mediaguardian

Media08

The Essential Guide to the Changing Media Landscape

Edited by **Janine Gibson**

First published in 2008 by
Guardian Books, 119 Farringdon Road, London EC1R 3ER
www.guardian.co.uk

Guardian Books is an imprint of Guardian News and Media Ltd.
Copyright © The Guardian 2008

ISBN 978-0-85265-091-2

Cover design: Two Associates
Text Design: Bryony Newhouse

Data updated by Keyways Publishing

Disclaimer
We have taken all steps possible to ensure the accuracy of the data
in this directory. If any information is incorrect, please send an email
with updated details to mediadirectory@guardian.co.uk

Printed by Cambridge University Press

10 9 8 7 6 5 4 3 2 1

Contents

How to use this book

Welcome to **Media 08: The Essential Guide to the Changing Media Landscape**.
It looks a little different from last year's Media Directory.

This guide's origins were in 1992, when the Guardian first began trying to map the diverse media industries in book form. In those days, it was possible to list pretty much every business involved in broadcasting, periodical publishing, advertising and marketing and still have room for listing major journalistic contacts without worrying about how many trees to plant in compensation. To even attempt such an exercise now seems impossible.

Over the past 15 years, we have annually modified, tweaked and restructured the book to give the best possible snapshot of the industry at that point in time. So this year, we've split the guide in two — to give due prominence to both offline and online businesses, their differences and the extraordinary number of new enterprises in the digital world. Strangely, of course, as we do this, the drive for integration (at least for the media companies who attempt to bridge both) has accelerated.

As the media has expanded to include (at one extreme) anyone with a blog or a playlist, the twin forces of globalisation and individualisation in publishing have made the notion of a fully comprehensive list unthinkable. Instead, the MediaGuardian teams have selected the most notable players and useful information that you're always a little too busy to search for. Our experts have provided comment on and analysis of the significant developments in their sector and we have selected key pieces from the year's breaking news to chart the mergers, auctions and — in the case of broadcasting especially — scandals that characterised 2007.

We have, naturally, massively expanded our digital section. Here we've included speeches, articles and news stories from the past year, to illustrate where our experts believe these industries are heading. A new listings section provides an at-a-glance overview of the many digital innovators in the UK, from game creators to internet service providers — a unique opportunity to grasp the reach of the new creative industries.

These are strange and unpredictable times for media owners. As even government and regulators will spend most of the next two years trying to assess the diverse directions of the media — largely for the purposes of divvying up the public money spent on ensuring plurality and diversity — we are confident that you, the users of this media directory, will have something of a headstart.

State of the media

Time was that the media was a glorious industry of plenty. A licence-to-print-money industry; a trebles-all-round-and-no-holding-back-on-the-expenses industry. I mention this only because that was a while ago now and though the image persists of an industry of plenty, free to indulge its creative whims, the reality is grinding and uncertain and altogether really quite perilous.

Take television. Long seen as an old boys' club, populated by groaning drinks trolleys and viewed as a branch of the arts, albeit a slightly downmarket one, the television industry has been reduced to a grasping swindler, out to fleece its viewers through sharp trading and dodgy dealings. The fines the channels have collectively incurred for their frauds and cackhandedness total into the millions and the inquiries are still not concluded at the time of publication.

Newspapers, which have not been backwards in expressing their wide-eyed horror at the antics of the broadcasters, are doing no better. Some shameless over-reporting of the — largely fictional — twists and turns in the Madeleine McCann kidnap case might have propped up the sales, but the general climate has continued to be pretty grim for print. Most of the titles, quick at least to catch on to

Whole-year trends		
	2006	**2005**
Total national newspaper average circulation (per day)	11.9 million	12.3 million
Total Sunday newspaper average circulation (per issue)	12.7 million	13.3 million
Total regional newspaper circulation/distribution (weekly)	63.4 million	64.3 million
Total consumer magazine copies (sales per annum)	1,377 million	1,438 million
Total households with multichannel TV	20.4 million	18.1 million
Total radio reach	45 million	44.4 million
total number of adults who own a DAB or claim to listen to the radio via DTV or the internet	27.2 million	24.6 million
total number of adult mp3 owners (aged 15+)	11.9 million	—
use their mp3 player to listen to podcasts	2.1 million	—
Total households with internet access	15.8 million	14.9 million
with broadband connections	12.4 million	9.4 million
Total volume of books sold by UK publishers	787 million	788 million
Total measured ad spend	£19.08 billion	£18.95 billion

Sources: ABC, PPA, Ofcom, RAJAR, Newspaper Society, Publishers Association, Advertising Association, The Advertising Statistics Yearbook 2007 for the Advertising Association

a zeitgeist, are now emphasising their online developments, throwing money at video and merging their reporting and editing teams, if not across print and online then across weekdays and weekends. The odds on a national newspaper closing in 2008 have shortened considerably, though most pragmatic observers bet the status quo will see out the decade.

Commercial radio, not long ago the scene of many a merger bonanza with venture capitalists banging down the door of every regional licence holder with a blank chequebook, is performing what tabloid papers call a "reverse ferret". Here we see the newcomer Global Radio, not content with having swallowed Chrysalis's Heart and Magic assets last year, now having a pop at the former big beast GCap. Global's first attempt at a takeover was rebuffed "out of hand" by the GCap board, but it is unlikely to be the final word on the matter. Weakened by its own ailing share price, GCap hasn't looked secure since GWR and Capital first bolted their businesses together and, following the departure of Ralph Bernard, who seemed to be holding it together through sheer will, some sort of definitive action seems inevitable.

It will be following Emap, which spent most of 2007 in limbo and finally divorced its consumer and trade businesses at the end of the year. Both now have found new partners – Bauer and the Guardian Media Group, publishers of this guide, respectively – and we must throw confetti and hope some domestic bliss can be rescued from the broken homes.

Still, the advertising business has undergone a creative renewal, even as its income has scattered. A media plan actually now has to involve a plan rather than a decision whether to go for Coronation Street, News at Ten or both. And the transfer of advertising pounds to the internet continues to be faster than that of dollars or, indeed euros.

This year, we are told, will be the year of the mobile – a whole new medium that few have yet understood to be a platform, though the launch of the iPhone helps with the transition. But a media landscape where writers are on strike in the US, where the TV networks are rather desperately trying to rebuild trust and the newspapers are cutting costs, isn't necessarily all that unfamiliar. We've been in all these places before.

The idea that the media industry is in a period of epoch-defining change is now as hackneyed as the idea that all big media is dead and the market will suffice. Actually and boringly the likelihood is that yes, the times of milk and honey are gone for a while, unless you work for Google – where apparently milk, honey and possibly ambrosia itself are not only free but mandatory. But the erosion of old media might take a little longer. Plus those beasts have a few ideas left.

Top ten media events of 2007

1. Television's year of shame

Not so much an event as an ongoing disaster, from the Blue Peter cat to massive phoneline fraud, television itself suffered a calamitous series of revelations. It seemed everyone was implicated, from GMTV to Ant and Dec, from the Queen to the BBC1 controller, and misleading the viewers was revealed to be something of an industry pastime. The whole murky business is in the hands of the regulators and will run and run.

2. The trial of Conrad Black

Another event that seemed to span most of 2007 was the trial and eventual sentencing of the disgraced Lord Black. Eventually given a six-and-half-year prison stretch to think about the $6.1m he stole from the newspaper empire, including the Daily Telegraph, that he built from scratch, Black remained extraordinarily defiant and unremorseful to the end.

3. Editor merry-go-round

Newspapers had another tough year, reflected in a sweeping change at the top level. The editors of the People, Sunday Telegraph, Times, Observer and Independent on Sunday all moved on for varying reasons, which can be summed up ultimately in two words: the internet.

4. Facebook opens up

A social networking site aimed at college students in the US decided to try its luck outside educational establishments and became the digital phenomenon of 2007, bumping Google from the list. Its extraordinary year peaked, perhaps, with the news that Microsoft paid its 23-year-old founder $240m for a minority stake in October, valuing the company at $15bn.

5. Murdoch buys the Wall Street Journal

Well it took a while, but in the end Rupert Murdoch pretty much always gets his way. Buying Dow Jones cost him $5bn. But more excitingly for NewsCorp watchers (and who in the media isn't one?), the acquisition prompted a major shake-up of personnel, leaving young James Murdoch the leading contender to replace the old man. Eventually.

6. Emap break-up

It looked uncomfortable in the digital era, but it took longer to offload the radio, magazine and television conglomerate than anyone anticipated owing, largely, to the global credit crisis. Or so its defenders said. Finally, by the end of 2007, Bauer took the consumer mags, radio and assorted music TV brands for £1.14bn, while Guardian Media Group (publishers of this guide) bought the business-to-business publishing arm, in partnership with the private equity firm Apax, for £1.2bn.

7. Radiohead offers album for free download

Pay what you want to was the idea and, sadly, many didn't. But Radiohead's brave move — to offer an album for download with the virtual equivalent of an honesty box — generated massive publicity and plenty of room for speculation on the future of the music industry.

8. Analogue switch-off

It was the Cumbrian town of Whitehaven that was the digital trailblazer in broadcasting. If the local inhabitants weren't aware that BBC2 would be the first station to switch off its analogue signal in November, then they certainly were when the national media arrived to document the moment. Which passed quite smoothly.

9. Global buys Chrysalis Radio

Former ITV chief executive Charles Allen's Global Radio moved into the big league in 2007 when it bought Chrysalis Radio for £170m, increasing the portfolio to include the Heart and Galaxy networks as well as LBC and its sister station LBC News.

10. The launch of the iPhone

Was it anti-climactic? Or the most significant development in media since the launch of the mobile phone? It's expensive, it isn't 3G and the email functionality is inferior to the BlackBerry, but the iPhone dominated 2007. With 5m sold, it's too expensive to saturate the market just yet, but it is what the experts call a "game changer".

MediaGuardian 100

» MediaGuardian   July 9 2007

The MediaGuardian 100 published in July 2007 is our annual guide to the most powerful people in the industry. Candidates are judged on three criteria — their cultural, economic and political influence in the UK. The list takes in all sectors of the media, including broadcasting, publishing, new media, advertising, marketing and PR. The aim was to take a snapshot of the individuals who run or influenced the UK media in 2007.

There are 47 new entries this year. Of those that survived from 2006, 28 went up, 23 went down and two stayed the same. A note on salaries — they are taken from the latest available official sources such as company annual reports. Where salaries are not publicly available, we have not included them. Wealth figures are from the Sunday Times Rich List and other sources.

1. Eric Schmidt

Job: chief executive, Google **Age:** 52
Industry: new media **Turnover:** $10.6bn (£5.25bn)
Staff: 12,238 **Salary:** $1 **Worth:** $5bn (£2.5bn)
2006 ranking: NEW ENTRY

Peter Morgan/Reuters

Don't know Eric Schmidt? Try Googling him. He is the chief executive of the internet search giant, the media big beast that got even bigger with the $1.65bn (£817m) purchase of YouTube last year. In the words of Chad Hurley, co-founder of the video-sharing website: "The king of search and the king of video have gotten together."

It is appropriate, then, that Schmidt is crowned number one in this year's MediaGuardian 100. The figures speak for themselves — revenue of $10.6bn in 2006, profit of $3.1bn, market capitalisation of $168bn, and estimated global unique users of half a billion. Not bad for a company founded less than a decade ago.

What began as the best and most efficient internet search engine has become the dominant player in the global online advertising market — a position that has been reinforced with its $3.1bn purchase of its largest independent competitor, the online advertising group DoubleClick. It was Google's biggest acquisition to date.

Google is now expanding its advertising business into TV, print, radio and mobile. No wonder everyone else is worried.

With millions of people using the search engine every day, Google controls the news and websites we see, and how we see them. But while website owners depend on Google for a proportion of their visitors, it also swallows up the advertising on which they depend for their existence. Unless you are the BBC, of course. Type "fear of Google" into the search engine and you will find 119,000 results — and counting.

The DoubleClick deal had Google's rivals crying foul and prompted an investigation into the online advertising market by the US federal trade commission.

It is not the only battle being fought by Google — YouTube has been accused of copyright abuse by showing broadcasters' content for free and is being sued for $1bn by MTV parent Viacom. It faces a similar action in the US from a group of sports rights owners including the Premier League.

Google has also been accused of invading its users' privacy by building up a vast history of email and search information, and was slated for launching a censored version of the site in China which limited results on search terms such as "Tiananmen Square".

Google, which had always been the acceptable face of big business with mottos such as "don't be evil", was suddenly feeling the heat.

So if you did Google Schmidt , what would you find out? Rather less, it turns out, than you would about its two co-founders, Larry Page and Sergey Brin.

Described as an "avid pilot" and "political junkie", Schmidt is also a member of the Apple board. Like Page and Brin, he takes an annual salary of just $1, but his stock options in Google make him worth about $5bn.

The trio run Google as a "triumvirate". But our panel of judges decided that, as chief executive, Schmidt should represent Google in this year's MediaGuardian 100, replacing Sergey and Brin who were at number four in last year's list.

Chief executive since 2001, Schmidt was

previously chairman and chief executive of the software company Novell and chief technology officer and chief executive of Sun Microsystems, where he led the development of Java programming technology. Google accounts revealed that he was paid more than $530,000 for his personal security, perks that include the use of private jets.

Schmidt said last year that he wanted to build a business with $100bn in annual revenues, around 10 times its current size. He addressed the Conservative party's annual conference last year and shared his vision of the future of the internet with readers of the Sun.

"And then there's my dream product – I call it serendipity. It works like this. You have two computer screens. On one you're typing, on the other comments appear checking the accuracy of what you are saying, suggesting better ways of making the same point. This would be good for journalists and politicians too!"

For Schmidt, it is a dream. For others, who fear the internet being dominated by a single company – be it Google or any other – it is a nightmare. How thin is the line between big business and big brother?

2. Rupert Murdoch

Job: chairman and chief executive, News Corporation
Age: 76 **Industry:** broadcasting, publishing, new media
Annual revenue: $25.33bn (£12.65bn) **Staff:** 57,000
Salary: $25.7m (£12.5m) (including $21m (£10m) bonus)
2006 ranking: 3

Murdoch is the old media baron who stole a march on his new media rivals. Two years after he bought social networking website MySpace, the News Corp chairman and chief executive showed he had lost none of his capacity to surprise with his audacious $5bn (£2.5bn) bid for Dow Jones, owner of the Wall Street Journal.

When Murdoch makes a move, he has a habit of bringing newsrooms to a halt: "He's done what?"

That was the case last November when BSkyB bought a 17.9% share of ITV to scupper NTL's hopes of a takeover. Credited to his son James, chief executive of BSkyB, it would undoubtedly have been approved by his father. It was a classic Murdoch manoeuvre.

Murdoch's old media empire – BSkyB, 39% owned by News Corp, and News International, home to the Sun, Times, News of the World and Sunday Times – has been transforming itself to take on its new media challengers.

Sky plunged into the broadband market while the Sun and the Times relaunched their websites. News International has also been cutting costs, with plans for around 100 redundancies, 7% of its editorial workforce, in a bid to save £30m. But it was the purchase of MySpace in 2005 that showed how far Murdoch was ahead of the game, giving him instant access to an online audience from which he had previously been isolated.

However, MySpace is now under pressure itself from the new breed of social networking sites such as Facebook, so much so that Murdoch reportedly considered exchanging it for a 25% stake in Yahoo!. Bought for $580m, it has turned out to be one of the bargains of the second dotcom boom.

The Dow Jones bid, if successful, would fulfil Murdoch's long-held ambition of owning a prestigious financial newspaper with which he could go head-to-head with the Financial Times. It would give him a global electronic financial brand in the WSJ.com website, one of the few newspapers able to charge for its online content. For Murdoch, global brands equal political influence.

"Rupert Murdoch is the most forward-thinking media tycoon and has made a huge leap forward compared with this time last year," said one of our panellists.

But Murdoch 's UK empire is under pressure on several fronts. BSkyB remains the dominant player in the pay-TV market but is locked in a battle with its most serious competitor for years, Virgin Media. The satellite broadcaster's activities are under investigation by Ofcom and the Competition Commission, and its row with Virgin Media over the withdrawal of Sky's basic channels from the cable TV platform is heading for the high court.

Declining circulations mean Murdoch's four newspapers are inevitably less of an influence than they once were. The Times continues to rack up huge losses and the previously dependable Sunday Times has suffered steep circulation declines since becoming the first £2 national newspaper last year. Sales of the Sun are on the verge of dropping below the 3m mark for the first time. No wonder he is investing so much online.

However, Murdoch 's political influence remains largely undiminished. "He is still the one chief executive that all politicians want to talk to," said one of our panellists. Murdoch is also pouring millions into the free newspaper war in London in his bid to break Associated Newspapers' monopoly in the capital, launching the London Paper from the News International stable.

In the US, News Corp owns the Fox TV and film business and newspapers including the New York Post. The global empire also includes publishing house HarperCollins, Star TV in Asia, Foxtel in Australia and Sky Italia.

The MediaGuardian 100, however, is about power and influence in the UK rather than around the world.

3. Mark Thompson

Job: director general, BBC **Age:** 49
Industry: broadcasting, new media, publishing
Total group income: £4bn **Staff:** 23,037
Salary: £788,000 (including benefits and other remuneration totalling £164,000) **2006 ranking:** 1

From the below-inflation licence fee settlement to the Blue Peter phone-in scandal, it has been a rotten year for the BBC director general. Worse, Thompson had to deal with the fallout from the "disappointing" licence fee increase without the man with whom he negotiated the BBC's charter renewal, Michael Grade – the corporation's chairman who unexpectedly jumped ship to ITV. A black mood turned blacker.

The fallout is likely to be hundreds, if not thousands more job cuts at the BBC, which has been left with a £2bn funding gap. Thompson's radical reorganisation of the corporation, which has already accounted for around 4,000 job losses, appears not to have been radical enough.

The BBC's online ambitions have also been hit, with the cancellation of its digital curriculum, BBC Jam, and the much-delayed launch of its iPlayer. The long-promised video-on-demand service was a key plank of Thompson's "Martini media" strategy, making BBC programmes available "anytime, anyplace, anywhere" and is finally due to launch this month.

Ranked number one last year, Thompson therefore slips two places to number three in this year's list. "He has had a terrible year," said one of our panellists.

Despite Thompson's travails, BBC1 is in good health and Radio 2 is the most listened-to radio station in the country. Thompson now needs to get their digital siblings, such as BBC3 and 6Music, the audiences that their considerable budgets deserve.

However, it was a year dominated by the licence fee deal. The BBC's hopes that the government would grant it a big increase in its income were punctured by the director general's questionable negotiating tactics and press revelations about the huge salaries paid to the corporation's biggest stars, including Radio 1 DJ Chris Moyles and £18m-man Jonathan Ross.

Thompson will find little sympathy from rivals struggling with declining advertising revenue who can only look on in envy at the BBC's guaranteed income over the next six years, with the cost of a licence due to increase from £135.50 today to £151.50 by 2012. He was appointed the BBC's director general in 2004 after three years as chief executive of Channel 4.

4. Michael Grade

Job: executive chairman, ITV Age: 64
Industry: broadcasting Turnover: £2.18bn
Staff: 5,957 Salary: £825,000 2006 ranking: 7

It was the most sensational media transfer of the past 12 months – Grade's defection from the BBC to become the new executive chairman of ITV. The corporation's former chairman decided the challenge of reviving Britain's biggest commercial broadcaster would be more interesting than overseeing the nascent BBC Trust which he had helped to create.

It will certainly be better rewarded, with a basic salary of £825,000 and potentially £11m more in ITV shares if he meets all his targets.

Grade is everything his ITV predecessor, former chief executive Charles Allen, is not – charismatic, steeped in programme-making, good with talent and possessing an uncanny knack for boosting morale just by walking into a room. He arrived at ITV, the network his uncle Lew helped establish half a century ago, to a standing ovation from staff. He immediately made his aggressive intentions clear when ITV poached the rights to live FA Cup and England home internationals from the BBC. Put that in your cigar and smoke it.

Little of Grade's influence will be seen on screen until the autumn at the earliest, but his arrival coincided with an upturn in the fortunes of ITV1 under its director of television Simon Shaps. The bottom line remains unmoved, however, and the task for Grade as daunting as ever. ITV's advertising revenues are down – despite the encouraging performance of its digital channels – and the

premium-rate phone-in scandal is likely to cost it millions.

Grade said the network needed to be "more innovative" and "take more risks", and said a turnaround in its fortunes was about "doing a hundred things maybe just 1% better ... There is still a great deal more to do." He's not kidding.

A 64-year-old former showbiz impresario may not sound like the obvious candidate to lead ITV into a bright new digital future. But Grade will be helped by one of his most important new signings, former Sky Network's managing director Dawn Airey, whose job as ITV director of global content will be to take the broadcaster's programming onto new platforms.

In his two-and-a-half years as BBC chairman, Grade made a formidable double act with director general Mark Thompson and was credited with helping to rescue the corporation from the depths of its post-Hutton despair. But the timing of his surprise departure last November could not have been worse, coming just weeks before the announcement by the government of its ultimately disappointing licence fee settlement, and the establishment of the new BBC Trust which Grade had been expected to head.

Grade rises three places from his position in last year's MediaGuardian 100, when he was still at the BBC, while ITV director of television Simon Shaps falls 12 places in this year's list. "It is a reflection of the shifting balance of power," said one panellist.

5. James Murdoch

Job: chief executive, BSkyB Age: 34
Industry: broadcasting Annual revenue: £4.15bn
Salary: £2.75m (including £1.65m bonus and £268,606 benefits) 2006 ranking: 15

He proved he is truly a chip off the old block with BSkyB's purchase of a 17.9% stake in ITV. The BSkyB chief executive was credited with the £940m raid that scuppered the potential merger of two of the satellite broadcaster's biggest rivals, ITV and NTL, at a stroke. "Of course it would have been approved by Rupert [Murdoch], but if James really did mastermind it then it was breathtaking," said one member of our panel.

"It was the most audacious media move of the year, the sort of boldness that only comes from being young and empowered."

However, Murdoch now finds himself fighting on several fronts. Alistair Darling referred to the purchase of Sky's ITV stake to the Competition Commission, Ofcom is investigating the entire pay-TV market, and Sky's battle with Virgin Media is heading for the high court.

But it is a badge of honour for a Murdoch to upset competitors and regulators – the fact that they included Richard Branson, Virgin Media's largest shareholder, was the icing on the cake. The best time to challenge regulation is at a moment of potential political weakness, and with Gordon Brown newly arrived in No 10, Sky may have timed it just right.

Murdoch succeeded Tony Ball as BSkyB chief executive at the end of 2003, an appointment that prompted fierce opposition from shareholders. He took hold of a business at a crossroads and transformed it, pitching into the broadband market, investing millions in the Sky brand and championing innovations such as its personal video recorder service Sky+ and high definition television. In 2004, Sky's annual revenue was £3.19bn and Murdoch was earning £950,000 a year. Its revenue has increased by one-third to £4.15bn and its chief executive is now on £2.75m. The one-time daddy's boy has now become his own man.

Will Murdoch still be at Sky by 2010? He is the only one of Rupert Murdoch's children still working in the family business and rumours persist he will leave to take up a senior role with News Corporation in New York. But we said that in last year's MediaGuardian 100 as well.

6. Richard Branson

Job: founder, Virgin's largest shareholder, Virgin Media **Age:** 56 **Industry:** broadcasting, telecommunications **Worth:** £3.1bn **2006 ranking:** 29

Few competitors stand toe-to-toe with Sky and live to tell the tale. Branson, the largest shareholder in Virgin Media, is bloodied but unbowed in his effort to take on the might of the Murdoch pay-TV empire. The next stage of the battle, the most compelling media story of the past 12 months, will be in front of a judge. The cable TV company filed high court papers accusing Sky of anti-competitive behaviour after it removed Sky One and other basic channels from the fledgling Virgin platform. Balderdash, said Sky. Ding ding, round three.

However, the fight for control of the pay-TV market took a new turn when US private equity group Carlyle bid £5.2bn for Virgin Media. The offer makes Branson, with a 10.5% share in the business, even more powerful. He can sell out or reinvest with Carlyle – or whoever buys Virgin Media – and take on Sky with new private equity backing.

Branson is one of this year's biggest risers and a NEW ENTRY in our top 10. He achieved his lifelong dream of becoming a player in the TV big league when he sold his Virgin Mobile business to NTL in a deal worth approximately £1bn last year. However, his plans of becoming an even bigger competitor to Sky by masterminding a £1bn merger with ITV were scuppered by – guess who? – Sky, when it took a 17.9% stake in the terrestrial broadcaster last year.

Sky said the purchase was an investment. Branson described the Murdoch empire as a "threat to democracy" and said Sky was trying to "strangle us at birth".

In any case, the purchase is now the subject of an investigation by the Competition Commission ordered by Alistair Darling. It is not the first time Branson has fought a one-man PR campaign against a multibillion-pound rival, the latest in a series of "David and Goliath" battles that have come to characterise his career.

"It is very hard to go up against Sky and come out with anything like a score draw," was the verdict of one of our panellists. "Branson did that. I never thought I would say this but Branson played it well. You actually sympathised with him."

7. Steve Jobs

Job: co-founder and chief executive, Apple **Age:** 52 **Industry:** new media **Turnover:** $21.59bn (year to March 31) **Salary:** $1 **2006 ranking:** 2

In the beginning was the iPod. Then there was the iPod mini, the nano, the shuffle, Apple TV and now the iPhone. Jobs keeps on innovating and the bubble shows no sign of bursting just yet.

The Apple co-founder and chief executive transformed the way we buy and consume music with iTunes and the iPod, launched in 2001. Rarely has a product become so ubiquitous and yet maintained its image as the cool "must-have" gadget. Jobs is also a master marketer.

But will the iPhone live up to the hype? The touchscreen handset, which combines a music player, mobile phone, video, email and the internet, launched in the US last month, and is due to arrive in Europe by this end of the year.

Jobs described it as a "leapfrog product" that would "change everything", while Time magazine predicted it would "do to the cellphone market what the iPod did to the portable music player market: crush it pitilessly beneath the weight of its own superiority". Not everyone on our panel was so convinced. "There is a lot of scepticism about the iPhone," said one panellist. "This could be the year when we see a lot of reaction against the Apple brand."

Jobs has already suffered a backlash over Apple's use of digital rights management, or DRM, which means songs downloaded from iTunes can only be played on an iPod. He responded by laying the blame firmly at the door of the big record companies, and signed a deal earlier this year with EMI to offer DRM-free music, albeit at a higher price, on iTunes.

8. Ed Richards

Job: chief executive, Ofcom **Age:** 41 **Industry:** regulation **Staff:** 776 **Salary:** £308,930 (including bonus, benefits and pension payments) **2006 ranking:** 77

The Ofcom chief executive faces a critical few months which will test not just his own ability but the effectiveness or otherwise of the three and a half-year-old regulator. Ofcom's recent interventions read like a list of the industry's biggest stories of the year so far – the Celebrity Big Brother race row, the premium-rate call-TV scandal, and BSkyB's purchase of a 17.9% share in ITV.

The Big Brother controversy ended with a landmark ruling from the regulator saying that Channel 4 had made "serious editorial misjudgments" that were "compounded by a serious failure of the compliance process".

Critics claimed Ofcom had made errors of its own by failing to react quickly enough to either the Big Brother row or the TV phone-in scandal, which began with Channel 4's Richard & Judy and spread to other broadcasters like a virus.

Ofcom is looking into Sky's purchase of a stake in ITV as well as the satellite broadcaster's pay-TV plans for Freeview, and has opened more than 20 investigations into irregularities on premium-rate phone-ins and interactive services.

"The next few months are going to be absolutely crucial for Ed Richards," said one of our panellists. "He has more to say about the shape of the media landscape over the next 12 months than almost anyone else on this list, but I fear he is going to be weak rather than directional."

Also in Richards' in-tray: what to do with analogue spectrum, the future funding of Channel 4, sharp practice in the cut-throat broadband market, the future regulation of commercial radio, the provision of public service content in the digital age, TV product placement, HDTV. The list goes on. And on.

Previously the regulator's number two, Richards succeeded Stephen Carter in the top job in October last year. The new regime made its first significant decision last year when it banned junk food advertising around children's TV programmes.

A quintessential New Labour man – Greg Dyke famously referred to him as a "jumped-up Millbank oik" – Richards has worked for both Gordon Brown and Tony Blair. It was as a media adviser to No 10 that he helped draft the Communications Act that brought Ofcom into being.

9. Lesley Douglas

Job: controller, BBC2 and 6Music, controller, BBC popular music **Age:** 44 **Industry:** broadcasting **Annual programming budget:** £35.7m (Radio 2), £4.5m (6Music) **Audience:** 13.25m (Radio 2), 477,000 (6Music) **Staff:** 110 **2006 ranking:** 37

The controller of the country's most popular radio station has her finger on the pulse of what middle England wants to listen to, Radio 2 is the Daily Mail of the airwaves. Controller of Radio 2 and its digital offshoot, 6Music, Douglas's empire expanded this year with her appointment as the BBC's first controller of popular music.

The role is as grand as the title suggests, coordinating all of the corporation's pop music output across radio, TV and online – appearing to usurp the responsibilities of her boss, Jenny Abramsky, in this area. She also becomes the first port

Martin Godwin

of call for record labels looking to promote their artists through the BBC.

"Douglas is single-handedly destroying commercial radio," said another of our judges. "She has got a chequebook and she is not afraid to use it."

Her most recent signing was Russell Brand. The stand-up comic and Sun's "shagger of the year" is an unlikely stablemate for other Radio 2 DJs such as Terry Wogan and Ken Bruce. However, his signing was a reflection of the broad church that Radio 2 has become, and how far the station has moved away from its stuffy old image of 10 years ago.

"Lesley wants to get everyone in the country listening to her station at some time in the week," said a panellist. "That's why she signed Russell Brand."

The station's relentless move towards the mainstream has meant some of its heritage programming, such as Your Hundred Best Tunes, has been axed. Where do the station's older listeners go next? But Douglas has managed the station's evolution without the sort of listener revolt that typically greets change on Radio 4.

The fiercest response from listeners came when Chris Evans replaced Johnnie Walker in the weekday drivetime slot. When Terry Wogan retires from the breakfast show – possibly in 2009 – dare she choose Evans to replace him?

10. Paul Dacre

Job: editor, Daily Mail editor-in-chief, Associated Newspapers **Age:** 58 **Industry:** publishing **Circulation:** Daily Mail 2,294,949 Mail on Sunday 2,274,551 London Evening Standard 273,537 (May 2007) **Salary:** £1.23m (including £249,000 benefits) **2006 ranking:** 10

The most powerful newspaper editor in the country has a pay packet to match. For the third successive year, he is the highest ranking editor in the list. His Daily Mail is the newspaper success story of its era, selling three times more than its one-time rival, the undernourished Daily Express, and with the Sun's circulation in its sights.

"He is a phenomenon, much more like a proprietor than he is a newspaper editor, with absolute confidence in his product," said one of our panellists. "While newspapers and their editors have changed all around him, Dacre and the Daily Mail have stayed the same – solid, reliable, and they still don't like anyone."

As the editor-in-chief of Associated Newspapers, Dacre's empire extends from the Daily Mail to the Mail on Sunday, the London Evening Standard and Metro, as well as afternoon freesheet London Lite which is locked in a bitter struggle with Rupert Murdoch's London Paper.

After years of the paper pouring scorn on Tony Blair, all eyes will be on the Mail to see how it reacts to the premiership of Gordon Brown whom Dacre described as "touched by the mantle of greatness".

Now in his 16th year in charge of the Mail, Dacre's ranking in the MediaGuardian 100 is boosted because he has a hands-off proprietor in Viscount Rothermere, a luxury enjoyed by few other national newspaper editors.

11. **Jana Bennett** director of Vision, BBC *broadcasting* (8)
12. **Peter Fincham** controller, BBC1 *broadcasting* (25)
13. **Sir Michael Lyons** chairman, BBC Trust *broadcasting* NEW ENTRY
14. **Steven Chen and Chad Hurley** co-founders, chief technology officer (Chen), chief executive (Hurley), YouTube *new media* NEW ENTRY
15. **Russell T Davies** writer, executive producer *broadcasting* (28)
16. **Julian Bellamy** head of programming, Channel 4 *broadcasting* (78)
17. **Peter Morgan** writer *TV, film* NEW ENTRY
18. **Jenny Abramsky** director, BBC audio and music *broadcasting* (11)
19. **James Purnell** culture secretary *politics* NEW ENTRY
20. **Simon Cowell** TV producer, presenter *broadcasting* (76)
21. **Kevin Lygo** director of television and content, Channel 4 *broadcasting* (14)
22. **Andy Duncan** chief executive, Channel 4 *broadcasting* (5)
23. **Rebekah Wade** editor, the Sun *publishing* (12)
24. **David Tennant** actor *broadcasting* NEW ENTRY
25. **Les Hinton** executive chairman, News International *publishing* (26)
26. **Robert Thomson** editor, the Times *publishing* (41)
27. **Trevor East** director of sport, Setanta *broadcasting* (44)
28. **Simon Shaps** director of television, ITV *broadcasting* (16)
29. **Helen Boaden** director, BBC News *broadcasting* (17)
30. **Richard Wallace** editor, Daily Mirror *publishing* (47)
31. **Viscount Rothermere** chairman, Daily Mail & General Trust *publishing* (24)
32. **Ashley Highfield** director of future media and technology, BBC *broadcasting* (21)
33. **Arun Sarin** chief executive, Vodafone *telecommunications* NEW ENTRY
34. **Sir David and Sir Frederick Barclay** owners of the Telegraph Group, Press Holdings *publishing* (30)
35. **Richard Desmond** chief executive, Northern & Shell, Express Newspapers *publishing* (49)
36. **Sly Bailey** chief executive, Trinity Mirror *publishing* (32)
37. **Murdoch MacLennan** chief executive, Telegraph Group *publishing* (34)
38. **Lisa Opie** managing director, content, Channel Five *broadcasting* NEW ENTRY
39. **Simon Fuller** chief executive, 19 Entertainment *broadcasting, music* NEW ENTRY
40. **Alan Rusbridger** editor, the Guardian, executive editor, the Observer *publishing, new media* (35)

41. **Marjorie Scardino** chief executive, Pearson *publishing* (36)
42. **John Witherow** editor, the Sunday Times *publishing* (45)
43. **Sir Martin Sorrell** group chief executive, WPP *advertising, marketing* (23)
44. **Will Lewis** editor, Daily Telegraph *publishing* NEW ENTRY
45. **Lionel Barber** editor, Financial Times *publishing* (79)
46. **Carolyn McCall** chief executive, Guardian Media Group (GMG) *publishing, broadcasting, new media* (94)
47. **Nick Robinson** political editor, BBC *broadcasting* (48)
48. **Ivan Fallon** UK chief executive, Independent News & Media *publishing* (39)
49. **Zarin Patel** group finance director, BBC non-executive director, BBC Worldwide *broadcasting* NEW ENTRY
50. **Dawn Airey** director of global content, ITV *broadcasting* (31)
51. **Simon Kelner** editor-in-chief, Independent, Independent on Sunday *publishing* (53)
52. **Paul Jackson** director of entertainment and comedy, ITV *broadcasting* (59)
53. **Patience Wheatcroft** editor, Sunday Telegraph *publishing* (87)
54. **Elisabeth Murdoch** chairman and chief executive, Shine *broadcasting* NEW ENTRY
55. **Roger Alton** editor, the Observer *publishing* (62)
56. **Steve Morrison** chief executive, All3Media *broadcasting* (80)
57. **David Frank** chief executive, RDF Media *broadcasting* NEW ENTRY
58. **Mark Sharman** director of news and sport ITV *broadcasting* NEW ENTRY
59. **David Kershaw** chief executive, M&C Saatchi plc *advertising* (64)
60. **David Mannion** editor-in-chief, ITV news *broadcasting* (73)
61. **Duncan Edwards** managing director and chief executive officer, the National Magazine Company *publishing* (90)
62. **Jane Featherstone** joint managing director, Kudos Productions *broadcasting* (74)
63. **Nicholas Coleridge** managing director, Conde Nast *publishing* (75)
64. **Richard Curtis** TV and film writer, producer, director charity fundraiser *TV, fundraising* NEW ENTRY
65. **Ant and Dec** presenters, producers *broadcasting* (81)
66. **Andy Harries** founder, Left Bank Pictures *broadcasting* NEW ENTRY
67. **Roly Keating** controller, BBC2 *broadcasting* (61)
68. **John Humphrys** presenter, Today *broadcasting* NEW ENTRY
69. **Danny Rimer** partner, Index Ventures *venture capital* NEW ENTRY
70. **Tom Loosemore** project director, BBC 2.0 *new media* NEW ENTRY

71. **Jane Bruton** editor, Grazia *publishing*
NEW ENTRY

72. **Jeremy Clarkson** TV presenter, newspaper columnist *broadcasting, publishing*
NEW ENTRY

73. **Robert Saville** partner and creative director, Mother *advertising* NEW ENTRY

74. **John Noel** agent *television* NEW ENTRY

75. **Russell Brand** presenter, columnist *broadcasting, publishing* NEW ENTRY

76. **Richard Eyre** deputy chairman and chairman elect, GCap Media *broadcasting* NEW ENTRY

77. **Alexandra Shulman** editor, Vogue *publishing* NEW ENTRY

78. **Michael Birch** co-founder, chief executive Bebo *new media* NEW ENTRY

79. **Polly Toynbee** columnist, Guardian *publishing* NEW ENTRY

80. **Steve Hilton** adviser to David Cameron *politics* NEW ENTRY

81. **Guido Fawkes** blogger *new media* NEW ENTRY

82. **Chris Evans** presenter, Radio 2 *broadcasting* NEW ENTRY

83. **Adam Boulton** political editor, Sky News *broadcasting* NEW ENTRY

84. **Charles Allen** chairman, Global Radio *broadcasting* (6)

85. **Andrew Neil** publishing executive, TV presenter *broadcasting, publishing* NEW ENTRY

86. **Matthew Freud** chairman, Freud Communications *public relations* (86)

87. **Colin Myler** editor, News of the World *publishing* NEW ENTRY

88. **Chris DeWolfe** co-founder, chief executive, MySpace *new media* NEW ENTRY

89. **Alan Parker** founder, chairman, Brunswick Group *public relations* NEW ENTRY

90. **Gordon Ramsay** TV chef, restaurant owner *broadcasting* NEW ENTRY

91. **John Whittingdale** chairman, House of Commons media select committee *politics* NEW ENTRY

92. **David Puttnam** deputy chairman, Channel 4 politics *broadcasting* NEW ENTRY

93. **Ajaz Ahmed** co-founder, chairman, AKQA *marketing* NEW ENTRY

94. **Allison Pearson** columnist, Daily Mail *publishing* NEW ENTRY

95. **Ford Ennals** chief executive, Digital UK *broadcasting* NEW ENTRY

96. **Kevin Maguire** associate editor (politics), Daily Mirror *publishing* NEW ENTRY

97. **Emily Bell** director of digital content, Guardian News & Media *new media* NEW ENTRY

98. **Andy Parfitt** controller, BBC Radio 1, 1Xtra, BBC teen tsar *broadcasting* (50)

99. **Peter Wright** editor, Mail on Sunday *publishing* NEW ENTRY

100. **Facebook** social networking *new media* NEW ENTRY

● The panellists

Lord Alli is chairman of entertainment content company Chorion, which owns the rights to Agatha Christie, Enid Blyton, Noddy and The Mr Men. He is also a non-executive director of Scottish Media Group, Paul O'Grady's TV company Olga Productions and online retail store, ASOS. The youngest peer in parliament when he was appointed nine years ago, aged 34, Lord Alli was co-founder of Big Breakfast and TFI Friday producer Planet 24. A former member of Labour's "kitchen cabinet", he is a working Labour peer taking a particular interest in equality issues.

Daisy McAndrew is the chief political correspondent for ITV News. She previously co-hosted BBC2's Daily Politics with Andrew Neil and presented the daily drive-time show for London talk radio station, LBC. She began her career as a researcher in the House of Commons and after a stint as a freelance political journalist spent two years as Charles Kennedy's press secretary. She returned to journalism after the 2001 general election, presenting Channel 4's lunchtime political programme, Powerhouse.

Jamie Kantrowitz is senior vice-president of marketing and content for MySpace.com in Europe. Based in London, she oversees strategic and media partnerships and events, as well as the brand and content acquisition for MySpace and its entertainment channels, focusing on music, film and TV. She was previously vice-president of marketing at its Los Angeles headquarters.

Richard Park is an executive director of Chrysalis Radio parent Global Radio. He joined the investment firm last week after two years as programme director of Magic, which he turned into London's number one station. A veteran radio executive, he previously spent 14 years at Capital Radio, working with the likes of Chris Tarrant, and became an unlikely household name as the head teacher of BBC1 talent show, Fame Academy.

Sarah Sands is a consultant editor of the Daily Mail. She previously spent a decade at the Telegraph Group, first as deputy editor on the Daily Telegraph, assuming responsibility for the Saturday edition, and later as the first female editor of the Sunday Telegraph. She started her career at the Sevenoaks Courier in Kent before joining the Evening Standard and editing the Londoner's Diary gossip column. She has also written two novels.

James Scroggs is vice-president, consumer business of SpinVox, the voice-to-screen messaging company. He was previously vice-president of marketing for MTV Networks UK and Ireland, where he was responsible for all advertising, digital events, products and brand experiences. He began his career as a graduate recruit at DMB&B before going on to join Lowe Howard-Spink. As senior brand manager of OnDigital, he drove its relaunch as ITV Digital with the "Al & Monkey" ad campaign.

Janine Gibson is executive editor of Guardian Unlimited and editor-in-chief of MediaGuardian.

Matt Wells is editor of MediaGuardian and presenter of the Media Talk podcast.

Rip it up and start again

John Plunkett

It's the biggest shakedown in the seven-year history of the Media 100. Old media are on the wane, and among the biggest-ever group of new entrants are the leading lights of the digital future. In this report we present the people who wield the most power in the British media industry. Big names have gone, fresh faces have arrived and there are plenty of surprises in this year's list. So how did our panel of experts reach their decisions?

The old media certainties are no more. In a world where print journalists have become podcasters, video-on-demand has replaced the video cassette, and two-year-old new media start-ups sell for $1.65bn, it is apt there should be a changing of the guard in the MediaGuardian 100. So this year we ripped up the list and started again with the help of several new members on our panel of judges. Out of the list go the likes of Radio 4 controller Mark Damazer and Daily Express editor Peter Hill, in come the vanguard of the social networking revolution – YouTube founders Chad Hurley and Steven Chen, MySpace chief executive Chris DeWolfe, and Bebo's Michael Birch. Nearly half of this year's list are new entries.

Channel 4 is among the big losers in the wake of the Celebrity Big Brother race row. Its chief executive Andy Duncan and director of television and content Kevin Lygo drop out of the top 20, while chairman Luke Johnson disappears altogether. It was also a year to forget for BBC director general Mark Thompson – last year's number one, down two places to number three. Thompson is replaced at the top by Eric Schmidt, chief executive of Google, the search engine turned media giant and most powerful brand in the world.

Also in the top 10 are the protagonists of the year's most entertaining media feud – BSkyB chief executive James Murdoch and Virgin Media's Richard Branson. The battle for dominance of the pay-TV market has only just begun, and was given an unexpected twist with US private equity group Carlyle's £5.2bn bid for the cable company. Murdoch moves up 10 places to five, one ahead of Branson.

It was a mixed year for Murdoch Senior. The News Corp chairman and chief executive's purchase of MySpace two years ago seems more far-sighted with every passing day, and his empire is on the verge of expanding still further with his $5bn bid for Wall Street Journal parent Dow Jones – still nail-bitingly incomplete at the time of writing. But MySpace's crown is under threat from the latest social networking craze, Facebook, this year's number 100.

Our panel was convinced that none of Murdoch's newspaper editors can match the power of Daily Mail editor and Associated Newspapers editor-in-chief Paul Dacre, number 10 and once again our top-ranked editor. Robert Thomson – editor of the Times and prospective new publisher of the Wall Street Journal – moves up 15 places to 26. Radio 2 controller and BBC controller of popular music Lesley Douglas, Ofcom chief executive Ed Richards and Michael Grade, who jumped ship from the BBC to become executive chairman of ITV, make up the rest of this year's top 10.

Sir Michael Lyons, appointed chairman of the BBC Trust after Grade changed channels, is our second highest new entry at 13. He is joined in the top 20 by the secretary for culture, media and sport, James Purnell, who will finally begin the process of digital switchover in October when the analogue signal is switched off in the Cumbrian town of Whitehaven. It is a PR disaster waiting to happen.

Doctor Who star David Tennant is a new entry at 24, nine places behind the show's lead writer and executive producer Russell T Davies. But Tennant is not this year's highest-placed on-screen star – that is Simon Cowell, up 56 places to 20 on the back of Britain's Got Talent, ITV's biggest new show of the year. Its presenters, Anthony McPartlin and Declan Donnelly, rise 16 places to 65. Other on-screen talent on this year's list includes Jeremy Clarkson, Gordon Ramsay, and Russell Brand.

Sir Martin Sorrell is once again the highest placed entry from the world of advertising. After a year that will be remembered for a libel trial involving two of his former colleagues, Sorrell falls 20 places to number 43, ahead of M&C Saatchi chief executive David Kershaw, Mother's Robert Saville, and Ajaz Ahmed of digital agency AKQA. But it is new media where many of the gains have been made, with Michael Birch, Chris DeWolfe, Chad Hurley and Steven Chen appearing for the first time. Hurley and Chen's YouTube revolutionised the way we put and watch video on the web. Had it not been bought by Google last year, the pair would probably have been even higher.

Other new entries include The Queen scriptwriter Peter Morgan; Radio 2 DJ Chris Evans, a double winner at this year's Sony radio awards; 19 Entertainment chief executive Simon Fuller, the man behind brand Beckham, American Idol and the Spice Girls; Shine chairman and chief executive Elisabeth Murdoch; and Jane Bruton, editor of Emap's Grazia and the highest ranked magazine editor.

But enough about the winners, what of the losers? Radio 4's Damazer is one of the highest-profile names to drop off this year's list, as is his colleague, Radio 5 Live controller Bob Shennan, reflecting a renewed effort by our judges to reward power, not job titles.

Bill Gates, number nine in last year's list, drops out too, showing the shift in balance of power from the PC to the internet. As does Richard Littlejohn, half the columnist at the Daily Mail that he was at the Sun, although his fellow Mail columnist Allison Pearson is a new entry at 94.

The MediaGuardian 100 takes economic, political and cultural influence into account, and is intended as a snapshot of individuals' power today. Ricky Gervais is another casualty, eclipsed in the second series of Extras by his writing and directing partner Stephen Merchant. GCap Media chief executive Ralph Bernard also goes, a reflection of the influence of the group's incoming chairman, Richard Eyre. Channel Five chief executive Jane Lighting is out but Five's managing director, content, Lisa Opie, is in.

Big names who have gone because they have changed or lost their jobs include former Emap chief executive Tom Moloney, News of the World editor turned Tory spin doctor Andy Coulson, and Chris Wright, whose Chrysalis radio business was sold to Charles Allen's new broadcast venture, Global Radio.

Last year's unofficial "survivor of the year", Allen was down and out of this year's list following his exit from ITV, only to return at the 11th hour after Global paid £170m for Chrysalis Radio. Now he is being linked with a possible takeover of Virgin Radio with Richard Branson. Will there ever be a MediaGuardian 100 without Allen?

Traditional media

Print media

Janine Gibson

The nationals

The Madeleine McCann story dominated tabloid headlines

Some of the hysteria around the imminent demise of the national press abated in 2007, due in part to a strong news agenda that breathed some life into the presses.

Why worry too much about those pesky DVDs propping up the sale, when they cost fortunes and provide no loyalty from the fickle consumer? So many other reliable sales props can be found in the more traditional (and, let's face it, cheaper) world of journalism.

Of course, this is why the fickle consumer spent the year gorging on rewritten Portuguese headlines about a couple whose daughter disappeared, or a princess who died 10 years ago and is finally getting an inquest. Extreme weather, particularly of the dramatic flood variety, does the trick and so, though less dramatically, do the more specialist delights of temporary election fever, agricultural disease outbreaks and scandals leading to repeated demands for public figures to be sacked.

The largely ignored story of newspapers then, is that news, too, sells. Madeleine McCann's disappearance – a classic one-fact story if ever there was one – provided such a fillip to sales (one tabloid editor admitted that the name McCann on the front page was worth 20,000 copies) that even the Express felt able to break into its Diana-all-the-time editorial policy.

For the broadsheets, though Maddy might not be quite so rewarding, a new prime minister and a flurry of electoral hopes kept sales respectable into the autumn. Within the general and inevitable decline, it was even possible to see signs of rallying, particularly in the quality and Sunday markets.

As ever, though, the genuine circulation gains have their roots in price-cutting (notably at the Sun) and giveaways. Here the Mail on Sunday takes the prize with its Prince CD bonanza. The giveaway of an entire, brand-new album generated landmark sales for the paper and caused a furore around the further eroding of the economic model of the music industry – one of the few creative businesses that the papers can regard pityingly.

Perhaps the biggest stories of the year for the print end of the newspaper business (increasingly preoccupied by its online presence) were the personnel changes at the big titles. The Observer editor, Roger Alton, resigned in October in favour of his long-time deputy John Mulholland. His departure came as the Observer's parent company, Guardian News and Media, announced the Guardian and Observer would integrate some of their operations with the website Guardian Unlimited. Though all the titles will continue to publish under separate identities, it is clear that some aspect of seven-day print operations will form part of the "24/7 online publishing" strategy announced by the Guardian's editor, Alan Rusbridger.

Alton's departure echoed that earlier in the year of the Sunday Telegraph's editor, Patience Wheatcroft, who had been in the post for a matter of months. Wheatcroft, formerly a highly respected business editor of the Times for many years, was said to have been opposed to and ultimately refused to participate in the greater integration of her paper with the Telegraph website. The Telegraph editor and digital evangelist Will Lewis shrugged off yet another senior departure and installed Ian McGregor – like many new Telegraph staffers, latterly of the Daily Mail – in the post. The Telegraph has undergone phenomenal change over the past three years and is probably the most advanced of the UK newspaper groups in transferring the focus of its operations online. It has not been without cost,

National daily circulations

	Editor	Jan-Jun 07	Jul-Dec 06	Jan-Jun 06	Year-on-year % change
Popular and midmarket titles					
Sun	Rebekah Wade	3,064,376	3,028,732	3,163,504	-3.23
Daily Mail	Paul Dacre	2,200,691	2,203,262	2,386,893	-8.46
Daily Mirror	Richard Wallace	1,565,711	1,540,917	1,653,431	-5.60
Daily Express	Peter Hill	770,403	773,768	838,165	-8.80
Daily Star	Dawn Neesom	795,891	750,374	791,732	0.52
Daily Record	Bruce Waddell	402,033	404,372	443,464	-10.31
Quality Press					
Daily Telegraph	William Lewis	801,333	816,521	902,769	-12.66
Times	Robert Thomson	584,378	586,097	666,018	-13.97
Financial Times	Lionel Barber	405,913	401,103	446,786	-10.07
Guardian	Alan Rusbridger	347,897	349,863	381,790	-9.74
Independent	Simon Kelner	198,575	199,844	254,827	-28.33

National Sunday circulations

	Editor	Jan-Jun 07	Jul-Dec 06	Jan-Jun 06	Year-on-year % change
Popular and midmarket titles					
News of the World	Colin Myler	3,269,483	3,380,746	3,552,119	-8.64
Mail on Sunday	Peter Wright	2,194,857	2,156,484	2,331,213	-6.21
Sunday Mail	Alan Rennie	503,894	498,632	532,545	-5.69
Sunday Mirror	Tina Weaver	1,411,428	1,322,720	1,463,809	-3.71
People	Mark Thomas	736,438	766,842	852,399	-15.75
Sunday Express	Martin Townsend	743,327	759,495	846,260	-13.85
Daily Star Sunday	Gareth Morgan	394,920	354,809	397,646	-0.69
Quality Press					
Sunday Times	John Witherow	1,154,059	1,191,553	1,339,111	-16.03
Sunday Telegraph	Ian MacGregor	594,825	590,533	673,528	-13.23
Observer	John Mulholland	421,210	407,242	487,307	-15.69
Independent on Sunday	Tristan Davies	208,083	161,129	233,769	-12.34

Source: ABC. Figures include bulks

The Telegraph leads the way with online video

however, certainly at management level. After Lewis, the next most senior member of staff in the Telegraph newsroom with length of service over a year is a reporter.

Though the Telegraph is still chasing the Guardian's web audience, it has had great success with online video – launching a news service supplied by ITN – and in publicly conveying a change of culture. The days of the editor Charles Moore, the proprietor Conrad Black (sentenced to six and a half years in an American prison for embezzlement) and a staff of gentleman-journalists are long gone.

All the main UK titles signed up to the ABCe audit of web user figures in 2007 in an attempt to bring sense to the complicated and oft-disputed audience metrics of the digital world. The Guardian retained its number one status, hitting record traffic and more than 18m users in October 2007. The Times, Telegraph and Daily Mail all saw huge gains over the year with wildly differing strategies. The Telegraph, focused on developing a strong video offering, is pitching itself straight up against the traditional broadcasters, Lewis told an audience of TV executives in September. It too reached an all-time best audience – 11m users – in the same set of figures. The Times, at 12.4m users, is putting money and strategic effort into Google optimisation and mobile telephone-based services and the Mail (another record, 13.5m) is successfully pursuing the search-engine friendly worlds of showbiz and celebrity. Their efforts show that the British press, once engaged, can be just as lively (and wildly competitive) online as in print.

ABC explainer

What is ABC?

ABC (the Audit Bureau of Circulations) is an independent, industry-owned organisation that verifies the circulation, distribution and traffic data of print, events and digital media.

When is ABC data issued?

National newspaper reports and online traffic figures (the latter from ABCe, the new media section of ABC) are published monthly. Regional newspaper and magazine print reports are published every six months, covering January–June and July–December each year. Other online traffic, B2B magazine and event attendance data is issued throughout the year.

What does ABC data include?

ABC presents circulation data by various categories, eg actively purchased, subscription, free distribution. The minimum metric for web traffic data (as agreed by the industry) is unique user.

The regionals

Further consolidation or ("offloading") of titles in the regional press was stymied by the global credit crunch (which also, by the way, sold a few papers in the autumn). Trinity Mirror realised, as Associated/Northcliffe did in 2006, that now is not a great time to sell. While shifting the sports division, including The Racing Post and a few other titles for somewhat less than expected, did keep the share price stable, a prolonged process to find a bidder for the Midlands titles failed to attract high enough prices.

DMGT, which owns Associated and Northcliffe, appointed a new chief executive, Martin Morgan, from within the house ranks to succeed Charles Sinclair when he retires in 2008. It is investing heavily online, particularly in property sites, and saw an increase in operating profits at the "unsellable" Northcliffe division. Along with Trinity Mirror, the company continues to protest that print is far from dead or even doomed. However, Lord Rothermere was the first of his line to proudly announce that 50 per cent of his company's operating profits are derived from "outside the newspaper industry". And the London Evening Standard, one of the company's flagship titles, is, at best, "stable", after a torrid time in the London freesheet wars.

Emap, too, fell victim to something of a personal crisis at a bad time for the markets. The radio owner/consumer magazine/trade publisher, which has outposts in most old media but has struggled with the digital world, began to implode midway through 2007 and the chief executive, Tom Moloney, an Emap lifer, resigned. The company put itself up to auction, essentially, and though several private equity firms and interested parties (including the Guardian Media Group) presented themselves, their intentions were reportedly focused on the trade publishing business.

A familiar pattern has now been established in media sell-offs where first the company puts the for sale sign up, causing a spate of stories and rumour about bidders. Then, several months later, details begin to leak out. Bidder x doesn't want the carpets; bidder y is only really interested in the self-contained granny flat; company z, it is reported, is only selling if someone takes the whole shebang including the leaky boiler. It looked as though Emap's future would remain in question until well into 2008 when two bids came to fruition in December. At the time of writing Bauer looks set to take the radio and consumer titles while GMG – publishers of this guide – and Apax have agreed the sale of the B2B arm.

Daily tabloids

Heather Mills McCartney's
GMTV meltdown

Meanwhile, at the more colourful end of the publishing business, Heather Mills McCartney decided to launch what was either a one-woman PR suicide campaign or a desperate bid to illuminate the murky world of the red-tops, depending on your perspective. As her seemingly interminable divorce from her Beatle husband dragged on, Mills McCartney went where few others (Britney Spears, most notably) have dared go, ditching her expensive advisers and their dull "say nothing" advice, to provide quite a show.

It began when she pitched up on GMTV one morning, at her own request, to tearfully rail against the press – fixating on the Sun – clutching a folder of her "4,000" negative and fictional cuttings. Unveiling a website aimed at banning the Sun and a campaign to get

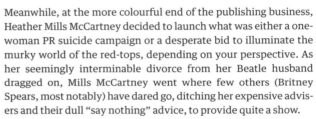

Group name	Market share		Titles	Executive control
National newspaper ownership				
	Jan–Jun 07	Jan–Jun 06		
News International	35.5%	34.4%	Sun Times Sunday Times News of the World	Rupert Murdoch
Daily Mail and General Trust	19.3%	20.5%	Daily Mail Mail on Sunday	Lord Rothermere
Trinity Mirror	20.3%	15.1%	Daily Mirror Sunday Mirror People Sunday Mail Daily Record	TM Board
Northern and Shell	11.9%	13.6%	Daily Express Sunday Express Daily Star Daily Star Sunday	Richard Desmond
Telegraph Media Group	6.1%	7.5%	Daily Telegraph Sunday Telegraph	Barclay Brothers
Guardian Media Group	3.4%	3.4%	Guardian Observer	Scott Trust
Pearson	1.8%	3.3%	Financial Times	Pearson Board
Independent News & Media	1.8%	2.2%	Independent Independent on Sunday	Anthony O'Reilly

Source: ABC

the European court to legislate and regulate the UK press, she might even have engaged some public sympathy for her cause. Few, let's face it, would go to the barricades for tabloid newspapers, no matter how firm their belief in free speech.

We'll likely never know how Mills McCartney might have fared with a serious campaign. This version, with its tone of overwrought desperation, was immediately dismissed — mockingly by her foes and with regret by possible sympathisers — as the last throw of the dice by an unbalanced, greedy, mendacious woman who threatened the happiness of a beloved national icon. Following on from her extensive announcements of defamation proceedings last year, it didn't seem to have been a well-executed campaign and certainly her experienced PR advisor, Phil Hall, (a former editor of the News of the World) publicly resigned, followed swiftly by her divorce lawyer, Anthony Julius.

But as some of the more thoughtful commentators point out, her personal PR can hardly get worse and she just might have a point.

● Janine Gibson is executive editor of Guardian Unlimited and editor-in-chief of MediaGuardian

Major PCC decisions

● **January 2007** The PCC published a series of six recommendations for best practice for newspapers and magazines after two men were convicted for their involvement in a phone-tapping scandal. The News of the World reporters Clive Goodman and Glenn Mulcaire were found guilty of intercepting private voicemail messages on phones belonging to members of the royal household. When Goodman was sentenced, the News of the World editor, Andy Coulson, announced his resignation.

In summary, the PCC's recommendations for best investigative practice are: contractual compliance with the PCC code of practice should be universal in the industry; editors must ensure all staff understand the PCC code of practice and the law; payments to external contributors must be monitored with rigorous audit controls; internal training in relation to privacy cases should be provided regularly; and the Data Protection Act should be referenced in staff contracts.

● **May 2007** The first enforcement of the new rules on reporting suicide was made against the Wigan Evening Post on May 25 2007. The article, headlined "Electrocuted", was found to be excessively detailed in describing how a man had electrocuted himself. The widow of the deceased man made a complaint, calling the Wigan Evening Post's reporting "irresponsible". Her late husband was a teacher and she felt the article was negligent because of the effect it might have had on the children he taught. The PCC upheld the complaint. Newspapers are free to report the proceedings of public inquests, but they have a responsibility to ensure that others are not given sufficient information to carry out copycat suicides.

● **July 2007** The first PCC ruling on video content was against the Hamilton Advertiser, which ran footage of unruly schoolchildren on its website in a story about insufficient discipline in the classroom. Two other papers, the Scottish Sun and the Scottish Daily Mirror, used stills from the same footage, but were said to be within their rights because none of the children were identifiable in the pictures. A pupil who had hoped to explain her poor test results to her parents took the footage on a mobile phone. The PCC agreed with the newspapers that it was in the public's interest to be informed of the lack of teacher supervision, but said that it infringed on the rights of the pupils who were recognisable in the film. Steps should have been taken to conceal their identity or gain consent.

● **August 2007** When the lads' mag FHM published a picture of a topless girl aged 14, it was found to be in breach of clause 3 (privacy) and clause 6 (Children) of the PCC code of practice. The complaint was made by the parents of the girl, whose picture was published without her consent. The snapshot was taken on a mobile phone and sent in by a reader of the magazine. He had informed FHM that he was in a cohabiting relationship with the girl so the magazine did not make further enquiries into her age and had "no reason to believe the image was taken without her consent". The PCC said that the publication of the photo without her consent would be damaging enough regardless, but this damage would have been significantly increased by her age. FHM has introduced new measures to prevent a repeat of the situation.

Traditional media

The digital challenge
Roy Greenslade

The future of newspapers is online – but how are they responding to the demands of different platforms and round-the-clock reporting? In December 2007, Roy Greenslade visited the high-tech newsrooms of three national newspapers to see just how the great integration plans were progressing.

Newspapers are playing a game of digital leapfrog. One paper does not merely catch up when another jumps ahead. It usually overtakes by taking advantage of technological developments its rival was unable to embrace. There is no possibility of standing still. What is state-of-the-art today will be old hat by tomorrow.

In a sense, the online revolution is like a train journey without a destination. As soon as one paper arrives at a station that had once appeared to be a terminus, another title has built a new line and sped onwards. Despite the differences, everyone seems clear about the general direction to take towards an otherwise mysterious objective: the future of news-gathering and news delivery is tied to the screen.

For the moment, given the need to keep on printing while simultaneously uploading, it means driving as fast as possible towards a brave new world while keeping the engines running at full power in the old – but still lucrative and popular – world of newsprint.

Inevitably, this split has proved uncomfortable, both in journalistic terms and, seen from the perspective of owners and managers, in financial terms too. In company with editors, they have set the course to reach a single station named "Integration". It is now clear that the days of binary staffing, with journalists for print and journalists for web, are virtually over. In most offices the initial scepticism about the utility and viability of online news has long since passed.

Regional newspapers, as so often, have been in the forefront of this cultural change. Their reporters and subeditors have been embracing multi-platform journalism for several years. The nationals have been slower off the mark, but – as you can see from the following examples – they are forging ahead now.

Editors, naturally enough, tend to justify the merging of print and digital staffs by talking of the journalistic imperative. But they are aware that there has been a commercial impulse too. With falling revenues from both circulation and advertising, it does not make financial sense to employ two sets of overlapping staff.

A similar, if somewhat controversial, financial logic has also dictated a reconsideration of the staffing requirements across seven days. Some dailies with Sunday counterparts have come to the conclusion that it is no longer feasible to have completely separate staffs.

One of digital transmission's greatest benefits is that it allows for the merging of staff on daily and Sunday titles in a way that proved unachievable 20 years ago. Some call it another wonder of the web others call it job cuts under a digital cloak.

But integration is about much more than internal office structures. It is really about the creation of a new journalistic culture, a method of working that reflects both the technological possibilities and the demands of a wised up, increasingly media-savvy public.

Indeed, it is also about the response to a new public because newspapers are no longer serving a geographically distinct area. Worldwide access to news sites means that the audience served by London-based national newspapers is no longer merely British.

Name	January	February	March	April	May	June	July	August
Guardian Unlimited	15,703,012	13,761,364	15,093,058	15,170,348	16,062,221	14,514,091	16,058,979	15,821,480
Sun.co.uk	9,543,772	8,028,211	7,797,032	8,235,925	9,002,325	9,021,249	9,435,509	10,594,198
telegraph.co.uk	7,473,939	7,199,166	7,392,803	7,359,312	7,275,288	7,053,297	8,992,526	9,770,562
Times.co.uk	10,891,378	—	8,048,029	8,905,701	8,730,026	9,647,607	10,536,915	10,239,223
Dailymail.co.uk			6,518,774	7,549,351	9,347,554	9,466,326	11,865,039	11,585,134

National newspaper websites (global monthly unique users, 2007)

Unique audience – does not count repeat visits by the same user   Source: ABCe

The challenge is to provide 24/7 news, to offer a minute-by-minute, round-the-clock news service. This can only be achieved through integration, by journalists responding to the demand of filing for website and newsprint paper, by them bringing into play audio and video material whenever relevant.

In my visits to the offices of the Financial Times, the Times and the Telegraph titles – where there are different forms of integration – I was struck by the way in which their journalists have grasped, or are beginning to grasp, the benefits of integration, not only at a practical level but as a philosophy.

Every executive I met was at pains to point out how the mindset of their editorial staffs has changed. They are no longer troubled by that old argument about whether a story should be web-first or print-first. With their news editors they are developing an instinct about the appropriate way to publish.

One persistent criticism by sceptics is that journalists are being asked to do too much. Again, that's not what I discovered. As far as I could ascertain, journalists are grasping the opportunities offered by online publishing to write more freely.

There is much more fulfilment involved in writing a developing story when you discover that there is no longer any need to cut it to ribbons to fit a space. Updating for newsprint editions tended to be dispiriting because some material would inevitably be lost. Now it can be accommodated without any loss of detail.

Similarly, there was no previous possibility of going off at a tangent. Those who have been given blogs can do just that, offering readers background material, plus comment.

It is true that on some papers, such as the Daily Telegraph, it took some prompting to encourage people to write regular blog contributions. Now that's not a problem. Journalists are seeing the value of the online medium even as they continue to delight in their newsprint bylines.

Finally, it is also clear that integration has stimulated journalists to become inventive. Once it was the journalist geeks among us who had to goad reluctant colleagues to change their attitudes, to learn the new way of doing things.

Now journalists are realising that integration is not only proving much less painless than expected, it is releasing them from the straitjacket of the single 24-hour deadline.

» MediaGuardian   September 10 2007

Why Patience wasn't enough

Peter Wilby

Another week, another Telegraph editor departs, the fourth in two years. Patience Wheatcroft's offence, apparently, was to be insufficiently enthused by the Telegraph's all-action, round-the-clock multimedia operation. Put simply, she wanted her modestly-sized staff to be accountable to her for producing a good Sunday paper, and not to be distracted by other editors demanding the instant reactions of a 24-hour website.

Even to daily newspaper journalists – let alone to managements bent on achieving "efficiencies" – this attitude will be incomprehensible, perhaps scandalous. Sunday journalists, they think, have nothing to do all week and will, therefore, have more free time for multimedia performances. But the natural instinct of a Sunday editor is to keep her powder dry and her staff on a tight rein. Her paper's credibility depends on a conjuring trick. Except in sport, there is no news on Saturdays; the

Sundays have nothing fresh in the way of significant events to report. But unlike magazines and local or professional weekly newspapers, they are on sale for a single day. No matter how good their book reviews, style sections and food magazines, they must therefore contrive news to create the necessary sense of urgency, with the political team commonly instructed to weave together a spurious "crisis" for the front page.

Sunday papers must also, on their comment and news feature pages, produce distinctive insights into the past week's events which supposedly require long reflection and detailed probing. As a former Sunday paper editor – and I congratulate Wheatcroft on exceeding my 17-month tenure at the Independent on Sunday by three weeks – I know many 2,000-word "focus" pieces are hastily knocked out, after a few phone calls, late on a Friday night. But that is not a secret one wishes to share with the outside world, and there is some truth in the view that Sunday journalists – who can rarely just rewrite a press release – have to work as hard as their daily colleagues, and draw on higher levels of ingenuity and writing skill. I worked for 23 years on Sunday papers, against three years on a daily, and certainly found the former more demanding. Though several Sunday papers, notably the IoS, now share some writing staff with their daily sisters, no British newspaper group has yet gone down the road of complete integration. All continue to market their Sundays as separate titles and to maintain separate editorial hierarchies.

Since several Sunday papers existed long before they were joined by ownership to their present daily partners, it makes sense to preserve them as distinct brands. The Sunday Telegraph was intended from its launch in 1961 as a seventh-day version of the Daily Telegraph and has always struggled to establish its own identity. The Observer, Sunday Times and News of the World, however, have their own character and history and can reach readers and advertisers that the Guardian, Times and Sun do not. Of these, the Sunday Times is probably the most distinct from its daily sister and, with twice the circulation and consistently high profits, is the more valuable property.

Yet even the Sunday Times does not have its own web address: enter sundaytimes.co.uk and you find yourself at timesonline.co.uk. Enter sundaytelegraph.co.uk and it is "unavailable". No newspaper group seriously attempts to promote its Sunday brands online. Where Sundays do have their own websites, they rarely show more than the latest issue's headlines and stories, plus breaking news identical to that on its daily sister's site. Most are not significantly active between Sunday morning and the following Saturday night.

The Observer website has a blog – but the latest entry is for November 16 2006. When newspaper people discuss the future of Sunday papers, this is the elephant in the room they never mention.

The most obscure weekly papers have an online presence; Sunday papers, for the most part, don't. Since their unique selling point is that they appear on Sundays, it is hard to see how they could develop one. The Times Educational Supplement, the New Statesman and your local rag may come out on Fridays, but they are not Friday papers. On a seven-day website, the Sundays inevitably become sub-sections with no more prominence than weekly sections such as Education Guardian or Femail.

Differentiated brands may continue to work for a few years yet. In the UK, attempts to integrate Sunday and daily operations have so far failed. That doesn't mean they are doomed forever. As more readers and advertisers migrate to the web, where news doesn't await a daily deadline, let alone a weekly one, Sunday titles will gradually cease to mean anything.

We may still get fat Sunday papers, just as we get fat Saturday ones, because people have more time for reading and shopping at weekends. An Alan Watkins or Andrew Rawnsley may continue to write a column only on Sundays, as a George Monbiot writes only on Tuesdays. The Sunday may have a special editor to oversee the package, as most Saturday papers do. But I fear the reporters, feature writers and news editors, saving their pearls for the weekend, and the designers sweating over distinctive mastheads and typefaces will, within a decade at most, all be gone.

The regionals

In a quiet year for the regional press, two companies owned by the Daily Mail and General Trust pointed to a possible way forward, both in print and online. Stephen Brook reported for Mediaguardian.co.uk in October:

Northcliffe Media, the regional division of the Daily Mail and General Trust, said today it was a "revitalised business" that would continue to launch local print titles. Briefing city journalists today, more than 18 months after it tried and failed to sell its regional newspaper arm, DMGT said its regional division had a "renewed sense of purpose".

Northcliffe, which includes the Hull Daily Mail and South Wales Evening Post, said its UK operating profits grew by 6.9% in the year to September 30. This was despite a fall in advertising revenue of 0.7% for the year. "We have a revitalised business, which is clearly focused, more efficient, operating on a much reduced cost base, and has a renewed sense of purpose," said Northcliffe managing director Michael Pelosi.

"We are aware of our key challenges. We must deliver local audiences if we are to achieve profitable revenue growth. Digital publishing has a key role to play here," Mr Pelosi added. "We are implementing solutions so as to address our challenges. Northcliffe is now an integrated local media publisher. Online, we are getting better by the day.

"But we still recognise the huge value of print and we will launch selectively where market opportunities present themselves." Northcliffe said it expected to report revenues of £448m and operating profits of not less than £92.5m before deductions for the year ending September 30.

Significantly, Northcliffe's declarations came a day after a "digital restructure" at sister company Associated Newspapers in which control of digital publishing reverted to the individual newspapers including London paper, Metro. The company's websites are a mix of newspaper-related spin-offs and lifestyle sites including Dailymail.co.uk, ThisisLondon.co.uk, SimplySwitch.com, FindaProperty.com, Jobsite.co.uk and LoopyLove.com.

Earlier in the year Northcliffe bought 25 titles in Surrey, Sussex, Kent and Dorset from Trinity Mirror for £64.15m. As Stephen Brook and Chris Tryhorn reported on MediaGuardian.co.uk in July:

The sale includes paid-for weeklies the Croydon Advertiser, the Surrey Mirror, the Folkestone and Dover Herald; and free weeklies including the Adscene series, Blackmore Vale Magazine, a free title published in Dorset and numerous local websites.

Trinity Mirror and Northcliffe expect to complete the sale by the end of the month. Northcliffe will use the sale to boost its south-east division, currently its smallest region, and extend its websites to a wider geographic area.

The local newspaper publisher has recently sold Aberdeen Journals, Northcliffe Retail and its 25% shareholding in the website Fish4.

The managing director of Northcliffe Media, Michael Pelosi, said that the company's transformation over the past year had been "dramatic".

"We believe that the division has an excellent future as a provider of high quality local media content and services," Mr Pelosi added.

"Today's acquisitions strengthen our publishing reach in a region demonstrating strong economic growth where digital opportunities are particularly attractive.

"We are acquiring strong products which are at the heart of their local communities and are looking forward to working with our new colleagues."

Was this piecemeal acquisition of regional newspaper groups simply a UK phenomenon? Peter Preston writing in the Observer in July pointed to a US giant, previously one of the acquisitors.

Pundits and union officials alike seem bemused. Why should the biggest newspaper company in America – 90 dailies, almost a thousand weeklies – be offering its British staff an unenviable pension choice: four pretty unpalatable options, from increasing your contributions to 12 per cent, to bailing out of the scheme altogether?

Didn't Gannett boast revenues of $8bn last year? Isn't its Newsquest wing – with 300 titles, including 18 dailies – the second biggest regional group in Britain, and performing rather better on ad revenue than Big Brother USA? How can a £65m pension-fund shortfall matter quite so much?

Alas, two little figures explain rather a lot. When Gannett bought Newsquest in 1999 the £1.06bn they paid came in at $1.55bn. Now… well, you've seen the latest pound/dollar exchange rate – two dollars plus, and rising. Eight years ago, the profits from Newsquest produced glowing Wall Street opinions. Gannett, which more than any other huge US newspaper company lives or dies by its share price, had done a great deal (especially since there was still a little fat to be carved off the bone).

But now all such fat has gone. How do you cut back on editions at the Bradford Telegraph & Argus when there's only one edition left?

Top 10 regional publishers			
	Number of papers	**Weekly circulation (m)**	**% share**
Trinity Mirror	185	11.2	16.7%
Newsquest Media Group	215	9.7	14.4%
Associated Newspapers	13	9.1	13.5%
Johnston Press	283	8.8	13.2%
Northcliffe Media	135	7.9	11.8%
Archant	74	2.7	4.0%
Guardian Media Group	43	2.6	3.9%
News International Newspapers	1	2.4	3.5%
The Midland News Association	19	2.0	2.9%
D.C. Thomson & Co	6	1.9	2.8%
Total top 10	**974**	**58.3**	**86.8%**
Total all regional publishers	**1,310**	**67.1**	

Source: PPA

It's no wonder, then, that succeeding Gannett investment reports have fallen to moaning about the strength of sterling. Nor is it wholly surprising to find American newspaper executives seeing Newsquest back in takeover play again. Remember, company pension deficits are a drag when buyers are summoned to market. Why not get that problem cleared up first? But remember, too, that regional papers in Britain are also harder to get rid of at a premium, as Northcliffe found to its dismay.

What am I bid? No... Who will open any bidding? There are real prospective difficulties here. America can't sell off whole chains with ease any longer – as first Knight Ridder then the Tribune Company proved. There have to be deals within deals. And the UK, if anything, is in a more complex state. Trinity Mirror, still number one, is a seller, not a buyer (it sold 25 titles on Friday). Johnston Press at number three is fighting hard to keep FTSE good opinions, but can't fancy having a great Newsquest banquet on its plate while problems like The Scotsman linger. Northcliffe, at number four, bought those Trinity tidbits, but suffers from indigestion. And monopoly regulations raise problems at every turn in any case.

Call for the rescue squad of first modern resort, aka private equity? Perhaps: but Gannett hasn't left much juice to squeeze out of Newsquest – and residual pensions won't help a jot. Which, with a glum glance at Wall Street, is where we came in.

Buying chains when the rate is right may be fine. But rates go down as well as up. Maybe the pound will fall off its perch again sometime soon. Maybe that gets everyone involved off an ominous hook. Don't bank on it as grimaces deepen, though. Purchase in haste, repent at leisure.

Regional newspaper circulations

	Average net circulation			Frequency	Editor
	Jan-Jun 07	Jan-Jun 06	% change		
Top 20 paid-for regionals					
Sunday Mail, Scotland	505,075	532,545	-5.2%	Sunday	Allan Rennie
Daily Record, Scotland	368,271	443,464	-17.0%	morning	Bruce Waddell
Evening Standard, London	270,718	326,132	-17.0%	evening	Veronica Wadley
Sunday Post, Scotland	277,217	451,530	-38.6%	Sunday	David Pollington
Express & Star, West Midlands	144,909	151,272	-4.2%	evening	Adrian Faber
Liverpool Echo	113,126	121,517	-6.9%	evening	Alastair Machray
Manchester Evening News	88,669	118,903	-25.4%	evening	Paul Horrocks
Evening Times, Glasgow	86,166	87,399	-1.4%	evening	Donald Martin
Belfast Telegraph	85,916	90,827	-5.4%	evening	Martin Lindsay
Yorkshire Post, Leeds	84,904	87,645	-3.1%	morning	Peter Charlton
Aberdeen Press & Journal	81,956	84,137	-2.6%	morning	Derek Tucker
Evening Chronicle, Newcastle	80,669	86,287	-6.5%	evening	Paul Robertson
Dundee Courier & Advertiser	77,451	76,917	0.7%	morning	Bill Hutcheon
Leicester Mercury	77,108	75,319	2.4%	evening	Nick Carter
Eastern Daily Press, Norwich	76,056	66,515	14.3%	morning	Peter Franzen
Sunday Life, Belfast	74,886	77,817	-3.8%	Sunday	Jim Flanagan
Birmingham Mail	74,347	78,178	-4.9%	evening	Steve Dyson
Shropshire Star	74,017	76,568	-3.3%	evening	Sarah Jane Smith
Sunday Sun, Newcastle	68,960	71,755	-3.9%	Sunday	Colin Patterson
The Sentinel, Stoke on Trent	64,685	70,567	-8.3%	daily	Mike Sassi
Top 10 frees					
Metro, London	546,959*	542,294**	0.9%	morning	Kenny Campbell
Manchester Metro News Trafford	309,103	309,613	-0.2%	weekly	Kate Stirrup
Nottingham & Long Eaton Topper	211,700	209,190	1.2%	weekly	John Howarth
Nottingham Recorder	150,102	150,525	-0.3%	weekly	Malcolm Pheby
Herald & Post Edinburgh	132,739	134,537	-1.3%	weekly	Gail Milne
Coventry Times	121,827	120,894	0.8%	weekly	Alan Kirby
Coventry Observer	121,577	122,209	-0.5%	weekly	Mike Green
Milton Keynes Citizen	103,119	101,002	2.1%	weekly	Jan Henderson
Croydon Guardian	100,894	100,712	0.2%	weekly	Danny Brierley
Bromley News Shopper	99,445	99,284	0.2%	weekly	Jean May

* Jul 30–Aug 26 07   ** Jul 31–Aug 27 06

Source: ABC

Magazines

David Hepworth

A few weeks ago I asked a very well-known, recently retired industry figure whether he would be looking to pick up any titles in the proposed Emap sale. "I wouldn't buy a magazine these days," he said. "Not even in a newsagent."

There was some gallows humour of that kind around this year, particularly from people who'd been used to selling a lot of magazines to young men. Even in the world of women's magazines it was clear to those paying attention that the virtues of the medium might no longer be quite so self-evident. I talked to a number of people at the helms of household-name titles who were watching their sales base erode and finding they were having to fight harder for advertising in what is becoming, for everyone but the phone company, a small portions world. The vessel of human attention has only a certain capacity and at some point somebody has to shout "when!".

The indisputably candid statement of the year came from Darren Styles of Brooklands, speaking in April after he'd closed the magazine Popworld Pulp within two weeks of its launch: "To be perfectly frank, the magazine has bombed in a way nobody connected with it could ever have envisaged." Brooklands put out more than 100,000 of the first issue and sold less than 4,000. This is not because it was rubbish. It's because the public has never taken more persuading to put its hand in its pocket and try something new. The Popworld closure took place just days after the equally premature demise of the upmarket property magazine So London, which gave up almost before it had started.

Launches not working is nothing new but this indifference was. Since the spring there's been little going on in the launch area at all. It's as if all the publishers recognise that the curiosity gap in which they used to flourish has been colonised by other media and the only new titles that seem to get traction are big weeklies. These are ruinously expensive to launch and consequently few and far between.

A model of success ...
free sports magazine Sport

What are the alternatives? On the face of it, the policy of actually stuffing your magazine in somebody's hand seems to get round the problem of the public unwillingness to sample. The success of the free sports magazine Sport encouraged Mike Soutar, previously editorial director at IPC, to come in with his general men's weekly ShortList and as I type this there is talk of Open Goal, which is to be given away at Premier League grounds, and even a Jewish lifestyle glossy, JLifestyle. We must assume that some time soon there will be a free weekly celeb title given away at travel points. However, because these free versions are compelled to offer more circulation than the paid-for titles (which, in the case of the celebrity market, would be a great deal) they're going to run into the mother and father of a littering problem. This is going to be an issue for the whole print industry before very long.

At the time of writing (early November) the other shoe has yet to drop in the biggest story of the year, the potential break-up of Emap. Hearst, the owner of National Magazines, seems to be the most likely buyer but there is talk of a David Arculus-led attempt to shake up the board and continue to run Emap as a media company. However, there will still be arguments over valuations, which are all rooted in an earlier age when profits were easier to predict than they are at the moment. If Hearst succeeds and finds itself the publisher of market-leading weeklies such as Heat and Closer as well as its traditional glossies, the balance of power in the magazine business will tilt significantly.

Felix Dennis offloaded his American operation in summer but his UK business remains strong thanks to the steady growth of The

Magazine top 10s

		Average circulation per issue			Year-on-year % change
		Jan–Jun 07	Jul–Dec 06	Jan–Jun 06	
Top 10 women's weeklies					
1	Take a Break	1,018,423	1,027,013	1,082,051	-5.9%
2	Closer	570,239	614,141	590,211	-3.4%
3	Heat	558,365	598,623	579,883	-3.7%
4	OK! Magazine	557,014	624,091	547,714	1.7%
5	Chat	511,510	537,464	554,375	-7.7%
6	Now	494,229	540,132	539,902	-8.5%
7	Pick Me Up	447,100	424,410	445,098	0.4%
8	That's Life	443,604	464,762	490,220	-9.5%
9	New!	442,003	456,987	458,751	-3.7%
10	Hello!*	419,814	412,807	403,666	4.0%
Top 10 women's lifestyle					
1	Glamour	544,653	588,539	586,056	-7.1%
2	Cosmopolitan	450,952	455,649	442,384	1.9%
3	Good Housekeeping	435,238	463,645	441,151	-1.3%
4	Yours	344,438	383,577	400,312	-14.0%
5	Marie Claire	332,705	334,729	331,127	0.5%
6	Woman & Home	320,934	316,034	325,223	-1.3%
7	Look*	318,907	–	–	
8	Candis	302,377	301,309	301,114	0.4%
9	Prima	300,025	315,149	321,617	-6.7%
10	Company	264,494	264,095	275,038	-3.8%
Top 10 men's lifestyle including weeklies					
1	Sport*	317,093	–	–	
2	FHM	311,590	371,263	420,688	-25.9%
3	Nuts	277,269	295,002	304,785	-9.0%
4	Men's Health	238,980	238,568	235,833	1.3%
5	Zoo	186,732	204,564	228,024	-18.1%
6	GQ	127,886	127,505	126,797	0.9%
7	Loaded	120,492	162,554	185,268	-35.0%
8	Maxim	107,687	131,497	146,043	-26.3%
9	Stuff	92,793	100,265	92,672	0.1%
10	Men's Fitness	65,366	65,135	67,674	-3.4%

* Not in last year's top 10   Source: ABC

Week, which now sells 150,000 copies every week. The fact that its entire readership sit down with it for the same two hours on a Saturday morning and only a small number of its copies actually go through the news trade could turn out to be a lesson for the entire industry. People love magazines just as much as they ever did. It's just that they bridle at being driven into newsagents to pay for them and they need to have the habit of reading them re-established.

Other medium to large companies, such as Future and Haymarket, reported good progress thanks to strict cost control, investment in well-aimed web services and limiting their exposure to the costly slugfests at the news stand. Once it had managed to successfully establish the celebrity and shopping weekly Look, IPC didn't do much on the magazine front, instead concentrating efforts on Nuts TV with the rumour of NME radio and the like not very far behind. These are likely to provide work for glamour models and third-party suppliers long before they produce work for journalists or ad revenue for the bottom line but there's something to be said for having something new to talk to your clients about.

It's been the same with the web in 2007. You couldn't afford not to but you couldn't honestly see how to. The chief executive of one major publisher of women's weeklies told me he'd given up pretending with investors and was prepared to confess that he couldn't see a way his company would ever make money out of the internet. History will either see this as a hopeless lack of vision or admirable good sense depending on how things work out. The truth is that the senior magazine executives (as a group among the least web-savvy in the media) making all the grand announcements don't know how well it's going to go, any more than their counterparts at newspapers, TV or radio do. "Mapmaking in an earthquake zone" they used to call it. That's the way it's going to be for everybody from now on. Could be fun.

● David Hepworth is editorial director of Development Hell Ltd.
mail@davidhepworth.com

Awards

British Press Awards 2007

- *Scoop of the year:* Stephen Moyes for the Daily Mirror, "John Prescott's Affair"
- *Front page of the year:* Daily Mirror, "My Affair: By Prezza"
- *Newspaper of the year:* Observer

Regional Press Awards 2007

- *Weekly newspaper of the year below 20,000 circulation:* North Shropshire Chronicle
- *Weekly newspaper of the year above 20,000 circulation:* The Cumberland News
- *Daily/Sunday newspaper of the year below 40,000 circulation:* Evening Star, Ipswich
- *Daily/Sunday newspaper of the year above 40,000 circulation:* Belfast Telegraph
- *Free newspaper of the year:* The Comet, Hertfordshire
- *Website of the year:* Evening Gazette, Teesside
- *Supplement of the year:* Food Monthly, Reading Evening Post

PPA Awards 2007

- *Consumer magazine of the year:* Harper's Bazaar (National Magazine Company)
- *Editor of the year, consumer:* Morgan Rees, Men's Health (NatMag Rodale)
- *Consumer specialist magazine of the year:* Focus (Bristol Magazines)
- *Consumer lifestyle magazine of the year:* Condé Nast Traveller (Condé Nast Publications)
- *Weekly business and professional magazine of the year:* Property Week (CMP Information)
- *Monthly business and professional magazine of the year:* Safety Health Practitioner (CMP Information)
- *Customer magazine of the year:* 33 Thoughts (John Brown, BDO Stoy Hayward)

Why are vintage magazines more popular than their modern day counterparts? Swoon! At the "gorgeous" centrefold. Gasp! At the outrageous fashion. Wallow! In 70s nostalgia. In 2007 a whole new market emerged of Christmas "retro annuals" producing the best (and the worst) of years gone by. Alice Wignall examined our obsession with retro magazines, and our ambivalence towards current titles.

The wonder years
Alice Wignall

Christmas is coming and novelty book publishers everywhere are hoping to get fat. And this year the tide of nostalgia publications seems to be rising higher than ever, washing in with it stacks of books bearing the names of iconic magazines and cover girls with improbable hair.

The current trend for anthologising articles and features from old magazines was kick-started in 2005 when Prion Books published The Best of Jackie, a collection of tidbits from the long-running teen magazine. It was a huge success, generating big sales, a great glut of "those were the days" articles, and spawning a slew of imitators. My Guy: the Best of the Photostories and The Best of Cosmopolitan: the 70s and 80s are but the most recent.

You can see the appeal for the bottom-line minded publisher. Set loose a researcher with plenty of stamina and a strong sense of the absurd on a pile of back issues, bind the whole lot together with some suitably retro styling on the front cover and then armies of readers of a certain age can ... squeal! At the terrible clothes. Chortle! At the hopeless naivety of teenagers three decades ago. Feel slightly sick as we survey the men we (apparently) once fancied.

It has proved a successful formula, but it is curious that as we are carting piles of these publications to the tills, we are marching right past the present-day examples of the same titles. The teen magazine market, the sector created by weeklies such as Jackie and My Guy, is virtually extinct. Neither of those titles exists any more – though they lasted a lot longer than you might suspect, up until 1993 and 2000 respectively.

And while Cosmopolitan considers itself a market leader among the women's glossies – the most recent ABC figures gave it a monthly circulation of 450,952, second only to Glamour – the market it is leading is pretty sickly, if not an outright terminal case. Even such an iconic brand as Cosmo is experiencing falling sales – those ABCs representing a 1% drop in circulation from the previous six-month period.

So how is it that we love the archive material, but are bored by the current output? The first and most obvious answer is that these nostalgia-fests provide something that magazines tend to be pretty light on: laughs, although that presumably was not the purpose at the time. One can only imagine that the people who originally laboured over Cosmo stories with titles like, The Most Beautiful Thing A Man Can Do For A Woman – and Michael Parkinson Has Done It (a tell-all interview on vasectomy, just in case you were unaware of the precise nature of the most beautiful thing a man can do for a woman) had nothing but the most serious of intentions at the time.

Now, however, there is not much one can do but laugh when faced with a technicolour photo of Ian McShane wearing a medallion, a beard and not much else, with only a surprisingly content-looking dachshund (Morrie) to protect his modesty. The My Guy annual lays it on even thicker, with the worst clothes, the most alarming youth slang and the least realistic stories of teenage adventures in a cabin cruiser ever committed to paper.

And then, of course, there is the other great joy – in fact, the whole purpose – of these anthologies: a great big serving of nostalgic reverie. But the particular type of nostalgia that the Cosmo collection is trying to inspire in its present-day readers is harder to define. Is it smug satisfaction at how far we have come? It is hard not to read an article that exhorts its readers to overturn the patriarchy with such daring moves as choosing the wine when you are out for dinner with your boyfriend, or phoning him at 6pm to say you have to work late, and not feel at least a little pleased at what women have achieved in the interim years (yes, yes, the right to get drunk and/or stuck in the office. Well, it is a start).

On the other hand, you cannot help but wonder

if the editors of the book are also trying to teach us a lesson or two. The same feature that suggests you help your partner with his tax return as a sign of your liberation casually mentions in its introduction that, "We know we all live with a double standard . . . " How many glossies these days would assume that all its readers were concerned with gender inequality, let alone mention it in print? As well as being, naturally, a hoot, The Best Of Cosmopolitan reminds us that it was a proud campaigner. Is feminism in 2007 not in Cosmo because it is not mainstream, or is it not mainstream because it's not in Cosmo? Are they trying to make us feel nostalgic for a time when magazines were political as well as pretty?

In any case, presumably the reason a few pages from an old magazine can inspire such floods of reverie is because they so accurately pinpoint the experience of being, say, a teenager in 1979. Maybe magazines now are struggling to do the same, if falling sales and dying-off titles are anything to go by (My Guy sold 300,000 copies a week in its heyday).

For teen magazines the template remains the same as that created by Jackie and My Guy — boys, friends, celebrities, causes, fashion, beauty, problems and periods. And there remains reaction from outsiders who think that the titles are leading young girls astray (though the precise nature of the concern — from too much kissing to too much oral sex — has shifted over time).

Even the photo-stories aren't that far removed from what you read today. The only real difference is that Best Kept Secret, a photo-story about school bullies publishing the contents of your diary, would these days be a real life-story, told in written-through copy and illustrated with a picture of a pretty-but-relateable real reader.

Which is why, no doubt, that various tweaked permutations of the teenage magazine thrived throughout the 80s and early 90s. It was only really with the advent of the internet age that they properly began to flounder. A once-a-month publication struggles to compete with a readership whose social currency depends on knowing what Britney Spears was doing in LA five hours ago. It cannot tell them; a website can.

Play it safe

What the teenage market has in common with its older sisters is a loss of its stranglehold. In 1979 if you, as a woman of any age, wanted to know about fashion, about relationships, where could you go? There might be a bit on TV or the radio, you could ask your friends. But for authoritative opinion on a wide range of subjects the magazine rack at your local newsagents was your only option. Now, readers drain away to the web and multiple TV channels.

No doubt these collections were put together with an eye for an easy laugh and a quick buck, but what they inadvertently showcase is a period when magazines had the upper hand over their readers. If you wanted to read anything at all, then this was what was on offer.

Now, the fierce competition between magazines for readers has led to a narrowing of their remit, in an attempt to avoid scaring any more of the precious commodity away. You could argue that this makes them leaner, fitter and more responsive to their market. But surveying the pages of The Best of Cosmopolitan and wondering if any magazine these days could just throw in a reference to Manet's Le Dejeuner sur l'Herbe in an introduction to a food piece — and deciding the answer is probably "no" — suggests magazines today play it safe at the risk of being bland. Which is maybe why they're being left on the shelf, while their 70s selves are invited out to play.

Top 50 consumer magazines

Title	Average circulation/issue			Year-on-year % change
	Jan–Jun 07	Jul–Dec 06	Jan–Jun 06	
1 Sky the magazine	7,034,310	7,002,232	6,798,495	3.5%
2 Sky Sports Magazine (UK)	4,362,228	–	–	–
3 Sky Movies Magazine (UK Edition)	3,767,906	–	–	–
4 Asda Magazine	2,805,052	2,743,005	2,974,793	-5.7%
5 Tesco Magazine	1,943,767	2,419,083	1,923,933	1.0%
6 Sainsbury's Fresh Ideas	1,507,766	1,473,800	1,422,102	6.0%
7 What's on TV	1,421,645	1,436,873	1,508,595	-5.8%
8 TV Choice	1,390,376	1,352,090	1,286,385	8.1%
9 The Somerfield Magazine	1,201,700	1,244,715	1,092,936	10.0%
10 Radio Times	1,041,705	1,078,156	1,066,734	-2.3%
11 Take a Break	1,009,795	1,015,010	1,073,145	-5.9%
12 Debenhams Desire	747,251	747,251	745,126	0.3%
13 Sky Kids	745,779	–	–	–
14 Reader's Digest	709,152	713,254	733,261	-3.3%
15 Saga Magazine	657,264	609,166	1,103,511	-40.4%
16 Birds	607,775	613,013	618,104	-1.7%
17 Closer	561,869	604,149	583,524	-3.7%
18 Heat	542,280	586,081	568,818	-4.7%
19 Unlimited	500,700	524,600	542,250	-7.7%
20 OK! Magazine	500,121	546,812	494,824	1.1%
21 Chat	499,626	523,630	543,950	-8.1%
22 Ikea Family Live	487,815	–	–	–
23 Now	483,858	517,383	528,027	-8.4%
24 Glamour	475,714	527,359	517,400	-8.1%
25 That's Life	440,583	459,281	487,432	-9.6%
26 Pick Me Up	436,150	416,959	437,185	-0.2%
27 Sky the magazine Ireland	430,143	413,683	397,478	8.2%
28 New!	424,489	427,686	438,379	-3.2%
29 Homebase Ideas	417,505	418,465	424,055	-1.5%
30 Good Housekeeping	416,200	446,165	422,905	-1.6%
31 Emma's Diary Pregnancy Guide	409,383	408,235	414,930	-1.3%
32 Village Life	400,002	–	–	–
33 Your Family	392,950	395,014	392,475	0.1%
34 Love It!	390,436	396,185	393,131	-0.7%
35 Cosmopolitan	379,401	386,864	373,360	1.6%
36 Woman	358,957	377,939	405,956	-11.6%
37 National Geographic Magazine	355,830	356,206	355,956	0.0%
38 TV Times	352,484	377,044	372,339	-5.3%
39 Hello!	352,076	354,101	345,480	1.9%
40 Sainsbury's: The Magazine	347,089	382,443	357,500	-2.9%
41 Reveal	342,151	337,612	338,877	1.0%
42 Yours	341,852	380,489	397,483	-14.0%
43 Woman's Own	336,317	346,360	356,413	-5.6%
44 The Garden	334,486	336,415	335,996	-0.4%
45 Best	332,789	351,798	353,586	-5.9%
46 Woman's Weekly	332,339	347,897	352,053	-5.6%
47 BMW Magazine UK	321,899	304,567	–	–
48 BBC Good Food	319,232	339,663	309,023	3.3%
49 Look	317,343	–	–	–
50 Sport	317,093	–	–	–

Newsstand titles in bold

Source: ABC

National press contacts

National daily newspapers

Daily Express
Express Newspapers, The Northern & Shell Building,
Number 10 Lower Thames Street, London EC3R 6EN
0871 434 1010
www.express.co.uk
firstname.surname@express.co.uk
Editor: Peter Hill
- *Deputy editor: Hugh Whittow; news: Greg Swift; political: Macer Hall*
- *Section editors – City: Stephen Kahn; comment: Laura Kibby; defence: John Ingham; features: Fergus Kelly; health: Victoria Fletcher; money: Holly Thomas; showbiz: Elisa Roche; sport: Bill Bradshaw; transport: John Ingham; TV: Charlotte Civil*
- *Production editor: Bob Smith; chief sub: Keith Ging*

Daily Mail
Associated Newspapers, Northcliffe House,
2 Derry Street, Kensington, London W8 5TT
020 7938 6000
www.dailymail.co.uk
firstname.surname@dailymail.co.uk
Editor: Paul Dacre
- *Deputy editor: Alistair Sinclair; news: Keith Poole; political: Ben Brogan*
- *Sections – city: Alex Brummer; Royal and diplomatic: Rebecca English; diary: Richard Kay; features: Leaf Kalfayan; money: Tony Hazell; showbiz: Richard Simpson; sport: Tim Jotischky; transport: Ray Massey*
- *Correspondents – consumer affairs: Sean Poulter; education: Sarah Harris; health: Jenny Hope; industry: Becky Barrow; political: James Chapman, Graeme Wilson; social affairs: Steve Doughty*
- *Editorial systems manager: Harbans Baga; chief subs: Matthew Gocher (news); Robin Popham (features)*
- *Assistant editor: Charles Garside, 020 7938 6000*

Daily Mirror
MGN, One Canada Square, Canary Wharf,
London E14 5AP
020 7293 3000
www.mirror.co.uk
firstname.surname@mirror.co.uk
Editor: Richard Wallace
- *Deputy editor: Conor Hanna; news: Anthony Harwood; political: Oonagh Blackman*
- *Sections – business: Clinton Manning; consumer: Ruki Sayid; fashion: Amber Morales; features: Carole Watson; foreign: Mark Ellis; health: Simone Cave; money: John Husband; sport: Dean Morse; TV: Nicola Methven*
- *Executive editor (production): Jon Moorhead; chief news sub: Pratima Sarwate; chief features sub: James Rettie; assistant editor (pictures): Ian Down; picture editor: Greg Bennett; managing editor: Eugene Duffy; editorial manager: John Honeywell*
- *Publicity: Sarah Vaughan-Brown, 020 7293 3222*

Daily Sport
Sport Newspapers, 19 Great Ancoats Street,
Manchester M60 4BT
0161 236 4466
www.dailysport.net
firstname.surname@sportsnewspapers.co.uk
- *Publicity: Paul Carter, 0161 238 8181*

Daily Star
Express Newspapers, The Northern & Shell Building,
Number 10 Lower Thames Street, London EC3R 6EN
0871 434 1010
www.dailystar.co.uk
firstname.surname@dailystar.co.uk
Editor: Dawn Neesom
- *Deputy editor: Jim Mansell; news: Kieron Saunders; political: Macer Hall; features: Samantha Taylor; sport: Howard Wheatcroft; Cashpoint: Michelle Carter*
- *Production editor: Bob Hadfield*

Daily Telegraph
Telegraph Group, 111 Buckingham Palace Road,
London SW1 0DT
020 7931 2000
www.telegraph.co.uk
firstname.surname@telegraph.co.uk
Editor: William Lewis
- *Assistant editors: Corinna Honan, Andrew Pierce; editor at large: Jeff Randall; associate editor: Simon Heffer; news: Chris Evans (executive head); political: Andrew Porter; home affairs: Philip Johnston*
- *Sections – assistant editor (arts): Sarah Crompton; business: Damian Reece; city: Richard Blackden; foreign editor: Michael Smith; fashion: Hilary Alexander; features: Liz Hunt; medical: Rebecca Smith; legal: Joshua Rozenberg and Christopher Hope; literary: Sam Leith; personal finance: Ian Cowie; science: Roger Highfield; sport: Keith Perry; TV: Neil Midgley; weekend: Jon Stock, education: Graeme Paton; consumer affairs: Harry Wallop*
- *Publicity: Danielle Howe, 020 7931 2000*

Financial Times
The Financial Times Group, 1 Southwark Bridge,
London SE1 9HL
020 7873 3000
www.ft.com
firstname.surname@ft.com
Editor: Lionel Barber
- *Deputy editor: Martin Dickson; news: Robert Shrimsley; political: James Blitz*
- *Sections – weekend: Michael Skapinker; Asia edition: John Ridding; FT magazine: Graham Watts; Europe: John Thornhill; comment: Brian Groom; public policy: Nick Timmins*
- *Production editor: Joe Russ*
- *Director of communications: Katy Hemmings; PR manager: Lucy Ellison*

The Guardian

Guardian News & Media, 119 Farringdon Road,
London EC1R 3ER
020 7278 2332
www.guardian.co.uk
firstname.surname@guardian.co.uk
Editor: Alan Rusbridger
- *Deputy editor: Paul Johnson; Managing editor: Chris Elliott*
- *Section editors – arts: Melissa Denes; books: Claire Armitstead; City: Deborah Hargreaves, Julia Finch; comment: Toby Manhire; Comment Is Free: Georgina Henry; country diary & weather: Celia Locks; diary: Hugh Muir; education: Claire Phipps; family: Harriet Green, Sally Weale; fashion: Jess Cartner-Morley; film & music: Michael Hann; food & wellbeing: Amy Hamilton-Fleming; foreign: Harriet Sherwood, David Munk; G2: Katharine Viner; work and graduate: Ian Wylie; graphics: Mark Porter; The Guide: Malik Meer; guide daily: Camilla Redmond; home news: Nick Hopkins, David Taylor; letters: Nigel Willmott; money: Patrick Collinson; northern: Martin Wainwright; obituaries: Robert White; office hours: Vicky Frost; picture desk: Roger Tooth; review: Lisa Allardice; saturday: Ian Katz, Charlie English; society: Patrick Butler; sport: Ben Clissitt; technology: Charles Arthur; travel: Isabel Choat; Weekend magazine: Merope Mills; women: Kira Cochrane; work: Ian Wylie*
- *Specialists – economics: Larry Elliott; environment: John Vidal; health: Sarah Boseley; home affairs: Alan Travis; education: Polly Curtis; defence & security: Richard Norton-Taylor; political: Patrick Wintour; social affairs: John Carvel*
- *Assistant editor (production): David Marsh; production editor, G2: Paul Howlett; production editor, weekend: Bill Mann*
- *Publicity: Sarah Jones: 020 7239 9818*

The Independent

Independent News and Media (UK), Independent
House, 191 Marsh Wall, London E14 9RS
020 7005 2000
www.independent.co.uk
initial.surname@independent.co.uk
firstname.surname@independent.co.uk
Editor-in-chief: Simon Kelner
- *Deputy editor: Ian Birrell; news: Julian Coman; political: Andrew Grice*
- *Sections – City: Jeremy Warner; diplomatic: Ann Penketh; education: Lucy Hodges; editor for education: Richard Garner; environment: Michael McCarthy; features: Guy Adams; foreign: Catherine Butler; health: Jeremy Laurance; media: Ian Burrell; science: Steve Connor; sport: Matt Tench*
- *Production editor: Carl Reader*
- *Executive director (marketing): David Greene, 020 7005 2000*

The Sun

News Group Newspapers, 1 Virginia Street,
London E98 1SN
020 7782 4000
www.thesun.co.uk
firstname.surname@the-sun.co.uk
Editor: Rebekah Wade
- *Deputy editor: Fergus Shanahan; executive editor: Chris Roycroft-Davis; managing editor: Graham Dudman; political: George Pascoe-Watson (Whitehall: David Wooding); news: Christopher Pharo; chief reporter: John Kay*
- *Sections – bizarre: Gordon Smart; business: Ian King; crime: Mike Sullivan; defence: Tom Newton Dunn; features: Dominic Mohan; motoring: Ken Gibson; sport: Steve Waring; Sun woman: Sharon Hendry; TV: Sara Nathan*
- *Chief editorial production editor: Mike Fairbairn; chief sub, news: Jim Holgate*
- *Publicity: Lorna Carmichael, 020 7782 5000*

The Times

Times Newspapers, 1 Pennington Street,
London E98 1TT
020 7782 5000
www.timesonline.co.uk
firstname.surname@thetimes.co.uk
Editor: James Harding
- *Deputy editor: Keith Blackmore; home news: John Wellman, Oliver Wright; political: Philip Webster; social affairs: Rosemary Bennett; assistant politics: Peter Riddell; Washington correspondent: Tom Baldwin; Brussels correspondent: David Chater; Moscow correspondent: Tony Halpin; Whitehall: Jill Sherman; chief political correspondent: Anthony Browne*
- *Sections – business and City: David Wighton; comment: Daniel Finkelstein; consumer and countryside: Valerie Elliott; defence: Michael Evans; diplomatic: Richard Beeston; education: Alex Frean; features: Michael Harvey; financial: Graham Searjeant; foreign: Bronwen Maddox; health: Nigel Hawkes; money: Andrew Ellson; sport: Tim Hallissey*
- *Executive editors/chief subs: Chris McKane (deputy managing editor), Simon Pearson (night editor)*
- *Communications director: Anoushka Healy, 020 7782 5000*

National Sunday newspapers

Daily Star Sunday

Express Newspapers, The Northern & Shell Building,
Number 10 Lower Thames Street, London EC3R 6EN
0871 434 1010
www.megastar.co.uk
firstname.surname@dailystar.co.uk
Editor: Gareth Morgan
- *Deputy editor: David Harbord; news: Michael Booker; political: Macer Hall*
- *Sections – features: Victoria Lissaman; sport: Ray Ansbro*
- *Chief sub: Mike Woods; picture editor: Tomassina Brittain*

The Independent on Sunday

Independent News and Media (UK), Independent
House, 191 Marsh Wall, London E14 9RS
020 7005 2000
www.independent.co.uk
initial.surname@independent.co.uk
Editor: John Mullin
- *Deputy editor: Michael Williams; political: Andy McSmith (deputy: Francis Elliott)*
- *Sections – education: Richard Garner; environment: Geoffrey Lean; features: Mike Higgins; sport: Neil Morton; travel: Kate Simon; women's: Elizabeth Heathcote*
- *Production editor: Keith Howitt*
- *Marketing manager: Jonathan Grogan, 020 7005 2000*

The Mail on Sunday

Associated Newspapers, Northcliffe House,
2 Derry Street, Kensington, London W8 5TT
020 7938 6000
www.mailonsunday.co.uk
firstname.surname@mailonsunday.co.uk
Editor: Peter Wright
- *Deputy editor: Eric Bailey; news: Sebastian Hamilton; home affairs: Christopher Leake; political: Simon Walters*
- *Sections – education: Glen Owen; defence: Christopher Leake; environment: Jo Knowsley; features: Sian James; show business: Katie Nicholl; sport: Malcolm Vallerius*
- *Production editor: Tim Smith; executive production editors: Nic Petkovic, Derek Whitfield*
- *Managing editor: John Wellington, 020 7938 7015*

News of the World

News Group Newspapers, 1 Virginia Street,
London E98 1NW
020 7782 4000
www.thenewsoftheworld.co.uk
firstname.surname@notw.co.uk
Editor: Colin Myler

- *Deputy editor: Jane Johnson; executive editor: Neil Wallis; news: James Mellor; assistant editor (news): Ian Edmondson; features: Matt Nixson; assistant editor (features): Jules Stenson; assistant editor (politics): Ian Kirby; investigations: Mazher Mahmood; senior associate editor: Harry Scott*
- *Production editor: Richard Rushworth, managing editor: Stuart Kuttner*
- *Publicity: Hayley Barlow, 020 7782 4529*

The Observer

Guardian News & Media, 3–7 Herbal Hill,
London EC1R 5EJ
020 7278 2332
www.observer.guardian.co.uk
firstname.surname@observer.co.uk
Editor: John Mulholland

- *Deputy editor: Paul Webster; managing editor: Jan Thompson; executive editor, news: Kamal Ahmed; political: Gaby Hinsliff*
- *Sections – arts: Sarah Donaldson; books: Robert McCrum; business: Ruth Sunderland; City: Richard Wachman; crime: Mark Townsend; economics: Heather Stewart; Escape: Joanne O'Connor; fashion: Jo Adams; foreign: Tracy McVeigh; health: Jo Revill; home affairs: Jamie Doward; media: Vanessa Thorpe; money and property: Jill Insley; Observer Magazine: Allan Jenkins; Observer Food Monthly: Nicola Jeal; Observer Woman: Nicola Jeal; Observer Music Monthly: Caspar Llewellyn Smith; Observer Sport Monthly: Jason Cowley; investigations editor: Antony Barnett; Review: Jane Ferguson; science: Robin McKie; 7 days: Rob Yates; sport: Brian Oliver; TV: Mike Bradley*
- *Production editor: Bob Poulton; chief news sub: David Pearson; art director: Carolyn Roberts; picture editor: Greg Whitmore*
- *Publicity: Diane Heath, 020 7239 9936*

The People

MGN, One Canada Square, Canary Wharf,
London E14 5AP
020 7293 3000
www.people.co.uk
firstname.surname@people.co.uk

- *Deputy editor and news: Ben Proctor; associate news editor: David Jeffs; political: Nigel Nelson*
- *Sections – features: Chris Bucktin; investigations: Roger Insall; showbiz: Debbie Manley; sport: Lee Horton*
- *Chief sub: Trisha Harbord; night editor: Matt Clarke; picture editor: Paula Derry*
- *Publicity: Sarah Vaughan-Brown, 020 7293 3222*

The Sunday Express

Express Newspapers, The Northern & Shell Building,
Number 10 Lower Thames Street, London EC3R 6EN
0871 434 1010
www.express.co.uk
firstname.surname@express.co.uk
Editor: Martin Townsend

- *Deputy editor: Richard Dismore; news: James Murray; political: Julia Hartley-Brewer*
- *Sections – arts: Rachel Jane; business: Lawrie Holmes; defence & diplomatic: Kirsty Buchanan; environment: Stuart Winter; features: Giulia Rhodes; health: Hilary Douglas; royal: Keith Perry; sport: Scott Wilson; travel: Jane Memmler*
- *Night editor: Andy Hoban; assistant night editor (features): Stuart Kershaw; chief news sub: Keith Ging*

Sunday Mirror

MGN, One Canada Square, Canary Wharf,
London E14 5AP
020 7293 3000
www.sundaymirror.co.uk
firstname.surname@sundaymirror.co.uk
Editor: Tina Weaver

- *Deputy editor: James Scott; associate editor: Mike Small; assistant editor (news): Nick Buckley; news: James Saville; political: Vincent Moss; deputy news editor: Euan Stretch*
- *Sections – features: Jill Main; investigations reporter: Nick Owens; showbusiness: Sean Hamilton; sport: David Walker*
- *Chief subs: Brian Hancill (news and features); Phil Davies (sport); picture editor: Mike Sharp*
- *Publicity: Rachel Muir-Brown, 020 7293 3222*

Sunday Sport

Sport Newspapers, 19 Great Ancoats Street,
Manchester M60 4BT
0161 236 4466
www.sundaysport.com
Editor: Paul Carter

- *News editor: Jane Field; features: Mark Harris; sports: Mark Smith*

The Sunday Telegraph

Telegraph Group, 111 Buckingham Palace Road,
London SW1 0DT
020 7931 2000
www.telegraph.co.uk
firstname.surname@telegraph.co.uk
Editor: Ian MacGregor

- *Deputy editor: Dan Roberts; assistant news: Tim Woodward; political: Patrick Hennessy; executive editor, politics: Iain Martin*
- *Sections – city: Mark Kleiman; foreign: David Wastell; economics: Liam Halligan; Seven: Ross Jones; Stella: Anna Murphy; sport: Mark Skipworth; picture editor: Mike Spillard; business: Damian Reece*
- *Publicity: Danielle Howe, 020 7931 2000*

The Sunday Times

Times Newspapers, 1 Pennington Street,
London E98 1ST
020 7782 5000
www.sunday-times.co.uk
firstname.surname@sunday-times.co.uk
Editor: John Witherow

- *Deputy editor: Martin Ivens; managing editor: Richard Caseby; news: Charles Hymas; associate editor: Bob Tyrer; managing editor, news: Charles Hymas; political: Jonathan Oliver (deputy: Isabel Oakeshott)*
- *Sections – arts: Richard Brooks; business: John Waples; City: Grant Ringshaw; culture: Helen Hawkins; In gear: Nick Rufford; Doors: David Johnson; economics: David Smith; financial editor: Paul Durman; Focus: Paul Nuki; foreign: Sean Ryan; home: Peter Conradi; home affairs: David Leppard; literary: Susannah Herbert; Insight: Jonathan Calvert; Ireland: Frank Fitzgibbon; medical: Sarah-Kate Templeton; money: Kathryn Cooper; News review: Eleanor Mills; science: Jonathan Leake; Scotland: Les Snowdon; sport: Alex Butler; Sunday Times Magazine: Robin Morgan; Style: Tiffanie Darke; travel: Christine Walker; TV: David Hutcheon*
- *Managing editor (production): Ian Coxon; chief subs: David Paton; Denise Boutall (arts and leisure); Arnis Biezais (business)*
- *Publicity: Sophie Bickford*

Regional press contacts

Main publishers

Archant
Prospect House, Rouen Road,
Norwich NR1 1RE
01603 772803
www.archant.co.uk
Chairman: Richard Jewson; CEO:
John Fry; corporate communications
manager: Keith Morris, 01603 772814
Archant Regional
01603 772824

Daily Mail & General Trust
Northcliffe House, 2 Derry Street,
London W8 5TT
020 7938 6000
www.dmgt.co.uk
Chairman: Viscount Rothermere;
CEO: CJF Sinclair
Associated Newspapers
Northcliffe House, 2 Derry Street,
London W8 5TT
020 7938 6000
www.associatednewspapers.co.uk
MD: Kevin Beatty; editor-in-chief:
Paul Dacre
Northcliffe Media Limited
Northcliffe House, 2 Derry Street,
London W8 5TT
020 7400 1401
www.thisisnorthcliffe.co.uk
MD: Michael Pelosi

DC Thomson
185 Fleet Street, London EC4A 2HS
020 7400 1030
www.dcthomson.co.uk

Guardian Media Group
75 Farringdon Road,
London EC1M 3JY
020 7278 2332
www.gmgplc.co.uk
Chairman: Paul Myners; CEO,
regionals: Mark Dodson

Independent News and Media
Independent House,
2023 Bianconi Avenue, Citywest
Business Campus, Naas Road,
Dublin 24, Ireland
00 353 1 466 3200
www.inmplc.com
Chief executive: Sir Anthony O'Reilly;
CEO, Ireland: Vincent Crowley; CEO,
UK: Ivan Fallon

Johnston Press
53 Manor Place, Edinburgh EH3 7EG
0131 225 3361
www.johnstonpress.co.uk
Non-executive chairman: Roger Parry;
CEO: Tim Bowdler

**Midland News Association/
Express & Star**
51-53 Queen Street,
Wolverhampton WV1 1ES
01902 313131
www.mna-research.com

Newsquest Media
58 Church Street, Weybridge,
Surrey KT13 8DP
01932 821212
www.newsquest.co.uk
Chairman and chief executive:
Paul Davidson

Scotsman Publications
Barclay House, 108 Holyrood
Road, Edinburgh EH8 8AS
0131 620 8620
www.scotsman.com
Publisher: Johnston Press;
MD: Michael Johnston

Trinity Mirror
One Canada Square, Canary
Wharf, London E14 5AP
020 7293 3000
www.trinitymirror.com
Chairman: Sir Ian Gibson;
CEO: Sly Bailey

Regional newspapers — England

● Major paid-for regionals

The Argus (Brighton)
Argus House, Crowhurst Road,
Hollingbury, Brighton BN1 8AR
01273 544544
www.theargus.co.uk
Daily. Owner: Newsquest. Editor:
Michael Beard; news: Frankie Taggart;
night news editor: James Glover;
features: Jacqui Phillips; production:
Chris Heath

Birmingham Mail
PO Box 78, Weaman Street,
Birmingham, West Midlands B4 6AY
0121 236 3366
www.icbirmingham.co.uk
Daily. Owner: Trinity Mirror. Editor:
Steve Dyson; news: Andy Richards;
features: Paul Fulford

Blackpool Gazette & Herald
Avroe House, Avroe Crescent,
Blackpool Business Park,
Blackpool FY4 2DP
01253 400888
www.blackpoolgazette.co.uk
Daily. Owner: Johnston Press. Editor:
David Halliwell; news: Jon Rhodes;
features: Steve Singleton; chief sub:
Peter Ward

Bolton News
Newspaper House, Churchgate,
Bolton, Lancs BL1 1DE
01204 522345
www.thisisbolton.co.uk
Daily. Owner: Newsquest. Editor-in-
chief: Ian Savage; news: James
Higgins; features: Andrew Mosley;
production: John Bird

Bristol Evening Post
Temple Way, Bristol BS99 7HD
0117 934 3000
www.thisisbristol.co.uk
Daily. Owner: Northcliffe Media.
Editor: Mike Norton; news: Rob
Perkins; features: David Webb;
chief sub: Richard Coulter

Coventry Evening Telegraph
Corporation Street,
Coventry CV1 1FP
024 7663 3633
www.iccoventry.co.uk
Daily. Owner: Trinity Mirror. Editor:
Alan Kirby; news: John West; features:
Steven Chilton; head of production:
Barry Matthew

Daily Echo
Richmond Hill,
Bournemouth BH2 6HH
01202 554601
www.bournemouthecho.co.uk
Daily. Owner: Newsquest. Editor: Neal Butterworth; news: Andy Martin; features: Kevin Nash

Derby Evening Telegraph
Northcliffe House, Meadow Road,
Derby, Derbyshire DE1 2DW
01332 291111
www.thisisderbyshire.co.uk
Daily. Owner: Northcliffe Media. Editor: Steve Hall; news: Nicola Hodgson; features: Cheryl Hague; chief sub: Ian Crowson

East Anglian Daily Times
Press House, 30 Lower Brook
Street, Ipswich IP4 1AN
01473 230023
www.eadt.co.uk
Daily. Owner: Archant. Editor: Terry Hunt; news: Brad Jones; features: Julian Ford

Eastern Daily Press
Prospect House, Rouen Road,
Norwich NR1 1RE
01603 628311
www.edp24.co.uk
Daily. Owner: Archant. Editor: Peter Franzen

Evening Chronicle (Newcastle)
Groat Market,
Newcastle upon Tyne NE1 1ED
0191 232 7500
www.icnewcastle.co.uk
Daily. Owner: Trinity Mirror. Editor: Paul Robertson; news: James Marley; features: Jennifer Bradbury; chief sub: Beverley Pearson

Evening Gazette
Borough Road,
Middlesbrough TS1 3AZ
01642 245401
www.icteesside.co.uk
Daily. Owner: Gazette Media Company (Trinity Mirror). Editor: Darren Thwaites; news: Jim Horsley; features: Barbara Argument

Evening Standard
Northcliffe House, 2 Derry Street,
London W8 5TT
020 7938 6000
www.thisislondon.co.uk
Daily. Owner: Associated Newspapers. Editor: Veronica Wadley; news: Ian Walker; features: Simon Davies

Express & Star
51-53 Queen Street,
Wolverhampton,
West Midlands WV1 1ES
01902 313131
www.expressandstar.com
Daily. Owner: Midland News Association. Editor: Adrian Faber; news: Mark Drew; features: Emma Farmer; chief sub: Tony Reynolds

The Herald (Plymouth)
17 Brest Road, Derriford Business
Park, Plymouth PL6 5AA
01752 765500
www.thisisplymouth.co.uk
Daily. Owner: Northcliffe Media. Editor: Bill Martin; news: James Garnett; features: Su Carroll

Hull Daily Mail
Blundell's Corner, Beverley Road,
Hull HU3 1XS
01482 327111
www.thisishull.co.uk
Daily. Owner: Northcliffe Media. Editor: John Meehan; news: Paul Baxter; features: Paul Johnson; chief sub: Daniel Urben

The Journal (Newcastle)
Groat Market,
Newcastle upon Tyne NE1 1ED
0191 201 6230
www.journallive.co.uk
Daily. Owner: Newcastle Chronicle & Journal (Trinity Mirror). Editor: Brian Aitken; night editor: Richard Kirkman; news: Matt McKenzie; features: Jane Hall

Lancashire Evening Post
Oliver's Place, Preston PR2 9ZA
01772 254841
www.lep.co.uk
Daily. Owner: Johnston Press. Editor: Simon Reynolds

Lancashire Telegraph
1 High Street, Blackburn,
Lancashire BB1 1HT
01254 678678
www.lancashiretelegraph.co.uk
Daily. Owner: Newsquest. Editor-in-chief: Kevin Young; news: Andrew Turner; features: John Anson

Leicester Mercury
St George Street, Leicester LE1 9FQ
0116 251 2512
www.thisisleicestershire.co.uk
Daily. Owner: Northcliffe Media. Editor: Nick Carter; news: Mark Charlton; features: Alex Dawson

Liverpool Daily Post
Old Hall Street, Liverpool L69 3EB
0151 227 2000
www.icliverpool.co.uk
Daily. Owner: Trinity Mirror. Editor: Mark Thomas; news: Andy Kelly

Liverpool Echo
Old Hall Street, Liverpool L69 3EB
0151 227 2000
www.icliverpool.co.uk
Daily. Owner: Trinity Mirror. Editor: Alastair Machray; news: Maria Breslin

Manchester Evening News
1 Scott Place, Manchester M3 3RN
0161 832 7200
www.manchestereveningnews.co.uk
Daily. Owner: Guardian Media Group. Editor: Paul Horrocks; news: Sarah Lester; deputy features editor: Graham McGilliard; features editor: Deanna Delamotta

The News (Portsmouth)
Portsmouth Publishing & Printing,
The News Centre, London Road,
Hilsea, Portsmouth,
Hampshire PO2 9SX
023 9266 4488
www.portsmouth.co.uk
Daily. Owner: Johnston Press. Editor: Mark Waldron; news: Colin McNeill; features: Graeme Patfield

Northern Echo (Darlington & South West Durham)
PO Box 14, Priestgate, Darlington,
County Durham DL1 1NF
01325 381313
www.thisisthenortheast.co.uk
Daily. Owner: Newsquest. Editor: Peter Barron; news: Nigel Burton; features: Lindsay Jennings; chief sub: Dave Horsley

Nottingham Evening Post
Castle Wharf House,
Nottingham NG1 7EU
0115 948 2000
www.thisisnottingham.co.uk
Daily. Owner: Northcliffe Media. Editor: Malcolm Pheby; news: Claire Catlow; features: Jeremy Lewis

The Press
76-86 Walmgate, York YO1 9YN
01904 653051
www.yorkpress.co.uk
Daily. Owner: Newsquest. Editor: Kevin Booth; news: Scott Armstrong; features: Steven Lewis; chief sub: Simon Ritchie

The Sentinel (Stoke-on-Trent)
Staffordshire Sentinel
Newspapers, Sentinel House,
Etruria, Stoke-on-Trent ST1 5SS
01782 602525
www.thisisthesentinel.co.uk
Daily. Owner: Northcliffe Media. Editor: Mike Sassi; news: Rob Cotterill; features: Richard Bramwell; chief sub: Charlotte Little-Jones

Shropshire Star
Waterloo Road, Ketley, Telford,
Shropshire TF1 5HU
01952 242424
www.shropshirestar.com
Daily. Owner: Midland News Association. Editor: Sarah Jane Smith; news: John Simcock; features: Carl Jones

Southern Daily Echo
Newspaper House, Test Lane,
Redbridge, Southampton SO16 9JX
023 8042 4777
www.dailyecho.co.uk
Daily. Owner: Newsquest. Editor: Ian Murray; news: Gordon Sutter; chief sub: Colin Jenkins

The Star (Sheffield)
York Street, Sheffield,
South Yorkshire S1 1PU
0114 276 7676
www.thestar.co.uk
Daily. Owner: Johnston Press. Editor: Alan Powell; news: Bob Westerdale; features: John Highfield; head of content: Paul License

41

Sunday Mercury
Weaman Street, Birmingham,
West Midlands B4 6AZ
0121 236 3366
www.icbirmingham.co.uk
Sunday. Owner: Trinity Mirror. Editor:
David Brookes; deputy editor: Paul
Cole; news: Tony Larner

Sunday Sun (Newcastle)
Groat Market,
Newcastle upon Tyne NE1 1ED
0191 232 7500
www.icnewcastle.co.uk
Sunday. Owner: Trinity Mirror. Editor:
Colin Patterson; news: Mike Kelly;
production: Lesley Oldfield; chief sub:
Lesley Oldfield

Telegraph & Argus (Bradford)
Hall Ings, Bradford BD1 1JR
01274 729511
www.thetelegraphandargus.co.uk
Daily. Owner: Newsquest. Editor:
Perry Austin-Clarke; news: Martin
Heminway; features: David Barnett;
chief sub: Mel Jones

Western Daily Press (Bristol)
Temple Way, Bristol BS99 7HD
0117 934 3000
www.westerndailypress.co.uk
Daily. Owner: Northcliffe Media.
Editor: Andrew Wright; backbench
executive editor: Dave Edler; news:
Cathy Ellis; features: Dave Webb; chief
sub: Chris Brown

Western Morning News
17 Brest Road, Derriford,
Plymouth PL6 5AA
01752 765500
www.westernmorningnews.co.uk
Daily. Owner: Northcliffe Media.
Editor-in-chief: Alan Qualtrough;
news: Steve Grant

Yorkshire Evening Post
PO Box 168, Wellington Street,
Leeds LS1 1RF
0113 243 2701
www.yorkshireeveningpost.co.uk
Daily. Owner: Johnston Press. Editor:
Paul Napier; news: Gillian Haworth;
features: Jayne Dawson; production:
Howard Corry

Yorkshire Post
PO Box 168, Wellington Street,
Leeds LS1 1RF
0113 243 2701
www.yorkshirepost.co.uk
Daily. Owner: Johnston Press. Editor:
Peter Charlton; news: Hannah Start;
features: Catherine Scott

Other local and regional papers – England

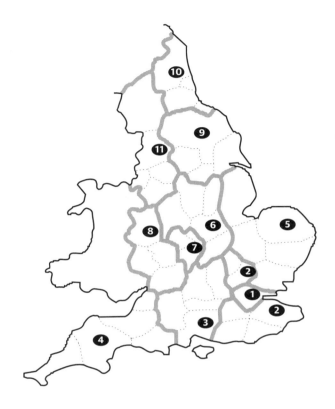

● London

Barnes, Mortlake & Sheen Times
020 8744 4200
www.richmondandtwickenham
times.co.uk
*Weekly (Fri). Owner: Newsquest.
Assistant editor: Scott Barr; news:
Michelle Curran*

Barnet & Potters Bar Times
020 8359 5959
www.barnettimes.co.uk
*Weekly (Thu). Owner: Newsquest.
Editor: Phil Crowther; chief reporter:
Ruth Holmes*

Barnet & Whetstone Press
020 8367 2345
*Weekly free (Thu). Owner: London &
Essex Newspaper. Editor: Gary
O'Keeffe; news: Ruth Holmes*

Brent & Wembley Leader
020 8427 4404
*Weekly free (Fri). Owner: Trinity
Mirror Southern. Editor: Lindsey
Coulson; news: Sophia Haque;
features: Dhruti Shah*

Bromley Times
020 8269 7000
www.bromleytimes.co.uk
*Weekly (Weds & Thu). Owner: Archant.
Editor: Melody Foreman; production:
Sarah Sharman*

Bromley News
01959 564766
www.bromley-today.co.uk
*Weekly (Thu). Owner: Tindle
Newspapers. Editor: Charlotte
McDonnall*

Bromley News Shopper
01689 836211
www.newsshopper.co.uk
*Weekly (Weds). Owner: Newsquest.
Editor: Jean May; news: Helen Backway*

Camden Gazette
020 8342 5777
www.camdengazette.co.uk
*Weekly (Weds). Owner: Archant. Editor:
Tony Allcock; news: Rob Bleaney*

Camden New Journal
020 7419 9000
www.camdennewjournal.co.uk
*Weekly (Thu). Owner: New Journal
Enterprises. Editor: Eric Gordon; news:
Dan Carrier; features: Sunita Rappai;
production: Kelvin Morrison*

Caterham & District Advertiser
020 8763 6666
www.thisiscroydontoday.co.uk
*Weekly (Fri). Owner: Northcliffe Media.
Editor: Ian Carter; news: Andy Worden*

Chingford Guardian
020 8498 3400
www.chingfordguardian.co.uk
*Weekly (Thu). Owner: Newsquest.
Editor: Pat Stannard*

The Chiswick
020 8744 4200
www.richmondandtwickenham
times.co.uk
*Weekly (Thurs). Owner: Newsquest.
Assistant Editor: Scott Barr; news:
Chris Briddon*

City AM
020 7015 1200
www.cityam.com
*Daily free. Owner: City AM Ltd.
Acting editor: David Hellier; news:
Ben Griffiths*

City of London & Dockland Times
020 7247 2524
*Fortnightly (Mon). Editor:
Mr D Delderfield*

Croydon Advertiser
020 8763 6666
www.croydonadvertiser.co.uk
*Weekly (Fri). Owner: Northcliffe Media.
Editor: Ian Carter; news: Andy Worden*

Croydon Borough Post
0800 073 1848
www.iccroydon.co.uk
*Weekly (Wed). Owner: Northcliffe
Media. Editor: Ian Carter; news:
Andy Worden*

Croydon Guardian
020 8329 9244
www.croydonguardian.co.uk
*Weekly (Wed). Owner: Newsquest.
Editor: Danny Brierley*

Ealing & Acton Gazette
020 8579 3131
www.icealing.co.uk
*Weekly (Fri). Owner: Trinity Mirror
Southern. Editor: Shajaul Azam;
news: Sachin Nakrani; features:
Victoria Prewer*

Ealing Informer
020 8579 3131
www.icealing.co.uk
*Weekly (Wed). Owner: Trinity Mirror
Southern. Editor: Shajaul Azam;
news: Sachin Nakrani; features:
Victoria Prewer*

Ealing Leader
020 8579 3131
www.ealinggazette.co.uk
*Weekly (Fri). Owner: Trinity Mirror
Southern. Editor: Shajaul Azam;
features: Victoria Prewer; chief sub:
Joyce McKim*

Ealing Times
01494 755000
www.ealingtimes.co.uk
*Weekly (Thu). Owner: Newsquest.
Editor: Rachel Sharp; news: James
Young*

East End Life
020 7364 3059
*Weekly free (Sun). Owner: London
Borough of Tower Hamlets. Editor:
Laraine Clay; news: Helen Watson*

East London Advertiser
020 7791 7799
*Weekly (Thu). Owner: Archant. Editor:
Malcolm Starbrook; news: Mike Brooke*

East London Enquirer
01277 627300
www.theenquirer.co.uk
Weekly (Thu). Editor: Carol Driver

Edgware & Mill Hill Press
020 8367 2345
www.icnorthlondononline.co.uk
*Weekly free (Thu). Owner: Tindle
Newspapers. Editor: Gary O'Keeffe;
news: Tom Hutchinson*

Edgware & Mill Hill Times
020 8359 5959
www.edgwaretimes.co.uk
*Weekly (Thu). Owner: Newsquest.
Editor: Phil Crowther*

Enfield Advertiser
020 8367 2345
www.icnorthlondononline.co.uk
*Weekly (Thu). Owner: Tindle
Newspapers. Editor: Gary O'Keeffe;
news: Tom Hutchinson*

Enfield Gazette
020 8367 2345
www.icnorthlondononline.co.uk
*Weekly (Thu). Owner: Tindle
Newspapers. Editor: Gary O'Keeffe;
news: Tom Hutchinson*

Enfield Independent
020 8362 1431
www.enfieldindependent.co.uk
*Weekly (Wed). Owner: Newsquest.
Editor: Charlie Stong*

Evening Standard
See page 41

Fulham Gazette
020 8579 3131
www.icealing.co.uk
*Weekly (Fri). Owner: Trinity Mirror
Southern. Editor: Shajaul Azam;
news editor: Sachin Nakrani*

Greenford & Northolt Gazette
020 8579 3131
www.icealing.co.uk
*Weekly (Fri). Owner: Trinity Mirror
Southern. Editor: Shajaul Azam;
news editor: Sachin Nakrani*

Greenwich Borough Mercury
020 8769 4444
www.icsouthlondon.co.uk
*Weekly (Wed). Owner: Tindle
Newspapers. Editor-in-chief:
Hannah Walker*

Hackney Gazette
020 7791 7788
www.hackneygazette.co.uk
*Weekly (Thu). Owner: Archant. Editor:
Mick Ferris; news: Russ Lawrence*

Fulham & Hammersmith Chronicle
020 8943 5171
www.trinitymirrorsouthern.co.uk
*Weekly (Thu). Owner: Trinity Mirror
Southern. Content editor: Janice
Raycroft; features: Gerri Besgrove;
news editor: Jo McDermott*

Hammersmith & Shepherd's Bush Gazette
020 8579 3131
www.ealinggazette.co.uk
Weekly (Fri). Owner: Trinity Mirror Southern. Editor: Shajaul Azam; news editor: Sachin Nakrani

Hampstead & Highgate Express
020 7433 0000
www.hamhigh.co.uk
Weekly (Fri). Owner: Archant. Editor: Geoff Martin; news: Bridget Galton; features: Melanie Smith

Harefield Gazette
01895 451000
www.icuxbridge.co.uk
Weekly (Wed). Owner: Trinity Mirror Southern. Editor-in-chief: Adrian Seal; content editor: David Tilley

Haringey Advertiser
020 8367 2345
www.icnorthlondononline.co.uk
Weekly (Wed). Owner: Tindle Newspapers. Editor: Gary O'Keeffe; news: Henry Ellis

Haringey Independent
020 8359 5959
Weekly (Fri). Owner: Newsquest. Editor: Phil Crowther; news: Ruth Holmes

Harrow Leader
020 8427 4404
www.icharrow.co.uk
Weekly free (Thu). Owner: Trinity Mirror Southern. Editor: Lindsay Coulson; news: Emily Twinch; production: Andre Erasmus

Harrow Observer
020 8427 4404
www.icharrow.co.uk
Weekly (Thu). Owner: Trinity Mirror Southern. Editor: Lindsay Coulson; news: Emily Twinch; production: Andre Erasmus

Harrow Times
01923 216216
www.harrowtimes.co.uk
Weekly (Thu). Owner: Newsquest. Editor: Rachel Sharp

Hayes & Harlington Gazette
01895 451000
www.icuxbridge.co.uk
Weekly (Wed). Owner: Trinity Mirror Southern. Editor-in-chief: Adrian Seal; content editor: David Tilley

Hendon & Finchley Press
020 8367 2345
www.icnorthlondononline.co.uk
Weekly free (Thu). Owner: Tindle Newspapers. Editor: Gary O'Keeffe; news: Tom Hutchinson

Hendon Times
020 8359 5959
www.hendontimes.co.uk
Weekly (Thu). Owner: Newsquest. Editor: Phil Crowther

Hillingdon & Uxbridge Times
01923 216216
www.hillingdontimes.co.uk
Weekly free (Thu). Owner: Newsquest. Editor: Rachel Sharp

Hornsey & Crouch End Journal
020 8340 6868
www.hornseyjournal.co.uk
Weekly (Thu). Owner: Archant. Editor: Tony Allcock; news: Alison Campsie

Hounslow, Brentford & Chiswick Informer
020 8572 1816
www.trinitymirrorsouthern.co.uk
Weekly free (Fri). Owner: Trinity Mirror Southern. News editor: Daniel Lyons

Hounslow Chronicle
020 8572 1816
www.trinitymirrorsouthern.co.uk
Weekly (Thu). Owner: Trinity Mirror Southern. News editor: Daniel Lyons; features: Gerri Besgrove

Hounslow Guardian
020 8329 9244
www.hounslowguardian.co.uk
Weekly (Thu). Owner: Newsquest. Editor: Scott Barr; news: Chris Briddon

Hounslow & Isleworth Informer
020 8572 1816
Weekly free (Fri). Owner: Trinity Mirror Southern. Features editor: Gerri Besgrove; content editor: Janice Raycroft

Ilford Recorder
020 8478 4444
www.ilfordrecorder.co.uk
Weekly (Thu). Owner: Archant. Editor: Chris Carter; production: Mike Cubitt

Islington Gazette
020 8342 5777
www.islingtongazette.co.uk
Weekly (Thu). Owner: Archant. Editor: Tony Allcock; news: Rob Bleaney

Islington Tribune
020 7419 9000
www.camdennewjournal.co.uk
Weekly (Fri). Owner: New Journal Enterprises. Editor: Eric Gordon; news: Mark Blunden

Kensington & Chelsea Informer
020 8572 1816
www.trinitymirrorsouthern.co.uk
Weekly (Thu). Owner: Trinity Mirror Southern. Content editor: Janice Raycroft; features: Gerri Besgrove

Kilburn Times
020 8962 6868
www.kbtimes.co.uk
Weekly (Thu). Owner: Archant. Editor: Tim Cole

Kingston & Surbiton Times
020 8744 4200
Weekly (Fri). Owner: Newsquest. Editor: Scott Barr; news: Chris Briddon

Kingston Guardian
020 8329 9244
www.kingstonguardian.co.uk
Weekly (Thu). Owner: Newsquest. Editor: Sean Duggan

Kingston Informer
020 8572 1816
www.trinitymirrorsouthern.co.uk
Weekly (Fri). Owner: Trinity Mirror Southern. Content editor: Janice Raycroft; features: Gerri Besgrove

Lewisham & Greenwich Mercury
020 8769 4444
www.icsouthlondon.co.uk
Weekly free. Owner: Tindle Newspapers. Editor-in-chief: Hannah Walker; news: Christina Salzano

Lewisham Borough Mercury
020 8769 4444
www.icsouthlondon.co.uk
Weekly (Wed). Owner: Tindle Newspapers. Editor-in-chief: Hannah Walker; chief reporter: Keely Sherbird

Lewisham News Shopper
01689 885714
www.newsshopper.co.uk
Weekly (Wed). Owner: Newsquest. Editor: Jean May; news: Helen Backway; chief sub: Tim Miles

Leyton & Leytonstone Guardian
020 8498 3400
www.leytonguardian.co.uk
Weekly (Thu). Owner: Newsquest. Editor: Pat Stannard

London Lite
020 7938 6000
www.thisislondon.co.uk
Daily free. Owner: Associated Newspapers. Editor: Ted Young

The London Paper
020 7782 4848
www.thelondonpaper.com
Daily free. Owner: News International. Editor: Stefano Hatfield

Marylebone & Paddington Mercury
020 8572 1816
www.trinitymirrorsouthern.co.uk
Weekly (Thu). Owner: Trinity Mirror Southern. Content editor: Janice Raycroft; features: Gerri Besgrove

Mayfair Times
020 7259 1050
www.mayfairtimes.co.uk
Monthly free (1st Mon). Editor-in-chief: Eric Brown; editor: Selma Day

Metro London
020 7651 5200
www.metro.co.uk
Daily. Owner: Associated Newspapers. Editor: Kenny Campbell; news: Sarah Getty; features: Kieran Meeke

Mitcham, Morden & Wimbledon Post
020 8769 4444
www.icsouthlondon.co.uk
Weekly free (Fri). Owner: Tindle Newspapers. Editor-in-chief: Hannah Walker; news: Christina Salzano

Muswell Hill Journal
020 8342 5700
www.london24.com
Weekly (Thu). Owner: Archant. Editor: Tony Allcock; news: Alison Campsie

New Addington Advertiser
020 8763 6666
www.thisiscroydontoday.co.uk
Weekly (Fri). Owner: Trinity Mirror Southern. Editor: Ian Carter; news: Andy Worden

Newham Recorder
020 8472 1421
www.newhamrecorder.co.uk
Weekly (Wed). Owner: Archant. Editor: Colin Grainger; deputy editor: John Finn; news: Pat Coughtrey

Pinner Observer
020 8427 4404
www.icharrow.co.uk
Weekly (Thu). Owner: Trinity Mirror Southern. Editor: Lindsay Coulson; news: Sophia Haque; features: Dhruti Shah; production: Andre Erasmus

The Press (North London)
020 8364 4040
Weekly free (Thu). Owner: Trinity Mirror Southern. Editor: Gary O'Keeffe; news: Henry Ellis

Richmond & Twickenham Informer
020 8572 1816
www.trinitymirrorsouthern.co.uk
Weekly (Fri). Owner: Trinity Mirror Southern. Content editor: Janice Raycroft; features: Gerri Besgrove

Richmond & Twickenham Times
020 8744 4200
www.richmondandtwickenham times.co.uk
Weekly (Fri). Owner: Newsquest. Assistant Editor: Scott Barr; news: Michelle Curran

Richmond Borough Guardian
020 8744 4200
www.kingstonguardian.co.uk
Weekly (Thu). Owner: Newsquest. Editor: Scott Barr; news: Chris Briddon

Ruislip & Northwood Gazette
01895 451000
www.icuxbridge.co.uk
Weekly (Wed). Owner: Trinity Mirror Southern. Editor-in-chief: Adrian Seal; content editor: David Tilley

St John's Wood & Maida Vale Express (Wood & Vale)
020 7433 0000
www.islingtonexpress.co.uk
Weekly (Fri). Owner: Archant. Editor: Geoff Martin; news: Jeni Conniveer; features: Bridget Galton: chief sub: Melanie Smith

South Bucks Star
01494 755000
www.southbucksstar.co.uk
Weekly free (Thu). Owner: Newsquest. Editor: Steve Cohen; news: Victoria Birch; features: Lindi Bilgorri

South London Press
020 8769 4444
www.icsouthlondon.co.uk
Twice-weekly (Tue, Fri). Owner: Tindle Newspapers. Editor: Hannah Walker; news: Sam Eversden

Southall Gazette
020 8579 3131
www.icealing.co.uk
Weekly (Fri). Owner: Trinity Mirror Southern. Editor: Shajaul Azam

Southwark Weekender
020 7231 5258
Monthly (Thu). Editor: Chris Mullany and Kevin Quinn

Stanmore Observer
020 8427 4404
www.icharrow.co.uk
Weekly (Thu). Owner: Trinity Mirror Southern. Editor: Lindsay Coulson; news: Sophia Haque; features: Dhruti Shah; production: Andre Erasmus

Streatham Guardian
020 8646 6336
www.streathamguardian.co.uk
Weekly (Thu). Owner: Newsquest. Editor: Jo Gumb; features: June Sampson

Streatham, Clapham & West Norwood Post
020 8769 4444
www.icsouthlondon.co.uk
Weekly free (Thu). Owner: Tindle Newspapers. Editor-in-chief: Hannah Walker; news: Christina Salzano

Tottenham, Wood Green & Edmonton Journal
020 8340 6868
www.tottenhamjournal.co.uk
Weekly (Thu). Owner: Archant. Editor: Tony Allcock; news: Alison Campsie

Tower Hamlets Recorder
020 8472 1421
www.www.towerhamletsrecorder .co.uk
Weekly (Wed). Owner: Archant. Editor: Colin Grainger; deputy editor: John Finn; news: Pat Coughtrey

Uxbridge & Hillingdon Leader
01895 451000
www.icuxbridge.co.uk
Weekly free (Thu). Owner: Trinity Mirror Southern. Editor-in-chief: Adrian Seal; content editor: David Tilley

Uxbridge & W Drayton Gazette
01895 451000
www.icuxbridge.co.uk
Weekly (Tue). Owner: Trinity Mirror Southern. Editor-in-chief: Adrian Seal; content editor: David Tilley

Walthamstow Guardian
020 8498 3400
www.walthamstowguardian.co.uk
Weekly (Thu). Owner: Newsquest. Editor: Pat Stannard

Wandsworth Guardian
020 8329 9244
www.wandsworthguardian.co.uk
Weekly (Thu). Owner: Newsquest. News editor: Vikki Thomas; features: June Sampson

Wembley & Kingsbury Times
020 8962 6868
www.wktimes.co.uk
Weekly (Thu). Owner: Archant. Editor: Tim Cole

Wembley Leader
020 8427 4404
www.icharrow.co.uk
Weekly (Thu). Owner: Trinity Mirror Southern. Editor: Lindsay Coulson; news: Claire Garner; features: Victoria Prewer; production: Andre Erasmus

Wembley Observer
020 8427 4404
www.icharrow.co.uk
Weekly (Thu). Owner: Trinity Mirror Southern. Editor: Lindsay Coulson; news: Claire Garner; features: Victoria Prewer; production: Andre Erasmus

West End Extra
020 7419 9000
www.camdennewjournal.co.uk
Weekly (Fri). Owner: New Journal Enterprises. Editor: Eric Gordon; news: Joel Taylor; features: Sunita Rappai; production: Kelvin Morrison

Westender
020 7607 6060
Monthly free (last week in month). Editor: Eileen Martin; news: Bina Gowrea; features: Eileen Duff; production: Jason Kent

Westminster & Pimlico News
020 8572 1816
www.trinitymirrorsouthern.co.uk
Weekly (Fri). Owner: Trinity Mirror Southern. Content editor: Janice Raycroft; features: Gerri Besgrove

Westminster Independent
01840 779255
www.londonlocals.co.uk
Monthly (last Fri). Editor: Jan Mappin; news: Jaz Walia

The Wharf
020 7510 6306
www.icthewharf.co.uk
Weekly free (Thu). Owner: Trinity Mirror Southern. Editor: Tom Derbyshire; deputy editor: Lucy Walters

Willesden & Brent Times
020 8962 6868
www.wbtimes.co.uk
Weekly (Thu). Owner: Archant. Editor: Tim Cole

Willesden Observer
020 8427 4404
www.icharrow.co.uk
Weekly (Thu). Owner: Trinity Mirror Southern. Editor: Lindsay Coulson; news: Sophia Haque; features: Dhruti Shah; production: Andre Erasmus

Wimbledon Guardian
020 8329 9244
www.wimbledonguardian.co.uk
Weekly (Thu). Owner: Newsquest. Editor: Vikki Thomas; features: June Sampson

Wimbledon News
020 8329 9244
www.wimbledonnews.co.uk
Weekly (Wed). Owner: Newsquest. Editor: Sean Duggan

● South-east England

Bedfordshire, East Sussex, Hertfordshire, Kent, Surrey, West Sussex

Addlestone and Byfleet Review
01483 508700
www.surreyadvertiser.co.uk
Weekly (Wed). Owner: Guardian Media Group. Group editorial director: Marnie Wilson

Adscene (Ashford & Tenterden)
01227 767321
www.thisiskent.co.uk
Weekly free (Fri). Owner: Northcliffe Media. Publishing director: Lesley Finlay; features: Julia Rogers; chief sub: Catherine Langston

Adscene (Canterbury)
01227 767321
www.thisiskent.co.uk
Weekly free (Fri). Owner: Northcliffe Media. Editor: John Nurden; features: Julia Rogers; chief sub: Paul Taylor; production: Mark Silva

Adscene (Folkestone & Dover)
01227 767321
www.thisiskent.co.uk
Weekly free (Wed). Owner: Northcliffe Media. Editor: Simon Finlay

Adscene (Maidstone)
01622 690339
Weekly free (Thu). Owner: Trinity Mirror Southern. Editor: Diane Nicholls

Adscene (Medway)
01227 767321
www.thisiskent.co.uk
Weekly free (Wed). Owner: Northcliffe Media. Editor: Diane Nicholls

Adscene (Sittingbourne & Sheppey)
01227 767321
www.thisiskent.co.uk
Weekly free (Thu). Owner: Northcliffe Media. Editor: Christine Rayner

Adscene (Thanet)
01227 767321
www.thisiskent.co.uk
Weekly free (Wed). Owner: Northcliffe Media. Editor: Rebecca Smith; news: Jenny De Freitas

Aldershot News
01483 508700
www.aldershot.co.uk
Weekly (Tue). Owner: Guardian Media Group. Group editorial director: Marnie Wilson

The Argus (Brighton)
See page 40

Ashford KM Extra
01233 623232
www.kentonline.co.uk
Weekly (Fri). Owner: Kent Messenger Group. Editor: Robert Barman; chief sub: Claire Stevens; production: Gary Barker

Barnet & Potters Bar Times
020 8359 5959
www.barnettimes.co.uk
Weekly (Thu). Owner: Newsquest. Group editor: Phil Crowther; news: Ruth Holmes

Bedford Times & Citizen
01234 405060
www.bedfordtoday.co.uk
Weekly (Thu). Owner: Johnston Press. Editor: Chris Hall; deputy editor: Olga Norford; news: Mark Lewis

Bedfordshire on Sunday
01234 304403
www.bedsonsunday.com
Weekly (Sun). Owner: LSN Media. Editor: Steve Lowe; news: Liz O'Reilly

Bexhill AdNews
01424 730555
www.bexhillobserver.net
Weekly free (Wed). Owner: Johnston Press. Deputy editor: John Dowling; news: Daniel Collins

Bexhill-on-Sea Observer
01424 730555
www.bexhillobserver.net
Weekly (Fri). Owner: Johnston Press. Deputy editor: John Dowling; news: Daniel Collins

Bexley Times
020 8269 7000
www.bexleytimes.co.uk
Weekly free (Wed). Owner: Archant. Editor: Melody Ryall; production: Mick Taylor

Bexley Mercury
020 8769 4444
www.icsouthlondon.co.uk
Weekly free (Wed). Owner: Tindle Newspapers. Editor: Hannah Walker

Bexleyheath & Welling Times
020 8269 7000
Weekly (Wed). Owner: Archant. Editor: Melody Ryall; production: Mick Taylor

Biggin Hill News
01959 564766
www.biggin-hill-today.co.uk
Weekly (Thu). Owner: Tindle Newspapers. Editor: Luke King

Biggleswade & Sandy Comet
01438 866000
www.thecomet.net
Weekly (Thu). Owner: Archant. Editor: Darren Isted; news: John Adams

Biggleswade Advertiser
01462 441020
www.intheadvertiser.co.uk
Weekly (Wed). Owner: Herts & Essex Newspapers. General manager: Ricky Allan

Biggleswade Chronicle
01767 222333
www.biggleswadetoday.co.uk
Weekly (Fri). Owner: Johnston Press. Editor: Jim Stewart

Bishops Stortford Citizen
01992 572285
www.bishopsstortfordcitizen.co.uk
Weekly (Thu). Owner: Newsquest. Editor: David Jackman

Bishops Stortford Herald
01279 624331
www.herald24.co.uk
Weekly (Thu). Owner: Archant. Editor: Barry Hunt; reporter: Elizabeth Aslington

Bognor Regis Guardian
01243 534133
www.bognor.co.uk
Weekly free (Wed). Owner: Johnston Press. Editor: Janet Philip

Bognor Regis Observer
01243 828777
www.bognor.co.uk
Weekly (Thu). Owner: Johnston Press. Chief sub: David Philip; features: Kevin Smith

Borehamwood & Elstree Times
020 8953 3391
www.borehamwoodtimes.co.uk
Weekly (Fri). Owner: Newsquest. Group editor: Phil Crowther; chief reporter: Marcus Dysch

Brighton & Hove Leader
01273 544544
www.thisisbrightonandhove.co.uk
Weekly (Fri). Owner: Newsquest. Editor: Chris Chandler; news: Mike Dunford

Bromley Times
020 8269 7000
www.bromleytimes.co.uk
Weekly (Thu). Owner: Archant. Editor: Melody Ryall; production: Mick Taylor

Camberley Courier
01252 339760
www.camberley.co.uk
Weekly free (Wed). Owner: Guardian Media Group. Editor: Elaine Cole; news: Andrew Milford

Camberley News & Mail
01252 339760
www.camberley.co.uk
Weekly (Fri). Owner: Guardian Media Group. Editor: Elaine Cole; news: Andrew Milford

Canterbury KM Extra
01227 768181
www.kentonline.co.uk
Weekly (Thu). Owner: Kent Messenger Group. Editor: Bob Bounds

Chichester & Selsey Journal
01243 534133
www.chichester.co.uk
Weekly free (Wed). Owner: Johnston Press. Editor: Janet Philips

Chichester Observer
01243 532532
www.chiobserver.co.uk
Weekly (Thu). Owner: Johnston Press. Chief sub: David Phillip; features: Sue Gilson

Crawley News
01737 732000
www.icsurrey.co.uk
Weekly (Wed). Owner: Northcliffe
Media. Editor-in-chief: Ian Carter;
content editor: Harriet Shelley

Crawley Observer
01293 562929
www.crawleyobserver.co.uk
Weekly (Wed). Owner: Johnston Press.
Editor: Lesley Hixon; news: Andrew
Newman; chief sub: Mark Dunford

Crowborough Courier
01892 681000
www.thisiskentandeastsussex.co.uk
Weekly (Fri). Owner: Northcliffe
Media. Editor: John Mcready; news:
Faith Lee; Today editor: Melanie Yey;
editorial production: Lindsay Jones

Croydon Advertiser
020 8763 6666
www.iccroydon.co.uk
Weekly (Fri). Owner: Trinity Mirror
Southern. Editor-in-chief: Ian Carter;
content editor: Andy Worden

Croydon Guardian
020 8330 9554
www.croydonguardian.co.uk
Weekly (Wed). Owner: Newsquest.
Editor: Danny Brierley

Croydon Post
01737 732000
www.iccroydon.co.uk
Weekly (Thu). Owner: Northcliffe
Media. Editor-in-chief: Ian Carter;
content editor: Andy Worden

Dartford & Gravesham
News Shopper
01689 885701
www.newsshopper.co.uk
Weekly (Wed). Editor: Jean May

Dartford & Swanley
Extra Informer
01634 227800
www.kentonline.co.uk
Weekly (Thu). Owner: Kent Messenger
Group. Editor: Denise Eaton; news:
Louise Edwards

Dartford Express
020 8269 7000
www.dartfordexpress.co.uk
Weekly free (Wed). Owner: Archant.
Editor: Melody Ryall; production:
Mick Taylor

Dartford Messenger
01322 220791
www.kentonline.co.uk
Weekly (Thu). Owner: Kent Messenger
Group. Editor: Sandra Hembury;
news: Louise Edwards

Dartford Times
020 8269 7000
www.dartfordtimes.co.uk
Weekly (Thu). Owner: Archant. Editor:
Melody Ryall; production: Mick Taylor

Dover Express
01227 767321
Weekly (Thu). Owner: Northcliffe
Media. Editor: Simon Finlay

Dover Mercury
01304 240380
Weekly (Thu). Owner: Kent Messenger
Group. Editor: Graham Smith

Downs Mail
01622 630330
www.downsmail.co.uk
Monthly (variable). Editor in chief:
Dennis Fowle

Dunstable Gazette
01582 526000
www.lutontoday.co.uk
Weekly (Wed). Owner: Johnston Press.
Editor: Geoff Cox

East Grinstead Courier
01892 681000
www.thisiskentandeastsussex.co.uk
Weekly (Fri). Owner: Northcliffe
Media. Editor in chief: John
McCready; news: Faith Lee; Today
editor: Melanie Yey; editorial
production: Lindsay Jones

East Grinstead Observer
01737 732000
www.icsurreyonline.co.uk
Weekly (Wed). Owner: Northcliffe
Media. Editor-in-chief: Ian Carter

East Kent Gazette
01227 767321
Weekly (Wed). Owner: Northcliffe
Media. Editor: Christine Rayner

East Kent Mercury
01304 238970
www.eastkentmercury.co.uk
Weekly (Thu). Owner: Kent Messenger
Group. Editor: Graham Smith

Eastbourne & District Advertiser
01323 722091
www.eastbournetoday.co.uk
Weekly free (Wed). Owner: Johnston
Press. Editor: Peter Austin;
commercial editor: Andrew Bennett;
sports editor: Ken McEwan

Eastbourne Gazette
01323 722091
www.eastbournetoday.co.uk
Weekly (Wed). Owner: Johnston Press.
Editor: Peter Austin; commercial
editor: Andrew Bennett; sports editor:
Ken McEwan

Eastbourne Herald
01323 722091
www.eastbournetoday.co.uk
Weekly (Fri). Owner: Johnston Press.
Editor: Peter Austin; commercial
editor: Andrew Bennett; sports editor:
Ken McEwan

Edenbridge Chronicle
01959 564766
www.edenbridge-today.co.uk
Weekly (Thu). Owner: Tindle
Newspapers. Editor: Signid Sherrell

Edenbridge County Border News
01959 564766
www.edenbridge-today.co.uk
Weekly (Thu). Owner: Tindle
Newspapers. Editor: Kevin Black

Edenbridge Courier
01892 681000
www.thisiscourier.co.uk
Weekly (Fri). Owner: Northcliffe
Media. Editor: John McCready; news:
Faith Lee; Today editor: Melanie Yey;
editorial production: Lindsay Jones

Edgware & Mill Hill Times
020 8359 5959
www.edgwaretimes.co.uk
Weekly (Thu). Owner: Newsquest.
Group editor: Phil Crowther; chief
reporter: Ruth Holmes

Elmbridge Guardian
020 8329 9244
www.elmbridgeguardian.co.uk
Weekly (Thu). Owner: Newsquest.
Editor: Sean Duggan

Epsom, Ewell & Banstead Post
020 8763 6666
www.iccroydon.co.uk
Weekly (Thu). Owner: Trinity Mirror
Southern. Editor: Ian Carter; news:
Patsy Payne

Epsom Guardian
020 8329 9244
www.epsomguardian.co.uk
Weekly (Thu). Owner: Newsquest.
Editor: Sean Duggan

Esher News & Mail
01483 508700
www.esher.co.uk
Weekly (Fri). Owner: Guardian Media
Group. Group editorial director:
Debbie Thompson

Farnham Herald
01252 725224
www.farnham-herald-today.co.uk
Weekly (Fri). Owner: Tindle
Newspapers. Editor: Tony Short;
chief reporter: Corina Larby

Farnham Post
01420 84446
Weekly free (Mon). Owner: Tindle
Newspapers. General manager:
Alan Wooler

Faversham KM Extra
01795 534545
www.kentonline.co.uk
Weekly (Tue). Owner: Kent Messenger
Group. Editor: Leo Whitlock; news:
Trisha Jamieson; production: Gary
Barker

Faversham News
01795 532345
www.kentonline.co.uk
Weekly (Thu). Owner: Kent Messenger
Group. Editor: Leo Whitlock; news:
Trisha Jamieson; production: Gary
Barker

Faversham Times
01795 536555
www.trinitymirrorsouthern.co.uk
Weekly (Thu). Owner: Trinity Mirror
Southern. Editor: Christine Rayner;
features: Julia Rogers

Folkestone & Hythe Extra
01303 850676
Weekly (Wed). Owner: Kent Messenger Group. Editor: Leo Whitlock; production: Gary Barker

Folkestone Express
01233 623232
www.kentonline.co.uk
Weekly (Wed). Owner: Kent Messenger Group. Editor: Robert Boman; news: Simon Alford; chief sub: Claire Stevens

Folkestone Herald
01303 850999
Weekly (Thu). Owner: Northcliffe Media. Editor: Simon Finlay

Friday-Ad
0870 162 9999
www.friday-ad.co.uk
Weekly (Fri). Editor: David Sommerville

Gatwick Skyport
020 8538 2236
www.trinitymirrorsouthern.co.uk
Weekly free (Fri). Owner: Trinity Mirror Southern. Editor: Carl Plunkett

Godalming Times
01483 508700
Weekly free (Wed). Owner: Guardian Media Group. Group editorial director: Marnie Wilson; news: Tony Green

Gravesend Express
020 8269 7000
www.gravesendexpress.co.uk
Weekly free (Wed). Owner: Archant. Editor: Melody Ryall; production: Mick Taylor

Gravesend KM Extra
020 8308 7407
www.kentonline.co.uk
Weekly (Fri). Owner: Kent Messenger Group. Editor: Denise Eaton

Gravesend Messenger
020 8308 7407
www.kent-online.co.uk
Weekly (Thu). Owner: Kent Messenger Group. Editor: Denise Eaton

Gravesend Reporter
020 8269 7000
www.gravesendreporter.co.uk
Weekly (Thu). Owner: Archant. Editor: Melody Ryall; production: Mick Taylor

Guildford Times
01483 508700
www.surreyadvertiser.co.uk
Weekly free (Wed). Owner: Guardian Media Group. Group editorial director: Marnie Wilson; news: Tony Green

Hailsham Gazette
01323 722091
www.eastbournetoday.co.uk
Weekly (Wed). Owner: Johnston Press. Editor: Peter Austin; commercial editor: Andrew Bennett; sports editor: Ken McEwan

Haslemere Times & Mail
01252 716444
www.haslemere-herald-today
.co.uk
Weekly free (Tue). Owner: Tindle Newspapers. Editor: Tony Short

Hastings & St Leonards Observer
01424 854242
www.hastingstoday.co.uk
Weekly (Fri). Owner: Johnston Press. Group editor: Peter Lindsey; chief reporter: Chris Pollard

Hastings AdNews
01424 854242
www.hastingstoday.co.uk
Weekly (Wed). Owner: Johnston Press. Group editor: Peter Lindsey; chief reporter: Chris Pollard

Hemel Hempstead Gazette
01442 262311
www.hemeltoday.co.uk
Weekly (Wed). Owner: Johnston Press. Editor: Adam Hollier; sports editor: Graham Caygill

Hendon & Finchley Times
020 8359 5959
www.hendontimes.co.uk
Weekly (Thu). Owner: Newsquest. Group editor: Phil Crowther; chief reporter: Ruth Holmes

Herne Bay Gazette
01227 475901
www.kentonline.co.uk
Weekly (Thu). Owner: Kent Messenger Group. Editor: Leo Whitlock; news: Trisha Jamieson; production: Gary Barker

Herne Bay KM Extra
01227 768181
www.kentonline.co.uk
Weekly (Tue). Owner: Kent Messenger Group. Editor: Leo Whitlock; news: Trisha Jamieson; production: Gary Barker

Herne Bay Times
01227 771515
Weekly (Thu). Owner: Northcliffe Media. Editor: John Nurden; features: Julia Rogers; chief sub: Paul Taylor

Hertford Times
01707 327551
www.whtimes.co.uk
Weekly (Wed). Owner: Archant. Editor: Terry Mitchinson; news: Chris Lennon

Hertfordshire Mercury
01992 526625
www.hertsessexnews.co.uk
Weekly (Fri). Owner: Herts & Essex Newspapers. Editor: Paul Winspear

Hertfordshire Star
01992 526625
www.hertsessexnews.co.uk
Weekly (Wed). Owner: Herts & Essex Newspapers. Editor: Ken Morley

Herts & Essex Observer
01279 866355
www.hertsessexnews.co.uk
Weekly (Thu). Owner: Yattenden News Media. Editor: Paul Winspear; news: Sandra Perry

Herts Advertiser
01727 865165
www.hertsad.co.uk
Weekly (Thu). Owner: Archant. Editor: Noel Cantillon

Hitchin Advertiser
01462 441020
www.intheadvertiser.co.uk
Weekly (Wed). Owner: Herts & Essex Newspapers. General manager: Ricky Allan

Hitchin Comet
01438 866200
www.thecomet.net
Weekly (Thu). Owner: Archant. Editor: Darren Isted; news: John Adams

Hoddesdon & Broxbourne Mercury
01992 526600
www.hertsessexnews.co.uk
Weekly (Fri). Owner: Herts & Essex Newspapers. Editor in chief: Paul Brackley

Horsham Advertiser
01403 751200
www.wscountytimes.co.uk
Weekly (Fri). Owner: Johnston Press. Editor: Gary Shipton; chief sub: Steve Payne

Hythe Herald
01303 850999
Weekly (Thu). Owner: Northcliffe Media. Editor: Simon Finlay

Isle of Thanet Gazette
01227 767321
www.thisiskent.co.uk
Weekly (Thu). Owner: Northcliffe Media. Editor: Rebecca Smith; news: Julian May

Kent & Sussex Courier
01892 681000
 www.thisiscourier.co.uk
Weekly (Fri). Owner: Northcliffe Media. Editor in chief: John McCready; features: Tony Durrant; production: Jo Lewis

Kent Messenger
01622 695666
www.kentonline.co.uk
Weekly (Fri). Owner: Kent Messenger Group. Editor: Bob Bounds; community editor: Cathy Tyce

Kent on Sunday
01303 817000
www.kentnews.co.uk
Weekly (Sun). Owner: KOS Media (Publishing). Editor: Ian Patel; news: Bernard Ginns; chief sub: Dave Hobday; production: Jason Pyne

Kentish Express
01233 623232
www.kentonline.co.uk
Weekly (Thu). Owner: Kent Messenger Group. Editor: Robert Barman; news: Simon Alford; chief sub: Claire Stevens; production: Gary Barker

Kentish Gazette
01227 768181
www.kentonline.co.uk
Weekly (Thu). Owner: Kent Messenger Group. Editor: Leo Whitlock; news: Trisha Jamieson; production: Gary Barker

Kingston Guardian
020 8329 9244
www.kingstonguardian.co.uk
Weekly (Thu). Owner: Newsquest.
Editor: Sean Duggan

Lea Valley Star
01992 526625
www.hertsessexnews.co.uk
Weekly (Wed). Owner: Herts & Essex
Newspapers. Editor: Ken Morley

Leatherhead Advertiser
01737 732000
www.icsurreyonline.co.uk
Weekly (Thu). Owner: Northcliffe
Media. Editor-in-chief: Ian Carter;
content editor: Katherine Newton

Leatherhead Guardian
020 8329 9244
www.leatherheadguardian.co.uk
Weekly (Thu). Owner: Newsquest.
Editor: Sean Duggan

Leighton Buzzard & Linslade Citizen
01908 651200
www.miltonkeynestoday.co.uk
Weekly free (Thu). Owner: Johnston
Press. Editor: Alan Legg

Leighton Buzzard Observer
01525 858400
www.miltonkeynestoday.co.uk
Weekly (Tue). Owner: Johnston Press.
Editor: Nick Wormley; news: Mike King

LB News
01908 242490
www.seriousaboutnews.com
Weds. Owner: LSN Media. Editor:
Craig Lewis

Letchworth & Baldock Comet
01438 866000
www.thecomet.net
Weekly (Thu). Owner: Archant. Editor:
Darren Isted; news: John Adams

Limited Edition (Hertfordshire)
01923 216220
Monthly. Owner: Newsquest.
Editor: Deborah Aspinall

Littlehampton Gazette
01903 714135
www.littlehamptontoday.co.uk
Weekly (Thu). Owner: Johnston Press.
Editor: Roger Green

Luton & Dunstable on Sunday
01582 707707
www.lutononsunday.com
Weekly (Sun). Owner: LSN Media.
Editor: Gaynor Selby; news: Craig Lewis

Luton Herald & Post
01582 700600
www.lutontoday.co.uk
Weekly (Thu). Owner: Johnston Press.
Editor: John Francis

Luton News
01582 526000
www.lutontoday.co.uk
Weekly (Wed). Owner: Johnston Press.
Assistant editor: Geoff Cox

Maidstone KM Extra
01622 695666
www.kentonline.co.uk
Weekly free (Fri). Owner: Kent
Messenger Group. Editor: Bob Bounds;
community editor: Cathy Tyce

Medway Messenger (Rochester, Chatham, Gravesend)
01634 227800
www.kentonline.co.uk
Weekly (Mon, Fri). Owner: Kent
Messenger Group. Editor: Bob Bounds

Medway News
01227 767321
Weekly (Fri). Editor: Diane Nicholls

Medway Standard
01227 767321
Weekly (Mon). Editor: Diane Nicholls

The Messenger (Haslemere)
01428 653999
www.messenger-online.co.uk
Weekly free (Wed). Editor: Joyce
Charland-Brown; news: Sheila Checkley

Mid Sussex Citizen
01444 452201
www.midsussextoday.co.uk
Weekly free (Wed). Owner: Johnston
Press. Editor: Grahame Campbell

Mid Sussex Leader
01273 544544
www.thisismidsussex.co.uk

Mid Sussex Times
01444 452201
www.midsussextoday.co.uk
Weekly (Thu). Owner: Johnston Press.
Editor: Grahame Campbell

Midhurst & Petworth Observer
01730 813557
www.midhurstandpetworth.co.uk
Weekly (Thu). Owner: Johnston Press.
Chief sub: John Carter; news: Jane Hunt

News & Mail
01483 508900
www.surreyad.co.uk
Weekly (Wed). Owner: Guardian Media
Group. Group editorial director:
Marnie Wilson

News in Focus
01732 228000
www.thisiskent.co.uk
Weekly (Tue). Owner: Northcliffe
Media. Editor: Ian Reid

News Shopper
01689 885772
www.newsshopper.co.uk
Weekly (Wed). Owner: Newsquest.
Editor:Jean May; news: Helen Backway;
chief sub: Tim Miles

Orpington & Petts Wood Times
020 8269 7000
Weekly (Thu). Owner: Archant. Editor:
Melody Ryall; production: Mick Taylor

Paddock Wood Courier
01892 681000
www.thisiscourier.co.uk
Weekly (Fri). Owner: Northcliffe
Media. Editor: John McCready;
features: Melanie Whittaker

Redhill, Reigate & Horley Life
01403 223180
www.redhillandreigatelife.co.uk
Weekly (Wed). Owner: Newsquest.
Editor: Chris Chandler

Reigate Post
020 8770 7171
www.icsurreyonline.co.uk
Weekly (Thu). Owner: Northcliffe
Media. Editor: Ian Carter; content
editor: James Osbourne

Reigate, Redhill & Horley Post
01737 732000
www.icsurreyonline.co.uk
Weekly (Wed). Owner: Northcliffe
Media. Editor-in-chief: Ian Carter;
content editor: James Osbourne

Romney Marsh Herald
01227 767321
Weekly (Wed). Editor: Simon Finlay

Royston & Buntingford Mercury
01992 526600
www.hertsmercury.co.uk
Weekly (Fri). Owner: Herts & Essex
Newspapers. Editor: Paul Brackley;
features: Bridget McAlpine

Royston Crow
01763 245241
www.royston-crow.co.uk
Weekly (Thu). Owner: Archant.
Editor: Les Baker

Rye & Battle Observer
01424 854242
www.ryeandbattletoday.co.uk
Weekly (Fri). Owner: Johnston Press.
Associate editor: Russell Claughton;
news: Andy Hemsley

St Albans & Harpenden Review
01727 834411
www.stalbansobserver.co.uk
Weekly free (Wed). Owner: Newsquest.
Editor: Martin Buhagiar

St Albans Observer
01727 834411
www.stalbansobserver.co.uk
Weekly (Thu). Owner: Newsquest.
Editor: Martin Buhagiar

Seaford Gazette
01323 722091
www.eastbournetoday.co.uk
Weekly (Wed). Owner: Johnston Press.
Editor: Peter Austin; commercial
editor: Andrew Bennett; sports editor:
Ken McEwan

Sevenoaks Chronicle
01732 228000
www.thisiskentandeastsussex.co.uk
Weekly (Thu). Owner: Northcliffe
Media. Editor: Ian Reid

Sheerness Times Guardian
01795 580300
Weekly (Thu). Owner: Kent Messenger
Group. Editor: Matt Ramsden; news:
Gemma Constable

Sheppey Gazette
01227 767321
Weekly (Wed). Editor: Christine Rayner

49

Shoreham Herald
01903 230051
www.shorehamtoday.co.uk
*Weekly (Thu). Owner: Johnston Press.
Editor: Michelle Neville*

Sittingbourne KM Extra
01795 426873
www.kentonline.co.uk
*Weekly (Wed). Owner: Kent Messenger
Group. Editor: Matt Ramsden; news:
Gemma Constable*

South Coast Leader
01273 544544
www.thisisbrightonandhove.co.uk
*Weekly (Fri). Owner: Newsquest. Editor:
Chris Chandler; news: Mike Dunford*

Staines & Ashford News
01932 561111
www.surreyheraldnews.co.uk
*Weekly (Wed). Owner: Trinity Mirror
Southern. Editor: Mike Hawkins;
publishing director: Liz Dixon*

Staines & Egham News
01932 561111
www.surreyheraldnews.co.uk
*Weekly (Wed). Owner: Trinity Mirror
Southern. Editor: Mike Hawkins;
publishing director: Liz Dixon*

Staines Guardian
020 8939 1500
www.yourlocalguardian.co.uk
*Weekly (Thu). Owner: Newsquest.
Editor: Chris Caulfield*

Staines Informer
01932 561111
www.surreyheraldnews.co.uk
*Weekly free (Thu). Owner: Trinity
Mirror Southern. Editor: Mike
Hawkins; publishing director: Liz Dixon*

Staines Leader
01932 561111
www.surreyheraldnews.co.uk
*Weekly (Thu). Owner: Trinity Mirror
Southern. Editor: Mike Hawkins*

Star Classified (Bishops Stortford)
01992 526625
www.hertsessexnews.co.uk
*Weekly (Tue). Owner: Archant. Editor:
Paul Winspear; news: Sandra Perry*

Stevenage Advertiser
01462 441020
www.intheadvertiser.co.uk
*Weekly (Wed). Owner: Herts & Essex
Newspapers. General manager:
Ricky Allan*

Stevenage Comet
01438 866000
www.thecomet.net
*Weekly (Thu). Owner: Archant. Editor:
Darren Isted; news: John Adams*

Stevenage Herald
01438 866000
www.thecomet.net
*Weekly free (Wed). Owner: Archant.
Editor: Darren Isted; news: John Adams*

Surrey & Hants News
01252 716444
www.farnham-herald-today.co.uk
*Weekly free (Tue). Owner: Tindle
Newspapers. Assistant Editor:
Tony Short*

Surrey Advertiser
01483 508700
www.surreyad.co.uk
*Weekly (Fri). Owner: Guardian Media
Group. Group editorial director:
Marnie Wilson*

Surrey Comet
020 8329 9244
www.surreycomet.co.uk
*Weekly (Wed). Owner: Newsquest.
Editor: Sean Duggan*

Surrey Hants Star
01252 316311
www.shstar.co.uk
*Weekly free (Thu). Owner: Guardian
Media Group. Editor: Joanne Jones*

Surrey Herald
01932 561111
www.surreyheraldnews.co.uk
*Weekly (Wed). Owner: Trinity Mirror
Southern. Editor: Mike Hawkins*

Surrey Mirror
020 8770 7171
www.icsurreyonline.co.uk
*Weekly (Wed). Owner: Northcliffe
Media. Editor: Ian Carter; news:
James Osbourne; features: Christine
Malthouse; chief sub: Sherif El Alfay*

Surrey Times
01483 508700
*Weekly free (Wed). Owner: Guardian
Media Group. Group editorial director:
Marnie Wilson*

Sussex Express
01273 480601
www.sussexexpress.co.uk
*Weekly (Fri). Owner: Johnston Press.
Editor: Paul Watson; deputy editor:
Michael McKenzy*

Sutton Advertiser
020 8763 6666
www.iccroydon.co.uk
*Weekly (Fri). Owner: Trinity Mirror
Southern. Editor: Ian Carter*

Sutton Borough Post
020 8763 6666
www.iccroydon.co.uk
*Weekly (Wed). Owner: Trinity Mirror
Southern. Editor: Ian Carter*

Sutton Guardian
020 8329 9244
www.suttonguardian.co.uk
*Weekly (Thu). Owner: Newsquest.
Editor: Sean Duggan*

Swanley Messenger
01474 564327
www.kent-online.co.uk
*Weekly (Thu). Owner: Kent Messenger
Group. Editor: Sandra Hembury;
news: Louise Edwards*

Swanley Times
020 8269 7000
*Weekly (Thu). Owner: Archant.
Editor: Melody Ryall*

Tandridge Chronicle
01959 564766
www.tandridge-today.co.uk
*Weekly (Thu). Owner: Tindle
Newspapers. Editor: Signid Sherrell*

Tandridge County Border News
01959 564766
www.tandridge-today.co.uk
*Weekly (Thu). Owner: Tindle
Newspapers. Editor: Kevin Black*

Tenterden Express
01233 623232
www.kentonline.co.uk
*Weekly (Tue). Owner: Kent Messenger
Group. Editor: Robert Barman; news:
Simon Alford; chief sub: Claire Stevens*

Tenterden KM Extra
01233 623232
www.kentonline.co.uk
*Weekly (Tue). Owner: Kent Messenger
Group. Editor: Robert Barman; news:
Simon Alford; chief sub: Claire Stevens*

Thanet KM Extra
01843 296969
www.kentonline.co.uk
*Weekly (Wed). Owner: Kent Messenger
Group. Editor: Carol Davis*

Thanet Times
01227 767321
*Weekly (Tues). Editor: Rebecca Smith;
news: Jenny De Freitas*

Tonbridge Courier
01892 681000
www.thisiskentandeastsussex.co.uk
*Weekly (Fri). Owner: Northcliffe Media.
Editor: John McCready; features:
Melanie Whittaker; production:
Richard Page*

Tunbridge Wells Courier
01892 681000
www.thisiskentandeastsussex.co.uk
*Weekly (Fri). Owner: Northcliffe
Media. Editor: John McCready;
production: Richard Page*

Tunbridge Wells Extra
01892 525111
www.kentonline.co.uk
*Weekly (Fri). Owner: Kent Messenger
Group. Editor: Bob Bounds; news:
Linda Mitchell*

Virginia Water Villager
01753 523355
*Fortnightly (Thu). Owner: Clyde &
Forth Press. Editor: Julie Swain*

Walton & Weybridge Informer
01932 561111
www.surreyheraldnews.co.uk
*Weekly free (Thu). Owner: Trinity
Mirror Southern. Editor: Mike Hawkins*

Watford Free Observer
01923 216220
www.watfordobserver.co.uk
*Weekly (Thu). Owner: Newsquest.
Editor: Peter Wilson-Leary; news:
Frazer Ansell*

Watford Review
01923 216220
www.stalbansobserver.co.uk
*Weekly free (Wed). Owner: Newsquest.
Editor: Peter Wilson-Leary*

Weald Courier
01892 681000
www.thisiskentandeastsussex.co.uk
*Weekly (Fri). Owner: Northcliffe
Media. Editor: John McCready;
features: Melanie Whittaker;
production: Richard Page*

Wealden Advertiser
01580 753322
www.wealdenad.co.uk
Weekly free (Fri). Editor: Graham Thorn

**Weekend Herald
(Crawley, Horsham, Horley)**
01293 562929
www.crawleyobserver.co.uk
*Weekly free (Fri). Owner: Johnston
Press. Editor: Lesley Hixon; chief sub:
Mark Dunford*

Welwyn & Hatfield Review
01923 216346
www.stalbansobserver.co.uk
*Weekly (Thu). Owner: Newsquest.
Editor: Martin Buhagiar*

Welwyn & Hatfield Times
01707 327551
www.whtimes.co.uk
*Weekly (Wed). Owner: Archant. Editor:
Terry Mitchinson; news: Chris Lennon*

Westerham County Border News
01959 564766
www.westerham-today.co.uk
*Weekly (Thu). Owner: Tindle
Newspapers. Editor: Kevin Black*

West Sussex County Times
01403 751200
www.horshamonline.co.uk
*Weekly (Fri). Owner: Johnston Press.
Editor: Gary Shipton; deputy editor:
Tim Hopewell-Ash*

West Sussex Gazette
01903 230051
www.westsussextoday.co.uk
*Weekly (Wed). Owner: Johnston Press.
Editor: John Hammond; chief sub:
Phil Reynolds*

Weybridge Villager
01753 523355
*Fortnightly (Thu). Owner: Clyde &
Forth Press. Editor: Sally Stevens*

Whitstable Gazette
01227 372233
www.kentonline.co.uk
*Weekly (Thu). Owner: Kent Messenger
Group. Editor: Leo Whitlock;
news: Trisha Jamieson; production:
Gary Barker*

Whitstable KM Extra
01227 768181
www.kentonline.co.uk
*Weekly (Tue). Owner: Kent Messenger
Group. Editor: Bob Bounds;
news: Trisha Jamieson; production:
Gary Barker*

Whitstable Times
01227 771515
*Weekly (Thu). Owner: Northcliffe
Media. Editor: John Nurden; features:
Julia Rogers; chief sub: Paul Taylor;
production: Mark Silva*

Woking Informer
01932 561111
www.surreyheraldnews.co.uk
*Weekly free (Thu). Owner: Trinity
Mirror Southern. Editor: Mike
Hawkins; news: Irlene Watchmore*

Woking News & Mail
01483 755755
www.woking.co.uk
*Weekly (Thu). Owner: Guardian Media
Group. Editor: Bridget Dakin*

Woking Review
01483 755755
www.woking.co.uk
*Weekly (Wed). Owner: Guardian Media
Group. Editor: Bridget Dakin*

Worthing Advertiser
01903 230051
www.worthingtoday.co.uk
*Weekly (Wed). Owner: Johnston Press.
Editor: Tony Mayes*

Worthing Guardian
01903 230051
www.worthingtoday.co.uk
*Weekly (Fri). Owner: Johnston Press.
Editor: Nikki Jeffrey*

Worthing Herald
01903 230051
www.worthingtoday.co.uk
*Weekly (Thu). Owner: Johnston Press.
Editor: John Buss; news: Nicola
McClaren*

● South England

Berkshire, Buckinghamshire,
Hampshire, Oxfordshire, Wiltshire

Abingdon Herald
01865 425262
www.thisisoxfordshire.co.uk
*Weekly (Thu). Owner: Newsquest.
Editor: Derek Holmes*

The Advertiser (Newbury)
01635 524111
www.newburytoday.co.uk
*Weekly (Tue). Owner: Blacket Turner.
Editor: Brien Beharrell; news:
Martin Robertshaw*

Aldershot Courier
01252 339760
www.aldershot.co.uk
*Weekly free (Wed). Owner: Guardian
Media Group. Editor: Elaine Cole;
news: Andrew Milford*

Aldershot Mail
01252 339760
www.aldershot.co.uk
*Weekly (Tue). Owner: Guardian Media
Group. Editor: Elaine Cole; news:
Andrew Milford*

Aldershot News
01252 339760
www.aldershot.co.uk
*Weekly (Fri). Owner: Guardian Media
Group. Editor: Elaine Cole; news:
Andrew Milford*

Alresford Advertiser
01420 84446
*Weekly (Wed). Owner: Tindle
Newspapers. Editor: Christine
McDerment; news: Martin Ford*

Alton Times & Mail
01252 716444
*Weekly free (Tue). Owner: Tindle
Newspapers. Editor: Tony Short*

Amersham & Chesham Free Press
01494 755081
www.bucksfreepress.co.uk
*Weekly (Fri). Owner: Newsquest.
Editor: Steve Cohen; news: Paul
Pickett; features: Lindi Bilgorri*

Amersham Examiner
01753 888333
www.buckinghamtoday.co.uk
*Weekly (Thu). Owner: Trinity Mirror
Southern. Editor: Julie Voyce; news:
Ben Steele*

Andover Advertiser
01264 323456
www.andoveradvertiser.co.uk
*Weekly (Fri). Owner: Newsquest.
Editor: Joe Scicluna; deputy editor:
Judy Belbin; features: Simon Reeve;
chief sub: Judith Hughes*

Andover Advertiser Midweek
01264 323456
www.andoveradvertiser.co.uk
*Weekly (Wed). Owner: Newsquest.
Editor: Joe Scicluna; deputy editor:
Judy Belbin; features: Simon Reeve;
chief sub: Judith Hughes*

Ascot News
01344 456611
www.icberkshire.co.uk
*Weekly (Thu). Owner: Clyde & Forth
Press. Editor: Richard Crowe*

Ash & Farnham Mail
01252 339760
www.aldershot.co.uk
*Weekly (Tue). Owner: Guardian Media
Group. Editor: Elaine Cole;
news: Lindsey Eudo-Mitchell*

Banbury Cake
01295 256111
www.thisisoxfordshire.co.uk
*Weekly (Thu). Owner: Newsquest.
Editor: Derek Holmes; news and
features: Jason Collie*

Banbury Review
01295 227777
www.banburyguardian.co.uk
*Weekly free (Fri). Owner: Johnston
Press. Editor: Jason Gibbins; news:
Stuart Kidman*

Banbury Guardian
01295 227777
www.banburyguardian.co.uk
*Weekly (Thu). Owner: Johnston Press.
Editor: Jason Gibbins; news: Stuart
Kidman*

Basingstoke & Northampton Gazette
01256 461131
www.thisishampshire.net
Weekly (Mon). Owner: Newsquest. Editor: Mark Jones; news: Hugh Cadman; chief sub: Jonathan Lee; production manager: Alan Cranham

Basingstoke Extra
01256 461131
www.thisishampshire.net
Weekly free (Wed). Owner: Newsquest. Editor: Mark Jones; news: Hugh Cadman; chief sub: Jonathan Lee; production manager: Alan Cranham

Basingstoke Independent
01962 859559
www.hantsmedia.co.uk
Weekly (Fri). Owner: Hampshire Media. Editor: Mark O'Connor

Basingstoke Observer
01256 694121
Weekly (Thu). Owner: Tri Media Publishing. Editor: Steve Davies; head of production: Tony Allsop

Beaconsfield Advertiser
01753 888333
www.buckinghamtoday.co.uk
Weekly (Thu). Owner: Trinity Mirror Southern. Editor: Julie Voyce; news: Ben Steele

Berkhamsted & Tring Gazette
01442 262311
www.hemeltoday.co.uk
Weekly (Wed). Owner: Johnston Press. News: Ann Traynor

Bicester Advertiser
01865 425262
www.thisisoxfordshire.co.uk
Weekly (Fri). Owner: Newsquest. Editor: Derek Holmes

Bicester Review
01280 813434
www.buckinghamtoday.co.uk
Weekly (Fri). Owner: Central Counties Newspapers. Editor: Rob Gibbard; deputy editor: Clare Wale

Bordon Post
01730 264811
www.petersfield.co.uk
Weekly (Wed). Owner: Johnston Press. Editor: Graeme Moir; chief reporter: Will Parsons

Bordon Times & Mail
01252 716444
Weekly free (Tue). Owner: Tindle Newspapers. Editor: Tony Short; features: Angie Williamson

Brackley & Towcester Advertiser
01280 813434
www.buckinghamtoday.co.uk
Weekly (Fri). Owner: Central Counties Newspapers. Editor: Rob Gibbard; deputy editor: Clare Wale

Bracknell & Ascot Times
0118 936 6180
www.getbracknell.co.uk
Weekly (Wed). Owner: Guardian Media Group. Editor: Adam D Smith; sports editor: Steve Skerry

Bracknell Midweek News
01344 456611
www.icberkshire.co.uk
Weekly (Wed). Owner: Clyde & Forth Press. News editor: Richard Crowe

Bracknell News
01344 456611
www.icberkshire.co.uk
Weekly (Thu). Owner: Clyde & Forth Press. News editor: Richard Crowe

Bracknell Standard
0118 936 6180
www.getbracknell.co.uk
Weekly (Thu). Owner: Guardian Media Group. Editor: Adam D Smith; sports editor: Steve Skerry

Buckingham & Winslow Advertiser
01280 813434
www.buckinghamtoday.co.uk
Weekly (Fri). Owner: Central Counties Newspapers. Editor: Rob Gibbard; deputy editor: Clare Wale

Buckinghamshire Advertiser
01753 888333
Weekly (Thu). Owner: Trinity Mirror Southern. Editor: Julie Voyce; news: Ben Steele

Buckinghamshire Examiner
01753 888333
www.buckinghamtoday.co.uk
Weekly (Thu). Owner: Trinity Mirror Southern. Editor: Julie Voyce; news: Ben Steele

Bucks Free Press
01494 755000
www.bucksfreepress.co.uk
Weekly (Fri). Owner: Newsquest. Editor: Steve Cohen; news: Paul Pickett

Bucks Free Press Midweek
01494 755081
www.bucksfreepress.co.uk
Weekly (Tue). Owner: Newsquest. Editor: Steve Cohen; news: Paul Pickett; features: Lindi Bilgorri

Bucks Herald
01296 619700
www.bucksherald.co.uk
Weekly (Wed). Owner: Johnston Press

Crowthorne & Sandhurst Times
0118 936 6180
www.getbracknell.co.uk
Weekly (Wed). Owner: Guardian Media Group. Editor: Adam D Smith; news: David Allan; sport: Steve Skerry

Crowthorne, Sandhurst, Owlsmoor Newsweek
01344 456611
www.icberkshire.co.uk
Weekly (Thu). Owner: Clyde & Forth Press. News Editor: Richard Crowe

Devizes, Melksham & Vale of Pewsey News
01793 528144
www.thisisswindon.co.uk
Weekly free (Wed). Owner: Newsquest. Editor: Gary Lawrence

Didcot Herald
01865 425262
www.thisisoxfordshire.co.uk
Weekly (Thu). Owner: Newsquest. Editor: Derek Holmes

Eastleigh News Extra
01962 841772
www.thisishampshire.net
Weekly free (Thu). Owner: Newsquest. Editor: Mary Payne; news: Kit Neilson

Fareham & Gosport Journal
023 9266 4488
www.portsmouth.co.uk
Weekly free (Thu). Owner: Johnston Press. News: Colin McNeill; features: Graham Patsfield

Fareham & Gosport News
See The News, page 41

Farnborough News & Mail
01252 339760
www.farnborough.co.uk
Weekly (Tue). Owner: Guardian Media Group. Editor: Elaine Cole

Fleet News & Mail
01252 339760
www.fleet-online.co.uk
Weekly (Tue). Owner: Guardian Media Group. Editor: Elaine Cole

Frome Times and White Horse News
01225 704761
www.frometimes.co.uk
Fortnightly free (Thu). Owner: Wiltshire Publications. Editor: Ian Drew

Hamble Valley Journal
023 9266 4488
www.portsmouth.co.uk
Weekly free (Thu). Owner: Johnston Press. News: Colin McNeill; features: Graham Patsfield

Hampshire Chronicle
01962 841772
www.thisishampshire.net
Weekly (Thu). Owner: Newsquest. Editor: Keith Redbourn; deputy editor: Brian Mustoe

Hants & Dorset Avon Advertiser
01722 426500
www.salisburyjournal.co.uk
Weekly (Wed). Owner: Newsquest. Editor: Bill Browne; news: David Vallis; features: Lesley Bates

Hart Courier
01252 339760
www.surreyad.co.uk
Weekly (Wed). Owner: Guardian Media Group. Editor: Elaine Cole

Havant & Waterlooville Journal
023 9266 4488
www.portsmouth.co.uk
Weekly free (Thu). Owner: Johnston Press. Editor: News: Colin McNeill; features: Graham Patsfield

Havant & Waterlooville News
See The News, page 41

Hemel Hempstead Herald Express
01442 262311
www.hemeltoday.co.uk
Weekly (Thu). Owner: Johnston Press. News: Ann Traynor

Henley Standard
01491 419444
www.henleystandard.co.uk
Weekly (Thurs). Editor: George Tuckfield; news: Richard Reid

Isle of Wight County Press
01983 521333
www.iwcp.co.uk
Weekly (Fri). Editor: Alan Marriott

Liphook Times & Mail
01252 716444
Weekly free (Tue). Owner: Tindle Newspapers. Editor: Tony Short

Lymington Times
01425 613384
Weekly (Fri). Editor: Charles Curry

Maidenhead Advertiser
01628 680680
www.maidenhead-advertiser.co.uk
Weekly (Thurs). Editor: Martin Trepte; news: Glenn Mitchell

Maidenhead Express
01753 825111
www.icberkshire.co.uk
Weekly (Fri). Owner: Clyde & Forth Press. Editor: Sally Stevens

Marlow Free Press
01494 755081
www.bucksfreepress.co.uk
Weekly (Fri). Owner: Newsquest. Editor: Steve Cohen; news: Victoria Birch; features: Lindi Bilgorri

Melksham Independent News
01225 704761
www.melkshamnews.com
Fortnightly free (Thu). Owner: Wiltshire Publications. Editor: Ian Drew

Meon Valley News
023 9263 2767
www.mvn.org.uk
Monthly (Mon). Owner: Tindle Newspapers. Editor: Christine Miller; assistant editor: Angela Ennis

Mid Hampshire Observer
01962 859559
www.hantsmedia.co.uk
Weekly (Wed). Owner: Hampshire Media. Editor: Mark O'Connor

Milton Keynes Citizen
01908 651200
www.miltonkeynes.co.uk
Weekly free (Thu). Owner: Johnston Press. Editor: Jan Henderson; news: Steve Larner

Milton Keynes News
01908 242490
www.mk-news.co.uk
Weekly (Wed). Owner: LSN Media. Editor: David Gale

Monday Gazette
01256 461131
www.thisishampshire.net
Weekly (Mon). Owner: Newsquest. Editor: Mark Jones; news: Hugh Cadman; chief sub: Jonathan Lee; production manager: Alan Cranham

New Forest Post
01590 613888
www.thisishampshire.net
Weekly (Thu). Owner: Newsquest. Editor: Ian Murray

New Milton Advertiser
01425 613384
Weekly (Fri). Editor: Charles Curry

Newbury & Thatcham Chronicle
01635 32812
www.icberkshire.co.uk
Weekly free (Wed). Owner: Clyde & Forth Press. News: Morris O'Brien

Newbury Weekly News
01635 524111
www.newburytoday.co.uk
Weekly (Thu). Owner: Blacket Turner. Editor: Brien Beharrell; news: Martin Robertshaw

The News (Portsmouth)
See page 41

Oxford Journal
01235 553444
www.youroxfordshire.co.uk
Weekly (Thu). Owner: Biz Publishing. Editor: Steve Davis

Oxford Mail
01865 425262
www.thisisoxfordshire.co.uk
Daily. Owner: Newsquest. Editor: Simon O'Neill

Oxford Star
01865 425262
www.thisisoxfordshire.co.uk
Weekly (Thu). Owner: Newsquest. Editor: Simon O'Neill

Oxford Times
01865 425262
www.thisisoxfordshire.co.uk
Weekly (Fri). Owner: Newsquest. Editor: Derek Holmes

Petersfield Mail
01252 716444
Weekly free (Tue). Owner: Tindle Newspapers. Editor: Tony Short

Petersfield Post
01730 264811
www.petersfield.co.uk
Weekly (Wed). Owner: Johnston Press. Editor: Graeme Moir; chief reporter: Will Parsons

Portsmouth & Southsea Journal
023 9266 4488
www.portsmouth.co.uk
Weekly free (Thu). Owner: Johnston Press. News: Colin McNeill; features: Graham Patsfield

Property Chronicle (Berkshire)
0118 950 3030
www.icberkshire.co.uk
Weekly (Tue, Thu). Owner: Trinity Mirror Southern. Editor: Sally Stevens

Reading Post
0118 918 3000
www.getreading.co.uk
Weekly (Wed). Owner: Clyde & Forth Press. Editor: Andy Murrill

Reading Chronicle
0118 950 3030
www.icberkshire.co.uk
Weekly (Thu). Owner: Clyde & Forth Press. Editor: Sally Stevens

Reading Evening Post
0118 918 3000
www.getreading.co.uk
Daily (Mon-Fri). Owner: Guardian Media Group. Editor: Andy Murrill; news: Lucy Allan; features: Phil Creighton; chief sub: Karen Neville

Romsey Advertiser
023 8042 4777
www.dailyecho.co.uk
Weekly (Fri). Owner: Newsquest. Editor: Ian Murray; news: Gordon Sutter; chief sub: Colin Jenkins

Salisbury Avon Advertiser
01722 426500
www.thisiswiltshire.co.uk
Weekly (Wed). Owner: Newsquest. Editor: Bill Browne; news: David Vallis; features: Lesley Bates; chief sub: Jane Warner

Salisbury Journal
01722 426500
www.thisissalisbury.co.uk
Weekly (Thu). Owner: Newsquest. Editor: Bill Browne; news: David Vallis; features: Lesley Bates; chief sub: Jane Warner

Sandhurst & Crowthorne Mail
01252 339760
www.aldershot.co.uk
Weekly (Tue). Owner: Guardian Media Group. Editor: Elaine Cole

Sandhurst & Crowthorne News
01252 339760
www.aldershot.co.uk
Weekly (Fri). Owner: Guardian Media Group. Editor: Elaine Cole

Slough Express
01753 825111
www.icberkshire.co.uk
Weekly (Fri). Owner: Clyde & Forth Press. Editor: Sally Stevens

Slough Observer
01753 523355
www.thisisslough.com
Weekly (Fri). Owner: Clyde & Forth Press. Editor: Roger Hawes

Southern Daily Echo
See page 41

South Bucks, Wycombe & Chiltern Star and Midweek
01494 755000
www.hillingdontimes.co.uk
Weekly (Tue, Thu). Owner: Newsquest. Editor: Steve Cohen; news: Paul Pickett

Southampton Advertiser
023 8042 4777
Weekly (Thu). Owner: Newsquest. Editor: Ian Murray; news: Gordon Sutter; chief sub: Colin Jenkins

Surrey & Hampshire Guardian
01788 543077
www.surreyandhampshire
guardian.co.uk
*Daily. Owner: Journal Publishing
Company. Editor: Jag Basra; news: Keith
Brailford; features: Andrew Woods*

Swindon Advertiser
01793 528144
www.thisisswindon.co.uk
*Daily. Owner: Newsquest. Editor:
Dave King*

Swindon Star
01793 528144
www.thisisswindon.co.uk
*Weekly free (Thu). Owner: Newsquest.
Editor: Dave King*

Thame Gazette
01296 619700
www.thametoday.co.uk
*Weekly (Fri). Owner: Johnston Press.
Editor: Chris East; news: Kim Green*

Twyford Times
0118 936 6180
www.getbracknell.co.uk
*Weekly (Wed). Owner: Guardian Media
Group. Editor: Adam D Smith; deputy
editor: David Allan; sports editor:
Steve Skerry*

Wallingford Herald
01865 425262
www.thisisoxfordshire.co.uk
*Weekly (Thu). Owner: Newsquest.
Editor: Derek Holmes*

Wantage Herald
01865 425262
www.thisisoxfordshire.co.uk
*Weekly (Thu). Owner: Newsquest.
Editor: Derek Holmes*

Warminster Journal
01985 213030
*Weekly (Fri). Editors: RC Shorto and
DJ Watkins*

West & North Wilts Star
01225 777292
www.thisiswiltshire.co.uk
*Weekly free (Fri). Owner: Newsquest.
Editor: Andy Sambidge; news: Craig
Evry; features: Amy Watkins*

**Wilts & Gloucestershire
Standard**
01285 642642
www.thisiscirencester.com
*Weekly (Thu). Owner: Newsquest.
Editor: Skip Walker; news: Simon Davis*

Wiltshire Gazette and Herald
01793 528144
www.thisisswindon.co.uk
*Weekly (Thu). Owner: Newsquest.
Editor: Gary Lawrence*

Wiltshire Guardian
024 7622 0742
*Weekly free (Thu). Owner: Journal
Publishing Company. Editor: Jag
Basra; features: Kelly Turrall*

Wiltshire Times
01225 777292
www.thisiswiltshire.co.uk
*Weekly (Fri). Owner: Newsquest.
Editor: Andy Sambidge; news: Craig
Evry; features: Amy Watkins*

Winchester News Extra
01962 841772
www.thisishampshire.net
*Weekly free (Thu). Owner: Newsquest.
Editor: Keith Redbourn; news: Brian
Mustoe*

Winchester Shopper
023 8042 4777
www.dailyecho.co.uk
*Weekly (Sun). Owner: Newsquest.
Editor: Ian Murray; news: Gordon
Sutter; chief sub: Colin Jenkins*

**Windsor, Ascot & Maidenhead
Observer**
01753 523355
www.thisiswindsor.com
*Weekly (Fri). Owner: Clyde & Forth
Press. Editor: Roger Hawes; assistant
editor: Mike Sim*

Windsor Express
01753 825111
www.icberkshire.co.uk
*Weekly free (Fri). Owner: Clyde &
Forth Press. Editor: Roger Hawes*

**Witney & West Oxfordshire
Gazette**
01865 425262
www.thisisoxfordshire.co.uk
*Weekly (Wed). Owner: Newsquest.
Editor: Derek Holmes*

Woodley Times
0118 936 6180
www.getbracknell.co.uk
*Weekly (Wed). Owner: Guardian Media
Group. Editor: Adam D Smith; deputy
editor: David Allan; sports editor:
Steve Skerry*

Woking Midweek
01344 456611
www.icberkshire.co.uk
*Weekly (Wed). Owner: Clyde & Forth
Press. News: Richard Crowe*

Wokingham News
01344 456611
www.icberkshire.co.uk
*Weekly (Wed). Owner: Clyde & Forth
Press. News: Richard Crowe*

Wokingham Standard
0118 936 6180
www.getbracknell.co.uk
*Weekly (Thu). Owner: Guardian Media
Group. Editor: Adam D Smith; deputy
editor: David Allan; sports editor:
Steve Skerry*

Wokingham Times
0118 936 6180
www.getbracknell.co.uk
*Weekly (Wed). Owner: Guardian Media
Group. Editor: Adam D Smith; deputy
editor: David Allan; sports editor:
Steve Skerry*

Woodley & Earley Chronicle
0118 963 3030
www.icberkshire.co.uk
*Weekly (Thu). Owner: Trinity Mirror
Southern. Editor: Simon Jones; news:
Maurice O'Brien; features: Alec
Kingham; production: Phil Atkinson*

Yateley Mail
01252 339760
www.aldershot.co.uk
*Weekly (Tue). Owner: Guardian Media
Group. Editor: Elaine Cole*

Yateley News
01252 339760
www.aldershot.co.uk
*Weekly (Fri). Owner: Guardian Media
Group. Editor: Elaine Cole*

● South-west England

Cornwall, Devon, Dorset,
Somerset & Avon

Bath Chronicle
01225 322322
www.thisisbath.co.uk
*Daily. Owner: Northcliffe Media.
Editor: Sam Holliday; news: Paul
Wiltshire; features: Georgette
McCready; chief sub: Graham Holburn*

Bath Times
01225 322322
www.thisisbath.co.uk
*Weekly (Tues). Owner: Northcliffe
Media. Editor: Sam Holliday; news:
Paul Wiltshire*

Bournemouth Advertiser
01202 554601
www.thisisbournemouth.co.uk
*Weekly free (Thu). Owner: Newsquest.
Editor: Neal Butterworth; news: Andy
Martin; features: Kevin Nash*

Bridgwater Mercury
01823 365151
www.thisisthewestcountry.co.uk
*Weekly (Tue). Owner: Newsquest.
Editor-in-chief: Ken Bird; deputy
group editor: Bob Drayton*

Bridgwater Star
01823 365151
www.thisisthewestcountry.co.uk
*Weekly (Thu). Owner: Newsquest.
Editor-in-chief: Ken Bird; deputy
group editor: Bob Drayton*

Bridgwater Times
01275 335100
www.thisissomerset.co.uk
*Weekly (Thu). Owner: Northcliffe
Media. Editor: Carol Deacon*

Bridport & Lyme Regis News
01308 425884
www.bridportnews.co.uk
*Weekly (Fri). Owner: Newsquest.
Editor: Holly Robinson*

Bristol Evening Post
See page 40

Brixham News
01803 864212
*Weekly free (Wed). Owner: Tindle
Newspapers. Editor: Gina Coles*

Bude & Stratton Post
01566 772424
Weekly (Thu). Owner: Tindle Newspapers. Editor: Geoff Seccombe; news: Keith Whitford

Burnham & Highbridge Mercury
01823 365151
www.thisisthewestcountry.co.uk
Weekly (Tue). Owner: Newsquest. Editor-in-chief: Ken Bird; deputy group editor: Bob Drayton

Burnham & Highbridge Times
01275 335100
www.thisissomerset.co.uk
Weekly (Thu). Owner: Northcliffe Media. Editor: Carol Deacon; news: Juliette Auty

Burnham & Highbridge Weekly News
01823 365151
www.thisisthewestcountry.co.uk
Weekly (Thu). Owner: Newsquest. Editor-in-chief: Ken Bird; deputy group editor: Bob Drayton

Camborne and Redruth Packet
01326 213333
www.thisisthewestcountry.co.uk
Weekly free (Wed). Owner: Newsquest. Editor: Terry Lambert; news: Stephen Ivall; chief sub: David Robinson

Camelford & Delabole Journal Gazette
01566 772424
Weekly (Fri). Owner: Tindle Newspapers. Editor: Keith Whitford

Camelford & Delabole Post
01566 772424
Weekly (Thu). Owner: Tindle Newspapers. Editor: Keith Whitford

Central Somerset Gazette
01749 832300
www.thisissomerset.co.uk
Weekly (Thurs). Owner: Northcliffe Media. Editor: Philip Welch

Chard & Ilminster News
01823 365151
www.thisisthewestcountry.co.uk
Weekly (Wed). Owner: Newsquest. Editor-in-chief: Ken Bird; deputy group editor: Bob Drayton

Chard & Ilminster News (Somerset)
01460 67474
www.thisisthewestcountry.co.uk
Weekly (Wed). Owner: Newsquest. Editor: Ken Bird; chief reporter: Alex Cameron

Chard Advertiser
01297 357504
www.chard-today.co.uk
Weekly free (Weds). Owner: Tindle Newspapers. Editor: Kate Mew

Cheddar Valley Gazette
01749 832300
www.thisissomerset.co.uk
Weekly (Thu). Owner: Northcliffe Media. Editor: Philip Welch

Chew Valley Gazette
01275 332266
www.chewvalleygazette.co.uk
Monthly (last Fri). Owner: Northcliffe Media. Editor: Rowland Janes; features: Anne Collier

Clevedon Mercury
01275 335142
www.thisissomerset.co.uk
Weekly (Thu). Owner: Northcliffe Media. Editor: Carol Deacon; chief sub: Kevin Lee

Cornish & Devon Post
01566 772424
Weekly (Thu). Owner: Tindle Newspapers. Editor: Keith Whitford

Cornish Guardian
01726 76815
www.thisiscornwall.co.uk
Weekly (Thu). Owner: Northcliffe Media. Editor: Andy Cooper; news: Matt Dixon; chief sub: Simon Fernley

The Cornishman
01736 363171
www.thisiscornwall.co.uk
Weekly (Thu). Owner: Northcliffe Media. Editor: Jeremy Ridge; features: Donna MacAllister

Cornish Times
01579 342174
www.cornwall-today.co.uk
Weekly (Fri). Owner: Tindle Newspapers. Editor: John Noble

Crewkerne Advertiser
01297 631120
www.crewkerne-today.co.uk
Weekly free (Fri). Owner: Tindle Newspapers. Editor: Tony Woodman

Culm, Crediton & Tiverton Gazette
01884 252725
Weekly (Tue). Owner: Northcliffe Media. Editor: Richard Best

Daily Echo
See page 41

Dartmouth Chronicle
01548 856353
www.dartmouth-today.co.uk
Weekly (Fri). Owner: Tindle Newspapers. Editor: Steve Harvey

Dawlish Gazette
01626 355566
www.dawlish-today.co.uk
Weekly (Fri). Owner: Tindle Newspapers. Editor: Ruth Davey; news: John Belment; chief sub: Steven Taylor

Dawlish Post
01626 355566
www.dawlish-today.co.uk
Weekly (Fri). Owner: Tindle Newspapers. Editor: Ruth Davey; news: John Belment; chief sub: Steven Taylor

Dorchester Advertiser
01305 830930
www.thisisdorset.net
Weekly (Thu). Owner: Newsquest. Editor: David Murdock; news: Paul Thomas; features: Dirmaid Macdonagh; chief sub: Nick Horton

Dorset Echo
01305 830930
www.thisisdorset.net
Weekly (Thu). Owner: Newsquest. Editor: David Murdock; news: Paul Thomas; features: Dirmaid Macdonagh

Exeter Express and Echo
01392 442211
www.thisisexeter.co.uk
Daily. Owner: Northcliffe Media. Editor: Mark Astley; news: Sue Kemp; features: Becky Moran; production: Jerry Charge

Exeter Leader
01392 442211
www.thisisexeter.co.uk
Weekly free (Wed). Owner: Northcliffe Media. Editor: Mark Astley; news: Sue Kemp; features: Becky Moran

Exmouth Herald
01392 888444
www.exmouthherald.co.uk
Weekly free (Fri). Owner: Archant. Chief sub: Phil Griffin

Falmouth Packet
01326 213333
www.thisisthewestcountry.co.uk
Weekly (Wed). Owner: Newsquest. Editor: Terry Lambert; news: Stephen Ivall

Frome & Somerset Standard
01225 322322
www.thisissomerset.co.uk
Weekly (Thu). Owner: Northcliffe Media. Editor: Stephanie Feldwicke; News Editor: Chloe Boyce

Frome Times
01225 704761
www.frometimes.co.uk
Fortnightly free (Thu). Editor: Ian Drew; news: Jessica Fox-Taylor

Hayle Times
01736 795813
www.stivesnews.co.uk
Weekly (Fri). Editor: Toni Carver; features: Tricia Carver

Helston Gazette
01326 213333
www.thisisthewestcountry.co.uk
Weekly (Wed). Owner: Newsquest. Editor: Terry Lambert; news: Stephen Ivall

The Herald (Plymouth)
See page 41

Holsworthy Post
01566 778220
Weekly (Thu). Owner: Tindle Newspapers. Editor: Keith Whitford

Honiton Advertiser
01297 35750
www.honiton-today.co.uk
Weekly (Wed). Owner: Tindle Newspapers. Editor: Kate Mew

Ivybridge, South Brent & South Hams Gazette
01548 853101
www.ivybridge-today.co.uk
Weekly (Fri). Owner: Tindle Newspapers. Editor: Steve Harvey

Journal (Exmouth)
01392 888444
www.devon24.co.uk
Weekly (Thu). Owner: Archant.
Editor: Phil Griffin

Kingsbridge & Salcombe Gazette
01548 853101
Weekly (Fri). Owner: Tindle
Newspapers. Editor: Steve Harvey

Launceston Journal Gazette
01566 772424
Weekly (Fri). Owner: Tindle
Newspapers. Editor: Keith Whitford

Liskeard Gazette & Journal
01579 342174
Weekly (Thu). Owner: Tindle
Newspapers. Editor: Will Doney

Mid Cornwall Advertiser
01726 66755
www.cornwalladvertisers.co.uk
Monthly (middle of month). Owner:
Tindle Newspapers. Editor: Fiona Jolley

Mid Devon Advertiser
01626 355566
www.newton-abbot-today.co.uk
Weekly (Fri). Owner: Tindle
Newspapers. Editor: Ruth Davey; news:
John Belment; chief sub: Steven Taylor

Mid Devon Star
01823 365151
www.thisisthewestcountry.co.uk
Weekly (Fri). Owner: Newsquest.
Editor-in-chief: Ken Bird; deputy
group editor: Bob Drayton

Midweek Herald
01392 888444
www.devon24.co.uk
Weekly (Wed). Owner: Archant. Editor:
Linda Bennett

Newquay Voice
01637 878298
www.newquayvoice.co.uk
Weekly (Wed). Editor: Matt Bond

North Cornwall Advertiser
01208 815096
www.northcornwall-today.co.uk
Monthly free (1st Wed). Owner: Tindle
Newspapers. Editor: Tony Gregan

North Devon Gazette & Advertiser
01271 344303
www.northdevongazette.co.uk
Weekly (Wed). Owner: Archant.
Editor: David Tanner

North Devon Journal
01271 343064
www.thisisnorthdevon.co.uk
Weekly (Thu). Owner: Northcliffe Media.
Managing editor: Andy Cooper; Editor:
Richard Best; features: Andrea Foster

North Somerset Times
01934 422622
www.thewestonmercury.co.uk
Weekly (Wed). Owner: Archant. Editor:
Heather Pickstock; news: Andy Ridgeway

Okehampton Times
01822 613666
www.okehampton-today.co.uk
Weekly (Thu). Owner: Tindle
Newspapers. Editor: Colin Brent

Ottery Advertiser
01297 35750
Weekly (Wed). Owner: Tindle
Newspapers. Editor: Kate Mew

Penwith Pirate
01326 213333
www.thisisthewestcountry.co.uk
Weekly free (Wed). Owner: Newsquest.
Editor: Terry Lambert; news: Stephen
Ivall; chief sub: Paul Jordan

Plymouth Extra
01752 765500
www.thisisplymouth.co.uk
Weekly free (Thu). Owner: Northcliffe
Media. Editor: Paul Atkins

Plympton Plymstock & Ivybridge News
01548 853101
Weekly (Fri). Owner: Tindle
Newspapers. Editor: Steve Harvey

Poole Advertiser
01202 675413
Weekly free (Thu). Owner: Newsquest.
Editor: Neal Butterworth; news:
Andy Martin; features: Kevin Nash

Post Advertiser
01305 830900
Monthly free (Mon). Owner:
Newsquest. Editor: Holly Robinson

Princetown Times
01822 613666
www.thisisthewestcountry.co.uk
Weekly (Thu). Owner: Tindle
Newspapers. Editor: Colin Brent

St Ives Times & Echo
01736 795813
www.stivesnews.co.uk
Weekly (Fri). Editor: Toni Carver;
features: Tricia Carver

Shepton Mallet Journal
01749 832300
www.thisissomerset.co.uk
Weekly (Thu). Owner: Northcliffe
Media. Editor: Philip Welch

Sidmouth Herald
01392 888444
www.archantdevon.co.uk
Weekly (Fri). Owner: Archant.
Editor: Emma Silverthorne

Somerset County Gazette
01823 365151
www.thisisthewestcountry.co.uk
Weekly (Fri). Owner: Newsquest.
Editor-in-chief: Ken Bird; deputy
group editor: Bob Drayton

Somerset Guardian
01225 322322
www.thisissomerset.co.uk
Weekly (Thu). Owner: Northcliffe
Media. Editor: Stephanie Feldwicke

South Devon & Plymouth Times
01584 856353
www.thisisthewestcountry.co.uk
Weekly (Thu). Owner: Tindle
Newspapers. Editor: Gina Coles

Swanage and Wareham District Advertiser
01929 427428
www.thisisdorset.net
Weekly free (Thu). Owner: Newsquest.
Editor: Neal Butterworth; news: Andy
Davey

Taunton Star
01823 365151
www.tauntonstar.co.uk
Weekly (Wed). Owner: Newsquest.
Editor: Ken Bird; deputy group editor:
Bob Drayton

Taunton Times
01823 250500
www.thisissomerset.co.uk
Weekly free (Thu). Owner: Northcliffe
Media. Editor: Martin Heale

Tavistock Times Gazette
01822 613666
www.tavistock-today.co.uk
Weekly (Thu). Owner: Tindle
Newspapers. Editor: Colin Brent

Teignmouth News
01626 355566
www.teignmouth-today.co.uk
Weekly (Fri). Owner: Tindle
Newspapers. Editor: Ruth Davey; news:
John Belment; chief sub: Steven Taylor

Teignmouth Post & Gazette
01626 355566
www.teignmouth-today.co.uk
Weekly (Fri). Owner: Tindle
Newspapers. Editor: Ruth Davey; news:
John Belment; chief sub: Steven Taylor

Torbay Weekender
01803 676000
www.thisissouthdevon.co.uk
Weekly (Thu). Owner: Northcliffe
Media. Editor: Andy Phelan; news:
Jim Parker; features: Tracy Gwynne;
chief sub: Nigel Lines

Torquay Herald Express
01803 676000
www.thisissouthdevon.co.uk
Weekly (Thu). Owner: Northcliffe
Media. Editor: Andy Phelan; news:
Jim Parker; features: Tracy Gwynne;
chief sub: Nigel Lines

Totnes News
01548 853101
Weekly (Fri). Owner: Tindle
Newspapers. Editor: Gina Coles

Totnes Times Gazette
01584 856353
www.thisisthewestcountry.co.uk
Weekly (Wed). Owner: Tindle
Newspapers. Editor: Gina Coles

Trader News (West Somerset)
01984 632731
Weekly free (Wed). Owner: Northcliffe
Media. Editor: Gareth Purcell

Truro Packet
01326 213333
www.thisisthewestcountry.co.uk
Weekly (Wed). Owner: Newsquest.
Editor: Terry Lambert; news:
Stephen Ivall

Wellington Weekly News
01823 250500
www.thisissomerset.co.uk
Weekly (Wed). Owner: Northcliffe Media. Editor: Debbie Rundle; news: Steve Weatherill

Wells Journal
01749 832300
www.thisissomerset.co.uk
Weekly (Thu). Owner: Northcliffe Media. Editor: Philip Welch

The West Briton
01872 271451
www.thisiscornwall.co.uk
Weekly (Thu). Owner: Northcliffe Media. Editor: Andy Cooper

West Somerset Free Press
01984 632731
www.west-somerset-today.co.uk
Weekly (Fri). Owner: Northcliffe Media. Editor: Gareth Purcell

Western Daily Press (Bristol)
See page 42

Western Gazette
01935 700500
www.westgaz.co.uk
Weekly (Thu). Owner: Northcliffe Media. Editor: Tim Dixon; news: Zena O'Rourke; features: Tori Birch

Western Morning News (Plymouth)
See page 42

Weston & Worle News
01275 335140
www.thisissomerset.co.uk
Weekly (Thu). Owner: Northcliffe Media. Editor: Carol Deacon; news: Juliette Auty; chief sub: Kevin Lee

Weston Mercury
01934 422622
www.thewestonmercury.co.uk
Weekly (Fri). Owner: Archant. Editor: Judy Kisiel; news: Clare Hayes

Weston-super-Mare Admag
01934 422622
www.thewestonmercury.co.uk
Weekly (Wed). Owner: Archant. Editor: Judy Kisiel; news: Clare Hayes

Weymouth & Portland Advertiser
01305 830930
www.thisisdorset.net
Weekly (Thu). Owner: Newsquest. Editor: David Murdock; news: Paul Thomas; features: Dirmaid Macdonagh

Yeovil Express
01823 365151
www.thisisthewestcountry.co.uk
Weekly (Thu). Owner: Newsquest. Editor-in-chief: Ken Bird; deputy group editor: Bob Drayton

Yeovil Times
01935 700500
Weekly free (Wed). Owner: Northcliffe Media. Editor: Tim Dixon; news: Zena O'Rourke; features: Carla Gale

● East England

Cambridgeshire, Essex, Lincolnshire, Norfolk, Suffolk

Alford Standard
01754 897120
www.skegnesstoday.co.uk
Weekly (Wed). Owner: Johnston Press. Editor: Becky Baker

Axholme Herald
01427 874417
Weekly (Wed). Owner: Northcliffe Media. Editor: Ron Shipley

Barking & Dagenham Post
0845 070 0161
www.bdpost.co.uk
Weekly (Wed). Owner: Archant. Editor: Barry Kirk

Barking & Dagenham Recorder
020 8478 4444
www.bdrecorder.co.uk
Weekly (Thu). Owner: Archant. Editor: Chris Carter

Barking & Dagenham Weekender
0845 070 0161
Weekly (Fri). Owner: Archant. Editor: Barry Kirk; chief sub: Graham Whitmore

Barking & Dagenham Yellow Advertiser
01268 503400
www.trinitymirrorsouthern.co.uk
Weekly (Thu). Owner: Trinity Mirror Southern

Basildon & Wickford Recorder
01268 522792
www.thisisessex.co.uk
Daily. Owner: Newsquest. Editor: Martin McNeill; news: Chris Hatton; chief sub: Neal Reeve

Basildon Yellow Advertiser
01268 503400
www.icessex.co.uk
Weekly (Thu). Owner: Trinity Mirror Southern. Features: Liz Wade

Beccles & Bungay Journal
01603 628311
www.edp24.co.uk
Weekly (Fri). Owner: Archant. Editor: Terry Redhead

Billericay & Wickford Gazette
01277 219222
www.thisisessex.co.uk
Weekly (Wed). Owner: Northcliffe Media. Editor: Ben Hall

Boston Citizen
01205 311433
www.bostontoday.co.uk
Weekly (Fri). Owner: Johnston Press. Deputy Editor: Warren Moody; news: Stephen Stray

Boston Standard
01205 311433
www.bostontoday.co.uk
Weekly (Wed). Owner: Johnston Press. Deputy Editor: Warren Moody; news: Stephen Stray

Boston Target
01522 820000
www.thisislincolnshire.co.uk
Weekly (Wed). Owner: Northcliffe Media. Acting Editor: Martin Finney

Braintree & Witham Times
01376 343344
www.thisisessex.co.uk
Weekly (Thu). Owner: Newsquest. Editor: Ainsley Davidson

Braintree Chronicle
01245 600700
www.thisisessex.co.uk
Weekly (Wed/Thu). Owner: Northcliffe Media. Editor: Matt Holder; news: Matt Adams; features: Darryl Webber

Brentwood, Billericay & Havering Recorder
01708 771500
www.romfordrecorder.co.uk
Weekly (Fri). Owner: Archant. Editor: Mark Sweetingham; news: Eden Black

Brentwood Gazette
01277 219222
www.thisisessex.co.uk
Weekly (Wed). Owner: Northcliffe Media. Editor: Matt Holder; news: Sheelagh Bree

Brentwood Weekly News
01268 522792
www.thisisessex.co.uk
Weekly (Thu). Owner: Newsquest. Editor: Martin McNeill; news: Chris Hatton; chief sub: Neal Reeve

Brentwood Yellow Advertiser
01268 503400
www.trinitymirrorsouthern.co.uk
Weekly (Thu). Owner: Trinity Mirror Southern. Features: Liz Wade

Bury Free Press
01284 768911
www.buryfreepress.co.uk
Weekly (Fri). Owner: Johnston Press. Editor: Barry Peters; news: Lesley Anslow; features: Sue Green

Bury St Edmunds Citizen
01284 768911
Weekly (Fri). Owner: Johnston Press. Editor: Barry Peters; news: Lesley Anslow; features: Sue Green

Bury St Edmunds Mercury
01284 702588
www.edp24.co.uk
Weekly (Fri). Owner: Archant.Editor: Paul Couch; news: Will Grahame-Clarke

Cambridge Crier
01223 434434
www.cambridge-news.co.uk
Weekly (Fri). Owner: Cambridge Newspapers. Editor: Nigel Brookes; features: James Fuller

Cambridge Evening News
01223 434434
www.cambridge-news.co.uk
Daily. Owner: Cambridge Newspapers. Editor: Murray Morse; news: John Deex; features: Paul Kirkley

Cambridge Weekly News
01223 434434
www.cambridge-news.co.uk
Weekly (Wed). Owner: Cambridge Newspapers. Editor: Nigel Brookes

Cambridgeshire Times
01354 652621
Weekly. Owner: Archant. Editor: Brian Asplin; news: John Elworthy; features: Maggie Gibson

Castle Point Yellow Advertiser
01268 503400
www.trinitymirrorsouthern.co.uk
Weekly (Thu). Owner: Trinity Mirror Southern

Castlepoint & Rayleigh Standard
01268 522792
www.thisisessex.co.uk
Weekly (Wed). Owner: Newsquest. Editor: Martin McNeill; news: Chris Hatton; chief sub: Neal Reeve

Chatteris Times
01354 652621
www.cambs-times.co.uk
Weekly (Thu). Owner: Archant. Editor: Brian Asplin; news: John Elworthy; features: Maggie Gibson

Chelmsford Chronicle
01245 600700
www.thisisessex.co.uk
Weekly (Wed, Thu). Owner: Northcliffe Media. Editor: Matt Holder; news: Matt Adams; features: Darryl Webber

Chelmsford Weekly News
01245 493444
www.thisisessex.co.uk
Weekly (Thu). Owner: Newsquest. Editor: Paul Gilham; news: Denise Rigby

Chelmsford Yellow Advertiser
01268 503400
www.trinitymirrorsouthern.co.uk
Weekly (Thu). Owner: Trinity Mirror Southern

Clacton & Frinton Gazette
01255 221221
www.thisisessex.co.uk
Weekly (Thu). Owner: Newsquest. Editor: James Wills

Colchester Evening Gazette
01206 506000
www.nqe.info
Daily. Owner: Newsquest. Editor-in-chief: Irene Kettle; news: Sally Teatheredge; features: Iris Clapp; chief sub: Will Bramhill

Dereham & Fakenham Times
01603 628311
www.edp24.co.uk
Weekly (Thu). Owner: Archant. Editor: Terry Redhead

Diss Express
01379 642264
www.dissexpress.co.uk
Weekly (Fri). Owner: Johnston Press. Editor: Stephen Penny

Diss Mercury
01603 628311
www.edp24.co.uk
Weekly (Fri). Owner: Archant. Editor: Terry Redhead

Dunmow & Stansted Chronicle
01245 600700
www.thisisessex.co.uk
Weekly (Wed/Thu). Owner: Northcliffe Media. Editor: Matt Holder; news: Matt Adams; features: Darryl Webber

Dunmow Broadcast and Recorder
01371 874537
www.dunmow-broadcast.co.uk
Weekly free (Thu). Owner: Archant. Editor: Barry Hunt; reporter: Michael Boyton

Dunmow Observer
01279 866355
www.herts-essex-news.co.uk
Weekly (Thu). Owner: Herts & Essex Newspapers. Editor: Paul Winspear; news: Sandra Perry

East Anglian Daily Times
See page 41

East Herts Herald
01279 624331
www.herald24.co.uk
Weekly (Thu). Owner: Archant. Editor: Barry Hunt; news: Tracey Hubbard

Eastern Daily Press
See page 41

Ely Standard
01353 667831
www.ely-standard.co.uk
Weekly free (Thu). Owner: Archant. Editor: Debbie Davies; news: Leslie Innes

Epping & Waltham Yellow Advertiser
01268 503400
www.trinitymirrorsouthern.co.uk
Weekly free (Fri). Owner: Trinity Mirror Southern

Epping Guardian
01992 572285
www.eppingguardian.co.uk
Weekly (Thu). Owner: Newsquest. Editor: David Jackman

Epping Independent
020 8498 3400
www.newsquest.co.uk
Weekly (Fri). Owner: Newsquest. Editor: David Jackman

Epworth Bells & Crowle Advertiser
01427 872202
www.epworthtoday.co.uk
Weekly (Thu). Owner: Johnston Press. Editor: Janet Harrison

Essex Chronicle
01245 600700
www.thisisessex.co.uk
Weekly (Wed/Thu). Owner: Northcliffe Media. Editor: Matt Holder; news: Matt Adams; features: Darryl Webber

Essex County Standard
01206 506000
www.nqe.info
Weekly (Fri). Owner: Newsquest. Editor: Irene Kettle; features: Iris Clapp; chief sub: Will Bramhill

Essex Enquirer
01277 627300
www.theenquirer.co.uk
Weekly (Thu). Editor: Carol Driver

Evening Echo (Essex)
01268 522792
www.thisisessex.co.uk
Daily. Owner: Newsquest. Editor: Martin McNeill; news: Chris Hatton; chief sub: Neal Reeve

Evening News (Norwich)
01603 628311
www.eveningnews24.co.uk
Daily. Owner: Archant. News editor: David Powles

Evening Star (Ipswich)
01473 324788
www.eveningstar.co.uk
Daily. Owner: Archant. Editor: Nigel Pickover; news: Jessica Gallagher; features: Tracy Sparling

Fenland Citizen
01945 586100
www.fenlandtoday.co.uk
Weekly (Wed). Owner: Johnston Press. Editor: Keith Drayton

Gainsborough Standard
01427 615323
www.gainsboroughtoday.co.uk
Weekly (Thu). Owner: Johnston Press. Editor: Janet Harrison

Gainsborough Target
01522 820000
www.thisislincolnshire.co.uk
Weekly (Fri). Owner: Northcliffe Media. Editor: Jon Grubb

Goole Courier
01405 782400
www.gooletoday.co.uk
Weekly (Thu). Owner: Johnston Press. Editor: Janet Harrison; news: Stephanie Bateman

Goole Times/Selby Post
01405 720110
www.gooletimes.co.uk
Weekly (Thu). Owner: Northcliffe Media. Editor: Peter Butler

Grantham Citizen
01476 562291
www.granthamtoday.co.uk
Weekly (Tue). Owner: Johnston Press. Editor: Tim Robinson; news: John Pinchbeck

Grantham Journal
01476 562291
www.granthamtoday.co.uk
Weekly (Tue). Owner: Johnston Press. Editor: Tim Robinson; news: John Pinchbeck

Great Yarmouth & Gorleston Advertiser
01493 601206
www.advertiser-online.co.uk
Weekly (Thu). Owner: Archant.
Editor: Anne Edwards

Great Yarmouth Mercury
01603 628311
www.edp24.co.uk
Weekly (Tue). Owner: Archant.
Editor: Terry Redhead

Grimsby Evening Telegraph
01472 360360
www.thisisgrimsby.co.uk
Daily. Owner: Northcliffe Media.
Editor: Michelle Lalor; news: Lucy
Wood; features: Barrie Farnsworth

Grimsby Target
01472 360360
www.thisisgrimsby.co.uk
Daily. Owner: Northcliffe Media.
Editor: Michelle Lalor; news: Lucy
Wood; features: Barrie Farnsworth

Halstead Gazette
01376 343344
www.thisisessex.co.uk
Weekly (Fri). Owner: Newsquest.
Editor: Ainsley Davidson

Harlow Herald
01279 624331
www.herald24.co.uk
Weekly (Thu). Owner: Archant. Editor:
Barry Hunt; news: Tracey Hubbard

Harlow Star
01279 451545
www.herts-essex-news.co.uk
Weekly (Thu). Owner: Herts & Essex
Newspapers. Editor: Ken Morley

Havering Gazette
01277 219222
www.thisisessex.co.uk
Weekly (Wed). Owner: Northcliffe
Media. Editor in chief: Matt Holder

Haverhill Echo
01440 703456
www.haverhilltoday.co.uk
Weekly (Thu). Owner: Johnston Press.
News editor: David Hart

Haverhill Weekly News
01223 434434
www.cambridge-news.co.uk
Weekly (Thu). Owner: Cambridge
Newspapers. Editor: Nigel Brookes

Havering Herald
0845 070 0161
Weekly free (Fri). Owner: Archant.
Editor: Richard Thompson

Havering Yellow Advertiser
01268 503400
www.trinitymirrorsouthern.co.uk
Weekly (Wed). Owner: Trinity Mirror
Southern

Horncastle News
01507 353200
www.horncastletoday.co.uk
Weekly (Wed). Owner: Johnston Press.
Managing editor: Tim Robinson

Huntingdon Town Crier
01480 402100
www.cambridge-news.co.uk
Weekly (Thu). Owner: Johnston Press.
Editor: Richard Yetman

Huntingdon Weekly News
01223 434434
www.cambridge-news.co.uk
Weekly (Wed). Owner: Newsquest.
Editor: Murray Morse; news: John Deex

Hunts Post
01480 411481
www.huntspost.co.uk
Weekly (Wed). Owner: Archant.
Editor: Andy Veale; deputy editor:
Angela Singer

Ilford & Redbridge Post
0845 070 0161
Weekly free (Wed). Owner: Archant.
Editor: Wayne Tuckfield; chief sub:
Graham Whitmore

Ipswich Advertiser
01473 324700
www.ipswichadvertiser.co.uk
Weekly (Thu). Owner: Archant.
Editor: Paul Couch

Island Times (Canvey Island)
01702 477666
Monthly (Tue). Owner: Archant.
Editor: Michael Guy

Leigh Times
01702 477666
Fortnightly (Tue). Owner: Archant.
Editor: Michael Guy

Lincoln Target
01522 820000
www.thisislincolnshire.co.uk
Weekly (Wed). Owner: Northcliffe
Media. Editor: Jon Grubb

Lincolnshire Echo
01522 820000
www.thisislincolnshire.co.uk
Daily. Owner: Northcliffe Media.
Editor: Jon Grubb

Lincolnshire Free Press
01775 725021
www.spaldingtoday.co.uk
Weekly (Tue). Owner: Johnston Press.
Editor: Nick Woodhead; news: David
Crossley; features: Julie Williams;
chief sub: Tracey Vale

The Local (Bourne)
01778 425876
Weekly (Fri). Owner: Johnston Press.
Editor: Lisa Bruen

Loughton, Chigwell & Buckhurst Hill Guardian
01992 572285
www.eppingguardian.co.uk
Weekly (Thu). Owner: Newsquest.
Editor: David Jackman

Louth Citizen
01507 353200
www.louthtoday.co.uk
Weekly (Fri). Owner: Johnston Press.
Managing editor: Tim Robinson;
editor: Charles Ladbrooke

Louth Leader
01507 353200
www.louthtoday.co.uk
Weekly (Wed). Owner: Johnston Press.
Managing editor: Tim Robinson;
editor: Charles Ladbrooke

Lowestoft Journal
01603 628311
www.edp24.co.uk
Weekly (Fri). Owner: Archant.
Editor: Terry Redhead

Lynn News
01553 761188
www.lynnnews.co.uk
Weekly (Tue, Fri). Owner: Johnston
Press. Editor: Malcolm Powell;
news: Donna Semmens

Maldon & Burnham Chronicle
01245 600700
www.thisisessex.co.uk
Weekly (Wed/Thu). Owner: Northcliffe
Media. Editor: Matt Holder; news:
Matt Adams; features: Darryl Webber

Maldon & Burnham Standard
01621 852233
Weekly (Thu). Owner: Newsquest.
Editor: Paul Gilham

Market Rasen Mail
01507 353200
www.marketrasentoday.co.uk
Weekly (Wed). Owner: Johnston Press.
Managing editor: Tim Robinson;
editor: Jason Hipsley

Newmarket Journal
01638 564104
www.newmarketjournal.co.uk
Weekly (Thu). Owner: Johnston Press.
Assistant editor: Philip Minett

Newmarket Weekly News
01223 434434
www.cambridge-news.co.uk
Weekly (Thu). Owner: Cambridge
Newspapers. Editor: Nigel Brookes

Norfolk Citizen
01553 761188
Weekly (Fri). Owner: Johnston Press.
Editor: Chris Hornby

Norfolk North Advertiser
01603 772487
www.advertiser24.co.uk
Weekly (Fri). Owner: Archant.
Editor: Terry Redhead

North Essex Advertiser
01473 324700
www.advertiser-online.co.uk
Weekly (Fri). Owner: Archant. Editor:
Paul Couch; news: Nicola Durrant

North Norfolk & Broadland Town & Country News
01692 582287
Monthly (Fri nearest 1st).
Editor: Lawrence Watts

North Norfolk News
01603 628311
www.edp24.co.uk
Weekly (Thu). Owner: Archant.
Editor: Terry Redhead

Norwich Advertiser
01603 772487
www.advertiser24.co.uk
*Weekly (Fri). Owner: Archant.
Editor: Terry Redhead*

Ongar & North Weald Gazette
01277 219222
www.thisisessex.co.uk
*Weekly (Wed). Owner: Northcliffe Media.
Editor: Matt Holder; news: Ben Hall*

Ongar Guardian
01992 572285
www.eppingguardian.co.uk
*Weekly (Thu). Owner: Newsquest.
Editor: David Jackman*

Peterborough Citizen
01733 555111
www.peterboroughnow.co.uk
*Weekly (Wed). Owner: Johnston Press.
Acting Editor: Nigel Thornton; news:
Rose Taylor; features: Julia Ogden;
production: Brad Barnes*

Peterborough Evening Telegraph
01733 555111
www.peterboroughnow.co.uk
*Daily. Owner: Johnston Press Acting
Editor: Nigel Thornton; news: Rose
Taylor; features: Julia Ogden;
production: Brad Barnes*

Peterborough Herald & Post
01733 318600
www.peterborough.net
/heraldandpost
*Weekly (Thu). Owner: Midlands
Weekly Media (Trinity Mirror).
Editor: Amanda Franklin*

Ramsey Post
01480 411481
*Weekly (Thu). Owner: Archant.
Editor: Andy Veale; deputy editor:
Angela Singer*

Rayleigh Times
01702 477666
*Monthly. Owner: Archant.
Editor: Michael Guy*

Redbridge Yellow Advertiser
01268 503400
www.trinitymirrorsouthern.co.uk
*Weekly (Thu). Owner: Trinity Mirror
Southern*

**Redbridge, Waltham Forest &
West Essex Guardian**
020 8498 3400
www.newsquest.co.uk
*Weekly (Thu). Owner: Newsquest.
Editor: Pat Stannard*

Romford & Havering Post
0845 070 0161
www.haveringpost.co.uk
*Weekly free (Wed). Owner: Archant.
Editorial director: Richard Thompson;
editor: Amanda Patterson*

Romford Recorder
01708 771500
www.recorderonline.co.uk
*Weekly (Fri). Owner: Archant. Editor:
Mark Sweetingham; news: Eden Black*

Royston Weekly News
01223 434434
www.cambridge-news.co.uk
*Weekly (Thu). Owner: Cambridge
Newspapers. Editor: Nigel Brookes*

Rutland & Stamford Mercury
01780 762255
www.stamfordtoday.co.uk
*Weekly (Fri). Owner: Johnston Press.
Editor: Eileen Green; news: Mike Roberts*

Saffron Walden Observer
01279 866355
www.herts-essex-news.co.uk
*Weekly (Thu). Owner: Herts & Essex
Newspapers. Editor: Paul Winspear;
news: Sandra Perry*

Saffron Walden Weekly News
01223 434434
www.cambridge-news.co.uk
*Weekly (Thu). Owner: Cambridge
Newspapers. Editor: Nigel Brookes*

**Saffron Walden, Stansted &
Sawston Reporter**
01799 525100
www.thisisessex.co.uk
*Weekly (Thu). Owner: Archant.
Editor: Barry Hunt*

St Ives Town Crier
01480 402100
www.stivestoday.co.uk
*Weekly (Thu). Owner: Johnston Press.
Editor: Matthew Cornish*

St Ives Weekly News
01223 434434
www.cambridge-news.co.uk
*Weekly (Thu). Owner: Cambridge
Newspapers. Editor: Murray Morse*

St Neots Town Crier
01480 402100
www.stneotstoday.co.uk
*Weekly (Thu). Owner: Johnston Press.
Editor: Matthew Cornish*

St Neots Weekly News
01223 434434
www.cambridge-news.co.uk
*Weekly (Wed). Owner: Newsquest.
Editor: Murray Morse*

Scunthorpe Target
01724 273273
www.thisisscunthorpe.co.uk
*Weekly (Thu). Owner: Northcliffe
Media. Editor: Jane Manning;
chief sub: John Curtis*

Scunthorpe Telegraph
01724 273273
www.thisisscunthorpe.co.uk
*Daily. Owner: Northcliffe Media. Editor:
Jane Manning; chief sub: John Curtis*

Skegness Citizen
01507 353200
*Weekly (Fri). Owner: Johnston Press.
Managing editor: Tim Robinson;
editor: John Cowpe*

Skegness Standard
01507 353200
www.skegnesstoday.co.uk
*Weekly (Wed). Owner: Johnston Press.
Managing editor: Tim Robinson;
editor: John Cowpe*

Skegness Target
01205 315000
*Weekly (Wed). Owner: Northcliffe
Media. Editor: Martin Finney*

Sleaford Citizen
01529 413646
*Weekly (Fri). Owner: Johnston Press.
Editor: John Lavery; news:
Andy Hubbert*

Sleaford Standard
01529 413646
*Weekly (Wed). Owner: Johnston Press.
Editor: John Lavery; news:
Andy Hubbert*

Sleaford Target
01522 820000
www.thisislincolnshire.co.uk
*Weekly (Wed). Owner: Northcliffe
Media. Editor: Martin Finney*

**South Woodham & Maldon
Weekly News**
01621 852233
www.thisisessex.co.uk
*Weekly (Thu). Owner: Newsquest.
Editor: Neil Thomas*

Southend Standard
01268 522792
www.thisisessex.co.uk
*Weekly (Thu). Owner: Newsquest.
Editor: Martin McNeill; news:
Chris Hatton; chief sub: Neal Reeve*

Southend Times
01702 477666
*Weekly (Tue). Owner: Archant.
Editor: Michael Guy*

Southend Yellow Advertiser
01268 503400
www.trinitymirrorsouthern.co.uk
*Weekly free (Thu). Owner: Trinity
Mirror Southern*

Spalding Guardian
01775 725021
www.spaldingtoday.co.uk
*Weekly (Thu). Owner: Johnston Press.
Editor: Nick Woodhead; news: David
Crossley; features: Julie Williams;
chief sub: Tracey Vale*

Spalding Herald
01775 713723
www.spaldingherald.co.uk
*Monthly free (1st of month).
Editor: Natalie Ward*

Spilsby Standard
01754 897120
www.skegnesstoday.co.uk
*Weekly (Wed). Owner: Johnston Press.
Editor: Rebecca Baker*

Spilsby Target
01205 315000
*Weekly (Wed). Owner: Northcliffe
Media. Editor: Martin Finney*

Stamford Citizen
01780 762255
www.stamfordmercury.co.uk
*Weekly free (Tue). Owner: Johnston
Press. Editor: Eileen Green; news:
Mike Roberts*

Stamford Herald & Post
01733 318600
*Weekly (Thu). Owner: Midlands
Weekly Media (Trinity Mirror). Editor:
Steve Rose; features: Amanda Franklin*

Stansted Observer
01279 866355
www.herts-essex-news.co.uk
*Weekly (Thu). Owner: Herts & Essex
Newspapers. Editor: Val Brown;
news: Sandra Perry*

Sudbury Mercury
01284 702588
www.edp24.co.uk
*Weekly (Fri). Owner: Archant. Editor:
Paul Couch; reporter: Will Wright*

Suffolk Advertiser
01473 324700
www.advertiser24.co.uk
*Weekly (Fri). Owner: Archant. Editor:
Paul Couch; news: Nicola Durrant*

Suffolk Free Press
01787 375271
www.sudburytoday.co.uk
*Weekly free (Thu). Owner: Johnston
Press. Editor: Mark Crossley;
news: Nick Wells*

Swaffham Mercury
01603 628311
www.edp24.co.uk
*Monthly. Owner: Archant.
Editor: Terry Redhead*

Swaffham News
01553 761188
*Weekly (Fri). Owner: Johnston Press.
Editor: Chris Hornby; news:
Donna Semmens*

Tendring Weekly News
01206 506000
www.thisisessex.co.uk
*Weekly free (Wed). Owner: Newsquest.
Editor-in-chief: Irene Kettle;
news: Sally Teatheredge*

Thetford & Brandon Times
01603 628311
www.edp24.co.uk
*Weekly (Wed). Owner: Archant.
Editor: Terry Redhead*

Thetford Citizen
01284 768911
www.burystedmundstoday.co.uk
*Weekly. Owner: Johnston Press.
Editor: Barry Peters; news: Lesley
Anslow; features: Sue Green*

Thurrock Gazette
01375 411502
www.thisisessex.co.uk
*Weekly free (Fri). Owner: Newsquest.
Editor: Neil Speight*

Thurrock, Lakeside & Grays Post
0845 070 0161
*Weekly (Thu). Owner: Archant. Editor:
Barry Kirk; news: Wayne Tuckfield;
chief sub: Graham Whitmore*

Thurrock Recorder
01708 771500
www.romfordrecorder.co.uk
*Weekly (Fri). Owner: Archant. Editor:
Mark Sweetingham; news: Eden Black*

Thurrock Yellow Advertiser
01268 503400
www.trinitymirrorsouthern.co.uk
*Weekly free (Thu). Owner: Trinity
Mirror Southern*

Walden Local
01799 516161
www.thisisessex.co.uk
Weekly (Wed). Editor: John Brooker

Waltham Forest Guardian
020 8498 3400
www.newsquest.co.uk
*Weekly (Thu). Owner: Newsquest.
Editor: Pat Stannard*

Waltham Forest Independent
020 8498 3400
www.newsquest.co.uk
*Weekly (Fri). Owner: Newsquest.
Editor: Pat Stannard*

Watton & Swaffham Times
01603 628311
www.edp24.co.uk
*Weekly (Fri). Owner: Archant.
Editor: Terry Redhead*

Waveney Advertiser
01493 601206
www.advertiser-online.co.uk
*Weekly (Fri). Owner: Archant.
Managing editor: Russell Cook*

Whittlesey Times
01354 652621
www.cambs-times.co.uk
*Weekly (Fri). Owner: Archant. Editor:
Brian Asplin; news: John Elworthy;
features: Maggie Gibson*

Wisbech Standard
01354 652621
www.wisbech-standard.co.uk
*Weekly (Thu). Owner: Archant. Editor:
Brian Asplin; news: John Elworthy;
features: Maggie Gibson*

Witham Chronicle
01245 600700
www.thisisessex.co.uk
*Weekly (Wed/Thu). Owner: Northcliffe
Media. Editor: Matt Holder; news:
Matt Adams; features: Darryl Webber*

Woodham Chronicle
01245 600700
www.thisisessex.co.uk
*Weekly (Wed/Thu). Owner: Northcliffe
Media. Editor: Matt Holder; news:
Matt Adams; features: Darryl Webber*

**Wymondham & Attleborough
Mercury**
01603 628311
www.edp24.co.uk
*Weekly (Fri). Owner: Archant.
Editor: Terry Redhead*

● Midlands

Derbyshire, Leicestershire,
Northamptonshire, Nottinghamshire,
Staffordshire

The Advertiser (Staffordshire)
01782 602525
www.thisisthesentinel.co.uk
*Weekly free (Thu). Owner: Northcliffe
Media. Editor: Mike Sassi; news:
Robert Cotterill; features: Charlotte
Little-Jones*

Alfreton & Ripley Echo
01773 514150
www.derbyshiretoday.com
*Weekly (Fri). Owner: Johnston Press.
Editor: David Hopkinson*

Alfreton Chad
01623 456789
www.chad.co.uk
*Weekly (Fri). Owner: Johnston Press.
Editor: Jeremy Plews; news: Ashley
Bucker; chief sub: Tim Morris*

Ashbourne News Telegraph
01283 512345
www.ashbournenewstelegraph.co.uk
*Weekly (Wed). Owner: Staffordshire
Newspapers. Editor: Paul Hazeldine;
news: Steve Doohan; features: Bill
Pritchard; production: Dave Finn*

Ashby & Coalville Mail
0116 251 2512
www.thisisleicestershire.co.uk
*Weekly (Tue). Owner: Northcliffe
Media. Editor: Ian Amos*

Ashby Times
01530 813101
*Weekly (Fri). Owner: Trident Midland
Newspapers*

Ashfield Chad
01623 456789
www.ashfieldtoday.co.uk
*Weekly (Wed). Owner: Johnston Press.
Editor: Jeremy Plews; news: Ashley
Bucker; chief sub: Tim Morris*

Atherstone Herald
01827 848535
*Weekly (Thu). Owner: Northcliffe
Media. Editor: Gary Phelps*

Belper Express
01332 291111
*Weekly free (Tue). Owner: Northcliffe
Media. Editor: Chris Ward*

Belper News
01773 881100
www.belpertoday.co.uk
*Weekly (Wed). Owner: Johnston Press.
Editor: Amanda Hatfield*

Biddulph Chronicle
01260 273737
www.chronicleseries.com
Weekly (Thu). Editor: Jeremy Condliffe

Birstall Post
0116 267 4213
www.birstallpost.co.uk
*Monthly free (1st of month). Owner:
The Birstall Post Society. Editor:
Jerry Jackson*

Bolsover & District Advertiser
01246 202291
www.chesterfieldtoday.co.uk
Weekly free (Wed). Owner: Johnston Press. Editor: Mike Wilson; assistant editor: Phil Bramley; news: Tracy Mitchell; assistant news editor: Sean Boyle

Brackley Post
01604 614600
www.midlandweeklymedia.co.uk
Weekly (Fri). Owner: Midlands Weekly Media (Trinity Mirror). Editor: Richard Howarth; production: Julie Fisher

Burntwood Mercury
01543 256501
Weekly (Thu). Owner: Northcliffe Media. Editor: Sam Holliday

Burton & South Derbyshire Advertiser
01283 512345
www.uttoxeteradvertiser.co.uk
Weekly (Wed). Owner: Staffordshire Newspapers. Editor: Paul Hazeldine; news: Steve Doohan; features: Bill Pritchard; production: Dave Finn

Burton Mail
01283 512345
www.burtonmail.co.uk
Daily. Owner: Staffordshire Newspapers. Editor: Paul Hazeldine; news: Steve Doohan; features: Bill Pritchard; production: Diane Finn

Burton Trader
01283 512200
Weekly (Wed). Owner: Midlands Weekly Media (Trinity Mirror). Editor: Pam Thomas; news: Paul Henshall

Buxton Advertiser
01298 767070
www.buxtontoday.co.uk
Weekly (Thu). Owner: Johnston Press. Editor: John Phillips; chief reporter: Emma Downes; subeditor: Alan Charnley

Buxton Times
01298 767070
www.buxtontoday.co.uk
Weekly free (Fri). Owner: Johnston Press. Editor: John Phillips; chief reporter: Emma Downes; subeditor: Alan Charnley

Cannock & Rugeley Chronicle
01543 506311
www.expressandstar.co.uk
Weekly (Thu). Owner: Midland News Association. Editor: Mark Ship

Cannock & Rugeley Mercury
01827 848535
Weekly (Thu). Owner: Northcliffe Media. Editor: Linda Young

Cannock Chase & Burntwood Post
01543 501700
Weekly (Thu). Owner: Midlands Weekly Media (Trinity Mirror). Editor: Mike Lockley

Cheadle & Tean Times
01538 753162
Weekly (Wed). Editor: Paul Campbell

Cheadle Post & Times
01538 750011
www.staffordshiresentinel.co.uk
Weekly (Wed). Owner: Northcliffe Media. Editor: Doug Pickford

Chesterfield Advertiser
01246 202291
www.chesterfieldtoday.co.uk
Weekly free (Fri). Owner: Johnston Press. Editor: Mike Wilson; news: Tracy Mitchell; assistant news editor: Sean Boyle

Chesterfield Express
01246 504500
Weekly free (Wed). Owner: Johnston Press. Editor: Mike Wilson; assistant editor: Phil Bramley; news: Tracy Mitchell; assistant news editor: Sean Boyle

Chronicle and Echo (Northampton)
01604 467000
www.northantsnews.com
Daily. Owner: Johnston Press. Editor: Mark Edwards; news: Richard Edmondson; production: Graham Tebbutt

Coalville & Ashby Echo
01509 635807
Weekly (Tue). Owner: Midlands Weekly Media (Trinity Mirror). Editor: Pete Warrington

Coalville Times
01530 813101
Weekly (Fri). Owner: Trident Midland Newspapers. Editor: Nick Hudson

Coleshill Herald
01827 848856
www.tamworthherald.co.uk
Weekly (Thu). Owner: Northcliffe Media. Editor: Gary Phelps

Corby Citizen
01536 506100
www.northantset.co.uk
Weekly (Thu). Owner: Johnston Press. Acting deputy editor: Nick Tite; assistant news editor: Kristy Ward; features: Joni Ager; production: Kathryn Dunn

Corby Herald & Post
01604 614600
www.midlandweeklymedia.co.uk
Weekly (Thu). Owner: Midlands Weekly Media (Trinity Mirror). Editor: Richard Howarth; production: Julie Fisher

Daventry Express
01327 703383
www.daventrytoday.co.uk
Weekly (Thu). Owner: Johnston Press. Editor: Chris Lillington

Derby Evening Telegraph
See page 41

Derby Express
01332 291111
Weekly free (Tue). Owner: Northcliffe Media. Editor: Andy Machin

Derby Trader
01332 253999
Weekly (Thu). Owner: Midlands Weekly Media (Trinity Mirror). Editor: Patrick O'Connor; features: Steve Eyley; chief sub: Patrick O'Connor

Derbyshire Times
01246 504500
www.derbyshiretimes.co.uk
Weekly (Thu). Owner: Johnston Press. Editor: Mike Wilson; assistant editor: Phil Bramley; news: Tracy Mitchell; assistant news editor: Sean Boyle

Dronfield Advertiser
01246 202291
www.chesterfieldtoday.co.uk
Weekly free (Wed). Owner: Johnston Press. Editor: Mike Wilson; assistant editor: Phil Bramley; news: Tracy Mitchell; assistant news editor: Sean Boyle

Dukeries Advertiser
01636 681234
Weekly (Fri). Editor: Harry Whitehouse; news: Lucy Millard; chief sub: Chris Prine

Eastwood & Kimberley Advertiser
01773 537850
www.eastwoodtoday.co.uk
Weekly (Fri). Owner: Johnston Press. Editor: John Shawcroft

Eckington Leader
01246 437310
Weekly (Fri). Owner: Johnston Press. Editor: Mike Wilson; assistant editor: Phil Bramley; news: Tracy Mitchell; assistant news editor: Sean Boyle

The Evening Telegraph (Northants)
01536 506100
www.northantset.co.uk
Daily. Owner: Johnston Press. Editor: Jeremy Clifford; deputy editor: Neil Pickford; assistant editor: Nick Tite; features: Joni Ager; assistant editor production: Kathryn Dunn

Glossop Chronicle
0161 304 7691
www.tamesidereporter.com
Weekly (Thu). Owner: Ashton Weekly Newspapers. Editor: Nigel Skinner

Harborough Mail
01858 436060
www.harboroughmail.co.uk
Weekly (Thu). Owner: Johnston Press. Editor: Brian Dodds; news: Alex Blackwell

High Peak Courier
01298 767070
www.buxtontoday.co.uk
Weekly free (Fri). Owner: Johnston Press. Editor: John Phillips; chief reporter: Emma Downes; subeditor: Alan Charnley

Hinckley Herald & Journal
01455 891981
www.hinckley-times.co.uk
Weekly (Wed). Owner: Coventry Newspapers (Trinity Mirror). Editor: Andrew Punchon

Hinckley Times
01455 891981
www.hinckley-times.co.uk
Weekly (Thu). Owner: Coventry
Newspapers (Trinity Mirror).
Editor: Andrew Punchon

Hucknall & Bulwell Dispatch
01623 456789
www.hucknalltoday.co.uk
Weekly (Fri). Owner: Johnston Press.
Editor: Richard Silverwood

Ilkeston Advertiser
0115 944 6160
www.ilkestontoday.co.uk
Weekly (Thu). Owner: Johnston Press.
Editor: David Horne

Ilkeston Express
01332 291111
Weekly free (Tue). Owner: Northcliffe
Media. Editor: Pete Noble

Ilkeston Shopper
0115 944 6160
www.ilkestontoday.co.uk
Weekly free (Tue). Owner: Johnston
Press. Editor: David Horne

Kenilworth Times
024 7663 3633
Weekly free (Wed). Owner: Coventry
Newspapers (Trinity Mirror).
Editor: Darren Parkin

Kettering Citizen and Mercury
01536 506100
www.northantsnews.com
Weekly (Thu). Owner: Johnston Press.
Editor: Jeremy Clifford; deputy editor:
Nick Pickford; assistant editor:
Nick Tite; features: Joni Ager;
chief sub: Kathryn Dunn

Kettering Evening Telegraph
01536 506100
www.northantsnews.com
Weekly (Thu). Owner: Johnston Press
Editor: Jeremy Clifford; deputy editor:
Nick Pickford; assistant editor:
Nick Tite; features: Joni Ager;
chief sub: Kathryn Dunn

Kettering Herald & Post
01604 614600
www.midlandweeklymedia.co.uk
Weekly (Thu). Owner: Midlands Weekly
Media (Trinity Mirror). Editor: Richard
Howarth; production: Julie Fisher

Leek Post & Times
01538 399599
www.leekpostandtimes.co.uk
Weekly (Wed). Owner: Northcliffe
Media. Editor: Doug Pickford;
news: Rob Cotterill

Leicester Mail
0116 251 2512
www.thisisleicestershire.co.uk
Weekly free (Tue). Owner: Northcliffe
Media. Editor: Nick Carter; news:
Mark Charlton; features: Alex Dawson

Leicester Mercury
See page 41

Lichfield & Burntwood Edition
Express and Star
01902 313131
www.expressandstar.com
Daily. Owner: Midland News
Association. Editor: Adrian Faber

Lichfield Mercury
01827 848535
www.lichfieldmercury.co.uk
Weekly (Thu). Owner: Northcliffe
Media. Editor: Sam Holliday

Lichfield Post
01543 258523
www.iclichfield.co.uk
Weekly (Thu). Owner: Midlands
Weekly Media (Trinity Mirror).
Editor: Pam Thomas

Long Eaton Advertiser
0115 946 2837
Weekly (Wed). Owner: Midlands
Weekly Media (Trinity Mirror).
Editor: David Godsall

Long Eaton Recorder
0115 948 2000
www.thisisnottingham.co.uk
Weekly free (Thu). Owner: Northcliffe
Media. Editor: Graham Glen; news:
Claire Catlow; features: Jeremy Lewis

Long Eaton Trader
0115 946 9909
Weekly (Thu). Owner: Midlands Weekly
Media (Trinity Mirror). Editor: Patrick
O'Connor; features: Steve Eyley

Loughborough Echo
01509 232632
Weekly (Thu). Owner: Midlands Weekly
Media (Trinity Mirror). Editor: Andy
Rush; news: Rachel Harrison

Loughborough Mail
0116 251 2512
www.thisisleicestershire.co.uk
Weekly (Tue). Owner: Northcliffe
Media. Editor: Nick Carter; news:
Mark Charlton; features: Alex Dawson

Lutterworth Advertiser
01858 462626
www.harboroughtoday.co.uk
Weekly (Thu). Owner: Johnston Press.

Mansfield & Ashfield Observer
01623 456789
Weekly free (Thu). Owner: Johnston
Press. Editor: Tony Spittles

Mansfield & Ashfield Recorder
01623 420000
Weekly free (Wed). Owner: Northcliffe
Media. Editor: Graham Glen

Mansfield Chad
01623 456789
www.mansfieldtoday.co.uk
Weekly (Wed). Owner: Johnston Press.
Editor: Jeremy Plews; news: Joy
Thompson; chief sub: Karen Robinson

Market Harborough Herald & Post
01604 614600
www.midlandweeklymedia.co.uk
Weekly (Thu, Fri). Owner: Midlands
Weekly Media (Trinity Mirror).
Editor: Richard Howarth; production:
Julie Fisher

Matlock Mercury
01629 762120
www.matlocktoday.co.uk
Weekly (Thu). Owner: Johnston Press.
Editor: Amanda Hatfield

Melton Citizen
01664 410041
www.meltontimes.co.uk
Weekly free (Tue). Owner: Johnston
Press. Editor: Michael Cooke

Melton Times
01664 410041
www.meltontimes.co.uk
Weekly (Thu). Owner: Johnston Press.
Editor: Michael Cooke

Mid Staffs Edition Express
and Star
01543 506311
www.expressandstar.com
Daily. Owner: Midland News
Association. Editor: Adrian Faber;
news: Mark Drew

Moorlands Advertiser
01782 602525
www.thisisthesentinel.co.uk
Weekly (Wed). Owner: Northcliffe
Media. Editor: Mike Sassi

Mountsorrel Post
0116 267 4213
4pa. Owner: The Birstall Post Society.
Editor: Jerry Jackson

Newark Advertiser
01636 681234
www.newarkadvertiser.co.uk
Weekly (Fri). Editor: Harry
Whitehouse; news: Lucy Millard

Newcastle Advertiser
01782 619830
www.thisisthesentinel.co.uk
Weekly (Thu). Owner: Northcliffe
Media. Editor: Mike Sassi; news:
Robert Cotterill; features: Charlotte
Little-Jones

North West Leics &
South Derbyshire Leader
01530 813101
Weekly (Wed). Owner: Trident Midland
Newspapers. Editor: Robin Slingsby

Northampton Herald & Post
01604 614600
www.midlandweeklymedia.co.uk
Weekly (Thu). Owner: Midlands
Weekly Media (Trinity Mirror).
Editor: Richard Howarth; production:
Julie Fisher

Northampton Mercury
01604 467000
www.northantsnews.com
Weekly (Thu). Owner: Johnston Press.
Editor: Steve Scholes; news:
Richard Edmondson; production:
Graham Tebbutt

Northants on Sunday
01604 467000
www.northantsnews.co.uk
Sunday. Owner: Johnston Press.
Editor: Steve Scoles; news: Richard
Edmondson; features: Lily Canter;
production manager: Graham Billing

Nottingham & Trent Valley Journal
0115 982 7337
Weekly (Fri). Owner: Journal Publishing Company. Editor: Ed Palmer

Nottingham & Long Eaton Topper
0115 969 6000
www.toppernewspapers.co.uk
Weekly free (Wed). Owner: Topper Newspapers. Editor: John Howarth

Nottingham Evening Post
See page 41

Nottingham Recorder
0115 948 2000
www.thisisnottingham.co.uk
Weekly free (Wed). Owner: Northcliffe Media. Editor: Malcolm Pheby; news: Claire Catlow; features: Jeremy Lewis

Oadby & Wigston Mail
0116 251 2512
www.thisisleicestershire.co.uk
Weekly (Tue). Owner: Northcliffe Media. Editor: Nick Carter; news: Mark Charlton; features: Alex Dawson

Peak Advertiser
01629 812159
Fortnightly free (Thu). Editor: Steve Wild

Peak Times
01629 582432
www.matlocktoday.co.uk
Weekly free (Fri). Owner: Johnston Press. Editor: Amanda Hatfield

Potteries Advertiser
01782 602525
www.thisisthesentinel.co.uk
Weekly free (Thu). Owner: Northcliffe Media. Editor: Mike Sassi; news: Robert Cotterill; features: Charlotte Little-Jones

Retford & Bawtry Guardian
01909 500500
www.retfordtoday.co.uk
Weekly (Thu). Owner: Johnston Press. Editor: George Robinson; news: Jackie Laver

Retford, Gainsborough & Worksop Times
01777 702275
Weekly (Thu). Owner: Northcliffe Media. Editor: Nick Purkiss

Retford Trader
01909 500500
www.retfordtoday.co.uk
Weekly free (Thu). Owner: Johnston Press. Editor: George Robinson; news: Jackie Laver

Ripley & Heanor News
01629 762120
www.ripleyandheanornews.co.uk
Weekly (Thu). Owner: Johnston Press. Editor: Amanda Hatfield; news: Helen Taylor

Rugeley Mercury
01543 414414
www.thisisstaffordshire.co.uk
Weekly (Thu). Owner: Northcliffe Media. Editor: Tim Hewitt; news: Andy Kerr

Rugeley Post
01543 258523
Weekly (Thu). Owner: Midlands Weekly Media (Trinity Mirror). Editor: Pam Thomas

Rutland Times
01572 757722
www.rutlandtoday.co.uk
Weekly (Thu). Owner: Johnston Press. Editor: Richard Yetman

The Sentinel (Stoke-on-Trent)
See page 41

Sentinel Sunday
See The Sentinel, page 41

Shepshed Echo
01509 232632
Weekly (Thu). Owner: Midlands Weekly Media (Trinity Mirror). Editor: Andy Rush; news: Rachel Harrison

Sherwood/Rainworth Chad
01623 456789
Weekly (Wed). Owner: Johnston Press. Editor: Jeremy Plews; news: Ashley Bucker

Shirebrook & Bolsover Chad
01623 456789
Weekly (Wed). Owner: Johnston Press. Editor: Jeremy Plews; news: Ashley Bucker

South Notts Advertiser
01636 681234
Weekly (Fri). Editor: Harry Whitehouse; news: Lucy Millard

Stafford & Stone Chronicle
01785 247290
www.expressandstar.com/chronicle
Weekly (Thu). Owner: Midland News Association. Editor: Richard Lockley

Stafford Post
01543 501700
www.icstafford.co.uk
Weekly (Thu). Owner: Midlands Weekly Media (Trinity Mirror). Editor: Mike Lockley

Staffordshire Newsletter
01785 257700
www.staffordshirenewsletter.co.uk
Weekly (Thu). Owner: Staffordshire Newspapers. Editor: Klooran Wills

Stapleford & Sandiacre News
0115 946 2837
Weekly (Wed). Owner: Midlands Weekly Media (Trinity Mirror). Editor: David Godsall

Stratford & Banbury Why
0845 600 9742
Weekly free (Fri). Owner: Northcliffe Media. Ad Director: Hazel Pilling

Swadlincote Times
01530 813101
Weekly (Fri). Owner: Trident Midland Newspapers

Tamworth Herald
01827 848535
www.tamworthherald.co.uk
Weekly (Thu). Owner: Northcliffe Media. Editor: Gary Phelps

Tamworth Times
01827 308000
Weekly (Thu). Owner: Midlands Weekly Media (Trinity Mirror). Editor: Pam Thomas

Towcester Post
01604 614600
www.midlandweeklymedia.co.uk
Weekly (Fri). Owner: Midlands Weekly Media (Trinity Mirror). Editor: Richard Howarth; production: Julie Fisher

Trader Pictorial
01636 681234
www.newarkadvertiser.co.uk/trader
Weekly (Wed). Editor: Harry Whitehouse; news: Lucy Millard

Uttoxeter Advertiser
01889 562050
www.uttoxeteradvertiser.co.uk
Weekly (Tue). Owner: Staffordshire Newspapers. Editor: Alan Harris

Uttoxeter Post & Times
01889 568999
Weekly (Fri). Owner: Northcliffe Media. Editor: Doug Pickford; news: Neil Gibson

Warsop Chad
01623 456789
Weekly (Wed). Owner: Johnston Press. Editor: Jeremy Plews; news: Joy Thompson; chief sub: Karen Robinson

Wellingborough & East Northants Evening Telegraph
01536 506100
www.northantsnews.com
Daily. Owner: Johnston Press. Acting deputy editor: Mark Edwards; acting news editor: Kristy Ward; features: Joni Ager; chief sub: Kathryn Dunn

Wellingborough & Rushden Citizen
01536 506100
www.northantsnews.com
Weekly (Thu). Owner: Johnston Press. Acting deputy editor: Mark Edwards; acting news editor: Kristy Ward; features: Joni Ager; chief sub: Kathryn Dunn

Wellingborough & Rushden Herald & Post
01604 614600
www.midlandweeklymedia.co.uk
Weekly (Thu). Owner: Midlands Weekly Media (Trinity Mirror). Editor: Richard Howarth; production: Julie Fisher

Worksop Guardian
01909 500500
www.worksoptoday.co.uk
Weekly (Thu). Owner: Johnston Press. Editor: George Robinson; news: Jackie Laver

Worksop Trader
01909 500500
Weekly free (Wed). Owner: Johnston Press. Editor: George Robinson; news: Jackie Laver

Your Leek Paper
01538 371807
www.yourleekpaper.co.uk
Weekly (Wed). Owner: Staffordshire Newspapers. Editor: Gary Shenton

● West Midlands

West Midlands, Warwickshire

Bedworth Echo
01455 891965
www.iccoventry.co.uk
Weekly (Fri). Owner: Coventry
Newspapers (Trinity Mirror). Editor:
Andrew Punchon; news: Emma Ray;
features: Emma Ray

Birmingham Mail
See page 40

Birmingham Independent
0121 446 1345
www.birminghamindependent.co.uk
Weekly (Fri). Owner: Birmingham
Independent. Editor: Paul Blair

Birmingham News
0121 234 5048
www.bhamnews.com
Weekly (Thu). Owner: Birmingham
Post & Mail (Trinity Mirror). Editor:
Russ Crawford; news: Victoria Thomas

Birmingham Post
0121 236 3366
www.icbirmingham.co.uk
Daily. Owner: Birmingham Post & Mail
(Trinity Mirror). Editor: Marc Reeves;
news: Mohammed Ilyas; features:
Sarah Probert

Black Country Bugle
01384 567678
www.blackcountrybugle.co.uk
Weekly (Thu). Owner: Staffordshire
Newspapers. Editor: Robert Taylor

Coventry Times
024 7663 3633
www.iccoventry.co.uk
Weekly (Thu). Owner: Coventry
Newspapers (Trinity Mirror). Editor:
Alan Kirby; news: John West; features:
Steven Chilton

Coventry Evening Telegraph
See page 40

Coventry Observer
024 7649 5900
www.coventryobserver.co.uk
Weekly free (Thu). Owner: Observer
Standard Newspapers. Editor:
Mike Green

Daventry Express
01327 703383
www.daventrytoday.co.uk
Weekly (Thu). Owner: Johnston Press.
Editor: Chris Lillington

Dudley Chronicle
01384 353211
www.expressandstar.com
Weekly (Thu). Owner: Midland News
Association. Editor: John Nash; features:
Dave Pearce; chief sub: Jane Reynolds

Dudley Edition Express & Star
01384 355355
www.expressandstar.com
Daily. Owner: Midland News
Association. Editor: Adrian Faber;
news: Mark Drew; features: Dylan
Evans; chief sub: Tony Reynolds

Dudley News
01384 358050
www.dudleynews.co.uk
Weekly (Thu). Owner: Newsquest.
Editor: Paul Walker

Express & Star
See page 41

Express & Star (Stourbridge)
01384 399914
www.expressandstar.com
Daily. Owner: Midland News
Association. Editor: Adrian Faber

Express & Star (Walsall)
01922 444444
www.expressandstar.com
Daily. Owner: Midland News
Association. Editor: Adrian Faber

Great Barr & Erdington Chronicle
0121 553 7171
www.expressandstar.com
Weekly free (Thu). Owner: Midland
News Association. Editor: Leon
Burakowski

Great Barr Observer
01827 848535
www.tamworthherald.co.uk
Weekly (Fri). Owner: Northcliffe
Media. Editor: Natalie Missenden

Halesowen Chronicle
01384 353211
www.expressandstar.com
Weekly (Fri). Owner: Midland News
Association. Editor: John Nash

Halesowen News
01384 358050
www.halesowennews.co.uk
Weekly (Fri). Owner: Newsquest.
Editor: Paul Walker

Heartland Evening News
024 7635 3534
www.hen-news.co.uk
Daily. Editor: Tony Parrott; news:
Claire Harrison; features: John Jevons

Kenilworth Times
024 7650 0375
Weekly (Wed). Owner: Trinity Mirror.
Editor: Darren Parkin

Kenilworth Weekly News
01926 457777
www.kenilworthonline.co.uk
Weekly (Fri). Owner: Johnston Press.
Editor: Lucia Clifford

Leamington Midweek Courier
01926 457777
www.leamingtontoday.co.uk
Weekly (Wed). Owner: Johnston Press.
Editor: Martin Lawson

Leamington Spa Courier
01926 457777
www.leamingtontoday.co.uk
Weekly (Fri). Owner: Johnston Press.
Editor: Martin Lawson

Leamington Spa Observer
01926 451900
www.leamington-now.com
Weekly free (Thu). Owner: Observer
Standard Newspapers. Editor:
Ian Hughes

Metro (Birmingham)
020 7938 6000
www.metrobirmingham.co.uk
Daily (Weekdays). Owner: Associated
Newspapers. Editor: Kenny Campbell;
news: Sarah Getty; features: Kieran
Meeke

Nuneaton Weekly Tribune
024 7663 3633
www.iccoverntry.co.uk
Weekly (Thu). Owner: Coventry
Newspapers (Trinity Mirror). Editor:
Alan Kirby; news: John West; features:
Steven Chilton

Royal Leamington Spa Times
024 7650 0375
Weekly (Wed). Owner: Trinity Mirror.
Editor: Darren Parkin

Rugby Advertiser
01788 535363
www.rugbyadvertiser.co.uk
Weekly (Thu). Owner: Johnston Press.
Editor: Peter Hengenheister

Rugby Observer
01788 535147
www.therugbyobserver.co.uk
Weekly free (Thu). Owner: Observer
Standard Newspapers. Editor:
Chris Smith

Rugby Review
01788 539999
www.rugbyreviewtoday.co.uk
Weekly (Thu). Owner: Johnston Press.
Editor: Peter Aengenheister

Rugby Times
01604 614643
Weekly (Tues). Owner: Trinity Mirror.
Editor: Duncan Gibbons

Sandwell Chronicle
0121 553 7171
www.expressandstar.com
Weekly free (Thu). Owner: Midland News
Association. Editor: Leon Burakowski

Solihull News
0121 711 5723
www.midlandweeklymedia.co.uk
Weekly (Fri). Owner: Midlands Weekly
Media (Trinity Mirror). Editor:
Ross Crawford

Solihull Observer
0121 683 0707
www.solihull.observertoday.co.uk
Weekly (Thurs). Owner: Observer
Standard Newspapers. Editor:
Charlotte Burch

Solihull Times
0121 711 5723
www.midlandweeklymedia.co.uk
Weekly (Wed). Owner: Midlands
Weekly. Media (Trinity Mirror)
Editor: Ross Crawford

Stourbridge Chronicle
01384 399914
www.expressandstar.com
Weekly (Thu). Owner: Midland News
Association. Editor: John Nash

Stourbridge News
01384 358050
www.thisisstourbridge.co.uk
Weekly (Thu). Owner: Newsquest.
Editor: Paul Walker

Stratford-upon-Avon Herald
01789 266261
www.stratford-herald.co.uk
Weekly (Thu). Owner: Stratford Herald.
Editor: Chris Towner; news: Dale Levack

Stratford-upon-Avon Midweek
01789 266261
www.stratford-herald.co.uk
Weekly (Tue). Owner: Stratford Herald.
Editor: Chris Towner; news: Dale Levack

Stratford-upon-Avon Observer
01789 415717
www.stratfordstandard.co.uk
Weekly free (Thu). Owner: Observer
Standard Newspapers. Editor:
Clare Fitzsimmons

Sunday Mercury (Birmingham)
0121 236 3366
www.icbirmingham.co.uk
Weekly (Sun). Owner: Birmingham
Post & Mail (Trinity Mirror). Editor:
David Brookes; news: Tony Larner;
features: Paul Cole

Sutton Coldfield News
0121 355 7070
www.icsuttoncoldfield.co.uk
Weekly (Fri). Owner: Midlands Weekly
Media (Trinity Mirror). Editor:
Pam Thomas

Sutton Coldfield Observer
01827 848535
www.tamworthherald.co.uk
Weekly (Fri). Owner: Northcliffe
Media. Editor: Charlotte Hart

Walsall Advertiser
01827 848535
www.tamworthherald.co.uk
Weekly (Thu). Owner: Northcliffe
Media. Editor: Natalie Missenden

Walsall Chronicle
01922 444444
www.expressandstar.com
Weekly (Thu). Owner: Midland News
Association. Editor: Leon Burakowski

Walsall Observer
01922 636666
www.thisiswalsall.co.uk
Weekly (Fri). Owner: Midlands Weekly
Media (Trinity Mirror). Editor:
Mike Lockley

Warwick Times
024 7650 0375
Weekly (Wed). Owner: Trinity Mirror.
Editor: Darren Parkin

Why Coventry, Nuneaton & Hinckley
0845 600 9742
Weekly free (Fri). Owner: Northcliffe
Media. Editor: Hazel Pilling

Why Solihull & District
0845 600 9742
Weekly free (Fri). Owner: Northcliffe
Media. Editor: Hazel Pilling

Why Warwick & Leamington
0845 600 9742
Weekly free (Fri). Owner: Northcliffe
Media. Editor: Hazel Pilling

Wolverhampton Ad News
01543 501700
Weekly (Wed). Owner: Midlands
Weekly Media (Trinity Mirror).
Editor: Mike Lockley

Wolverhampton Chronicle
01902 313131
www.expressandstar.com
Weekly free (Thu). Owner: Midland
News Association. Editor: John Nash;
news: Mark Drew; features: Dave
Pearce; chief sub: Tony Reynolds

● West England

Gloucestershire, Herefordshire,
Shropshire, Worcestershire

Alcester Chronicle
01527 453500
www.thisisworcestershire.co.uk
Weekly (Wed). Owner: Newsquest.
Editor: Paul Walker; news:
Emily Bridgwater

Berrow's Worcester Journal
01905 748200
www.berrowsjournal.co.uk
Weekly. Owner: Newsquest. Editor:
Stewart Gilbert; news: Stephanie
Preece; chief sub: Jim Collins

Bridgnorth Journal
01746 761411
www.bridgnorthjournal.co.uk
Weekly (Fri). Owner: Midland News
Association. Editor: John Griffiths

Bromsgrove Advertiser
01527 837000
www.thisisworcestershire.co.uk
Weekly (Wed). Owner: Newsquest.
Editor: Alan Wallcroft; chief reporter:
Peter Lammas

Bromsgrove Messenger
01527 837000
www.thisisworcestershire.co.uk
Weekly (Wed). Owner: Newsquest.
Editor: Alan Wallcroft; chief reporter:
Peter Lammas

Bromsgrove Standard
01527 574111
www.bromsgrovestandard.co.uk
Weekly free (Fri). Owner: Observer
Standard Newspapers. Editor:
Tristan Harris

Cheltenham Independent
01453 762412
www.thisisstroud.com
Weekly (Wed). Owner: Newsquest.
Editor: Sue Smith; news: Tamash Lal

Cheltenham News
01242 271900
www.thisisgloucestershire.co.uk
Weekly free (Thu). Owner: Northcliffe
Media. Editor: Anita Syvret

Chipping Sodbury/Yate Gazette
01453 544000
www.thisisthesouthcotswolds.co.uk
Weekly (Thu). Owner: Newsquest.
Editor: Cathryn Turnbull

Cotswold Journal
01608 651456
www.cotswoldjournal.co.uk
Weekly (Thu). Owner: Newsquest.
Editor: John Murphy; news: Tony
Donnelly

County Independent
01453 762412
www.thisisstroud.com
Weekly (Wed). Owner: Newsquest.
Editor: Sue Smith; news: Tamash Lal

Droitwich Spa Advertiser
01527 837000
www.thisisdroitwichspa.co.uk
Weekly (Wed). Owner: Newsquest.
Editor: Alan Wallcroft; deputy editor:
Alex Wellings

Droitwich Standard
01527 574111
www.droitwich.standardtoday.co.uk

Evesham Journal
01608 651456
www.thisisworcestershire.co.uk
Weekly (Thu). Owner: Newsquest.
Editor: John Murphy; news:
Tony Donnelly

Express and Star (Kidderminster)
01902 313131
www.expressandstar.com
Daily. Owner: Midland News
Association. Editor: Adrian Faber

Forest of Dean and Wye Valley Review
01594 841113
www.forest-and-wye-today.co.uk
Weekly free (Wed). Owner: Tindle
Newspapers. Editor: Ted Lamb

The Forester
01594 820600
www.thisisgloucestershire.co.uk
Weekly (Thu). Owner: Northcliffe
Media. Editor: Viv Hargreaves

Gloucester Citizen
01242 271900
www.thisisgloucestershire.co.uk
Daily. Owner: Northcliffe Media.
Editor: Ian Mean

Gloucester Independent
01453 762412
www.thisisstroud.com
Weekly (Thu). Owner: Newsquest.
Editor: Sue Smith; news: Tamash Lal

Gloucester News
01242 271900
www.thisisgloucestershire.co.uk
Weekly free (Thu). Owner: Northcliffe
Media. Editor: Chris Hill

Gloucestershire County Gazette
01453 544000
www.thisisthesouthcotswolds.co.uk
Weekly (Thu). Owner: Newsquest.
Editor: Cathryn Turner; news:
Jeff Bolitho

Gloucestershire Echo
01242 271900
www.thisisgloucestershire.co.uk
Daily. Owner: Northcliffe Media.
Editor: Anita Syvret; news: Sam
Shepherd; features: Tanya Gledhill;
chief sub: Peter Gavan

Hereford Admag
01432 376120
Weekly (Wed). Owner: Northcliffe
Media. Features editor: Richard Green

Hereford Journal
01432 355353
www.herefordjournal.co.uk
Weekly free (Wed). Owner: Midland
News Association. Editor: Mike
Robinson; news: Colin Osborne

Hereford Times
01432 274413
www.thisisherefordshire.co.uk
Weekly (Thu). Owner: Newsquest.
Editor: Liz Griffin; news: Nigel Heins

Jobs Today
(Cheltenham & Gloucester)
01453 544000
www.thisisthesouthcotswolds.co.uk
Weekly (Thu). Owner: Newsquest.
Editor: Cathryn Turnbull

Kidderminster Chronicle
01562 829500
www.expressandstar.com
Weekly (Thu). Owner: Midland News
Association. Editor: Sue Attwater;
chief reporter: Katie Swan

Kidderminster Shuttle
incorporating Kidderminster
Times and Stourport News
01562 633300
www.kidderminstershuttle.co.uk
Weekly (Thu). Owner: Newsquest.
Editor: Clive Joyce; chief reporter:
Peter McMillan

Ledbury Reporter
01684 892200
www.thisisworcestershire.co.uk
Weekly (Fri). Owner: Newsquest. Editor:
Nick Howells; news: Suzanne Black

Leominster Journal
01432 355353
www.leominsterjournal.com
Weekly free (Wed). Owner: Midland
News Association. Editor: Mike
Robinson; news: Colin Osborne

Ludlow Advertiser
01584 873796
www.ludlowadvertiser.co.uk
Weekly (Thu). Owner: Newsquest.
News editor: Jean Kingdon; general
reporter: Michael Baws

Ludlow Journal
01743 248248
www.ludlowjournal.co.uk
Weekly free (Fri). Owner: Midland
News Association. Editor: Mike
Robinson; chief reporter: Vince Buston

Malvern Gazette
01684 892200
www.thisisworcestershire.co.uk
Weekly (Fri). Owner: Newsquest.
Editor: Nick Howells

Market Drayton Advertiser
01630 698113
www.marketdraytonadvertiser
.co.uk
Weekly (Fri). Owner: Midland News
Association. Editor: Samantha Taylor;
deputy editor: Gary Scattergood

Newport Advertiser
01952 811500
www.newportadvertiser.co.uk
Weekly (Fri). Owner: Midland News
Association. Editor: Samantha Taylor;
deputy editor: Gary Scattergood

North Shropshire Chronicle
01743 248248
www.northshropshirechronicle.com
Weekly (Thu). Owner: Midland News
Association. Editor: John Butterworth

Oswestry & Border Counties
Advertiser
01691 655321
www.bordercountiesadvertiser
.co.uk
Weekly (Tue). Owner: North Wales
Newspapers. Editor: Sue Perry

Redditch Advertiser
01527 453500
www.redditchadvertiser.co.uk
Weekly (Wed). Owner: Newsquest.
Editor: Alan Wallcroft; news: Helen
Clarke

Redditch Standard
01527 588688
www.redditchstandard.co.uk
Weekly free (Fri). Owner: Observer
Standard Newspapers. Editor:
Andrew Powell

Ross Gazette
01989 562007
www.ross-today.co.uk
Weekly (Thu). Owner: Tindle
Newspapers. Editor: Chris Robertson;
chief reporter: Jo Scriven

Ross-on-Wye Journal
01432 355353
www.rossonwyejournal.com
Weekly free (Wed). Owner: Midland
News Association. Editor: Mike
Robinson; news: Colin Osborne

Shrewsbury Admag
01743 241414
Weekly (Thu). Owner: Northcliffe
Media. General manager: Jan Edwards

Shrewsbury Chronicle
01743 248248
www.shrewsburychronicle.co.uk
Weekly (Thu). Owner: Midland News
Association. Editor: John Butterworth

Shropshire Star
See page 41

South Shropshire Journal
01584 876311
www.southshropshirejournal.co.uk
Weekly (Fri). Owner: Midland News
Association. Editor: Mike Robinson;
news: Vince Buston

Stratford Observer
01789 415717
www.stratfordobserver.co.uk
Weekly (Thu). Owner: Observer
Standard Newspapers. Editor: Clare
Fitzsimmons

Stroud News & Journal
01453 762142
www.thisisstroud.com
Weekly (Wed). Owner: Newsquest.
Editor: Sue Smith; news: Tamash Lal

Telford Journal
01743 248248
www.telfordjournal.co.uk
Weekly free (Thu). Owner: Midland
News Association. Editor: David Sharpe

Tenbury Wells Advertiser
01584 873796
www.ludlowadvertiser.co.uk
Weekly (Thu). Owner: Newsquest.
Editor: Liz Griffin

Tewkesbury News
01452 271900
www.thisisgloucestershire.co.uk
Weekly free (Thu). Owner: Northcliffe
Media. Editor: Chris Hill

Thornbury Gazette
01453 544000
www.thisisthesouthcotswolds.co.uk
Weekly (Fri). Owner: Newsquest.
Editor: Cathryn Turnbull

Why Evesham
0845 600 9742
Weekly free (Fri). Owner: Northcliffe
Media. Editor: Tushy Sanghera

Why Redditch & District
0845 600 9742
Weekly free (Fri). Owner: Northcliffe
Media. Editor: Tushy Sanghera

Why Worcester, Malvern &
Kidderminster
0845 600 9742
Weekly free (Fri). Owner: Northcliffe
Media. Editor: Tushy Sanghera

Wilts & Gloucestershire Standard
01285 642642
www.thisiscirencester.com
Weekly (Thu). Owner: Newsquest.
Editor: Skip Walker; news: Simon Davies

Worcester News
01905 748200
www.thisisworcestershire.co.uk
Daily. Owner: Newsquest. Editor:
Stewart Gilbert; news: Stephanie Preece

Worcester Standard
01905 726200
www.worcesterstandard.co.uk
Weekly free (Thu). Owner: Observer
Standard Newspapers. Editor:
James Iles; news: Tim Clarke

● North England

East, North, South & West Yorkshire

Aire Valley Target
01274 729511
*Weekly (Thu). Owner: Newsquest.
Editor: Perry Austin-Clarke; news:
Martin Heminway; features: David
Barnett; chief sub: Mel Jones*

Axholme Herald
01472 874417
*Weekly (Fri). Owner: Northcliffe
Media. Editor: Ron Shipley*

Barnsley Chronicle
01226 734734
www.barnsley-chronicle.co.uk
*Weekly (Fri). Editor: Robert Cockroft;
news: Stephanie Daley; features:
Maureen Middleton; chief sub:
John Threlkeld*

Barnsley Independent
01226 734734
www.barnsley-chronicle.co.uk
*Weekly (Tue). Editor: Robert Cockroft;
news: Stephanie Daley; features:
Maureen Middleton; chief sub:
John Threlkeld*

Batley News
01924 468282
www.dewsburytoday.co.uk
*Weekly (Thu). Owner: Johnston Press.
Editor: Richard Firth; news: Vicky Dacre*

Beverley Advertiser
01482 327111
*Weekly (Thu). Owner: Northcliffe
Media. Editor: Alex Leys*

Beverley Guardian
01377 241122
www.beverleytoday.co.uk
*Weekly free (Fri). Owner: Johnston
Press. Editor: Dennis Sissons; news:
Steve Petch; chief sub: Gill Pick*

Birstall News
01924 468282
www.dewsburyreporter.co.uk
*Weekly (Thu). Owner: Johnston Press.
Editor: Richard Firth*

Bradford Target
01274 729511
*Weekly (Thu). Owner: Newsquest.
Editor: Perry Austin-Clarke; news:
Martin Heminway; features: David
Barnett; chief sub: Mel Jones*

Bridlington Free Press
01262 606606
www.bridlingtonfreepress.co.uk
*Weekly (Thu). Owner: Johnston Press.
Editor: Nick Procter; news: Simon
Haldenby; features: John Edwards*

Bridlington Gazette & Herald
01262 606606
www.bridlingtonfreepress.co.uk
*Weekly free (Tue). Owner: Johnston
Press. Editor: Nick Procter; news: Simon
Haldenby; features: John Edwards*

Brighouse Echo
01422 260200
www.brighousetoday.co.uk
*Weekly (Fri). Owner: Johnston Press.
Editor: Stephen Firth*

Calderdale News
01422 260200
www.halifaxcourier.co.uk
*Weekly free (Wed). Owner: Johnston
Press. Editor: John Furbisher;
production: Gordon Samson*

Colne Valley Chronicle
01484 430000
www.ichuddersfield.co.uk
*Weekly (Fri). Owner: Trinity Mirror
Huddersfield. Editor: Chris Burgess*

Craven Herald & Pioneer
01756 794117
www.cravenherald.co.uk
*Weekly (Fri). Owner: Newsquest.
Editor: Ian Lockwood; deputy editor:
Lindsey Moore*

Dearne Advertiser
01709 303050
www.doncasterfreepress.co.uk
*Weekly (Fri). Owner: Johnston Press.
Editor-in-chief: Graham Huston*

Dearne Valley Weekender
01709 571111
www.rotherhamadvertiser.com
*Weekly (Fri). Owner: Garnet Dickinson
Publishing. Editor: Doug Melloy*

Dewsbury Reporter
01924 468282
www.dewsburytoday.co.uk
*Weekly (Fri). Owner: Johnston Press.
Editor: Richard Firth; news: Vicky Dacre*

Dinnington & Maltby Guardian
01909 550500
www.dinningtontoday.co.uk
*Weekly (Fri). Owner: Johnston Press.
Editor: George Robinson; news:
Jackie Laver*

Dinnington & Maltby Trader News
01909 550500
*Weekly (Thu). Owner: Johnston Press.
Editor: George Robinson; news:
Jackie Laver*

Doncaster Advertiser
01302 347213
*Weekly (Fri). Owner: Johnston Press.
Editor: Martin Edmunds; news:
John Hepperstall*

Doncaster Free Press
01302 347264
www.doncasterfreepress.co.uk
*Weekly (Thu). Owner: Johnston Press.
Editor: Graham Huston; news: Kath
Finlay; features: Darren Burke;
production: David Crossland*

Doncaster Star
01302 348500
www.doncastertoday.co.uk
*Daily. Owner: Johnston Press.
Editor: David Kessen*

Driffield Post
01377 241122
www.driffieldtoday.co.uk
*Weekly (Fri). Owner: Johnston Press.
Editor: Dennis Sissons; news: Steve
Petch; chief sub: Gill Pick*

Driffield Times
01377 241122
www.driffieldtoday.co.uk
*Weekly (Wed). Owner: Johnston Press.
Editor: Dennis Sissons; news: Steve
Petch; chief sub: Gill Pick*

**Easingwold Advertiser &
Weekly News**
01347 821329
www.ghsmith.com/advertiser
Weekly (Thu). Editor: Margery Smith

East Hull Advertiser
01482 327111
*Weekly (Wed). Owner: Northcliffe
Media. Editor: Alex Leys*

East Riding Advertiser
01482 327111
*Weekly (Thu). Owner: Northcliffe
Media. Editor: Alex Leys*

East Riding News
01482 887700
www.eastridinggov.co.uk
*Monthly (1st week). Editor: Sarah
Mainprize*

Elmsall & South Elmsall Express
01977 640107
www.wakefieldexpress.co.uk
*Weekly (Thu). Owner: Johnston Press.
Editor: Delia Kitson*

Epworth Bells & Crowle Advertiser
01427 615323
*Weekly (Thu). Owner: Johnston Press.
Editor: Janet Harrison; deputy editor:
Eddie Mardell*

Filey & Hunmanby Mercury
01723 363636
www.fileytoday.co.uk
*Weekly. Owner: Johnston Press.
Editor: Ed Asquith; news: Steve
Hartley; chief sub: Steve Banbridge*

Gainsborough News
01427 872202
*Weekly free (Fri). Owner: Johnston
Press. Editor: Janet Harrison; deputy
editor: Chris Burton*

Gainsborough Standard
01427 615323
*Weekly (Thu). Owner: Johnston Press.
Editor: Janet Harrison; deputy editor:
Chris Burton*

Halifax Evening Courier
01422 260200
www.halifaxcourier.co.uk
*Daily. Owner: Johnston Press.
Editor: John Furbisher*

Harrogate Advertiser
01423 564321
www.harrogatetoday.co.uk
*Weekly (Fri). Owner: Johnston Press.
Editor: Jean Macquarrie; assistant
editor: Sophie Bradley; chief sub:
Sophie McCandlish*

Harrogate Herald
01423 564321
www.harrogatetoday.co.uk
Weekly free (Tue). Owner: Johnston Press. Editor: Jean Macquarrie; assistant editor: Sophie Bradley; chief sub: Sophie McCandlish

Hebden Bridge Times
01422 260200
www.halifaxtoday.co.uk
Weekly (Thu). Owner: Johnston Press. Editor: Sheila Tordoff

Heckmondwike Herald
01924 468282
www.dewsburytoday.co.uk
Weekly (Fri). Owner: Johnston Press. Editor: Richard Firth

Holderness & Hornsea Gazette
01964 612777
www.holderness-gazette.com
Weekly (Thu). Publisher: Brian Adcock; news: Chris Leek

Holderness Advertiser
01482 327111
Weekly (Wed). Owner: Northcliffe Media. Editor: Alex Leys

Holme Valley Express
01484 430000
www.ichuddersfield.co.uk
Weekly (Fri). Owner: Trinity Mirror Huddersfield. Editor: Chris Burgess

Huddersfield Daily Examiner
01484 430000
www.ichuddersfield.co.uk
Daily. Owner: Trinity Mirror Huddersfield. Editor: Roy Wright; news: Neil Atkinson; features: Andrew Flynn

Huddersfield District Chronicle
01484 430000
www.ichuddersfield.co.uk
Weekly (Fri). Owner: Trinity Mirror Huddersfield. Editor: Chris Burgess

Hull Daily Mail
See page 41

Ilkley Gazette
01943 607022
www.ilkleygazette.co.uk
Weekly (Thu). Owner: Newsquest. Editor: Mel Vasey; chief reporter: Paul Langan

The Journal (Hull)
01482 327111
Monthly (24th). Owner: Northcliffe Media. Editor: Roy Woodcock

Keighley & Craven Target
01274 729511
Weekly (Tue). Owner: Newsquest. Editor: Perry Austin-Clarke; news: Martin Heminway; features: David Barnett; chief sub: Mel Jones

Keighley News
01535 606611
www.keighleynews.co.uk
Weekly (Thu). Owner: Newsquest. Editor: Malcolm Hoddy; news: Alistair Shand; chief sub: Ralph Badham

Knaresborough Post
01423 564321
www.knaresboroughtoday.co.uk
Weekly (Fri). Owner: Johnston Press. Editor: Jean Macquarrie; assistant editor: Sophie Bradley; chief sub: Sophie McCandlish

Leeds Weekly News
0113 243 2701
Weekly (Thu). Owner: Johnston Press. Editor: Sheila Holmes

Look Local (Sheffield)
0114 283 1100
www.looklocal.org.uk
Weekly (Wed). Editor: James Evans; head of production: Adrian von Werzbach

Malton & Pickering Mercury
01723 363636
www.maltontoday.co.uk
Weekly. Owner: Johnston Press. Editor: Ed Asquith; news: Steve Hartley; chief sub: Steve Banbridge

Metro Yorkshire
020 7651 5200
www.metro.co.uk
Daily. Owner: Associated Newspapers. Editor: Kenny Campbell; news: Sarah Getty; features: Kieran Meeke

Mirfield Reporter
01924 468282
www.dewsburytoday.co.uk
Weekly (Fri). Owner: Johnston Press. Editor: Richard Firth

Morley Observer & Advertiser
01924 468282
www.morleyobserver.co.uk
Weekly (Wed). Owner: Johnston Press. Editor: Richard Firth

North Yorkshire Advertiser
01325 381313
www.theadvertiserseries.co.uk
Weekly free (Tue). Owner: Newsquest. Editor: Sally Taylor

North Yorkshire Herald & Post
01642 245401
www.icteeside.co.uk
/herald and post
Weekly (Thu). Owner: Gazette Media Company (Trinity Mirror). Editor: Sue Giles

North Yorkshire News
01765 601248
www.northallertontoday.co.uk
Weekly free (Wed). Owner: Johnston Press. Editor: Steve Barton; news: Stephen Pass

Northallerton, Thirsk & Bedale Times
01765 601248
www.northallertontoday.co.uk
Weekly (Fri). Owner: Johnston Press. Editor: Steve Barton; news: Stephen Pass

Ossett Observer
01924 375111
www.wakefieldexpress.co.uk
Weekly free (Fri). Owner: Johnston Press. Editor: Mark Bradley; news: Lisa Rookes

Pateley Bridge & Nidderdale Herald
01423 564321
www.nidderdaleherald.co.uk
Weekly (Fri). Owner: Johnston Press. Editor: Jean Macquarrie; assistant editor: Sophie Bradley; chief sub: Sophie McCandlish

Pocklington Post
01759 301003
www.pocklingtontoday.co.uk
Weekly (Thu). Owner: Johnston Press. Chief reporter: Nick Frame

Pontefract & Castleford Express
01977 737200
www.wakefieldexpress.co.uk
Weekly (Thu). Owner: Johnston Press. Editor: David Ward; news: Julie Hawksworth

Pontefract & Castleford Extra
01977 737200
www.wakefieldexpress.co.uk
Weekly free (Fri). Owner: Johnston Press. Editor: David Ward; news: Julie Hawksworth

The Press
See page 41

Pudsey Times
01943 466750
Weekly (Thu). Owner: Johnston Press. Editor: Kate Evans

Reporter Extra
01924 468282
www.dewsburyreporter.co.uk
Weekly free (Thu). Owner: Johnston Press. Editor: Richard Firth

Ripon Gazette & Boroughbridge Herald
01423 564321
www.ripontoday.co.uk
Weekly (Fri). Owner: Johnston Press. Editor: Jean Macquarrie; assistant editor: Sophie Bradley; chief sub: Sophie McCandlish

Rotherham & South Yorkshire Advertiser
01709 768000
www.rotherhamadvertiser.com
Weekly (Fri). Owner: Garnet Dickinson Publishing. Editor: Doug Melloy; news: Ann Charlton

Rotherham Record
01709 768000
www.rotherhamadvertiser.com
Weekly (Wed). Owner: Garnet Dickinson Publishing. Editor: Doug Melloy; news: Ann Charlton

Scarborough Evening News
01723 363636
www.scarboroughtoday.co.uk
Daily. Owner: Johnston Press. Editor: Ed Asquith; news: Steve Hartley; chief sub: Steve Banbridge

Scarborough Trader
01723 352269
www.tradertoday.co.uk
Weekly free (Thu). Owner: Johnston Press. Editor: Ed Asquith

Selby Extra
01757 702198
www.selbytoday.co.uk
Weekly free (Fri). Owner: Johnston Press. Editor: Chris Page; news: Richard Parker

Selby Post
01405 720110
www.selbypost.co.uk
Weekly (Thu). Owner: Northcliffe Media. Editor: Peter Butler

Selby Star
01904 653051
www.yorkpress.co.uk
Weekly free (Wed). Owner: Newsquest. Editor: Lynne Martin

Selby Times
01757 702802
www.selbytoday.co.uk
Weekly (Thu). Owner: Johnston Press. Editor: Chris Page; news: Richard Parker

Sheffield Journal
0114 276 7676
www.sheffieldtoday.net
Weekly free (Thu). Owner: Johnston Press. Editor: Alan Powell; news: Charles Smith; features: John Highfield; head of content: Paul License

Sheffield Mercury
0114 276 3633
Weekly (Wed). Editor: David Hayes

Sheffield Telegraph
0114 276 7676
www.sheffieldtoday.net
Weekly (Fri). Owner: Johnston Press. Editor: David Todd; news: Peter Kay; head of content: Paul License

Sheffield Weekly Gazette
0114 276 7676
www.sheffieldtoday.net
Weekly free (Thu). Owner: Johnston Press. Editor: Alan Powell; news: Bob Westerdale; features: John Highfield; head of content: Paul License

South Yorkshire Times
01709 303050
www.southyorkshiretimes.co.uk
Weekly (Thu). Owner: Johnston Press. Deputy Editor: David Jones

Spenborough Guardian
01924 468282
www.spenboroughguardian.co.uk
Weekly (Fri). Owner: Johnston Press. Editor: Richard Firth

The Star (Sheffield)
See page 41

Telegraph and Argus (Bradford)
See page 42

Todmorden News & Advertiser
01422 260200
www.halifaxtoday.co.uk
Weekly (Fri). Owner: Johnston Press. Editor: Sheila Tordoff

Thirsk Weekly News
01347 821349
www.ghsmith.com
Weekly (Wed). Editor: Rupert Smith

Wakefield Express
01924 375111
www.wakefieldexpress.co.uk
Weekly (Fri). Owner: Johnston Press. Editor: Mark Bradley; news: Lisa Rookes

Wakefield, Rothwell & Alton Extra
01924 375111
www.wakefieldexpress.co.uk
Weekly free (Thu). Owner: Johnston Press. Editor: Mark Bradley; news: Lisa Rookes

West Hull Advertiser
01482 327111
Weekly (Wed). Owner: Northcliffe Media. Editor: Alex Leys

Wetherby News
01423 564321
www.harrogatetoday.co.uk
Weekly (Fri). Owner: Johnston Press. Editor: Jean Macquarrie; assistant editor: Sophie Bradley; chief sub: Sophie McCandlish

Wharfe Valley Times
01943 466750
Weekly (Thu). Owner: Johnston Press. Editor: Kate Evans

Wharfedale & Airedale Observer
01943 465555
www.wharfedaleobserver.co.uk
Weekly (Thu). Owner: Newsquest. Editor: Mel Vasey; chief reporter: Paul Langhan

Whitby Gazette
01947 602836
www.whitbytoday.co.uk
Twice-weekly (Tue, Fri). Owner: Johnston Press. Editor: Damien Holmes

York Star
01904 653051
www.yorkstar.co.uk
Weekly free (Wed). Owner: Newsquest. Editor: Lynne Martin

Yorkshire Evening Post
See page 42

Yorkshire Gazette & Herald
01904 653051
www.gazetteherald.co.uk
Weekly (Wed). Owner: Newsquest. Editor: Chris Buxton

Yorkshire Post
See page 42

● North-east England

Cleveland, Durham, Northumberland, Tyne & Wear

Berwick Advertiser
01289 306677
www.berwick-advertiser.co.uk
Weekly (Thu). Owner: Johnston Press. Editor: Janet Wakenshaw; news: Ian Smith; chief sub: Keith Hamblin

Berwick Gazette
01289 306677
www.tweedalepress.co.uk
Weekly (Fri). Owner: Johnston Press. Editor: Janet Wakenshaw; news: Ian Smith; chief sub: Keith Hamblin

Chester-le-Street Advertiser
01325 381313
www.thisisthenortheast.co.uk
Weekly free (Thu). Owner: Newsquest. Editor: Peter Barron; news: Nigel Burton; features: Lindsey Jennings; chief sub: Ken Farrier

Citylife (Newcastle)
0191 211 5093
www.newcastle.gov.uk/citylife
Monthly (last week of month). Editor: Jane Byrne

Consett & Stanley Advertiser
01325 381313
www.thisisthenortheast.co.uk
Weekly free (Thu). Owner: Newsquest. Editor: Peter Barron; news: Nigel Burton; features: Lindsey Jennings; chief sub: Ken Farrier

Darlington & Stockton Times
01325 381313
www.thisisthenortheast.co.uk
Weekly (Fri). Owner: Newsquest. Editor: Malcolm Warne; news: Nigel Burton; chief sub: Andy Brown

Darlington, Aycliffe & Sedgefield Advertiser
01325 381313
www.thisisthenortheast.co.uk
Weekly free (Wed). Owner: Newsquest. Editor: Peter Barron; news: Nigel Burton; features: Lindsey Jennings; chief sub: Ken Farrier

Darlington Herald & Post
01325 262000
www.icteesside.co.uk
Weekly (Thu). Owner: Johnston Press. Editor: Sue Giles

Durham Advertiser
01325 381313
www.thisisthenortheast.co.uk
Weekly free (Thu). Owner: Newsquest. Editor: Peter Barron; news: Nigel Burton; features: Lindsey Jennings; chief sub: Ken Farrier

East Cleveland Advertiser
01325 381313
www.theclarion.co.uk
Weekly free (Fri). Owner: Newsquest. Editor: Peter Barron; news: Nigel Burton; features: Lindsey Jennings; chief sub: Ken Farrier

East Cleveland Herald & Post
01642 234227
www.icteesside.co.uk
Weekly (Wed). Owner: Gazette Media Company (Trinity Mirror). Editor: Sue Giles

Evening Chronicle (Newcastle)
See page 41

Evening Gazette
See page 41

Gateshead Herald and Post
0191 201 6405
www.icnewcastle.co.uk
Weekly (Wed). Owner: Newcastle Chronicle & Journal (Trinity Mirror). Editor: Catherine Welford; news: Zoe Burn

Hartlepool Mail
01429 239333
www.hartlepoolmail.co.uk
Daily. Owner: Johnston Press. Editor: Joy Yates; deputy editor: Brian Nuttley

Hartlepool Star
01429 239333
www.hartlepoolmail.co.uk
Weekly free (Thu). Owner: Johnston Press. Editor: Joy Yates; deputy editor: Brian Nuttley

Hexham Courant
01434 602351
www.hexham-courant.co.uk
Weekly (Fri). Owner: Cumbrian News Group. Editor: Collin Tapping; news: Brian Tilley

Houghton Star
0191 501 5800
Weekly free (Thu). Owner: Johnston Press. Editor: Betty Long

The Journal (Newcastle)
See page 41

Metro North East
0191 477 7445
www.metro.co.uk
Daily. Owner: Owner: Associated Newspapers. Editor: Deane Hodgson

Middlesbrough Herald & Post
01642 234227
www.icteesside.co.uk
Weekly (Wed). Owner: Gazette Media Company (Trinity Mirror). Editor: Sue Giles

Morpeth Herald
01670 510522
www.morpethherald.co.uk
Weekly (Thu). Owner: Johnston Press. Editor: Terry Hackett

Newcastle Herald & Post
0191 201 6405
www.icnewcastle.co.uk
Weekly (Wed). Owner: Newcastle Chronicle & Journal (Trinity Mirror). Editor: Catherine Welford; news: Zoe Burn

Newcastle Times & Teesside Focus
01332 365811
www.newcastletimes.co.uk
Weekly (Thu). Owner: Journal Publishing Company. Editor: Charlie Davenport; news: Simon Howorth; features: Katie Doherty; production: Fiona Smith

News Post Leader (Whitley Bay)
0191 251 8484
www.newspostleader.co.uk
Weekly (Thu). Owner: Johnston Press. Editor: Ross Weeks

Northeast Guardian
01452 300037
www.cmcnewspapers.co.uk
Weekly (Thurs). Owner: Gazette. Editor: Philip Fletcher

North Tyneside Herald & Post
0191 201 6405
www.icnewcastle.co.uk
Weekly (Wed). Owner: Newcastle Chronicle & Journal (Trinity Mirror). Editor: Catherine Welford; news: Zoe Burn

Northern Echo
See page 41

Northumberland Gazette
01665 602234
www.northumberlandgazette.co.uk
Weekly (Thu). Owner: Johnston Press. Editor: Paul Larkin

Northumberland Herald and Post
0191 201 6405
Weekly (Wed). Owner: Newcastle Chronicle & Journal (Trinity Mirror). Editor: Catherine Welford; news: Zoe Burn

Peterlee Star
0191 501 5800
Weekly free (Thu). Owner: Johnston Press. Editor: Betty Long

Seaham Star
0191 501 5800
Weekly free (Thu). Owner: Johnston Press. Editor: Betty Long

South Durham Herald & Post
01642 234227
www.icteesside.co.uk
Weekly (Fri). Owner: Gazette Media Company (Trinity Mirror). Editor: Sue Giles

South Shields Gazette
0191 455 4661
www.southtynesidetoday.co.uk
Daily. Owner: Johnston Press. Editor: John Syzmanski

South Tyne Star
0191 455 4661
Weekly free (Thu). Owner: Johnston Press. Editor: John Syzmanski

South Tyneside Herald & Post
0191 201 6405
www.icnewcastle.co.uk
Weekly (Wed). Owner: Newcastle Chronicle & Journal (Trinity Mirror). Editor: Catherine Welford; news: Zoe Burn

Stockton & Billingham Herald & Post
01642 234227
www.icteesside.co.uk
Weekly (Wed). Owner: Gazette Media Company (Trinity Mirror). Editor: Sue Giles

Sunday Sun (Newcastle)
See page 42

Sunderland Echo
0191 501 5800
www.sunderland-today.co.uk
Daily. Owner: Johnston Press. Editor: Rob Lawson; news: Gavin Foster; features: Paul Taylor; production: Jerry Kenny

Sunderland Star
0191 501 5800
Weekly free (Thu). Owner: Johnston Press. Editor: Betty Long

Teesside Herald & Post
01642 234227
www.icteesside.co.uk
Weekly (Wed). Owner: Gazette Media Company (Trinity Mirror). Editor: Sue Giles

Wallsend News Guardian
0191 251 8484
www.newsguardian.co.uk
Weekly free (Thu). Owner: Johnston Press. Editor: Ross Weeks

Washington Star
0191 501 5800
Weekly free (Thu). Owner: Johnston Press. Editor: Betty Long

Wear Valley Mercury
01388 768758
www.wearvalleymercury.co.uk
Weekly (Fri). Owner: Teesdale Mercury. Editor: Adrian Braddy

Whitley Bay News Guardian
0191 251 8566
www.newsguardian.co.uk
Weekly free (Thu). Owner: Johnston Press. Editor: Ross Weeks

● North-west England

Cheshire, Cumbria, Lancashire, Manchester, Merseyside

Accrington Observer
01254 871444
www.accringtonobserver.co.uk
Weekly (Fri). Owner: Guardian Media Group. Editor: Mervyn Kay; news: Stephanie Turner

Anfield and Walton Star
0151 472 2701
www.icliverpool.co.uk
Weekly (Thu). Owner: Trinity Mirror Merseyside. Editor: Jane Daly; news editor: Ed Casson

Ashton-under-Lyne Reporter
0161 303 1910
Weekly (Thu). Editor: Nigel Skinner

Asian News
01706 354321
www.theasiannews.co.uk
*Monthly (4th Fri). Owner: Guardian
Media Group. Editor: Steve Hammond*

Barnoldswick & Earby Times
01282 612561
www.eastlancashireonline.co.uk
*Weekly (Fri). Owner: Johnston Press.
Editor: Roy Prenton; news:
Peter Dewhurst*

Barrow Advertiser
01229 840150
www.cumbria-online.co.uk
*Weekly free (Thu). Owner: Cumbrian
News Group. Editor: Steve Brauner;
news: Jon Townend; features: Pete
Leach; chief sub: Ann McVea*

Bentham Guardian
01524 32525
*Weekly (Fri). Owner: Johnston Press.
Editor: Sue Riley; news: Louise
Bryning; features: Peter Gibbons;
chief sub: Michael Gardner*

Birkenhead News
0151 647 7111
www.icwirral.co.uk
*Weekly (Wed). Owner: Trinity Mirror
Merseyside. Editor: Sue McCann*

Blackburn Citizen
01254 678678
www.thisislancashire.co.uk
*Weekly (Thu). Owner: Newsquest.
Editor-in-chief: Kevin Young; news:
Andrew Turner; features: John Anson*

Blackpool & Fylde Citizen
01253 292005
www.thisislancashire.co.uk
*Weekly (Thu). Owner: Newsquest.
Editor: Jill Ellis; news: Steve
Dunthorne*

Blackpool Gazette & Herald
See page 40

Blackpool Reporter
01253 361842
www.blackpoolonline.co.uk
*Weekly free. Owner: Johnston Press.
Assistant Editor: Alison Bott*

Bolton News
See page 40

Bolton Journal
01204 522345
www.thisisbolton.co.uk
*Weekly (Thu). Owner: Newsquest.
Editor-in-chief: Steve Hughes; editor:
Derrick Grewcock; news: James
Higgins; features: Andrew Mosley;
production: John Bird*

Bootle Times
0151 932 1000
www.icliverpool.co.uk
*Weekly (Thu). Owner: Trinity Mirror
Merseyside. Editor: Hazel Shaw;
news: Lloyd Jones*

Bromborough & Bebington News
0151 647 7111
*Weekly (Wed). Owner: Trinity Mirror
Merseyside. Editor: Sue McCann*

Burnley Citizen
01254 678678
www.thisislancashire.co.uk
*Weekly (Thu). Owner: Newsquest.
Editor-in-chief: Kevin Young; news:
Andrew Turner; features: John Anson*

Burnley Express
01282 426161
www.burnleyexpress.co.uk
*Weekly (Tue, Fri). Owner: Johnston
Press. Editor: Chris Daggett; news:
Margaret Parsons; features: Barry
Bradshaw; production: Paul Watson*

Bury Journal
0161 764 9421
www.thisisbury.co.uk
*Weekly free (Wed). Owner: Newsquest.
Editor: Ian Savage; news: Steve Orrell;
chief sub: John Ellavy*

Bury Times
0161 764 9421
www.thisisbury.co.uk
*Weekly (Thu). Owner: Newsquest.
Editor: Ian Savage; news: Steve Orrell;
chief sub: John Ellavy*

Buy Sell Cheshire
0151 330 4991
www.cheshirenews.co.uk
*Weekly (Thu). Owner: Trinity Mirror
Cheshire. Editor: Ali McRae*

Carnforth Guardian
01524 32525
*Weekly (Fri). Owner: Johnston Press.
Editor: Sue Riley; news: Louise
Bryning; features: Paul Collins;
chief sub: Michael Gardner*

Chester & District Standard
01244 304500
www.chesterstandard.co.uk
*Weekly (Thu). Owner: North Wales
Newspapers. Editor: Jonathan White*

Chester Chronicle
01244 340151
www.cheshirenews.co.uk
*Weekly (Fri). Owner: Trinity Mirror
Cheshire. Editor-in-chief: Eric Langton*

Chester Mail
01244 340151
www.cheshirenews.co.uk
*Weekly (Fri). Owner: Trinity Mirror
Cheshire. Editor-in-chief: Eric Langton*

Chorley Citizen
01257 269313
www.thisislancashire.co.uk
  /lancashire/chorley
*Weekly (Wed). Owner: Newsquest.
Editor-in-chief: Kevin Young*

Chorley Guardian
01257 264911
www.chorleytoday.co.uk
*Weekly (Wed). Owner: Johnston Press.
Editor: Chris Maguire; news: Vanessa
Taylor; chief sub: Mal Morris*

Chronicle Weekend (Oldham)
0161 633 2121
www.oldham-chronicle.co.uk
*Weekly (Sat). Editor: Jim Williams;
news: Mike Attenborough; chief sub:
Steve Sutcliffe*

Clitheroe Advertiser & Times
01200 422324
www.clitheroe.co.uk
*Weekly (Thu). Owner: Johnston Press.
Editor: Vivien Meath; news:
Duncan Smith*

Colne Times
01282 612561
www.pendletoday.co.uk
*Weekly (Fri). Owner: Johnston Press.
Editor: Roy Prenton; news:
Peter Dewhurst*

Community News (Macclesfield)
01625 503322
*Weekly (Thu). Owner: Newsquest.
Editor: Jean Ellis*

Congleton Advertiser
01782 602525
*Weekly free (Fri). Owner: Northcliffe
Media. Editor: Micheal Saffy; news:
Robert Cotterill; features: Charlotte
Little-Jones*

Congleton Chronicle
01260 273737
www.chronicleseries.com
Weekly (Fri). Editor: Jeremy Condliffe

Congleton Guardian
01260 296545
www.thisischeshire.co.uk
*Weekly (Thu). Owner: Newsquest.
Editor: Carla Slynn; news: Ian Ross*

Crewe & Nantwich Guardian
01925 434000
www.thisischeshire.co.uk
*Weekly (Thu). Owner: Newsquest.
Editor: Keith Morris*

Crewe Chronicle
01270 256631
www.cheshirenews.co.uk
*Weekly (Wed). Owner: Trinity Mirror
Cheshire. Editor: Dave Fox; news:
Jan Roberts*

Crewe Mail
01270 256631
www.cheshirenews.co.uk
*Weekly (Fri). Owner: Trinity Mirror
Cheshire. Editor: Dave Fox; news:
Jan Roberts*

Crosby Herald
0151 932 1000
www.icseftonandwestlancs.co.uk
*Weekly (Thu). Owner: Trinity Mirror
Merseyside. Editor: Hazel Shaw;
news: Lloyd Jones*

**Cumberland and Westmorland
Herald**
01768 862313
www.cwherald.com
*Weekly (Sat). Editor: Colin Maughan;
news: Liz Stannard; features:
Helen Phillips*

Cumberland News
01228 612600
www.cumberland-news.co.uk
*Weekly (Fri). Owner: Cumbrian News
Group. Editor: Neil Hodgkinson; news:
Sue Crawford; features: Mary Ingham;
production: Andy Nixon*

Deeside Chronicle
01244 340151
www.cheshirenews.co.uk
Weekly (Fri). Owner: Trinity Mirror
Cheshire. Editor-in-chief: Eric Langton

East Cumbrian Gazette
01228 612600
www.cumbria-online.co.uk
Weekly free (Thu). Owner: Cumbrian
News Group. Editor: Neil Hodgkinson;
news: Sue Crawford; features: Mary
Ingham; production: Andy Nixon

Ellesmere Port Pioneer
0151 355 5181
www.cheshirenews.co.uk
Weekly (Wed). Owner: Trinity Mirror
Cheshire. Editor: Phil Robinson

Ellesmere Port Standard
01244 304500
www.ellesmereportstandard.co.uk
Weekly (Thu). Owner: North Wales
Newspapers. Editor: Jonathan White

Evening Leader (Chester)
01352 707707
www.chestereveningleader.co.uk
Daily. Editor: Barry Jones; chief sub:
Joanne Shone; production: Karen Perry

Fleetwood Weekly News and
Chronicle
01253 772950
www.fleetwoodtoday.co.uk
Weekly (Wed). Owner: Johnston Press.
Editor: Gary Miller; news: Karen Evans

Flint & Holywell Chronicle
01244 821911
www.cheshirenews.co.uk
Weekly (Fri). Owner: Trinity Mirror
Cheshire. Editor: Kevin Hughes; news:
James Shepherd

Formby Champion
01704 392392
www.championline.net
Weekly (Wed). Owner: Champion
Media Group. Editor: Martin Hovden

Formby Times
01704 872237
www.icformby.co.uk
Weekly (Thu). Owner: Trinity Mirror
Merseyside. Editor: Hazel Shaw

Frodsham & Helsby Chronicle
01244 340151
www.cheshirenews.co.uk
Weekly (Fri). Owner: Trinity Mirror
Cheshire. Editor-in-chief: Eric Langton

Garstang Courier
01995 602494
www.garstangtoday.co.uk
Weekly (Fri). Owner: Johnston Press.
Editor: Richard Machin; news:
Tony Coppin

Garstang Guardian
01524 32525
www.prestontoday.net
Weekly (Fri). Owner: Johnston Press.
Editor: Sue Riley; news: Louise Bryning;
features: Peter Gibbons; chief sub:
Michael Gradner

Heswall News
0151 647 7111
Weekly (Wed). Owner: Trinity Mirror
Merseyside. Editor: Sue McCann

Heywood Advertiser
01706 360626
www.heywoodadvertiser.co.uk
Weekly (Wed). Owner: Guardian Media
Group. Editor: Paul Harrison

Hoylake & West Kirby News
0151 647 7111
Weekly (Wed). Owner: Trinity Mirror
Merseyside. Editor: Sue McCann

Huyton & Roby Star
0151 236 2000
Weekly (Thu). Owner: Trinity Mirror
Merseyside. News editor: Jane Daly

Keswick Reminder
01768 772140
www.keswickreminder.co.uk
Weekly (Fri). Editor: Jane Grave

Kirkby Extra
07831 090566
Monthly (1st Wed). Editor: Chris O'Shea

Kirkham Express
01253 724236
Weekly (Wed). Owner: Johnston Press.
Editor: Gary Miller; news: Karen Evans

Knowsley Challenge
0151 709 7567
www.knowsleychallenge.co.uk
Monthly (15th). Owner: Trinity Mirror
Merseyside. Editor: Alan Birkett

Knutsford Guardian
01925 434000
www.thisischeshire.co.uk
Weekly (Wed). Owner: Newsquest.
Editor: Nicola Priest

Lakeland Echo
01524 833111
www.lakelandtoday.co.uk
Weekly (Tue). Owner: Johnston Press.
Editor: David Waddington

Lancashire Evening Post
See page 41

Lancashire Telegraph
See page 41

Lancaster & Morecambe Citizen
01524 382121
www.thelancasterandmorecambe
citizen.co.uk
Weekly (Wed). Owner: Newsquest
Media Group. Editor: Phil Fleming

Lancaster Guardian
01524 32525
www.lancastertoday.co.uk
Weekly (Fri). Owner: Johnston Press.
Editor: Sue Riley; news: Louise Bryning;
features: Peter Gibbons; chief sub:
Michael Gardner

Leigh Journal
01942 672241
www.leighjournal.co.uk
Weekly (Thu). Owner: Newsquest.
Editor: Mike Hulme

Leigh Reporter
01942 603334
www.leightoday.co.uk
Weekly free (Wed). Owner: Johnston
Press. Editor: Wendy Moss

Leyland Guardian
01257 264911
www.leylandtoday.co.uk
Weekly (Wed). Owner: Johnston Press.
Editor: Christopher Maguire; news:
Vanessa Taylor; chief sub: Mal Morris

Liverpool Daily Post
See page 41

Liverpool Echo
See page 41

Longridge News
01772 783265
www.longridgenews.co.uk
Weekly (Wed). Owner: Johnston Press.
Editor: Richard Machin

Lytham St Annes & Fylde Express
01253 724236
Weekly (Wed). Owner: Johnston Press.
Editor: Gary Miller; news: Karen Evans

Macclesfield Express
01625 424445
www.macclesfield-express.co.uk
Weekly (Wed). Owner: Guardian Media
Group. Editor: David Lafferty;
news: Pat Hills

Macclesfield Times
01625 424445
www.manchesteronline.co.uk
/newspapers/macctimes.html
Weekly free (Thu). Owner: Guardian
Media Group. Editor: David Lafferty;
news: Pat Hills

Maghull & Aintree Star
0151 236 2000
www.icseftonandwestlancs.co.uk
/icmaghull
Weekly (Thu). Owner: Trinity Mirror
Merseyside. News editor: Jane Daly

Maghull Champion
01704 392392
www.champnews.com
Weekly (Wed). Owner: Champion
Media Group. Editor: Martin Hovden

Manchester Evening News
See page 41

Manchester Metro News
0161 475 4898
www.metronews.co.uk
Weekly. Editor: Kate Stirrup

Marketplace (Wirral)
0151 906 3000
Weekly (Thu). Owner: Newsquest.
Editor: Leigh Marles

Metro North West
0161 836 5152
www.metro.co.uk
Daily free. Owner: Associated
Newspapers. Editor: Kenny Campbell

Middleton & North Manchester
Guardian
0161 643 3615
www.middletonguardian.co.uk
Weekly (Thu). Owner: Guardian Media
Group. Editor: Gerry Sammon

Middlewich Chronicle
01244 340151
www.cheshirenews.co.uk
*Weekly (Fri). Owner: Trinity Mirror
Cheshire. Editor-in-chief: Eric Langton*

Middlewich Guardian
01925 434000
www.thisischeshire.co.uk
*Weekly (Wed). Owner: Newsquest.
Editor: Nicola Priest*

Midweek Advertiser
01695 572501
*Weekly (Thu). Owner: Trinity Mirror
Merseyside. Editor: Peter Harvey;
news: David Sudworth*

Mold & Buckley Chronicle
01244 340151
www.cheshirenews.co.uk
*Weekly (Fri). Owner: Trinity Mirror
Cheshire. Editor-in-chief: Eric Langton*

Morecambe Guardian
01524 32525
*Weekly (Fri). Owner: Johnston Press.
Editor: Sue Riley; news: Louise
Bryning; features: Paul Collins;
chief sub: Michael Gardner*

Morecambe Visitor
01524 833111
www.thevisitor.co.uk
*Weekly (Wed). Owner: Johnston Press.
Editor: Glen Cooper; news: Ingrid Kent*

Nantwich Chronicle
01244 340151
www.cheshirenews.co.uk
*Weekly (Fri). Owner: Trinity Mirror
Cheshire. Editor-in-chief: Eric Langton*

Nelson Leader
01282 612561
www.pendletoday.co.uk
*Weekly (Fri). Owner: Johnston Press.
Editor: Roy Prenton; news:
Peter Dewhurst*

Neston News
0151 647 7111
*Weekly (Wed). Owner: Trinity Mirror
Merseyside. Editor: Sue McCann*

News & Star (Carlisle)
01228 612600
www.news-and-star.co.uk
*Daily (Mon-Sat). Owner: Cumbrian
News Group. Editor: Neil Hodgkinson;
news: Sue Crawford; features: Mary
Ingham; production: Andy Nixon*

Northwest Evening Mail (Barrow)
01229 821835
www.nwemail.co.uk
*Daily. Owner: Cumbrian News Group.
Editor: Steve Brauner; news: Jon
Townend; features: Pete Leach;
chief sub: Ann McVea*

Northwich & District Guardian
01925 434000
www.thisischeshire.co.uk
*Weekly (Wed). Owner: Newsquest.
Editor: Keith Morris*

Northwich Chronicle
01244 340151
www.cheshirenews.co.uk
*Weekly (Wed). Owner: Trinity Mirror
Cheshire. Editor-in-chief: Eric Langton*

Northwich Herald & Post
01244 340151
www.cheshirenews.co.uk
*Weekly (Wed). Owner: Trinity Mirror
Cheshire. Editor-in-chief: Eric Langton*

Northwich Mail
01606 42272
*Weekly (Wed). Owner: Trinity Mirror
Cheshire. Editor: Simon Drury*

Oldham Evening Chronicle
0161 633 2121
www.oldham-chronicle.co.uk
*Daily (Mon-Fri) Editor: Jim Williams;
news: Mike Attenborough; chief sub:
Steve Sutcliffe*

Ormskirk Advertiser
01695 572501
*Weekly (Thu). Owner: Trinity Mirror
Merseyside. Editor: Peter Harvey;
news: David Sudworth*

Ormskirk Champion
01704 392392
www.champnews.com
*Weekly (Wed). Owner: Champion
Media Group. Editor: Malcolm Hindell*

Padiham Express
01282 426161
www.burnleytoday.co.uk
*Weekly (Tue, Fri). Owner: Johnston
Press. Editor: Chris Daggett; news:
Margaret Parsons*

Pendle & Burnley Reporter
01282 612561
*Weekly free (Fri). Owner: Johnston
Press. Editor: Roy Prenton; news:
Peter Dewhurst*

Pendle Express
01282 612561
www.pendletoday.co.uk
*Weekly (Tue, Fri). Owner: Johnston
Press. Editor: Roy Prenton; news:
Peter Dewhurst*

Poynton Times
01625 424445
www.manchesteronline.co.uk
*Weekly (Wed). Owner: Guardian Media
Group. Editor: David Lafferty; news:
Pat Hills*

Preston & Leyland Reporter
01772 838103
*Weekly free (Thu). Owner: Johnston
Press. Editor: Simon Reynolds*

Preston & Leyland Citizen
01772 824631
www.thisislancashire.co.uk
*Weekly (Thu). Owner: Newsquest.
Editor: Gill Ellis; news: Jane Willis*

Prestwich & Whitefield Guide
0161 764 9421
www.thisisbury.co.uk
*Weekly (Wed). Owner: Newsquest.
Editor: Ian Savage; news: Steve Orrell;
chief sub: John Ellavy*

Prestwich Advertiser
0161 789 5015
www.prestwichadvertiser.co.uk
*Weekly (Fri). Owner: Guardian Media
Group. Editor: Vince Hale*

Radcliffe Times
0161 764 9421
www.thisisbury.co.uk
*Weekly (Wed). Owner: Newsquest.
Editor: Ian Savage; news: Steve Orrell;
chief sub: John Ellavy*

Rochdale Express
01706 354321
www.manchesteronline.co.uk/news
papers/rochdaleexpress.html
*Weekly free (Fri). Owner: Guardian
Media Group. Editor: Claire Mooney*

Rochdale Observer
01706 354321
www.rochdaleobserver.co.uk
*Weekly (Wed, Sat). Owner: Guardian
Media Group. Editor: Claire Mooney*

Rossendale Free Press
01706 213311
www.therossendalefreepress.co.uk
*Weekly (Thu). Owner: Guardian Media
Group. Editor: Stuart Robertson*

Runcorn and Widnes Herald & Post
0151 424 5921
*Weekly (Fri). Owner: Trinity Mirror
Cheshire. Editor: Ian Douglas; news:
Simon Drury*

Runcorn Weekly News
0151 424 5921
www.cheshireonline.icnetwork
.co.uk
*Weekly (Thu). Owner: Trinity Mirror
Cheshire. Editor: Ian Douglas; news:
Simon Drury*

Runcorn World
0845 603 7854
www.runcornworld.co.uk
*Weekly (Wed). Owner: Newsquest.
Editor: Nicola Priest; assistant editor:
Stephen Hallmark*

St Helens Star
01925 434000
www.thisisst-helens.co.uk
*Weekly (Thu). Owner: Newsquest.
Editor: Nicola Priest*

St Helens, Prescot & Knowsley Reporter
01744 22285
www.sthelenstoday.net
*Weekly (Wed). Owner: Johnston Press.
Editor: Andy Moffatt*

Sale & Altrincham Messenger
0161 908 3360
www.messengernewspapers.co.uk
*Weekly (Thu). Owner: Newsquest.
Editor: Lynn Hughes*

Salford Advertiser
0161 789 5015
www.salfordadvertiser.co.uk
*Weekly (Thu). Owner: Guardian Media
Group. Editor: Vince Hale*

Skelmersdale Advertiser
01695 572501
www.icseftonandwestlancs.co.uk
*Weekly (Thu). Owner: Trinity Mirror
Merseyside. Editor: Peter Harvey;
news: David Sudworth*

Skelmersdale Champion
01704 392392
www.champnews.com
Weekly (Wed). Owner: Champion Media Group. Editor: Malcolm Hindell

South Cheshire Advertiser
01782 602525
Weekly free (Thu). Owner: Northcliffe Media. Editor: Michael Saffy; news: Robert Cotterill; features: Charlotte Little-Jones

South Cheshire Guardian
01925 434000
www.thisischeshire.co.uk
Weekly (Wed). Owner: Newsquest. Editor: Nicola Priest

South Cheshire Mail
01270 256631
www.cheshirenews.co.uk
Weekly (Wed). Owner: Trinity Mirror Cheshire. Editor: Dave Fox; news: Jan Roberts

South Lakes Citizen
01539 720555
www.thisisthelakedistrict.co.uk
Weekly free (Wed). Owner: Newsquest. Editor: Mike Glover; news: Mike Addison; chief sub: Richard Belk

South Liverpool Merseymart
0151 734 4000
Weekly (Thu). Owner: Trinity Mirror Merseyside. News editor: Jane Daly

South Manchester Reporter
0161 446 2213
www.southmanchesterreporter.co.uk
Weekly (Thu). Owner: Guardian Media Group. Editor: Laurence Matheson; news: Gareth Tidman

South Wirral News
0151 355 5181
Weekly free (Fri). Owner: Trinity Mirror Cheshire. Editor: Phil Robinson

Southport Champion
01704 392392
www.champnews.com
Weekly (Wed). Owner: Champion Media Group. Editor: Martin Hovden

Stockport Citizen
0161 491 5700
Fortnightly (Thu). Independent. Editor: Mike Shields

Stockport Express
0161 480 4491
www.stockportexpress.co.uk
Weekly (Wed). Owner: Guardian Media Group. Editor: Mandy Leigh; news: Duncan Ponter; features: Lisa Cooper

Stockport Times East
0161 475 4834
www.stockportexpress.co.uk
Weekly free (Thu). Owner: Guardian Media Group. Editor: Mandy Leigh; news: Duncan Ponter; features: Lisa Cooper

Stockport Times West
0161 475 4834
www.stockportexpress.co.uk
Weekly free (Thu). Owner: Guardian Media Group. Editor: Mandy Leigh; news: Duncan Ponter; features: Lisa Cooper

Stretford & Urmston Messenger
0161 908 3360
www.messengernewspapers.co.uk
Weekly (Thu). Owner: Newsquest. Editor: Lynn Hughes

Tameside Advertiser
0161 339 7611
www.tamesideadvertiser.co.uk
Weekly free (Thu). Owner: Guardian Media Group. Editor: David Porter

Tameside Reporter
0161 304 7691
www.tamesidereporter.com
Weekly (Thu). Owner: Ashton Weekly Newspapers. Editor: Nigel Skinner

Thornton, Cleveleys & Poulton Citizen
01772 824631
www.thisislancashire.co.uk
Weekly (Thu). Owner: Newsquest. Editor: Jill Ellis; news: Steve Dunthorne

Village Visiter (Lancashire)
01695 572501
Weekly (Thu). Owner: Trinity Mirror Merseyside. Editor: Peter Harvey; news: David Sudworth

Wallasey News
0151 647 7111
Weekly (Wed). Owner: Trinity Mirror Merseyside. Editor: Sue McCann

Warrington Guardian
01925 434000
www.thisischeshire.co.uk
Weekly (Thu). Owner: Newsquest. Editor: Nicola Priest; news: Gareth Dunning

Warrington Guardian Midweek
01925 434000
www.thisischeshire.co.uk
Weekly free (Tue). Owner: Newsquest. Editor: Nicola Priest

West Cumberland Times and Star
01900 607600
www.times-and-star.co.uk
Weekly (Fri). Owner: Cumbrian News Group. Editor: Stephen Johnson; deputy editor: Ian Brogden

West Cumbrian Gazette
01228 612600
www.cumbria-online.co.uk
Weekly free (Thu). Owner: Cumbrian News Group. Editor: Neil Hodgkinson; news: Sue Crawford; features: Mary Ingham; production: Andy Nixon

West Derby & Tuebrook Star
0151 236 2000
Weekly (Thu). Owner: Trinity Mirror Merseyside. Editor: Jane Daly; news editor: Ed Casson

Westmorland Gazette
01539 720555
www.thisisthelakedistrict.co.uk
Weekly (Fri). Owner: Newsquest. Editor: Mike Glover; news: Mike Addison; chief sub: Richard Belk

Westmorland Messenger
01539 720555
www.thisisthelakedistrict.co.uk
Weekly (Wed). Owner: Newsquest. Editor: Mike Glover; news: Mike Addison; chief sub: Richard Belk

Whitchurch Herald
01948 662332
Weekly (Thu). Owner: Trinity Mirror Cheshire. Editor: Andrew Bowan

Whitehaven News
01946 595100
www.whitehaven-news.co.uk
Weekly (Thu). Owner: Cumbrian News Group. Editor: Colin Edgar; deputy editor: Alan Cleaver; news: David Siddall

Widnes Weekly News
0151 424 5921
www.iccheshire.co.uk
Weekly (Thu). Owner: Trinity Mirror Cheshire. Editor: Rob Hopkins; news: Adrian Short

Widnes World
01925 434000
www.runcornandwidnesworld.co.uk
Weekly (Wed). Owner: Newsquest. Editor: Nicola Priest; assistant editor: Stephen Hallmark

Wigan Courier
01257 400026
www.wigancourier.co.uk
Three-weekly (Tue). Independent. Editor: John Callon

Wigan Evening Post
01902 228000
www.wigantoday.net
Daily. Owner: Johnston Press. Editor: Gillan Gray; head of content: Blaise Tapp

Wigan Observer
01902 228000
www.wigantoday.net
Weekly (Tue). Owner: Johnston Press. Editor: Gillan Gray; head of content: Blaise Tapp

Wigan Reporter
01772 838103
www.wigantoday.net
Weekly free (Thu). Owner: Johnston Press. Editor: Gillan Gray; head of content: Blaise Tapp

Wilmslow Citizen
0161 491 5700
Fortnightly (Thu). Independent. Editor: Mike Shields

Wilmslow Express
01625 529333
www.thewilmslowexpress.co.uk
Weekly (Thu). Owner: Guardian Media Group. Editor: Jackie Doran; news: Betty Anderson

Winsford Chronicle
01244 340151
www.cheshirenews.co.uk
Weekly (Wed). Owner: Trinity Mirror
Cheshire. Editor-in-chief: Eric Langton

Winsford Guardian
01925 434000
www.thisischeshire.co.uk
Weekly (Wed). Owner: Newsquest.
Editor: Nicola Priest

Wirral Chronicle
01244 340151
www.cheshirenews.co.uk
Weekly (Fri). Owner: Trinity Mirror
Cheshire. Editor-in-chief: Eric Langton

Wirral Globe
0151 906 3000
www.thisiswirral.co.uk
Weekly (Wed). Owner: Newsquest.
Editor: Leigh Marles

Wirral Target
0151 906 3000
www.thisiswirral.co.uk
Fortnightly free (Wed). Owner:
Newsquest. Editor: Leigh Marles

Wythenshawe World
0161 998 4786
Fortnightly free (Fri). Editor: John
Oatway

Isle of Man

Isle of Man Courier
01624 695695
www.iomtoday.co.im
Weekly (Thu). Owner: Johnston Press.
Editor: John Sherrocks; news: Jo Overty;
chief sub: Dave Corbett

Isle of Man Examiner
01624 695695
www.iomtoday.co.im
Weekly (Tue). Owner: Johnston Press.
Editor: John Sherrocks; news: Jo Overty;
chief sub: Dave Corbett

The Manx Independent
01624 695695
www.iomtoday.co.im
Weekly (Fri). Owner: Johnston Press.
Editor: John Sherrocks; news: Jo Overty;
chief sub: Dave Corbett

Regional newspapers — Wales

● Major regionals

Wales on Sunday
Thomson House, Havelock Street,
Cardiff CF10 1XR
029 2058 3583
www.icwales.co.uk
Weekly (Sun). Owner: Western Mail
& Echo (Trinity Mirror). Editor:
Tim Gordon; news: Laura Kemp

Western Mail
Thomson House, Havelock Street,
Cardiff CF10 1XR
029 2022 3333
www.icwales.co.uk
Daily. Owner: Western Mail & Echo
(Trinity Mirror). Editor: Alan Edmunds

South Wales Echo
Thomson House, Havelock Street,
Cardiff CF10 1XR
029 2022 3333
www.icwales.co.uk
Daily. Owner: Western Mail & Echo
(Trinity Mirror). Editor: Mike Hill;
news: Cathy Owen

South Wales Evening Post
PO Box 14, Adelaide Street,
Swansea SA1 1QT
01792 510000
www.thisissouthwales.co.uk
Daily. Owner: Northcliffe Media.
Editor: Spencer Feeney; news: Chris
Davies; features: Peter Slee; chief sub:
Lynne Fernquest

● North Wales

Abergele Visitor
01492 584321
www.icnorthwales.co.uk
Weekly (Wed). Owner: Trinity Mirror
North Wales. Editor: Alan Davies;
news: Steve Stratford

Bangor Chronicle
01248 387400
www.northwaleschronicle.co.uk
Weekly (Thu). Owner: North Wales
Newspapers. Editor: Matt Warner;
features: Tony Coates

Bangor/Anglesey Mail
01286 671111
www.icnorthwales.co.uk
Weekly (Wed). Owner: Trinity Mirror
North Wales. Editor: Jeff Eames; news:
Linda Roberts; production: Mark Jones

Buy Sell (Flintshire Edition)
01978 290400
Weekly (Wed). Owner: Trinity Mirror
Cheshire. No editorial

Caernarfon & Denbigh Herald
01286 671111
www.icnorthwales.co.uk
Weekly (Thu). Owner: Trinity Mirror
North Wales. Editor: Jeff Eames; news:
Linda Roberts; production: Mark Jones

Y Cymro
01970 615000
www.y-cymro.co.uk
Weekly (Fri). Owner: Tindle
Newspapers. Editor: Carol Taylor

Daily Post & Yr Herald
01492 574455
www.icnorthwales.co.uk
Daily. Owner: Trinity Mirror North
Wales. Editor: Rob Irvine

Denbighshire Free Press
01745 813535
www.denbighshirefreepress.co.uk
Weekly (Thu). Owner: North Wales
Newspapers. Editor: Alistair Syme

Flintshire Chronicle
01244 821911
www.icnorthwales.co.uk
Weekly (Fri). Owner: Trinity Mirror.
Editor: Kevin Hughes; news: James
Shepherd

Flintshire Evening Leader
01244 304500
www.chesterstandard.co.uk
Weekly (Thu). Owner: North Wales
Newspapers. Editor: Barrie Jones

Flintshire Leader & Standard
01352 707707
www.flintshirestandard.co.uk
Weekly (Thu). Editor: Barrie Jones;
features: Joanne Shone; chief sub:
Joanne Shone; production: Karen Perry

Gwynedd Chronicle
01248 387400
www.chroniclenow.co.uk
Weekly (Thu). Owner: North Wales
Newspapers. Editor: Matt Warner;
features: Tony Coates

Holyhead & Anglesey Mail
01286 671111
www.icnorthwales.co.uk
Weekly (Wed). Owner: Trinity Mirror
North Wales. Editor: Jeff Eames; news:
Linda Roberts; production: Mark Jones

North Wales Chronicle
01248 387400
www.chroniclenow.co.uk
Weekly (Thu). Owner: North Wales
Newspapers. Editor: Matt Warner;
features: Tony Coates

North Wales Pioneer
01492 531188
www.northwalespioneer.co.uk
Weekly (Wed). Owner: North Wales
Newspapers. Editor: Steve Rogers

North Wales Weekly News
01492 584321
www.icnorthwales.co.uk
Weekly (Thu). Owner: Trinity Mirror
North Wales. Editor: Alan Davies;
news: Steve Stratford

Rhyl & Prestatyn Visitor
01745 334144
www.icnorthwales.co.uk
Weekly free (Wed). Owner: Trinity
Mirror North Wales. Editor: Alan
Davies; news: Dave Jones

Rhyl, Prestatyn & Abergele Journal
01745 357500
www.rhyljournal.co.uk
Weekly (Wed). Owner: North Wales Newspapers. Editor: Steve Rogers; deputy editor: Terry Canty

Vale Advertiser
01492 584321
icnorthwales.icnetwork.co.uk /news/valeadvertiser
Weekly (Fri). Owner: Trinity Mirror North Wales. Editor: Alan Davies; news: Steve Stratford

Wrexham Evening Leader
01978 355151
www.eveningleader.co.uk
Daily. Owner: North Wales Newspapers. Editor: Barrie Jones

Wrexham Leader
01978 355151
www.bigleader.co.uk
Weekly free (Fri). Owner: North Wales Newspapers. Editor: Barrie Jones

Wrexham Mail
01978 351515
www.icnorthwales.co.uk
Weekly (Thu). Owner: Trinity Mirror Cheshire. Editor: Kevin Hughes; news: James Shepherd

Ynys Mon Chronicle
01248 387400
www.chroniclenow.co.uk
Weekly (Thu). Owner: North Wales Newspapers. Editor: Matt Warner; features: Tony Coates

● South Wales

Abergavenny Chronicle
01873 852187
www.abergavenny.co.uk
Weekly (Thu). Owner: Tindle Newspapers. Editor: Liz Davies

Abergavenny Free Press
01873 857497
www.thisismonmouthshire.co.uk
Weekly (Wed). Owner: Newsquest. Editor: Andy Downie

Barry & District News
01446 704981
www.thisisbarry.co.uk
Weekly (Thu). Owner: North Wales Newspapers. Editor: Shira Valek

Barry Gem
01446 774484
www.barry-today.co.uk
Weekly (Thu). Owner: Tindle Newspapers. Editor: Caroline Patuto

Brecon & Radnor Express
01874 610111
www.brecon-radnor.co.uk
Weekly (Wed). Owner: Tindle Newspapers. Editor: Clare Graham

Bridgend & District Recorder
01446 774484
Weekly (Tue). Owner: Tindle Newspapers. Editor: Caroline Patuto

Cambrian News
01970 615000
www.aberystwyth-today.co.uk
Weekly (Wed). Owner: Tindle Newspapers. Editor: Beverly Davies; news: Simon Middlehurst

Campaign Blackwood
01633 777212
www.thisisgwent.co.uk
Weekly (Thu). Owner: Newsquest. Editor: Andy Downie; chief sub: Gina Robertson

Campaign Caerphilly
01633 777212
www.thisisgwent.co.uk
Weekly (Thu). Owner: Newsquest. Editor: Andy Downie; chief sub: Gina Robertson

Campaign North Gwent
01633 777212
www.thisisgwent.co.uk
Weekly (Thu). Owner: Newsquest. Editor: Andy Downie; chief sub: Gina Robertson

Campaign Pontypridd
01633 777212
www.thisisgwent.co.uk
Weekly (Thu). Owner: North Wales Newspapers. Editor: Andy Downie; chief sub: Gina Robertson

Cardiff Advertiser & Property Times
029 2030 3900
www.thecardiffandsouthwales advertiser.co.uk
Weekly (Fri). Independent. Editor: David Hynes

Cardigan & Tivyside Advertiser
01239 614343
www.thisistivyside.net
Weekly (Tue). Owner: Newsquest. Editor: Areurin Evans; news: Sue Lewis

Carmarthen Herald
01267 227222
www.thisissouthwales.co.uk
Weekly free (Fri). Owner: Northcliffe Media. Editor: Robert Lloyd; news: Rachael Misstear

Carmarthen Journal
01267 227222
www.thisissouthwales.co.uk
Weekly (Wed). Owner: Northcliffe Media. Editor: David Hardy

Chepstow Free Press
01291 621882
www.thisismonmouthshire.co.uk
Weekly (Wed). Owner: Newsquest. Editor: Andy Downie; news: Alex Cinus

County Echo (Newport)
01348 874445
www.newport-today.co.uk
Weekly (Fri). Owner: Tindle Newspapers. Editor: Bev Davies

County Times & Gazette (Brecon)
01938 553354
www.countytimes.co.uk
Weekly (Fri). Owner: North Wales Newspapers. Editor: Nick Knight

Courier (Neath)
01792 510000
Weekly (Tue). Owner: Northcliffe Media. Editor: Paul Turner

Cowbridge Gem
01446 774484
www.cowbridge-today.co.uk
Weekly (Thu). Owner: Tindle Newspapers. Editor: Caroline Patuto

Cynon Valley Leader
01685 873136
www.icwales.co.uk
Weekly (Wed). Owner: Western Mail & Echo (Trinity Mirror). Editor: Gary Marsh

Glamorgan Gazette
01656 304924
www.icwales.co.uk
Weekly (Thu). Owner: Western Mail & Echo (Trinity Mirror). Editor: Deborah Rees

Gwent Gazette
01495 304589
www.icwales.co.uk
Weekly (Tue). Owner: Western Mail & Echo (Trinity Mirror). Editor: Sarah Harris

Llanelli Star
01554 745300
www.thisissouthwales.co.uk
Weekly (Thu). Owner: Northcliffe Media. Editor: Rob Lloyd; assistant editor: Susanne Oakley

Llantwit Major Gem
01446 774484
www.llantwit-major-today.co.uk
Weekly (Thu). Owner: Tindle Newspapers. Editor: Caroline Patuto

Metro Cardiff
01179 343 728
www.metro.co.uk
Daily. Owner: Associated Newspapers. Editor: Clare Ogden

Merthyr Express
01685 856500
Weekly (Thu). Owner: Western Mail & Echo (Trinity Mirror). Editor: Gordon Caldicott

Mid Wales Journal
01743 283312
www.midwalesjournal.co.uk
Weekly (Fri). Owner: Midland News Association. Editor: Mike Robinson; deputy editor: Mary Queally

Milford & West Wales Mercury
01646 698971
www.thisismilfordhaven.co.uk
Weekly (Thu). Owner: Newsquest. Editor: Fiona Phillips; news editor: Richard Harris

Monmouth Free Press
01600 713631
www.thisismonmouthshire.co.uk
Weekly (Wed). Owner: Newsquest. Editor: Andy Downie; news: Andy Sherwill

Monmouthshire Beacon
01600 712142
www.monmouth-today.co.uk
Weekly (Wed). Owner: Tindle Newspapers. Editor: Robert Williams

Traditional media

Narbeth & Whitland Observer
01834 843262
*Weekly (Fri). Owner: Tindle
Newspapers. Editor: Neil Dickinson*

Neath & Port Talbot Guardian
01639 778885
*Weekly (Wed). Owner: Western Mail
& Echo (Trinity Mirror). Editor:
Rhodri Evans*

Neath & Port Talbot Tribune
01792 510000
*Monthly (3rd Mon). Owner: Northcliffe
Media. Editor: Paul Turner*

Penarth Times
029 2070 7234
www.thisispenarth.co.uk
*Weekly (Thu). Owner: North Wales
Newspapers. News editor: Shira Valek*

Pontypool Free Press
01495 751133
www.thisismonmouthshire.co.uk
*Weekly (Wed). Owner: Newsquest.
Editor: Andy Downie; news:
Lorna Phelan*

Pontypridd Observer
01443 665161
www.icwales.com
*Weekly (Wed). Owner: Western Mail
& Echo (Trinity Mirror). Editor:
Wayne Nowaczyk*

Rhondda Leader
01443 665151
*Weekly (Thu). Owner: Western Mail
& Echo (Trinity Mirror). Editor:
Kayrin Davies; news: Dave Edwards*

South Wales Argus
01633 810000
www.thisisgwent.co.uk
*Daily. Owner: Newsquest. Editor: Gerry
Keighley; chief sub: Caroline Woolard*

South Wales Guardian
01269 592781
www.thisisammanford.co.uk
*Weekly (Wed). Owner: Newsquest.
Editor: Mike Lewis; features:
Richard Sharpe*

Swansea Herald
01792 514630
*Weekly (Thu). Owner: Northcliffe
Media. Editor: Spencer Feeney*

Tenby Observer
01834 843262
www.tenby-today.co.uk
*Weekly (Fri). Owner: Tindle
Newspapers. Editor: Neil Dickinson*

Tenby Times
01834 843262
*Monthly free (1st Wed). Owner: Tindle
Newspapers. Editor: Neil Dickinson*

Weekly Argus
01633 810000
www.thisisgwent.co.uk
*Weekly (Thu). Owner: Newsquest.
Editor: Gerry Keighley; chief sub:
Caroline Woolard*

Western Telegraph
01437 763133
www.thisispembrokeshire.net
*Weekly (Wed). Owner: Newsquest.
Editor: Fiona Philips*

Regional newspapers – Scotland

● Main regionals

Aberdeen Press and Journal
Aberdeen Journals, Lang Stracht,
Mastrick, Aberdeen AB15 6DF
01224 690222
www.pressandjournal.co.uk
*Daily. Owner: DC Thomson. Editor:
Derek Tucker; news: Andrew Hebdon;
features: Sonja Cox; chief sub:
Alexander Lossen*

Courier and Advertiser
80 Kingsway East, Dundee DD4 8SL
01382 223131
www.thecourier.co.uk
*Daily. Owner: DC Thomson. Editor:
Bill Hutcheon; news: Mike Alexander;
features: Catriona Macinnes;
production: Brian Clarkson*

Daily Record
One Central Quay, Glasgow G3 8DA
0141 309 3000
www.dailyrecord.co.uk
*Daily. Owner: Trinity Mirror. Editor:
Bruce Waddell; news: Andy Lynes;
features: Melanie Harvey*

Edinburgh Evening News
Barclay House, 108 Holyrood
Road, Edinburgh EH8 8AS
0131 620 8620
www.edinburghnews.com
*Daily. Owner: Scotsman Publications.
Editor: John McLellan; news: Euan
McGrory; features: Gina Davidson;
chief sub: Howard Dorman;
production: Mark Eadie*

Glasgow Evening Times
200 Renfield Street,
Glasgow G2 3QB
0141 302 7000
www.eveningtimes.co.uk
*Daily. Owner: Newsquest. Editor:
Donald Martin; news: Hugh Boag;
features: Garry Scott; chief sub:
Andy Clark*

Glasgow Herald
200 Renfield Street,
Glasgow G2 3QB
0141 302 7000
www.theherald.co.uk
*Daily. Owner: Newsquest. Editor:
Charles McGhee; senior assistant
editor: Magnus Llewellin; features:
Mark Smith; chief sub: Chris Macrae*

Scotland On Sunday
Barclay House, 108 Holyrood
Road, Edinburgh EH8 8AS
0131 620 8620
www.scotlandonsunday.com
*Sunday. Owner: Scotsman
Publications. Editor: Les Snowdon;
news: Peter Laing; features: Claire
Hay; chief sub: Martin Allen;
production: Chris Dry*

The Scotsman
Barclay House, 108 Holyrood
Road, Edinburgh EH8 8AS
0131 620 8620
www.scotsman.com
*Daily. Owner: Scotsman Publications.
Editor: Mike Gilson; news: James Hall;
assistant features editor: Gaby Soutar;
production editors: John Ellingham
and Alistair Norman (subs), Alastair
Clark (opinion)*

Scottish Daily Mirror
1 Central Quay, Glasgow G3 8DA
0141 221 2121
www.mirror.co.uk
*Daily. Owner: Trinity Mirror. News:
Stephen White*

Sunday Herald
200 Renfield Street,
Glasgow G2 3QB
0141 302 7800
www.sundayherald.com
*Sunday. Owner: Newsquest. Editor:
Richard Walker; news: Charlene
Sweeney; features: Susan Flockhart;
production: Roxanne Sorooshian*

Sunday Mail
One Central Quay, Glasgow G3 8DA
0141 309 3000
www.sundaymail.co.uk
*Sunday. Owner: Trinity Mirror. Editor:
Allan Rennie; news: Brendan McGinty*

Sunday Post
2 Albert Square, Dundee DD1 9QJ
01382 223131
www.sundaypost.com
*Sunday. Owner: DC Thomson. Editor:
David Pollington; deputy editor:
Alastair Bennett; news: Tom McKay;
features: Bruce Allan*

● Other newspapers

Aberdeen & District Independent
01224 618300
www.aberdeen-indy.co.uk
*Weekly (Thu). Independent. Editor:
Derek Piper; news: John Storrie*

Aberdeen Citizen
01224 690222
*Weekly (Wed). Owner: Northcliffe
Media. Editor: Damien Bates; deputy:
Richard Prest; news: Louise Redvers;
chief sub: James Donaldson*

Aberdeen Evening Express
01224 690222
www.eveningexpress.co.uk
*Daily. Owner: Northcliffe Media.
Editor: Damien Bates; deputy: Richard
Prest; news: Louise Redvers; chief sub:
James Donaldson*

The Advertiser (Midlothian)
0131 561 6600
*Weekly (Wed). Owner: Johnston Press.
Editor: Roy Scott; news: Alex Hogg*

Airdrie & Coatbridge Advertiser
01236 748648
www.icscotland.co.uk
*Weekly (Wed). Owner: Scottish &
Universal Newspapers (Trinity
Mirror). Editor: John Murdoch*

Alloa & Hillfoots Advertiser
01259 214416
Weekly (Thu). Owner: Dunfermline Press Group. Editor: Kevin McRoberts; news: Faye Thomson

Annandale Herald
01461 202078
Weekly (Thu). Owner: Dumfriesshire Newspapers. Editor: Bryan Armstrong; news: Alan Hall

Annandale Observer
01461 202078
Weekly (Fri). Owner: Dumfriesshire Newspapers. Editor: Bryan Armstrong; news: Alan Hall

Arbroath Herald
01241 872274
Weekly (Fri). Owner: Johnston Press. Editor: Craig Nisbet; news: Brian Forsythe

Ardrossan & Saltcoats Herald
01294 464321
www.ardrossanherald.com
Weekly (Wed). Owner: Clyde & Forth. Editor: Alex Clarke; news: Craig Nisbet

Argyllshire Advertiser
01631 563058
www.argyllshireadvertiser.co.uk
Weekly (Fri). Owner: Oban Times. Editor: Stewart Mackenzie; news: Joanne Simms

Arran Banner
01631 568000
www.obantimes.co.uk
Weekly (Sat). Owner: Oban Times. Editor: Stewart Mackenzie

Ayr Advertiser
01292 267631
Weekly (Tue). Owner: Ayrshire Weekly Press. Editor: Alex Clarke; news: Caroline Paterson

Ayrshire Extra
01292 611666
Weekly (Thu). Owner: Johnston Press. Editor: John Matthews

Ayrshire Post
01292 261111
www.icscotland.co.uk
Weekly (Wed). Owner: Scottish & Universal Newspapers (Trinity Mirror). Editor: Alan Woodison; deputy editor: Cheryl McEvoy; features: Yonnie McInnes

Ayrshire Weekly Press
01294 464321
Weekly (Fri). Owner: Scottish & Universal Newspapers (Trinity Mirror). Editor: Alex Clarke; news: Craig Nisbet

Ayrshire World
01294 272233
www.icscotland.co.uk
Weekly free (Wed). Owner: Scottish & Universal Newspapers (Trinity Mirror). Editor: Alan Woodison; news: Lex Brown

Banffshire Journal
01542 886262
www.banffshire-journal.com
Weekly (Wed). Owner: Scottish Provincial Press. Editor: George Boardman

Barrhead News
0141 887 7055
Weekly (Wed). Owner: Clyde & Forth Press. Editor: Scott Reid

Bearsden, Milngavie & Glasgow Extra
0141 427 7878
www.icscotland.co.uk
Weekly (Thu). Owner: Archant. Editor: Allan Hodge; news: Colin Macdonald; chief sub: Jim Cameron

Bellshill Speaker
01698 264611
Weekly (Thu). Owner: Johnston Press. Editor: Archie Fleming

Berwick Gazette
01289 306677
www.berwicktoday.co.uk
Weekly free (Fri). Owner: Johnston Press. Editor: Janet Wakenshaw

Berwickshire News
01289 306677
www.berwickshiretoday.co.uk
Weekly (Thu). Owner: Johnston Press. Editor: Sandy Brydon

Blairgowrie Advertiser
01250 872854
www.icscotland.co.uk
Weekly (Thu). Owner: Scottish & Universal Newspapers (Trinity Mirror). Editor: Alison Lowson

Border Telegraph
01896 758395
www.bordertelegraph.com
Weekly (Tue). Owner: Dunfermline Press. Editor: Atholl Innes

Brechin Advertiser
01356 622767
www.brechinadvertiser.com
Weekly (Thu). Owner: Angus County Press. Editor: Alan Ducat; news: Phillip Murray; features: Jenny Hill

Buchan Observer
01779 472017
www.buchanie.co.uk
Weekly (Tue). Owner: Johnston Press. Editor: Ken Duncan

The Buteman
01700 502503
www.icscotland.co.uk
Weekly (Fri). Owner: Angus County Press. Editor: Craig Borland

Caithness Courier
01955 602424
www.caithness-courier.co.uk
Weekly (Wed). Owner: North of Scotland Newspapers. Editor: Alan Henry; news: Karen Macdonald

Campbell Times Courier
01631 563058
Weekly (Sat). Owner: Oban Times. Editor: Stewart Mackenzie; news: Joanne Simms

Campbeltown Courier
01586 554646
www.campbeltowncourier.co.uk
Weekly (Fri). Owner: Oban Times. Senior Reporter: Aileen McLennon

Carrick Gazette
01671 402503
Weekly (Thu). Owner: Johnston Press. Editor: Stephen Norris

Central Fife Times & Advertiser
01383 728201
Weekly (Thu). Owner: Dunfermline Press Group. Editor: Jim Stark; chief sub: Susan Dryburgh

Clydebank Post
0141 952 0565
Weekly (Thu). Owner: Clyde & Forth Press. Editor: James Walsh

Clyde Weekly News
01294 273421
www.icScotland.co.uk
Weekly (Wed). Owner: Scottish & Universal Newspapers (Trinity Mirror). Editor: Alex Clarke

Craigmillar Chronicle
0131 661 0791
www.southedinburgh.net
Monthly free (1st of month). Editor: Sally Fraser

Cumbernauld News & Advertiser
01236 725578
www.falkirktoday.co.uk
Weekly free (Fri). Owner: Johnston Press. Editor: Alistair Blyth; chief sub: Neil Smith

Cumbernauld News & Kilsyth Chronicle
01236 725578
www.falkirktoday.co.uk
Weekly (Wed). Owner: Johnston Press. Editor: Alistair Blyth; chief sub: Neil Smith

Cumnock Chronicle
01290 421633
Weekly (Wed). Owner: Ayrshire Weekly Press. Editor: Douglas Skelton

Deeside Piper
01330 824955
www.deesidepiper.com
Weekly (Fri). Owner: Angus County Press. Editor: Phil Allan

Donside Piper & Herald
01330 824955
www.donsidepiper.com
Weekly (Fri). Owner: Angus County Press. Editor: Phil Allan

Dumbarton & Vale Of Leven Reporter
01436 673434
Weekly (Tue). Owner: Clyde & Forth Press. Editor: James Walsh; news: Steve MacIlroy

Dumfries & Galloway Standard
01387 240342
www.icscotland.co.uk
Weekly (Wed & Fri). Owner: Scottish & Universal Newspapers (Trinity Mirror). Editor: Elizabeth Martin; news: Ian Pollock

Dumfries and Galloway Today
01387 240342
www.icscotland.co.uk
Weekly (Thu). Owner: Scottish & Universal Newspapers (Trinity Mirror). Editor: Elizabeth Martin; news: Ian Pollock

Dumfries Courier
01461 202078
Weekly free (Fri). Owner: Dumfriesshire Newspapers. Editor: Bryan Armstrong; news: Alan Hall

Dunfermline Press & West of Fife Advertiser
01383 728201
www.dunfermlinepress.co.uk
Weekly (Wed). Owner: Dunfermline Press Group. Editor: Tom Davidson; news: Simon Harris

Dunoon Observer & Argyllshire Standard
01369 703218
www.dunoon-observer.co.uk
Weekly (Fri). Owner: E&R Ingles. Editor: Bill Jardin

East Fife Mail
01592 261451
www.fifenow.co.uk
Weekly (Wed). Owner: Johnston Press. Editor: Ian Muirhead

East Kilbride Mail
01355 270510
www.eastkilbridemail.com
Weekly (Wed). Owner: Forth Independent. Editor: Willie Mack

East Kilbride News
01355 265000
www.iclanarkshire.co.uk
Weekly (Wed). Owner: Scottish & Universal Newspapers (Trinity Mirror). Editor: Gordon Bury; news: Lynda Nichol

East Kilbride World
01698 283200
Weekly free (Fri). Owner: Scottish & Universal Newspapers (Trinity Mirror). Editor: Joseph Kelly

East Lothian Courier
01620 822451
www.eastlothiancourier.com
Weekly (Thu). Owner: Dunfermline Press Group. Editor: Robbie Scott

East Lothian News
0131 561 6600
www.eastlothiantoday.co.uk
Weekly (Thu). Owner: Johnston Press. Editor: Roy Scott; news: Alex Hogg

East Lothian Times
0131 561 6600
Weekly free (Fri). Owner: Johnston Press. Editor: Roy Scott; news: Alex Hogg

Ellon Advertiser
01888 563589
Weekly (Fri). Owner: W Peters & Son. Editor: Joyce Summers

Ellon Times & East Gordon Advertiser
01779 472017
Weekly (Thu). Owner: Johnston Press. Acting editor: Ken Duncan

Eskdale and Liddesdale Advertiser
01387 380012
Weekly (Thu). Owner: Cumbrian News Group. Editor: Neil Hodgkinson; news: Rachael Norris

Evening Telegraph (Dundee)
01382 223131
Daily. Owner: DC Thomson. Editor: Gordon Wishart; news: Elaine Harrison; features: Phillip Smith

Falkirk Herald
01324 624959
www.falkirktoday.co.uk
Weekly (Thu). Owner: Johnston Press. Editor: Colin Hume; assistant editor: Duncan McCallum

Falkirk, Grangemouth & Linlithgow Advertiser
01324 638314
Weekly (Wed). Owner: Johnston Press. Editor: Colin Hume; assistant editor: Duncan McCallum

Fife & Kinross Extra
01383 728201
Weekly free (Fri). Owner: Dunfermline Press Group. Editor: Andrew Cowie

Fife Free Press
01592 261451
www.fifenow.co.uk
Weekly (Fri). Owner: Johnston Press. Editor: Allen Crow

Fife Herald
01592 261451
www.fifenow.co.uk
Weekly (Fri). Owner: Johnston Press. Editor: Graham Scott

Fife Leader
01592 261451
www.fifenow.co.uk
Weekly free (Tue). Owner: Johnston Press. Editor: Jack Snedden

Forfar Dispatch
01307 464899
www.forfardispatch.com
Weekly (Thu). Owner: Angus County Press. Editor: Alan Ducat

Forres Gazette
01309 672615
www.forres-gazette.co.uk
Weekly (Wed). Scottish Provincial Press. Editor: Ken Smith

Fraserburgh Herald
01779 472017
Weekly (Fri). Owner: Johnston Press. Editor: Alex Shand

Galloway Gazette
01671 402503
www.gallowaygazette.com
Weekly (Fri). Owner: Johnston Press. Editor: Stephen Norris

Galloway News
01556 504141
www.icscotland.co.uk
Weekly (Thu). Owner: Scottish & Universal Newspapers (Trinity Mirror). Editor: Elizabeth Martin; chief sub: Lee Kerr

The Gazette (Paisley)
0141 887 7055
Weekly (Wed). Owner: Clyde & Forth Press. Editor: Scott Reid

Glasgow East News
0141 573 5060
Weekly (Fri). Owner: Johnston Press. Editor: Jim Holland; chief sub: Allan Muir

Glasgow South & Eastwood Extra
0141 427 7878
www.icscotland.co.uk
Weekly (Thu). Owner: Archant. Editor: Allan Hodge; news: Colin Macdonald; chief sub: Jim Cameron

Glasgow West Extra
0141 427 7878
www.icscotland.co.uk
Weekly (Thu). Owner: Archant. Editor: Allan Hodge; news: Colin Macdonald; chief sub: Jim Cameron

The Glaswegian
0141 309 3132
Weekly free (Thu). Owner: Scottish Daily Record & Sunday Mail (Trinity Mirror). Editor: Garry Thomas

Glenrothes Gazette
01592 261451
www.fifenow.co.uk
Weekly (Wed). Owner: Johnston Press. Editor: Brian Stormont

Gorgie Dalry Gazette
0131 337 2457
Monthly (Fri). Independent. Editor: Brian Montgomery

Greenock Telegraph
01475 726511
www.greenocktelegraph.co.uk
Weekly (Wed). Owner: Clyde & Forth Press. Editor: Tom McConingley

Hamilton Advertiser
01698 283200
www.icscotland.co.uk
Weekly (Thu). Owner: Scottish & Universal Newspapers (Trinity Mirror). Editor: Joseph Kelly

Hamilton Extra People
01698 261321
Weekly (Thu). Owner: Johnston. Editor: Martin Clark

Hawick News
01750 21581
www.hawicktoday.co.uk
Weekly (Fri). Owner: Johnston Press. Editor: Jason Marshall

Helensburgh Advertiser
01436 673434
Weekly (Thu). Owner: Clyde & Forth Press. Editor: Alan Greenwood

Herald & Post Edinburgh
0131 620 8620
Weekly free (Thu). Owner: Scotsman Publications. Editor: Gail Milne

Highland News
01463 732222
www.highland-news.co.uk
Weekly (Thu). Owner: Scottish Provincial Press. Editor: Paul Breen

Huntly Express
01466 793622
Weekly (Fri). Owner: J&M Publishing. Editor: Pat Scott

Ileach (Islay & Jura)
01496 810355
www.ileach.co.uk
Fortnightly (Sat). Independent. Editor: Carl Reavey

Inverclyde Extra
01475 726511
Weekly free (Wed). Owner: Clyde & Forth Press. Editor: Anne Caine

Inverness & Nairnshire Herald
01463 732222
Weekly (Thu). Owner: Scottish Provincial Press. Editor: Paul Breen

Inverness Courier
01463 233059
www.inverness-courier.co.uk
Twice-weekly (Tue, Fri). Owner: Scottish Provincial Press. Editor: Robert Taylor

Inverurie Advertiser
01888 563589
Weekly (Fri). Owner: W Peters & Son. Editor: Joyce Summers

Inverurie Herald
01467 625150
www.inverurieherald.com
Weekly (Thu). Owner: Angus County Press. Editor: David Duncan

Irvine & North Ayrshire Extra
01292 611666
www.theextra24.co.uk
Weekly (Thu). Owner: Johnston Press. Editor: John Matthews

Irvine Herald
01294 222288
www.icscotland.co.uk
Weekly (Wed). Owner: Scottish & Universal Newspapers (Trinity Mirror). Editor: Alan Woodison; news: Lex Brown; chief sub: Kenny Barr

Irvine Times
01294 273421
Weekly (Wed). Owner: Scottish & Universal Newspapers (Trinity Mirror). Editor: Alex Clarke

John O'Groat Journal
01955 602424
www.johnogroat-journal.co.uk
Weekly (Fri). Owner: North of Scotland Newspapers. Editor: Alan Henry; news: Karen Macdonald

Kilmarnock & District Extra
01292 611666
www.theextra24.co.uk
Weekly (Thu). Owner: Archant. Editor: John Matthews

Kilmarnock Standard
01563 525115
www.icscotland.co.uk
Weekly (Wed). Owner: Scottish & Universal Newspapers (Trinity Mirror). Editor: Alan Woodison; news: Steph Lach

Kincardineshire Observer
01561 377283
Weekly (Fri). Owner: Angus County Press. Editor: Charles Wallace

Kirkintilloch Herald
0141 775 0040
www.kirkintillochtoday.co.uk
Weekly (Wed). Owner: Johnston Press. Editor: Jim Holland; chief sub: Allan Muir

Kirriemuir Herald
01307 464899
www.kirriemuirherald.com
Weekly (Thu). Owner: Angus County Press. Editor: Alan Ducat

Lanark Gazette
01555 663937
Weekly (Thu). Owner: Johnston Press. Editor: Aileen McCulloch

Lanarkshire Extra
01698 261321
www.icscotland.co.uk
Weekly (Thu). Owner: Johnston Press. Editor: Martin Clark

Lanarkshire World
01698 283200
www.icscotland.co.uk
Weekly (Thu). Owner: Scottish & Universal Newspapers (Trinity Mirror). Editor: Joseph Kelly

Largs & Millport Weekly News
01475 689009
Weekly (Wed). Owner: Clyde & Forth Press. Editor: Andrew Cochrane

Lennox Herald
01389 742299
www.icscotland.co.uk
Weekly (Wed). Owner: Scottish & Universal Newspapers (Trinity Mirror). Editor: Alan Woodison

Linlithgowshire Journal & Gazette
01506 844592
www.icscotland.co.uk
Weekly (Fri). Owner: Johnston Press. Editor: Jack Shennan; features: Julie Currie

Lochaber News
01463 732222
www.lochaber-news.co.uk
Weekly (Thu). Owner: Scottish Provincial Press. Editor: Paul Breen

Lothian Times East
0131 561 6600
Weekly free (Fri). Owner: Johnston Press. Editor: Roy Scott; news: Alex Hogg

Mearns Leader
01569 762139
www.mearnsleader.com
Weekly (Fri). Owner: Angus County Press. Editor: John McIntosh

Metro Scotland
020 7651 5200
www.metroscot.co.uk
Daily. Owner: Associated Newspapers. Editor: Kenny Campbell

Midlothian Times
0131 561 6600
Weekly free (Fri). Owner: Johnston Press. Editor: Roy Scott; news: Alex Hogg

Midlothian Advertiser
0131 561 6600
Weekly (Wed). Owner: Johnston Press. Editor: Roy Scott; news: Alex Hogg

Milngavie & Bearsden Herald
0141 956 3533
Weekly (Fri). Owner: Johnston Press. Editor: Allan McIntyre; news: Rena O'Neill

Moffat News
01461 202078
Weekly (Thu). Owner: Dumfriesshire Newspapers. Editor: Bryan Armstrong; news: Alan Hall

Montrose Review
01674 672605
www.montrosereview.net
Weekly (Thu). Owner: Angus County Press. Editor: Douglas Hill

Motherwell Extra
01698 261321
Weekly (Fri). Owner: Johnston Press. Editor: Martin Clark

Motherwell Times
01698 264611
Weekly (Thu). Owner: Johnston Press. Editor: Archie Fleming

Musselburgh News
0131 561 6600
Weekly (Thu). Owner: Johnston Press. Editor: Roy Scott; news: Alex Hogg

North Ayrshire World
01294 272233
www.icscotland.co.uk
Weekly (Wed). Owner: Scottish & Universal Newspapers (Trinity Mirror). Editor: Alan Woodison; news: Lex Brown

North East Gazette
01224 618300
www.indy-online.co.uk
Weekly (Thu). Editor: Derek Piper; news: John Storrie

North Edinburgh News
0131 467 3972
www.northedinburghnews.co.uk
Monthly free (2nd Wed). Editor: Mary Burnside

North Star
01463 732222
www.highland-news.co.uk
Weekly (Thu). Owner: Scottish Provincial Press. Editor: Paul Breen

North West Highlands Bratach
01641 561214
www.bratach.co.uk
Monthly (1st Thu). Editor: Donald McCloud

Northern Scot
01343 548777
www.northern-scot.co.uk
*Weekly (Fri). Owner: Scottish
Provincial Press. Editor: Mike Collins*

Northern Times
01408 633993
www.northern-times.co.uk
*Weekly (Thu). Owner: Scottish
Provincial Press. Editor: Duncan Ross*

Oban Times
01631 563058
www.obantimes.co.uk
*Weekly (Thu). Owner: Oban Times.
Editor: Stewart Mackenzie; news:
Joanne Simms*

The Orcadian
01856 879000
www.orcadian.co.uk
*Weekly (Thu). Owner: Orkney Media
Group. Editor: Margaret Carr*

Paisley & District People
0141 887 7055
*Weekly free (Fri). Owner: Clyde &
Forth Press. Editor: Scott Reid*

Paisley & Renfrewshire Extra
0141 427 7878
www.icscotland.co.uk
*Weekly (Thu). Owner: Archant. Editor:
Allan Hodge; news: Colin Macdonald;
chief sub: Jim Cameron*

Paisley Daily Express
0141 887 7911
www.icscotland.co.uk
*Daily. Owner: Scottish & Universal
Newspapers (Trinity Mirror).
Editor: Anne Dalrymple*

Peebles Times
0131 561 6600
*Weekly free (Fri). Owner: Johnston
Press. Editor: Roy Scott; news:
Alex Hogg*

Peeblesshire News
01896 758395
www.peeblesshirenews.com
*Weekly (Fri). Owner: Dunfermline
Press. Editor: Atholl Innes*

Perth Shopper
01738 626211
*Weekly (Fri). Owner: Scottish &
Universal Newspapers (Trinity Mirror).
Editor: Alison Lowson*

Perthshire Advertiser
01738 626211
www.icperthshire.co.uk
*Weekly (Tue, Fri). Owner: Scottish &
Universal Newspapers (Trinity Mirror).
Editor: Alison Lowson*

Ross-shire Herald
01349 863436
*Weekly (Thu). Owner: Scottish
Provincial Press. Editor: Paul Breen*

Ross-shire Journal
01349 863436
www.rsjournal.co.uk
*Weekly (Fri). Owner: Scottish
Provincial Press. Editor: Hector
McKenzie; features: Shirley Hastings*

Rutherglen Reformer
0141 647 2271
www.icscotland.co.uk
*Weekly (Thu). Owner: Scottish &
Universal Newspapers (Trinity Mirror).
Editor: Joe Kelly*

St Andrews Citizen
01592 261451
www.fifetoday.co.uk
*Weekly (Fri). Owner: Johnston Press.
Editor: Mike Rankin*

Selkirk Advertiser
01750 21581
www.selkirktoday.co.uk
*Weekly (Fri). Owner: Johnston Press.
Editor: Susan Windram*

Shetland Life
01595 693622
www.shetlandtoday.co.uk
*Monthly (1st Fri). Editor: Mallachy
Tallack*

Shetland News
01806 577332
www.shetland-news.co.uk
Daily, online. Editor: Hans Marter

Shetland Times
01595 693622
www.shetlandtoday.co.uk
Weekly (Fri). Editor: Jonathan Lee

Southern Reporter
01750 21581
www.borderstoday.co.uk
*Weekly (Thu). Owner: Johnston Press.
Editor: Susan Windram*

Stirling News
01259 214416
*Weekly free (Thu). Owner: Dunfermline
Press Group. Editor: Kevin McRoberts*

Stirling Observer
01786 451110
www.icstirlingshire.co.uk
*Twice-weekly free (Wed, Fri). Owner:
Scottish & Universal Newspapers
(Trinity Mirror). Editor: Alan Rennie;
deputy editor: Donald Morton*

Stirling/Alloa & Hillfoots Shopper
01786 451110
*Weekly free (Thu). Owner: Scottish &
Universal Newspapers (Trinity Mirror).
Editor: Alan Rennie; deputy editor:
Donald Morton*

**Stornoway Gazette & West Coast
Advertiser**
01851 702687
www.stornowaygazette.co.uk
Weekly (Thu). Editor: Melinda Gillen

**Stranraer & Wigtownshire
Free Press**
01776 702551
www.stranraer.org/freepress
Weekly (Wed). Editor: John Neil

Strathkelvin Advertiser
0141 775 0040
*Weekly free (Sat). Owner: Johnston
Press. Editor: Jim Holland; chief sub:
Allan Muir*

Strathspey Herald
01479 872102
www.sbherald.co.uk
*Weekly (Wed). Owner: Scottish
Provincial Press. Editor: Gavin
Musgrove*

Turriff Advertiser
01888 563589
*Weekly (Fri). Owner: W Peters & Son.
Editor: Joyce Summers*

Wee County News
01259 724724
www.wee-county-news.co.uk
*Weekly (Wed). Editor: Joan McCann;
chief sub: Ronnie Paterson;
production: Bryan Watson*

West Highland Free Press
01471 822464
www.whfp.co.uk
Weekly (Fri). Editor: Ian McCormack

West Lothian Courier
01506 633544
www.icscotland.co.uk
*Weekly (Thu). Owner: Scottish &
Universal Newspapers (Trinity
Mirror). Acting editor: John Murdoch*

West Lothian Herald & Post
0131 620 8620
*Weekly free (Thu). Owner: Scotsman
Publications. Editor: Gail Milne*

Wishaw Press
01698 373111
www.icscotland.co.uk
*Weekly (Wed). Owner: Scottish &
Universal Newspapers (Trinity Mirror).
Editor: John Murdoch*

Wishaw World
01698 283200
www.icscotland.co.uk
*Weekly (Fri). Owner: Scottish &
Universal Newspapers (Trinity Mirror).
Editor: Joseph Kelly*

Regional newspapers — Northern Ireland

● Main regionals

Belfast Telegraph
124–144 Royal Avenue,
Belfast BT1 1EB
028 9026 4000
www.belfasttelegraph.co.uk
Daily. Owner: Independent News & Media. Editor: Martin Lindsay; news: Paul Connolly; features: Gail Walker

Sunday Life
124–144 Royal Avenue,
Belfast BT1 1EB
028 9026 4000
www.sundaylife.co.uk
Sunday. Owner: Independent News & Media. Editor: Jim Flanagan; news: Martin Hill; features: Audrey Watson

The Daily Mirror (NI)
028 9056 8000
www.mirror.co.uk
Daily. Owner: Mirror Group. Editor: Jerry Miller; news: Morris Fitzmaurice; features: Jilly Beattie

Irish News
028 9032 2226
www.irishnews.com
Daily. Independent. Editor: Noel Doran; news: Billy Foley; features: Joanna Braniff

News Letter
028 9089 7700
www.newsletter.co.uk
Daily. Owner: Johnston Press. Editor: Darwin Templeton; news: Darwin Templeton; features: Jeff Hill

Sunday Mirror (NI)
028 9056 8000
www.sundaymirror.co.uk
Sunday. Owner: Mirror Group. Editor: Christian McCashin; assistant editor: Donna Carton

● Other newspapers

Andersonstown News
028 9061 9000
www.irelandclick.com
Twice-weekly (Mon, Thu). Owner: Andersonstown News Group. Editor: Robin Livingstone

Antrim Guardian
028 9446 2624
www.ulster-ni.co.uk
Weekly (Wed). Owner: Alpha Group. Editor: Liam Hesfron

Armagh Observer
028 8772 2557
Weekly (Wed). Independent. Editor: Desmond Mallon; news: Desmond Mallon Junior

Armagh-Down Observer
028 8772 2557
Weekly (Thu). Independent. Editor: Desmond Mallon; news: Desmond Mallon Junior

Ballycastle Chronicle
028 7034 3344
www.ulsternet-ni.co.uk/chronicle/pages/ballycastle.htm
Weekly (Wed). Owner: Northern News Group. Editor: John Fillis

Ballyclare Advertiser
028 9336 3651
www.ulsternet-ni.co.uk
Weekly (Wed). Owner: Alpha Group. Editor: Raymond Hughes

Ballyclare Gazette
028 9336 3651
www.ulster-ni.co.uk
Weekly (Wed). Owner: Alpha Group. Editor: David Hull

Ballymena Chronicle
028 8772 2557
Weekly (Wed). Independent. Editor: Desmond Mallon; news: Desmond Mallon Junior

Ballymena Guardian
028 2564 1221
www.ulsternet-ni.co.uk
Weekly (Wed). Owner: Alpha Group. Editor: Maurice O'Neil; assistant editor: Shaun O'Neil

Ballymena Times
028 2565 3300
www.ballymenatoday.co.uk
Weekly (Tue). Owner: Morton News Group. Editor: Desmond Blackadder; advertising: Stephanie Manson

Ballymoney & Coleraine Chronicle
028 7034 3344
www.ulsternet-ni.co.uk/chronicle/pages/ballymoney.htm
Weekly (Wed). Owner: Northern News Group. Editor: John Fillis

Ballymoney & Moyle Times
028 2766 6216
www.ballymoneytoday.co.uk
Weekly (Tue). Owner: Morton News Group. Editor: Lyle McMullen; news & features: Clare Smith

Banbridge Chronicle
028 4066 2322
Weekly (Wed). Independent. Editor: Bryan Hooks

Banbridge Leader
028 4066 2745
www.banbridgetoday.co.uk
Weekly (Thu). Owner: Morton News Group. Editor: Mark Weir

Bangor Spectator
028 9127 0270
Weekly (Thu). Owner: DE Alexander & Sons. Editor: Paul Flowers

Belfast News
028 9087 7700
www.icnorthernireland.co.uk
Weekly (Thu). Owner: Century Newspaper. Editor: Julie McClay; news: Rick Clarke; features: Jeff Hill

Carrick Gazette
028 9336 3651
www.carricktoday.co.uk
Weekly (Wed). Owner: Alpha Group. Editor: David Hull

Carrick Times
028 9335 1992
www.carricktoday.co.uk
Weekly (Thu). Owner: Morton News Group. Editor: Hugh Vance; assistant editor: Valerie Martin

Carrickfergus Advertiser
028 8772 2274
www.carricktoday.co.uk
Weekly (Wed). Owner: Alpha Group. Editor: David Hull

City News
028 7127 2200
www.derrytoday.com
Weekly free (Thu). Owner: Local Press. Editor: Martin McGinley; deputy editor: Bernie Mullen

Coleraine Times
028 7035 5260
www.colerainetoday.co.uk
Weekly (Wed). Owner: Morton News Group. Editor: David Rankin

County Down Spectator
028 9127 0270
Weekly (Thu). Owner: Spectator Newspapers. Editor: Paul Flowers

Craigavon Echo
028 3839 3939
www.craigavontoday.co.uk
Weekly free (Wed). Owner: Morton News Group. Editor: Hugh Vance

Derry Journal
028 7127 2200
www.derrytoday.com
Twice-weekly (Tues, Fri). Owner: Local Press. Editor: Martin McGinley; deputy editor: Bernie Mullen

Derry Journal (Sunday)
028 7127 2200
www.derrytoday.com
Weekly (Sun). Owner: Local Press. Editor: Eamonn MacDermott; deputy editor: Bernie Mullen

Derry News
028 7129 6600
Twice-weekly (Mon, Thu). Independent. Editor: Mark Mullen; head of production: Eamonn Kelly

Down Democrat
028 4461 4400
www.downdemocrat.com
Weekly (Tue). Owner: TCH Group. Editor: Ciara Byrne; sales editor: Veronica Barr

Down Recorder
028 4461 3711
www.thedownrecorder.co.uk
Weekly (Wed). Independent. Editor: Paul Symington

Dromore Leader
028 9269 2217
www.dromoretoday.co.uk
Weekly (Wed). Owner: Morton News Group. Editor: Marc Weir

Dungannon News & Tyrone Courier
028 8772 2271
www.ulsternet-ni.co.uk/courier
/cpages/cmain.htm
*Weekly (Wed). Owner: Alpha Group.
Editor: Ian Grear*

Dungannon Observer
028 8772 2557
*Weekly (Fri). Independent.
Editor: Desmond Mallon;
news: Desmond Mallon Jr*

East Antrim Advertiser
028 2827 2303
*Monthly. Owner: Morton News Group.
Editor: Hugh Vance*

East Antrim Guardian
028 2564 1221
www.macunlimited.net
*Weekly (Wed). Owner: Northern Alpha
Group. Editor: Maurice O'Neil;
assistant editor: Shaun O'Neil*

Farming Life
028 3839 5593
www.farminglife.com
*Twice-weekly (Wed, Sat). Owner:
Century Newspapers. Editor: David
McCoy; news: Karen Quinn; features:
Jeff Hill*

Fermanagh Herald
028 6632 2066
www.fermanaghherald.com
*Weekly (Wed). Owner: North West
of Ireland Printing Co. Editor:
Pauline Leary*

Fermanagh News
028 8772 2557
*Weekly (Fri). Independent. Editor:
Desmond Mallon; news: Desmond
Mallon Junior*

Foyle News
028 7127 2200
www.derryjournal.com
*Weekly (Weds). Owner: Local Press.
Editor: Martin McGinley; deputy
editor: Bernie Mullen*

Impartial Reporter
028 6632 4422
www.impartialreporter.com
*Weekly (Thu). Independent. Editor:
Denzil McDaniel; news: Sarah
Sanderson; features: Lily Dane; head
of production: Tony Quinn*

The Journal (Derry)
028 7127 2200
www.derryjournal.com
Weekly (Thu). Owner: Local Press

Lakeland Extra
028 6632 4422
www.impartialreporter.com
*Monthly free (3rd Mon). Independent.
Editor: Denzil McDaniel*

Larne Gazette
028 9336 3651
www.ulster-ni.co.uk
*Weekly (Wed). Owner: Alpha Group.
Editor: David Hull*

Larne Times
028 2827 2303
www.larnetoday.co.uk
*Weekly (Thu). Owner: Morton News
Group. Editor: Hugh Vance*

The Leader (Banbridge/Dromore)
028 4066 2745
*Weekly (Tue). Owner: Morton News
Group. Editor: Mark Weir*

The Leader (Coleraine)
028 7034 3344
www.ulsternet-ni.co.uk/leader
/pages/leader.htm
*Weekly (Mon). Owner: Northern News
Group. Editor: Linda Faithkelly*

Limavady Chronicle
028 7034 3344
www.ulsternet-ni.co.uk/chronicle
/pages/limavady.htm
*Weekly (Wed). Owner: Northern News
Group. Editor: John Fillis*

Lisburn Echo
028 3839 3939
www.lisburntoday.co.uk
*Weekly free (Wed). Owner: Morton
News Group. Editor: Hugh Vance*

Londonderry Sentinel
028 7134 8889
www.londonderrytoday.co.uk
*Weekly (Wed). Owner: Morton News
Group. Editor: Robin Young*

Lurgan & Portadown Examiner
028 8772 2557
*Weekly (Wed). Independent. Editor:
Desmond Mallon; news: Desmond
Mallon Junior*

Lurgan Mail
028 3832 7777
www.lurgantoday.co.uk
*Weekly (Thu). Owner: Johnston Press.
Editor: Clint Aitken; assistant editor:
John Bingham; head of production:
Lawrence Cinnamond*

Magherafelt & Limavady Constitution
028 7034 3344
www.ulsternet-ni.co.uk/ncon
/pages/limavady.htm
*Weekly (Thu). Owner: Northern News
Group. Editor: Jennifer Church*

Mid-Ulster Echo
028 8676 2288
www.midulstermail.co.uk
*Weekly free (Wed). Owner: Morton
News Group. Editor: Mark Bain*

Mid-Ulster Mail
028 8676 2288
www.midulstermail.co.uk
*Weekly (Thu). Owner: Morton News
Group. Editor: Mark Bain*

Mid-Ulster Observer
028 8772 2557
*Weekly (Wed). Independent.
Editor: Desmond Mallon;
news: Desmond Mallon Jr*

Mourne Observer & County Down News
028 4372 2666
www.mourneobserver.com
*Weekly (Wed). Independent.
Editor: Terrance Bowman*

Newry Advertiser
028 8772 2557
*Monthly free. Independent.
Editor: Desmond Mallon;
news: Desmond Mallon Jr*

Newry Democrat
028 3025 1250
www.newrydemocrat.com
*Weekly (Tue). Owner: Thomas Crosby
Holdings. Editor: Jacky Mckeown;
features: Patrick Ryan; head of
production: Paul Murphy*

Newtownabbey Times
028 3839 3939
www.newtownabbeytoday.co.uk
*Weekly (Thu). Owner: Morton News
Group. Editor: Hugh Vance*

Newtownards Chronicle
028 9127 0270
*Weekly (Thu). Owner: Spectator
Newspapers. Editor: John Savage*

Newtownards Spectator
028 9127 0270
*Weekly (Thu). Owner: Spectator
Newspapers. Editor: Paul Flowers*

North Belfast News
028 9058 4444
www.irelandclick.com
*Weekly (Fri). Owner: Andersonstown
News Group. Editor: John Macguire;
features: Aine McEntee*

North West Echo
028 3839 3939
*Weekly free (Wed). Owner: Morton
News Group. Editor: Hugh Vance;
assistant editor: John Fillis*

Northern Constitution
028 7034 3344
www.ulsternet-ni.co.uk/ncon
/pages/coleraine.htm
*Weekly (Wed). Owner: Northern News
Group. Editor: John Fillis*

The Outlook (Portadown)
028 4063 0202
www.ulsternet-ni.co.uk
*Weekly (Wed). Owner: Alpha Group.
Editor: Alan McVeigh*

Portadown Times
028 3833 6111
www.portadowntimes.com
*Weekly (Fri). Owner: Morton News
Group. Editor: David Armstrong*

Roe Valley Sentinel
028 7134 8889
www.roevalleytoday.co.uk
*Weekly (Wed). Owner: Morton News
Group. Editor: David Armstrong*

South Belfast News
028 9061 9000
www.irelandclick.com
*Weekly (Fri). Owner: Andersonstown
News Group. Editor: Maria McCourt*

Strabane Chronicle
028 8224 3444
www.strabanechronicle.com
Weekly (Thu). Owner: North West of Ireland Printing Co. Editor: Darach Mcdonald

Strabane Weekly News
028 8224 2721
www.ulsternet-ni.co.uk
Weekly (Thu). Owner: Alpha Group. Editor: Wesley Atchison; features: Geraldine Wilson

Tyrone Constitution
028 8224 2721
www.ulsternet-ni.co.uk
Weekly (Thu). Owner: Alpha Group. Editor: Wesley Atchison; features: Geraldine Wilson

Tyrone Herald
028 8224 3444
www.tyroneherald.com
Weekly (Mon). Owner: The North West of Ireland Printing & Publishing Co. Editor: Morris Kennedy

Tyrone Times
028 8775 2801
www.tyronetoday.co.uk
Weekly (Tue). Owner: Morton News Group. Editor: Peter Bayne

Ulster Gazette & Armagh Standard
028 3752 2639
www.ulsternet-ni.co.uk
Weekly (Wed). Owner: Alpha Group. Editor: Richard Stewart

Ulster Herald
028 8224 3444
www.ulsterherald.com
Weekly (Thu). Owner: North West of Ireland Printing Co. Editor: Darach McDonald

Ulster Star
028 9267 9111
www.ulsterstar.com
Weekly (Fri). Owner: Morton News Group. Editor: David Fletcher; news: Mary McGee

Magazine contacts

Main magazine & contract magazine publishers

Archant
Prospect House, Rouen Road,
Norwich NR1 1RE
01603 772814
www.archant.co.uk
Chief executive: John Fry; MD,
Archant Life: Johnny Hustler, 01603
664242; general manager, Archant
Dialogue customer publishing: Chris
Rainer, 01603 772532
Archant Specialist
The Mill, Bearwalden Business
Park, Royston Road, Wendens
Ambo, Essex CB11 4GB
01799 544200
MD: Farine Clarke
Press: Keith Morris, 01603 772814

Brooklands Group
Westgate, 120–128 Station Road,
Redhill, Surrey RH1 1ET
01737 786800
mail@brooklandsgroup.com
www.brooklandsgroup.com
Chief executive: Darren Styles;
account director: Matthew Jenns
Press: 020 8875 2850

BBC Worldwide
Woodlands, 80 Wood Lane,
London W12 0TT
020 8433 2000
www.bbcworldwide.com
MD: Peter Phippen

Cedar
Pegasus House, 37–43 Sackville
Street, London W1S 3EH
020 7534 2400
info@cedarcom.co.uk
www.cedarcom.co.uk
MD: Clare Broadbent; editorial
director: Mark Jones

Centaur
50 Poland Street, London W1F 7AX
020 7970 4000
firstname.secondname@
  centaur.co.uk
www.centaur.co.uk
Publishing directors: Robin Coates,
Roger Beckett, Howard Sharman,
Tim Potter, Annie Swift

CMP Information
Ludgate House, 245 Blackfriars
Road, London SE1 9UY
020 7921 5000
www.cmpinformation.com
Part of United Business Media. Chief
executive: Gary Hughes

Condé Nast
Vogue House, Hanover Square,
London W1S 1JU
020 7499 9080
www.condenast.co.uk
MD: Nicholas Coleridge

DC Thomson
185 Fleet Street, London EC4A 2HS
020 7400 1030
shout@dcthomson.co.uk
www.dcthomson.co.uk

Dennis
30 Cleveland Street,
London W1T 4JD
020 7907 6000
firstname_secondname@
  dennis.co.uk
www.dennis.co.uk
Chief executive: James Tye;
MD, consumer: Bruce Sandell

Emap
Greater London House,
Hampstead Road, London NW1 7EJ
020 7728 5000
www.emap.com
Group chief executive: Alun Cathcart

Future
Beauford Court, 30 Monmouth
Street, Bath BA1 2BW
01225 442244
firstname.secondname@
  futurenet.com
www.futurenet.com
Chief executive: Stevie Spring;
MD: Robert Price

London office
2 Balcombe Street,
London NW1 6NW
020 7042 4000
Press: 01225 732235/822517

H Bauer
Academic House, 24–28 Oval Road,
London NW1 7DT
020 7241 8000
www.bauer.co.uk
MD: Simon Young

Hachette Filipacchi
64 North Row, London W1K 7LL
020 7150 7000
Firstname.secondname@hf-uk.com
www.hf-uk.com
Chairman: Kevin Hand; general
manager women's group: Julie Harris

Haymarket
174 Hammersmith Road,
London W6 7JP
020 8267 4210
hpg@haymarketgroup.com
www.haymarketgroup.com
Group MD: Simon Daukes; joint MDs,
Haymarket magazines: Kevin Costello,
Simon Daukes; chairman and MD,
Haymarket business publications:
Martin Durham

Haymarket Customer Publishing
Broom Road, Teddington,
Middlesex TW11 9BE
020 8267 5000
haycustpub@haynet.com
www.haycustpub.com
MD: Patrick Fuller

IPC Media
Blue Fin Building,
110 Southwark Street,
London SE1 0SU
020 3148 5000
www.ipcmedia.com
Owned by Time Warner. CEO: Sylvia
Auton

John Brown Citrus
The New Boathouse, 136–142
Bramley Road, London W10 6SR
020 7565 3000
www.jbcp.co.uk
MD: Dean Fitzpatrick, 020 7565 3202;
editorial director: Paul Colbert

National Magazine Company
National Magazine House,
72 Broadwick St, London W1F 9EP
020 7439 5000
www.natmags.co.uk
MD: Jessica Burley

Publicis Blueprint
Whitfield House, 83–89 Whitfield
Street, London W1A 4XA
020 7462 7777
www.publicis-blueprint.com
MD: Jason Frost

Rare Publishing
102 Sydney Street, London SW3 6NJ
020 7368 9600
Bristol office 0117 989 7800
www.rarecontent.co.uk
Part of Chime Communications.
MD: Julian Downing; publishing and
commercial director: Sarah Kermode;
editorial director: Maureen Rice;
editor-in-chief: Matthew Cowen

Redwood
7 St Martin's Place,
London WC2N 4HA
020 7747 0700
info@redwoodgroup.net
www.redwoodgroup.net
MD: Keith Grainger

Reed Business Information
Quadrant House, The Quadrant,
Sutton SM2 5AS
020 8652 3500
www.reedbusiness.co.uk
Part of Reed Elsevier. Chief executive:
Keith Jones

River Group
Victory House, Leicester Square,
London WC2H 7BZ
020 7306 0304
info@river.com
www.therivergroup.co.uk
Joint MD and sales and marketing
director: Nicola Murphy; joint MD and
editorial director: Jane Wynn

Seven
20 Upper Ground, London SE1 9PD
020 7775 7775
info@7publishing.co.uk
www.7publishing.com
Chairman: Michael Potter

VNU Business
VNU House, 32–34 Broadwick Street, London W1A 2HG
020 7316 9000
firstname_secondname@vnu.co.uk
www.vnunet.com
MD: Brin Bucknor

Consumer magazines

● Adult

Escort
020 7292 8000
Monthly. Owner: Paul Raymond. Editor: James Hundleby

Fiesta
01376 534549
www.fiesta.co.uk
13pa. Owner: Galaxy. Editor: Ross Gilfillan

Knave
01376 534549
www.knave.co.uk
13pa. Owner: Galaxy. Editor: Ross Gilfillan

Mayfair
020 7292 8000
Monthly. Owner: Paul Raymond. Editor: David Rider

Men Only
020 7292 8000
Monthly. Owner: Paul Raymond. Editor: Pierre Perrone

Skin Two
020 8487 9528
www.skintwo.co.uk
4pa. Owner: Tim Woodward. Editor: Tim Woodward

Viz
020 7907 6000
www.viz.co.uk
Monthly. Owner: Dennis

● Arts, music, film & TV

247
01752 294130
www.twenty4-seven.co.uk
Monthly. Owner: Afterdark Media. Editor: Lucy Griffiths

All About Soap
020 7150 7000
www.allaboutsoap.co.uk
Fortnightly. Owner: Hachette Filipacchi UK. Editor: Jonathan Hughes

Amateur Photographer
020 3148 5000
www.amateurphotographer.co.uk
Weekly. Owner: IPC Media. Editor: Garry Coward-Williams

AN Magazine
0191 241 8000
www.a-n.co.uk
Monthly. Owner: The Artists Information Company. Editor: Gillian Nicol

The Art Book
01865 776868
www.blackwellpublishing.com
4pa. Owner: Blackwell Publishing. Editor: Sue Ward, Marion Arnold

The Art Newspaper
020 7735 3331
www.theartnewspaper.com
Monthly. Independent. Editor: Cristina Ruiz

Art Quarterly
020 7225 4800
www.artfund.org
4pa. Owner: National Art Collection Fund. Editor: Caroline Bugler

Art Review
020 7017 2760
www.art-review.com
Monthly. Owner: ArtReview. Editor: Daniel Kunitz

The Artist
01580 763315
www.theartistmagazine.co.uk
Monthly. Owner: The Artists' Publishing Company. Editor: Sally Bulgin

Artists & Illustrators
020 7349 3150
www.aimag.co.uk
Monthly. Owner: Quarto Magazines. Editor: John Swinfield

Arts East
01223 434434
www.cambridgenewspapers.co.uk
Monthly. Owner: Cambridge Newspapers. Editor: Louise Cummings

BBC Music Magazine
0117 927 9009
Monthly. Owner: Origin Publishing. Editor: Oliver Condy

The Big Cheese
020 7607 0303
www.bigcheesemagazine.com
Monthly. Independent. Editor: Eugene Butcher

Billboard
020 7420 6000
www.billboard.com
Weekly. Owner: VNU. Group Editorial Director: Tom Ferguson

Blues & Soul
020 7402 6897
www.bluesandsoul.com
Fortnightly. Owner: Blues & Soul. Editor: Bob Killbourn

The Brighton Source
01273 561617
www.brightonsource.co.uk
Monthly. Owner: Newsquest. Editor: Richard Gilpin

Buzz Magazine
029 2025 6883
Monthly. Editor: Kirsten Chapman

Cineworld
01225 737300
www.cineworld.co.uk
Bi-monthly. Owner: Concept. Editor: Sally Thomson

Classic FM — The Magazine
020 8267 5000
www.haymarket.com
www.classicfm.com
Monthly. Owner: Haymarket. Editor: John Evans

Classic Rock
www.classicrockmagazine.com
Owner: Future. Editor: Scott Rowley

Classical Music
020 7333 1742
www.rhinegold.co.uk
Fortnightly. Owner: Rhinegold. Editor: Keith Clarke

Country Music People
020 8854 7217
www.countrymusicpeople.com
Monthly. Owner: Music Farm. Editor: Craig Baguley

Country Music Round-up
www.cmru.co.uk
Monthly. Owner: CMRU. Editor: John Emptage

The Crack
0191 230 3038
www.thecrackmagazine.com
Monthly. Editor: Robert Meddes

Cult Times
020 8875 1520
www.visimag.com
Monthly. Owner: Visual Imagination. Editor: Paul Spragg

Dance Europe
020 8985 7767
www.danceeurope.net
Monthly. Editor: Emma Manning

Dance Gazette
020 7326 8000
www.rad.org.uk
3pa. Owner: Royal Academy of Dance. Editor: David Jays

DJ
020 7770 6180
www.djmag.com
Fortnightly. Owner: Future. Editor: Lesley Wright

DMC Update
01628 667124
www.dmcworld.com/update
Weekly. Owner: DMC. Publisher: Tony Prince

DVD Monthly
01392 434477
www.predatorpublishing.co.uk
Monthly. Owner: Predator. Editor: Tim Isaac

DVD Review
www.dvdreview.net
13pa. Owner: Future. Editor: Paul Morgan

Early Music Today
020 7333 1744
www.rhinegold.co.uk
6pa. Owner: Rhinegold. Editor: Johnathon Wikley

Empire
020 7182 8093
www.empireonline.com
Monthly. Owner: Bauer. Editor: Mark Dinning

Entertainer
01302 347225
www.doncastertoday.co.uk
Weekly. Owner: Johnston Press.
Editor: Graeme Huston

EP Magazine
0845 644 5513
www.vigilante.co.uk
10pa. Owner: Vigilante Publications.
Editor: Jon Ewing

Film Review
020 8875 1520
www.visimag.com
Monthly. Owner: Visual Imagination.
Editor: Nikki Baughan

The Fly
020 7691 4555
www.the-fly.co.uk
Monthly. Owner: Channelfly
Enterprises. Editor: Will Kinsman

Freetime
01252 621513
www.freetimemag.co.uk
4pa. Owner: VRA. Editor: Vic Robbie

fRoots
020 8340 9651
www.frootsmag.com
Monthly. Owner: Southern Rag.
Editor: Ian Anderson

Future Music
01225 442244
www.futuremusic.co.uk
13pa. Owner: Future. Editor: Daniel
Griffith

Gramophone
020 8267 5136
www.gramophone.co.uk
Monthly. Owner: Haymarket.
Editor: James Invern

Granta
020 7605 1360
www.granta.com
4pa. Owner: Granta. Editor: Jason
Cowley

Guitar
020 8726 8306
www.ipcmedia.com
Monthly. Owner: IPC Media.
Editor: Marcus Leadley

Guitar Buyer
01353 665577
Monthly. Owner: MB Media.
Editor: David Greeves

Guitar Techniques
01225 442244
www.futurenet.com
/guitartechniques
13pa. Owner: Future.
Editor: Neville Marten

Guitarist
01225 442244
www.futurenet.com/guitarist
13pa. Owner: Future.
Editor: Mick Taylor

Hip Hop Connection
01223 210536
www.hiphop.co.uk
Monthly. Owner: Infamous Ink.
Editor: Andy Cowan

Hollywood Reporter
020 7420 6004
www.hollywoodreporter.com
Weekly. Owner: VNU.
Editor: Ralph Ludermann

Home Cinema Choice
020 7331 1000
www.homecinemachoice.com
Monthly. Owner: Future.
Editor: Steve May

Impact
01484 435011
www.martialartsltd.co.uk/impact/
Monthly. Owner: MAI Publications.
Editor: John Mosby

Inside Soap
020 7150 7000
www.insidesoap.co.uk
Weekly. Owner: Hachette Filipacchi
UK. Editor: Steven Murphy

It's Hot
020 8433 3910
www.bbcmagazines.com/hot
13pa. Owner: BBC Worldwide. Acting
editor: Shelley Moulden

Jazz at Ronnie Scott's
020 7485 9803
www.ronniescotts.co.uk
Bi-monthly. Editor: Jim Godbolt

Jazz Guide
01908 312392
Monthly. Editor: Bernie Tyrrell

Jazz UK
029 2066 5161
www.jazzservices.org.uk
Bi-monthly. Owner: Jazz Services.
Editor: John Fordham

Kerrang!
020 7182 8000
www.kerrang.com
Weekly. Owner: Bauer.
Editor: Paul Brannigan

Knowledge
020 8871 2062
www.knowledgemag.co.uk
10pa. Owner: Vision Publishing.
Editor: Colin Steven

Leisure Painter
01580 763315
www.leisurepainter.co.uk
Monthly. Owner: The Artists' Publishing
Company. Editor: Ingrid Lyon

The List
0131 550 3050
www.list.co.uk
Fortnightly; extra festival issues in
August. Editor: Velire Prentice

London Review of Books
020 7209 1101
www.lrb.co.uk
Fortnightly. Owner: LRB.
Editor: Mary-Kay Wilmers

London Theatre Guide
020 7557 6700
www.officiallondontheatre.co.uk
Fortnightly. Owner: The Society of
London Theatre. Editor: Philippa
Smart, Matthew Aimer

M8
0141 840 5980
www.m8magazine.com
Monthly. Editor: Kevin McFarlane

Magpie
08700 711 611
www.magpiedirect.com
Bi-monthly. Editor: Mark Rye

Metal Hammer
www.metalhammer.co.uk
13pa. Owner: Future.
Editor: Jamie Hibbard

Mixmag
020 7817 8805
www.mixmag.net
Monthly. Owner: Development Hell.
Features editor: Andrew Harrison

Mojo
020 7436 1515
www.mojo4music.com
Monthly. Owner: Bauer.
Editor: Phil Alexander

Movie Mag International
020 8567 3662
www.movie-mag.net
Monthly. Editor: Bharathi Pradhan

Music Tech
01225 489984
www.musictechmag.co.uk
Monthly. Owner: Anthem Publishing.
Editor: Neil Worley

Music-Zine
01279 865070
www.music-zine.com
Bi-monthly. Editor: Simon Baker

National Gallery Season Guide
020 7747 2836
www.nationalgallery.org.uk
3pa. Owner: National Gallery.
Editor: Andrea Easey

NME
020 3148 5000
www.nme.com
Weekly. Owner: IPC Media.
Editor: Conor McNicholas

Opera
020 8563 8893
www.opera.co.uk
Monthly. Editor: John Allison

Opera Now
020 7333 1740
www.rhinegold.co.uk
6pa. Owner: Rhinegold.
Editor: Ash Khandekar

Piano
020 7333 1724
www.rhinegold.co.uk
6pa. Owner: Rhinegold.
Editor: Jeremy Siepmann

Q
020 7182 8000
www.q4music.com
Monthly. Owner: Emap.
Editor: Paul Rees

RA Magazine
020 7300 5820
www.ramagazine.org.uk
4pa. Owner: Royal Academy of Arts.
Editor: Sarah Greenberg

Radio Times
0870 608 4455
www.radiotimes.com
Weekly. Owner: BBC Worldwide.
Editor: Gill Hudson

Record Buyer
01522 511265
Monthly. Owner: Aceville.
Editor: Paul Rigby

Rhythm
01225 442244
www.rhythmmag.co.uk
13pa. Owner: Future.
Editor: Phill Ascott

Rock Sound
020 7877 8770
www.rock-sound.net
Monthly. Editor: Darren Taylor

Rolling Stone
00 1 212 484 1616
www.rollingstone.com
26pa. Owner: Rolling Stone Magazine.
Editor: Jann S Wenner

Screen International
020 7505 8096
www.screendaily.com
Weekly. Owner: Emap.
Editor: Michael Gubbins

SFX
01225 442244
www.sfx.co.uk
13pa. Owner: Future.
Editor: Dave Bradley

Shivers
020 8875 1520
www.visimag.com
Monthly. Owner: Visual Imagination.
Editor: David Miller

Sight & Sound
020 7255 1444
www.bfi.org.uk/sightandsound
Monthly. Owner: British Film Institute.
Editor: Nick James

Soaplife
020 3148 5000
www.ipcmedia.com
Fortnightly. Owner: IPC Media.
Editor: Hellen Gardner

Songlines
020 7371 2777
www.songlines.co.uk
Bi-monthly. Editor: Simon Broughton

Sound on Sound
01954 789888
www.soundonsound.com
Monthly. Owner: SOS Publications
Group. Editor: Paul White

The Stage
020 7403 1818
www.thestage.co.uk
Weekly. Editor: Brian Attwood

Starburst
020 8875 1520
www.visimag.com
Monthly. Owner: Visual Imagination.
Editor: Stephen Payne

Stardust International
020 7486 8409
www.stardustindia.com
Monthly. Owner: Magna.
Editor: Ashwin Varde

The Strad
020 7618 3095
www.thestrad.com
Monthly. Owner: Newsquest.
Editor: Aravenen Teodes

Straight No Chaser
020 8533 9999
www.straightnochaser.co.uk
Bi-monthly. Editor: Paul Bradshaw

Theatregoer
020 7907 7020
www.whatsonstage.com
Monthly. Owner: Whatsonstage.
Editor: Terri Paddock

This is London Magazine
020 7434 1281
www.thisislondontickets.co.uk
Weekly. Publisher: Julie Jones

Time Out
020 7813 3000
www.timeout.com
Weekly. Owner: Time Out Group.
Editor: Gordon Thompson

Time Out Student Guide
020 7813 3000
www.timeout.com
Annually. Owner: Time Out Group.
Editor: Tom Lomont

Times Literary Supplement
020 7782 3000
www.the-tls.co.uk
Weekly. Owner: TSL Education.
Editor: Peter Stothard

Top of the Pops Magazine
020 8433 3910
www.bbcmagazines.com/totp
Monthly. Owner: BBC Worldwide.
Editor: Peter Hart

Total Film
020 7042 4000
www.totalfilm.co.uk
13pa. Owner: Future.
Editor: Nev Pierce

Total Guitar
01225 442244
www.totalguitar.co.uk
13pa. Owner: Future.
Editor: Stephen Lawson

Total TV Guide
020 7241 8000
www.bauer.co.uk
Weekly. Owner: H Bauer.
Editor: Jon Peake

TV & Satellite Week
020 3148 5000
www.tvandsatelliteweek.com
Weekly. Owner: IPC Media.
Editor: Jonathan Bowman

TV Choice
020 7241 8000
www.bauer.co.uk
Weekly. Owner: H Bauer.
Editor: Jon Peake

TV easy
020 3148 5000
www.ipcmedia.com
Weekly. Owner: IPC Media.
Editor: Richard Clark

TV Hits!
01206 851117
www.tvhits.co.uk
Monthly. Owner: Hachette Filipacchi
UK. Assistant Editor: Charlotte Acock

TV Quick
020 7241 8000
www.bauer.co.uk
Weekly. Owner: H Bauer.
Editor: Jon Peake

TV Times
020 7261 7816
www.ipcmedia.com
Weekly. Owner: IPC Media.
Editor: Ian Abbott

TV Zone
020 8875 1520
www.visimag.com
Monthly. Owner: Visual Imagination.
Editor: Jan Vincent-Rudzki

Ultimate DVD
020 8875 1520
www.visimag.com
Monthly. Owner: Visual Imagination.
Editor: David Richardson

Uncut
020 7261 6992
www.uncut.co.uk
Monthly. Owner: IPC Media.
Editor: Allan Jones

V&A Magazine
020 7942 2000
www.vam.ac.uk
3pa. Owner: Culture Shock.
Editor: Charlotte Mullins

Variety
020 7611 4580
www.variety.com
Daily and weekly. Owner: Reed
Business Information. Editor: Alex
Romanelli

What's on in London
www.whatsoninlondon.co.uk
Weekly. Editor: Michael Darvell

What's on TV
020 7261 7535
www.ipcmedia.com
Weekly. Owner: IPC Media.
Editor: Colin Tough

Where London
020 7611 7885
Monthly. Owner: Where Publications.
Editor: Mary Anne Evans

The Wire
020 7422 5014
www.thewire.co.uk
Monthly. Editor: Chris Bohn

Word
020 7078 8400
www.wordmagazine.co.uk
Monthly. Owner: Development Hell.
Editor: Mark Ellen

Writers' News
0113 200 2929
www.writersnews.co.uk
Monthly. Owner: Warners.
Editor: Jonathan Telfer

X-pose
020 8875 1520
www.visimag.com
Monthly. Owner: Visual Imagination.
Editor: Anthony Brown

● Children and teenage

2000 AD
01865 200603
www.2000adonline.com
Weekly. Owner: DC Thomson.
Editor: Matt Smith

Action Man
01892 500100
www.paninicomics.co.uk
18pa. Owner: Panini UK.
Editor: Simon Frith

Animal Action
0870 010 1181
www.rspca.org.uk
Bi-monthly. Owner: RSPCA.
Editor: Sarah Evans

Animals and You
01382 223131
www.dcthomson.co.uk
Monthly. Owner: DC Thomson.
Editor: Margaret Monaghan

Aquila Children's Magazine
01323 431313
www.aquila.co.uk
Monthly. Owner: New Leaf Publishing.
Editor: Jackie Berry

Art Attack
01892 500100
www.paninicomics.co.uk
18pa. Owner: Panini UK.
Editor: Karen Brown

Balamory Magazine
020 8433 2356
www.bbcmagazines.com
13pa. Owner: BBC Worldwide.
Editor: Siobhan Keeler

Barbie
020 7380 6452
www.egmontmagazines.co.uk
Fortnightly. Owner: Egmont
Magazines. Editor: Rebecca Jamieson

BBC Toybox
020 8433 2356
www.bbcmagazines.com/toybox/
13pa. Owner: BBC Worldwide. Editors:
Nora Kerezovic, Paddy Kempshall

Beano
01382 223131
www.beanotown.com
Weekly. Owner: DC Thomson.
Editor: Alan Digby

Bliss
020 7321 0701
www.blissmag.co.uk
Monthly. Owner: Panini.
Editor: Anna Wakeford

Breakout
01235 553444
www.couriergroup.com
6pa. Owner: Courier Newspaper
Group. Editor: Lawrence Webb

CosmoGirl!
020 7439 5000
www.cosmogirl.co.uk
Monthly. Owner: National Magazine
Company. Editor: Celia Duncan

Daisy
020 7380 6430
www.egmontmagazines.co.uk
Monthly. Owner: Egmont.
Editor: Joanna Tubbs

Dandy
01382 223131
www.dandy.com
Weekly. Owner: DC Thomson.
Editor: Craig Graham

Disney & Me
020 7380 6430
www.egmontmagazines.co.uk
Fortnightly. Owner: Egmont
Magazines. Editor: Jeanette Ryall

Disney Princess
020 7380 6430
www.egmontmagazines.co.uk
Fortnightly. Owner: Egmont
Magazines. Editor: Jeanette Ryall

Dora the Explorer
020 7565 3000
Monthly. Owner: G E Magazines.
Editor: Harriet Murphy

Elle Girl
020 7150 7000
Monthly. Owner: Hachette Filipacchi
UK. Editor: Claire Irvin

Fimbles Magazine
020 8433 2000
www.bbcmagazines.com
13pa. Owner: BBC Worldwide.
Editor: Nora Kerezovic

Girl
01392 664141
Monthly. Owner: LCD Publishing.
Editor: Joanne Trump

Girl Talk
020 8433 3825
www.bbcmagazines.com/girltalk
Fortnightly. Owner: BBC Worldwide.
Editor: Samantha McEvoy

Go Girl
020 7380 6430
www.egmontmagazines.co.uk
Fortnightly. Owner: Egmont
Magazines. Editor: Sarah Delmege

Guiding
020 7592 1821
www.girlguiding.org.uk
Monthly. Owner: GirlGuiding UK.
Editor: Wendy Kewley

Hot Wheels
020 7380 6430
www.egmontmagazines.co.uk
Monthly. Owner: Egmont Magazines.
Editor: Matt Crossick

Mizz
01892 500105
Fortnighty. Owner: Panini UK

Pony
01428 601020
www.ponymag.com
Monthly. Owner: DJ Murphy
Publishers. Editor: Janet Rising

Postman Pat
01892 500100
www.paninicomics.co.uk
3 weekly. Owner: Panini.
Editor: Karen Brown

Power Rangers
020 7380 6430
www.egmontmagazines.co.uk
Monthly. Owner: Egmont Magazines.
Editor: Jeanette Ryall

Rugrats
0161 624 0414
13pa. Owner: Toontastic Publishing.
Editor: Emma Boff

Scouting Magazine
020 8433 7219
www.scouts.org.uk/magazine/
Bi-monthly. Owner: Redactive
Publishing. Joint Editors: Matt Oakes
and Hillary Galloway

Shout Magazine
01382 223131
www.dcthomson.co.uk
Fortnightly. Owner: DC Thomson.
Editor: Ria Welch

Simpsons Comic
020 7620 0200
www.titanmagazines.com
Monthly. Owner: Titan Publishing.
Editor: Steve White

Spectacular Spider-Man
01892 500100
www.paninicomics.co.uk
17pa. Owner: Panini UK.
Editor: Tom O'Malley

Sugar
020 7150 7087
www.sugarmagazine.co.uk
Monthly. Owner: Hachette Filipacchi
UK. Editor: Annabel Brog

Thomas & Friends
020 7380 6430
www.egmontmagazines.co.uk
Fortnightly. Owner: Egmont
Magazines. Editor: Jane Tarrant

Toxic
020 7380 6465
www.egmontmagazines.co.uk
Fortnightly. Owner: Egmont
Magazines. Editor: Matt Yeo

Tweenies Magazine
020 8433 2356
www.bbcmagazines.com
Fortnightly. Owner: BBC Worldwide

Wallace & Gromit
0870 428 8203
www.titanmagazines.com
Monthly. Owner: Titan Magazines.
Editor: Steve White

Winnie the Pooh
020 7380 6449
www.egmontmagazines.co.uk
Monthly. Owner: Egmont Magazines.
Editor: Jeanette Ryall

Witch
020 8433 3825
www.bbcmagazines.com/content
/magazines/witch
Monthly. Owner: BBC.
Editor: Bea Appleby

Wolverine & Deadpool
01892 500100
www.paninicomics.co.uk
13pa. Owner: Panini UK.
Editor: Scott Gray

Young Scot
0131 313 2488
www.youngscot.org
Monthly. Editor: Fiona McIntyre

● Computing & gadgets

.net
01225 442244
www.netmag.co.uk
13pa. Owner: Future. Editor: Dan Oliver

3D World
01225 442244
www.3dworldmag.co.uk
13pa. Owner: Future.
Editor: Jim Thacker

Computer Arts
01225 442244
www.computerarts.co.uk
13pa. Owner: Future.
Editor: Gillian Carson

Computer Arts Projects
01225 442244
www.computerarts.co.uk
13pa. Owner: Future.
Editor: Rob Carney

Computer Buyer
020 7907 6000
www.computerbuyer.co.uk
Monthly. Owner: Dennis.
Editor: Adam Banks

Computer Shopper
020 7907 6000
www.computershopper.co.uk
Monthly. Owner: Dennis.
Editor: Paul Sanders

ComputerActive
020 7316 9000
www.computeractive.co.uk
Fortnightly. Owner: VNU.
Editor: Dylan Armbrust

Computing Which?
020 7770 7564
www.computingwhich.co.uk
Bi-monthly. Owner: Which?
Editor: Nicole Shymans

Digital Camera Buyer
01202 586200
www.imagine-publishing.co.uk
6pa. Owner: Imagine Publishing.
Editor: Chris Lean

Digital Home
www.digitalhomemag.co.uk
13pa. Owner: Future.
Editor: Dean Evans

Digital Photo
01733 468000
www.bauer.co.uk
Monthly. Owner: Bauer.
Editor: Jon Adams

Digital Video
www.digitalvideomag.co.uk
13pa. Owner: Future.
Editor: Robert Hull

Edge
01225 442244
www.edge-online.co.uk
13pa. Owner: Future. Editor: Tony Mott

Games Domain
0121 326 0900
www.gamesdomain.com
Website, updated daily. Owner: Yahoo!

Games TM
01202 586257
www.gamestm.co.uk
13pa. Owner: Imagine Publishing.
Editor: Paul Morgan

GamesMaster
01225 442244
www.futurenet.com/gamesmaster
13pa. Owner: Future.
Editor: Robin Alway

Hi-Fi Choice
020 7042 4000
www.hifichoice.co.uk
13pa. Owner: Future.
Editor: Dan George

Hi-Fi News
020 8726 8000
www.hifinews.com
Monthly. Owner: IPC Media.
Editor: Paul Miller

Hi-Fi World
01275 371386
www.hi-fiworld.co.uk
Monthly. Editor: David Price

Home Cinema Choice
020 7042 4000
www.homecinemachoice.co.uk
Monthly. Owner: Future.
Editor: Rick Hemson

iCreate
01202 586205
www.icreatemagazine.com
9pa. Owner:Imagine Publishing.
Editor: Ben Harvell

Internet and Broadband Advisor
01225 442244
www.netmag.co.uk
13pa. Owner: Future.
Editor: Dan Oliver

Jetix
01225 442244
www.jetix.co.uk
13pa. Owner: Future.
Editor: Cavan Scott

Linux Format
01225 442244
www.linuxformat.co.uk
13pa. Owner: Future. Editor: Nick Veitch

Login Magazine
01702 589169
www.imagine-publishing.co.uk
Monthly. Owner: Enterbrain.
Editor: Rick Haynes

MacFormat
01225 442244
www.macformat.co.uk
13pa. Owner: Future.
Editor: Graham Barlow

MacUser
020 7907 6000
www.macuser.co.uk
Fortnightly. Owner: Dennis.
Editor: Nick Rawlinson

Macworld
020 7071 3621
www.macworld.co.uk
13pa. Owner: IDG London.
Editor: Mark Hattersley

Micro Mart
020 7907 6000
www.micromart.co.uk
Weekly. Owner: Dennis.
Editor: Simon Brew

Official PlayStation 2 Magazine
01225 442244
www.playstation.co.uk
13pa. Owner: Future.
Editor: Nick Ellis

Official Xbox Magazine
020 7042 4000
www.officialxboxmagazine.co.uk
13pa. Owner: Future.
Editor: Steve Brown

PC Advisor
020 7071 3615
www.pcadvisor.co.uk
Monthly. Owner: IDG London.
Editor: Matthew Bath

PC Answers
01225 442244
www.pcanswers.co.uk
13pa. Owner: Future.
Editor: Simon Pickstock

PC Format
01225 442244
www.pcformat.co.uk
13pa. Owner: Future.
Editor: Adam Oxford

PC Gamer
01225 442244
www.pcgamer.co.uk
13pa. Owner: Future.
Editor: Ross Atherton

PC Plus
01225 442244
www.pcplus.co.uk
13pa. Owner: Future. Editor: Ian Robson

PC Pro
020 7907 6000
www.pcpro.co.uk
Monthly. Owner: Dennis.
Editor: Tim Danson

PC Utilities
0871 223 1112
www.pc-utilities.co.uk
13pa. Owner: Magnesium Media
International. Editor: Gavin Burrell

PC Zone
020 7042 4000
www.pczone.co.uk
13pa. Owner: Future.
Editor: Jamie Sefton

PDA Essentials
01202 586254
www.pda-essentials.co.uk
13pa. Owner: Imagine.
Deputy editor: Andy Betts

Personal Computer World
01858 438881
www.pcw.co.uk
Monthly. Owner: VNU.
Editor: Rob Jones

Play
01202 586216
www.play-mag.co.uk
13pa. Owner: Imagine.
Editor: Simon Phillips

PSM2
01225 442244
www.futurenet.com/psm2
13pa. Owner: Future. Editor: Daniel
Griffith

PSW
020 7042 4000
www.myfavouritemagazines.co.uk
13pa. Owner: Future. Editor: Ian Dean

Stuff
020 8267 5036
www.stuffmagazine.co.uk
Monthly. Owner: Haymarket.
Editor: Jamie Clarke

T3
020 7042 4000
www.t3.co.uk
13pa. Owner: Future.
Editor: Michael Brooke

Total Mobile
www.totalmobilemag.co.uk
13pa. Owner: Future.
Editor: Robert Hull

Web Designer
www.webdesignermag.co.uk
13pa. Owner:Imagine.
Editor: Mark Billen

Web User
020 3148 5000
www.webuser.co.uk
Fortnightly. Owner: IPC Media.
Editor: Claire Woffenden

What Digital Camcorder
www.whatcamcorder.net
13pa. Owner: Future. Editor: Robert Hull

What Hi-Fi? Sound and Vision
020 8267 5000
www.whathifi.com
Monthly, plus awards issue. Owner:
Haymarket. Editor: Claire Eason

What Home Cinema
020 7331 1000
www.homecinemachoice.com
/whathomecinema/magazine
Monthly. Owner: Future.
Editor: Adrian Justins

What Satellite and Digital TV
www.wotsat.com
Monthly. Owner: Future.
Editor: Alex Lane

What Video and Widescreen TV
www.whatvideomag.com
Monthly. Owner: Future.
Editor: Danny Phillips

Windows XP Made Easy
01202 586253
www.windowsmadeeasy.co.uk
13pa. Owner: Imagine.
Editor: Stuart Tarrant

Windows XP:
The Official Magazine
01225 442244
www.windowsxpmagazine.co.uk
13pa. Owner: Future.
Editor: Paul Douglas

● Current affairs

AFF Families Journal
01980 615525
www.aff.org.uk
4pa. Owner: Army Families
Federation. Editor: Catherine Moss

The American
01747 830520
www.the-american.co.uk
Monthly. Owner: Blue Edge Publishing.
Editor: Michael Burland

Big Issue
020 7526 3388
www.bigissue.com
Weekly. Editor: A. John Bird

Big Issue in Scotland
0141 418 7000
www.bigissuescotland.com
Weekly. Editor: Claire Harris

Big Issue in the North
0161 834 6300
www.bigissueinthenorth.com
Weekly. Editor: Ato Erzan

Challenge Newsline
0845 166 8463
www.challengenewsline.com
Monthly. Owner: Verité.
Editor: Debbie Bunn

Connect Magazine
020 7865 8100
www.greenpeace.org.uk
4pa. Owner: Greenpeace.
Editor: Stokeley Webster

Diplo
020 7833 9766
www.diplo-magazine.co.uk
Monthy. Owner: Editor: Charles Baker

EarthMatters
020 7490 1555
www.foe.co.uk
3pa. Owner: Friends of the Earth.
Editor: Adam Bradbury

Ecologist
020 7422 8100
www.theecologist.org
10pa. Editor: Pat Thomas

Economist
020 7830 7000
www.economist.com
Weekly. Owner: The Economist
Newspaper. Editor: John Micklethwait

Glasgow Magazine
0141 287 0907
www.glasgow.gov.uk
Bi-monthly. Owner: Glasgow City
Council. Editor: John Keil

Green Futures
020 7324 3660
www.greenfutures.org.uk
Bi-monthly. Owner: Forum for the
Future. Editor: Roger East

The House Magazine
020 7091 7530
www.epolitix.com
Weekly. Owner: Dods Parliamentary
Communications.
Editor: Gisela Stuart

Impact International
020 7263 1417
www.impact-magazine.com
Monthly. Owner: News and Media.
Editor: Ahmad Irfan

Index on Censorship
020 7278 2313
www.indexonline.org
4pa. Owner: Taylor & Francis.
Editor: Jo Glanville

The Liberty Newsletter
020 7403 3888
www.liberty-human-rights.org.uk
4pa. Owner: Liberty, The National
Council for Civil Liberties.
Editor: Zoe Gillard

New African
020 7713 7711
www.africasia.com
Monthly. Owner: IC Publications.
Editor: Baffour Ankomah

New Internationalist
01865 811400
www.newint.org
Monthly. Editorial contact:
David Ransom

New Statesman
020 7730 3444
www.newstatesman.com
Weekly. Editor: John Kampfner

News Africa
020 7394 4030
www.newsafrica.net
Monthly. Editor: Moffat Ekoriko

Newsweek
020 7851 9799
www.newsweek.com
Weekly. Editor: Fareed Zakaria

Outrage — magazine of Animal
Aid
01732 364546
www.animalaid.co.uk
4pa. Editor: Mark Gold

Parliamentary Brief
020 7381 1611
www.thepolitician.org
Monthly. Editor: Roderick Crawford

Party Politics
020 7324 8500
www.sagepub.co.uk
6pa. Owner: Sage Publications.
Editor: Paul Webb

Private Eye
020 7437 4017
www.private-eye.co.uk
Fortnightly. Owner: Pressdram.
Editor: Ian Hislop

Prospect
020 7255 1281
www.prospect-magazine.co.uk
Monthly. Owner: Prospect Publishing.
Editor: David Goodhart

Red Pepper
020 7281 7024
www.redpepper.org.uk
Monthly. Owner: Socialist
Newspaper (Publications).
Editor: Hilary Wainwright

Report
020 7930 6441
www.askatl.org.uk
10pa. Owner: Association of Teachers
and Lecturers. Editor: Guy Goodwin

SchNEWS
01273 685913
www.schnews.org.uk
Weekly. Editor: Jo Makepeace

Socialism Today
020 8988 8773
www.socialismtoday.org
Monthly. Editor: Lynn Walsh

The Socialist
020 8988 8777
www.socialistparty.org.uk
Weekly. Owner: Eastway Offset.
Editor: Ken Smith

Socialist Review
020 7819 1176
www.socialistreview.org.uk
11pa. Owner: Socialist Workers Party
(Britain). Editor: Judith Orr

Socialist Worker
020 7819 1180
www.socialistworker.co.uk
Weekly. Owner: Newsfax.
Editor: Chris Bambery

Spectator
020 7405 1706
www.spectator.co.uk
Weekly. Editor: Matthew d'Ancona

Time
020 7499 4080
www.time.com
Weekly. Owner: Time.
Editor: Michael Elliot

Tribune
020 7433 6410
www.tribuneweb.co.uk
Weekly. Editor: Chris McLaughlin

Unite
01582 663880
www.pensioneronline.com
8pa. Owner: National Federation
of Royal Mail and BT Pensioners.
Editor: Lee Wilson

The Week
020 7907 6180
www.theweek.co.uk
Weekly. Owner: Dennis.
Editor: Caroline Law

The World Today
020 7957 5712
www.theworldtoday.org
Monthly. Owner: The Royal Institute
of International Affairs.
Editor: Graham Walker

WWF UK News
01483 426444
www.wwf.org.uk
Quarterly. Owner: WWF.
Editor: Guy Jowett

● Food & drink

BBC Good Food
020 8433 3342
www.bbcmagazines.com/goodfood
Monthly. Owner: BBC Worldwide.
Editor: Gillian Carter

Big Cook Little Cook
020 8433 2356
www.bbcmagazines.com/content
/magazines/bigcooklittlecook
Monthly. Owner: BBC Worldwide.
Editor: Sarah O'Neill

Decanter
020 3148 5000
www.decanter.com
Monthly. Owner: IPC Media.
Editor: Guy Woodward

Delicious
020 7775 7757
www.deliciousmagazine.co.uk
Monthly. Owner: Seven Publishing.
Editor: Matthew Drennan

Easy Cook
020 8433 2000
www.bbcmagazines.com
Bi-monthly. Owner: BBC Worldwide.
Editor: Sarah Giles

Food & Travel
020 7501 0511
www.foodandtravel.com
Monthly. Owner: Green Pea
Publishing. Editor: Claire Shiells

Food Chain
01603 274130
www.foodchain-magazine.com
Bi-monthly. Owner: Schofield
Publishing. Editor: Libbie Hammond

Foodie Magazine
01527 61122
www.thefoodie.co.uk/magazine.php
Monthly. Owner: CW Corporate
Communications. Editor: Alison
Davison

M&S Magazine
020 7747 0700
www.redwoodgroup.net
4pa. Owner: Redwood.
Editor: Drew Clawson

Olive
0870 458 3991
www.olivemagazine.co.uk
Monthly. Owner: BBC Worldwide.
Editor: Christine Hayes

Sainsbury's Magazine
020 7633 0266
www.sainsburysmagazine.co.uk
Monthly. Owner: New Crane
Publishing. Editor: Sue Robinson

Somerfield Magazine
0117 989 7808
www.somerfield.co.uk
13pa. Owner: Rare Publishing.
Editor: Hannah Smith

The Vegetarian
0161 925 2000
www.vegsoc.org
4pa. Owner: The Vegetarian Society of
the United Kingdom. Editor: Jane Bowler

Waitrose Food Illustrated
020 7565 3000
www.jbcp.co.uk
Monthly. Owner: John Brown Publishing
Group. Editor: William Sitwell

What's Brewing
01727 798454
www.camra.org.uk
Monthly. Owner: Camra.
Editor: Tom Stainer

Whisky Magazine
01603 633808
www.whiskymag.com
8pa. Owner: Paragraph Publishing.
Editor: Rob Allanson

Wine and spirit
01293 846550
www.wineint.com
Monthly. Owner: Quest Magazines &
Events. Editor: David Williams

● Gay and lesbian

» See page 120

● General interest

American in Britain
020 8661 0186
www.americaninbritain.co.uk
4pa. Owner: The American Hour.
Editor: Helen Elliott

Another Magazine
020 7336 0766
www.anothermag.com
2pa. Owner: Dazed Group.
Editor: Jefferson Hack

Asian Image
01254 298263
www.asianimage.co.uk
Monthly. Owner: Newsquest.
Editor: Shuiab Khan

Astronomy Now
www.astronomynow.com
Monthly. Owner: Pole Star
Publications. Editor: Stuart Clark

BBC History Magazine
0117 927 9009
www.bbchistorymagazine.com
Monthly. Owner: Origin Publishing.
Editor: David Musgrove

Brighton & Hove Life
01903 604226
www.archantlife.co.uk
Monthly. Owner: Archant.
Editorial contact: Jonathan Keeble

Cambridge Agenda
01223 309227
www.thecambridgeagenda.co.uk
Monthly. Owner: Life Publishing.
Editor: Justin Coleman

Cheshire Life
01772 722022
www.archantlife.co.uk
Monthly. Owner: Archant.
Editor: Patrick O'Neill

Choice
01733 555123
www.choicemag.co.uk
Monthly. Editor: Norman Wright

Contemporary
020 7740 1704
www.contemporary-magazine.com
Monthly. Owner: Art 21.
Editor: Brian Muller

Cornwall Life
01803 860910
www.archantlife.co.uk
Monthly. Owner: Archant.
Publisher: Anita Newcombe

Cotswold Life
01242 216050
www.archantlife.co.uk
Monthly. Owner: Archant.
Editor: Mick Lowe

Dazed & Confused
020 7336 0766
Monthly. Owner: Dazed Group.
Editor: Tim Lough

Der Spiegel
020 8605 3893
www.spiegel.de
Weekly. Editor: Stefan Aust

Devon Life
01803 860910
www.archantlife.co.uk
Monthly. Owner: Archant.
Editor: Jan Barwick

Dorset
01305 211840
www.archantlife.co.uk
Monthly. Owner: Archant.
Editor: Bridget Swann

DV8
01202 388388
www.dv8online.co.uk
Monthly. Editor: Helen Mayson

EDP Norfolk Magazine
01603 772469
www.edp24.co.uk
Monthly. Owner: Archant.
Editor: Peter Franzen

Epicurean Life
020 7376 5959
www.epicureanlife.co.uk
4pa. Editor: Azzy Asghar

Essex Life
01799 544273
www.archant.co.uk
Monthly. Owner: Archant.
Editor: Robyn Bechelet

Expression
01392 263052
www.exeter.ac.uk/alumni
2pa. Owner: University of Exeter Alumni
Network. Editor: Stuart Franklin

Focus
0117 933 8040
www.focusmag.co.uk
Monthly. Owner: Origin Publishing.
Editor: Paul Parsons

Folio
0117 942 8491
www.foliomag.com
Monthly. Owner: Venue Publishing.

Forward
0118 983 8364
www.guidedogs.org.uk
4pa. Editor: Sarah Hall

Freemasonry Today
01359 240820
www.freemasonrytoday.co.uk
4pa. Editor: Michael Baigent

Fresh Direction
020 7449 0900
www.freshdirection.co.uk
3pa. Owner: Antonville.
Editor: Paul Russell

The Green
020 7792 2626
www.archantlife.co.uk
Monthly. Owner: Archant.
Editor: Claire Kelly

The Guide Magazine
01603 772772
www.archantlife.co.uk
Monthly. Owner: Archant.
Editor: Lee Cheshire

H&E Naturist
01405 760298
www.henaturist.co.uk
Monthly. Owner: New Freedom
Publications. Editor: Sara Backhouse

Hampshire Life
01242 216053
www.archantlife.co.uk
Monthly. Owner: Archant.
Editor: Emma Coulston

Hertfordshire Life
01799 544273
www.archantlife.co.uk
Monthly. Owner: Archant.
Editor: Robyn Bechelet

The Hill
020 7792 2626
www.archantlife.co.uk
Monthly. Owner: Archant.
Editor: Pendle Harte

History Today
020 7534 8000
www.historytoday.com
Monthly. Owner: History Today.
Editor: Peter Furtado

Hot Press
00 353 1 241 1500
www.hotpress.com
Fortnightly. Owner: Osnovina.
Editor: Niall Stokes

Hotline (Virgin Trains)
020 7306 0304
www.therivergroup.co.uk
Quarterly. Owner: River Publishing.
Editorial director: Jane Wynn

i-D
020 7490 9710
www.i-dmagazine.co.uk
Monthly. Editor: Ben Reardon

Illustrated London News
020 7805 5555
www.ilng.co.uk
Bi-annual. Owner: Illustrated London
News. Editor: Alison Booth

The Insight
01273 765200
www.theinsight.co.uk
Monthly. Owner: The Insight.
Publisher: Mike Holland

Kent Life
01622 762818
www.archantlife.co.uk
Monthly. Owner: Archant.
Editor: Sarah Stuart

Kindred Spirit
01803 866686
www.kindredspirit.co.uk
6pa. Editor: Kate Osbourne

Lancashire Life
01772 722022
www.archantlife.co.uk
Monthly. Owner: Archant.
Editor: Roger Borrell

Let's Talk!
01603 772413
www.edp24.co.uk
Monthly. Owner: Archant.
Editor: Anne Gould

The Lifeboat
01202 662254
www.rnli.org.uk
4pa. Owner: RNLI. Editor: Liz Cook

Limited Edition
01689 885661
www.newsshopper.co.uk
/limitededition
Monthly. Owner: Newsquest.
Editor: Jean May

Living South
020 7223 0022
www.archantlife.co.uk
Monthly. Owner: Archant.
Editor: Shannon Denny

Magnet — The Village Communicator
01825 732796
www.magnetpublications.com
Monthly. Editor: Mary Hillyar

Majesty
020 7436 4006
www.majestymagazine.com
Monthly. Owner: Rex Publications.
Editor-in-chief: Ingrid Seward

MQ — Masonic Quarterly
www.mqmagazine.co.uk
Quarterly. Owner: Grand Lodge
Publications. Editor: John Jackson

New Humanist
020 7436 1151
www.newhumanist.org.uk
Bi-monthly. Owner: Rationalist Press
Association. Editor: Casper Melville

Nexus
01342 322854
www.nexusmagazine.com
Bi-monthly. Editor: Duncan Roads

North Magazine
020 7359 5500
www.archantlife.co.uk
Monthly. Owner: Archant.
Editor: Mark Kebble

NW
020 7359 5500
www.archantlife.co.uk
Monthly. Owner: Archant.
Editor: Danielle Monroe

Occasions
020 7650 2000
www.occasions-mag.com
4pa. Owner: Ethnic Media Group.
Editor: Sheri Mill

The Oldie
020 7436 8801
www.theoldie.co.uk
Monthly. Owner: Oldie Publications.
Editor: Richard Ingrams

Oxfordshire Life
01242 216050
www.archantlife.co.uk
Monthly. Owner: Archant.
Publisher: Tim Thurston

Password
020 7261 9878
Bi-monthly. Editor: Alistair Gordon

Platform
0115 848 1510
www.trentstudents.org
Fortnightly. Owner: Nottingham Trent
Students Union
Editor: Andrea Vassallo

Psychologies
0870 129 8800
www.psychologies.co.uk
Monthly. Owner: Hachette Fillipacchi.
Editor: Maureen Rice

Quicksilver Magazine
020 7747 9390
www.pspcom.com
Bi-monthly. Owner: PSP
Communications. Editor: Garth Gibbs

Reader's Digest
020 7715 8000
www.readersdigest.co.uk
Monthly. Owner: Reader's Digest.
Editor: Rob Lowe

Reform
020 7916 8630
www.urc.org.uk
11pa. Owner: United Reformed Church.
Editor: Guest Editors

The Resident
020 7384 9124
www.metropolispublishing.co.uk
Monthly. Owner: Metropolis
Publishing. Editor: Amanda Constance

Royal Berkshire Life
01242 216050
www.archantlife.co.uk
Monthly. Owner: Archant.
Publisher: Tessa Harris

Royalty
020 8201 9978
www.royalty-magazine.com
Monthly. Owner: Sena Julia
Publicatus. Editor: Bob Houston

Salvationist
020 7367 4890
www.salvationarmy.org.uk
/salvationist
Weekly. Owner: Salvation Army.
Editor: Dean Pallant

Scots Magazine
01382 223131
www.scotsmagazine.com
Monthly. Owner: DC Thomson.
Editor: John Methven

Sixer
0114 250 6300
www.northernlifestyle.com
Monthly. Owner: Regional Magazine
Company. Editor: Chris Wilson

Somerset Life
01803 860910
www.archantlife.co.uk
Monthly. Owner: Archant.
Editor: Nicki Lukehurst

The Spark
0117 914 3434
www.thespark.co.uk
4pa. Editor: John Dawson

Surrey Life
01737 247188
www.archantlife.co.uk
Monthly. Owner: Archant.
Editor: Caroline Harrap

Sussex Life
01903 604200
www.archantlife.co.uk
Monthly. Owner: Archant.
Editor: Jonathan Keeble

SW
020 7223 0022
www.archantlife.co.uk
Monthly. Owner: Archant.
Editor: Bernard Driscoll

Tank
020 7434 0110
www.tankmagazine.com
Quarterly. Owner: Tank Publications.
Editor: Masoud Golsorkhi

Toni & Guy
020 7462 7777
www.publicis-blueprint.co.uk
4pa. Owner: Publicis Blueprint.
Editor: Scarlett Brady

Town & Country News
01692 582287
Monthly. Owner: Leisure Publishing.
Editor: Laurence Watts

Trafford Magazine
020 7387 9888
www.babersmith.co.uk
2pa. Owner: Baber Smith.
Editor: Heather Wood

The Visitor
01963 351256
Monthly. Editor: Helen Dunion

Wavelength
01872 247456
www.wavelengthmag.co.uk
Monthly. Owner: Cornwall & Devon
Media. Editor: Tim Nunn

Weekly News
01382 223131
www.dcthomson.co.uk
Weekly. Owner: DC Thomson.
Editor: Dave Burness

Which?
020 7770 7373
www.which.co.uk
Monthly. Owner: Which?
Editor: Neil Fowler

Yorkshire Life
01772 722022
www.archantlife.co.uk
Monthly. Owner: Archant.
Editor: Esther Leach

You Can! Magazine
01242 544905
3pa. Owner: Independent News &
Media (UK). Editor: Anthony McClaran

Your Family Tree
01225 442244
www.yourfamilytreemag.co.uk
Monthly. Owner: Future.
Editor: Russell James

Yours
01733 468000
www.bauer.co.uk
Monthly. Owner: Bauer.
Editor: Valerie McConnell

● Home and garden

25 Beautiful Homes
020 3148 5000
www.ipcmedia.com
Monthly. Owner: IPC Media.
Editor: John Smigielski

25 Beautiful Kitchens
020 7261 5015
www.ipcmedia.com
10pa. Owner: IPC Media.
Editor: Ysanne Brooks

Amateur Gardening
01202 440840
www.ipcmedia.com
Weekly. Owner: IPC Media.
Editor: Tim Rumball

BBC Gardeners' World
020 8433 3959
www.gardenersworld.com
Monthly. Owner: BBC Worldwide.
Editor: Adam Pasco

BBC Good Homes
0870 444 2607
www.bbcmagazines.com
/goodhomes
Monthly. Owner: BBC Worldwide.
Editor: Bernie Herlihy

BBC Homes & Antiques
0117 927 9009
www.bbcmagazines.com
/homesandantiques
Monthly. Owner: BBC Magazines
Bristol. Editor: Angela Linsforth

Country Homes & Interiors
020 7261 6434
www.ipcmedia.com
Monthly. Owner: IPC Media.
Editor: Rhoda Parry

Country Living
020 7439 5000
www.countryliving.co.uk
Monthly. Owner: National Magazine
Company. Editor: Susy Smith

Horsemart
0870 122 2710
www.country-mkt.co.uk
Monthly. Editor: David Somerville

Easy Living
0870 837 8507
www.easylivingmagazine.co.uk
Monthly. Owner: Condé Nast.
Editor in chief: Abigail Chisman

Elle Decoration
020 7150 7000
www.hf-uk.com
Monthly. Owner: Hachette Filipacchi
UK. Editor: Michelle Ogunadehin

The English Garden
020 7751 4800
www.theenglishgarden.co.uk
Monthly. Owner: Archant.
Editor: Janine Wookey

The English Home
020 7751 4800
www.theenglishhome.co.uk
Monthly. Owner: Archant.
Editor: Sharon Parsons

The Essential Kitchen, Bathroom & Bedroom Magazine
01206 851117
www.essentialpublishing.co.uk
Monthly. Owner: Essential Publishing.
Editor: Natalie Kelly

Fabric
020 7747 0700
www.redwoodgroup.net
Monthly. Owner: Redwood.
Editor: Steven Short

The Garden
01733 775775
www.rhs.org.uk
Monthly. Owner: RHS Publications.
Editor: Ian Hodgson

Garden Answers
01733 264666
www.bauer.co.uk
Monthly. Owner: Bauer.
Editor: Neil Pope

Garden News
01733 264666
www.bauer.co.uk
Weekly. Owner: Bauer

Gardening Which?
020 7770 7564
www.which.co.uk/gardeningwhich
10pa. Owner: Which?
Editor: Kerri Thomas

Gardens Illustrated
0870 444 2611
www.bbcmagazines.com
/gardensillustrated
10pa. Owner: BBC Worldwide.
Editor: Juliet Roberts

Gardens Monthly
01689 899297
www.gardening.co.uk
11pa. Owner: Magicalia Media.
Editor: Liz Dobbs

Good Housekeeping
020 7439 5000
www.goodhousekeeping.co.uk
Monthly. Owner: National Magazine
Company. Editor: Louise Chunn

WI Life
020 7731 5777
www.womens-institute.co.uk
Monthly. Owner: Women's Institute.
Editor: Penny Kitchen

Home View
01277 366134
www.homeviewproperty
magazine.com
Bi-monthly. Editor: Garry Clarke

Homebase Ideas
020 7462 7777
www.publicis-blueprint.co.uk
Quarterly. Owner: Publicis Blueprint.
Editor: Ward Hellewell

Homebuilding & Renovating
01527 834400
www.moveorimprove.co.uk
Monthly. Owner: Centaur.
Editor: Jason Orme

Homes & Gardens
020 3148 5000
www.homesandgardens.com
Monthly. Owner: IPC Media.
Editor: Deborah Barker

Homes & Interiors Scotland
0141 221 5559
www.homesandinteriors
scotland.com
Bi-monthly. Owner: International
Magazines. Editor: Kate Hamilton

Homes Overseas
020 7002 8300
www.homesoverseas.co.uk
Monthly. Owner: Blendon
Communications. Editor: Mike Hayes

Homes Review
01206 506249
Monthly. Owner: MS Publications
Bonnie Howard

House & Garden
020 7499 9080
www.houseandgarden.co.uk
Monthly. Owner: Condé Nast.
Editor: Susan Crewe

House & Home Ideas
01823 288344
www.houseandhomeideas.co.uk
Monthly. Owner: Giraffe Media.
Editor: Sarah Messenger

House Beautiful
020 7439 5000
www.housebeautiful.co.uk
Monthly. Owner: National Magazine
Company. Editor: Julia Goodwin

Ideal Home
020 7261 6474
www.ipcmedia.com
Monthly. Owner: IPC Media.
Acting Editor: Sarah Warwick

International Homes
01245 358877
www.international-homes.com
Monthly. Editor: Jill Keene

Ireland's Homes Interiors & Living
028 9147 3979
www.irelandshomesinteriors
andliving.com
Monthly. Editor: Heather McGarrigle

KBB — Kitchens, Bedrooms & Bathrooms Magazine
020 8515 2000
www.dmgworldmedia.com
Monthly. Owner: DMG World Media.
Editor: Jackie Daly

Key
020 7494 3155
www.real-london.com
2pa. Owner: Real London Ltd.
Editor: Clare Weatherall

Livingetc
020 7261 6603
www.ipcmedia.com
Monthly. Owner: IPC Media.
Editor: Suzanne Imre

Period House
01206 851117
www.essentialpublishing.co.uk
Monthly. Owner: Essential Publishing.
Editor: Charlotte Barber

Period Ideas
01206 505976
www.periodideas.com
Monthly. Owner: Aceville Publications.
Editor: Rebecca Winward

Period Living & Traditional Homes
020 7970 4000
www.periodliving.co.uk
Monthly. Owner: Centaur.
Editor: Sarah Whelan

Real Homes Magazine
020 7150 7000
www.hf-uk.com
Monthly. Owner: Hachette Filipacchi.
Editor: Lisa McFarlane

Renovations
020 7384 1985
4pa. Editor: Liz Cowley

Scottish Home & Country
www.swri.org.uk
Monthly. Owner: Scottish Women's
Rural Institutes. Editor: Liz Ferguson

Traditional Homes & Interiors
01795 599191
www.cplmedia.co.uk
11pa. Owner: CPL Media.
Editor: Vicki Watson

Wallpaper
020 3148 5000
www.wallpaper.com
Monthly. Owner: IPC Media.
Editor: Tony Chambers

World of Interiors
020 7499 9080
www.worldofinteriors.co.uk
Monthly. Owner: Condé Nast.
Editor: Rupert Thomas

Your Home
01206 851117
www.essentialpublishing.co.uk
Monthly. Owner: Essential Publishing.
Editor: Hayley Chilver

Your New Home
01732 878800
www.yournewhome.co.uk
4pa. Owner: New Concept Group.
Editor: Karen Keeman

● Leisure

Absolute Horse
01473 731220
www.ahmagazine.com
Monthly. Owner: PCD Media.
Editor: Diana Goldstone

Aeroplane
020 7261 5849
www.aeroplanemonthly.com
Monthly. Owner: IPC Media.
Editor: Michael Oakey

Air Enthusiast
01780 755131
www.airenthusiast.com
Bi-monthly. Owner: Key Publishing.
Editor: Ken Ellis

Air Transport World
01628 477775
www.atwonline.com
Monthly. Owner: Penton Media.
Editor: Perry Flint

Aircraft Illustrated
01932 266600
www.aircraftillustrated.com
Monthly. Owner: Ian Allan Publishing.
Editor: Alan Burney

Airliner World
01780 755131
www.airlinerworld.com
Monthly. Owner: Key Publishing.
Editor: Tony Dixon

Animal Life
0870 010 1181
www.rspca.org.uk
Quarterly. Owner: RSPCA.
Editor: Amanda Bailey

Antique Collecting
01394 389950
www.antique-acc.com
10pa. Owner: Antique Collectors Club.
Editor: Susan Wilson

Antique Dealer & Collectors Guide
020 8691 4820
www.antiquecollectorsguide.co.uk
Bi-monthly. Owner: Status Court.
Editor: Philip Bartlam

Antiques and Collectibles
01225 786835
www.antiques-collectables.co.uk
13pa. Owner: Merricks Media.
Editor: Rachel Harrison

At Home in Cardiff Bay
029 2045 0532
www.athomeincardiffbay.com
Bi-monthly. Owner: City Publications.
Editor: Alison Tucker

Aviation News
01424 720477
www.aviation-news.co.uk
Monthly. Owner: HPC Publishing.
Editor: Barry Wheeler

**Aviation Week &
Space Technology**
020 7434 3126
www.aviationnow.com
Weekly. Owner: McGraw-Hill.
Editor-in-chief: Anthony Velocci;
London bureau chief: Douglas Barrie

Award Journal
01753 727470
www.theaward.org
3pa. Editor: Dave Wood

BBC Wildlife Magazine
0117 927 9009
www.bbcwildlifemagazine.com
Monthly. Publisher: Bristol Magazines
Ltd. Editor: Sophie Stafford

Bird Life
01767 680551
www.rspb.org.uk
Bi-monthly. Owner: RSPB.
Editor: Rob Hume

Birds
01767 680551
www.rspb.org.uk
4pa. Owner: RSPB. Editor: Rob Hume

Birdwatch
020 8881 0550
www.birdwatch.co.uk
Monthly. Owner: Solo Publishing.
Editor: Dominic Mitchell

Bird Watching
01733 468000
www.bauer.co.uk
Monthly. Owner: Bauer.
Editor: Kevin Wilmott

BMFA News
0116 244 0028
www.bmfa.org/news
Bi-monthly. Editor: Eric Clark

Boat International
020 8547 2662
www.boatinternational.com
Monthly. Owner: Edisea.
Editor: Amanda McCracken

Boats & Yachts for Sale
01243 533394
www.boatshop24.co.uk
Monthly. Owner: Marine Trader Media.
Commercial director: John Dupree

Book & Magazine Collector
0870 732 8080
13pa. Publisher: Diamond.
Editor: Jonathan Scott

Bridge Magazine
020 7388 2404
www.bridgemagazine.co.uk
Monthly. Editor: Mark Horton

British Birds
01424 755155
www.britishbirds.co.uk
Monthly. Editor: Roger Riddington

British Horse
0870 120 2244
www.bhs.org.uk
Bi-monthly. Owner: The British Horse
Society. Editor: David Prince

British Naturism
01604 620361
www.british-naturism.org.uk
4pa. Editor: Tracey Major

Budgerigar World
01678 520262
Monthly. Owner: County Press.
Editor: G Evans

Boat Trader
01243 533394
www.boatshop24.co.uk
Monthly. Owner: Marine Trader Media.
Commercial director: John Dupree

Cage & Aviary Birds
020 7261 6201
www.ipcmedia.com
Weekly. Owner: IPC Media.
Editor: Kim Forrester

Camping & Caravanning
024 7647 5270
www.campingandcaravanning
   club.co.uk
Monthly. Owner: The Camping &
Caravanning Club. Editor: Nick
Harding

Camping Magazine
01778 391000
www.campingmagazine.co.uk
10pa. Owner: Warners.
Editor: Clive Garrett

Canal & Riverboat
01603 708930
www.canalsandrivers.co.uk
Monthly. Owner: Morgan Publications.
Editor: Chris Cattrall

Canal Boat
0118 977 1677
www.canalboatmag.co.uk
Monthly. Owner: Archant.
Editor: Kevin Blick

Caravan Club Magazine
01342 336804
www.caravanclub.co.uk
Monthly. Owner: The Caravan Club.
Editor: Gary Martin

Caravan Magazine
020 8726 8249
www.ipcmedia.com
Monthly. Owner: IPC Media.
Editor: Victoria Heath

Cat World
01903 884988
www.catworld.co.uk
Monthly. Owner: Ashdown.
Editor: Laura Quiggan

Chess
020 7388 2404
www.chess.co.uk
Monthly. Editor: Jimmy Adams

Church Music Quarterly
01722 424848
www.rscm.com
4pa. Owner: Royal School of Church
Music. Editor: Esther Jones

Classic Boat
020 8726 8130
www.ipcmedia.com
Monthly. Owner: IPC Media.
Editor: Dan Houston

Coast
020 7439 5000
www.coastmagazine.co.uk
Monthly. Publisher: National Magazine
Company. Editor: Susy Smith

Coin News
01404 46972
www.tokenpublishing.com
Monthly. Owner: Token Publishing.
Editor: John Mussell

Coin Yearbook
01404 46972
www.tokenpublishing.com
Yearly. Owner: Token Publishing.
Editor: John Mussell

Collect it!
01778 391000
www.collectit.info
Monthly. Owner: Warner Publishing
Group. Editor: Jean Hodge

Collections
020 7870 9000
www.bostonhannah.co.uk
3pa. Owner: Boston Hannah
International. Editor: Charles Ford

Collector
020 8740 7020
www.artefact.co.uk
Bi-monthly. Owner: Barrington
Publications. Editor: Paul Hooper

Collectors Gazette
01778 391000
www.collectorsgazette.com
Monthly. Owner: Warners.
Editor: Denise Burrows

Companions Magazine
01952 290999
www.pdsa.org.uk
4pa. Owner: PDSA. Editor: Clare Evans

Continental Modeller
01297 20580
www.peco-uk.com
Monthly. Owner: Peco Publications &
Publicity. Editor: Andrew Burnham

Country Illustrated
020 7291 8609
www.countryclubuk.com
Monthly. Owner: St Martin's
Magazines. Editor: Julie Spencer

Country Life
020 7261 6400
www.countrylife.co.uk
Weekly. Owner: IPC Media.
Editor: Mark Hedges

Country Smallholding
01392 888481
www.countrysmallholding.com
Monthly. Owner: Archant.
Editor: Diane Cowgill

Country Walking
01733 468000
www.bauer.co.uk
Monthly. Owner: Bauer.
Editor: Jonathan Manning

The Countryman
01756 701381
www.countrymanmagazine.co.uk
*Monthly. Owner: Country
Publications. Editor: Paul Jackson*

The Countryman's Weekly
01822 855281
www.countrymansweekly.com
*Weekly. Owner: Diamond.
Editor: David Venner*

Countryside La Vie
0116 212 2555
www.countryside-lavie.com
Bi-monthly. Editor: Sue Brindley

Crafts
020 7806 2538
www.craftscouncil.org.uk
*Bi-monthly. Owner: Crafts Council.
Editor: Emma Mills*

Crafts Beautiful
01206 505989
www.crafts-beautiful.com
*Monthly. Owner: Aceville Publications.
Editor: Sarah Crosland*

Crafty Carper
0114 258 0812
www.anglingpublications.co.uk
*Monthly. Owner: Angling Publications.
Editorial director: Martin Ford*

Cross Stitch Collection
01225 442244
www.crossstitchcollection.co.uk
*13pa. Owner: Future.
Editor: Catherine Hood*

Cross Stitcher
01225 442244
www.cross-stitchermagazine.co.uk
*13pa. Owner: Future.
Editor: Cathy Lewis*

Cumbria
01756 701033
www.dalesman.co.uk
*Monthly. Owner: Country
Publications. Editor: Terry Fletcher*

Dalesman
01756 701033
www.dalesman.co.uk
*Monthly. Owner: Country
Publications. Editor: Terry Fletcher*

Dartmoor Magazine
01822 614899
www.dartmoormagazine.co.uk
*4pa. Owner: Quay Publications.
Editor: Elisabeth Stanbrook*

Dog World
01233 621877
www.dogworld.co.uk
Weekly. Editor: Stuart Baillie

Dogs Today
01276 858880
www.dogstodaymagazine.co.uk
Monthly. Editor: Beverley Cuddy

Doll Magazine
01903 884988
www.dollmagazine.com
*Bi-Monthly. Owner: Ashdown.
Editor: Sue Brewer*

Dolls House World
01903 884988
www.dollshouseworld.com
*Monthly. Owner: Ashdown.
Editor: Joyce Dean*

Engineering in Miniature
01926 614101
www.engineeringinminiature.co.uk
*Monthly. Owner: Tee Publishing.
Editor: CL Deith*

EOS Magazine
01869 331741
www.eos-magazine.com
*4pa. Owner: Robert Scott Associates.
Editor: Angela August*

ESP Magazine
www.espmag.co.uk
Monthly. Editor: Sharon McAllister

Evergreen
01242 537900
www.thisengland.co.uk
*4pa. Owner: This England.
Editor: Stephen Garnet*

Everyday Practical Electronics
01202 873872
www.epemag.co.uk
*Monthly. Owner: Wimborne
Publishing. Editor: Mike Kenward*

Families East
020 8694 8694
www.familiesonline.co.uk
*Bi-monthly. Owner: Families
Magazines. Editor: Mewe Mechese*

Families Edinburgh
0131 624 0049
www.familiesonline.co.uk
*Bi-monthly. Owner: Families
Magazines. Editor: Sarah Adir*

Families Liverpool
0151 601 8270
www.familiesonline.co.uk
*Bi-monthly. Owner: Families Magazines.
Editor: Jennifer-Paige Deenihan*

Families North
020 7794 5690
www.familiesonline.co.uk
*Bi-monthly. Owner: Families
Magazines. Editor: Cathy Youd*

Families Together
01903 821082
www.cfnetwork.co.uk
*3pa. Owner: Christian Publishing and
Outreach. Editor: Anne Atkins*

Families Upon Thames
01932 254584
www.familiesonline.co.uk
*Bi-monthly. Owner: Families
Magazines. Editor: Francis Loates*

The Flower Arranger
020 8748 2673
www.theflowerarrangermagazine
.co.uk
*4pa. Owner: The National Association
of Flower Arrangement Societies
(NAFAS). Editor: Judith Blacklock*

Flyer
01225 481440
www.flyer.co.uk
*13pa. Owner: Seager Publishing.
Editor: Philip Whiteman*

FlyPast
01780 755131
www.flypast.com
*13pa. Owner: Key Publishing.
Editor: Ken Ellis*

Fortean Times
020 7907 6000
www.forteantimes.com
*13pa. Owner: Dennis.
Editor: David Sutton*

Galleries
020 8740 7020
www.galleries.co.uk
*Monthly. Owner: Barrington
Publications. Editor: Andrew Aitkin*

Gibbons Stamp Monthly
01425 472363
www.gibbonsstampmonthly.com
*Monthly. Owner: Stanley Gibbons
Publications. Editor: Hugh Jefferies*

The Great Outdoors
0141 302 7700
www.newsquest.co.uk
*Monthly. Owner: Newsquest.
Editor: Cameron McNeish*

Gulliver's World
01228 404350
www.lilliputlane.co.uk
*4pa. Owner: Enesco.
Editor: Lynne Thompson*

Hali
020 7970 4000
www.hali.co.uk
*6pa. Owner: Centaur.
Editor: Ben Evans*

Heritage Magazine
020 7751 4800
www.heritagemagazine.co.uk
*Bi-monthly. Owner: Archant.
Editor: Penelope Rance*

Hoofprint
01565 872107
*Monthly. Owner: Penn House
Publishing. Editor: Barry Hook*

Horoscope
01202 873872
www.horoscope.co.uk
*Monthly. Owner: Wimborne
Publishing. Editor: Mike Kenward*

Horse
020 7261 5867
www.ipcmedia.com
*Monthly. Owner: IPC Media.
Editor: Jo Pyatt*

Horse & Hound
020 7261 6453
www.horseandhound.co.uk
*Weekly. Owner: IPC Media.
Editor: Lucy Higginson*

Horse & Rider
01428 601020
www.horseandrider.com
*Monthly. Owner: DJ Murphy
Publishers. Editorial Director:
Jennifer Forsberg Meyer*

International Boat Industry
020 8726 8134
www.ibinews.com
*Monthly. Owner: IPC Media.
Editor: Ed Slack*

K9 Magazine
0870 011 4115
www.k9magazine.com
*Quarterly. Owner: K9 Media Solutions.
Editor: Ryan O'Meara*

Kew
020 8332 5906
www.rbgkew.org.uk
4pa. Editor: Sue Seddon

Koi Carp
01202 735090
www.koi-carp.com
Monthly. Owner: Freestyle Publications. Editor: Christina Evatt

Lakeland Walker
01778 391000
www.warnersgroup.co.uk
Bi-monthly. Owner: Warners Group. Editor: Michael Cowton

Legion — Royal British Legion
020 7880 7666
www.britishlegion.org.uk
Bi-monthly. Owner: Redactive Publishing. Editor: Claire Townley-Jones

Leisure Painter
01580 763315
www.leisurepainter.co.uk
Monthly. Owner: The Artists' Publishing Company. Editor: Ingrid Lyon

Leisure Scene
01494 888433
www.cssc.co.uk
3pa. Owner: CSSC Sports & Leisure. Editor: Ian Cooper

Lifewatch Magazine
020 7449 6363
www.zsl.org
3pa. Owner: Zoological Society of London. Editor: Debbie Curtis

Marine Modelling International
01684 588500
www.marinemodelmagazine.com
Monthly. Owner: Traplet Publications. Editor: Chris Jackson

Microlight Flying (The British Microlight Aircraft Association official magazine)
01524 841010
www.pagefast.co.uk
6pa. Owner: Pagefast. Editor: David Bremner

Military Illustrated Past & Present
0870 870 2345
www.publishingnews.co.uk
Monthly. Owner: Publishing News. Editor: Liz Thomson

Military in Scale
01684 588500
www.militaryinscale.com
Monthly. Owner: Traplet Publications. Editor: Spencer Pollard

Military Modelling
01525 370389
www.militarymodelling.com
15pa. Owner: Magicalia Media. Editor: Vinnie Branigan

Miniature Wargames
01202 297344
www.miniwargames.com
Monthly. Owner: Pireme Publishing. Editor: Iain Dickie

Model & Collectors Mart
0121 233 8712
www.modelmart.co.uk
Monthly. Owner: Trinity Publications. Editor: Dean Shepherd

Model Boats
01525 382847
www.modelboats.co.uk
13pa. Owner: Magicalica Media Editor: John Cundell

Model Collector
020 8726 8238
www.modelcollector.co.uk
Monthly. Owner: IPC Media. Editor: Lindsey Amrani

Model Engineer
01689 899255
26pa. Owner: Magicalia Media Editor: David Carpenter

Model Engineers' Workshop
01738 583832
11pa. Owner: Magicalia Media Editor: Graham Marsden

Model Helicopter World
01684 588500
www.modelheliworld.com
Monthly. Owner: Traplet Publications. Editor: Jon Tanner

Motor Boat & Yachting
020 7261 7257
www.ybw.com
Monthly. Owner: IPC Media. Editor: Hugo Andreae

Motor Boats Monthly
020 7261 5308
www.motorboatsmonthly.com
Monthly. Owner: IPC Media. Editor: Simon Collis

Motor Caravan Magazine
020 8726 8248
www.motorcaravanmagazine.co.uk
Monthly. Owner: IPC Media. Editor: Helen Avery

Motor Caravanner
01480 496130
www.motorcaravanners.org.uk
Monthly. Owner: The Motor Caravanners' Club. Editor: Helen Avery

Motorcaravan & Camping Mart
01778 391000
www.caravanmart.co.uk
11pa. Owner: Warners Group. Editor: Peter Sharpe

Motorhome Monthly
020 8302 6150
www.stoneleisure.com
Monthly. Owner: Stone Leisure. Editor: Robert Griffiths

Natural World
020 8962 3020
www.thinkpublishing.co.uk
3pa. Owner: Think Publishing. Editor: Rupert Paul

New Stitches
01227 750215
www.newstitches.com
Monthly. Owner: Creative Crafts Publishing. Editor: Janice Broadstocks

Our Dogs
0870 731 6500
www.ourdogs.co.uk
Weekly. Owner: Our Dogs Publishing. Editor: Anne Williams

Paddles
01202 735090
www.freestyle-group.com
Monthly. Owner: Freestyle Publications. Editor: Richard Parkin

PaperCraft Inspirations
01225 442244
www.futurenet.com/papercraft
13pa. Owner: Future. Editor: Jenny Dixon

Park Home & Holiday Caravan
020 8726 8253
www.ipcmedia.com
Monthly. Owner: IPC Media. Editor: Emma Bartlett

Patchwork & Quilting
01684 588500
www.pandqmagazine.com
Monthly. Owner: Traplet Publications. Editor: Gerald M Knox

Paws
020 7627 9293
www.dogshome.org
4pa. Owner: Battersea Dogs Home. Editor: Helen Tennant

The People's Friend
01382 223131
www.dcthomson.co.uk
Weekly. Owner: DC Thomson. Editor: Margaret McCoi

Pet Patter
020 7415 7100
www.mediamark.co.uk
Quarterly. Owner: Mediamark Publishing. Editor: Pip Jones

Pilot
01799 544200
www.pilotweb.aero
Monthly. Owner: Archant. Editor: Nick Bloom

Popular Patchwork
01727 866664
13pa. Owner: Magicalia Media Editor: Davina Thomas

Practical Boat Owner
01202 440820
www.pbo.co.uk
Monthly. Owner: IPC Media. Editor: Sarah Norbury

Practical Caravan
020 8267 5000
www.practicalcaravan.com
Monthly. Owner: Haymarket. Editor: Carl Rodgerson

Practical Fishkeeping
01733 282764
www.bauer.co.uk
Monthly. Owner: Bauer. Editor: Karen Youngs

Practical Wireless
0870 224 7810
www.pwpublishing.co.uk
Monthly. Owner: PW Publishing. Editor: Rob Mannion

Practical Woodworking
01689 899256
www.getwoodworking.com
13pa. Owner: Magicalia Media

Prediction
020 8726 8257
www.predictionmagazine.co.uk
Monthly. Owner: IPC Media. Editor: Marion Williamson

Quick & Crafty
01206 505980
www.crafts-beautiful.com
Monthly. Owner: Aceville Publications. Editor: Holly Markham

Quick & Easy Stitch and Craft
01225 442244
www.futurenet.com/quickandeasy
crossstitch
13pa. Owner: Future.
Editor: Ruth Southorn

RA Magazine
020 7300 5820
www.royalacademy.org.uk
4pa. Owner: Royal Academy of Arts.
Editor: Sarah Greenberg

Racecar Engineering
020 8726 8362
www.racecar-engineering.com
Monthly. Owner: IPC Media.
Editor: Charles Armstrong-Wilson

RadCom
0870 904 7373
www.rsgb.org
Monthly. Owner: Radio Society of
Great Britain. Editor: Giles Reed

Radio Control Jet International
01684 588500
www.rcjetinternational.com
Bi-monthly. Owner: Traplet
Publications. Editor: John Wright

Radio Control Model Flyer
01525 222573
www.modelflyermagazine.com
Monthly. Owner: ADH Publishing.
Editor: Ken Shepherd

Radio Control Model World
01684 588500
www.rcmodelworld.com
Monthly. Owner: Traplet Publications.
Editor: Tony Van Geffen

Radio Race Car International
01684 588500
www.radioracecar.com
Monthly. Owner: Traplet Publications.
Editor: Des Chand

Rail Express
01780 470086
www.railexpress.co.uk
Monthly. Owner: Foursight
Publications. Editor: Philip Sutton

Railway Modeller
01297 20580
www.peco-uk.com
Monthly. Owner: Peco Publications
& Publicity. Editor: John Brewer

Raw Vision
01923 856644
www.rawvision.com
4pa. Editor: John Maizels

RCM & E
01689 899258
13pa. Owner: Magicalia Media
Editor: Graham Ashby

RIB International
01884 266100
www.ribmagazine.com
Bi-monthly.
Editor: Hugo Montgomery-Swan

RYA Magazine
023 8060 4100
www.rya.org.uk
Quarterly. Owner: Royal Yachting
Association. Editor: Deborah Cornick

Sailing Today
01489 580836
www.sailingtoday.co.uk
Monthly. Editor: Rodger Witt

Scale Aviation Modeller
0870 733 3373
Monthly. Owner: Sam Publications.
Editor: Neil Robinson

ScrapBook Inspirations
01225 442244
13pa. Owner: Future.
Editor: Joanne Mullen

Sew Bridal
01243 379009
www.sewbridal.co.uk
Annually. Owner: McCall Butterick &
Vogue. Editor: Julie Watkins

Sewing World
01684 588500
www.sewingworldmagazine.com
Monthly. Owner: Traplet Publications.
Editor: Wendy Gardiner

Sew Today
01243 379009
www.sewdirect.com
10pa. Owner: McCall Butterick & Vogue.
Editor: Julie Watkins

Ships Monthly
01283 542741
www.ipcmedia.com
Monthly. Owner: IPC Media.
Editor: Iain Wakefield

Radio User Magazine
0870 224 7810
www.pwpublishing.co.uk
Monthly. Owner: PW Publishing.
Editor: Elaine Richards

Simply Knitting
01225 442244
www.futurenet.com
/simplyknittingmagazine
13pa. Owner: Future.
Editor: Debora Bradley

Stamp Magazine
020 8726 8243
www.stampmagazine.co.uk
Monthly. Owner: IPC Media.
Editor: Guy Thomas

Steam Days
01202 304849
www.steamdaysmag.co.uk
Monthly. Owner: Redgauntlet
Publications Ltd. Editor: Douglas
Kennedy

Steam Railway
01733 264666
www.bauer.co.uk
Monthly. Owner: Bauer.
Editor: Tony Streeter

Surrey Nature
01483 795440
www.surreywildlifetrust.org
3pa. Owner: Surrey Wildlife Trust.
Editor: Chris Parker

The Teddy Bear Club International
01903 884988
www.teddybeartimes.com
Monthly. Owner: Ashdown.
Editor: Kirste McCool

Time Out Shopping Guide
020 7813 3000
www.timeout.com
Annual. Owner: Time Out Group.
Editor: Jan Fuscoe

Toy Soldier & Model Figure
01903 884988
www.toy-soldier.com
Monthly. Owner: Ashdown.
Editor: Stuart Hessney

Treasure Hunting
01376 521900
www.greenlightpublishing.co.uk
Monthly. Owner: Greenlight
Publishing. Editor: Greg Payne

Trends
020 8342 5777
www.independentregionals.com
4pa. Owner: Archant. Editor: Tony
Allcock

Truck Model World
01684 588500
Monthly. Owner: Traplet Publications.
Editor: Peter White

Used Bike Guide
01507 529300
www.usedbikeguide.com
Monthly. Owner: Mortons Media
Group. Editor: Chris Pearson

Wag
020 7837 0006
www.dogstrust.org.uk
3pa. Owner: Dogs Trust.
Editor: Deana Selby

Walk
020 7339 8500
www.ramblers.org.uk
Quarterly. Owner: The Ramblers
Association / Think Publishing.
Editor: Christopher Ord

Waterways
01283 790447
www.waterways.org.uk
Quarterly. Owner: Inland Waterways
Association. Editor: Harry Arnold

Waterways World
01283 742951
Monthly. Editor: Richard Berhear

Which Caravan
01778 391000
www.whichcaravan.co.uk
Monthly. Owner: Warners Group.
Editor: Mark Sutcliffe

Wild Times
01767 680551
www.rspb.org.uk
Quarterly. Owner: RSPB.
Editor: Derek Niemann

Wildfowl & Wetlands
01453 891187
www.wwt.org.uk
4pa. Owner: Wildfowl & Wetlands
Trust. Editor: Mike Daw

Woodcarving
01273 477374
www.thegmcgroup.com
Bi-monthly. Owner: Guild of Master
Craftsmen. Editor: Mark Baker

Woodturning
01273 477374
www.thegmcgroup.com
13pa. Owner: Guild of Master
Craftsmen. Editor: Colin Simpson

The Woodworker
01689 899256
www.getwoodworking.com
14pa. Owner: Magicalia Media.
Editor: Mark Ramuz

Workbox
01579 340100
www.ebony.co.uk/workbox
Bi-monthly. Owner: Ebony Media.
Editor: Victor Briggs
**The World of Yachts & Boats
(pan-Arab)**
020 7328 3334
www.worldofyachts.com
*Bi-monthly. Owner: The World of
Yachts & Boats. Editor: Nabil Farhat*
The Yellow Book
01483 211535
www.ngs.org.uk
*Yearly. Owner: National Garden
Scheme. Editor: Julia Grant*
You & Your Vet
020 7636 6541
www.bva-awf.org.uk
*4pa. Owner: British Veterinary
Association. Editor: Martin Alder*
Your Cat
01780 766199
www.yourcat.co.uk
*Monthly. Owner: Bourne Publishing
Group. Editor: Sue Parslow*
Your Dog
01780 766199
www.yourdog.co.uk
*Monthly. Owner: Bourne Publishing
Group. Editor: Sarah Wright*
Your Horse
01733 264666
www.bauer.co.uk
*Monthly. Owner: Bauer.
Editor: Nicola Dela-Croix*

● Men's interest

Arena
020 7437 9011
www.bauer.co.uk
*Monthly. Owner: Bauer.
Editor: Giles Hattersley*
Bizarre
020 7907 6000
www.bizarremag.com
*Monthly. Owner: Dennis.
Editor: Jenni Davis*
Boys Toys
01202 735090
www.boystoys.co.uk
*Monthly. Owner: Freestyle
Publications. Editor: Duncan Madden*
Details
020 7240 0420
www.men.style.com/details
*10pa. Owner: Fairchild.
Editor: Daniel Peres*
DNR
020 7240 0420
www.dnrnews.com
*Weekly. Owner: Fairchild.
Editor: John Birmingham*
Esquire
020 7439 5000
www.esquire.co.uk
*Monthly. Owner: National Magazine
Company. Editor: Jeremy Langmead*

FHM
020 7436 1515
www.fhm.com
*Monthly. Owner: Bauer. Editor: David
Moynihan*
GQ
020 7499 9080
www.gq.com
*Monthly. Owner: Condé Nast.
Editor: Dylan Jones*
Loaded
020 7261 5562
www.loaded.co.uk
*Monthly. Owner: IPC Media.
Editor: Martin Daubney*
Maxim
020 7907 6000
www.maxim-magazine.co.uk
*Monthly. Owner: Dennis.
Editors: Martin Robinson, Nick Leftley*
Men's Fitness
020 7907 6000
www.mensfitnessmagazine.co.uk
*Monthly. Owner: Dennis.
Editor: Martin Robinson, Nick Leftley*
Men's Health
020 7439 5000
www.menshealth.co.uk
*11pa. Owner: National Magazine
Company. Editor: Morgan Rees*
Muscle & Fitness
01423 504516
www.muscle-fitness.co.uk
*Monthly. Owner: Weider Publishing.
Editor: Geoff Evans*
Musclemag International
0845 345 0916
www.emusclemag.com
*Monthly. Owner: Tropicana Health &
Fitness. Editor: Gary Hill; Sophie Adey*
Nuts
020 7261 5660
www.nuts.co.uk
*Weekly. Owner: IPC Media.
Editor: Dominic Smith*
Zoo Weekly
020 7182 8000
www.zootoday.com
*Weekly. Owner: Bauer.
Editor: Anthony Noguera*

● Money and property

Bloomberg Money
020 7034 2713
www.investegate.co.uk
*Monthly. Owner: Incisive Media.
Editor: Julian Marr*
The Business
020 7961 0000
www.thebusinessonline.com
*Weekly. Owner: Press Holdings.
Publisher and editor-in-chief:
Andrew Neil; editor: Alistair Heath*
Business Week
020 7176 6060
www.businessweek.com
*Weekly. Owner: McGraw-Hill.
Bureau chief: Stanley Reed*

**Country Landowner
and Rural Business**
01392 447766
www.cla.org.uk
*Monthly. Owner: Country Land and
Business Association. Publisher:
Archant. Editor: Tom Quinn*
Euroslot
01622 687031
www.datateam.co.uk
*Monthly. Owner: Datateam
Publishing. Editor: Stephanie Norbury*
Forbes
020 7534 3900
www.forbes.com
*Fortnightly. Owner: Forbes.
Editor: William Baldwin*
Fortune
www.fortune.com
*Fortnightly. European editor, Fortune
Europe: Robert Friedman*
Investors Chronicle
020 7775 6292
www.investorschronicle.co.uk
*Weekly. Owner: Financial Times
Business. Editor: Matthew Vincent*
ISA Direct
020 7409 1111
www.allenbridge.co.uk
*2pa. Owner: Allenbridge.
Editor: Anthony Yadgaroff*
The MBA Career Guide
020 7284 7200
www.topmba.com/careers
2pa. Editor: Cameron Ahmedx
Money Observer
020 7713 4188
www.moneyobserver.com
*Monthly. Owner: Guardian Media
Group. Editor: Andrew Pitts*
Moneywise
020 7680 3600
www.moneywise.co.uk
Monthly. Editor: Rachel Williams
Mortgage Finance Gazette
020 7827 5457
www.mfgonline.co.uk
*Monthly. Owner: Charterhouse
Communications. Editor: Jo Atkin*
Mortgage Introducer
020 7827 5429
www.mortgageintroducer.com
*Weekly. Owner: Charterhouse
Communications. Editor: Angela
Faherty*
Negotiator
01252 843566
www.negotiator-magazine.co.uk
*Fortnightly. Owner: Ocean Media.
Editor: Rosalind Renshaw*
Optima
020 8420 4488
www.optimamagazine.co.uk
Fortnightly. Editor: Jill Glenn
Personal Finance Confidential
020 7633 3600
www.agoralifestyles.com
*Monthly. Owner: Agora Lifestyles.
Managing editor: Dave Fedash*

MAGAZINE contacts **Print media**

101

Post Magazine
020 7316 9000
www.postmagazine.co.uk
Weekly. Owner: Incisive Media.
Editor: Jonathan Swift

The Property Magazine
01480 494944
www.property-platform.com
Monthly. Owner: Guild of Professional
Estate Agents. Editor: Malcolm Lindley

Scotland's New Home Buyer
0131 556 9702
4pa. Owner: Pinpoint Scotland.
Editor: Anna Baird

What Investment
020 7827 5454
www.what-investment-mag.co.uk
Monthly. Owner: Charterhouse
Communications. Editor: Kieron Root

What Investment Trust
020 7827 5454
www.charterhouse-
    communications.co.uk
3pa. Owner: Charterhouse
Communications. Editor: Kieron Root

What ISA
020 7250 7010
www.charterhouse-
    communications.co.uk
3pa. Owner: Vitesse Media.
Editor: Kieron Root

What Mortgage
020 7827 5454
www.what-mortgage-mag.co.uk
Monthly. Owner: Charterhouse
Communications. Editor: Nia Williams

Your Money:
Savings & Investments
020 7484 9700
www.yourmoney.com
Quarterly. Owner: Incisive Media.
Editor: Mike Collins

Your Mortgage
020 7484 9700
www.yourmortgage.co.uk
Monthly. Owner: Incisive Media.
Editor: Paula John

Your New Home
01732 878800
www.yournewhome.co.uk
6pa. Owner: New Concept.
Editor: Karen Keeman

● Motoring

4x4 Magazine
020 8726 8374
www.4x4i.com
Monthly. Owner: IPC Media.
Editor: John Carroll

100% Biker
01244 663400
www.100-biker.co.uk
Monthly. Owner: Jazz Publishing.
Editor: Nick Samson

911 & Porsche World Magazine
020 8655 6400
www.chpltd.com
Monthly. Owner: CH Publications.
Editor: Steve Bennett

Advanced Driving
01483 230300
www.iam.org.uk
3pa. Owner: Institute of Advanced
Motorists. Editor: Ian Webb

American Motorcycle Dealer
01892 511516
www.dealer-world.com
Monthly. Owner: Dealer World.
Editor: Robin Bradley

Audi Driver
01525 750500
www.autometrix.co.uk
Monthly. Owner: AutoMetrix
Publications. Editor: Paul Harris

Autocar
020 8267 5000
www.autocarmagazine.co.uk
Weekly. Owner: Haymarket.
Editor: Steve Copley

Auto Express
020 7907 6000
www.autoexpress.co.uk
Weekly. Owner: Dennis.
Editor: David Johns

Auto Italia
01707 273999
www.auto-italia.co.uk
13pa. Owner: TRMG. Editor: Philip Ward

AutoTrader
020 8544 7000
www.autotrader.co.uk
Weekly. Owner: Trader Media Group

The Automobile
01483 268818
Monthly. Owner: Enthusiast
Publishing. Editor: Michael Bowler

Back Street Heroes
020 7772 8300
www.insidecom.co.uk
Monthly. Owner: Ocean Media.
Editor: Stu Garland

Banzai
01732 748000
www.banzaimagazine.com
Monthly. Owner: Unity Media.
Editor: Joe Clifford

BBC Top Gear
020 8433 2313
www.topgear.com
Monthly. Owner: BBC Worldwide.
Editor: Michael Harvey

Bike
01733 468000
www.bikemagazine.co.uk
12pa. Owner: Bauer.
Editor: John Westlake

BMW Car
01732 748000
www.bmwcarmagazine.com
Monthly. Owner: Unity Media.
Editor: Bob Harper

Car
01733 468379
www.car-magazine.co.uk
12pa. Owner: Bauer.
Editor: Jason Barlow

Car Mechanics
01959 541444
www.carmechanicsmag.co.uk
Monthly. Owner: Kelsey Publishing.
Editor: Peter Simpson

CarSport Magazine
028 9078 3200
www.carsportmag.net
Monthly. Owner: Greer Publications.
Editor: Pat Burns

Classic & Sports Car
020 8267 5000
www.classicandsportscar.com
Monthly. Owner: Haymarket.
Editor: James Elliott

Classic American
0161 877 9977
www.classic-american.com
Monthly. Owner: Guardian Media
Group. Editor: Ben Klemenzson

Classic Bike
01733 468000
www.bauer.co.uk
12pa. Owner: Bauer. Editor: Hugo Wilson

The Classic Bike Guide
01507 529404
www.classicbikeguide.com
Monthly. Owner: Mortons Media
Group. Editor: Tim Britton

Classic Car
01733 468000
www.classiccarmagazine.co.uk
12pa. Owner: Bauer. Editor: Phil Bell

Classic Car Weekly
01733 347559
www.classic-car-weekly.co.uk
Weekly. Owner: Kelsey Publishing.
Editor: Phil Weaving

Classic Ford
01225 442244
www.classicfordmag.co.uk
Monthly. Owner: Future.
Editor: Steve Phillips

Classic Military Vehicle
01959 541444
www.kelsey.co.uk
Monthly. Owner: Kelsey Publishing.
Editor: John Blackman

Classic Motor Monthly
01204 657212
www.classicmotor.co.uk
Monthly. Editor: John Hodson

Classic Motorcycle
01507 529300
www.classicmotorcycle.co.uk
Monthly. Owner: Mortons Media
Group. Editor: James Robinson

Classic Racer
01507 529300
www.classicracer.com
Bi-monthly. Owner: Mortons Media
Group. Editor: Malcolm Wheeler

Classics
01225 442244
www.futurenet.com
13pa. Owner: Future.
Editor: Gary Stretton

Custom Car
01959 541444
www.kelsey.co.uk
Monthly. Owner: Kelsey Publishing.
Editor: Dave Biggadyke

Dirt Bike Rider
01524 834077
www.dirtbikerider.com
Monthly. Editor: Sean Lawless

Enjoying MG
01954 231125
www.mgcars.org.uk
Monthly. Owner: Polestar Colchester.
Editor: Richard Ladds

Evo
020 7907 6000
www.evo.co.uk
Monthly. Owner: Dennis.
Editor: Harrison Metcalfe

Fast Bikes
01225 442244
www.fastbikesmag.com
www.futurenet.com
13pa. Owner: Future.
Editor: Richard Newland

Fast Car
01689 887200
www.fastcar.co.uk
www.futurenet.com
13pa. Owner: Future.
Editor: Steve Chalmers

Fast Ford
01225 442244
www.fastfordmag.co.uk
Monthly. Owner: Future.
Editor: Simon Woolley

Good Motoring
01342 825676
www.motoringassist.com
Quarterly. Owner: Gem Motoring
Assistant editor: James Luckhurst

Intersection
020 7608 1166
www.intersectionmagazine.com
Quarterly. Owner: Intersection Media.
Editor: Dan Ross

Jaguar Driver
01582 419332
www.jaguardriver.co.uk
Monthly. Owner: Jaguar Drivers Club.
Editor: Steve Fermore

Jaguar World Monthly
01959 541444
www.jaguar-world.com
Monthly. Owner: Kelsey Publishing.
Editor: Matt Skelton

Land Rover Enthusiast
01379 890056
www.landroverenthusiast.com
Monthly. Editor: James Taylor

Land Rover Owner International
01733 468000
www.lro.com
13pa. Owner: Bauer.
Editor: John Pearson

Land Rover World
020 8726 8000
www.landroverworld.co.uk
Monthly. Owner: IPC Media.
Editor: John Carroll

Lexus Magazine
020 7449 1500
www.mccann.com
4pa. Owner: Story Worldwide.
Editor: Claire Dobel

LRM — Land Rover Monthly
01359 240066
www.lrm.co.uk
*Monthly. Editor: Richard Howell-
Thomas*

MaxPower
01733 468000
www.maxpower.co.uk
13pa. Owner: Bauer.
Editor: Simon Penson

Mercedes
01789 490530
3pa. Owner: Impact Press & PR.
Editor: Eric Lafone

Mercedes Enthusiast
020 8639 4400
www.mercedesenthusiast.co.uk
Monthly. Owner: Sundial Magazines.
Editor: Dan Trent

MG Enthusiast Magazine
01733 246500
www.mg-enthusiast.com
6pa. Editor: Simon Goldsworthy

Mini Magazine
01225 442244
www.minimag.co.uk
Monthly. Owner: Future.
Editor: Mark Robinson

MiniWorld
020 8726 8364
www.ipcmedia.com
Monthly. Owner: IPC Media.
Editor: Monty Watkins

Motor Cycle News (MCN)
01733 468000
www.motorcyclenews.com
Weekly. Owner: Bauer.
Editor: Marc Potter

Motor Sport
020 8267 5000
www.haymarketpublishing.co.uk
Monthly. Owner: Haymarket.
Editor: Matt Burt

Motorcycle Mechanics
01507 529442
www.classicmechanics.com
*Monthly. Owner: Mortons Media
Group. Editor: Rod Gibson*

Motorcycle Racer
01353 665577
www.motorcycleracer.com
Monthly. Owner: MB Media.
Editor: Larry Carter

Motorcycle Rider
01652 680060
www.bmf.co.uk
4pa. Owner: RBP. Editor: Andy Dukes

Motorcycle Sport & Leisure
01507 529300
www.mslmagazine.co.uk
*Monthly. Owner: Mortons Media
Group. Editor: Phil Turner*

Motoring & Leisure
01273 744757
www.csma.uk.com
10pa. Owner: CSMA.
Editor: David Arnold

Performance Bikes
01733 468000
www.performancebikes.co,uk
Monthly. Owner: Bauer.
Editor: Tim Thompson

Performance VW
01732 748000
www.performancevwmag.com
Monthly. Owner: Unity Media.
Editor: Elliot Roberts

Peugeot Rapport
0117 925 1696
www.specialistuk.com
3pa. Owner: Specialist.
Editor: Karen Ellison

Porsche Post
01608 652911
www.porscheclubgb.com
Monthly. Owner: Stephen Mummery

Post Office Motoring
0191 418 3970
4pa. Owner: The Post Office Auto Club.
Editor: Alan Fairbairn

Practical Classics
01733 468000
www.bauer.co.uk
13pa. Owner: Bauer. Editor: Matt Wright

Redline
01225 442244
www.redlinemag.co.uk
13pa. Owner: Future. Editor: Dan Lewis

The Renault Magazine
01737 786800
www.brooklandsgroup.com
4pa. Owner: Brooklands Publishing.
Editor: Ann Wallace

Ride
01733 468000
www.bauer.co.uk
13pa. Owner: Bauer. Editor: Steve Rose

Saab Magazine
01603 664242
www.archant.co.uk
2pa. Owner: Archant. Editor: Zoe Francis

Safety Fast!
01235 555552
www.mgcc.co.uk
Monthly. Editor: Andy Knott

Scootering
01507 529300
www.scootering.com
*Monthly. Owner: Mortons Media
Group. Editor: Andy Gillard*

Street Fighters
020 7772 8300
www.insidecom.co.uk
*Monthly. Owner: Inside
Communications. Editor: Stu Garland*

SuperBike Magagazine
020 8726 8445
www.superbike.co.uk
Monthly. Owner: IPC Media.
Editor: Kenny Pryde

Tag Magazine
01507 529408
www.twistngo.com
*Bi-Monthly. Owner: Mortons Media
Group. Editor: Mau Spencer*

Torque
01455 891515
www.triumph.co.uk
*Quarterly. Owner: Riders Association
of Triumph. Editor: Simon Carter*

Total Vauxhall
01225 442244
www.totalvauxhall.co.uk
Monthly. Owner: Future.
Editor: Barton Brisland

Used Bike Guide
01507 529300
www.usedbikeguide.com
*Monthly. Owner: Mortons Media
Group. Editor: Chris Pearson*

VM — Vauxhall
01582 426909
www.vmonline.co.uk
*3pa. Owner: Brooklands Publishing.
Editor: Michelle Howard*

Volks World
020 8726 8347
www.volksworld.com
*Monthly. Owner: IPC Media.
Editor: Ivan McCutcheon*

Volkswagen Driver
01525 750500
www.autometrix.co.uk
*Monthly. Owner: AutoMetrix
Publications. Editor: Neil Birkitt*

The Volvo Magazine
020 7747 0700
www.redwoodgroup.net
*3pa. Owner: Redwood.
Editor: Zac Assemakis*

What Car?
020 8267 5000
www.whatcar.co.uk
*Monthly. Owner: Haymarket.
Editor: Steve Fowler*

● Photography

Digital Camera Buyer
01202 5862000
www.digicambuyer.co.uk
*13pa. Owner: Imagine.
Editor: Chris Lean*

Digital Camera Magazine
01225 442244
www.dcmag.co.uk
*13pa. Owner: Future.
Editor: Marcus Hawkins*

Digital Photographer
01202 5862000
www.dphotographer.co.uk
*13pa. Owner: Imagine.
Deputy editor: Debbie Allen*

Photography Monthly
0845 650 1065
www.photographymonthly.co.uk
*Monthly. Owner: Archant.
Editor: Will Cheung*

What Digital Camera
020 3148 5000
www.what-digital-camera.com
*Monthly. Owner: IPC Media.
Editor: Nigel Atherton*

Which Digital Camera?
01799 544240
www.archant.co.uk
*Monthly. Owner: Archant.
Deputy editor: Darren Harbar*

● Puzzles

100 Crosswords
01737 378700
www.puzzler.co.uk
*13pa. Owner: Puzzler Media.
Editor: Debbie Hardy*

Code Crackers
01737 378700
www.puzzler.co.uk
*13pa. Owner: Puzzler Media.
Editor: Charles Sloan*

Fundoku
0870 787 9234
www.puzzler.co.uk
*Monthly. Owner: Puzzler Media.
Editor: Ariane Blok*

Kakuro
0870 428 1295
www.puzzler.co.uk
*Monthly. Owner: Puzzler Media.
Editor: Ariane Blok*

Kriss Kross
01737 378700
www.puzzler.co.uk
*13pa. Owner: Puzzler Media.
Editor: Jo MacLeod*

Logic Problems
01737 378700
www.puzzler.co.uk
*13pa. Owner: Puzzler Media.
Editor: Steve Bull*

Pocket Puzzler Crosswords
01737 378700
www.puzzler.co.uk
13pa. Owner: Puzzler Media.

Puzzle Compendium
01737 378700
www.puzzler.co.uk
*10pa. Owner: Puzzler Media.
Editor: Birgitta Bingham*

Puzzle Corner Special
01737 378700
www.puzzler.co.uk
*10pa. Owner: Puzzler Media.
Editor: Debbie Hardy*

Puzzle Selection
020 7241 8000
www.bauer.co.uk
*Monthly. Owner: H Bauer.
Editor: Francesca Clementis*

Puzzler
01737 378700
www.puzzler.co.uk
*13pa. Owner: Puzzler Media.
Editor: Catherine Filby*

Puzzler Quiz Kids
01737 378700
www.puzzler.co.uk
*7pa. Owner: Puzzler Media.
Editor: Jackie Guthrie*

Sudoku
01737 378700
www.puzzler.co.uk
*8pa. Owner: Puzzler Media.
Contact: Ariane Blok*

Sudoku Puzzles
0870 787 9306
www.puzzler.co.uk
*Monthly. Owner: Puzzler Media.
Editor: Ariane Blok*

Take a Break
020 7241 8000
www.bauer.co.uk
*Weekly. Owner: H Bauer.
Editor: John Dale*

Take a Crossword
020 7241 8000
www.bauer.co.uk
*13pa. Owner: H Bauer.
Editor: David Moore*

Take a Puzzle
020 7241 8000
www.bauer.co.uk
*13pa. Owner: H Bauer.
Editor: Michael Jones*

● Sport

LCA
020 8847 0100
*Monthly. Owner: Tennis GB.
Editor: Nigel Billen*

Air Gun World
01672 870453
www.airgunshooting.org
*Monthly. Owner: Archant.
Editor: Terry Doe*

Air Gunner
01275 848649
www.archant.co.uk
*Monthly. Owner: Archant.
Editor: Nigel Allen*

Angler's Mail
020 7261 5829
www.ipcmedia.com
*Weekly. Owner: IPC Media.
Editor: Tim Knight*

Angling Times
01733 237111
www.gofishing.co.uk
*Weekly. Owner: Bauer.
Editor: Richard Lee*

The Arsenal Magazine
020 7704 4138
www.arsenal.com
*Monthly. Owner: Arsenal Football
Club. Editor: Andy Exley*

Athletics Weekly
01733 898440
www.athletics-weekly.com
*Weekly. Owner: Descartes Publishing.
Editor: Jason Henderson*

Autosport
020 8267 5000
www.autosport.com
*Weekly. Owner: Haymarket.
Editor: Biranit Goren*

Badminton Magazine
01908 268400
www.badmintonengland.co.uk
*Quarterly. Owner: Badminton
England. Editor: Rachel Pullen*

Boxing Monthly
020 8986 4141
www.boxing-monthly.co.uk
*Monthly. Owner: Topwave.
Editor: Glyn Leach*

Boxing News
020 7618 3069
www.boxingnewsonline.net
*Weekly. Owner: Newsquest.
Editor: Claude Abrams*

British Homing World
01938 552360
www.pigeonracing.com
Weekly. Editor: Steven Richards

British Waterski & Wakeboard
01932 570885
www.britishwaterski.org.uk
5pa. Owner: British Water Ski.
Editor: Nikki Patefield

Bunkered
0141 950 2216
www.bunkered.co.uk
8pa. Owner: Pro Sports Promotions.
Editor: Martin Dempster

Calcio Italia
01225 489984
www.calcioitalia.co.uk
Monthly. Owner: Anthem Publishing.
Editor: John Taylor

Canoe Focus
01480 465081
www.canoefocus.co.uk
Bi-monthly. Owner: 2B Graphic
Design. Editor: Peter Tranter

Carpworld
0114 258 0812
www.anglingpublications.co.uk
Monthly. Owner: Angling Publications.
Publishing editor: Tim Paisley

Carve Surfing Magazine
01637 878074
www.orcasurf.co.uk
8pa. Owner: Orca Publications.
Editor: Chris Power

Celtic View
0141 551 4218
www.celticfc.net
Weekly. Owner: Cre8.
Editor: Paul Cuddihy

Climb
01298 72801
www.planetfear.com
Monthly. Owner: Greenshires Group.
Editor: Neil Pearson

Climber
01778 391000
www.climber.co.uk
Monthly. Owner: Warners.
Editor: Bernard Newman

Combat
0121 344 3737
www.martialartsinprint.com
Monthly. Owner: Martial Arts
Publications. Editor: Paul Clifton

Combat & Survival
01484 435011
www.combatandsurvival.com
Monthly. Owner: MAI Publications.
Editor: Bob Morrison

Country Walking
01733 468000
www.livefortheoutdoors.com
Monthly. Owner: Bauer.
Editor: Jonathan Manning

Cricket World Magazine
01476 530176
www.cricketworld.com
Quarterly. Editor: Alistair Symondson

Cycle
01723 377521
www.ctc.org.uk
Bi-monthly. Owner: Cyclists' Touring
Club. Editor: Dan Joyce

Cycle Sport
020 8726 8000
www.cyclesport.co.uk
Monthly. Owner: IPC Media.
Editor: Robert Garbutt

Cycling Plus
01225 442244
www.cyclingplus.co.uk
13pa. Owner: Future.
Editor: Tony Farrelly

Cycling Weekly
020 8726 8000
www.cyclingweekly.co.uk
Weekly. Owner: IPC Media.
Editor: Robert Garbutt

Daily Mail Ski & Snowboard Magazine
020 8515 2000
www.metroskishow.co.uk
6pa (Sep-Mar). Owner: DMG World
Media. Editor: Henry Druce

Darts World
020 8650 6580
www.dartsworld.com
Monthly. Owner: World Magazines.
Editor: Tony Wood

Direct Hit
08712 461100
www.surreycricket.com
5pa. Owner: Trinorth.
Editor: Matt Thacker

Dirt MTB Magazine
01202 606118
www.dirtmag.co.uk
Bi-monthly. Owner: 4130 Publications.
Editor: Mike Rose

Distance Running
020 7209 3193
www.inpositionmedia.co.uk
4pa. Owner: In Position Media.
Editor: Hugh Jones

DIVE Magazine
020 8332 8401
www.divemagazine.co.uk
Monthly. Editor: Simon Rogerson

Diver
020 8943 4288
www.divernet.com
Monthly. Owner: The Diver Group.
Editor: Steve Weinman

Document Skateboard
01202 606118
www.documentskateboard.com
9pa. Owner: 4130 Publications.
Editor: Percy Dean

Document Snowboard
01733 293250
www.fall-line.co.uk
7pa (Oct-Mar). Owner: Fall-Line
Media. Editor: Rachel Devlin

Dog Training Weekly
01348 875011
www.dogtrainingweekly.com
Weekly. Owner: Canine Press.
Editor: Angela Barrah

England Rugby
01707 273999
www.rfu.com
Quarterly. Owner: TRMG.
Editor: Howard Johnson

Equi-Ads
01738 567700
www.equiads.net
Monthly. Editor: Mary Moore

Evening Times Wee Red Book
0141 302 6606
Yearly. Owner: Newsquest.
Editor: Frasier Gibson

Eventing
020 3148 5000
www.ipcmedia.com
Monthly. Owner: IPC Media.
Editor: Julie Harding

The Evertonian
0151 285 8412
Monthly. Owner: Trinity Mirror.
Editor: Steve Hanrahan

F1 Racing
020 8267 5000
www.haymarketpublishing.co.uk
Monthly. Owner: Haymarket.
Editor: Matt Bishop

The Fairway Golfing News
01633 666700
www.fairway.org.uk
Monthly. Editor: John Doherty

Fall-Line Skiing
01733 293250
www.fall-line.co.uk
Monthly (Oct-Feb). Owner: Fall-Line
Media. Editor: Hannah Engelkamp

The Field
020 3148 5000
www.thefield.co.uk
Monthly. Owner: IPC Media.
Editor: Jonathan Young

Fighters
0121 344 3737
www.martialartsinprint.com
Monthly. Owner: Martial Arts
Publications. Editor: Marcus Haig

First Down
020 7005 2000
www.independent.co.uk
Weekly. Owner: Independent News &
Media (UK). Editor: Tony Prince

FitPro
0870 513 3434
www.fitpro.com
Bi-monthly. Owner: Fitness
Professionals. Editor: Heather Brown

Flex
01423 504516
www.flex-europe.com
Monthly. Owner: Weider Publishing.
Editor: Geoff Evans

Football Insider
020 7963 7888
www.sportservicesgroup.com
Bi-annual; also daily email.
Owner: PA Sport Services Group.
Editor: Stuart.info@yahoo.com

Football Italia
01494 564564
www.channel4.co.uk/sport
/football_italia
Monthly. Owner: Anthem Publishing.
Editor: John Taylor

FourFourTwo
020 8267 5000
www.haymarketpublishing.co.uk
Monthly. Owner: Haymarket.
Editor: Hugh Sleight

Gamefisher
020 7283 5838
www.salmon-trout.org
2pa. Owner: Salmon & Trout Association. Editor: Carmel Jorgensen

Going for Golf
01268 554100
www.goingforgolf.com
Quarterly. Editor: Neil Webber

The Golf Guide:
Where to Play / Where to Stay
0141 887 0428
www.holidayguides.com
Yearly. Owner: FHG Guides.
Editor: Anne Cuthbertson

Golf International
020 7828 3003
www.golfinternationalmag.co.uk
10pa. Editor: Richard Simmons

Golf Monthly
020 3148 5000
www.golf-monthly.co.uk
Monthly. Owner: IPC Media.
Editor: Michael Harris

Golf News
01273 772752
www.golfnews.co.uk
Monthly. Owner: BlueGreen.
Editor: Nick Bayly

Golf World
01733 468000
www.bauer.co.uk
Monthly. Owner: Bauer.
Editor: Chris Jones

Good Ski Guide
01372 468140
www.goodskiguide.com
4pa in winter. Owner: Profile Sports Media. Editor: John Hill

The Gymnast
0116 247 8766
www.british-gymnastics.org
Bi-monthly. Editor: Trevor Low

Improve Your Coarse Fishing
01733 237111
www.gofishing.co.uk
Monthly. Owner: Bauer.
Editor: Kevin Green

In The Know
0870 333 2062
www.itkonline.com
Monthly. Editor: Darren Croft

International Rugby News
020 7005 2000
www.independent.co.uk
Monthly. Owner: Independent News & Media (UK). Editor: John Edwards

Ireland's Equestrian Magazine
01623 474227
www.irelandsequestrian.co.uk
Bi-monthly. Owner: MAI Publications. Editor: Sue Porter

Karting
01689 897123
www.kartingmagazine.com
Monthly. Owner: Lodgemark Press.
Editor: Mark Burgess

The Kop
0151 285 8412
Monthly. Owner: Trinity Mirror.
Editor: Paul Dove

Lady Golfer
01274 851323
Monthly. Owner: Sports Publications.
Editor: Mickey Walker

LFC
0151 285 8412
Weekly. Owner: Trinity Mirror.
Editor: Steve Hanrahan

Liverpool Monthly
01392 664141
Monthly. Owner: LCD Publishing.
Editor: Joanne Trump

London Cyclist
020 7234 9310
www.lcc.org.uk
Bi-monthly. Owner: London Cycling Campaign. Editor: Lynette Eyb

Martial Arts Illustrated
01484 435011
www.martialarts.co.uk
Monthly. Owner: MAI Publications.
Editor: Bob Sykes

Match
01733 468000
www.matchmag.co.uk
Weekly. Owner: Bauer.
Editor: Ian Forster

Match Fishing Magazine
01327 311999
www.total-fishing.com
Monthly. Owner: DHP.
Editor: Dave Harrell

Moto
01202 606118
www.motomagazine.co.uk
Monthly. Owner: 4130 Publications.
Editor: Geoff Perrett

Motor Sport
020 7349 3150
Monthly. Owner: Stratfield Ltd.
Editor: Gordon Crookshank

Motorsport News
020 8267 5385
www.haymarketpublishing.co.uk
Weekly. Owner: Haymarket.
Editor: Matt Burt

Motorsports Now!
01691 830175
www.msauk.org
Quarterly. Owner: The Really Motoring Group (TRMG). Editor: Pete Wadsworth

Mountain Bike Rider
020 8726 8000
www.mountainbikerider.co.uk
Monthly. Owner: IPC Media.
Editor: John Kitchiner

Mountain Biking UK
01225 442244
www.mbuk.com
13pa. Owner: Future.
Editor: Tim Manley

Muscle & Fitness
01423 504516
www.muscle-fitness-europe.com
Monthly. Owner: Weider Publishing.
Editor: Geoff Evans

Musclemag International
0845 345 0916
www.emusclemag.com
Monthly. Owner: Tropicana Health & Fitness. Editor: Gary Hill

National Club Golfer
01274 851323
www.nationalclubgolfer.com
Monthly. Owner: Sports Publications Ltd. Editor: Dan Murphy

The Non-League Paper
020 8971 4333
www.thenlp.net
Weekly. Owner: Football Paper Ltd.
Editor: David Emery

The Official Tour de France Guide
020 7042 4761
www.procycling.com
Yearly. Owner: Future.
Editor: Peter Cossins

PQ International
020 7622 1048
www.pqinternational.co.uk
4pa. Owner: Euromedia Services.
Editor: Roger Chatterton-Newman

Procycling
020 7042 4000
www.procycling.com
Monthly. Owner: Future.
Editor: Pete Cossings

Pull!
01780 766199
www.countrypursuits.co.uk
10pa. Owner: Bourne Publishing Group. Editor: Mike Barnes

Raceform Update
020 7293 3000
www.racingpost.co.uk
Weekly. Owner: Trinity Mirror.
Editor: Bernie Ford

Racing Calendar
0870 871 2000
www.britishcycling.org.uk
Quarterly. Owner: British Cycling Federation. Editor: Phil Ingham

Racing Pigeon Weekly
01689 600006
www.racingpigeon.co.uk
Weekly. Editor: Steve Dunn

Racing Post
020 7293 3000
www.racingpost.co.uk
Daily. Owner: Trinity Mirror.
Editor: Chris Smith

Ride BMX
01202 606118
www.ridebmxmag.co.uk
12pa. Owner: 4130 Publications.
Editor: Mark Noble

Rugby League World
01484 401895
www.totalrl.com
Monthly. Owner: League Publications.
Editor: Richard De La Riviere

Rugby Leaguer & League Express
01484 401895
www.totalrl.com
Weekly. Owner: League Publications.
Editor: Martyn Sadler

Rugby Times
01484 401895
www.rugbytimes.com
Weekly. Owner: League Publications.
Editor: Jon Newcombe

Rugby World
020 3148 5000
www.rugbyworld.com
Monthly. Owner: IPC Media.
Editor: Paul Morgan

Runner's World
020 7439 5000
www.runnersworld.co.uk
Monthly. Owner: National Magazine
Company. Editor: Andy Dickson

Running Fitness
01733 347559
www.running-fitness.co.uk
Monthly. Owner: Kelsey Publishing.
Editor: David Castle

Sea Angler
01733 237111
www.bauer.co.uk
Monthly. Owner: Bauer.
Editor: Mel Russ

Seahorse
01590 671899
www.seahorsemagazine.com
Monthly. Owner: Fairmead
Communications. Editor: Andrew Hurst

Shoot Monthly
020 3148 5000
www.shootmonthly.co.uk
Monthly. Owner: IPC Media.
Editor: Colin Mitchell

The Shooting Gazette
020 3148 5000
www.ipcmedia.com
Monthly. Owner: IPC Media.
Editor: Will Hetherington

Shooting Sports
01206 525697
www.shooting-sports.net
Monthly. Owner: Aceville Publications.
Editor: Peter Moore

Shooting Times
020 3148 5000
www.shootingtimes.co.uk
Weekly. Owner: IPC Media.
Editor: Camilla Clarke

Sidewalk Skateboarding Magazine
020 7332 9700
www.sidewalkmag.com
Monthly. Owner: Factory Media.
Editor: Ben Powell

Snooker Scene
0121 585 9188
www.snookersceneshop.co.uk
Monthly. Owner: Evertons News
Agency. Editor: Clive Everton

Speedway Star
020 8335 1100
www.speedwaystar.net
Weekly. Owner: Pinegen.
Editor: Richard Clark

Sport Cities and Venues
020 7963 7888
www.sportservicesgroup.com
Bi-annual; also weekly email.
Owner: PA Sport Services Group.
Editor: Rory Squires

Sport Diver
01799 544200
www.sportdiver.co.uk
Monthly. Owner: Archant.
Editor: Mark Evans

Sport Insider
020 7963 7888
www.sportservicesgroup.com
Bi-annual; weekly email, Sport Insider.
Owner: PA Sport Services Group.
Editor: Rory Squires.

Sporting Gun
020 3148 5000
www.ipcmedia.com
Monthly. Owner: IPC Media.
Editor: Robin Scott

Sporting Shooter
020 7751 4800
www.sportingshooter.co.uk
Monthly. Owner: Archant.
Editor: James Marchington

Sportsbetting Update
020 7963 7888
www.sportservicesgroup.com
Weekly email. Owner: PA Sport
Services Group. Editor: Rory Squires

Sportsmedia
020 7963 7888
www.sportservicesgroup.com
Bi-annual; also daily email.
Owner: PA Sport Services Group.
Editor: Rory Squires

The Squash Player
01753 775511
www.squashplayer.co.uk
6pa. Owner: McKenzie Publishing.
Editor: Ian McKenzie

Summit
0870 010 4878
www.thebmc.co.uk
Quarterly. Owner: Warners Group.
Editor: Alex Messenger

Surf News
01637 878074
www.britsurf.co.uk
8pa. Owner: Orca Publications.
Editor: Chris Power

The Surfer's Path
020 7886 0680
www.surferspath.com
Bi-monthly. Owner: Factory Media.
Editor: Alex Dick-Read

Swimming
01509 632230
www.britishswimming.org
Monthly. Owner: Amateur Swimming
Association. Editor: Peter Hassall

Swimming Pool News
0870 442 0935, 01954 212906
www.swimmingpoolnews.co.uk
Bi-monthly. Owner: Go Publishing.
Editor: Alan Lewis

Taekwondo & Korean Martial Arts Magazine
0121 344 3737
www.martialartsinprint.com
Monthly. Owner: Martial Arts
Publications. Editor: Paul Clifton

Thoroughbred Owner and Breeder
020 7408 0903
www.racehorseowners.net
Monthly. Owner: Racehorse Owners
Association. Editor: Richard Griffiths

Today's Golfer
01733 468000
www.bauer.co.uk
Monthly. Owner: Bauer.
Editor: Andy Calton

Today's Pilot
01780 755131
www.todayspilot.co.uk
Monthly. Owner: Key Publishing.
Editor: Dave Unwin

Total Carp
01327 311999
www.total-fishing.com
Monthly. Owner: DHP.
Editor: Mark Coulson

Traditional Karate
0121 344 3737
www.martialartsinprint.com
Monthly. Owner: Martial Arts
Publications. Editor: Paul Clifton

Trail
01733 468000
www.trailroutes.com
Monthly. Owner: Bauer.
Editor: Guy Procter

Trials & Motorcross News
01524 834030
www.tmxnews.co.uk
Weekly. Owner: Johnston Press.
Editor: John Dickinson

Trout & Salmon
01733 237111
www.gofishing.co.uk
Monthly. Owner: Bauer.
Editor: Andrew Flitcroft

Ultra-Fit
01736 350204
www.ultra-fitmagazine.com
9pa. Editor: Charles Mays

Warren Miller's Tour Magazine
020 7240 4071
www.warrenmiller.co.uk
Yearly. Owner: Black Diamond.
Editor: Guy Chambers

What Mountain Bike
01225 442244
www.whatmtb.co.uk
4pa. Owner: Future.
Editor: Jane Bentley

When Saturday Comes
020 7729 1110
www.wsc.co.uk
Monthly. Editor: Andy Lyons

White Lines Snowboarding Magazine
020 7332 9700
www.whitelines.com
6pa (Oct–Mar). Owner: Spectrum
Media. Editor: Ed Blomfield

Windsurf Magazine
01993 811181
www.windsurf.co.uk
10pa. Owner: Arcwind.
Editor: Mark Kasprowicz

World Soccer
020 7261 5714
www.worldsoccer.com
Monthly. Owner: IPC Media.
Editor: Gavin Hamilton

Yachting Monthly
020 7261 6040
www.yachtingmonthly.com
Monthly. Owner: IPC Media.
Editor: Paul Gelder
Yachting World
020 7261 6800
www.ybw.com
Monthly. Owner: IPC Media.
Editor: Andrew Bray
Yachts & Yachting
01702 582245
www.yachtsandyachting.com
Fortnightly. Editor: Gael Pawson

● Travel

A Place in the Sun
01737 786820
www.aplaceinthesunmag.co.uk
Monthly. Owner: Brooklands Media.
Editor: Matt Havercroft
Activity Wales
01437 766888
www.activitywales.com
Yearly. Editor: Matthew Evans
Adventure Travel
01789 450000
www.atmagazine.co.uk
Bi-monthly. Editor: Lara Dunn
Arab Traveller
01621 842745
Bi-monthly. Owner: Fanar Publishing
WLL. Editor: Jeremy Wright
Bradmans Business Travel Guides
020 7613 8777
www.bradmans.com
Yearly. Owner: Ink Publishing.
Editor: Richard Bence
Canada News
01323 726040
www.worldofproperty.co.uk
Monthly. Owner: Outbound
Publishing. Editor: Paul Beasley
CN Traveller
(Condé Nast Traveller)
020 7499 9080
www.cntraveller.com
Monthly. Owner: Condé Nast.
Editor: Sarah Miller
Destination New Zealand
01323 726040
www.worldofproperty.co.uk
Monthly. Owner: Outbound
Publishing. Editor: Paul Beasley
Easyjet Magazine
020 7613 8777
www.easyjetinflight.com
Monthly. Owner: Ink Publishing.
Editor: Piers Townley
Edinburgh Shopping
& Tourist Guide
01506 508001
2pa. Owner: Capital Group.
Editor: Roger Sadler
Education Travel Magazine
020 7440 4025
www.hothousemedia.com
Bi-monthly. Owner: Hothouse Media.
Editor: Amy Baker

Emigrate America
01323 726040
www.worldofproperty.co.uk
Monthly. Owner: Outbound
Publishing. Editor: Paul Beasley
Emigrate Australia
www.worldofproperty.co.uk
www.emigrate2006.co.uk
Monthly. Owner: Outbound
Publishing. Editor: Paul Beasley
Enjoy Dorset & Hampshire
Magazine
01202 737678
www.enjoydorset.co.uk
Yearly. Owner: Eastwick Publishing.
Editor: Zoe Wilson
Ensign
01202 414200
Yearly. Editor: Karen Portnall
Essentially America
020 7243 6954
www.phoenixip.com
Quarterly. Owner: Phoenix
International Publishing.
Editor: Mary Moore Mason
Flybe. Uncovered
020 8649 7233
www.bmipublications.com
Bi-monthly. Owner: BMI Publications.
Editor: Alan Orbell
Food & Travel
020 7501 0511
www.foodandtravel.com
Monthly. Owner: Green Pea
Publishing. Editor: Claire Shiells
France
01242 216050
www.francemag.com
Monthly. Owner: Archant.
Editor: Nick Wall
French Property News
020 8543 3113
www.french-property-news.com
Monthly. Owner: Archant.
Editor: Caroline Pentonvoak
Gap Year
0870 241 6704
www.gapyear.com
Website. Editor: Tom Griffiths
Geographical
020 8332 2713
www.geographical.co.uk
Monthly. Owner: Circle Publishing.
Editor: Geordie Torr
Greece
01225 786835
www.merricksmedia.co.uk
10pa. Owner: Merricks Media.
Editor: Diana Cambridge
High Life
020 7534 2400
www.cedarcom.co.uk
Monthly. Owner: Cedar.
Editor: Kerry Smith
Holiday Which?
020 7770 7564
www.which.co.uk
4pa. Owner: Which?
Editor: Lorna Cowan

Holiday, The RCI Magazine
01536 310101
www.rci.com
3pa. Owner: RCI Europe.
Editor: Simon McGrath
Homes Overseas
020 7002 8300
www.homesoverseas.co.uk
Monthly. Owner: Globespan Media.
Editor: Mike Hayes
In Britain
020 7751 4800
www.archant.co.uk
Bi-monthly. Owner: Archant.
Editor: Andrea Spain
In London
020 7611 7891
www.morriseurope.com
Bi-monthly. Owner: Morris Visitor
Publications. Editor: Chris Johnson
Italia
01225 489984
www.italia-magazine.com
Monthly. Owner: Anthem Publishing.
Editor: Amanda Robinson
Italy
01305 266360
www.italymag.co.uk
Monthly. Owner: Poundbury
Publishing. Editor: Melissa Ormaston
Kuoni World Magazine
01306 744555
www.kuoni.co.uk
4pa. Owner: Kuoni Travel.
Editor: Naomi Wilkinson
Livewire
020 7805 5555
www.ilng.co.uk
Quarterly. Owner: The Illustrated
London News Group.
Editor: Claire Roberts
Living France
01242 216050
www.livingfrance.com
Monthly. Owner: Archant.
Editor: Nick Wall
The London Guide
020 7611 7891
www.morriseurope.com
Monthly. Owner: Morris Visitor
Publications. Editor: Chris Johnson
London Hotel Magazine
020 7373 7282
www.goodlifemedia.co.uk
Bi-monthly. Owner: Goodlife Media.
Editor: ER Spence
London Planner
020 7242 5222
www.archant.co.uk
Monthly. Owner: Morris Visitor
Editor: Hermione Grant
Med Life
020 7841 0340
www.touchline.com
Quarterly. Owner: Touchline
Publishing. Editor: Danielle Green
My Travel Recline & Life
Magazines
020 7613 8777
www.mytravelmag.com
Quarterly. Owner: Ink Publishing.
Editor: Chloe Greenbank

National Geographic
00 1 813 979 6845
www.nationalgeographic.com
Monthly. Editor: Chris Johns

Orient-Express Magazine
020 7805 5555
4pa. Owner: The Illustrated London News Group. Editor: Alison Booth

Overseas
020 7408 0214 x205
www.rosl.org.uk
4pa. Owner: The Royal Over-Seas League. Editor: Vicky Baker

Pride of Britain
020 7389 0870
www.prideofbritainhotels.com
2pa. Owner: Freeway Media. Editor: Sophie MacKenzie

The Railway Magazine
020 3148 5000
www.ipcmedia.com
Monthly. Owner: IPC Media. Editor: Nick Pigott

Redhot Magazine
020 7613 8777
www.ontoeurope.com
Quarterly. Owner: Ink Publishing. Editor: Bethen Rider

South Africa News
01323 726040
www.southafricanews.co.uk
Bi-monthly. Owner: Outbound Publishing. Editor: Paul Beasley

Spain
0131 226 7766
www.spainmagazine.co.uk
Monthly. Owner: The Media Company. Editor: Sue Hitchen

Sunday Times Travel
020 7413 9302
www.sundaytimestravel.co.uk
Monthly. Owner: River Publishing. Editor: Ed Grenby

TNT Magazine
020 7373 3377
www.tntmagazine.com
Weekly (Mon). Owner: TNT. Editor: Christine Booth

Travel & Leisure
020 8554 4456
www.tlmags.com
4pa. Owner: Travel & Leisure Magazines. Editor: Helen Hodge

Travel Australia
01424 223111
www.consylpublishing.co.uk
2pa. Owner: Consyl Publishing. Editor: Shirley Gilbertson

Travel GBI
020 7729 4337
Monthly. Editor: Richard Cawthorne

Traveller
020 7589 3315
www.traveller.org.uk
Quarterly. Owner: WEXAS. Editor: Amy Sohanpaul

Travelmag
01672 810202
www.travelmag.co.uk
Online magazine. Editor: Jack Barker

Wanderlust
01753 620426
www.wanderlust.co.uk
Bi-monthly. Editor: Lyn Hughes

Welcome to London
020 8297 4444
www.welcometolondon.com
Bi-monthly. Owner: Pareto. Editor: Melanie Armstrong

Where London
020 7611 7891
www.morriseurope.com
Monthly. Owner: Morris Visitor Publications. Editor: Mary Anne Evans

---

● Women and health

Accent Magazine
0191 284 9994
Monthly. Editor: Kevin Wright

Al-Jamila
020 7831 8181
www.hhsaudi.com
Monthly. Owner: Saudi Research & Publishing. Editor: Sanaa Elhadethee

Asian Woman
0870 755 5501
www.asianwomanmag.com
Monthly. Owner: Asian Interactive Media. Editor: Brianne Ragel

Asthma
020 7786 5000
www.asthma.org.uk
4pa. Owner: Asthma UK. Editor: Laura Smith

A–Z of Calories
01984 623014
Bi-monthly. Owner: Octavo Publications. Editor: Gertrude Sharrock

Balance
020 7424 1010
www.diabetes.org.uk
Bi-monthly. Owner: Diabetes UK. Editor: Martin Cullen

Be Slim
01984 623014
4pa. Owner: Octavo Publications. Editor: Gertrude Sharrock

Beautiful Brides
0117 934 3742
www.thisisbristol.co.uk /beautifulbrides
4pa. Owner: BUP Niche Publications. Editor: Harry Mottram

Bella
020 7241 8000
www.bauer.co.uk
Weekly. Owner: H Bauer. Editor: Jayne Marsden

Best
020 7439 5000
www.natmags.co.uk
Weekly. Owner: National Magazine Company. Editor: Michelle Hather

Black Beauty & Hair
020 7720 2108
www.blackbeautyandhair.com
Bi-monthly. Owner: Hawker Consumer Publications. Editor: Irene Shelley

Blackhair
01376 534549
Bi-monthly. Owner: Haversham Publications. Editor: Jane MacArthur

Brides
020 7499 9080
www.bridesmagazine.co.uk
Bi-monthly. Owner: Condé Nast. Editor: Debra Joseph

Caduceus Journal
www.caduceus.info
4pa. Editor: Sarida Brown

Candis
0870 745 3002
www.candis.co.uk
Monthly. Owner: New Hall Publications. Editor: Debbie Atwell

Chat
020 3148 5000
www.ipcmedia.com
Weekly. Owner: IPC Media. Editor: Gilly Sinclair

Closer
020 7437 9011
www.closeronline.co.uk
Weekly. Owner: Bauer. Editor: Jane Johnson

Company
020 7439 5000
www.company.co.uk
Monthly. Owner: National Magazine Company. Editor: Victoria White

Cosmopolitan
020 7439 5000
www.cosmopolitan.co.uk
Monthly. Owner: National Magazine Company. Editor: Louise Court

Elle
020 7150 7000
www.hf-uk.com
Monthly. Owner: Hachette Filipacchi UK. Editor: Lorraine Candy

Emma's Diary Pregnancy Guide
media@emmasdiary.co.uk
www.emmasdiary.co.uk
Weekly. Owner: Lifecycle Marketing

Essentials
020 3148 5000
www.ipcmedia.com
Monthly. Owner: IPC Media. Editor: Julie Barton-Breck

Eve
020 8267 8223
www.evemagazine.co.uk
Monthly. Owner: Haymarket. Editor: Sara Cremer

Family Magazine
01200 453000
www.family-mag.co.uk
Quarterly. Owner: RVPL. Editor: Jeremy Nicholls

First
020 7437 9011
www.bauer.co.uk
Weekly. Owner: Bauer. Editor: Jane Ennis

For the Bride
01376 534549
www.forthebride.co.uk
Bi-monthly. Owner: For the Bride Publishing. Editor: Angela Cole

Full House
020 7406 1582
www.fullhousemagazine.co.uk
Weekly. Owner: Hubert Burda Media UK. Editor: Samm Taylor

Glamour
020 7499 9080
www.glamourmagazine.co.uk
Monthly. Owner: Condé Nast.
Editor: Jo Elvin

Grazia
020 7437 9011
www.graziamagazine.co.uk
Weekly. Owner: Bauer. Editor-in-chief:
Fiona McIntosh; editor: Jane Bruton

Hair
020 3148 5000
www.ipcmedia.com
Bi-monthly. Owner: IPC Media.
Editor: Zoe Richards

Hairflair
01376 534549
6pa. Owner: Hairflair Magazines.
Editor: Ruth Page

Hairstyles Only
01376 534549
6pa. Owner: Hairflair Magazines.
Editor: Ruth Page

Harpers & Queen
020 7439 5000
www.harpersandqueen.co.uk
Monthly. Owner: National Magazine
Company. Editor: Lucy Yeomans

Health & Fitness
01225 224422
www.hfonline.co.uk
Monthly. Owner: Future.
Editor: Mary Comber

The Health Store Magazine
0115 976 7200
www.thehealthstore.co.uk
Bi-monthly. Editor: Alison Millington

Healthy
020 7306 0304
www.therivergroup.co.uk
Bi-monthly. Owner: River Publishing.
Editor: Heather Beresford

Healthy Times
020 7819 1111
www.squareonegroup.co.uk
Quarterly. Owner: Square One Group.
Editor: Michelle Simmons

Heat
020 7437 9011
www.heatworld.com
Weekly. Owner: Bauer.
Editor: Mark Frith

Hello!
020 7667 8901
www.hellomagazine.com
Weekly; website updated daily.
Editor: Ronnie Whelan

Hia
020 7539 2270
Monthly. Owner: Saudi Printing &
Packaging Company. Editor: Mai Badr

InStyle
020 3148 5000
www.ipcmedia.com
Monthly. Owner: IPC Media.
Editor: Trish Halpin

Junior
01225 224422
www.juniormagazine.co.uk
Monthly. Owner: Future.
Editor: Catherine O'Dolan

Junior Pregnancy & Baby
020 7761 8900
www.juniormagazine.co.uk
Monthly. Owner: Future.
Editor: Debora Stottor

Ladies First
029 2039 6600
www.hilspublications.com
4pa. Owner: Hils Publications.
Editor: Hilary Ferda

The Lady
020 7379 4717
www.lady.co.uk
Weekly. Editor: Arline Usden

Marie Claire
020 3148 5000
www.ipcmedia.com
Monthly. Owner: IPC Media.
Editor: Marie O'Riordan

More!
020 7437 9011
www.moremagazine.co.uk
Fortnightly. Owner: Bauer.
Editor: Lisa Mosarski

Mother & Baby
020 7874 0200
www.bauer.co.uk
Monthly. Owner: Bauer.
Editor: Eleanor Dalrymple

MS Matters
020 8438 0700
www.mssociety.org.uk
Bi-monthly. Owner: Multiple Sclerosis
Society. Editor: Debbie Reeves

My Weekly
01382 223131
www.dcthomson.co.uk
Weekly. Owner: DC Thomson.
Editor: Sally Hampton

New Woman
020 7437 9011
www.newwoman.co.uk
Monthly. Owner: Bauer.
Editor: Lauren Libbert

New!
0871 434 1010
Weekly. Owner: Northern and Shell.
Editor: Kirsty Mouatt

Now
020 3148 5000
www.nowmagazine.com
Weekly. Owner: IPC Media.
Editor: Helen Johnson

Number Ten
020 7439 9100
www.numberten.co.uk
Bi-annual. Owner: Arberry Pink.
Editor: Laura Sheed

OK!
0871 434 1010
www.ok-magazine.com
Weekly. Owner: Northern and Shell.
Editor: Lisa Palta

Parent News UK
020 8337 6337
www.parents-news.co.uk
Monthly. Editor: Penny McCarthy

Parent Talk
020 7921 4234
www.parentalk.co.uk
Website updated weekly.
Editor: Hannah Jenkins

People
020 7322 1134
www.people.com
Weekly. Owner: Time Life.
Editor: Simon Perry

Pick Me Up
020 7261 5588
www.pick-me-up.co.uk
Weekly. Owner: IPC Media.
Editor: June Smith-Sheppard

Practical Parenting
020 3148 5000
www.ipcmedia.com
Monthly. Owner: IPC Media.
Editor: Susie Boon

Pregnancy and Birth
020 7347 1885
www.bauer.co.uk
Monthly. Owner: Bauer.
Acting Editor: Katie Holland

Pregnancy, Baby and You Magazine
01225 442244
Monthly. Owner: Future.
Editor: Claire Roberts

Pride Magazine
020 7228 3110
www.pridemagazine.com
Monthly. Owner: Pride Media.
Editor: CJ Cushnie

Prima
020 7439 5000
www.primamagazine.co.uk
Monthly. Owner: National Magazine
Company. Editor: Maire Fahey

Prima Baby
020 7439 5000
www.primababy.co.uk
Monthly. Owner: National Magazine
Company. Editor: Elaine Griffiths

Healthy For Men
020 7306 0304
www.therivergroup.co.uk
Bi-monthly. Owner: River Publishing.
Editor: Andy Darling

Red
020 7150 7000
www.redmagazine.co.uk
Monthly. Owner: Hachette Filipacchi
UK. Editor: Pam Baker

Reveal
020 7439 5000
www.natmags.co.uk
Weekly. Owner: National Magazine
Company. Editor: Michael Butcher

Rosemary Conley Diet & Fitness Magazine
01509 620444
www.rosemary-conley.co.uk
9pa. Owner: Quorn House Publishing.
Editor: Allison Barlow

She
020 7439 5000
www.she.co.uk
Monthly. Owner: National Magazine
Company. Editor: Sian Rees

Slimmer, Healthier, Fitter
01206 505972
www.slimmerrecipes.co.uk
10pa. Owner: Aceville Publications.
Editor: Rachel Callen

Slimming World
01773 546360
www.slimming-world.com
7pa. Editor: Elise Wells

Star
0871 434 1010
Weekly. Owner: Northern and Shell.
Editor: Busola Odulate

Take a Break
020 7241 8000
www.bauer.co.uk
Weekly. Owner: H Bauer.
Editor: John Dale

Tatler
020 7499 9080
www.tatler.co.uk
Monthly. Owner: Condé Nast.
Editor: Geordie Greig

That's Life!
020 7241 8000
www.bauer.co.uk
Weekly. Owner: H Bauer.
Editor: Jo Checkley

Tiara
029 2039 6600
www.hilspublications.com
3pa. Owner: Hils Publications.
Editor: Kara Williams

Top Santé Health & Beauty
020 7728 5000
www.bauer.co.uk
Monthly. Owner: Bauer.
Editor: Marina Crook

Twins, Triplets & More Magazine
0870 770 3305
www.tamba.org.uk
4pa. Owner: The Twins and
Multiple Births Association.
Editor: Jane Williams

Ulster Bride
028 9066 3311
www.ulstertatler.com
Quarterly. Owner: Ulster Tatler
Publications. Editor: Christopher Sherry

Ulster Tatler
028 9066 3311
www.ulstertatler.com
Monthly. Owner: Ulster Tatler
Publications. Editor: Christopher
Sherry

Ultra-Fit
01736 350204
www.ultra-fitmagazine.com
9pa. Editor: Charles Mays

Vanity Fair
020 7499 9080
www.vanityfair.co.uk
Monthly. Owner: Condé Nast.
Editor: Henry Porter

Vogue
020 7499 9080
www.vogue.com
Monthly. Owner: Condé Nast.
Editor: Alexandra Shulman

W
020 7240 0420
www.style.com/w
Monthly. Owner: Fairchild.
Editor: Patrick McCarthy

Wave
01273 818160
www.wavemagazine.co.uk
Monthly. Owner: The Latest.
Editor: Pearl Bates

Wedding
020 3148 5000
www.weddingandhome.co.uk
Bi-monthly. Owner: IPC Media.
Editor: Katherine Westwood

Wedding Journal
028 9045 7457
www.weddingjournalonline.com
Quarterly. Owner: Penton Group.
Editor: Tara Craig

WeightWatchers
0845 788 999
8pa. Owner: Castlebar Publishing.
Editor: Mary Francis

WM
029 2022 3333
www.icwales.co.uk
Quarterly. Owner: Trinity Mirror.
Editor: Sarah Drew Jones

Woman
020 3148 5000
020 3148 6488
www.ipcmedia.com
Weekly. Owner: IPC Media.
Editor: Jackie Hatton

Woman & Home
020 3148 5000
www.womanandhome.com
Monthly. Owner: IPC Media.
Editor: Sue James

Woman Alive
01903 821082
www.womanalive.co.uk
Monthly. Owner: Christian Publishing
and Outreach. Editor: Jackie Stead

Woman's Own
020 3148 5000
www.ipcmedia.com
Weekly. Owner: IPC Media.
Editor: Elsa McAlonan

Woman's Weekly
020 3148 5000
www.ipcmedia.com
Weekly. Owner: IPC Media.
Editor: Gilly Sinclair

Women's Wear Daily (WWD)
020 7240 0420
www.wwd.com
Daily. Owner: Fairchild.
Editor: Jim Fallon

Yoga and Health
020 7480 5456
www.yogaandhealthmag.co.uk
Monthly. Owner: Yoga Today.
Editor: Jane Sill

You & Your Wedding
020 7439 5000
www.youandyourwedding.co.uk
6pa. Owner: National Magazine
Company. Editor: Colette Harris

Zest
020 7439 5000
www.zest.co.uk
Monthly. Owner: National Magazine
Company. Editor: Alison Pylkkanen

Major customer magazines

Asda Magazine
020 7462 7777
www.publicis-blueprint.co.uk
Monthly. Publisher: Publicis Blueprint.
Editor: Helen Williams

Boots Health and Beauty
020 7747 0700
www.redwoodgroup.net
6pa. Publisher: Redwood.
Editor: Nina Ahmed

Caravan Club Magazine
01342 336804
www.caravanclub.co.uk
Monthly. Publisher: The Caravan Club.
Editor: Gary Martin

Dare
020 7306 0304
www.therivergroup.co.uk
Monthly. Publisher: River Publishing.
Editor: Natalie Gibbons

Debenhams Desire
020 7462 7777
www.publicis-blueprint.co.uk
5pa. Publisher: Publicis Blueprint.
Editor: Amanda Morgan

Harrods
020 7499 9080
2pa. Owner: Condé Nast.
Editor: Nicola Loftus

Harvey Nichols Edit
020 7747 0700
Bi-annual. Editor: Neil Holbrook

Heritage Today
020 7565 3000
www.english-heritage-books
.org.uk
Quarterly. Publisher: John Brown
Publishing Group. Editor: Francine
Lawrence

High Life
020 7534 2400
www.cedarcom.co.uk
Monthly. Publisher: Cedar.
Editor: Kerry Smith

Homebase Ideas
020 7462 7777
www.publicis-blueprint.co.uk
Quarterly. Publisher: Publicis
Blueprint. Editor: Ward Hellewell

Honda Dream
020 7306 0304
www.therivergroup.co.uk
Quarterly. Publisher: River Publishing.
Editor: Chris Hatherill

Hotline (Virgin Trains)
020 7306 0304
www.therivergroup.co.uk
Quarterly. Publisher: River Publishing.
Editor: Rod Stanley

M&S Magazine
020 7747 0700
www.redwoodgroup.net
4pa. Publisher: Redwood.
Editor: Michelle Pamment

Motoring & Leisure
01273 744757
www.csma.uk.com
10pa. Publisher: CSMA.
Editor: David Arnold

National Trust Magazine
01793 817400
www.nationaltrust.org.uk
3pa. Publisher: National Trust.
Editor: Sue Herdman

The Renault Magazine — Vanguard
020 7462 7777
www.publicis-blueprint.co.uk
Quarterly. Publisher: Publicis
Blueprint. Editor: Neil Anderson

Saga Magazine
01303 771523
www.saga.co.uk
Monthly. Publisher: Saga Group.
Editor: Emma Soames

Sainsbury's Magazine
020 7633 0266
www.sainsburysmagazine.co.uk
Monthly. Publisher: New Crane
Publishing. Editor: Sue Robinson

Sky The Magazine
020 7198 3000
www.jbcp.co.uk
Monthly. Publisher: John Brown
Publishing Group. Editor: Lysanne
Currie

Somerfield Magazine
0117 989 7808
www.somerfield.co.uk
13pa. Publisher: Rare Publishing.
Editor: Hannah Smith

Unlimited
0117 927 9009
www.originpublishing.co.uk
10pa. Publisher: Origin Publishing.
Editor: Pat Reid

VM — Vauxhall
01582 426909
http://vauxhall.co.uk/vmmagazine/
3pa. Publisher: Brooklands Publishing.
Editor: Michelle Howard

Waitrose Food Illustrated
020 7565 3000
www.jbcp.co.uk
Monthly. Publisher: John Brown
Publishing Group. Editor: William Sitwell

Business and trade press

● Business

Accountancy Age
020 7316 9000
www.accountancyage.com
Weekly. Owner: VNU.
Editor: Damian Wild

Accounting & Business
020 7059 5966
www.accaglobal.com
10pa. Owner: Certified Accountants
(Publications). Editor: John Prosser

Accounting Technician
020 7837 8600
www.accountingtechnician.co.uk
Monthly. Owner: Association of
Accounting Agencies.
Editor: Fritha Sutherland

Assessment
020 7801 2884
www.pcs.org.uk/revenue
8pa. Owner: Public & Commercial
Services Union. Editor: Colin Edwards

Bradmans Business Travel Guides
020 7613 8777
www.bradmans.com
Yearly. Owner: Ink Publishing.
Editor: Richard Bence

Brand Strategy
020 7970 4000
www.mad.co.uk
Monthly. Owner: Centaur.
Editor: Ruth Mortimer

Business Informer
0191 518 4281
Bi-monthly. Owner: Deneholme
Publishing. Editor: Alan Roxborough

Business Traveller
020 7647 6330
www.businesstraveller.com
10pa. Owner: Panacea Publishing
International. Editor: Tom Otley

CFO Europe
020 7830 1090
www.cfoeurope.com
11pa. Owner: The Economist
Newspaper. Editor: Janet Kersnar

CorpComms Magazine
020 7251 7500
www.thecrossbordergroup.com
Monthly. Owner: Cross Border Ltd.
Editor: Helen Dunne

Corporate Citizenship Briefing
020 7940 5610
www.ccbriefing.co.uk
Bi-monthly. Editor: Mienke Retief

Creative Review
020 7970 4000
www.mad.co.uk
Monthly. Owner: Centaur.
Editor: Patrick Burgoyne

Design Week
020 7970 4000
www.mad.co.uk
Weekly. Owner: Centaur.
Editor: Lynda Relph-Knight

Director
020 7766 8950
www.iod.com
Monthly. Owner: Director
Publications. Editor: Joanna Higgins

Employee Benefits
020 7970 4000
www.employeebenefits.co.uk
Monthly. Owner: Centaur.
Editor: Amanda Wilkinson

Euromoney
020 7779 8888
www.euromoneyplc.com
Monthly. Owner: Euromoney
Institutional Investor. Editor: Peter Lee

Financial Advisor
00 1 732 450 8866
www.financialadvisormagazine.com
Weekly. Owner: Charter Financial
Publishing Network. Senior editor:
Jeff Schlegel

Financial Management
020 7368 7177
www.cimaglobal.com
Monthly. Owner: Caspian.
Editor: Ruth Prickett

Financial News
020 7426 3333
www.efinancialnews.com
Weekly. Editor: William Wright

Financial World
01227 818609
www.financialworld.co.uk
Monthly. Owner: Caspian.
Editor: Denise Smith

First Voice of Business
01223 477411
www.campublishers.com
Monthly. Owner: Cambridge
Publishers. Editor: Mike Sewell

Fund Strategy
020 7970 4000
www.fundstrategy.co.uk
Weekly. Owner: Centaur.
Editor: Daniel Ben-Ami

Growing Business
020 8334 1661
www.gbmag.co.uk
Monthly. Owner: Crimson Publishing.
Editor: Ian Wallace

Human Resources
020 8267 4641
www.humanresourcesmagazine
.com
12pa. Owner: Haymarket.
Editor: Sian Harrington

Industrial Focus
020 7014 0300
www.industrialfocus.co.uk
Bi-monthly. Owner: Tower Publishing.
Editor: Mike Wearing

Institutional Investor —
International Edition
020 7779 8888
www.iilondon.co.uk
Monthly. Owner: Euromoney
Institutional Investor.
Editor: Michael Carol

In-Store
020 7970 4000
www.mad.co.uk
Monthly. Owner: Centaur.
Editor: Matthew Valentine

Insurance Age
020 7484 9776
www.insuranceage.com
Monthly. Owner: Incisive Media.
Editor: Michelle Worvell

Investor Relations
020 7251 7500
www.thecrossbordergroup.com
Monthly. Owner: Cross Border Ltd.
Executive editor: Neil Stewart

The Journal
020 7534 2400
www.cedarcom.co.uk
Bi-monthly. Owner: Cedar.
Editor: Kevin Pratt

Landscape and Amenity Product
Update
01952 200809
www.landscapespecification.com
6pa. Owner: Tanner Stiles Publishing.
Editor: Katie Wilcox

Logistics Manager
020 7970 4000
www.logisticsmanager.co.uk
Monthly. Owner: Centaur.

Management Today
020 8267 5000
www.mtmagazine.co.uk
Monthly. Owner: Haymarket.
Editor: Emma de Bita

Marketing Week
020 7970 4000
www.mad.co.uk
Weekly. Owner: Centaur.
Editor: Anita Asthana

Money Marketing
020 7970 4000
www.centaur.co.uk
Weekly. Owner: Centaur.
Editor: Kate Baier

Mortgage Strategy
020 7970 4000
www.mortgagestrategy.co.uk
Weekly. Owner: Centaur.
Editor: Robyn Hall

New Business
020 7407 9800
www.newbusiness.co.uk
Quarterly. Owner: IBMG.
Editor: Nick Martindale

New Media Age
020 7970 4000
www.nma.co.uk/
Weekly. Owner: Centaur.
Editor: Angela Gilling

OS Magazine
0141 567 6000
www.peeblesmedia.com
Bi-monthly. Owner: Peebles Media Group. Editor: Mike Travers

Overseas Trade
020 7566 9910
www.overseas-trade.co.uk
Monthly. Owner: Rare Publishing.
Editor: Janet Tibble

Pensions & Investments
020 7457 1430
www.pionline.com
Fortnightly. Owner: Crain Communications.
Editor: Nancy Webman

Pensions Age
020 7562 2401
www.pensions-age.com
Monthly. Owner: Pensions Age Magazine. Editor: Marek Handzel

People Management
020 7880 6200
www.peoplemanagement.co.uk
Fortnightly. Owner: Redactive Publishing. Editor: Steve Crabb

Personnel Today
020 8652 3941
www.personneltoday.com
Weekly. Owner: Reed Business Information. Editor: Rob Willett

Professional Manager
020 7421 2705
www.managers.org.uk
Bi-monthly. Owner: Chartered Management Institute. Editor: Sue Mann

Public Private Finance
020 7970 4000
www.publicprivatefinance.co.uk
11pa. Owner: Centaur.
Editor: Michael Kapoor

Real Business
020 7368 7177
www.realbusiness.co.uk
Monthly. Owner: Caspian.
Editor: Kate Pritchard

Recruiter Magazine
020 7970 4000
www.recruitermagazine.co.uk
Fortnightly. Owner: Centaur.
Editor: Dee Dee Doke

StartUps.co.uk
020 8334 1721
www.startups.co.uk
Website, updated hourly.
Online editor: Matt Thomas

Supply Management
020 7880 6200
www.supplymanagement.co.uk
Fortnightly. Owner: Redactive Publishing. Editor: Geraint John

What's New In Industry
020 7970 4000
www.centaur.co.uk
Bi-monthly. Owner: Centaur.
Editor: David Keighley

● Construction
and engineering

ABC&D
01527 834400
www.abc-d.co.uk
Monthly. Owner: Centaur.
Editor: Claire Mackle

Architecture Today
020 7837 0143
www.architecturetoday.co.uk
10pa. Editor: Chris Foges

Builder & Engineer
0161 236 2782
www.builderandengineer.co.uk
Monthly. Owner: Excel Publishing.
Editor: Richard Stirling

Building
020 7560 4149
www.building.co.uk
Weekly. Owner: CMP Information.
Editor: Denise Chevin

Building Design
020 7921 5000
www.bdonline.co.uk
Weekly. Owner: CMP Information.
Editor: Amanda Baillieu

Building Products
0870 049 4424
www.buildingproducts.co.uk
Monthly. Owner: Quantum Business Media.

Construction Manager
020 7560 4153
www.construction-manager.co.uk
10pa. Owner: The Builder Group.
Editor: Kristina Smith

Construction News
020 7728 5000
www.cnplus.co.uk
Weekly. Owner: Emap.
Editor: Nick Edwards

Contract Journal
020 8652 4761
www.contractjournal.com
Weekly. Owner: Reed Business Information. Editor: Emma Penny

Electronics
01622 699162
www.connectingindustry.com
11pa. Editor: Paul March

Electronics Weekly
020 8652 3650
www.electronicsweekly.com
Weekly. Owner: Reed Business Information. Editor: Richard Wilson

Engineering and Technology
01438 313311
www.iee.org/Publish/Journals
Monthly. Owner: The Institution of Electrical Engineers. Editor: Dominic Lenton

The Engineer
020 7970 4000
www.e4engineering.com
Fortnightly. Owner: Centaur.
Editor: Andrew Lee

Gas Installer
0870 401 2529
www.shoreline-media.com
Monthly. Owner: Corgi.
Editor: Euan McManus

Global Pipeline Monthly
01494 675139
www.pipemag.com
Monthly. Owner: Scientific Surveys.
Editor: John Tiratsoo

Metal Working Production
020 7970 4000
www.mwp.co.uk
Bi-monthly. Owner: Centaur.
Editor: Mike Excell

New Civil Engineer
020 7505 6600
www.nceplus.co.uk
Weekly. Owner: Emap.
Editor: Antony Oliver

Offshore
01992 656657
www.offshore-mag.com
Monthly. Owner: Penwell Corporation.
Editor: Eldon Ball

PIR Construction
0870 749 0220
www.pirnet.co.uk
6pa. Owner: The Bellmont Agency.
Editor: Steve Lucas

Process Engineering
020 7970 4000
www.processengineering.co.uk
Monthly. Owner: Centaur.
Editor: Patrick Raleigh

Professional Electrician & Installer
01923 237799
www.hamerville.co.uk
11pa. Owner: Hamerville Magazines.
Editor: Jonathon Carl

Professional Engineering
020 7973 1299
www.profeng.com
*Fortnightly. Owner: Professional Engineering Publishing.
Editor: John Pullin*

Professional Heating & Plumbing Installer
01923 237799
www.hamerville.co.uk
*11pa. Owner: Hamerville Magazines.
Editor: Stuart Hamilton*

Public Sector Building
01527 834400
www.centaur.co.uk
*6pa. Owner: Centaur.
Editor: Angela Smith*

RIBA Journal
020 7921 8560
www.ribajournal.com
*Monthly. Owner: The Builder Group.
Editor: Hugh Pearman*

What's New In Building
020 7560 4245
www.wnibonline.com
*Monthly. Owner: CMP Information.
Editor: Mark Pennington*

● Defence

Airforces Monthly
01780 755131
www.airforcesmonthly.com
*Monthly. Owner: Key Publishing.
Editor: Alan Warnes*

Jane's Defence Weekly
020 8700 3700
www.janes.com
*Weekly. Owner: Jane's.
Editor: Peter Felstead*

Navy News
023 9229 4228
www.navynews.co.uk
Monthly. Editor: Sarah Fletcher

Soldier
01252 347356
www.soldiermagazine.co.uk
Monthly. Editor: Andy Simms

● Education

Child Education
01926 887799
www.scholastic.co.uk
*Monthly. Owner: Scholastic.
Editor: Michael Ward*

Education Today
020 7947 9536
www.collegeofteachers.ac.uk
*Quarterly. Owner: College of Teachers.
Editorial assistant: Morag Hughes*

Education Travel Magazine
020 7440 4025
www.hothousemedia.com
*Monthly. Owner: Hothouse Media.
Editor: Amy Baker*

English Teaching Professional
01243 576600
www.keywayspublishing.com
*Monthly. Owner: Keyways.
Editor: Helena Gomm*

FE Now
020 7005 2741
www.aoc.co.uk
4pa. Owner: The Association of Colleges. Editor: Kate Hilpern

Gair Rhydd
029 2078 1400
www.cardiffstudents.com
Weekly. Owner: Cardiff Union Services. Editor: Amy Harrison

Governors' News
0121 643 5787
www.nagm.org.uk
5pa. Owner: National Association of School Governors. Editor: Sally Thorne

Higher Education Review
020 8341 1366
www.highereducationreview.com
3pa. Editor: John Pratt

ICT for Education
020 8334 1600
www.ictforeducation.co.uk
*Monthly. Owner: Crimson Publishing.
Editor: Ian Delaney*

LSE Magazine
020 7955 7582
www.lse.ac.uk
2pa. Owner: London School of Economics. Editor: Judith Higgin

Nursery Education
01926 887799
www.scholastic.co.uk
*Monthly. Owner: Scholastic.
Editor: Helen Dean*

Nursery World
020 8267 5000
www.nurseryworld.co.uk
*Weekly. Owner: Haymarket.
Editor: Liz Roberts*

Oxford Today
01865 280545
www.oxfordtoday.ox.ac.uk
*3pa. Owner: University of Oxford.
Editor: Greg Neale*

Report
020 7930 6441
www.askatl.org.uk
10pa. Owner: Association of Teachers and Lecturers. Editor: Victoria Poskit

Right Start
020 7878 2338
www.rightstartmagazine.co.uk
*Bi-monthly. Owner: McMillan-Scott.
Editor: Lynette Lowthian*

Scottish Educational Journal
0131 225 6244
www.eis.org.uk
5pa. Owner: Educational Institute of Scotland. Editor: Simon MacAulay

Sesame
01908 653011
www.open.ac.uk/sesame
*4pa. Owner: Open University.
Editor: Tracy Archbold*

Special Schools Guide
020 7970 4000
www.centaur.co.uk
*Annual. Owner: Centaur.
Editor: Derek Rogers*

Student Direct
0161 275 2943
www.student-direct.co.uk
*Weekly during term.
Editor: Dominic Kolle*

The Teacher
020 7380 4708
www.teachers.org.uk
8pa. Owner: National Union of Teachers. Editor: Elyssa Campbell-Barr

Teaching Today
0121 453 6150
www.teachersunion.org.uk
5pa. Owner: NASUWT. Editor: Joe Devo

Times Educational Supplement
020 7782 3000
www.tes.co.uk
*Weekly. Owner: TSL Education.
Editor: Karen Dempsey*

Times Higher Education Supplement
020 7782 3000
www.thes.co.uk
*Weekly. Owner: TSL Education.
Editor: Gerard Kelly*

UC
020 7837 3636
www.ucu.org.uk
*5pa. Owner: UCU.
Editor: Brenda Kirsch*

● Farming

British Dairying
01438 716220
*Monthly. Owner: WB Publishing.
Editor: Mike Green*

Crop Production Magazine
01743 861122
www.cpm.gb.net
*Monthly (Feb-Oct).
Editor: Angus McKirdy*

Crops
020 8652 4923
www.reedbusiness.co.uk
Fortnightly. Owner: Reed Business Information. Editor: Charles Abel

Dairy Farmer
01732 377273
*16pa. Owner: CMP Information.
Editor: Peter Hollinshead*

Farmers Guardian
01772 799411
www.farmersguardian.com
*Weekly. Owner: CMP Information.
Editor: Liz Falkingham*

Farmers Weekly
020 8652 4940
www.fwi.co.uk
Weekly. Owner: Reed Business Information. Editor: Julian Gardener

Feed International
00 31 30 659 2236
www.wattnet.com
*Monthly. Owner: Watt Publishing.
Editor: Clayton Gill*

Living Earth
0117 914 2434
www.soilassociation.org
3pa. Editor: Elisabeth Winkler

NFU Horticulture
020 7331 7359
www.nfuonline.com
3pa. Owner: NFU.
Editor: Martin Stanhope

Poultry International
00 31 30 659 2234
www.wattnet.com
Monthly. Owner: Watt Publishing.
Editor: Jackie Linden

Scottish Farmer
0141 302 7700
www.newsquest.co.uk
Weekly. Owner: Newsquest.
Editor: Alistair Fletcher

Tractor & Machinery
01959 541444
www.kelsey.co.uk
Monthly. Owner: Kelsey Publishing.
Editor: Michael Oldacre

● Health and social care

Arthritis News
020 7380 6521
www.arthritiscare.org.uk
Bi-monthly. Owner: Arthritis Care.
Editor: Rosie Loft

BMJ
020 7387 4499
www.bmj.com
Weekly. Owner: BMJ Publishing Group.
Editor: Fiona Godlee

Community Care
020 8652 4886
www.communitycare.co.uk
Weekly. Owner: Reed Business
Information. Editor: Mike Broad

Doctor
020 8652 8740
www.doctorupdate.net
Weekly. Owner: Reed Business
Information. Editor: Charles Creswell

Druglink
020 7940 7500
www.drugscope.org.uk
Bi-monthly. Owner: DrugScope.
Editor: Harry Shapiro

GP
020 8267 4846
www.gponline.com
Weekly. Owner: Haymarket.
Editor: Bronagh Miskelly

Health Service Journal
020 7874 0200
www.hsj.co.uk
Weekly. Owner: Emap.
Editor: Richard Vize

Hospital Doctor
020 8652 8745
www.hospital-doctor.net
Weekly. Owner: Reed Business
Information. Editor: Rob Finch

Journal of Family Healthcare
01243 576600
www.keywayspublishing.com
Bi-monthly. Owner: Keyways
Publishing. Editor: Pat Scowan

The Lancet
020 7424 4910
www.lancet.com
Weekly. Owner: Elsevier.
Editor: Richard Horton

Medeconomics
020 8267 5000
www.gponline.com
Monthly. Owner: Haymarket.
Editor: Jacki Buist

MIMS
020 8267 5000
www.gponline.com
Monthly. Owner: Haymarket.
Editor: Kelly Gowans

Nursing Standard
020 8423 1066
www.nursing-standard.co.uk
Weekly. Owner: RCN Publishing.
Editor: Ken Edwards

Nursing Times
020 7874 0502
www.nursingtimes.net
Weekly. Owner: Emap.
Editor: Rachel Downey

The Pharmaceutical Journal
020 7572 2414
www.pjonline.com
Weekly. Owner: Royal Pharmaceutical
Society of Great Britain.
Editor: Olivia Timbs

The Practitioner
020 7921 8113
www.practitioner-i.co.uk
Monthly. Owner: CMP Information.
Editor: Gavin Atkin

The Psychologist
0116 252 9573
www.bps.org.uk/publications
/thepsychologist
Monthly. Owner: The British
Psychological Society.
Editor: Dr Jon Sutton

Pulse
020 7921 8106
www.pulse-i.co.uk
50pa. Owner: CMP Information.
Editor: Joe Haynes

RCN Bulletin
020 8423 1066
www.nursing-standard.co.uk
Fortnightly. Owner: RCN Publishing.
Editor: Ken Edwards

Update
020 8652 8760
www.doctorupdate.net
Monthly. Owner: Reed Business
Information. Editor: Anna Sayburn

» See also disability   page 119

● Housing

Housing Association Magazine
0121 682 8881
www.wavcoms.co.uk
8pa. Owner: Waverley
Communications. Editor: Bruce
Meecham

Inside Housing
020 7772 8300
www.insidehousing.co.uk
Weekly. Owner: Ocean Media.
Editor: Kate Murray

Regeneration & Renewal
020 8267 4381
www.regenerationmagazine.com
Weekly. Owner: Haymarket.
Editor: Richard Garlick

Roof
0844 515 2036
www.roofmag.org.uk
Bi-monthly. Owner: Shelter.
Editor: Emma Hawkey

● Law

The In-House Lawyer
020 7396 5672
10pa. Editor: Eduardo Reyes

The Lawyer
020 7970 4000
www.centaur.co.uk
Weekly. Owner: Centaur.
Editor: Catrin Griffiths

Law Society Gazette
020 7841 5546
www.lawgazette.co.uk
Weekly. Owner: The Law Society.
Editor: Neil Rose

Legal Business
020 7396 9308
www.legalbusiness.co.uk
10pa. Editor: James Baxter

Legal Week
020 7316 5000
www.legalweek.com
Weekly. Owner: Legal Week Global
Media. Editor: Caroline Pearce

Media Lawyer
01229 716622
www.medialawyer.press.net
Bi-monthly. Owner: Press Association.
Editor: Mike Dodd

● Media

● Police

Constabulary Magazine
0870 350 1892
Monthly. Owner: National Press
Publishers. Editor-in-chief:
Christopher Locke

Police Magazine
020 8335 1000
www.polfed.org
Monthly. Owner: Police Federation of
England & Wales. Editor: Metin Enver

Police Review
020 8276 4729
www.policereview.com
Weekly. Owner: Jane's.
Editor: Chris Herbert

Policing Today
01243 576600
www.keywayspublishing.com
Quarterly. Owner: Keyways
Publishing. Editor: Peter Shipley

● Property

Estates Gazette
020 7911 1805
www.reedbusiness.co.uk
Weekly. Owner: Reed Business
Information. Editor: Peter Bill

Facilities Management Journal
020 8771 3614
www.fmarena.com
Monthly. Owner: Market Place
Publishing. Editor: Martin Reed

Facilities Management UK
0161 683 8032
www.worldsfair.co.uk
Bi-monthly. Owner: World's Fair.
Editor: John Kirkbride

● Retail and catering

Asian Trader
020 7928 1234
www.gg2.net
Fortnightly. Owner: Garavi Gujarat
Publications. Editor: R Solanki

Caterer and Hotelkeeper
020 8652 4210
www.reedbusinessinformation
.co.uk
Weekly. Owner: Reed Business
Information. Editor: Mark Lewis

Caterer and Licensee News
01202 552333
www.catererlicensee.co.uk
Monthly. Owner: RBC Publishing.
Editor: Peter Adams

Class
01293 610442
www.william-reed.co.uk
Monthly. Owner: William Reed
Publishing. Editor: Paul Wootton

Convenience Store
01293 610218
www.william-reed.co.uk
Fortnightly. Owner: William Reed
Publishing. Editor: David Rees

DNR
020 7240 0420
www.dnrnews.com
Weekly, Owner: Fairchild.
Editor: Jean Palmieri

Drapers
020 7812 3700
www.drapersonline.com
Weekly. Owner: Emap.
Editor: Khabi Mirza

Eat Out
01474 574436
www.dewberryredpoint.co.uk
Monthly. Owner: Dewberry Redpoint.
Editor: David Foad

Food Manufacture
01293 610231
www.foodmanufacture.co.uk
Monthly. Owner: William Reed
Publishing. Editor: Rick Pendrous

Footwear News (FN)
020 7240 0420
www.footwearnews.com
Weekly. Owner: Fairchild.
Editor: Michael Atmoore

Forecourt Trader
01293 610219
www.william-reed.co.uk
Monthly. Owner: William Reed
Publishing. Editor: Merril Boulton

The Franchise Magazine
01603 620301
www.franchise-group.com
8pa. Owner: Franchise Development
Services. Editor: Stuart Anderson

The Grocer
01293 610259
www.grocertoday.co.uk
Weekly. Owner: William Reed
Publishing. Editor: Adam Leyland

Independent Retail News
01322 611240
www.irn-talkingshop.co.uk
Fortnightly. Owner: Nexus Media
Editor: John Kirwan

Leisure Report
01293 846559
www.martin-info.com
Monthly. Owner: William Reed
Publishing. Editor: Duncan Rowe

On Trade Scotland
0141 222 5389
www.william-reed.co.uk
Fortnightly. Owner: William Reed
Publishing. Editor: Michelle Robertson

MBR
01293 610268
www.william-reed.co.uk
Monthly. Owner: William Reed
Publishing. Editor: Mary Carmichael

Morning Advertiser
01293 610480
www.william-reed.co.uk
Weekly. Owner: William Reed
Publishing. Editor: Andrew Pring

Off Licence News
01293 610226
www.william-reed.co.uk
Fortnightly. Owner: William Reed
Publishing. Editor: Graham Holter

PubChef
01293 610487
www.william-reed.co.uk
Monthly. Owner: William Reed
Publishing. Editor: Jo Bruce

The Publican
020 7955 3736
www.thepublican.com
48pa. Owner: United Advertising
Publications. Editor: Caroline Nodder

Shopping Centre
01293 610294
www.william-reed.co.uk
Monthly. Owner: William Reed
Publishing. Editor: Graham Harvey

Toy News
01992 535646
www.toynewsmag.com
Monthly. Owner: Intent Media.
Editor: Ronnie Dungan

The Trader
0870 049 4363
www.thetrader.co.uk
Monthly. Owner: United Advertising
Publications. Editor: John Fuller

Women's Wear Daily (WWD)
020 7240 0420
www.wwd.com
Daily. Owner: Fairchild.
Editor: Jim Fallon

WWDBeautyBiz
020 7240 0420
www.wwd.com
9pa. Owner: Fairchild.
Editor: Jenny Fine

● Science

Clinical Laboratory International
01442 877777
www.cli-online.com
8pa. Owner: Lansdowne Media.
Editor: Frances Bushrod

Nature
020 7833 4000
www.nature.com
Weekly. Owner: Nature Publishing
Group. Editor: Phil Campbell

New Scientist
020 7611 1201
www.newscientist.com
Weekly. Owner: Reed Business
Information. Editor: Jeremy Webb

Science
01223 326500
www.sciencemag.org
Weekly. Owner: American Association
for the Advancement of Science.
Editor: Andrew Sugden

● Technology

British Photographic Industry News
01799 544200
www.archant.co.uk
Monthly. Owner: Archant.
Editor: Lynn Maxwell

Computer Business Review
020 7675 7910
www.cbronline.com
Monthly. Owner: Business Review.
Editor: Jason Stamper

Computer Weekly
020 8652 8450
www.computerweekly.com
Weekly. Owner: Reed Business
Information. Editor: Hooman Bassirian

Computing
020 7316 9000
www.computing.co.uk
Weekly. Owner: VNU.
Editor: Toby Wolpe

Develop
01992 535646
www.developmag.com
Monthly. Owner: Intent Media.
Editor: Michael French

Developer Network Journal
0117 930 0255
www.dnjonline.com
Website. Owner: Matt Publishing.
Editor: Matt Nicholson

Information Age
020 7612 9300
www.infoconomy.com
Monthly. Owner: Infoconomy.
Editor: Kenny MacIver

IT Week
020 7316 9000
www.itweek.co.uk
Weekly. Owner: VNU.
Editor: Lem Bingley

ITNOW
01793 417474
www.bcs.org
Bi-monthly. Owner: British Computer
Society. Editor: Brian Runciman

Mobile Entertainment
01992 535646
www.mobile-ent.biz
Monthly and website. Owner: Intent
Media. Editor: Stuart O'Brien

PC Retail
01992 535646
www.pcretailmag.com
Monthly. Owner: Intent Media.
Editor: Scott Bicheno

Professional Photographer
01799 544200
www.professionalphotographer
.co.uk
Monthly. Owner: Archant.
Editor: Lynn Maxwell

Scientific Computing World
01223 477411
www.europascience.com
Bi-monthly. Owner: Europa Science.
Editor: Tom Wilkie

● Transport

Aerospace International
020 7670 4300
www.aerosociety.com
Monthly. Owner: The Royal Aeronautical
Society. Editor: Richard Gardner

Air International
01780 755131
www.airinternational.com
Monthly. Owner: Key Publishing.
Editor: Malcolm English

Automotive Engineer
020 7304 6809
www.pepublishing.com
Monthly. Owner: Professional
Engineering Publishing.
Editor: Tristan Honeywell

Autowired
01565 872107
www.autowired.co.uk
Daily. Owner: Eurotax Glass.
Editor: Barry Hook

Commercial Motor
020 8652 3612
www.reedbusinessinformation
.co.uk
Weekly. Owner: Reed Business
Information. Editor: Brian Weatherly

Flight International
020 8652 4395
www.flightinternational.com
Weekly. Owner: Reed Business
Information. Editor: Murdo Morrison

Helicopter International
01934 822524
www.helidata.rotor.com
Bi-monthly. Owner: Avia Press
Associates. Editor: Elfan ap Rees

Motor Trader
01322 611301
www.motortrader.co.uk
Weekly. Owner: Nexus Holdings.
Editor: Curtis Hutchinson

Motor Transport
020 8652 3285
www.reedbusinessinformation
.co.uk
Weekly. Owner: Reed Business
Information. Editor: Andrew Brown

Professional Motor Mechanic
01923 237799
www.hamerville.co.uk
11pa. Owner: Hamerville Magazines.
Editor: Richard Bowler

Rail
01733 237111
www.rail-magazine.com
Fortnightly. Owner: Bauer.
Editor: Nigel Harris

Railnews
020 7278 6100
www.railnews.co.uk
Monthly. Owner: Rail News Limited.
Editor: Paul Whiting

Truck & Driver
020 8652 3303
www.reedbusinessinformation
.co.uk
Weekly. Owner: Reed Business
Information. Editor: Dave Young

Trucking
01225 442244
www.truckingmag.co.uk
Monthly. Owner: Future.
Editor: Steve Hayes

● Travel

Travel Trade Gazette
020 7921 8029
www.ttglive.com
Weekly. Owner: CMP Information.
Editor: John Welsh

Travel Weekly
020 8652 8227
www.travelweekly.co.uk
Weekly. Owner: Reed Business
Information. Editor: Sarah Longbottom

● Cultural and ethnic minorities

Ad-Diplomasi News Report
Focus Press (UK)
020 7286 1372
subscribe@ad-diplomasi.com
www.ad-diplomasi.com
Monthly. Arabic and English. Political
affairs covering the Middle East.
Editor: Raymond Atallah

Al-Ahram
Al-Ahram
weeklymail@ahram.org.eg
http://weekly.ahram.org.eg
Weekly. English, serving Arab world.
Editor-in-chief: Assem El-Kersh

Al-Arab
Al Arab Publishing House
020 7735 9977
editor@alarab.co.uk
www.alarabonline.org
Daily and online. Arabic.
Editor: Elhouni Mohammed

Anandabazar Patrika
subscription@abpmail.com
www.anandabazar.com
Daily. Bengali. Editor: Shrabani Basu

Anglo–Hellenic Review
Anglo–Hellenic League
020 7267 3877
paul.watkins@virgin.net
www.hellenicbookservice.com
/ahr.htm
2pa. Cultural affairs covering Greece
and Britain. Editor: Paul Watkins

Ashraq Al Awsat
Saudi Research and Marketing UK
020 7831 8181
editorial@asharqalawsat.com
www.aawsat.com
Daily. Arabic. Editor: Tariq Al Homayed

Asian Entertainment Guide
020 7723 6797
Weekly. Editor: N Gosai

Asian News
Guardian Media Group
01706 357086
asiannews@gmwn.co.uk
www.theasiannews.co.uk
Monthly. Editor: Steve Hammond;
chief reporter: Shelina Begum

Asian Post
Hussain Media
020 8558 9127
leali@theasianpost.co.uk
Weekly. English. Editor: Murtaza
Ali Shah

Asian Times
Ethnic Media Group
020 7650 2000
news@asiantimes.co.uk
www.asiantimesonline.co.uk
Weekly. English. Editor: Hamant Verma

Asians in Media
020 8893 5646
sunny.hundal@asiansinmedia.org
www.asiansinmedia.org
Weekly. Guide to the British Asian
media industry. Editor: Sunny Hundal

MAGAZINE contacts **Print media**

117

Awaaz
Awaaz Multi Media
01924 510512
info@awaaz.com
www.awaaznews.com
Monthly. English, Urdu and Gujarati.
Head of Comms: Shakir Daji

Barficulture.com
www.barficulture.com
Website. Young British Asians.
Editor: Sunny Hundal

Blacknet
0870 746 5000
junior@blacknet.co.uk
www.blacknet.co.uk
Community website for black people in
Britain. Editor: Junior Wilson

Black Information Link
020 7582 1990
blink1990@blink.org.uk
www.blink.org.uk
Website. Editor: Lester Holloway

Canada Post
020 8840 9765
info@canadapost.co.uk
www.canadapost.co.uk
Monthly. Managing editor:
Paula Adamick

Caribbean Times
Ethnic Media Group
020 7650 2000
caribbeantimes@ethnicmedia.co.uk
www.caribbeantimes.co.uk
Weekly. Editor: Ron Shillingford

Chinatown
CTM Publishing
0161 245 3252
enquiries@chinatownthemagazine
.com
www.chinatownthemagazine.com
Bi-monthly. English for Chinese.
Publisher: William Ong; editor:
Davidine Sim

Chup magazine
info@chupmagazine.com
www.chupmagazine.com
Bi-monthly. English for British
Bengalis. Editor: Jasmine

Clickwalla.com
MeMedia
0845 0138 401
amit@memediagroup.com
www.clickwalla.com
Website. Editor: Ahmed Patel

Daily AUSAF
020 8521 8555
ausaflondon@aol.com
www.dailyausaf.com
Daily. Urdu. Chief editor: Mehtab Khan

Daily Jang London
Jang Publications
020 7403 5833
editor@janglondon.co.uk
www.jang.com.pk
Daily. English and Urdu.
Editor: Zahoor Niazi

Des Pardes
020 8571 1127
despardesuk@btconnect.com
Weekly. Punjabi for Indian
expatriates. Editor: GS Virk

Dziennik Polski
The Polish Daily (Publishers)
020 8740 1991
editor@dziennikpolski.co.uk
www.polishdailynews.com
Daily. Polish. Editor: Taroslaw
Kozminski

Eastern Eye
Ethnic Media Group
020 7650 2000
editor@easterneyeuk.co.uk
www.easterneyeonline.co.uk
Weekly. For Indian, Pakistani, Sri
Lankan and Bangladeshi communities
in Britain. Editor: Hamnt Verma

Eikoku News Digest
News Digest International
020 7611 0166
info@newsdigest.co.uk
www.newsdigest.co.uk
Weekly. Japanese. Editor: Mikiko
Toshima

Euro Bangla
Newsfax
020 7377 0311
info@eurobangla.co.uk
www.eurobangla.co.uk
Weekly. Bangla and English.
Managing Director: Masaddik Ahmed

Garavi Gujarat
Asian Media & Marketing Group
020 7928 1234
garavi@gujarat.co.uk
www.gg2.net
Weekly. English and Gujarati.
Editor: Ramniklal Solanki

The Gleaner
020 7510 0340
www.jamaica-gleaner.com
Weekly. Head of News: Andrew Clunis

Gujarat Samachar/ Asian Voice
Asian Business Publications
020 7749 4000
support@abplgroup.com
www.gujarat-samachar.com
Weekly. Editor: C Patel

Hia
Saudi Printing & Packaging
Company
020 7831 8181
hia@hhsaudi.com
Monthly. Arab women. Editor: Mai Badr

Hurriyet
020 7734 1211
www.hurriyetim.com
Daily. Turkish. Editor: Aysegul
Richardson

Impact International
020 7263 1417
editor@impact-magazine.com
Monthly. Muslim current affairs.
Editor: Ahmed Irfan

India Monitor
shiv@journalist.com
www.indiamonitor.com
Website

India Times
servicedesk@timesgroup.com
http://timesofindia.indiatimes.com
Daily and website. Managing director
& chief executive officer: Dinesh
Wadhawan

Irish Post
020 8741 0649
irishpost@irishpost.co.uk
www.irishpost.co.uk
Weekly. Editor: John Miles

Irish World
Newsfax
020 8453 7800
sales@theirishworld.com
www.theirishworld.com
Weekly. Editor: Frank Murphy

Janomot
Publication 1969
020 7377 6032
janomot@btconnect.com
www.janomotnews.com
Weekly. Bengali. Editor: Nabab Uddin

Jewish Chronicle
020 7415 1500
webmaster@thejc.com
www.thejc.com
Weekly and website.
Editor: David Rowan

Jewish Telegraph
0161 740 9321
mail@jewishtelegraph.com
www.jewishtelegraph.com
Weekly. Editor: Paul Harris

KAL
020 7439 9100
www.kalmagazine.com
Bi-annual. Careers and recruitment
for ethnic minority students.
Editor: Laura Sheed

La Voce degli Italiani
020 7735 5164
www.lavoce.com
Bi-Monthly. Italians in Europe.
Editor: Padre Giandomenico Ziliotto

London Turkish Gazette
020 8889 5025
news@londragazete.com
www.londragazete.com
Weekly. Turkish and English.
Publisher: Yilmaz Ozyigit; editor:
Cihan Algan

London Welsh Magazine
London Welsh Association
020 7837 3722
ddaniel@streamline-cm.co.uk
www.londonwelsh.org
Quarterly. Editor: David Daniel

Maghreb Review
020 7388 1840
maghrab@maghrabreview.com
www.maghrabreview.com
Quarterly. English and French. North
Africa, sub-Saharan Africa, Middle
East and Islam. Islamic studies:
history, geopolitics, environment.
Editor: Mohammed Ban-madani

MIL Matchmaker Magazine
Matchmaker International
020 8868 1879
info@perfect-partner.com
www.perfect-partner.com
3pa. Asians seeking partners.
Editor: Mr Bharat Raithatha

Mauritian Abroad
Sankris Publishing
01795 539499
eveer77807@aol.com
Quarterly. English and French.
Editor: Krish Veeramah

Mauritius News
020 7498 3066
editor@mauritiusnews.co.uk
www.mauritiusnews.co.uk
Monthly. Editor: Peter Chellen

Milap Weekly
020 7385 8966
*Weekly. Urdu-speaking community.
Editor: Ramesh Soni*

Muslim News
Visitcrest
020 8863 8586
editor@muslimnews.co.uk
www.muslimnews.co.uk
Monthly. Editor: Ahmed Versi

Muslim Weekly
020 7377 1919
info@themuslimweekly.com
www.themuslimweekly.com
Weekly. Editor: Ahmed Malik

Navin Weekly
020 7385 8966
Weekly. Hindi. Editor: Ramesh Kumar

New Nation
Ethnic Media Group
020 7650 2000
general@ethnicmedia.co.uk
www.newnation.co.uk
*Weekly. Black African-Caribbean news.
Editorial director: Michael Eboda*

New World
020 7700 2673
dhirennewworld@blueyonder.co.uk
*Fortnightly. Editor and publisher:
Dhiren Basu*

New Zealand News UK
Southern Link Media
0845 270 7903
editor@southernlink.co.uk
www.nznewsuk.co.uk
Weekly. Editor: Scott Oliver

The News
Jang Publications
020 7403 5833
thenewsse1@yahoo.com
www.jang.com.pk
*Daily. English and Urdu.
Editor: Shahid Sadullah*

Notun Din Bengali Newsweekly
Din Publishers
020 7247 6280
news@notundin.plus.com
*Weekly. Bengali.
Editor: Mohib Chowdhury*

Opportunity
020 7005 2250
*Quarterly. 16-25, all ethnic minority
backgrounds. Magazine manager:
Brian Keith*

Pakistan Post
Hussain Media
020 8558 9127
editor@thepakistanpost.net
www.thepakistanpost.net
*Weekly. Urdu and English. Editor in
Urdu: Faizan Arif; editor in English:
Murtaza Ali Shah*

Parikiaki
info@parikia.com
www.parikia.com/greek
/parikiaki.html
Weekly. Cypriots in UK

Pride Magazine
020 7228 3110
info@pridemagazine.com
www.pridemagazine.com
*Monthly. Black African, black
Caribbean, mixed race. Publisher:
Carl Cushnie*

Punjab Mail International
020 8522 0901
*Monthly. Punjabi and English.
Editor: Gurdip Singh Sandhu*

Punjab Times International
PTI Derby Media
01332 372851
panjabtimes@aol.com
*Weekly. Punjabi and English. Punjabi
community in UK. Editor: Ms Purewal*

Red Hot Curry
01707 269666
www.redhotcurry.com
*Website. South Asian, British Asian,
and East African Asian. Editor:
Lopa Patel*

Sayidaty
Saudi Research and Marketing UK
020 7831 8181
sayidaty@hhsaudi.com
www.sayidaty.net
*Weekly. Arab issues.
Editor: Hani Nakshabandi*

Sikh Courier International
The World Sikh Foundation
020 8864 9228
2pa. Sikhs. Editor: SS Kapoor

Sikh Messenger
020 8540 4148
sikhmessenger@aol.com
Quarterly. Editor: Indarjit Singh

Sikh Times
Eastern Media Group
0121 523 0115
info@thesikh-times.co.uk
www.thesikh-times.co.uk
*Weekly. English, Punjabi.
Editor: Gurjeet Kaur Bains*

SomethingJewish.co.uk
07976 220273
editor@somethingjewish.co.uk
www.somethingjewish.co.uk
*Website. UK Jewish.
Editor: Leslie Bunder*

Spectrum
020 7439 9100
laura@arberrypink.co.uk
www.spectrummagazine.co.uk
*Bi-annual. Careers and recruitment
for ethnic minority students.
Editor: Laura Sheed*

Surma
020 7377 9787
info@surmanewsgroup.co.uk
www.surmanewsgroup.co.uk
*Weekly. Bangla. Publisher: Sarz
Ahmed; editor: Mohammed Emadadul
Choudhury*

TNT Magazine
Trader Media Group
020 7373 3377
enquiries@tntmag.co.uk
www.tntmagazine.com
*Weekly. International travellers.
Editor: Lyn Eyb*

Travellers' Times
c/o The Rural Media Company
01432 344039
travellerstimes@ruralmedia.co.uk
www.travellerstimes.org.uk
*Quarterly. Gypsies and Travellers.
Editor: Bill Laws*

Ukrainian Thought
Association of Ukrainians in GB
020 7229 8392
administrator@augb.co.uk
www.augb.co.uk/ukrainian
_thought.htm
*Bi-weekly. Ukrainian. Administrator:
Mrs Anna Mikulin*

Ultra Journey
Japan Journals
020 7255 3838
info@japanjournals.com
www.japanjournals.com
Weekly. Japanese. Editor: Ko Tejima

The Voice
020 7737 7377
www.voice-online.co.uk
*Weekly. For black community in
Britain. Editor: Andrew Clunis*

Weekly Journey
Japan Journals
020 7255 3838
lina@japanjournals.com
www.japanjournals.com
*Weekly. Japanese in Britain.
Editor: Ko Tejima*

● Disability

Big Print
0800 124007
bigprint@rnib.org.uk
www.big-print.co.uk
*Weekly. Large print news.
Editor: Trevor Buckley*

Breathing Space
The British Lung Foundation
0845 850 5020
enquiries@blf-uk.org
www.lunguk.org/
*Quarterly. Lung disease.
Editor: Daniel Spears*

Communication
The National Autistic Society
020 7833 2299
publications@nas.org.uk
www.nas.org.uk
3pa. Autism. Editor: Miranda Kemp

Devon Link
Devon County Council and Torbay
Council
01392 382332
joanne.white@devon.gov.uk
www.devon.gov.uk/devonlink
*Quarterly. People with physical and
sensory disabilities, and carers.
Editor: Sarah Wilson*

Disability Now
Scope
020 7619 7323
editor@disabilitynow.org.uk
www.disabilitynow.org.uk
Monthly. Editor: John Pring

Disabled and Supportive Carer
Euromedia Associates
01254 390066
editorial@euromedia-al.com
6pa. Editor: Richard Cheeseborough

Epilepsy Today
Epilepsy Action
0113 210 8800
smitchell@epilepsy.org.uk
www.epilepsy.org.uk
6pa. Editor: Peter Fox

FreeHand
Abucon
020 7834 1066
info@abucon.co.uk
www.abucon.co.uk
4pa. Elderly disabled in their own homes. Editor: Liza Jones

MS Matters
MS Society
020 8438 0700
info@mssociety.org.uk
www.mssociety.org.uk
6pa. Editor: Debbie Reeves

New Beacon
Royal National Institute of the Blind
020 7878 2307
beacon@rnib.org.uk
www.rnib.org.uk
11pa. For those with sight problems. Editor: Ann Lee

New Pathways
The MS Resource Centre
01206 505444
info@msrc.co.uk
www.msrc.co.uk
6pa. MS issues. Editor: Debbie Reeves.

Ouch!
020 8752 5444
ouch@bbc.co.uk
www.bbc.co.uk/ouch
Website. Editor: Damon Rose

One in Seven Magazine
The Royal National Institute for Deaf People
020 7296 8000
oneinseven@rnid.org.uk
www.rnid.org.uk
6pa. For the deaf. Editor: Dawn Diamond

The Parkinson Magazine
Parkinson's Disease Society of the UK
020 7931 8080
lhurst@parkinsons.org.uk
www.parkinsons.org.uk
Quarterly. Editor: Katie Moss

Soundaround
Soundaround Associations
020 8741 3332
nigel@soundaround.org
www.soundaround.org
Monthly. Visually impaired, worldwide. Executive editor: Nigel Vee

Stroke News
The Stroke Association
020 7566 0300
www.stroke.org.uk
Quarterly. Editor: Maggie Warburton

Talk
The National Deaf Children's Society
020 7490 8656
ndcs@ndcs.org.uk
www.ndcs.org.uk
6pa. For deaf children.
Editor: Jane Fookes

Talking Sense
Sense, National Deafblind and Rubella Association
020 7272 7774
enquiries@sense.org.uk
www.sense.org.uk
3pa. Deafblind. Editor: Sue Brown

Viewpoint
Mencap
020 7696 5599
viewpoint@mencap.org.uk
www.mencap.org.uk/viewpoint
6pa. Learning disabilities. Editor: Faiza Fareed

Vitalise
(formerly Winged Fellowship Trust)
020 7017 3420
admin@vitalise.org.uk
www.vitalise.org.uk
3pa. Disabled people and their carers. Editor: Colin Brook

● **Gay and lesbian**

3sixty
City Pride Publications
01273 570570
info@3sixtymag.co.uk
www.3sixtymag.co.uk
Monthly. Editor: David Harvey

Attitude
Northern & Shell
020 7479 7939
adam.mattera@attitudemag.co.uk
www.attitude.co.uk
Monthly. Editor: Adam Mattera

AXM
Millivres-Prowler
020 7424 7400
m.miles@axm-mag.com
www.axm-mag.com
Monthly. Editor: Matthew Miles

Bent
All Points North Publications
08712 246 511
editor@bent.com
www.bent.com
11-12pa. Editor: Gordon Hopps

Boyz
020 7025 6120
gage@boyz.co.uk
www.boyz.co.uk
Weekly. Editor: Simon Gage

Diva
Millivres-Prowler
020 7424 7400
edit@divamag.co.uk
www.divamag.co.uk
Monthly. Editor: Jane Czyzselska

G3
G3 Magazine
020 7258 1777
info@g3mag.co.uk
www.g3magazine.co.uk
Monthly. Editor: Sarah Garrett

Gay Times
Millivres-Prowler
020 7424 7400
joseph@gaytimes.co.uk
www.gaytimes.co.uk
Monthly. Editor: Joseph Galliano

Gay.com UK
020 7440 0660
stewart.who@planetoutinc.co.uk
www.uk.gay.com

Midlands Zone
What's On Magazine Group
01743 281777
info@zonemag.com
www.zonemag.com
Monthly. Editor: Martin Monahan

Outnorthwest
0161 235 8035
editor@outnorthwest.com
www.lgf.org.uk
Monthly free, published by the Lesbian and Gay Foundation. Editor: Grahame Robertson

Pink Paper
Millivres-Prowler
020 7424 7400
tris@pinkpaper.com
www.pinkpaper.com
Weekly. Editor: Tris Reid-Smith

Refresh
Wild Publishing
020 7277 4523
david@wildpublishing.com
www.refreshmag.co.uk
Monthly. Editor: David Tickner

Stonewall Newsletter
Stonewall
020 7593 1850
info@stonewall.org.uk
www.stonewall.org.uk
Quarterly. Editor: Jodie West

UKBlackOut.com
www.ukblackout.com
Website. For black lesbians and gays

● **Religion**

All The World
The Salvation Army
020 7332 0101
kevin_sims@salvationarmy.org
www.salvationarmy.org
Quarterly. Editor: Kevin Sims

Baptist Times
Baptist Times
01235 517670
editor@baptisttimes.co.uk
www.baptisttimes.co.uk
Weekly. Church leaders. Editor: Mark Woods

Catholic Herald
020 7588 3101
editorial@catholicherald.co.uk
www.catholicherald.co.uk
Weekly. Editor: Luke Coppen

Catholic Times
Gabriel Communications
0161 488 1700
kevin.flaherty@totalcatholic.com
www.totalcatholic.com
Weekly. Editor: Kevin Flaherty

Christianity and Renewal
Premier Media Group (PMG)
020 7316 1450
ccp@premier.org.uk
www.christianitymagazine.com
Monthly. Editor: John Buckeridge

Daily Bread
Scripture Union Publishing
01908 856000
nigelh@scriptureunion.org.uk
www.dailybread.org.uk
*Quarterly. Adult Bible readers.
Editor: Tricia Williams*

Home and Family
The Mothers' Union
020 7222 5533
homeandfamily@
    themothersunion.org
www.themothersunion.org
Quarterly. Editor: Jill Worth

Jewish Chronicle
020 7415 1500
editorial@thejc.com
www.thejc.com
*Weekly and website.
Editor: David Rowan*

Jewish Telegraph
0161 740 9321
mail@jewishtelegraph.com
www.jewishtelegraph.com
Weekly. Editor: Paul Harris

Jewish.net
07976 220273
admin@jewish.net
www.jewish.net
Website

The Life
Scripture Union Publishing
01908 856000
media@scriptureunion.org.uk
Quarterly

Life and Work
Board of Communications
0131 225 5722
magazine@lifeandwork.org
www.lifeandwork.org
*Monthly. Church of Scotland.
Editor: Lynne McNeil*

The Muslim News
Visitcrest
020 8863 8586
editor@muslimnews.co.uk
www.muslimnews.co.uk
Monthly. Editor: A Versi

New Day
The Leprosy Mission
01733 370505
karendup@tlmew.org.uk
www.leprosy.org.uk
2pa. Editor: Claire Tuck

Presbyterian Herald
Presbyterian Church in Ireland
028 9032 2284
herald@presbyterianireland.org
www.presbyterianireland.org
Monthly. Editor: Rev Arthur Clarke

Scottish Catholic Observer
0141 221 4956
info@scottishcatholicobserver.com
www.scottishcatholicobserver.com
Weekly. Editor: Harry Conroy

Sikh Courier International
The World Sikh Foundation
020 8864 9228
2pa. Sikhs. Editor: SS Kapoor

SomethingJewish.co.uk
07976 220273
editor@somethingjewish.co.uk
www.somethingjewish.co.uk
*UK Jewish website.
Editor: Leslie Bunder*

Ummah.com
info@ummah.com
www.ummah.org.uk
Website. English. Islam

The Universe
Gabriel Communications
0161 488 1700
newsdesk@the-universe.net
www.totalcatholic.com
*Weekly. Roman Catholics and Ireland.
Editor: Joe Kelly*

War Cry
Salvation Army
020 7367 4900
warcry@salvationarmy.org.uk
www.salvationarmy.org.uk/warcry
*Weekly. Evangelical Christian Tabloid.
Editor: Major Nigel Bovey*

Journalism trade press

Best Sellers
020 7689 3357
sarah.longbottom@newtrade.co.uk
www.newtrade.co.uk
*2pa. Owner: Newtrade Publishing.
Consumer magazine data and ABC
results. Editor: Sarah Longbottom*

British Journalism Review
020 7324 8500
editor@bjr.org.uk
www.bjr.org.uk
*Quarterly. Owner: SAGE Publications.
Managing editor: Brian Bass;
editor: Bill Hagerty*

CPU Quarterly
020 7583 7733
cpu@cpu.org.uk
www.cpu.org.uk
*Quarterly. Owner: Commonwealth
Press Union. In-house newspaper of
the Association of Commonwealth
Newspapers. Executive director:
Lindsay Ross; advertising contact:
Rosie Vlasto; news editor: Harry
Wilson, editor: Ian Beales O.B.E.*

The Journal
020 7252 1187
memberservices@ioj.co.uk
www.ioj.co.uk
*Owner: The Chartered Institute
of Journalists. Quarterly.
Editor: Andy Smith*

journalism.co.uk
Mousetrap Media
01273 384293
info@journalism.co.uk
www.journalism.co.uk
*Website. Editor/publisher: John
Thompson; news: Oliver Luft*

The Journalist
020 7278 7916
timg@nuj.org.uk
www.nuj.org.uk
*10pa. Owner: National Union of
Journalists. Free to union members.
Editor: Tim Gopsill*

Magazine Retailer
020 7689 3357
sarah.longbottom@newtrade.co.uk
www.newtrade.co.uk
*2pa. Owner: Newtrade Publishing.
Information on magazine sales in all
sectors. Editor: Sarah Longbottom*

Magazine World
020 7404 4169
info@fipp.com
www.fipp.com
*Quarterly. Owner: FIPP. International
consumer and B2B publishing trends.
Editor: Christina Esposito*

News from NewstrAid
01371 874198
oldben@newstraid.org.uk
www.newstraid.org.uk
*Annual. Owner: Newstraid Benevolent
Society. Charity for the newspaper
industry. Editor: Alex van Straubenzee*

Press Gazette
020 7936 6402
ianr@pressgazette.co.uk
www.pressgazette.co.uk
*Weekly. Independent. Editor: Ian
Reeves; features editor: Julie Tomlyn*

Ulrich's Periodical Directory
01342 310450
sales@bowker.co.uk
www.ulrichsweb.com
*Annual; updated quarterly on CD,
monthly on website. Owner: Bowker.
Editor: Laurie Kaplan*

Useful associations

Association of American Correspondents in London
c/o Time Life International,
Brettenham House, Lancaster
Place, London WC2E 7TL
020 7499 4080
monique_jessen@peoplemag.com

Association of British Science Writers
Wellcome Wolfson Building,
165 Queen's Gate, London SW7 5HE
0870 770 3361
absw@absw.org.uk
www.absw.org.uk

Association of Freelance Writers
Sevendale House, 7 Dale Street,
Manchester M1 1JB
0161 228 2362
fmn@writersbureau.com
www.writersbureau.com
    /resources.htm

Audit Bureau of Circulations (ABC)
Saxon House, 211 High Street,
Berkhamsted, Hertfordshire HP4
1AD
01442 870800
marketing@abc.org.uk
www.abc.org.uk

Authors' Club
40 Dover Street, London W1S 4NP
020 7499 8581
circles@author.co.uk
www.author.co.uk

British Copyright Council
29-33 Berners Street,
London W1T 3AB
01986 788122
secretary@britishcopyright.org
www.britishcopyright.org

British Guild of Beer Writers
Woodcote, 2 Jury Road,
Dulverton, Somerset TA22 9DU
01398 324314
tierneyjones@btinternet.com
www.beerwriters.co.uk

British Guild of Travel Writers
51B Askew Crescent,
London W12 9DN
020 8749 1128
charlotte.c@virtualnecessities.com
www.bgtw.org

British Newspaper Library
The British Library, Newspaper
Library, Colindale Avenue,
London NW9 5HE
020 7412 7353
newspaper@bl.uk
www.bl.uk/catalogues
/newspapers.html

British Society of Magazine Editors
137 Hale Lane, Edgware,
Middlesex HA8 9QP
020 8906 4664
admin@bsme.com
www.bsme.com

Broadcasting Press Guild
Tiverton, The Ridge, Woking,
Surrey GU22 7EQ
01483 764895
torin.douglas@bbc.co.uk

Bureau of Freelance Photographers
Focus House, 497 Green Lanes,
London N13 4BP
020 8882 3315
info@thebfp.com
www.thebfp.com

Campaign for Freedom of Information
Suite 102, 16 Baldwins Gardens,
London EC1N 7RJ
020 7831 7477
admin@cfoi.demon.co.uk
www.cfoi.org.uk

Campaign for Press and Broadcasting Freedom
2nd Floor, Vi and Garner Smith
House, 23 Orford Road,
Walthamstow, London E17 9NL
020 8521 5932
freepress@cpbf.org.uk
www.cpbf.org.uk

Chartered Institute of Journalists
2 Dock Offices, Surrey Quays
Road, London SE16 2XU
020 7252 1187
memberservices@ioj.co.uk
www.ioj.co.uk

Foreign Press Association in London
11 Carlton House Terrace,
London SW1Y 5AJ
020 7930 0445
reception@foreign-press.org.uk
www.foreign-press.org.uk

Garden Writers' Guild
c/o Institute of Horticulture,
14/15 Belgrave Square,
London SW1X 8PS
020 7245 6943
gwg@horticulture.org.uk
www.gardenwriters.co.uk

Guild of Agricultural Journalists
Denmill Cottage,
Burnett Street, Auchenblae,
Kincardineshire AB30 1WP
01561 320248
www.gaj.org.uk

Guild of Food Writers
020 8659 0422
guild@gfw.co.uk
www.gfw.co.uk

Guild of Motoring Writers
Hengistby Head
Bournemouth BH6 4DT
01202 424781
chris@whizzco.freeserve.co.uk
www.guildofmotoringwriters.co.uk

International Newspaper Marketing Association
10300 North Central Expressway,
Suite 467, Texas 75231 USA
00 1 214 373 9111
www.inma.org

MediaWise Trust
University of the West of England,
Canon Kitson, Oldbury Court
Road, Bristol BS16 2JP
0117 939 9333
info@mediawise.org.uk
www.mediawise.org.uk
Media ethics charity

Medical Writers' Group
The Society of Authors,
84 Drayton Gardens,
London SW10 9SB
020 7373 6642
info@societyofauthors.org
www.societyofauthors.org

National Union of Journalists
Headland House, 308-312 Gray's
Inn Road, London WC1X 8DP
020 7278 7916
info@nuj.org.uk
www.nuj.org.uk

Newspaper Marketing Agency
Empire House, 175 Piccadilly,
London W1J 9EN
020 7182 1700
enquiries@nmauk.co.uk
www.nmauk.co.uk

Newspaper Society
Saint Andrew's House, 18-20 Saint
Andrew Street, London EC4A 3AY
020 7632 7400
ns@newspapersoc.org.uk
www.newspapersoc.org.uk

Outdoor Writers' Guild
PO Box 520, Bamber Bridge,
Preston, Lancashire PR5 8LF
01772 321243
secretary@owg.org.uk
www.owg.org.uk

Periodical Publishers Association (PPA)
Queens House, 28 Kingsway,
London WC2B 6JR
020 7404 4166
info1@ppa.co.uk
www.ppa.co.uk

Picture Research Association
c/o 1 Willow Court, off Willow
Street, London EC2A 4QB
chair@picture-research.org.uk
www.picture-research.org.uk

Press Complaints Commission
Halton House, 20/23 Holborn,
London EC1N 2JD
020 7831 0022
complaints@pcc.org.uk
www.pcc.org.uk

Scottish Newspaper Publishers Association
48 Palmerston Place,
Edinburgh EH12 5DE
0131 220 4353
info@snpa.org.uk
www.snpa.org.uk

Scottish Print Employers Federation and Scottish Daily Newspaper Society
48 Palmerston Place,
Edinburgh EH12 5DE
0131 220 4353
info@spef.org.uk
www.spef.org.uk

Society of Editors
University Centre, Granta Place,
Mill Lane, Cambridge CB2 1RU
01223 304080
info@societyofeditors.org
www.societyofeditors.org

Society of Women Writers and Journalists
swwriters@aol.com
www.swwj.co.uk

Sports Journalists' Association of Great Britain
c/o Start2Finish Event
Management, Unit 92, Capital
Business Centre, 22 Carlton Road,
Surrey CR2 0BS
020 8916 2234
petta.naylor@sportengland.org
www.sportsjournalists.co.uk

Television

Steve Hewlett

Don Chung

Tough times for Mark Thompson

The Queen's had one and ITV has had a few that felt like one but this really has been traditional television's "annus horribilis". As scandal followed scandal a perfect storm ensued leaving public trust in TV (and especially public TV ...) in tatters and broadcasters' confidence in themselves at an all-time low. Marketing and PR are usually about attracting as much attention as possible to your programme or channel, but this year's efforts have mostly been about the reverse. In the game of corporate pass-the-parcel that has dominated the year, PR's success will be measured according to the fewest number of column inches you were unfortunate enough to attract. The only moments of relief came when competitors got their turn in the stocks. But shocking as they have proved to be, many of this year's outbreaks of fraud and fakery were, in reality, accidents waiting to happen or, in many cases, to be discovered.

For Channel 4 it all went wrong as early as the third week of January. The combination of the football Wag Danielle Lloyd, the ex-S CLUB 7 singer Jo O'Meara and Jade Goody with the Indian actress Shilpa Shetty — which must have looked like such a clever wheeze when the producers dreamt it up — blew up into probably the biggest racism row British television has ever had. To the liberals who inhabit TV land the behaviour of the inmates, with its heavily racial undertones, was genuinely shocking but to viewers in their millions it was nowhere near as shocking as Channel 4's almost complete failure to deal with it. On the morning of January 18 — the day the secretary of state was due to announce the BBC licence fee settlement — C4's chairman appeared on the Today programme, presumably to luxuriate in the BBC's likely misfortune. Instead he inadvertently found his place in broadcasting history by refusing to comment on C4's handling of the Big Brother racism row, which by then had literally gone global. Channel 4 found itself well and truly on the run. Not, it should be remembered, because of what happened in the programme but because of its handling of it. A subsequent Ofcom enquiry found that there had been a catastrophic failure by senior management at the channel to see that they had a problem and to deal with it effectively. To the surprise of many observers — but in keeping with most modern public broadcasting practice, apparently — they all kept their jobs.

Unfortunately for Channel 4 this all played straight into another much bigger question that had been brewing in the public policy bazaars. What was Channel 4 for? Was it being too commercial and was it too dependent on a small number of key programmes (ie Big Brother and Deal Or No Deal) and highly priced imports to raise its revenues? And, above all, was it deserving of public cash to support it through the difficult financial times the company said it faced?

Subsequently Ofcom accepted most of a report on C4's finances that found that the channel might well face problems in the future, but insisted on a wholesale review of governance arrangements and the development of a new "vision" for the channel in return. Whether any vision – and we still haven't seen it – worth having is commensurate with public funding and the type of accountability that will come with it remains to be seen.

Over at ITV, its executive chairman, Michael Grade, appeared to be having a pretty good year. With very positive comments about the new more creative leadership he brought to the company following the departure of his predecessor, Charles Allen, underpinned by significant improvements (or at least much slower deterioration) in the business fundamentals – ratings and revenues – Grade was looking good. As the BBC wrestled with fake guests on Blue Peter and Comic Relief, and the commercial broadcasters (including ITV) began to comprehend the true scale of the fraud perpetrated on viewers through premium-rate telephone services (from quiz questions with no right answers to competitions that couldn't possibly be won), Grade was able to stand above the fray. He gave a speech to the Royal Television Society about the importance of audience trust to broadcasting as an institution and proclaimed "zero tolerance" and "one strike and you're out" for anyone found to have been involved in misleading audiences at ITV or any of the independent producers that supplied it with programmes.

So far so good. Then Ofcom's report into GMTV's telephone competitions came out with scathing criticism of the company and a record £2m fine attached. The managing director, Paul Corley, did the honourable thing and resigned. Cue sharp intake of breath as

Audience share in all homes 2007

	Aug	Jul	Jun	May	April	March	Feb	Jan	Total % share 2006
Terrestrial channels									
BBC 1 (inc Breakfast News)	20.6	21.0	22.7	22.2	21.5	22.0	22.5	22.3	22.8
BBC 2	8.3	8.4	8.2	8.8	8.7	8.6	8.8	8.8	8.8
ITV (inc GMTV)	18.3	18.6	18.8	18.9	18.8	19.7	19.7	19.2	19.6
C4/S4C	8.7	9.2	9.4	8.7	8.4	8.8	9.1	10.6	9.8
Five	5.1	5.2	5.3	5.2	5.3	5.5	5.5	5.3	5.7
Other viewing	38.8	37.5	35.6	36.3	37.3	35.5	34.5	33.9	33.3
Audience share of viewing in multichannel homes									
Total Sky Movies	1.7	1.6	1.4	1.4	1.5	1.6	1.8	1.9	
Total Sky Sports	3.5	2.2	2.7	3.2	4.3	3.6	3.0	3.3	
Total Sky	8.0	6.8	6.9	7.6	8.8	8.0	8.1	8.3	
Total of all other channels	3.9	3.9	3.8	3.7	3.6	3.8	3.6	3.3	
Total non terrestrial channels	**45.8**	**44.6**	**42.3**	**43.7**	**44.9**	**43.0**	**42.1**	**41.5**	
Total terrestrial	**54.2**	**55.4**	**57.8**	**56.3**	**55.1**	**57.0**	**57.9**	**58.5**	

Source: BARB

Ofcom bared its teeth. As it had earlier accused the industry of being "in denial" about taking cash off viewers without worrying over whether they got anything in return, interest mounted in what was going to happen once the scale of malpractice at big sister ITV was revealed. And now we have it. ITV's own report into premium rate services (PRS) activity on ITV, commissioned from the accountants Deloittes, finally burst on to the scene in mid-October. As predicted, this made for pretty uncomfortable reading. Along with a dose of the usual, it revealed paid-for competitions that couldn't be won actually built into Ant and Dec's programme format. It also found viewers' paid-for choices of songs and contestants disregarded by producers where they thought they knew better. The disturbing picture that emerges is not just one of viewers being taken for granted but taken for a ride. And although the dash for PRS cash to buttress declining advertising revenues was Charles Allen's strategy, most of the people who implemented it and who failed to ensure any form of compliance financially or editorially are still in their jobs too. Grade's failure to act on his earlier "zero tolerance" pronouncement and the fact that as of the time of writing some major shows featuring PRS voting (such as The X Factor) have not been examined at all, have not improved his standing in the industry or the city.

And what of poor old Auntie? Fined £50,000 for faking a competition winner on Blue Peter, its director general, Mark Thompson, must have thought it couldn't get any worse. But like all the other terrestrial top-bods he almost couldn't have been more wrong. An internal enquiry from BBC Vision gave them a post Blue Peter clean bill of health only to be shown up days later by an amnesty that threw up at least seven new examples of dodgy dealing. And then came "Queengate". A trailer for a documentary series about the queen was doctored to show her leaving a photoshoot in a huff when nothing of the sort had actually happened. Worse, once discovered, senior BBC executives allowed the entire press (and all their own BBC news outlets) to carry on leading with the story for some 15 hours before they told the truth and withdrew the footage. Unusually, in this case three people did resign — Peter Fincham, the controller of BBC1; his head of press; and Stephen Lambert, the creative director of RDF Media, the independent producer responsible. Meanwhile, the rest of the senior management, under whose

Peter Fincham was forced to resign over the 'Queengate' affair

Martin Godwin

Digital and multichannel TV					
	Main operators	**Connected homes**		**Year-on-year rise**	**Audience share at 31 Mar 07**
		31 Mar 07	**31 Mar 06**		
Analogue terrestrial					18.3%
Satellite	Sky	8m	7.7m	3.9%	31.6%
	Free-to-view	885,000	645,000	37.2%	3.5%
Digital terrestrial	Freeview	8.3m	6.4m	29.7%	33.0%
Cable	Virgin Media	3.3m	3.3m	1.2%	13.4%
of which digital		*3.1m*	*2.8m*	*10.7%*	
ADSL		62,000	50,400	23.0%	0.2%
Total digital		**20.4m**	**17.6m**	**15.9%**	**80.5%**
Total multichannel		**20.7m**	**18.1m**	**14.4%**	**81.7%**

Source: Ofcom, Sky

authority the whole catalogue of errors and misjudgments has occurred, all remain firmly on the payroll.

The licence fee settlement announced by Tessa Jowell back on that day in January was a lot less than the BBC had asked for and is already proving difficult to manage. The staff, feeling let down by senior management's handling of the licence fee campaign and sore over fakery and the way it was dealt with, and now facing significant redundancies, are unhappy. But the bigger issue – which encompasses funding and fakery – is the sense that over the years of expanding services into new markets on one hand, and trying to deal with a much more competitive TV marketplace on the other, the organisation's core purposes and values have been left behind somewhere.

Meanwhile, at Sky there is no such problem. In a normal year one would probably be writing about Sky's impending difficulties on the regulatory front and its mutually damaging falling-out with Virgin Media, not to mention the prospect that it might be forced to dispose of its 18% stake in ITV at a loss. But all that feels like business as usual next to the storm that has engulfed terrestrial public-service TV. With improved penetration of Sky+ and more than a million people signed up to its broadband service, and in the absence of any obvious crisis of confidence over their core purposes, you'd have to say Sky has had a pretty good year.

But as the rest of the industry stares down the barrel, Ofcom's next review of public service broadcasting, which gets into full swing in 2008, will bring to the fore big questions of vision, values and purposes. And on that front you wouldn't, as they say, want to start from here.

● Steve Hewlett is media columnist at the Guardian

Awards

Bafta TV Awards 2007

- *Best actor:* Jim Broadbent, Longford (Channel 4)
- *Best actress:* Victoria Wood, Housewife, 49 (ITV1)
- *Best entertainment performance:* Jonathan Ross, Friday Night With Jonathan Ross (BBC1)
- *Best comedy performance:* Ricky Gervais, Extras (BBC2)
- *Best single drama:* Housewife, 49 (ITV1)
- *Best drama serial:* See No Evil: The Moors Murderers (ITV1)
- *Best drama series:* The Street (BBC1)
- *Best continuing drama:* Casualty (BBC1)
- *Best factual series:* Ross Kemp on Gangs (Sky One)
- *Best entertainment programme:* The X Factor (ITV1)
- *Best situation comedy:* The Royle Family: Queen of Sheba (BBC1)
- *Best comedy programme or series:* That Mitchell and Webb Look (BBC2)

Bong! News at Ten is back — but is this just ITV's attempt to bury bad news?

Janine Gibson

Television

There we were, going about our business, raking through the undergrowth trying to find out where all that ITV viewers' money went, when an apparition appears. Like something out of The Lion King, it's Sir Trevor McDonald in the night sky. He's pretty distant but he seems to be saying that News at Ten is back. Maybe. At some point next year.

Startled, we are distracted from the job in hand — and instead start searching for the dusty files on this eight-year-old saga of when to screen the news. Which was always, let's face it, an analogue debate of marginal significance outside of Westminster and the ITV network centre in the first place. Still, it takes our collective mind off all that unpleasantness with the phone calls.

Why on earth would ITV go down this particular road again when they are only going to lose in a head-to-head fight with the, now well-established, BBC 10pm bulletin?

First, I'm not convinced — and nor will I be till I hear those bongs on the hour and see Sir Trevor's ever-so-slightly wearier eyes staring back at me — that News at Ten will even return. Can we be absolutely certain that this is a genuine plan and not just an attempt to dazzle the fraud squad and Ofcom by wheeling out the patron saint of ITN?

Even assuming it is on the level, the best reason for bringing back News at Ten is a veil of respectability based on a reputation long squandered. The argument goes that ITV will inevitably lose money on the slot, but it will be "good" lost money; "we've put news on in primetime again" lost money. That then allows the network to argue to the regulator that it should be allowed to make slightly more money in other areas of the schedule (so can we please get rid of some of those advertising rules).

Here's the strange thing though. In the same week, ITN, which makes News at Ten, announced it would be putting its programmes on iTunes for free, funded by advertisers including BMW. It will be using the content it already produces for its customised ITN Mobile service — sports, showbiz, film, you choose what you want.

That deal comes a week after it launched a YouTube channel offering a range of news, sport and entertainment programmes, funded by advertisers, making ITN one of the first UK media companies to take advantage of YouTube's new in-video ads.

At the risk of sounding like the brochure, it's not just news either: it has some nifty archive-using tricks such as "this day in history" or "most requested" celebrity stories from its archives. A couple of months ago, it did a deal with the Telegraph, rumoured to be worth £1m, to produce news for its website.

Those of us who wearily remember every cough and spit of the News at When wars can recall that ITN was the loudest voice protesting against the move of News at Ten in the first place. Its then chief executive Stewart Purvis was back this week with a small and well-deserved "I told you so".

But now, at the moment of triumph, ITN doesn't seem to be all that confident about its analogue business model. Doubtless every last penny of extra cash will be mined out of the agreement and Sir Trevor, certainly, is not going to do badly out of this deal. His agent is, I'm sure, quite happy.

But ITN? ITN isn't focused on one slot on ITV anymore. ITN is looking to get its news out there anywhere it can. Messed about by its most important client eight years ago and forced to close its rolling news channel, it has finally learned that it can be on almost any platform you can imagine. And that it doesn't need Trevor McDonald either.

Sean Smith

Top Shows of 2006

	Title	Viewers (m)	% Share	Broadcaster/producer
1	World Cup 2006: Sweden v England	14.40	57.32	ITV1
2	World Cup Match of the Day Live	14.25	74.41	BBC1
3	Coronation Street	12.20	51.57	ITV1
4	The Vicar of Dibley	12.19	47.13	BBC1 Tiger Aspect
5	EastEnders	12.07	45.67	BBC1
6	Strictly Come Dancing	11.96	46.86	BBC1
7	Dancing on Ice: The Bolero Results	11.11	43.96	ITV1
8	Lewis	11.11	46.66	ITV1
9	Wild at Heart	10.63	40.33	ITV1
10	The X Factor — The Final Result	10.53	43.96	ITV1 Talkback Thames Syco
11	Pirates of the Caribbean	10.24	42.27	BBC1
12	A Touch of Frost	9.89	40.19	ITV1
13	Emmerdale	9.66	43.35	ITV1
14	I'm a Celebrity... Get Me out of Here! Final	9.65	41.26	ITV1
15	Heartbeat	9.48	36.56	ITV1
16	Ghostboat	9.45	37.05	ITV1
17	Planet Earth	9.37	33.21	BBC1
18	Doctor Who	9.28	37.80	BBC1
19	Match of the Day Live	9.28	38.93	BBC1
20	The Royal	8.99	36.10	ITV1
21	Children in Need	8.93	38.75	BBC1
22	Little Britain Abroad	8.75	37.66	BBC1
23	Midsomer Murders	8.70	34.59	ITV1 Bentley
24	Rebus	8.68	32.99	ITV1 SMG
25	Champions League Final	8.67	37.07	ITV1
26	Cracker	8.62	38.47	ITV1
27	Agatha Christie's Marple	8.61	36.81	ITV1
28	New Tricks	8.61	33.87	BBC1 Wall to Wall
29	Robin Hood	8.56	37.65	BBC1 Tiger Aspect
30	Holby City	8.53	34.42	BBC1
31	BBC News	8.53	36.60	BBC1
32	Housewife, 49	8.52	33.99	ITV1
33	Soapstar Superstar Results	8.35	33.79	ITV1
34	Doc Martin	8.33	31.71	ITV1 Buffalo Pictures
35	Casualty	8.30	34.32	BBC1
36	Eurovision Song Contest 2006	8.29	36.96	BBC1
37	Prime Suspect	8.26	35.82	ITV1
38	The Royle Family	8.24	33.58	BBC1
39	How Do You Solve a Problem Like Maria?	8.13	35.60	BBC1
40	Ant and Dec's Saturday Night Takeaway	8.07	35.83	ITV1
41	Foyle's War	8.05	32.97	ITV1 Greenlit
42	The Royal	8.02	32.69	ITV1
43	The Royal Variety Performance 2006	7.97	33.60	BBC1
44	Ten O'Clock News	7.91	37.59	BBC1
45	Calendar Girls	7.90	36.13	BBC1
46	My Family	7.85	33.26	BBC1 DLT Rude Boy
47	Big Brother: Live Final	7.73	38.64	C4 Brighter Pictures
48	Agatha Christie's Poirot	7.67	30.61	ITV1
49	The Children's Party at the Palace	7.62	39.57	BBC1
50	Who Wants to/be Millionaire? Celebrity	7.50	30.73	ITV1 Celador

	Title	Viewers (m)	% Share	Broadcaster/producer
51	Judge John Deed	7.49	30.44	BBC1
52	Bruce Almighty	7.49	32.45	BBC1
53	Life on Mars	7.40	28.16	BBC1 Kudos
54	Ant & Dec's Saturday Night Takeaway	7.34	34.11	ITV1
55	Sharpe's Challenge	7.33	31.18	ITV1
56	Dalziel and Pascoe	7.25	30.91	BBC1
57	Full Length and Fabulous	7.24	32.89	ITV1
58	Silent Witness	7.22	30.26	BBC1
59	The Funny Side of the Street	7.20	33.24	ITV1
60	The National Lottery: In It to Win It	7.20	35.11	BBC1
61	New Year Live	7.13	44.72	BBC1
62	Ice Age	7.10	32.28	ITV1
63	The Bill	7.10	29.91	ITV1 Talkback Thames
64	The National Lottery Jet Set	7.07	33.56	BBC1
65	Jane Eyre	7.06	27.50	BBC1
66	Ruby in the Smoke	7.02	28.43	BBC1
67	Mrs Henderson Presents	6.96	31.49	BBC1
68	Antiques Roadshow	6.91	29.33	BBC1
69	Blue Murder	6.81	32.11	ITV1
70	Jam and Jerusalem	6.81	27.84	BBC1
71	The National Lottery: 1 vs 100	6.80	30.66	BBC1
72	Soapstar Superstar	6.78	27.10	ITV1
73	The National Television Awards	6.78	29.53	ITV1
74	Hustle	6.77	29.02	BBC1 Kudos
75	Have I Got News for You	6.75	31.73	BBC1 Hat Trick
76	Northern Lights	6.73	26.28	ITV1
77	Poirot	6.73	28.63	ITV1
78	Sweeney Todd	6.71	27.28	BBC1
79	Krakatoa: The Last Days	6.68	27.34	BBC1
80	Driving Lessons	6.66	28.24	ITV1
81	You've Been Framed at Christmas	6.63	29.65	ITV1
82	The Booze Cruise III	6.57	29.48	ITV1
83	Seaside Rescue	6.57	28.24	BBC1
84	The Incredible Journey of Mary Bryant	6.57	30.01	ITV1
85	Where the Heart Is	6.55	29.14	ITV1
86	Celebrity Big Brother Live Launch Show	6.52	25.16	C4
87	All Star Family Fortunes	6.51	27.68	ITV1
88	ITV Evening News	6.47	35.18	ITV1 ITN
89	Tonight with Trevor McDonald	6.46	27.13	ITV1
90	My Name Is Earl	6.46	35.53	C4
91	Antiques Roadshow	6.46	28.33	BBC1
92	Just the Two of Us	6.45	27.19	BBC1
93	Spooks	6.45	25.88	BBC1 Kudos
94	9/11: The Twin Towers	6.44	30.00	BBC1
95	Who Do You Think You Are?	6.39	27.94	BBC1 Wall to Wall
96	The Inspector Lynley Mysteries	6.38	30.85	BBC1
97	See No Evil: The Moors Murders	6.38	32.12	ITV1
98	The Queen by Rolf	6.37	23.78	BBC1
99	If I Had You	6.37	27.47	ITV1
100	What We Did on Our Holiday	6.30	28.02	ITV1

Reproduced by kind permission of Broadcast magazine

Television contacts

BBC

BBC
020 8743 8000
info@bbc.co.uk
www.bbc.co.uk
Executive Board:
Director General: Mark Thompson;
deputy director-general: Mark Byford;
audio & music: Jenny Abramsky;
vision: Jana Bennett; marketing,
communications & audiences:
Tim Davie; future media & technology:
Ashley Highfield; BBC people: Stephen
Kelly; group finance director: Zarin
Patel; CEO BBC worldwide: John Smith;
chief operating officer: Caroline
Thomson; senior independent director:
Marcus Agius; non-executive directors:
Dr Mike Lynch, David Robbie, Dr Samir
Shah, Robert Webb.
BBC Trust: Chairman: Sir Michael
Lyons, Trustees: Chitra Bharucha;
Dermot Gleeson; Patricia Hodgson;
Janet Lewis-Jones; Jeremy Peat; Diane
Coyle; Alison Hastings; Rotha
Johnston; David Liddiment; Mehmuda
Mian Pritchard; Richard Tait.
Press: 020 8576 1865
  press.office@bbc.co.uk
  www.bbc.co.uk/pressoffice

Addresses

Television Centre
Wood Lane, London W12 7RJ

BBC White City
201 Wood Lane, London W12 7TS

Broadcasting House
Portland Place, London W1A 1AA

● BBC TV

Television Centre
020 8743 8000
www.bbc.co.uk/television
Director of BBC Vision: Jana Bennett;
controller, programme acquisition:
George McGhee
Press: 020 8576 9900
  publicity.frontdesk@bbc.co.uk

● Nations and regions

Director of nations and regions:
Pat Loughrey

BBC Northern Ireland
Broadcasting House, Ormeau
Avenue, Belfast BT2 8HQ
028 9033 8000
www.bbc.co.uk/northernireland
Controller: Peter Johnston

BBC Scotland
BBC Scotland, 40 Pacific Quay,
Glasgow, G51 1BA
0141 422 6000
www.bbc.co.uk/scotland
Controller: Ken MacQuarrie

BBC Wales
Broadcasting House, Llandaff,
Cardiff CF5 2YQ
029 2032 2000
www.bbc.co.uk/wales
Controller: Menna Richards

BBC ENGLISH REGIONS

Controller: Andy Griffee

BBC London
35c Marylebone High Street,
London W1U 4QA
020 7224 2424
yourlondon@bbc.co.uk
www.bbc.co.uk/london
Head of regional and local
programmes: Michael MacFarlane

BBC East
The Forum, Millennium Plain,
Norwich NR2 1BH
01603 619331
look.east@bbc.co.uk
www.bbc.co.uk/england/lookeast
Head of regional and local
programmes: Tim Bishop

BBC East Midlands
London Road, Nottingham NG2 4UU
0115 955 0500
emt@bbc.co.uk
www.bbc.co.uk/england
  /eastmidlandstoday
Head of regional and local
programmes: Aziz Rashid

BBC North
2 St Peter's Square, Leeds LS9 8AH
0113 244 1188
look.north@bbc.co.uk
www.bbc.co.uk/england
  /looknorthyorkslincs
Head of regional and local
programmes: Helen Thomas

BBC North East and Cumbria
Broadcasting Centre, Barrack Road,
Newcastle upon Tyne NE99 2NE
0191 232 1313
newcastlenews@bbc.co.uk
www.bbc.co.uk/tyne
Head of regional and local
programmes: Wendy Pilmer

BBC North West
New Broadcasting House,
Oxford Road, Manchester M60 1SJ
0161 200 2020
nwt@bbc.co.uk
www.bbc.co.uk/manchester
Head of regional and local
programmes: Tamsin O'Brien

BBC South
Broadcasting House, Havelock
Road, Southampton SO14 7PU
023 8022 6201
south.today@bbc.co.uk
www.bbc.co.uk/england
  /southtoday
Head of regional and local
programmes: Mike Hapgood

BBC South East
The Great Hall, Mount Pleasant
Road, Tunbridge Wells TN1 1QQ
01892 670000
southeasttoday@bbc.co.uk
www.bbc.co.uk/england
  /southeasttoday
Head of regional and local
programmes: Mike Hapgood

BBC South West
Broadcasting House, Seymour Road,
Mannamead, Plymouth PL3 5BD
01752 229201
spotlight@bbc.co.uk
www.bbc.co.uk/england/devon
Head of regional and local
programmes: John Lilley

BBC West
Broadcasting House,
Whiteladies Road, Bristol BS8 2LR
0117 973 2211
pointswest@bbc.co.uk
www.bbc.co.uk/england
  /pointswest
Head of regional and local
programmes: Andrew Wilson

BBC West Midlands
The Mailbox, Birmingham B1 1XL
0121 567 6767
midlands.today@bbc.co.uk
www.bbc.co.uk/birmingham
Head of regional and local
programmes: David Holdsworth

● Channels

BBC1
Television Centre
020 8743 8000
www.bbc.co.uk/bbcone
Controller: Jay Hunt

BBC2
Television Centre
020 8743 8000
www.bbc.co.uk/bbctwo
Controller: Roly Keating; controller of
daytime: Liam Keelan

BBC3
Television Centre
020 8743 8000
www.bbc.co.uk/bbcthree
Controller: Danny Cohen

BBC4
Television Centre
0870 010 0222
www.bbc.co.uk/bbcfour
Controller: Janice Hadlow

CBBC
Television Centre
020 8743 8000
www.bbc.co.uk/cbbc
Controller: Richard Deverell

CBeebies
Television Centre
020 8743 8000
www.bbc.co.uk/cbeebies
Controller: Richard Deverell

BBC America
747 Third Avenue, New York,
10017, NY, USA
00 1 859 342 4070
www.bbcamerica.com
Programme executive: Alison Fredericks

BBC Canada
121 Bloor Street East, Suite 200,
Toronto, Ontario, Canada M4W 3M5
00 1 416 967 1174
feedback@bbccanada.com
www.bbccanada.com

BBC Food
PO Box 5054, London W12 0ZY
020 8433 2221
www.bbcfood.com
Editor: David Weiland

BBC News 24
Television Centre
020 8743 8000
bbcnews24@bbc.co.uk
www.bbc.co.uk/bbcnews24
Controller: Kevin Bakhurst

BBC Parliament
4 Millbank, London SW1P 3JA
020 7973 6216
parliament@bbc.co.uk
www.bbc.co.uk/bbcparliament
Controller: Kevin Bakhurst

BBC Prime
PO Box 5054, London W12 0ZY
020 8433 2221
bbcprime@bbc.co.uk
www.bbcprime.com
Editor: David Weiland

BBC World
PO Box 5054, London W12 0ZY
020 8433 2221
bbcworld@bbc.co.uk
www.bbcworld.com
Editorial director: Sian Kevill

● Interactive TV

BBCi
Television Centre
020 8743 8000
www.bbc.co.uk/digital/tv
Controller: Rahul Chakkara; head, interactive TV programming: Emma Somerville

● Ceefax
Television Centre
020 8743 8000

Genres

● BBC News
Television Centre
020 8743 8000
www.bbc.co.uk/news
Director of BBC News: Helen Boaden; deputy: Adrian Van Klaveren; head of newsgathering: Fran Unsworth
- Editors – business: Robert Preston; diplomatic: Brian Hanrahan; home: Mark Easton; Middle East: Jeremy Bowen; political: Nick Robinson; world affairs: John Simpson
- UK correspondents – defence: Paul Adams; diplomatic: Jonathan Marcus; education: Mike Baker; health: Adam Brimelow, Sophie Hutchinson; home affairs: Margaret Gilmore; political: Laura Trevelyan; royal: Nicholas Witchell, Peter Hunt; rural affairs: Tom Heap; security: Frank Gardner; social affairs: Daniel Sandford
- Special correspondents – Fergal Keane, Gavin Hewitt; TV news: Ben Brown; BBC News 24: Philippa Thomas
- World correspondents – world affairs: Peter Biles. Europe: Tim Franks, Chris Morris, Stephen Sackur; Paris: Allan Little, Caroline Wyatt; Berlin: Ray Furlong; Rome: David Willey; Greece: Richard Galpin; Moscow: Damian Grammaticas; south Europe: Brian Barron; central Europe: Nick Thorpe. Middle East: Orla Guerin, Paul Wood; Turkey: Jonny Dymond. Americas – Washington: Nick Bryant, Matt Frei, Jon Leyne, Clive Myrie, Ian Pannell, Justin Webb; California: David Willis; Mexico and central America: Claire Marshall; South America: Elliott Gotkine. Other – Africa: Hilary Andersson; east Africa: Andrew Harding; south Asia: Adam Mynott; central Asia: Monica Whitlock. World media: Sebastian Usher. Also Dominic Hughes, Jill McGivering, Matthew Price

Political programmes unit
BBC Westminster, 4 Millbank,
London SW1P 3JA
020 7973 6000
Head of political programmes: Sue Inglish; political editor: Nick Robinson

TV News
Room 1502, Television Centre
020 8624 9141
Head of television news: Peter Horrocks

Breakfast
Room 1605, News Centre,
Television Centre
020 8624 9700
breakfasttv@bbc.co.uk
Editor: Richard Porter; presenters: Sian Williams and Bill Turnbull

Newsnight
Television Centre
020 8624 9800
Editor: Peter Barron; presenters: Jeremy Paxman, Kirsty Wark, Gavin Esler, Emily Maitlis

Panorama
Room 1118, BBC White City
020 8752 7152
panorama@bbc.co.uk
Editor: Sandy Smith; deputy editors: Frank Simmonds and Ingrid Kelly

Politics Show
4 Millbank, London SW1P 3JQ
020 7973 6199
politicsshow@bbc.co.uk
Presenter: Jon Sopel

Question Time
Mentorn, 77 Fulham Palace Road,
Hammersmith, London W6 8JA
020 7258 6800
Presenter: David Dimbleby

Six O'Clock News
Television Centre
020 8624 9996
Editor: Mark Popescu; presenters: George Alagiah, Sian Williams

Ten O'Clock News
Television Centre
020 8624 9999
Editor: Craig Oliver; presenters: Huw Edwards, Fiona Bruce

● Factual and learning

Director of factual and learning
Bridget Boseley
020 8752 6501

Controller of Knowledge, BBC Vision
Glenwyn Benson
020 8743 8000

Head of factual TV
Charlotte Ashton
020 8743 8000

Arts
2nd Floor, BBC White City
020 8752 4092
claire.lewis.02@bbc.co.uk
Executive producer: Claire Lewis; commissioner, arts and culture: Franny Moyle

Arts (Wales)
Room 3023, BBC Wales
029 2032 3012
Head of arts commissioning, Wales: Ceri Sherlock

contacts **Television**

131

Classical music
Room 3223, BBC White City
020 8752 6868
*Head of TV, classical music and
performance: Peter Maniura*

Current affairs
Room 1172, BBC White City
020 8752 7005
Head of current affairs: George Entwistle

Documentaries and contemporary factual
Room 3559, BBC White City
020 8743 8000
genfact.proposals@bbc.co.uk
Head of documentaries: Keith Scholey

Education
Room 3416, BBC White City
020 8752 5241
Executive editor: Karen Johnson

Education (Northern Ireland)
Education Unit, First Floor,
BBC Northern Ireland
028 9033 8445
Editor, learning, NI: Kieran Hegarty

Education (Scotland)
Zone 3.33, BBC Scotland
0141 422 6493
Editor, education, Scotland: Nick Simons

Education (Wales)
Room E3106, BBC Wales
029 2032 2834
*Head of education and learning,
Wales: Dr Eleri Wyn Williams*

Factual (Northern Ireland)
2nd Floor, BBC Northern Ireland
028 9033 8371
Editor, factual TV: Paul McGuigan

Factual (Scotland)
Zone 2.25, BBC Scotland
0141 422 6090
andrea.miller.01@bbc.co.uk
*Head of factual programmes,
Scotland: Andrea Miller*

Factual (Wales)
Room 4020, BBC Wales
029 2032 2976
*Head of factual programmes, Wales:
Adrian Davies*

Lifeskills TV
Room 2308, BBC White City
020 8752 4574
Head of Lifeskills TV: Seetha Kumar

Music (Wales)
Room E4113, BBC Wales
029 2032 2111
davidm.jackson@bbc.co.uk
Head of music, Wales: David Jackson

Specialist factual, current affairs and arts
Room 2156, BBC White City
020 8743 8000
specfact.proposals@bbc.co.uk
*Head of independent commissioning:
Adam Kemp; commissioner, head of
BBC Vision, multimedia: Emma Swain;
senior commissioning executives:
Krishan Arora, Lucy Hetherington;
executive editor: Jacquie Hughes*

PROGRAMMES

Arena
Room 2168, BBC White City
020 8752 5172
Series editor: Anthony Wall

Everyman
Room 5048, BBC Manchester,
Broadcasting House, Oxford Road,
Manchester M60 1SJ
0161 244 3321
ruth.pitt@bbc.co.uk
Creative director: Ruth Pitt

Horizon
Room 5100, BBC White City
020 8752 6134
horizon@bbc.co.uk
Editor: Andrew Cohen

Imagine
Arts Department, 2nd Floor,
BBC White City
020 8752 4092
ian.macmillan@bbc.co.uk
Series producer: Ian Macmillan

Money programme
Room 4606, BBC White City
020 8752 7432
Series editor: Clive Edwards

One Life
Room 5503, BBC White City
020 8752 6608
todd.austin@bbc.co.uk
Commissioning editor: Todd Austin

Panorama
Room 1118, BBC White City
020 8752 7152
Editor: Sandy Smith

Storyville
2nd Floor, Grafton House, Euston
Road 379-381, London NW1 3AU
020 7765 5211
storyville@bbc.co.uk
Commissioning editor: Nick Fraser

This World
Room 1362, BBC White City
020 8752 7500
thisworld@bbc.co.uk
Editor: Louise Norman

Timewatch
Room 3150, BBC White City
020 8752 7079
Editor: John Farren

● Drama and entertainment

*Director of drama, entertainment
and Children's:* Alan Yentob

Comedy
Room 4045, Television Centre
020 8576 7786
*Controller of comedy commissioning:
Lucy Lumsden*

*Comedy and entertainment
(Scotland)*
Zone 2.13, BBC Scotland
0141 422 6336
*Head of comedy and entertainment,
Scotland: Alan Tyler*

Daytime
Room 3560, BBC White City
020 8752 6225
*Senior commissioning executive,
daytime: Lindsay Bradbury*

Daytime entertainment
Room 6070, Television Centre
020 8576 9960
*Commissioning executive, daytime
entertainment: Gilly Hall*

Drama
Room 2145, Television Centre,
56 Wood Lane, London W12 7RJ
020 8576 1861

Drama (Northern Ireland)
BBC Northern Ireland
020 8576 1664
Head of drama, NI: Patrick Spence

Drama (Scotland)
Zone 2.08, BBC Scotland
0141 422 6081
*Head of television drama, Scotland:
Anne Mensah*

Drama (Wales)
Room E2106, BBC Wales
029 2032 2935
Head of drama, Wales: Julie Gardner

Entertainment
Room 6070, Television Centre
020 8225 6992
*Controller, entertainment
commissioning: Elaine Bedell*

Entertainment (Northern Ireland)
Room 229, BBC Northern Ireland
028 9033 8375
mike.edgar@bbc.co.uk
*Head of entertainment, events and
sport, NI: Cindy Hanson*

● Children

CBBC
Room E1012, Television Centre
020 8576 1280
*Director: Anne Gilchrist; controller:
Richard Deverell*

Acquisitions
Room E185, Television Centre
020 8576 8245
*Head of acquisitions and co-
productions: Jesse Cleverly*

CBeebies
Room E1015, Television Centre
020 8225 7968
*Creative director, CBeebies:
Michael Carrington*

CBBC Scotland
Room 2104, BBC Scotland
0141 422 6793
*Head of children's, Scotland:
Simon Parsons*

Drama
Room E817, Television Centre
020 8576 8245
Head of drama: Jon East

Entertainment
Room E701, Television Centre
020 8225 7925
Head of entertainment: Jo Godwin

News and factual
Room E111, Television Centre
020 8576 3118
Head of news and factual: Tim Levell

Pre-school
Room E219, Television Centre
020 8228 7072
Head of pre-school: Clare Elstow

● Sport

Director of sport: Roger Mosey

Live sport and highlights
Room 5060, Television Centre
020 8225 8400
andrew.thompson.01@bbc.co.uk
Head of new media, sports news and development: Andrew Thompson

● Films

BBC Films
Grafton House, 379 Euston Road,
London NW1 3AU
020 7765 0251

» *See page 222*

● Radio

» *See page 172*

● Digital media

BBC Future Media
Broadcast Centre, Media Village,
201 Wood Lane, London W12 7TP
020 8008 1300
www.bbc.co.uk
Director of new media and technology: Ashley Highfield; controller, internet: Tony Ageh; controller; multi platform distribution: Simon Nelson

» *See page 261*

● Business services

BBC Costumes and Wigs
Victoria Road, London W3 6UL
020 8576 1761
costume@bbc.co.uk
wigs@bbc.co.uk
www.bbcresources.com

BBC International Unit
020 8576 1173
international.unit@bbc.co.uk
www.bbc.co.uk/international
Supplies TV facilities to overseas broadcasters transmitting from UK. Manager: Peter James

BBC Monitoring
Marketing Unit, Caversham Park,
Reading RG4 8TZ
0118 948 6289
csu@mon.bbc.co.uk
www.bbcmonitoringonline.com
www.monitor.bbc.co.uk
Monitors world media

BBC Outside Broadcasts
Station Road, Langley, SL3 6DB
01753 588088
ob@bbc.co.uk
www.bbcresources.com

BBC Post-Production
Television Centre
020 8225 7702
postproduction@bbc.co.uk
www.bbcresources.com
Bristol
Broadcasting House,
White Ladies Road, Bristol BS8 2LR
0117 974 6666
Birmingham
The Mailbox, Birmingham B1 1XL
0121 567 7029

BBC R&D
BBC Kingswood Warren,
Tadworth, Surrey KT20 6NP
01737 839500
info@rd.bbc.co.uk
www.bbc.co.uk/rd
Head of research: Ian Childs

BBC Research Central
Broadcasting House
research-central@bbc.co.uk
www.bbcresearchcentral.com
Information, footage, pronunciation, radio and photo research services. Senior researchers: Helen Turner, Huw Martin, Guy Watkins, Angie Francis, Kyla Thorogood, Richard Jeffery, Jacqueline Faulkner, Michael Paige

BBC Studios
Television Centre, Wood Lane,
London, W12 7RJ
020 8576 7666
tvstudio.sales@bbc.co.uk
www.bbcresources.com

BBC Training and Development
Wood Norton Training Centre
Evesham, Worcestershire WR11 4YB
0870 122 0216
training@bbc.co.uk
www.bbctraining.co.uk
Training for programme-making, broadcasting and new media

Elstree
Clarendon Road, Borehamwood,
Herts WD6 1JF

London
35 Marylebone High Street,
London W1U 4PX

BBC Worldwide
Woodlands, 80 Wood Lane,
London W12 0TT
020 8433 2000
www.bbcworldwide.com
Commercial arm: businesses include distribution, TV channels, magazines, books, videos, spoken word, music, DVDs, licensed products, CD-ROMs, English language teaching, videos for education and training, interactive telephony, co-production, library footage. Chief executive: John Smith Offices Worldwide: New York, Sydney, Paris, Hollywood, Tokyo, Cologne, Florida, Hong Kong, Sao Paulo, Singapore, Toronto.

Audience Council for England
www.bbc.co.uk/england/ace
English Regions, BBC Birmingham,
The Mailbox, Birmingham B1 1XL
0121 567 6767
12 regional Audience Councils based in BBC English regions

Audience Council for Scotland
BBC Scotland, 40 Pacific Quay,
Glasgow, G51 1BA
0141 422 6076

Audience Council for Wales
BBC Wales, Broadcasting House,
Llandaff, Cardiff CF5 2YQ
029 2032 2004

Audience Council for Northern Ireland
Accountability Manager NI, Trish Davey, Broadcasting House,
Ormeau Avenue, Belfast BT2 8HQ
028 9033 8854

Television contacts

Traditional media

● ITV Network (ITV1)

200 Grays Inn Road,
London WC1X 8HF
0844 881 8000
www.itv.com/itv1
www.itvregions.com
Controllers run commissioning and scheduling across ITV1 national network – including non-ITV plc regions. Network controllers – acquisitions: Jay Kandola, 020 7843 8120; regulatory and public affairs: Sophie Cohen; factual and daytime: Alison Sharman, 020 7843 8132; comedy: Paul Jackson, 020 7843 8093; drama: Nick Elliot, 020 7843 8202 (head of continuing series: Corinne Hollingworth); entertainment: Paul Jackson, 020 7843 8105; sport: Mark Sharman

● ITV plc

London Television Centre,
Upper Ground, London SE1 9LT
0844 881 8000
Controls 11 of the 15 ITV1 franchises, ITV2, ITV3 and Granada production company. Executive chairman: Michael Grade; director of regional affairs: Susan Woodward; controller of regional affairs: Jane Luca; communications director: Brigitte Trafford
Press Office: 0844 881 8000

ITV Broadcast
020 7843 8000
Runs ITV plc's 11 regional ITV1 franchises; runs ITV2 and ITV3 Director of Television: Simon Shaps

ITV1 FRANCHISES

ITV Anglia
Anglia House, Norwich NR1 3JG
01603 615151
firstname.lastname@itv.com
www.itvlocal.com/anglia
MD: Neil Thompson; controller of programmes and regional news: Neil Thompson; head of regional affairs: Jim Woodrow

News at Anglia
0870 240 6003
news@angliatv.com

Cambridge regional office
26 Newmarket Road,
Cambridge CB5 8DT
01223 467076

Chelmsford regional office
64–68 New London Road,
Chelmsford CM2 0YU
01245 357676

Ipswich regional office
Hubbard House, Ipswich IP1 2QA
01473 226157

Luton regional office
16 Park Street, Luton LU1 2DP
01582 729666

Northampton regional office
77b Abington Street,
Northampton NN1 2BH
01604 624343

Peterborough regional office
6 Bretton Green,
Peterborough PE3 8DY
01733 269440

ITV Border
The Television Centre, Durranhill,
Carlisle CA1 3NT
01228 525101
www.itvregions.com/border
MD: Paddy Merrall; head of news: Ian Proniewicz
Press and regional affairs manager: Louise Maving

ITV Central
Gas Street, Birmingham B1 2JT
0844 881 4000
firstname.lastname@itv.com
www.itvlocal.com/central
MD: Ian Squires; controller of news and operations: Mike Blair; head of regional programming: Philip Braund; editor, Central News West: Dan Barton
Press officer: Christopher Strange

ITV Granada
Quay Street, Manchester M60 9EA
0161 832 7211
firstname.lastname@itv.com
www.itvregions.com/granada
MD: Susan Woodward; controller of programmes: Duncan Rycroft; controller of regional affairs: Jane Luca; news editor: Richard Frediani

Liverpool office
The Liver Building,
Liverpool L3 1HU
0808 101 0045

Lancaster office
Lancaster University, Bailrigg,
Lancaster LA1 4YW
01524 594594

ITV London
London Television Centre,
Upper Grounds, London SE1 9LT
020 7620 1620
firstname.lastname@itv.com
www.itvlocal.com/london
MD: Christy Swords; controller of regional programming: Emma Barker; head of regional affairs: Helen Andrews

London News Network
200 Grays Inn Road,
London WC1X 8HF
020 7430 4000
firstname.lastname@itvlondon.com
www.itvlocal.com/london
Planning editor: Anne Mulhall; head of news: Stuart Thomas; news editors: Brendan McGowan, Lizzie Hill

ITV Meridian
Forum One, Parkway,
Solent Business Park, Whiteley,
Hampshire PO15 7PA
0844 881 2000
news@meridiantv.com
www.itvlocal.com/meridian

Maidstone news office
Maidstone Studios, Vinters Park,
Maidstone, Kent ME14 5NZ
08448814300

Abingdon news office
9 Windrush Court, Abingdon
Business Park, Abingdon, Oxford,
OX14 1SA
0844 8814515

ITV Tyne Tees
Television House, The Watermark,
Gateshead NE11 9SZ
0844 881 5000
news@tynetees.tv
firstname.lastname@itv.com
www.itvlocal.com/tynetees
MD and controller of programmes: Graeme Thompson; regional affairs manager: Brenda Mitchell; head of news: Graham Marples

Tees Valley & North Yorkshire news office
Belasis Hall Technology Park,
Billingham, Teesside TS23 4EG
01642 566999
newstoday@tynetees.tv
Senior editor: Lucy West

ITV Wales
The Television Centre,
Culverhouse Cross, Cardiff CF5 6XJ
0844 881 0100
info@itvwales.com
news@itvwales.com
firstname.lastname@itvwales.com
www.itvregions.com/wales
MD: Roger Lewis; controller of programmes: Elis Owen; regional affairs manager: Shone Hughes; head of news: Philip Hemfey
Press contact: Shone Hughes

Carmarthen news office
19-20 Coopers Chambers, Lammas
Street, Carmarthen, SA31 3AL
01267 236806
West Wales correspondent: Giles Smith

Colwyn Bay news office
Celtic Business Centre, Plas
Eiriasm Heritage Gate, Abergele
Road, Colwyn Bay LL29 8BW
01492 513888
colwyn@itvwales.com
North Wales correspondents: Carole Green, Ian Lang

Newtown news office
St David's House,
Newtown SY16 1RB
01686 623381
Mid-Wales correspondent: Rob Shelley

Wrexham news office
Crown Buildings, 31 Chester
Street, Wrexham LL13 8BG
01978 261462
North Wales correspondent: Paul Mewies

ITV West

Television Centre, Bath Road,
Bristol BS4 3HG
0117 972 2722
reception@itv.com
firstname.lastname@itv.com
www.itvlocal.com/west
*MD: Mark Haskell; controller of
programmes: Jane McCloskey; head
of features and current affairs: James
Garrett; head of regional affairs:
Richard Lister*
Press: 0117 972 2214

Newsdesk
0117 972 2151/2
itvwestnews@itv.com
Head of news: Liz Hannam

ITV Westcountry

Langage Science Park, Western
Wood Way, Plymouth PL7 5BQ
01752 333333
firstname.lastname@itv.com
www.itvlocal.com/westcountry
*MD: Mark Haskell; director of
programmes: Jane McCloskey;
controller; director of production
technology: Mark Chaplin; regional
affairs: Rebecca Payne*

Main newsdesk
01752 333341
news@westcountry.co.uk
Controller of news: Phil Carrodus

Barnstaple news office
1 Summerland Terrace,
Barnstaple EX32 8JL
01271 324244

Exeter news office
St Luke's Campus, Magdalene
Road, Exeter EX4 4WT
01392 499400

Penzance news office
Parade Chambers, 10 Parade
Street, Penzance TR18 4BU
01736 331483

Taunton news office
Foundry Cottage, Riverside Place,
St James Street, Taunton TA1 1JH
01823 322335

Truro news office
Courtleigh House, Lemon Street,
Truro TR1 2PN
01872 262244

Weymouth news office
8 King Street, Weymouth DT4 7BP
01305 760860

ITV Yorkshire

The Television Centre, Kirkstall
Road, Leeds, West Yorkshire LS3 1JS
0113 243 8283
firstname.lastname@itv.com
www.itvlocal.com/yorkshire
*MD: David Croft, 0113 222 7184;
controller of regional programmes:
Neil Thompson, 0113 222 8724;
head of regional affairs: Mark Covell,
0113 222 7091*
Press: 0113 222 7129

Grimsby office
Image Studios, Margaret Street,
Immingham, Grimsby DN40 1LE
01469 510661
Head of news: Will Venters

Hull office
23 The Prospect Centre,
Hull HU2 8PM
01482 324488

Lincoln office
88 Bailgate, Lincoln LN1 3AR
01522 530738

Sheffield office
23 Charter Square, Sheffield S1 4HS
0114 272 7772

York office
8 Coppergate, York YO1 9NT
01904 610066

● Channels

ITV2
0844 881 3000
www.itv.com/itv2

ITV3
0884 881 3000
www.itv.com/itv3

● ITV News Group

020 7396 6000
*Includes ITV1's national and
international news output, and
regional news for ITV plc franchises
(see above); plus ITV plc's 40% stake in
ITN. Chief executive: Clive Jones*

ITV News
ITN, 200 Grays Inn Road,
London WC1X 8XZ
020 7833 3000
www.itv.com/news
*ITN is 40% owned by ITV plc.
Editor-in-chief: David Mannion;
editor: Deborah Turness; deputy
editor: Jonathan Munro; managing
editor: Robin Elias*
• Key presenters: *Mary Nightingale;
Katie Derham; Mark Austin; Alistair
Stewart; Nina Hossain*
• Editors – business: *Mark Eddo;
consumer affairs: Chris Choi;
international: Bill Neely; political:
Tom Bradby; science: Lawrence
McGinty; senior correspondent:
James Mates; UK correspondents –
news: Juliet Bremner, Neil Connery,
Paul Davies, Tim Ewart, Philip Reay-
Smith; Harry Smith; political: Libby
Wiener, Chris Ship; UK editor: Angus
Walker; north of England: Tim
Rogers; Wales and west of England:
Helen Callaghan; medical: Sue
Saville; crime: Adrian Britton; media
and arts: Nina Nannar; royalty:
Romilly Weeks; social affairs: Helen
Wright; sport: Geraint Vincent*
• World correspondents – Europe:
*Robert Moore; Washington: John
Irvine; Middle East: Julian Manyon;
Africa: Martin Geissler; China:
John Ray*

Press: 020 7430 4825
saskia.wirth@itn.co.uk
Press releases to:
itvplanning@itn.co.uk

Regional news offices
*Part of ITV News Group; listed under
ITV franchises, above*

● Other ITV plc divisions

ITV Consumer
0844 881 8000
*Builds direct consumer revenues.
Chief executive officer: Jeff Henry*

ITV Commercial
020 7396 6000
*Director of business management:
Andy Bagnall; director of customer
relationship management: Gary Digby;
Nicky Buss; sponsorship: Gary Knight;
regional sales: David Cross; London
sales: Simon Lent*

● Other ITV1 franchise-holders

Scottish Media Group
Acting chief executive: Donald Emslie

STV North
Television Centre, Craigshaw
Business Park, West Tullos,
Aberdeen AB12 3QH
01224 848848
firstname.lastname@smg.plc.uk
www.grampiantv.co.uk
*MD and controller of regional
programmes: Derrick Thomson; head
of news: Gordon Macmillan*
Press: Caroline Frost
01224 848820
caroline.frost@grampiantv.co.uk

Scottish TV
Pacific Quay, Glasgow, G51 1PQ
0141 300 3000
firstname.lastname@smg.plc.uk
www.scottishtv.co.uk
*MD and controller of regional
programmes: Bobby Hain; head
of news: Paul McKinney. Newsdesk:
0141 300 3360*
Press: Kirsten Elsby
0141 300 3670
kirstin.elsby@smg.plc.uk

INDEPENDENT FRANCHISES

Channel Television
Television Centre, La Pouquelaye,
St Helier, Jersey JE1 3ZD
01534 816816
broadcast@channeltv.co.uk
www.channeltv.co.uk
*MD: Michael Lucas; director of
programmes: Karen Rankine
(karen.rankine@channeltv.co.uk);
director of special projects: Gordon de
Ste Croix (gordon@channeltv.co.uk);
director of resources and transmission:
Kevin Banner. Newsroom: 01534 816688*

Guernsey office
Television House, Bulwer Avenue,
St Sampson, Guernsey GY2 4LA
01481 241888
broadcast.gsy@channeltv.co.uk

London office
Enterprise House, 1-2 Hatfields,
London SE1 9PG
020 7633 9902

UTV
Ormeau Road, Belfast BT7 1EB
028 9032 8122
info@utvplc.com
www.utv.com
*Group chief executive: John McCann;
director of television: Alan Bremner*
Press: 028 9026 2187

Channel Four

124 Horseferry Road,
London SW1P 2TX
020 7396 4444
www.channel4.co.uk
*Chief executive: Andy Duncan, 020
7306 8700; director of sales: Andy
Barnes, 020 7306 8200; director
of television and content: Kevin Lygo,
020 7306 3775*
Press: Matt Baker, 020 7306 8666

● Commissioning

*Managing editor: Janey Walker,
020 7306 8623 (assistant: Rachel
Postgate, 020 7306 8282); disability
advisor: Alison Walsh, 020 7306 8125*

Comedy
*Editor of comedy: Darren Smith,
assistant: Cathy Mason, 020 7306
8066; Caroline Leddy, 020 7306 8718*

Daytime and features
*Commissioning editor, daytime:
Adam MacDonald, 020 7306 8033;
commissioning editor, features:
Walter Iuzzolino, assistant: Jo Higlett,
020 7306 8517*

Documentaries
*Assistant: Clothilde Redfern 020 7306
8010; commissioning editors:
Meredith Chambers, 020 7306 5571;
Simon Dickson, 020 7306 3799, (arts)
Jan Younghusband, 020 7306 5153*

E4
*Head: Angela Jain, 020 7306 8515;
editor, Big Brother: David Williams,
020 7306 6971, editor, music content:
Steven Edwards, 020 7306 6429*

Education
*Head: Janey Walker; commissioning
editors: Deborah Ward, new media:
Matt Locke*

Entertainment (& Comedy)
*Head: Andrew Newman, 020 7306 6382,
assistant: Dylan Todd, 020 7396 8678*

Factual entertainment
*Head: Andrew Mackenzie , assistant:
Helena Peacock, 020 7306 6432; editors:
Nav Raman, 020 7306 8746, Dominique
Walker, assistant: Natalie Marsh, 020
7306 6912, Ruby Kuraishe, assistant:
Helena Peacock, 020 7306 6432*

Features
*Head: Sue Murphy, 020 7306 8279;
commissioning editors: Andrew
Jackson, 020 7306 8476, Philippa
Ransford, 020 7306 8424, and Liam
Humphreys, 020 7306 6932, Walter
Iuzzolino, assistant: Jo Higlett,
020 7306 8517*

Film and drama
*Head: Tessa Ross, 020 7306 6455;
senior commissioning editor:
Peter Carlton, 020 7306 8071;
deputy commissioning editor:
Robert Wullf-Cochrane 020 7306 5536
(events); assistant editor: Liz Pilling,
020 7306 8621; head of development:
Katherine Butler; head of Filmfour
Lab: Peter Carlton*

Specialist Factual
*Head: Hamish Mykura, 020 7306
1036; commissioning editors: Aaqil
Ahmed, 020 7306 8065 (religion),
Ralph Lee, 020 7306 6960 (history),
deputy commissioning editor: Tabitha
Jackson, 020 7306 8447 (history and
science)*

Nations and regions
Director: Stuart Cosgrove, 0141 568 7105

News and current affairs
*Head: Dorothy Byrne, 020 7306 8568;
commissioning editor (investigations):
Kevin Sutcliffe, 020 7306 1068*

**Programming planning and
strategy**
*Head of schedules & music, youth
& T4: Jules Oldroyd, 020 7306 8229;
commissioning editor: Neil McCallum,
020 7306 8588; assistant editor:
Cath Lovesey, 020 7306 5622*

Sport
*Head of sport: Andrew Thompson;
deputy commissioning editor: Deborah
Poulton, 020 7306 8501; assistant:
Miranda Little 020 7306 8281*

Programme acquisition
*Jeff Ford, 020 7306 8747; assistant:
Sarah Lloyd, 020 7306 8733*

● Broadcasting

*Controller: Rosemary Newell,
020 7306 8620; head of schedules:
Jules Oldroyd, 020 7306 8229;
deputy scheduler: John Williams,
020 7306 8257; senior planner:
Lucy Rogers, 020 7306 8401
Sales and marketing – agency sales:
Matt Shreeve, 020 7306 8240; airtime
management: Merlin Inkley, 020 7306
8254; marketing director: Polly
Cochrane, 020 7306 6446; research
and insight: Claire Grimmond, 020
7306 8779; sponsorship: David
Charlesworth, 020 7306 8043;
strategic sales: Mike Parker 020 7306
8242; strategy: Jonathan Thompson,
020 7306 8799*

● Business services

124 Facilities
Tony Chamberlain, 020 7306 8110

Channel Four International
Graeme Mason, 020 7306 3796

Consumer products
Mike Morris, 020 7306 5364

Digital channels
E4
Angela Jain, 020 7306 6436
FilmFour
Tom Sykes, 020 7306 6442
MoreFour
Peter Dale, 020 7306 8749

New media
Andy Taylor, 020 7306 3651

● Channel 4 News

ITN
200 Grays Inn Road,
London WC1X 8XZ
020 7833 3000
www.channel4.com/news
*Editor: Jim Gray; deputy editor:
Martin Fewell; managing editor: Gay
Flashman. Newsdesk: 020 7430 4601*
• *Presenters – anchor: Jon Snow; noon
anchor: Krishnan Guru-Murthy;
senior reporter: Sue Turton;
presenter: Samira Ahmed*
• *Senior editors – home: Yvette
Edwards; foreign: Deborah Rayner;
international editor: Lindsey Hilsum*
• *Commissioning editor, independent
productions: Fiona Campbell*
• *Chief correspondent: Alex Thomson.
Other correspondents – arts: Nicholas
Glass; economics: Faisal Islam; foreign
affairs: Jonathan Miller; home affairs:
Simon Israel; Midlands: Carl Dinnen;
political: Gary Gibbon; science: Tom
Clarke; science/defence: Julian Rush;
social affairs: Victoria Macdonald;
Washington correspondent: Sarah
Smith*
Press: 020 7430 4220
fiona.railton@itn.co.uk

FIVE

2 Long Acre, London WC2E 9LY
020 7550 5555
firstname.lastname@five.tv
www.five.tv
*Chief executive: Jane Lighting;
managing director of content: Lisa
Opie, 020 7550 5673 (PA: Sarah
Jackson, 020 7550 5522); controller of
broadcast services: David Burge, 020
7691 6260; history: Alex Sutherland*
• *Controllers – arts, daytime and
religion: Kim Peat, 020 7421 7107;
children's programmes: Nick Wilson;
factual entertainment: Steve Gowans
(deputy commissioning editor: Ian
Dunkley, 020 7550 5659); features
and entertainment: Ben Frow, 020
7421 7118; news: Chris Shaw, 020
7421 7122 (deputy: Ian Russell, 020
7550 5529); science: Justine Kershaw,
020 7421 7112; sport: Robert Charles,
020 7421 7185; special events and
pop features: Sham Sandhu, 020
7421 7184*
• *Drama editor: Abigail Webber*
• *Press: 020 7550 5533
Head of press and corporate affairs:
Paul Leather, 020 7550 5541; deputy:
Tracey O'Connor, 020 7550 5553;
marketing and publicity executive:
Louise Bowers, 020 7550 5662*
• *Heads of publicity – acquisitions
and drama: Tamara Bishopp, 020
7550 5539; factual and features:
Louise Plank, 020 7550 5659*
• *Publicists – arts, history and
daytime: Allison Broodie, 020 7550
5587; entertainment: Nick Dear,
020 7550 5634; factual and features:
Stephanie Faber, 020 7550 5589;
science and pop features: Elin Rees,
020 7550 5538*

● Five news

Unit 1, Sky News, Grant Way,
Isleworth, Middlesex TW7 5QD
020 7800 2705
www.five.tv/news
*Editor: Mark Calvert; deputy editor:
Josie MacRae; head of newsgathering:
James Birtles*
• *Presenters: John Suchet, Kate
Sanderson, Lara Lewington*
• *Political editor: Andy Bell*
• *Correspondents – northern: Peter
Lane; sport: Alex Thomas*
• *Reporters and correspondents:
Cathy Jones, Catherine Jacob,
Lindley Gooden, Jason Farrel*
Press: 020 7800 4289
Senior publicist: Stella Tooth

● Other departments

Acquisitions
*Director: Jay Kandona, 020 7421 7166
Controller: Vanessa Brookman,
020 7421 7166*

Interactive
Producer: Steven Bonner, 020 7550 5663

Scheduling and planning
*Director: Susanna Dinnage,
020 7550 5588*

RTÉ (Ireland)

Radio Telefís Éireann
Donnybrook, Dublin 4, Ireland
00 353 1 208 3111
Information: 00 353 1 208 3434
info@rte.ie
www.rte.ie
Irish national broadcaster.

*Managing director of television: Noel
Curran; managing director of news
and current affairs: Ed Mulhall;
managing director of radio: Adrian
Moynes; executive director of
publishing: Múirne Laffan; director
of communications: Bride Rosney*
Press contacts
(firstname.lastname@rte.ie)
*News and current affairs: Carolyn
Fisher; radio: Sarah Martin;
television: Cathriona Edwards;
corporate: Rory Coveney; corporate:
Peter Feeney*

Multichannel

KEY GOVERNMENT CONTACTS FOR DIGITAL TV

Department for Culture, Media and Sport
2-4 Cockspur Street,
London SW1Y 5DH
020 7211 6000
firstname.surname@
culture.gsi.gov.uk
www.culture.gov.uk
Culture secretary: Andy Burnham
Press: 020 7211 6267
mark.devane@culture.gsi.gov.uk
SwitchCo press office:
020 7737 7008

Department for Business, Enterprise and Regulatory Reform
1 Victoria Street, London SW1H 0ET
020 7215 5000
www.dberr.gov.uk/industries
/broadcasting
*Secretary of State for Business, Enterprise and Regulatory Reform: John Hutton
Head of broadcasting policy: Dave Thomas; project manager, digital television: Ian Lomas; head of broadcasting technology: Ian Dixon*
Press: 020 7215 6403

● BSkyB

British Sky Broadcasting
Grant Way, Isleworth TW7 5QD
0870 240 3000
www.sky.com
Chief executive: Jeremy Darroch; chief operating officer: Richard Freudenstein; chief marketing officer: Jon Florsheim; MD, Sky Sports: Vic Wakeling; director of corporate communications: Kate Oppenheim; head of programme publicity: Richard Turner; Sky One: Chris Aylott; Sky Movies: Phil Evans; consumer PR: Gabby Bennett
Press: 0870 240 3000

SKY CHANNELS

Grant Way, Isleworth TW7 5QD
0870 240 3000

Sky Bet
www.skybet.com
Marketing director: Simon Miller; consumer PR manager: Heidi Bruckland
Press: 020 7705 3275

Sky Box Office
www.skymovies.com
Head of pay-per-view: Karen Saunders; publicity manager: Phil Evans
Press: 020 7800 4252
skymoviespublicity@bskyb.com

Sky Cinema 1 & 2
www.skymovies.com
Director of film channels and acquisitions: Sophie Turner-Laing; publicity manager: Phil Evans
Press: 020 7800 4252
skymoviespublicity@bskyb.com

Sky Customer Channel
Consumer PR manager: Heidi Bruckland
Press: 020 7705 3275

Sky Movies 1-9
www.skymovies.com
Director of film channels and acquisitions: Sophie Turner-Laing; publicity manager: Phil Evans
Press: 020 7800 4252
skymoviespublicity@bskyb.com

Sky News
Newsdesk: news.plan@bskyb.com
www.skynews.co.uk
Head of Sky News: Nick Pollard
• Key presenters – *Sunrise: Eamonn Holmes; Sky News Today: Anna Jones, Martin Stanford; Lunchtime Live: Kay Burley; Sky News Today PM: Julie Etchington, Colin Brazier; Live At Five: Jeremy Thompson; Evening: Anna Botting, Gillian Joseph*
• Correspondents – *business: Michael Wilson; crime: Martin Brunt; entertainment: Neil Sean, Matt Smith; foreign: Tim Marshall, Lisa Holland, Stuart Ramsey, Robert Nisbet, Michelle Clifford, Alex Crawford, Peter Sharp, Greg Millam, Alex Rossi, Dominic Waughan; health: Thomas Moore; political: Adam Boulton, Jon Craig, Jenny Percival, Peter Spencer, Glen O'Glaza; royal: Sarah Hughes*
Press: 020 7800 4289
Senior publicist: Stella Tooth

Sky One
www.skyone.co.uk
Controller: James Baker. Acting publicity manager: Chris Aylott; head of programme publicity: Richard Turner; publicists for programmes – 24: Tom Mackey; Battlestar Galactica, Law & Order, Enterprise: Chris Aylott; Cold Case, Malcolm in the Middle: Gayle Hemmings and Melanie Adorian; Nip/Tuck, The Simpsons: Lee Robson
Press: 020 7805 7276

Sky Mix
www.skyone.co.uk
Controller: James Baker
Press: 020 7805 7276
Acting publicity manager: Chris Aylott; head of programme publicity: Richard Turner

Sky Sports 1, 2 & 3
www.skysports.com
MD: Vic Wakeling
Press: 020 7800 4254
Head of press and publicity: Chris Haynes

Sky Sports Extra
www.skysports.com
MD: Vic Wakeling
Press: 020 7800 4254
Head of press and publicity: Chris Haynes

Sky Sports News
www.skysports.com
MD: Vic Wakeling
Press: 020 7800 4254
Head of press and publicity: Chris Haynes

Sky Travel
www.skytravel.co.uk
General manager: Barbara Gibbon
Press: richard.turner@bskyb.com

Sky Travel Extra
www.skytravel.co.uk
General manager: Barbara Gibbon
Press: richard.turner@bskyb.com

Sky Travel Shop
www.skytravel.co.uk
General manager: Barbara Gibbon
Press: richard.turner@bskyb.com

Sky Travel +1
www.skytravel.co.uk
General manager: Barbara Gibbon
Press: richard.turner@bskyb.com

Sky Vegas Live
www.skyvegaslive.com
Executive producer: Peter Ward
Press: 020 7705 3416
Consumer PR executive: Tara Hicks

DEPARTMENTS

Sky Active
www.sky.com/skyactive
MD, Sky Interactive: Ian Shepherd

Sky Business
www.sky.com/business
Sales to non-domestic clients. Commercial marketing director: Iain Holden

Sky Ventures
www.sky.com/ventures
Joint venture channels and services. Director of Sky Ventures: Matthew Imi

● Cable

Cablecom Investments
The Coach House, Bill Hill Park,
Wokingham, Berks RG40 5QT
0845 230 0028
customer@cablecom.co.uk
www.cablecom.co.uk
MD: Charles Tompkins

SmallWorld Media
3 Chalmers Place, Riverside
Business Park, Irvine, North
Ayrshire KA11 5DH
0800 070 6150
enquiries@smallworldmedia.com
www.smallworldmedia.com
CEO: David Durnford
Press: Keith Annand

Tiscali
205 Holland Park Avenue,
London W11 4XB
020 7087 2000
www.tiscali.co.uk
Chairman and CEO: Mary Turner
Head of PR: Jody Haskayne

Virgin Media
Bartley Wood Business Park,
Bartley Way, Hook,
Hampshire RG27 9UP
01256 752000
01483 750900
www.virginmedia.com
CEO: Steve Burch
Press: 0207 909 2048
Head of business PR: Liz Nicholson;
head of customer PR: John Moorwood

WightCable
56 Love Lane, Cowes,
Isle of Wight PO31 7EU
01983 242424
enquiries@wightcable.com
www.wightcable.com
CEO: Ian Renshaw

● Digital terrestrial

Freeview
Broadcast Centre, (BC3 D5),
201 Wood Lane, London W12 7TP
020 7229 4400
www.freeview.co.uk
Free-to-view digital terrestrial service,
owned by National Grid Wireless, BBC
and BSkyB. General manager: Lib
Charlesworth
Press: 020 7229 4400
Consumer: Alison Wallace;
corporate: Nick Clark – both
firstname.lastname@nelsonbostock.com

Arqiva
Crawley Court, Winchester,
Hampshire SO21 2QA
01962 823434
firstname.surname@arqiva.com
www.arqiva.com
Formerly NTL Broadcast. CEO:
Tom Bennie; MD, media solutions:
Steve Holebrook
Press: 01962 822582
Communications manager:
Bruce Randall

National Grid Wireless
Warwick Technology Park,
Gallows Hill, Heathcote Lane,
Warwick CV34 6TN
01926 416000
MarketingUK@ngridwireless.co.uk
www.nationalgridwireless.com
Digital terrestrial transmitter
operator; part-owner of Freeview.
MD: Peter Abery
Press: 01926 416000
Communications manager:
Stephen Arnold

Top-Up TV
PO Box 801, Kirkaldy,
Fife KY2 6WW
0870 054 3210
enquiries@topuptv.com
www.topuptv.com
Offers top-up pay channels for
Freeview viewers. Chairman: David
Chance, CEO: Nick Markham

● TV Channels

ABC1
Chiswick Park, Building 12,
566 Chiswick High Road,
London W4 5AN
020 8636 2000
www.abc1tv.co.uk
VP programming: James Neal
Press:
rachel.babington@disney.com

Animal Planet
Discovery House, Chiswick Park
Building 2, 566 Chiswick High
Road, London W4 5YB
020 8811 3000
www.discoverychannel.co.uk
Channel director: Mark Wilde
Press: delyth_hughes@
discovery-europe.com

AsiaNet
Asianet Complex, Puliyarakonam
PO, Trivandrum 695 573 India
00 91 471 237 8407
www.asianetglobal.com

ATN Bangla
WASA Bhaban, 1st Floor,
98 Kazi Nazrul Islam Avenue,
Kawran Bazar, Dhaka 1215,
Bangladesh
00 880 811 1207/08/09/10
info@atnbangla.tv
www.atnbangla.tv

attheraces
11–13 Charlotte Street,
London W1T 1RH
020 7566 8911
studio@attheraces.com
www.attheraces.com
MD: Matthew Imi

Authentic TV
www.authentictv.tv

B4
8 Chelseagate Studios, 37
Harwood Road, London SW6 4QP
020 7371 5999
sarah.gauhan@chartshow.tv
CEO: David Docherty

B4U
Transputec House, 19 Heather
Park Drive, Wembley HA0 1SS
020 8795 7171
www.b4utv.com
Programme controller: Bala Iyer
Press: Kevin Rego

B4U Music
Transputec House, 19 Heather
Park Drive, Wembley HA0 1SS
020 8795 7171
www.b4utv.com
Programme controller: Bala Iyer
Press: Kevin Rego

BBC America
PO Box 6266, Florence,
KY 41022-6266 USA
00 1 859 342 4070
www.bbcamerica.com
Programme executive: Alison
Fredericks

BBC Canada
121 Bloor Street East, Suite 200,
Toronto, Ontario, Canada M4W 3M5
00 416 967 3249
feedback@bbccanada.com
www.bbccanada.com

BBC Food
PO Box 5054, London W12 0ZY
020 8433 2221
www.bbcfood.com
Editor: David Weiland

BBC Four
Television Centre
0870 010 0222
www.bbc.co.uk/bbcfour
Controller: Janice Hadlow

BBC Japan
PO Box 5054, London W12 0ZY
www.bbcjapan.tv

BBC News 24
Television Centre
020 8743 8000
bbcnews24@bbc.co.uk
www.bbc.co.uk/bbcnews24
Editoral director: Kevin Bakhurst

BBC One
Television Centre
020 8743 8000
www.bbc.co.uk/bbcone
Controller: Jay Hunt

BBC Parliament
4 Millbank, London SW1P 3JA
020 7973 6216
parliament@bbc.co.uk
www.bbc.co.uk/bbcparliament

BBC Prime
PO Box 5054, London W12 0ZY
020 8433 2221
bbcprime@bbc.co.uk
www.bbcprime.com
Editor: David Weiland

BBC Three
Television Centre
020 8743 8000
www.bbc.co.uk/bbcthree
Controller: Danny Cohen

BBC Two
Television Centre
020 8743 8000
www.bbc.co.uk/bbctwo
Controller: Roly Keating; controller of
daytime: Liam Keelan

BBC World
PO Box 5054, London W12 0ZY
020 8433 2221
bbcworld@bbc.co.uk
www.bbcworld.com
Editorial director: Sian Kevill

BBCi (interactive TV)
Television Centre
020 8743 8000
www.bbc.co.uk/digital/tv
Controller: Rahul Chakkara;
head, interactive TV programming:
Emma Somerville

BEN
25 Ashley Road, London N17 9LJ
020 8808 8800
info@bentelevision.com
www.bentelevision.com
Head of programming: Ife Akim,
CEO: Alistair Soyode

Best Direct
Sentinel House, Poundwell,
Modbury PL21 0ZZ
0871 555 2003
www.bestdirect.tv
CEO: Michael Levene

Bid TV
Sit-Up House, 179-181 The Vale,
London W3 7RW
0870 165 1647
www.bid.tv

Big Game TV
PO Box 5372, London W1A 8WN
020 7432 7300

Biography Channel
Grant Way, Isleworth TW7 5QD
020 7705 3000
www.biography.com
Channel director: Richard Melman
Press: biographychannelpress@
bskyb.com

Bloomberg
City Gate House, 39-45 Finsbury
Square, London EC2A 1PQ
020 7330 7797
newsalert@bloomberg.net
www.bloomberg.com/tv
Executive editor, broadcast: Michael
Clancy

Boomerang
Turner House, 16 Great
Marlborough Street,
London W1F 7HS
020 7693 1000
www.boomerangtv.co.uk
Press: nibs.dearsley@turner.com
www.europe.turnerinfo.com

The Box
Mappin House, 4 Winsley Street,
London W1W 8HF
020 7182 8000
www.emap.com
Programme director: Dave Young;
director of music: Simon Sadler
Press:
maureen.corish@emap.com

Bravo
160 Great Portland Street,
London W1W 5QA
020 7299 5000
www.bravo.co.uk
Programme controller: David Clarke
Press:
jakki.lewis@virginmediatv.co.uk

British Eurosport
Feltham Media Centre,
Sussex House, 2 Plane Tree
Crescent, Felthambrook Industrial
Estate, Middlesex TW13 7HF
020 7468 7777
www.eurosport.com
Programming director: Dave Kerr
Press: mhorler@eurosport.com
0845 672 1010

British Eurosport 2
Feltham Media Centre, Sussex
House, 2 Plane Tree Crescent,
Felthambrook Industrial Estate,
Middlesex TW13 7HF
020 7468 7777
www.eurosport.com
Programming director: Dave Kerr
Press: mhorler@eurosport.com
0845 672 1010

Channel 4
124 Horseferry Road,
London SW1P 2TX
020 7396 4444
www.channel4.com
Chief executive: Andy Duncan, 020
7306 8700; commercial director: Andy
Barnes, 020 7306 8200; director of
television: Kevin Lygo, 020 7306 3775

Cartoon Network
Turner House, 16 Great
Marlborough Street,
London W1F 7HS
020 7693 1000
www.cartoonnetwork.co.uk
www.cartoonito.co.uk
www.cartoonnetworktoo.co.uk
Press: nibs.dearsley@turner.com
www.europe.turnerinfo.com

CBBC
Television Centre
020 8743 8000
www.bbc.co.uk/cbbc
Controller: Richard Deverell

CBeebies
Television Centre
020 8743 8000
www.bbc.co.uk/cbeebies
Controller: Richard Deverell

CCTV9
CCTV International, 11B Fuxting
Road, Media Centre, Beijing,
China, 100038
cctv-9-mail1@cctv-9.com
www.cctv9.tv

CFC TV
The Christian Family Channel,
2 Silver Rd, Shepherds Bush,
London W12 7SG
www.cfctv.com

Challenge
160 Great Portland Street,
London W1W 5QA
020 7299 5000
www.challenge.co.uk
Programme controller: Jonathan Webb
Press:
jakki.lewis@virginmediatv.co.uk

Channel U
Video Interactive Television,
Studio4, 3 Lever Street,
London EC1V 3QU
020 7054 9010
info@vitv.co.uk
www.channelu.tv

Chart Show TV
37 Harwood Road, London SW6 4QP
020 7371 5999
info@chartshow.tv
www.chartshow.tv
Music coordinator: Sarah Gaughan

Chelsea TV
Stamford Bridge, Fulham Road,
London SW6 1HS
020 7915 1980
chelseatv@chelseafc.com
www.chelseafc.com
MD: Chris Tate

Chinese Channel
Teddington Studios, Broom Road,
Teddington TW11 9NT
020 8614 8364
newseditor@chinese-channel.co.uk
www.chinese-channel.co.uk
Head of programming: Desmond Ng

Classic FM TV
7 Swallow Place, London W1B 2AG
020 7343 9000
classicfmtv@classicfm.com
www.classicfm.com/tv
Station manager: Darren Henley

CNBC Europe
10 Fleet Place, London EC4M 7QS
020 7653 9300
www.cnbceurope.com
Executive producers: Helen Alexander,
Patrick Allen
Press:
cblenkinsop@cnbceurope.com

CNN
Turner House, 16 Great
Marlborough Street,
London W1F 7HS
020 7693 1000
www.cnn.com
International managing editor for
EMEA: Nick Wrenn
Press: 020 7693 0967
joel.brown@turner.com

Community Channel
3-7 Euston Centre, Regent's Place,
London NW1 3JG
020 7874 7626
info@communitychannel.org
www.communitychannel.org
Channel controller: Nick Ware

Create and Craft
Ideal Home House,
Newark Road, Peterborough,
Cambridgeshire PE1 5WG
0870 077 7002
customerservices@
idealshoppingdirect.co.uk
www.createandcraft.tv
CEO: Andrew Fryatt

Dating Channel
Suite 101, Copper Gate House,
16 Brune Street, London, E1 7NJ
020 7748 1500
info@thedatingchannel.com
www.thedatingchannel.com
Mobile technical manager: Paul Doyle

Discovery Channel
Discovery House, Chiswick Park
Building 2, 566 Chiswick High
Road, London W4 5YB
020 8811 3000
www.discoverychannel.co.uk
General manager: Dan Brooke
Press: lynn_li@
    discovery-europe.com

Discovery Civilisation
Discovery House, Chiswick Park
Building 2, 566 Chiswick High
Road, London W4 5YB
020 8811 3000
www.discoverychannel.co.uk
General Manager: Dan Brooke
Press: kate_buddle@
    discovery-europe.com

Discovery Home & Health
Discovery House, Chiswick Park
Building 2, 566 Chiswick High
Road, London W4 5YB
020 8811 3000
www.discoverychannel.co.uk
General manager: Dan Brooke
Press: caroline_watt@
    discovery-europe.com

Discovery Kids
Discovery House, Chiswick Park
Building 2, 566 Chiswick High
Road, London W4 5YB
020 8811 3000
www.discoverychannel.co.uk
General manager: Dan Brooke
Press: libby_rowley@
    discovery-europe.com

Discovery Real Time
Discovery House, Chiswick Park
Building 2, 566 Chiswick High
Road, London W4 5YB
020 8811 3000
www.realtimetv.co.uk
General Manager: Dan Brooke
Press: caroline_watt@
    discovery-europe.com

Discovery Science
Discovery House, Chiswick Park
Building 2, 566 Chiswick High
Road, London W4 5YB
020 8811 3000
www.discoverychannel.co.uk
General Manager: Dan Brooke
Press: kate_buddle@
    discovery-europe.com

Discovery Travel and Living
Discovery House, Chiswick Park
Building 2, 566 Chiswick High
Road, London W4 5YB
020 8811 3000
www.travelandliving.co.uk
General Manager: Dan Brooke
Press: caroline_watt@
    discovery-europe.com

Discovery Turbo
Discovery House, Chiswick Park
Building 2, 566 Chiswick High
Road, London W4 5YB
020 8811 3000
www.discoveryturbo.co.uk
General Manager: Dan Brooke
Press: kate_buddle@
    discovery-europe.com

Discovery Wings
Discovery House, Chiswick Park
Building 2, 566 Chiswick High
Road, London W4 5YB
020 8811 3000
www.discoverychannel.co.uk
General Manager: Dan Brooke
Press: kate_buddle@
    discovery-europe.com

Disney Channel
Chiswick Park, Building 12,
566 Chiswick High Road,
London W4 5AN
020 8636 2000
www.disneychannel.co.uk
VP programming: James Neal
Press: rachel.babington@
    disney.com

DM Digital
Lower Ground Floor,
33/35 Turner Street,
Manchester M4 1DW
0161 833 1555
chairman@dmdigitaltv.co.uk
Contact: Zahidh Hussain

DW-TV
Voltastr. 6, D-13355 Berlin,
Germany
00 49 30 4646 0
www.dw-world.de/dw
Head DW-TV: Christoph Lanz

E!
www.eonline.com

E4
124 Horseferry Road,
London SW1P 2TX
020 7396 4444
www.channel4.com/e4
Head: Angela Jain

Euro News
60, Chemin des Mouilles, BP 131,
F-69131 Lyon-Ecully, France
00 33 4 7218 8000
www.euronews.net
Press: 00 33 4 72 18 80 56

Extreme Sports Channel
The Media Centre, 19 Bolsover
Street, London W1W 5NA
020 7644 8758
www.extreme.com
Head of acquisitions: Alex Barnes
Press: stuart@extreme
    sportschannel.com

Fashion TV
Production Paris,
12 rue Hammunen,
70016 Paris, France
00 33 1 4505 4545
info@ftv.com
www.ftv.com
London office: jessica@ftv.com

FilmFour
124 Horseferry Road,
London SW1P 2TX
020 7396 4444
www.channel4.com/film
Head: Tom Sykes, 020 7306 6442

five
22 Long Acre, London WC2E 9LY
020 7550 5555
firstname.lastname@five.tv
www.five.tv
*Director of programmes: Lisa Opie,
020 7550 5673 (PA Sarah Jackson,
020 7550 5522); controller of broadcast
services: David Burge, 020 7691 6260*
Press: 020 7550 5533

Fizz
Video Interactive Television,
Studio4, 3 Lever Street,
London EC1V 3QU
020 7054 9010
info@vitv.co.uk
www.fizzmusic.com
Contact: Darren Platt

Flaunt
Grant Way, Isleworth TW7 5QD
0870 240 3000
www.myspace.com/flaunttv

Fox News
1211 Avenue of the Americas,
New York NY 10036
00 1 888 369 4762
foxaroundtheworld@foxnews.com
www.foxnews.com
*Senior vice-president, corporate
communications: Brian Lewis, 001 212
301 3301, brian.lewis@foxnews.com;
vice-president, media relations: Irena
Briganti, 001 212 301 3046,
irena.briganti@foxnews.com*

FX and Fox Movie Channel
10000 Santa Monica Blvd,
Los Angeles, CA 90067 USA
00 1 310 286 3800
www.fxnetworks.com
*Vice-president, public relations:
John Solberg, 00 1 310 369 0935;
manager, public relations: Scott
Seomin, 00 1 310 369 0938*

Game Network
Via Bisceglie 71\73,
20152 Milano, Italy
www.game-network.net

Gay Date TV
Suite 101, Copper Gate House,
16 Brune Street, London, E1 7NJ
020 7748 1500
info@gaydatetv.co.uk
www.gaydatetv.co.uk
Mobile technical manager: Mark Adams

Gems TV
Eagle Road Studios, Eagle Road,
Redditch B98 9HF
0845 658 8663
www.gemstv.co.uk
MD: Steve Bennett

GEO TV
geouk@geo.tv
www.geo.tv

Get Lucky TV
www.getlucky.tv

God TV
Angel House,
Borough Road, Sunderland,
Tyne and Wear SR1 1HW
0191 568 0800
info@god.tv
www.god.tv
UK regional director: Chris Cole

The Golf Channel UK
1 Kingsgate, Bradford Business
Park, Canal Road, Bradford,
West Yorkshire BD1 4SJ
www.thegolfchanneluk.com
Press: press@golftvinfo.co.uk

Hallmark
234a Kings Road, London SW3 5UA
020 7368 9100
info@hallmarkchannel.co.uk
www.hallmarkchannel.co.uk
Director of acquisitions: Rosie Hill-Davies
Press: janemuirhead@
hallmarkchannel.com

History Channel
Grant Way, Isleworth TW7 5QD
020 7705 3000
www.thehistorychannel.co.uk
Channel director: Richard Melman
Press: 020 7941 5199
historychannelpress@bskyb.com

Hits Channel
Mappin House, 4 Winsley Street,
London W1W 8HF
020 7182 8000
www.emapadvertising.com
*Programme director: Dave Young;
director of music: Simon Sadler*
Press:
maureen.corish@emap.com

Hollywood.com Television (HTV)
2255 Glades Road, Suite 219A,
Boca Raton, FL 33431 USA
00 1 561 998 8000
www.hollywood.com
Chairman and CEO: Mitchell Rubenstein

The Horror Channel
info@horrorchannel.com
www.thehorrorchannel.tv

Ideal Vitality
Ideal Home House,
Newark Road, Peterborough,
Cambridgeshire PE1 5WG
0870 077 7002
customerservices@
idealshoppingdirect.co.uk
www.idealvitality.tv
CEO: Andrew Fryatt

Ideal World
Ideal Home House,
Newark Road, Peterborough,
Cambridgeshire PE1 5WG
0870 077 7002
customerservices@
idealshoppingdirect.co.uk
www.idealworld.tv
CEO: Andrew Fryatt

**INI (Inspiration Network
International)**
5th Floor, 7910 Crescent
Executive Drive, Charlotte,
North Carolina USA
00 1 704 525 9800
info@ini.tv
www.ini.tv

Islam Channel
14 Bonhill Street,
London EC2A 4BX
020 7374 4511
www.islamchannel.tv
Press: pr@islamchannel.tv

ITV News
200 Grays Inn Road,
London WC1X 8XZ
020 7833 3000
www.itv.com/news
Editor: Ben Rayner

ITV1
200 Grays Inn Road,
London WC1X 8HF
020 7843 8000
www.itv.com/itv1

» *ITV Network contacts:*
see page 134

ITV2
200 Grays Inn Road,
London WC1X 8HF
020 7843 8000
www.itv.com/itv2

ITV3
200 Grays Inn Road,
London WC1X 8HF
020 7843 8000
www.itv.com/itv3

Jetix
3 Queen Caroline Street,
Hammersmith, London W6 9PE
020 8222 3600
www.jetix.co.uk

JML Direct
Regis Road, Kentish Town,
London NW5 3EG
0870 1287 288
www.jmldirect.com
Press: 020 7691 3822
press@jmldirect.com

Kerrang TV
Mappin House, 4 Winsley Street,
London W1W 8HF
020 7182 8000
www.emapadvertising.com
*Programme director: Dave Young;
director of music: Simon Sadler*
Press:
maureen.corish@emap.com

Kiss TV
Mappin House, 4 Winsley Street,
London W1W 8HF
020 7182 8000
www.emapadvertising.com
*Programme director: Dave Young;
director of music: Simon Sadler*
Press:
maureen.corish@emap.com

Living
160 Great Portland Street,
London W1W 5QA
020 7299 5000
www.livingtv.co.uk
*Programme controller: Claudia
Rosencrantz*
Press:
jessica.alder@virginmediatv.co.uk

Look4Love TV
Unit 20, Intec 2, Basingstoke,
Hampshire RG24 8NE
0871 550 0055
enquiries@look4love.tv
www.look4love.tv

Magic TV
Mappin House, 4 Winsley Street,
London W1W 8HF
020 7182 8000
www.emapadvertising.com
*Programme director: Dave Young;
director of music: Simon Sadler*
Press:
maureen.corish@emap.com

Majestic TV
CC.Comercial La Colonia Edificio
II, Locales 25–27, San Pedro de
Alcantara, 29670 Malaga
www.majestictv.co.uk

Matinee Movies
179–181 The Vale, London W3 7RW
020 8600 9700
www.sit-up.tv
MD: Chris Manson

MATV National
Combine House, 7 Woodboy
Street, Leicester LE1 3NJ
0116 253 2288
info@matv.co.uk
www.matv.co.uk
MD: Vinod Popat

Men and Motors
200 Grays Inn Road,
London WC1X 8HF
020 7843 8000
info@menandmotors.co.uk
www.menandmotors.co.uk
Commissioning editor: Joe Talbot
Press: 020 7737 8719
natalie.philips@itv.com

Motors TV
855, avenue Roger Salengro,
92370 Chaville, France
00 33 1 4115 9852
www.motorstv.com
Press:
service.presse@motorstv.com

MTA — Muslim TV
16 Gressenhall Road,
London SW18 5QL
020 8870 0922
info@mta.tv
www.mta.tv

MTV, MTV2, Base, Dance, Hits
MTV, Hawley Crescent,
London NW1 8TT
020 7284 7777
www.mtv.co.uk
Head of development (for programme commissions): Chris Sice
Press:
curlewis.samantha@mtvne.com

Music Choice Europe
The Old Truman Brewery,
91 Brick Lane, London E1 6QL
020 3107 0300
contactus@musicchoice.co.uk
www.musicchoice.co.uk

Musicians Channel
PO BOX 5784,
Southend on Sea SS1 9BYN
01702 350530
info@musicianschannel.tv
www.musicianschannel.tv

MUTV
4th Floor, 274 Deansgate,
Manchester M3 4JB
0161 834 1111
mutv@mutv.com
www.manutd.com/mutv

National Geographic Channel
3rd Floor, Shepherds Building
East, Richmond Way,
London W14 0DQ
020 7705 3000
natgeoweb@bskyb.com
www.natgeochannel.co.uk
General manager: Simon Bohrsmann

Nat Geo Wild
3rd Floor, Shepherds Building
East, Richmond Way,
London W14 0DQ
020 7705 3000
natgeoweb@bskyb.com
www.natgeowild.co.uk
General manager: Simon Bohrsmann

Nick Jr
Nickelodeon, 15–18 Rathbone
Place, London W1T 1HU
020 7462 1000
david.reiss@nickelodeon.co.uk
www.nickjr.co.uk
*Senior vice-president & MD:
Howard Litton*

Nick Toons TV
Nickelodeon, 15–18 Rathbone
Place, London W1T 1HU
020 7462 1000
david.reiss@nickelodeon.co.uk
www.nick.co.uk/toons
*Senior vice-president & MD:
Howard Litton*

Nickelodeon
Nickelodeon, 15–18 Rathbone
Place, London W1T 1HU
020 7462 1000
david.reiss@nickelodeon.co.uk
www.nick.co.uk
*Senior vice-president & MD:
Howard Litton*

OBE
Portall West Business Centre, Unit
4, 6 Portall Way, London W3 6RU
0870 240 4474
info@obetv.co.uk
www.obetv.co.uk

Open Access
6 Hoxton Square, London N1 6NU
0870 744 2041
info@openaccess.tv
www.openaccess.tv

Paramount Comedy
UK House, 4th Floor, 180 Oxford
Street, London W1D 1DS
020 7478 5300
www.paramountcomedy.co.uk
Director of programming: Heather Jones
Press: zoe.diver@
paramountcomedy.com

**PCNE Phoenix Chinese News &
Entertainment**
The Chiswick Centre, 414 Chiswick
High Road, London W4 5TF
020 8987 4320/1
info@phoenixtv.com
www.phoenixtv.com
MD: Wen Guang Shal

Performance
4 Farleigh Court, Long Ashton,
Bristol BS48 1UL
0870 850 8102
info@performancetv.co.uk
www.performance-channel.com
*CEO: Steve Timmins; channel
manager: Matthew Clements*

Poker Channel
020 8600 2698
info@thepokerchannel.co.uk
www.thepokerchannel.co.uk
*CEO: Crispin Nieboer; head of
programming: James Hopkins*
Press: angus.gardner@
thepokerchannel.co.uk

Price Drop TV
Sit-Up House, 179–181 The Vale,
London W3 7RW
0870 165 1647
www.price-drop.tv

Q TV
Mappin House, 4 Winsley Street,
London W1W 8HF
020 7182 8000
www.emapadvertising.com
*Programme director: Dave Young;
director of music: Simon Sadler*
Press:
maureen.corish@emap.com

QVC
Marco Polo House,
346 Queenstown Road,
Chelsea Bridge, London SW8 4NQ
020 7705 5600
www.qvcuk.com
Planning manager: Susan Hellyar
Press: 020 7886 8440

Real Estate TV
1–6 Falconberg Court,
London W1D 3AB
020 7440 1090
info@realestatetv.tv
www.realestatetv.tv
Head of channel: Mark Dodds

Reality TV
105–109 Salusbury Road,
London NW6 6RG
020 7328 8808
www.reality.tv
Press:
george.hills@zonevision.com

Record TV
tvrecord@recordnetwork.net
www.rederecord.com.br
*Spanish-language channel broadcast
on Sky*

Revelation TV
117a Cleveland Street,
London W1T 6PX
020 7631 4446
howard@revelationtv.com
lesley@revelationtv.com
www.revelationtv.com
Head of programming: Howard Conder

RTÉ 1 + 2
Donnybrook, Dublin 4, Ireland
00 353 1 208 3111
info@rte.ie
www.rte.ie/tv
*Commissioning editor, Irish language,
multiculture and education
programmes: Máiread Ní Nuadháin*

S4C
Parc Ty Glas, Llanishen,
Cardiff CF14 5DU
Cardiff: 029 20747444
Caernarfon: 01286 674622
www.s4c.co.uk

Sci-Fi
76 Oxford Street,
London W1D 1BS
020 7307 6600
www.scifi.com
*Head of programming and
acquisitions: Monica Iglesias*

Screenshop
179–181 The Vale, London W3 7RW
020 8600 9700
www.sit-up.tv
MD: Chris Manson

Scuzz
Grant Way, Isleworth TW7 5QD
0870 240 3000
www.scuzz.tv

Setanta Sport UK
4th Floor, 8 Waterloo Place,
London SW1Y 4BE
0870 050 6980
setantauk@setanta.com
www.setanta.com
MD, Setanta GB & Ireland: Roger Hall

Shop on TV
020 8453 1120
enquiries@shopon.tv
www.shopon.tv

Shop Vector
Betima House, 168–172 Old
Street, London EC1V 9BP
020 8104 0493
customerservice@simplymedia.tv
fran.hales@simplymedia.tv
www.vectordirect.tv
Media manager: Fran Hales

Simply Ideas
Betima House, 168–172 Old
Street, London EC1V 9BP
020 8104 0493
customerservice@simplymedia.tv
fran.hales@simplymedia.tv
www.simplyshoppingtv.co.uk
Media manager: Fran Hales

Simply Shopping
Betima House, 168–172 Old
Street, London EC1V 9BP
020 8104 0493
customerservice@simplymedia.tv
fran.hales@simplymedia.tv
www.simplyshoppingtv.co.uk
Media manager: Fran Hales

Sky Arts
Grant Way, Isleworth, TW7 5DQ
020 7805 2384
www.skyarts.co.uk
Controller: John Cassy
Press:
samantha.jones@bskyb.com

Sky Bet
Grant Way, Isleworth TW7 5QD
0870 240 3000
www.skybet.com
Press: 020 7705 3275
Consumer PR manager: Heidi Bruckland

Sky Box Office
Grant Way, Isleworth TW7 5QD
0870 240 3000
www.skymovies.com
Head of PPV: Karen Saunders
Press: 020 7800 4252
skymoviespublicity@bskyb.com
Publicity manager: Phil Evans

Sky Cinema 1 & 2
Grant Way, Isleworth TW7 5QD
0870 240 3000
www.skymovies.com
Director of movies: Ian Lewis
Press: 020 7800 4252
skymoviespublicity@bskyb.com
Publicity manager: Phil Evans

Sky Customer Channel
Grant Way, Isleworth TW7 5QD
0870 240 3000
Press: 020 7705 3275
Consumer PR manager: Tara Hicks

Sky Mix
Grant Way, Isleworth TW7 5QD
0870 240 3000
www.skyone.co.uk
Controller: James Baker
Press: 020 7805 7276
*Publicity manager: Chris Aylott; head
of programme publicity: Richard Turner*

Sky Movies 1–9
Grant Way, Isleworth TW7 5QD
0870 240 3000
www.skymovies.com
Director of movies: Ian Lewis
Press: 020 7800 4252
skymoviespublicity@bskyb.com
Publicity manager: Phil Evans

Sky News
Grant Way, Isleworth TW7 5QD
0870 240 3000
Newsdesk: news.plan@bskyb.com
www.skynews.co.uk
*Head of Sky News: John Riley.
Presenters and correspondents:
see page 138*
Press: 020 7800 4289
*Senior publicist: Stella Tooth; head of
programme publicity: Richard Turner*

Sky One
Grant Way, Isleworth TW7 5QD
0870 240 3071
www.skyone.co.uk
Controller: Richard Woolfe
Press: 020 7805 7276
*Publicity manager: Chris Aylott; head
of programme publicity: Richard
Turner. Publicists for programmes –
24: Louise Snell; Battlestar Galactica,
Law & Order, Enterprise: Chris Aylott;
Cold Case, Malcolm in the Middle:
Gayle Hemmings and Melanie
Adorian; Nip/Tuck, The Simpsons: Lee
Robson, Lost, Brainiac: Susan Collins*

Sky Sports 1, 2 & 3
Grant Way, Isleworth TW7 5QD
0870 240 3000
www.skysports.com
MD: Vic Wakeling
Press: 020 7800 4254
*Head of press and publicity:
Chris Haynes*

Sky Sports Extra
Grant Way, Isleworth TW7 5QD
0870 240 3000
www.skysports.com
MD: Vic Wakeling
Press: 020 7800 4254
*Head of press and publicity:
Chris Haynes*

Sky Sports News
Grant Way, Isleworth TW7 5QD
0870 240 3000
www.skysports.com
MD: Vic Wakeling
Press: 020 7800 4254
*Head of press and publicity:
Chris Haynes*

Sky Travel
Grant Way, Isleworth TW7 5QD
0870 240 3000
www.skytravel.co.uk
General manager: Barbara Gibbon
Press:
henrietta.svensen@bskyb.com

Sky Travel +1
Grant Way, Isleworth TW7 5QD
0870 240 3000
www.skytravel.co.uk
General manager: Barbara Gibbon
Press:
henrietta.svensen@bskyb.com

Sky Travel Extra
Grant Way, Isleworth TW7 5QD
0870 240 3000
www.skytravel.co.uk
General manager: Barbara Gibbon
Press:
henrietta.svensen@bskyb.com

Sky Travel Shop
Grant Way, Isleworth TW7 5QD
0870 240 3000
www.skytravel.co.uk
General manager: Barbara Gibbon
Press:
henrietta.svensen@bskyb.com

Sky Vegas Live
Grant Way, Isleworth TW7 5QD
0870 240 3000
www.skyvegaslive.com
*Executive producer: Peter Ward.
Consumer PR executive: Tara Hicks*
Press: 020 7705 3416

Sky Welcome
Grant Way, Isleworth TW7 5QD
0870 240 3000
Consumer PR executive: Tara Hicks
Press: 020 7705 3416

Smash Hits Channel
Mappin House, 4 Winsley Street,
London W1W 8HF
020 7182 8000
www.emapadvertising.com
*Programme director: Dave Young;
director of music: Simon Sadler*
Press:
maureen.corish@emap.com

Sony Entertainment TV Asia
Unit 24, Park Royal Metro Centre,
Britannia Way, London, NW10 7PA
020 7534 7575
www.setasia.tv
*Vice president for international
business: Neeraj Arora*
Press:
shalin_patel@spe.sony.com

Soundtrack Channel
1335 Fourth Street, Santa Monica,
California 90401 USA
00 1 310 899 1315
contactstc@stcchannel.com
www.stcchannel.com

Star TV/ News/ Plus/ Gold/ One
Great West House (15th floor),
Great West Road, Brentford,
Middlesex TW8 9DF
0870 240 3000
www.uk.startv.com
Senior marketing executive:
Gurpreet Braich
Press:
gurpreet.braich@bskyb.com

SUBtv
140 Buckingham Palace Road,
London SW1 9SA
020 7881 2540
info@sub.tv
www.sub.tv
Creative director: Jon Kingdon

Superstore TV
64–66 Coleman Street,
London EC2R 5BX
020 8104 0493
customerservice@simplymedia.tv
fran.hales@simplymedia.tv
www.superstore.tv
Media manager: Fran Hales

TBN Europe
PO Box 240, Hatfield,
Hertfordshire AL9 6BH
01707 655444
info@tbneurope.org
www.tbneurope.org

TCM
Turner House, 16 Great
Marlborough Street,
London W1V 1AF
020 7693 1000
tcminfo@turner.com
www.tcm.com

Teachers' TV
16-18 Berners Street,
London W1T 3LN
020 7182 7430
info@teachers.tv
www.teachers.tv
Chief executive: Andrew Bethell

Teletext Holidays
Building 10, Chiswick Park,
566 Chiswick High Road,
London W4 5TS
0870 731 3000
www.teletextholidays.co.uk

Television X
Suite 14, Burlington House,
St Saviours Road, St Helier,
Jersey JE2 4LA
01534 703700
pfarell@nasnet.je
Programme controller: Peter Farell

TG4
Baile na hAbhann,
Co. na Gaillimhe, Ireland
00 353 91 505050
eolas@tg4.ie
www.tg4.ie
Director of television: Alan Esslemont;
programmes department: Michéal Ó
Meallaigh

Thane Direct
248-250 Tottenham Court Road,
London W1T 7RA
020 7580 6110
info@thanedirect.tv
www.thanedirect.co.uk
MD: Thomas Parrot

Thane Stop and Shop
248-250 Tottenham Court Road,
London W1T 7RA
020 7580 6110
info@thanedirect.tv
www.thanedirect.co.uk
MD: Thomas Parrot

Thomas Cook TV
8 Park Place, Lawn Lane,
Vauxhall, London SW8 1UD
020 7820 4470
www.thomascooktv.com

Tiny POP
37 Harwood Road,
London SW6 4QP
020 7384 2243
francesca@chartshow.tv
www.popclub.tv
Head of channels: Keith MacMillan

TMF
MTV, Hawley Crescent,
London NW1 8TT
020 7284 7777
www.mtv.co.uk
General manager: Heather Jones
Press:
herson.mandy@mtvne.com

Toonami
Turner House, 16 Great
Marlborough Street,
London W1V 1AF
020 7693 1000
www.toonami.co.uk

Travel Channel
64 Newman Street,
London W1T 3EF
020 7636 5401
www.travelchannel.co.uk
Head of programming:
Annabelle Parmes
Press: petra@travelchannel.co.uk

Trouble
160 Great Portland Street,
London W1W 5QA
020 7299 5000
www.trouble.co.uk
Programme controller: Jonathan Webb
Press:
jakki.lewis@virginmediatv.co.uk

True Movies
020 7371 5999

Turner Classic Movies
Turner House, 16 Great
Marlborough Street,
London W1F 7HS
020 7693 1000
www.tcmonline.co.uk
Channel manager: Alan Musa
Press: ann.rosen@turner.com
www.europe.turnerinfo.com

TV Warehouse
Chalfont Grove,
Narcot Lane, Chalfont St Peter,
Buckinghamshire SL9 8TW
0800 013 1464
www.tvwarehouseonline.co.uk
MD: John Bramm

TV-Shop
P.O Box 64, Hadleigh IP7 6WF
0870 411 1345
tvshop-support@portica.co.uk
www.tvshop.com
MD: Ruth Oliver

UCB TV
UCB Broadcast Centre, Hanchurch
Lane, Stoke-on-Trent ST4 8RY
0845 604 0401
www.ucb.co.uk
TV broadcasting manager: John Green

UKTV Bright Ideas
160 Great Portland Street,
London W1W 5QA
020 7299 6200
www.uktv.co.uk
Channel editor: Steve Hornsey
Press:
rebecca.schutze@uktv.co.uk

UKTV Documentary
160 Great Portland Street,
London W1W 5QA
020 7299 6200
www.uktv.co.uk
Channel editor: Adrian Wills
Press:
tamsyn.zietsman@uktv.co.uk

UKTV Drama
160 Great Portland Street,
London W1W 5QA
020 7299 6200
www.uktv.co.uk
Channel editor: Lucy Clubbe
Press: zoe.clapp@uktv.co.uk

UKTV Food
160 Great Portland Street,
London W1W 5QA
020 7299 6200
www.uktvfood.co.uk
Channel editor: Paul Morton
Press:
rebecca.schutze@uktv.co.uk

UKTV G2
160 Great Portland Street,
London W1W 5QA
020 7299 6200
www.uktv.co.uk
Channel editor: Steve North
Press: zoe.clapp@uktv.co.uk

UKTV Gold
160 Great Portland Street,
London W1W 5QA
020 7299 6200
www.uktv.co.uk
Channel editor: James Newton
Press: zoe.clapp@uktv.co.uk

UKTV History
160 Great Portland Street,
London W1W 5QA
020 7299 6200
www.uktv.co.uk
Channel editor: Adrian Wills

UKTV People
160 Great Portland Street,
London W1W 5QA
020 7299 6200
www.uktv.co.uk
Channel editor: Adrian Wills

UKTV Style
160 Great Portland Street,
London W1W 5QA
020 7299 6200
www.uktvstyle.co.uk
Channel editor: Catherine Cattion
Press:
rebecca.schutze@uktv.co.uk

The Vault
37 Harwood Road,
London SW6 4QP
020 7384 2243
sarah.gauhan@chartshow.tv

VH1
MTV, Hawley Crescent,
London NW1 8TT
020 7284 7777
www.vh1.co.uk
General manager: Heather Jones
Press:
hershon.mandy@mtvne.com

VH1 Classic
MTV, Hawley Crescent,
London NW1 8TT
020 7284 7777
www.vh1.co.uk
General manager: Heather Jones
Press:
hershon.mandy@mtvne.com

VH2
MTV, Hawley Crescent,
London NW1 8TT
020 7284 7777
www.vh1.co.uk
General manager: Heather Jones
Press:
hershon.mandy@mtvne.com

Virgin 1
160 Great Portland Street,
London W1W 5QA
020 7299 5000
www.virginmedia.com
Programme controller: Celia Taylor
Press:
jessica.alder@virginmediatv.co.uk

Wine Network
88 Kearny Street, Suite 2100,
San Francisco CA 94108 USA
00 1 415 772 3601
info@winetv.tv
www.winetv.tv
CEO: Patrick Brunet; COO: Lorie Kim

Wrestling Channel
114 St Martins Lane,
London WC2N 4BE
020 7599 8959
info@thewrestlingchannel.tv
www.thewrestlingchannel.tv

YES661
Harper Road,
Sharston Industrial Estate,
Sharston, Manchester M22 4RG
0161 947 2580
www.yes661.com
MD: David Ades

YooPlay
Northumberland House,
155-157 Great Portland Street,
London W1W 6QP
020 7462 0870
oiyoo@yooplay.com
www.yoomedia.com/yooplay

Zee TV
Unit 7, Belvue Business Centre,
Belvue Road, Northolt UB5 5QQ
020 8839 4000
www.zeetv.co.uk
Programmes manager: Pranab Kapadia
Press: media@zeenetwork.com

Data services

Ceefax
BBC Television Centre, Wood
Lane, London W12 7RJ
020 8743 8000

Teletext
Building 10, Chiswick Park,
566 Chiswick High Road,
London W4 5TS
0870 731 3000
editor@teletext.co.uk
www.teletext.co.uk
Has a licence to use spare capacity within the Channel 3 (ITV) signal.
Head of television: Mishma Patel

Other broadcasters

Abacus TV
01603 812800
sales@abacustv.co.uk
www.abacustv.co.uk
Producer: Jane Scarfe

BFBS Forces Radio and TV
01494 878290
sarah.dornford-may@ssvc.com
www.ssvc.com
Controller of television: Helen Williams

Capital TV (Wales)
029 2070 2777
enquiries@capital.tv
www.capital.tv
MD: David Morris Jones

Channel M
0161 475 4855
info@channelM.co.uk
www.channelm.co.uk
Operations manager: Susan Steenson

EBS New Media
01462 895999
ben@ebsnewmedia.com
www.ebsnewmedia.com
MD: Ben Tagg

Glasgow University Student Television (GUST)
0141 341 6216
gust@src.gla.ac.uk
www.gust.tv
Station controller: Gemma Hanley

Leeds University Union TV (ls:tv)
0113 380 1423
stationmanager@lstv.co.uk
www.lstv.co.uk

Loughborough Students Union TV (LSUTV)
01509 635045
manager@lsutv.co.uk
www.lsutv.co.uk
Head of media: Holly Saunders

Middlesex Broadcasting Corporation (MATV Channel 6)
0116 253 2288
info@matv.co.uk
www.matv.co.uk
MD: Vinod Popat

Nerve TV
01202 965777
jhawkins@bournemouth.ac.uk
www.nervemedia.net
Media services manager: Jason Hawkins

Nexus UTV
01603 592270
nexusutv@gmail.com
www.nexusutv.co.uk

North West Television Services (Channel 9 — Coleraine, Limavady, Londonderry/Derry)
028 7131 4400
info@c9tv.tv
www.c9tv.tv
Director: Gary Porter

Northern Visions
028 9024 5495
info@northernvisions.org
www.northernvisions.org

SIX TV
01865 314700
info@sixtv.co.uk
www.sixtv.co.uk

STOIC Student Television of Imperial College
020 7594 8104
info@stoictv.com
www.stoictv.com
Contact: John Anderson

XTV
01392 263598
xtv@ex.ac.uk
www.xtv.org.uk

YCTV — Youth Culture Television
020 8964 4646
stuartr@yctv.org
www.yctv.org

York University Student Television (YSTV)
01904 431431
marketing@york.ac.uk
www.ystv.york.ac.uk

Independent production companies

● Key companies

ALL3MEDIA
168–173 High Holborn,
London WC1V 7AA
020 7845 4377
information@all3media.co.uk
www.all3media.com
CEO: Steve Morrison; head of press and marketing: Rachel Glaister; senior sales and marketing executive: Peter Grant

Assembly TV
Riverside Studios, Crisp Road,
London W6 9RL
020 8237 1075
judithmurrell@
   riversidestudios.co.uk
www.allthreemedia.com
Chief executive: William Burdett-Coutts
• *Black Books; Jo Brand's Hot Potatoes; In Exile*

Bentley Productions
Pinewood Studios, Pinewood Road, Iver, Bucks SL0 0NH
01753 656594
www.all3media.com
MD: Brian True-May
• *Midsomer Murders; Ultimate Force*

Cactus TV
373 Kennington Road,
London SE11 4PS
020 7091 4900
touch.us@cactustv.co.uk
www.cactustv.co.uk
MDs: Simon Ross, Amanda Ross
• *Richard & Judy; Saturday Kitchen*

Lion Television
Lion House, 26 Paddenswick Road, London W6 0UB
020 8846 2000
Scotland: 0141 331 0450
New York: 00 1 212 206 8633
LA: 00 1 310 566 6285
mail@liontv.co.uk
www.liontv.co.uk
MDs: Richard Bradley, Nick Catliff, Shahana Meer, Jeremy Mills
• *Bad Behaviour; Days That Shook the World; Britain's Finest; Castles; Royal Deaths and Diseases; Passport to the Sun*

North One TV
Mayward House, 46–52 Pentonville Road, London N1 9HF
020 7502 6000
annelise.unitt@northonetv.com
www.all3media.com
MD: Neil Duncanson; chief executive: John Wohlgemuth
• *Formula One; World Rally; The Top Ten series; Speed Sunday; Fifth Gear; The Gadget Show; The Victoria Cross*

At It Productions
68 Salusbury Road, Queens Park,
London NW6 6NU
020 8964 2122
enquiries@atitproductions.com
www.atitproductions.com
MDs: Martin Cunning, Chris Fouracre
• *T4; LA Pool Party; Sun Sea and Silicone; Perfect Getaway; Chancers; Popworld, 25 Years of Smash Hits; Bride and Grooming; Born Without a Face*

Celador Productions
39 Long Acre, London WC2 9LG
020 7845 6999
tvhits@celador.co.uk
www.celador.co.uk
CEO: Danielle Lux; director of production: Heather Hampson; director of factual: Murray Boland; director of entertainment: Ruth Wrigley; development executives, comedy: Vanessa Haynes, Humphrey Barclay
• *You Are What You Eat; 24 Carrott Gold; 3 Fat Brides, 1 Thin Dress; Commercial Breakdown; Popcorn; Perfect Strangers*

Diverse
Gorleston Street, London W14 8XS
020 7603 4567
reception@diverse.tv
www.diverse.tv
MD: Paul Sowerbutts; creative director: Roy Ackerman; head of post production: Paul Bates; head of production: Janet Smyth; executive producer: Adam Barker
• *Musicality: Badger Or Bust; Shalom In The Home; Born Survivor: Bear Grylls; Brits Behind Bars: America's Toughest Jail; The Real Dad's Army*

Endemol UK
Shepherds Building Centre,
Clarecroft Way, Shepherds Bush,
London W14 0EE
0870 333 1700
info@endemoluk.com
www.endemoluk.com
Chief creative officer: Tim Hincks; director of production: Clare Pickering
• *Big Brother; Fame Academy; Orange British Academy Film Awards; Ground Force; Changing Rooms; Restoration; 8 Out of 10 Cats; Soccer Aid; 1 Versus 100; Ready Steady Cook; Deal Or No Deal*

Hat Trick Productions
10 Livonia Street, London W1F 8AF
020 7434 2451
info@hattrick.com
www.hattrick.com
MD: Jimmy Mulville; head of entertainment: Leon Wilde
• *Have I Got News For You; Bodies; Bromwell High; Room 101; The Kumars at No 42; Father Ted; Underworld; Drop The Dead Donkey; News Knight; Fonejacker; Drop Dead Gorgeous*

HIT Entertainment
Maple House, 5th Floor,
149–150 Tottenham Court Road,
London W1T 7NF
020 7554 2500
www.hitentertainment.com
MD: Bruce Steinberg; head of production: Karen Davidsen
• *Barney and Friends; Art Attack; Angelina Ballerina; Pingu; Toddworld; Fireman Sam; Bob the Builder; Rubbadubbers; Sooty; Thomas the Tank Engine*

IWC Media
St George's Studio,
93–97 St George's Road,
Glasgow G3 6JA
0141 353 3222
London: 020 7013 4000
info@iwcmedia.co.uk
www.iwcmedia.co.uk
MD: Sue Oriel; creative directors: Alan Clements, Zad Rogers; head of production: Jonathan Warne; director of drama: Eileen Quinn
• *Ultimate Cars; Other Side; Location, Location, Location; Changemakers; Survival of the Richest; Relocation Relocation; Root of all Evil; Mountains*

Princess Productions
Whiteley's Centre,
151 Queensway, London W2 4YN
020 7985 1985
reception@princesstv.com
www.princesstv.com
MD: Sebastian Scott, Henrietta Conrad; head of production: Sarah Buckenham
• *Bump 'n' Grind; The Wright Stuff; The Friday Night Project; Doctor Doctor; The Big Art Project; Something For The Weekend*

Prospect Pictures
Wandsworth Plain,
London SW18 1ET
020 7636 1234
Capital studios,
London: 020 8877 1234
Wales 029 2055 1177
rhys@prospect-uk.com
www.prospect-uk.com
MD: Liam Hamilton
• *Ready Steady Cook; Saturday Cooks; Call Me A Cabbie*

Ragdoll (UK)
Timothy's Bridge Road,
Stratford Upon Avon CV37 9NQ
01789 404100
USA: 00 1 212 966 4477
info@ragdoll.co.uk
www.ragdoll.co.uk
Director of production: Sue James
• *Open a Door; Rosie and Jim; Tots TV; Brum; Teletubbies; Teletubbies Everywhere; Boohbah; In The Night Garden*

RDF Media
The Gloucester Building,
Kensington Village, Avonmore
Road, London W14 8RF
020 7013 4000
contactus@rdfmedia.com
www.rdfmedia.com
*Chief executive: David Frank; creative
officer: Grant Mansfield; chief
operating officer: Joely Fether*
- *Faking It 4; Wife Swap; Celebrity Wife
Swap; Scrapheap Challenge 5; Century
of the Self; Holiday Showdown; Ian
Wright's Supersize Kids; Britain's Top
Dog; A Year With The Queen*

September Films
Glen House, 22 Glenthorne Road,
London W6 0NG
020 8563 9393
USA: 00 1 323 960 8085
september@septemberfilms.com
www.septemberfilms.com
*Chief executive: Sammy Nourmand;
director of production: Elaine Day;
head of drama and film development:
Nadine Mellor*
- *Beauty & The Geek; Haunted Homes;
Generation Xcess; Bridezillas 5;
Hollywood Live; The Duchess*

Shine
140–142 Kensington Church Street,
Notting Hill, London W8 4BN
020 7985 7000
info@shinelimited.com
www.shinelimited.com
MD: Elizabeth Murdoch
- *Dispatches; MasterChef Goes Large;
Project Catwalk; 100 Greatest Series*

Talkback Thames Productions
20–21 Newman Street,
London W1T 1PG
020 7861 8000
reception@talkbackthames.tv
www.talkbackthames.tv
Chief executive: Lorraine Heggessey
- *Jamie's Kitchen; The Apprentice;
Grand Designs; How Clean Is Your
House?; House Doctor; The Bill, The
X Factor; The IT Crowd*

Tiger Aspect Productions
7 Soho Street, London W1D 3DQ
020 7434 6700
general@tigeraspect.co.uk
www.tigeraspect.co.uk
*MD: Andrew Zein; executive producer,
entertainment: Drew Pearce; head of
factual: Paul Sommers; head of
comedy: Sophie Clarke-Jervoise.
Comedy, drama, entertainment,
factual and animation.*
- *Teachers; Streetmate; Vicar of
Dibley; Lenny Henry Show; Murphy's
Law; Vital Signs; 3 Minute Wonder;
Charlie & Lola; Mr Bean*

Tinopolis
Tinopolis Centre, Park Street,
Llanelli, Carmarthenshire SA15 3YE
01554 880880
Mentorn London: 020 7258 6800
Oxford Mentorn: 01865 318 450
Glasgow Mentorn: 0141 204 6600
info@tinopolis.com
www.tinopolis.com
Executive chairman: Ron Jones
- *Robot Wars; Britain's Worst ...;
Gillette World Sport; Club Culture;
Question Time; The Real Monty;
Traffic Cops; Car Wars; Hotel Paradise*

TWI (Trans World International)
Pier House, Strand on the Green,
London W4 3NN
020 8233 5000
kmullins@imgworld.com
www.imgworld.com
Head of production: Graham Fry
- *Japan's War (in colour series);
Wimbledon; The Olympics; Premier
League; PGA European Tour;
Colour of War*

Twofour Productions
3 Bush Park, Estover,
Plymouth PL6 7RG
01752 727400
enq@twofour.co.uk
www.twofour.co.uk
*CEO: Charles Wace; managing director
of communications: Charles Mills;
managing director of broadcast:
Melanie Leach*
- *Are You Smarter Than A Ten Year
Old?; Dirty Cows; The Baron; Open
Gardens; The Hotel Inspector 24 Hours
With...; Exposed: Life Through A Lens*

Wall To Wall
8/9 Spring Place, Kentish Town,
London NW5 3ER
020 7485 7424
mail@walltowall.co.uk
www.walltowall.co.uk
*CEO: Alex Graham; Head of production:
Helena Ely*
- *New Tricks; The Battle That Made
Britain; The History of Photography;
Who Do You Think You Are?; Crisis At
The Castle; Empire's Children; 100%
English; Filth: The Mary Whitehouse
Story; Child Genius*

Zig Zag Productions
13-14 Great Sutton St,
Clerkenwell, London EC1V 0BX
020 7017 8755
production@zigzag.uk.com
www.zigzag.uk.com
*MD: Danny Fenton; head of factual
entertainment: Jes Wilkins; head of
production: Sophie Ardern; head of
development: Ben Paul*
- *Fashion is Football Challenge; Inside
the Mind of Frank Bruno; Three Lions;
DIY Births; Celebrity Gladiators;
X-Rated: The Ads They Couldn't
Show; That's So Last Week; Essex Boys*

● Other production companies

1A Productions
01360 620855
office@1AProductions.co.uk
MD: Norman Stone
- *Tales From the Madhouse; Man
Dancin'; CS Lewis: Beyond Narnia;
Songs Of Praise; The Final Fix?;
The Journey; Breathless*

3BM Television
020 8740 4780
3bmtv@3bmtv.co.uk
www.3bmtv.co.uk
*Chairman and creative director:
Simon Berthon*
- *War Lords; Children of Abraham;
Zero Hour 2: Ten Days to D-Day;
Bird Flu; The British Working Class;
Tsunami: Where Was God?*

12 Yard Productions
020 7432 2929
contact@12yard.com
www.12yard.com
MD: David Young
- *Weakest Link; In It To Win It; Without
Prejudice?; EggHeads; Here Comes
The Sun; Three's A Crowd; Coach Trip*

The 400 Company
020 8746 1400
info@the400.co.uk
www.the400.co.uk
MD: Mark Sloper
- *Who's Wedding Is It?; Property
Ladder; To Buy Or Not To Buy;
Conflicts; How To Look Good Naked;
Extreme Makeover; Empire's Children*

Aardman Animations
0117 984 8485
mail@aardman.co.uk
www.aardman.com
Chief operations officer: Stephen Moore
- *Walkers' Mr Potato Head
commercial; Robinson's Boogie
commercial; Chicken Run; Wallace
And Gromit; Shaun The Sheep*

Absolutely Productions
020 7644 5575
info@absolutely-uk.com
www.absolutely.biz
MD: Pete Baikie
- *Barry Welsh; Stressed Eric; Trigger
Happy TV; Baggage; Historyville*

Acacia Productions
020 8341 9392
projects@acaciaproductions.co.uk
www.acaciaproductions.co.uk
MD: J Edward Milner
- *Documentary and news, environment,
current affairs and human rights;
Open University programming*

Accomplice Television
00 353 1 660 3235
office@accomplice-tv.com
www.accomplice-tv.com
MD: David Collins
- *Pure Mule; Bachelors Walk Series 1,
2 & 3; Watermelon; Dan & Becs*

Addictive Television
020 7700 0333
mail@addictive.com
www.addictive.com
*Head of production: Nik Clarke;
Graham Daniels*
• *Spaced Out; Transambient; Night
Shift; The Web Review; Mixmasters
(ITV1); Visual Stings (Magnetic
Channel); Optronica*

Aimimage Production Company
020 7482 4340
atif@aimimage.com
www.aimimage.com
MD: Ahmad Zadeh
• *Terra Circa; Balls to Basra;
The Family Portrait*

Angel Eye
0845 230 0062
office@angeleye.co.uk
www.angeleye.co.uk
MD: Richard Osborne
• *Holy Offensive; Beginners Luck;
Estate Agents; Lady Macbeth; The
Last Chances; Cowards; Pam Ann's
Mile High*

Antelope
01243 370806
mick.csaky@antelope.co.uk
www.antelope.co.uk
*Chief executive and creative director:
Mike Csaky*
• *Docs: Mozart in Turkey; Rebel Music:
The Bob Marley Story; Geiko Girl;
Africa Live; Epic Journey; 13-part
series about Kyoto; The Pier*

APT Films
020 8280 9125
admin@aptfilms.com
www.aptfilms.com
MD: Jonny Persey
• *Wondrous Oblivion (feature);
Solomon and Gaenor (Oscar
nomination, best foreign film); The
Chosen Ones; Solo One; When I Lived
in Modern Times; Deep Water*

Atlantic Productions
020 8735 9300
info@atlanticproductions.tv
www.atlanticproductions.tv
MD: Anthony Geffen
• *The War On Britain's Jews?; Egypt's
New Tomb; Bhutan; Lost Worlds;
Munich; Atlas Italy; Apollo 13;
Everest; Jack The Ripper; Hanssen;
Seven Wonders; Real Miami Vice;
Real Untouchables; Real LAPD;
Mummy Autopsy; Conquistadors*

Attaboy TV
020 7740 3000
info@attaboytv.com
www.attaboytv.com
MD: Michael Wood
• *The High Road; End of the Line; A
Question of Colin; Life at the Sport;
Vets in Hong Kong*

Avalon
020 7598 8000
info@avalonuk.com
www.avalonuk.com
MD: John Thoday
• *Harry Hill's TV Burp; The Frank
Skinner Show; Jerry Springer – The
Opera; Kelsey Grammer presents
The Sketch Show (Fox Network USA)*

Betty TV
020 7290 0660
info@bettytv.co.uk
www.betty.co.uk
MD: Liz Warner
• *Spendaholics; Rude Britannia;
Let's Talk Sex; Breaking Up With The
Joneses; Arrange Me A Marriage*

Big Bear Films
020 7229 5982
office@bigbearfilms.co.uk
www.bigbearfilms.co.uk
*Directors: John Stroud, Marcus
Mortimer*
• *My Hero; Strange; Hairy Bikers
Cookbook, MUD*

Big Heart Media
020 7608 0352
info@bigheartmedia.com
www.bigheartmedia.com
MD: Colin Izod
• *GridClub/music studio; Spin 'n
Groove; Street Corner Symphony;
Rewind; Cape Farewell; Teachers'
TV; Pearson Education, WWF*

Big Umbrella Media
0121 506 9620
production@bigumbrellamedia
.co.uk
www.bigumbrellamedia.co.uk
MD: Martin Head
• *Living with the New Cross Fire; Sir
Frank Whittle: The Man who Shrank
the World*

Big Wave Productions
01243 532531
info@bigwavetv.com
www.bigwavetv.com
MD: Sarah Cunliffe
• *Bug Attack; Death on the Amazon;
Secret Weapons; Revenge of the
Crocodiles; Runaways; Alien Worlds;
Saved By Dolphins*

Blackwatch Productions
0141 222 2640
info@blackwatchtv.com
www.blackwatchtv.com
MD: Nicola Black
• *Boys with Breasts; Snorting Coke
with the BBC; Designer Vagina;
Braking The Cycle*

Blast! Films
020 7267 4260
blast@blastfilms.co.uk
www.blastfilms.co.uk
MD: Edmund Coulthard
• *Principles of Lust; The Death of
Klinghoffer; Tales from Pleasure
Beach; Days in the Life; Boys & Girls;
Lawless*

**Blue Egg Television/
Blue Egg Studios**
01873 851 885
info@blueegg.tv
www.blueeggproductions.com
MD: Jill Scott
• *James Bond: Die Another Day; San
Antonio; Orange commercial; Return
Journey*

Box TV
020 7297 8040
info@box-tv.co.uk
www.box-tv.co.uk
MD: Justin Thomson-Glover
• *Sunday; Trust; Boudica; Gunpowder,
Treason and Plot; Sweeney Todd;
Shades Of Black*

Brechin Productions
020 8876 2046
clivedoig@blueyonder.co.uk
www.brechin.com
CEO: Clive Doig
• *Jigsaw; See it, Saw it; Turnabout;
Eureka*

Brighter Pictures
020 8222 4100
info@endemoluk.com
www.endemoluk.com
  /brighterpictures
MD: Richard Johnston/ Lucas Church
• *Take the Mike; Bombay Blush; Diet
Another Day; You Can't Fire Me I'm
Famous; Larger Than Life; A Girls
Guide to 21st Century Sex; Chantelle's
Dream Dates*

Brighter Pictures Scotland
0141 572 0861
angela.donnolly@endemoluk.com
www.endemoluk.com
  /brighterpictures
MD: Paul Murray
• *Get a New Life (BBC2); Tabloid Tales
(BBC1); Nick Nairn and the Dinner
Ladies (BBC Scotland)*

Brighton TV
01273 224280
info@brighton.tv
www.brighton.tv
MD: David Pounds
• *Tales of the Living Dead; Big Boutique;
Secrets of the Bog People; Sleepwalkers
Who Kill; Selling Houses; Supernanny*

Broadway
0115 955 6909
info@intermedianotts.co.uk
www.broadway.org.uk
MD: Ceris Morris
• *One For The Road; Slot Art; Shifting
Units; The Entertainer; First Cut*

Brook Lapping Productions
020 7428 3100
info@brooklapping.com
www.brooklapping.com
MD: Brian Lapping
• *I Met Osama Bin Laden; The Fall of
Milosevic; Avenging Terror; Before
the Booker; I Met Adolf Eichmann;
The Death of Yugoslavia; Israel and
the Arabs; Live Aid Remembered
(2 parts); Surviving Katrina; Europe's
9/11; Stanley Goes to Europe*

Cactus TV
020 7091 4900
touch.us@cactustv.co.uk
www.cactustv.co.uk
MDs: Amanda Ross, Simon Ross
• *The Spirit of Diana, The Debate;
Songs of Bond; Cliff Richard, The Hits
I Missed; Richard & Judy; British
Soap Awards; Saturday Kitchen*

Caledonia TV
0141 564 9100
info@caledonia.tv
www.caledonia.tv
MD: Seona Robertson
• *Sun Worshippers; King Jamie and the
Angel; The Real Tartan Army II,
Shooting Franz Ferdinand;
Scotland's History: The Top Ten*

Carnival (Films and Theatre)
020 7317 1370
info@carnivalfilms.co.uk
www.carnivalfilms.co.uk
MD: Gareth Neames
• *Shadowlands; Firelight; Bugs; As If;
Poirot; Rosemary and Thyme; Hotel
Babylon*

Century Films
020 7378 6106
info@centuryfilmsltd.com
www.centuryfilmsltd.com
MDs: Brian Hill
• *Drinking for England; Feltham Sings;
Shot; Men at Fifty; David Beckham:
A Footballer's Story; Tightwads;
Songbirds; Bully 4 U*

Chameleon TV
0113 205 0040
www.chameleontv.com
MD: Allen Jewhurst
• *Edge of the City; Love 2 shop; Faith
and Music Series; Britain's First
Suicide Bombers; Undercover
Teacher; Young, Angry & Muslim*

Channel X
020 7566 8160
info@channelx.co.uk
www.channelx.co.uk
MD: Alan Marke
• *Reeves & Mortimer; Date That;
Popetown; Catterick; Snuff Box;
Blunder; Modern Toss*

Cicada Films
020 7266 4646
cicada@cicadafilms.com
www.cicadafilms.com
MD: Frances Berrigan
• *Ancient inventions; NYPD Animal
Squad; Fat Fiancees; The Abyss;
Beyond Pompeii; Bikini; Tiger
Traffic; A Year Without Summer*

Clearcut Communications
0161 427 3052
info@clearcut.freeserve.co.uk
MD: Robin Anderson
• *Sex and the Village; On the Edge
(Granada); Sense of Place (BBC1);
Shanghai'd (BBC2); Proof Positive
(pilot for Discovery America)*

Clerkenwell Films
020 7608 2726
andy@clerkenwellfilms.com
MD: Murray Ferguson
• *Dr Jekyll and Mr Hyde (Universal TV);
Rebus; Afterlife Series 1 & 2; Losing It;
Persuasion; Diary Of A Nobody*

Collingwood O'Hare Entertainment
020 8993 3666
info@crownstreet.co.uk
www.collingwoodohare.com
MD: Christopher O'Hare
• *Animal Stories; Eddy and the Bear;
The King's Beard; Yoko! Jakamoko!
Toto!*

The Comedy Unit
0141 305 6666
comedyunit@comedyunit.co.uk
www.comedyunit.co.uk
MDs: Colin Gilbert, April Chamberlain
• *Still Game; The Karen Dunbar Show;
Offside; Yo! Diary!; Taxi for Cowan
Spanish Special; New Year specials:
Chewin' The Fat; Only An Excuse?*

Company Pictures
020 7380 3900
enquiries@companypictures.co.uk
www.companypictures.co.uk
MDs: Charlie Pattinson, George Faber
• *Shameless; Forty; White Teeth; Anna
Karenina; Wild at Heart; Mansfield
Park; Skins; Talk To Me*

Cosgrove Hall Films
0161 882 2500
animation@chf.co.uk
www.chf.co.uk
MD: Anthony Utley
• *Andy Pandy; Bill & Ben; Postman
Pat; Enjie Benji; Dangermouse;
Rupert the Bear*

CTVC
020 7940 8480
ctvc@ctvc.co.uk
www.ctvc.co.uk
CEO: Nick Stuart
• *Imber, Britain's Lost Village;
Tonight; Shariah TV; Victim 001;
Bethlehem Year Zero; John Meets
Paul; A Mediterranean Journey;
Understanding Islam; The M25
Rapist; Codex*

Dai4Films
01570 471368
info@dai4films.com
www.dai4films.com
MD: Neil Davies
• *The Montserrat Volcano; Islands in
the Sun; Working Machines; Double
or Nothing; Raw Spice; Dirty Streets*

Dan Films
020 7916 4771
enquiries@danfilms.com
www.danfilms.com
Director: Julie Baines
• *Creep; Sons of the Wind; The
Republic of Love; Severance*

Darlow Smithson Productions
020 7482 7027
mail@darlowsmithson.com
www.darlowsmithson.com
MD: Iain Pelling
• *Touching the Void; We Built this City;
Falling Man; Lusitania; Waco; Deep
Water; The Da Vinci Detective*

Darrall Macqueen
020 7407 2322
info@darrallmacqueen.com
www.darrallmacqueen.com
MDs: Maddy Darrall, Billy Macqueen
• *The Crust; Play the Game; Smile
series 1, 2, 3; U Get Me series 1, 2, 3;
Animal Spies; Feel the Fear; Smile;
The Rory Stories*

Dazed Film and TV
020 7549 6840
info.film&tv@dazegroup.com
www.dazedfilmtv.com
MD: Laura Hastings-Smith
• *Perfect; Stop for a Minute; Untold
Beauty; The Lives of the Saints;
Hero2Hero*

DLT Entertainment UK
020 7631 1184
jbartlett@dltentertainment.co.uk
www.dltentertainment.com
MD: John Bartlett
• *As Time Goes By; Love on a Branch
Line; My Family; Meet My Folks*

DNA Films
020 7292 8700
info@dnafilms.com
www.dnafilms.com
MD: Andrew MacDonald
• *28 Days Later; Sunshine; Notes On
A Scandal; Last King Of Scotland;
28 Weeks Later; The History Boys*

Eagle and Eagle
020 8995 1884
producer@eagletv.co.uk
www.eagletv.co.uk
Producer: Robert Eagle
• *The Nuclear Boy Scout; Robo
Sapiens; Big Questions; Space:
The Final Junkyard; Picture This*

Eagle Films
01372 844484
info@eaglefilms.co.uk
www.eaglefilms.co.uk
Producer: Katrina Moss
• *Let's Do Lunch; Tears For Delaney;
It Started with a Kiss; The Road to
Somewhere; Shaking Dreamland*

Ecosse Films
020 7371 0290
webmail@ecossefilms.com
www.ecossefilms.com
MD: Douglas Rae
• *Monarch of the Glen; The
Ambassador; Mrs Brown; Charlotte
Gray; Heartless; Under the Greenwood
Tree; Wilderness; Becoming Jane; The
Water Horse; Cape Wrath; Kitchen;
My Boy Jack; Mistresses*

Educational Broadcasting Services Trust
020 7613 5082
enquiries@ebst.co.uk
www.ebsonline.co.uk
Chief executive: Dr Jim Stevenson
• *Looking at Learning; Maths for Engineers; Maths tutor (Series)*

Electric Sky
01273 224240
info@electricsky.com
www.electricsky.com
CEO: David Pounds
• *Who Killed Diana; Clash of Worlds; 37 Uses of a Dead Sheep; Fireballs of Tutankhamun; Sashan Avenue with Jodie Kidd*

The Elstree Production Company
01932 572680
enquiries@elsprod.com
www.elsprod.com
Producer: Greg Smith
• *Agnes Brown; George Orwell's Animal Farm; David Copperfield*

FACE Television
01256 350022
paula@facetv.co.uk
www.facetv.co.uk
MD: Paul Friend
• *Wildlife SOS series 1, 2; Lifeboat Rescue; Wildlife Photographer*

Faction Films
020 7690 4446
faction@factionfilms.co.uk
www.factionfilms.co.uk
MDs: David Fox, Sylvia Stevens, Peter Day
• *Aphrodite's Drop; Murder in the Family; Love for Sale; Resistencia; Cinematic Orchestra; Sonic Revolution; Point Annihilation*

The Farnham Film Company
01252 710313
info@farnfilm.com
www.farnfilm.com
MD: Ian Lewis
• *Dance with the Devil; Intergalactic Kevin; Mona the Vampire; The Druid's Tune; The Lake*

Festival Film and TV
020 8297 9999
info@festivalfilm.com
www.festivalfilm.com
MD: Ray Marshall
• *Feature films: Man Dancin'; The Colour; Grievous Angel*

Film and Music Entertainment
020 7131 5757
info@fame.uk.com
www.fame.uk.com
MD: Mike Downey
• *Guy X; Deathwatch; The Enemy; Border Post; Anastezsi; Son Of Man*

Films of Record
020 7286 0333
films@filmsofrecord.com
www.filmsofrecord.com
MD: Roger Graef
• *Malaria; The Protectors; Remember the Secret Policeman's Ball; Rail Cops*

Flame Television
020 7713 6868
contact@flametv.co.uk
www.theflamegroup.co.uk
Chairman: Roger Bolton; MD and head of production: Clare Featherstone
• *Don't Get Done, Get Dom; Tarrence Way; Churchill's Girl; Celebrity Swap; Heir Hunters*

Flashback Television
020 7490 8996
Bristol: 0117 973 8755
mailbox@flashbacktv.co.uk
bristol@flashbacktv.co.uk
www.flashbacktv.co.uk
MD: Taylor Downing
• *Europe: The Lost Evidence; Human Rights With Cherie Booth; Weaponology; Nigella's Christmas Bites; Married To The Prime Minister; Secret Life Of The Classroom*

Flick Features
020 7385 7338
info@flickfeatures.com
www.flickfeatures.com
Director: John Deery
• *Hell4Leather; Conspiracy of Silence; Pictures of Anna (in development)*

Flying Elephant Films
020 7871 0686
info@flyingelephant.co.uk
www.flyingelephant.co.uk
MD: Preeyf Nair
• *A Story That Begins at the End; A Different Life; You Know What I'm Saying; Miracles Of Faith; My Story; First Kiss*

Focus Productions
0790 1978 902
Stratford-upon-Avon:
  01789 298948
martinweitz@
  focusproductions.co.uk
maddern@focusproductions.co.uk
www.focusproductions.co.uk
MD: Martin Weitz
• *This Sceptred Isle; The Jewish Journey. Winner, Sony Gold Award. Projects 2003: Witness on Saint-making; The Godfather of the Blues; The Real Rainman; Brainman; Painting the Mind; The Musical Genius; Brainman*

Footstep Productions
020 7836 9990
info@footstep-productions.com
www.footstepproductions.com
MD: Collette Thomson
• *Worktalk; Voces Espanolas; A Christmas Card From England*

Free@Last TV
020 7242 4333
info@freeatlasttv.co.uk
www.freeatlasttv.co.uk
Executive producer: Barry Ryan
• *Revisiting Brideshead; The Wonderful World of Roald Dahl; Super Sleuths; 20 Reasons to Love Star Trek; A Portrait of George Galloway; The Story of Punk*

Fresh One Productions
020 7359 1000
www.freemantlemedia.com
MD: Andrew Conran
• *Jamie's School Dinners; Oliver's Twist; Jamie's Kitchen*

Fulcrum TV
020 7939 3160
team@fulcrumtv.com
www.fulcrumtv.com
MDs: Christopher Hird, Richard Belfield
• *Don't Worry; Can You Live Without?... (Series 1 & 2); Egypt Week Live; Top Ten Comic Book Heroes; What Would Jesus Drive?*

Genesis Media Group
029 2066 6007
info@genesis-media.co.uk
www.genesis-media.co.uk
Producer and programme director: Alan Torjussen
• *Peter Warlock; Ceiri and his Music; Love Talk; Leila Megane*

Ginger Television
020 7882 1000
production@ginger.tv
www.ginger.tv
MD: Elisabeth Partyka
• *Jack Osbourne — Adrenaline Junkie; Crucify Me; Whatever; Extreme Celebrity Detox; Don't Drop The Coffin*

Glasshead
020 8742 6800
lambros@glasshead.co.uk
www.glasshead.co.uk
MD: Lambros Atteshlis
• *Blue Dragon; Watch Magic Grandad; Real Science; Science In Focus; Magic Grandad*

Grand Slamm Children's Films
020 7388 0789
studio@gscfilms.com
www.gscfilms.com
MD: Ginger Gibbons
• *Percy the Park Keeper; Angelina Ballerina; Kipper; Dot Wot; The Hairdresser's Dog; The Magic Bed; Sheeep*

Green Bay Media
029 2064 2370
john-geriant@green-bay.tv
www.green-bay.tv
Creative directors: Phil George, John Geraint
• *An Archbishop Like This; A Bloody Good Friday; Do Not Go Gentle; The World's Most Dangerous Roads; The Physics Of Rock Guitar; Going for Growth*

Green Inc Productions
028 9057 3000
tv@greeninc.tv
www.greeninc.tv
MD: Stephen Stewart
• *The Afternoon Show; Patrick Kielty Almost Live; Red Bull DJ Academy; Anderson In; Brendan Courtney Show*

Green Umbrella
0117 906 4336
postmaster@umbrella.co.uk
www.umbrella.co.uk
MD: Nigel Ashcroft
- Journey to Centre of the Earth; Escape from Berlin; Galileo's Daughter; John and Abigail Adams: American Experience; Elephant Exodus; Bridging the Atlantic

Greenlit Productions
020 7287 3545
info@greenlit.co.uk
www.greenlit.co.uk
MD: Jill Green
- Foyle's War; The Swap; Menace; Trust

Greenpoint Films
020 7240 7066
info@greenpointfilms.com
www.greenpointfilms.co.uk
MDs: Patrick Cassavetti, Ann Scott, Simon Relph
- Only Human; Hideous Kinky; The Land Girls; The Only Boy For Me

Grosvenor Park Productions
020 7486 4639
chris.chrisafis@grosvenorpark.com
www.grosvenorpark.com
MD: Daniel Taylor
- Colour Me Kubrick; Count of Monte Cristo; Spider; The Battle In Seattle; Defiance; Mutant Chronicles

Gruber Films
0870 366 9313
office@gruberfilms.com
www.gruberfilms.com
MD: Richard Holmes
- Shooting Fish; Waking Ned; The Abduction Club; The Great Pretender

Hand Pict Productions
0131 346 1111
ask@handpict.com
www.handpict.com
Director: George Cathro
- East Coast Boy, West Coast Man; Numero Una; Gretna – A Different League; Jute Jam & Islam

Hanrahan Media
01789 450182
info@hanrahanmedia.com
www.hanrahanmedia.tv
MD: Will Hanrahan
- Renovation Creation; Star Lives; World's Biggest Ghost Hunt; Most Haunted Live; Men's Health; Cash Crop Circles; Verdict; Going to Work Naked; Conversion

Hasan Shah Films
020 7722 2419
hsfilms@blueyonder.co.uk
MD: Hasan Shah
- Short: Art Of The Critic; A Little Scary; Supernatural

Hewland International
020 8215 3345
jcook@hewland.co.uk
www.hewland.co.uk
MD: Jane Hewland
- Dream Team; Stranger than Fiction; Dial a Date; Dream Team Retro; Mile High; Can't Buy Me Love

Hopscotch Films
0141 221 2828
info@hopscotchfilms.co.uk
www.hopscotchfilms.co.uk
MDs: Charlotte Wontner, Clara Glynn, John Archer
- Writing Scotland; Detox or Die; Last Train to Beechwood; Is It Just Me; Cinema Iran; On the Road with Kiarostami; Bracken White; The Sickhouse

Hot Shot Films
028 9031 3332
info@hotshotfilms.com
www.hotshotfilms.com
MDs: Brendan J. Byrne
- The Secret Life of Words; Living History; Blind Vision; Street Detectives; So You Thought You Knew the Plantation; Heroes; Sons of Ulster; The Visitors

Hotbed Media
0121 248 3900
mail@hotbedmedia.co.uk
www.hotbedmedia.co.uk
MD: Johannah Dyer
- Under the Hammer; Songs of Praise; Real Brassed Off; 100 Worst Britons; Everything Must Go; 100 Worst Pop Records; Star Portraits with Rolf Harris; Build, Buy or Restore

Hourglass Productions
productions@hourglass.co.uk
www.hourglass.co.uk
MD: Martin Chilcott
- Energy for Nature; DNA and Rocket Science, Living Donation

HRTV
020 598 9430
mail@hra-online.com
www.hra-online.com
MD: Jerry Hibbert
- Tractor Tom; Stressed Eric series II; Hibbert Ralph Animations: TV adverts

Hyphen Films
020 7734 0632
nmk@hyphenfilms.com
MD: N.M. Kabir
- Spotlights and Saris; Bollywood Dancing; Bollywood Women – Intros 2007; Bismillah of Benaras; Bollywood Celebrities

I2I Productions
01698 794100
enquiries@i2itv.com
www.i2itv.com
Director: Gordon Ross
- Crimewatch; Panorama; Holiday Programme; Country File, What Not To Wear

Icon Films
0117 970 6882
info@iconfilms.co.uk
www.iconfilms.co.uk
MD: Laura Marshall
- Belgrano; King Cobra; Einstein's Brain; Tiger Kill; Last Lions Of India

Illumina Digital
020 8600 9300
info@illumina.co.uk
www.illumina.co.uk
MD: Andrew Chitty
- DCSF; National Theatre; Culture; Net Cymru; Empire's Children; Get Cooking

Illuminations Films
020 7288 8400
seb@illuminationsmedia.co.uk
www.illuminationsmedia.co.uk
MD: Linda Zuck
- The Piano Tuner of Earthquakes; London Orbital; Little Otik; TV Heaven; The A-Z of TV; 1001 Nights of TV

Images Of War
020 7430 4480
derek@warfootage.co.uk
www.warfootage.com
MD: Derek Blades
- Mass for Peace; Invasion; D-Day; Footage for Hitler's Britain; 300 hours of war-related material

Imago Productions
01603 727600
mail@imagoproductions.tv
www.imagoproductions.tv
MD: Vivica Parsons
- Grudge Match; Perfect Man; The Coach; Sporty Facts; Bryan's Olde and Bitter; Coastal Kitchen; Coastal Inspirations; My Horror Home; Secrets Beneath Our Feet

Independent Image
01883 654867
info@indimage.com
www.indimage.com
MD: David Wickham
- Chefs in the City; Cannabis from the Chemist; Interpol's Most Wanted; David Dimbleby's India; Quest for the Lost Civilisation

Infonation
020 7598 0273
mail@infonation.org.uk
www.infonation.org.uk
MD: Ron Blythe
- Under One Umbrella; Protected Meal Times; Challenge UK

International Media Productions (IMP)
020 8690 9674
improductions@tiscali.co.uk
www.improductions.co.uk
Producer, director: Paul Moody
- Arriva; Tiny Lives; A Beacon for Culture

ITN Factual
020 7430 4511
itn.factual@itn.co.uk
www.itn.co.uk
Head of ITN Factual: Philip Armstrong
- Reign of Terror; Europe's Richest; Madam Cyn's Home Movies; Travels with Diana; The First Head Transplant

Jay Media
01270 884453
media@jaymedia.co.uk
www.jaymedia.co.uk
MD: Nigel Jay
• Skill City; Manchester Evening News;
  Preston City Council; Mersey Family
  Business Awards; UK Trade &
  Investment; Manchester City
  Council; Scope

The Jim Henson Company
020 7428 4000
fanmail@henson.com
www.henson.com
CEOs: Brian Henson, Lisa Henson
• Muppet series; Aliens in the Family;
  Bear in the Big Blue House; Sesame
  Street

Juniperblue
020 7479 4812
richard@juniperblue.com
www.juniperblue.com
MD: Richard Moore
• Tate — Henry Moore Recumbent
  Figure; Marine Conservation Society;
  Good Beach Guide; Wild Battlefields
  Wolf and Polar Bear; Allied Domecq-
  Courvoisier XO; Turtles In Trouble

Keo Films
020 7490 3580
news@keofilms.com
www.keofilms.com
MD: Andrew Palmer
• River Cottage Series; Surviving
  Extremes; The Great Race; Save
  Lullingstone Castle

Kudos
020 7812 3270
info@kudosproductions.co.uk
www.kudosproductions.co.uk
MDs: Stephen Garrett, Jane
Featherstone
• Spooks; Life on Mars; Hustle;
  Pleasureland; Comfortably Numb;
  Confidence Lab

Landmark Films
01865 297220
information@landmarkfilms.com
www.landmarkfilms.com
MD: Nick O'Dwyer
• Strangest Hotel In Britain; Sleep
  Clinic; Animal Addicts; Big Red Bus

Landseer Productions
020 7485 7333
db@landseerfilms.com
www.landseerfilms.com
MD and producer: Derek Bailey

Leopard Films
0870 420 4232
enquiry@leopardfilms.com
www.leopardfilms.com
MD: Susie Field
• Car Booty; Cash in the Attic; Money
  Spinners; Elvis Mob; Stately Suppers;
  Found

Liberty Bell Productions
Newcastle: 0191 222 1200
London: 020 7598 7255
info@libertybell.tv
www.libertybell.tv
MD: Stuart Prebble; head of features:
Judith Holder
• Grumpy Old Men; Grumpy Old
  Women; Victoria Wood's Big Fat
  Documentary; Stella's Story; For the
  Benefit of Mr Parris; Heroes for Six
  Minutes; After They Were Famous —
  Grease; Stars Reunited; National
  Trust: National Treasures; Three
  Men In A Bed

Libra Television
0161 236 5599
hq@libratelevision.com
www.libratelevision.com
MDs: Madeline Wiltshire, Louise Lynch
• Citizen Power; How to be a Bully;
  Copycat Kids; Road Safety; Sorted 2;
  Curriculum Bites RE; Exploring
  Beliefs; History Busters

Little Bird
00 353 1 613 1710
info@littlebird.ie
www.littlebird.ie
Co Chairmen: James Mitchell,
Jonathan Cavendish
• Bridget Jones 2 — The Edge of Reason;
  Trauma; Churchill the Hollywood
  Years; Anner House; Uncle Max

Loose Moose
020 7287 3821
info@loosemoose.net
www.loosemoose.net
MD: Glenn Holberton
• Peperami; Chips Ahoy!; Brisk Iced
  Tea; Alone Amongst Friends; League
  of Gentlemen; Thunder Pig

Lupus Films
020 7419 0997
info@lupusfilms.net
www.lupusfilms.net
MDs: Camilla Deakin, Ruth Fielding
• Little Wolf's Book of Badness; Wilde
  Stories; Little Wolf's Adventure
  Academy; Mia, Cool Hunter

Macmillan Media
0870 350 2150
info@macmillanmedia.co.uk
www.macmillanmedia.co.uk
MD: Michael Macmillan
• Corporate video

Malachite
01790 763538
info@malachite.co.uk
www.malachite.co.uk
MD: Charles Mapleston
• Fiore; Children of the Mafia; Dressing
  up for the Carnival — a Portrait of
  Carol Shields; Cities With A Future?

Maverick Television
Birmingham: 0121 771 1812
London: 020 7383 2727
mail@mavericktv.co.uk
www.mavericktv.co.uk
MD: Jim Sayer
• Ten Years Younger; Celebrity
  Disfigurement; How to Look Good
  Naked; Embarrassing Illnesses

Maya Vision International
020 7796 4842
john@mayavisionint.com
www.mayavisionint.com
Producer and director: Rebecca Dobbs
• Hitler's Search for the Holy Grail;
  Conquistadors; In Search of
  Shakespeare; Two Moons; In Search of
  Myths and Heroes; The Story Of India

Mentorn
020 7258 6700
mentorn@mentorn.co.uk
www.mentorn.co.uk
MD: Steve Anderson
• Robot Wars; Question Time;
  30 minutes; Body Shock; Big Ideas
  that Change the World

Mint Productions
028 9024 0555
Belfast: 028 9024 0555
Dublin: 00 353 1 491 3333
info@mint.ie
www.mint.ie
Executive producers: Steve Carson,
Miriam O' Callaghan
• Abu Hamza; Two Day Coup;
  De Lorean; Workers Strike; Crash;
  Emmet; All the Queen's Men;
  Who Kidnapped Shergar?

Monkey
020 7749 3110
info@monkeykingdom.com
www.monkeykingdom.com
MD: Dom Loehnis
• What Sadie Did Next; He's Starsky
  I'm Hutch; The Charlotte Church
  Show; Girls Aloud: Off The Record

Multi Media Arts
0161 374 5566
info@mmarts.com
www.mmarts.com
MD: Michael Spencer
• Powerhouse; The Blizzard of Odd;
  Reality Bites; Supporting Acts; Icons;
  The Real Middle Earth

Mute Marmalade
020 7449 2552
info@mutemarmalade.com
www.mutemarmalade.com
MD: Jonathan Bentata
• Black Soles; The Runner; Making
  Mistakes

Nexus Productions
020 7749 7500
info@nexusproductions.com
www.nexusproductions.com
MD: Chris O'Reilly
• Honda; Vodafone; Thunderbirds;
  iToy; Coca Cola; Franz Ferdinand;
  Coldcut; Cravendale

Objective Productions
020 7202 2300
info@objectiveproductions.com
www.objectiveproductions.net
MDs: Andrew O'Connor, Michael Vine
• Derren Brown: Trick of the Mind;
  Peep Show; Dirty Tricks; Balls of
  Steel; Greatest TV Moments

October Films
020 7284 6868
info@octoberfilms.co.uk
www.octoberfilms.co.uk
MD: Denman Rooke
• *The Insurgency; True Horror with Anthony Head; Srebrenica: Never Again?; Godless In America; She Stole My Foetus*

Open Mind Productions
0845 890 9192
enquiries@openmind.co.uk
www.openmind.co.uk
Executive producer: Roland Tongue
• *Paz; The Shiny Show; The Number Crew; Numberjacks; Mathmateers; Webwhizz; Word Machine*

Optomen
020 7967 1234
otv@optomen.com
www.optomen.com
MD: Patricia Llewellyn
• *Ramsay's Kitchen Nightmares; The F Word; Jump London; Japanese Schoolgirls*

Outline Productions
020 7428 1560
mail@outlineproductions.co.uk
www.outlineproductions.co.uk
MDs: Helen Veale, Laura Mansfield
• *House of Tiny Tearaways; Mongrel Nation; Homefront; Violent Nation; Conspiracies On Trial*

ORTV
020 8614 7200
reception@ortv.co.uk
www.ortv.co.uk
MD: Christopher Mitchell
• *John McCarthy – Out of the Shadows; Heart of the Lioness; Saddam's Iraq; The Elephant Story*

Oxford Film And Television
020 7483 3637
email@oftv.co.uk
www.oftv.co.uk
Creative director: Nicholas Kent
• *Lionheart – The Crusade; Second Generation (C4); Superfly, Terry Jones' Medieval Tales, National Trust (BBC); The Spectator Affair; Vic Reeves: Rogues Gallery; Building Britain; 2003 Visions Of Space*

Paladin Invision
020 7348 1950
clive@pitv.com
www.pitv.com
MDs: William Cran, Clive Syddall
• *Commanding Heights; Do You Speak American; Dark Star; All Or Nothing At All: The Life of Frank Sinatra*

Pepper's Ghost Productions
020 8546 4900
enquiries@peppersghost.com
www.peppersghost.com
MD: Paul Michael
• *Tiny Planets; Policecat Fuzz; Bus Stop; Kingfisher Tailor*

Pesky
020 7703 2080
hodge@pesky.com
www.pesky.com
Partners: David Hodgson, Clare Underwood
• *Stress Maniacs; Amazing Adrenalini Brothers; MissyMiss; Invisible INK; CyberPest*

Pilot Film and TV Productions
020 8960 2771
info@pilot.co.uk
www.pilotguides.com
Director: Ian Cross
• *Globe Trekker; Pilot Guides; Planet Food; Ian Wright Live; Bazaar*

Pioneer Productions
020 8748 0888
pioneer@pioneertv.com
www.pioneertv.com
MD: Stuart Carter
• *Naked Science; Danger Man; Tycoon Toys; The Bible Revolution*

Presentable
029 2057 5729
all@presentable.co.uk
www.presentable.co.uk
MD: Megan Stuart
• *Poker Nations Cup, Late Night Poker, Wales: The Making of a People, Family Detectives*

Prism Entertainment
020 8969 1212
info@prism-e.com
www.prismentertainment.co.uk
MDs: Mike Crosby, Amelia Johnson
• *The Stables; FAQ series 3; Beat the Cyborgs; PXG; Star Munchies; Invention SOS*

The Producers
020 7636 4226
info@theproducersfilms.co.uk
www.theproducersfilms.co.uk
MDs: Jenny Edwards, Jeanna Polley
• *Belonging; Seeing Red; The Politician's Wife; Air City; My Brilliant Life*

Quickfire Media
0117 946 6838
info@quickfiremedia.com
www.quickfiremedia.com
MD: Mark Fielder
• *The Bobby Moore Story – The Secret Life of a Superhero; In the Footsteps of Churchill; Dispatches: Barrack Room Bullies; Natural World; Wolves of the Barren Lands*

Raw Charm
029 2064 1511
enquiries@rawcharm.tv
www.rawcharm.tv
MD: Kate Jones-Davies
• *War Stories; Grave Detectives; Simon Weston's War Heroes; The Weston Front*

Real Life Media Productions
0113 237 1005
info@reallife.co.uk
www.reallife.co.uk
MD: Simon Schofield
• *Mum, I'm a Muslim; Baby Baby; Britain's Most Dangerous Prisoner; Great British Muslim; China: Going For Gold*

Red Green and Blue Company
020 8749 3354
max@rgbco.com
www.rgbco.com
Directors: Max Whitby, Cathy Collis
• *DNA Interactive*

Red Kite Animations
0131 554 0060
info@redkite-animation.com
www.redkite-animation.com
MD: Ken Anderson
• *The Secret World of Benjamin Bear; The Loch Ness Kelpie; Wilf the Witch's Dog; The Imp; BBC Radio Scotland*

Red Production Company
0161 827 2530
info@redlimited.co.uk
www.redproductioncompany.com
MD: Andrew Critchley
• *Conviction; Jane Hall; Mine All Mine; New Street Law; The Mark Of Cain*

Reef Television
020 7836 8595
mail@reeftv.com
www.reef.tv
MD: Richard Farmbrough
• *Sun, Sea & Bargain Spotting; Put Your Money Where Your House Is; Foreign Exchange; Uncharted Territory; The People's Museum; My Favourite Garden*

Renting Eyeballs Entertainment
020 7437 4188
entertainment@rentingeyeballs.com
www.rentingeyeballs.com
MD: Mark Maco
• *Commercials, promos, brand television, motion pictures*

Resource Base
023 8023 6806
jane@resource-base.co.uk
www.resource-base.co.uk
MD: Karen Gilchrist, Hilary Durman
• *VEE-TV; Without You; World of Difference; Lion Mountain; Who Cares?*

Ricochet Films
020 7251 6966
mail@ricochet.co.uk
www.ricochet.co.uk
MD: Nick Southgate
• *Supernanny; Living in the Sun; Flying Heavy Metal; How Not to Decorate; Risking It All; Mirror, Signal, Manoeuvre; Big Wide World; Sex In Court*

Ronin Entertainment
020 7734 3884
mail@ronintv.com
www.ronintv.com
MDs: Richard Hearsey, Robin Greene
• *The Impressionable Jon Culshaw; Fort Boyard; It's a Knockout; Alter Ego; Seefeld*

RS Productions
0191 224 4301
info@rsproductions.co.uk
www.rsproductions.co.uk
MD: Mark Lavender
• *Frozen; Elephants and Angels; Laughter When We're Dead; Thereby Hangs a Tale*

Sally Head Productions
020 8607 8730
admin@shpl.demon.co.uk
MD: Sally Head
• *Forefathers; Plastic Man; Tipping The Velvet; The Cry; Mayor of Casterbridge; The Return; Fingersmith; A Good Murder*

Samson Films
00 353 1 667 0533
info@samsonfilms.com
www.samsonfilms.com
MD: David Collins
• *Co-producer: Blind Flight; Honeymooners; Abduction Club; Most Fertile Man in Ireland. Feature development: Mir Friends; Immortal; Havoc*

Scream Films
020 8995 8255
info@screamfilms.co.uk
www.screamfilms.co.uk
MD: Susie Dark
• *Famous and Frightened; Dale Winton's Wedding; Terror Alert*

Screenhouse Productions
0113 266 8881
info@screenhouse.co.uk
www.screenhouse.co.uk
Chief executive: Barbara Govan
• *Star Date; Science Shack; Snapshot; Timewatch: The Hidden Children*

Seventh Art Productions
01273 777678
info@seventh-art.com
www.seventh-art.com
MD: Phil Grabsky
• *Tim Marlow on … Edward Hopper; Easter in Art; Pelé – World Cup Hero; Great Artists II; The Boy Who Plays on the Buddhas of Bamiyan; In Search of Mozart*

Shed Productions
020 7239 1010
shed@shedproductions.com
www.shedproductions.com
MD: Brian Park
• *Footballers Wives; Bad Girls; Waterloo Road; Supernanny*

SMG Productions
0141 300 3000
website@smgproductions.tv
www.smgproductions.tv
MD: Elizabeth Partyka
• *Taggart; Club Reps: The Workers; Good Bye Mr Chips; Medics of the Glen; Squeak!; How 2*

Slinky Pictures
020 7247 6444
info@slinkypics.com
www.slinkypics.com
MD: Maria Manton
• *Who I Am and What I Want; Look For Me; Stalk; The Census Taker*

Smith And Watson Productions
01803 863033
info@smithandwatson.com
www.smithandwatson.com
MD: Nick Smith
• *Building a Dream; Bill Wyman's Blues; A Story of Peter Rabbit and Beatrix Potter; Joss Stone in Uganda*

Smoking Dogs Films
020 7249 6644
info@smokingdogsfilms.com
www.smokingdogsfilms.com
MD: David Lawson
• *Urban Soul – Making of Modern R&B; The Wonderful World of Louis Armstrong; Goldie – When Satin Returns*

So Television
020 7960 2000
info@sotelevision.co.uk
www.sotelevision.co.uk
Director: Jon Magnusson
• *Comedy Lab; V Graham Norton; Bigger Picture; The Graham Norton Show; School's Out 2*

Specific Films
020 7580 7476
info@specificfilms.com
MD: Michael Hamlyn
• *Last Seduction II; Paws; Mr Reliable; Priscilla, Queen of the Desert; The Proposition*

Spire Films
01865 371979
mail@spirefilms.co.uk
www.spirefilms.co.uk
MD: David Willcock
• *Delia Smith; Romans*

Stampede
01582 727330
dave@stampede.co.uk
www.stampede.co.uk
MD: Mike Chamberlain
• *Putting the Fun in Fundamental; Lin and Ralph – A Love Story; Fierce People; Before The Flood*

Sunset + Vine
020 7478 7400
reception@sunsetvine.co.uk
www.sunsetvine.co.uk
MD: John Leach
• *Channel 4 Cricket; Gillette World Sport; Rad; European Poker Tour; Football on Five; John Barnes Football Night*

Sunstone Films
sunstonefilms@aol.com
www.sunstonefilms.co.uk
• *Before Columbus; Lords of the Maya; Warhorse; Gladiators: The Brutal Truth; It Ain't Necessarily So*

Talent Television
020 7421 7800
entertainment@talenttv.com
www.talenttv.com
Creative director: John Kaye Cooper
• *Best of Friends; Casino, Casino; Test The Nation; The Man With Eighty Wives*

Telemagination
020 7434 1551
mail@tmation.co.uk
www.telemagination.co.uk
MD & head of studio: Beth Parker
• *Pongwiffy; Little Ghosts; Something Else; Metalheads; Cramp Twins; Heidi*

Television Junction
0121 248 4466
info@televisionjunction.co.uk
www.televisionjunction.co.uk
MDs: Paul Davies, Yvonne Davies
• *Double Act; Seeing Science; Think About It; The Way We Were*

Wish Films
020 8324 2308
info@wishfilms.com
www.wishfilms.com
MD: Helen Cadwallader
• *Jim Jam and Sunny*

Ten Alps TV
020 7878 2311
info@tenalps.com
www.tenalps.com
MD: Nigel Dacre
• *Peaches Geldof: Inside the Mind of a Teenager; Jeremy Vine Meets… series 2; Geldof on Fathers; Geldof on Divorce; 50 Greatest Goals; Top Dog*

Tern Television
01224 211123
Glasgow: 0141 243 5658
Belfast: 028 9099 8163
info@terntv.com
www.terntv.com
MDs: David Strachan, Gwyneth Hardy
• *Chancers; Fraserburgh; 2003 Reloaded; Mapman; Beachgrove Garden; The Greenmount Garden; The Woman Who Ate Scotland*

Testimony Films
0117 925 8589
mail@testimonyfilms.com
Executive producer: Steve Humphries
• *Lovechild; Sex in a Cold Climate; Britain's Boy Soldiers; Some Liked It Hot*

Tigress Productions
Bristol: 0117 933 5600
London: 020 7434 4411
general@tigressproductions.co.uk
general@tigressbristol.co.uk
www.tigressproductions.co.uk
MD: Andrew Jackson
• *Snakemaster; The Jeff Corwin Experience; Dolphin Murders; The Science of Combat; Dartmoor Zoo, Out Of This World*

Torpedo
01443 231989
info@torpedoltd.co.uk
www.torpedoltd.co.uk
Chairman: Mark Jones
• *Fishlock's Sea Stories II; Jigsaw III; V.E.T.S*

Touch Productions
01225 484666
enquiries@touchproductions.co.uk
www.touchproductions.co.uk
MD: Malcolm Brinkworth
• *Mind Shock: Transplanting Minds; Separating Twins; Angela's Dying Wish; British Made; Paris In The Sun; Brit School; The Four-Year-Old Boy Who Ran 40 Miles; Human Footprint*

TransAtlantic Films
020 8735 0505
Hereford: 01497 831800
mail@transatlanticfilms.com
www.transatlanticfilms.com
MD: Corisande Albert
• *Amazing Animal Adaptors; Extreme Body Parts; Science of Love*

Turn On Television
0161 247 7700
mail@turnontv.co.uk
www.turnontv.co.uk
MD: Angela Smith
• *Unlikely Lovers; Baby's Birthday; Inside Criminal Minds*

TV6
020 7610 0266
mail@tv6.co.uk
www.tv6.co.uk
MD: Richard Reisz
• *Horizon: Percy Pilcher's Flying Machines; Horizon: King Solomon's Tablet of Stone; Landscape Mysteries; Into the Great Pyramid; Tutankhamun's Fireball*

Unique Communications Group
020 7605 1200
ucg@uniquegroup.co.uk
info@uniquecomms.com
www.uniquecomms.com
MD: Michael Hurll
• *British Comedy Awards 2003; Stars Behind Bars; Harley Street; I'm the Answer; Survivors; Make Me Rich*

Vera Productions
020 7436 6116
cree@vera.co.uk
MD: Geoff Atkinson
• *Bremner Bird and Fortune*

Vivum Intelligent Media
020 7729 2749
livewire@vivum.net
www.vivum.net
MD: Nick Rosen
• *2003 World Trade Centre series; high-brow factual content*

Waddell Media
028 9042 7646
info@waddellmedia.com
www.waddellmedia.com
MD: Brian Waddell
• *Futureweapons; When Sports Stars See Red; Ireland's Richest; Getaways; How Long Will You Live?; Belfast Zoo; The Formal; Wanted Farmers; House Traders*

Wag TV
020 7688 1711
post@wagtv.com
www.wagtv.com
MD: Martin Durkin
• *Divine Designs; Dave Courtney's Underworld; The Great Scientist; Kings of Construction; Industrial Revelations; Face of Britain; How Do They Do It?*

Wild Dream Films
01432 840732
mail@wild-dream.com
www.wild-dream.com
MD: Stuart Clarke
• *Map Makers; Ancient Discoveries series 1/2*

Wild Rover Productions
028 9050 0980
enquiries@wild-rover.com
www.wild-rover.com
MD: Philip Morrow
• *Just For Laughs; A Day In The Westlife of Shane; Would You Pass the Eleven Plus?; Get Smarter in a Week*

Wilton Films
020 7749 7282
paul@wiltonfilms.com
tania@wiltonfilms.com
www.wiltonfilms.com
MD: Paul Mitchell
• *Hotspots; Chechnya; The Alternative Rock 'n' Roll Years; Lords of the Spin; Future for Lebanon; How to Make a Revolution; How Putin Came to Power*

Windfall Films
020 7251 7676
postmaster@windfallfilms.com
www.windfallfilms.com
MD: David Dugan
• *D-Day: The Ultimate Conflict; The Great Escape Revealed; Men of Iron*

World Of Wonder
020 7428 3444
wow@worldofwonder.co.uk
www.worldofwonder.net
Chief executive: Fenton Bailey
• *Matt's Old Masters; Housebusters; The Art Show — Spoils of War*

World Wide Pictures
020 7434 1121
info@worldwidegroup.ltd.uk
www.worldwidegroup.ltd.uk
MDs: Chris Courtenay-Taylor
• *Bad Girls; Road To Democracy; A Never-Ending Discovery: Moore In China*

World's End Productions
020 7386 4900
info@worldsendproductions.com
www.worldsendproductions.com
MDs: Jim Philips, Jerry Drew
• *Shoot Me; Going Down to South Park; Dead Casual; Live at Johnny's; Fighting Talk. Co-production with Celador: Johnny & Denise*

Zeal Television
020 8780 4600
info@zealtv.net
www.zealtv.net
Chief executive: Peter Christiansen
• *Building the Dream; Britain's Hardest; Resistance; Demolition; Super Human; Sushi TV*

Zeppotron
0870 333 1700
contact@zeppotron.com
www.zeppotron.com
Creative directors: Neil Webster, Ben Caudell, Charlie Brooker
• *People's Book of Records; Playing Tricks; The Cowboy Trap; Space Cadets*

TV and film studios

124 Facilities
124 Horseferry Road,
London SW1P 2TX
020 7306 8040
www.124.co.uk
Part of the Channel 4 group. General manager: Tony Chamberlain; studio managers: Tony Kibbles, Tim Moulson

3 Mills Studios
Three Mill Lane, London E3 3DU
020 7363 3336
info@3mills.com
www.3mills.com
MD: Daniel Dark; studio manager: Jason Taylor

3sixtymedia
Quay Street, Manchester M60 9EA
0161 839 0360
enquiry@3sixtymedia.com
www.the-manchester-studios.tv
Director of Northern Resources: Paul Bennett

400 Company
B3 The Workshops,
2A Askew Crescent, Shepherds Bush, London W12 9DP
020 8746 1400
info@the400.co.uk
www.the400.co.uk
Studio manager: Christian Riov

Air Studios
Lyndhurst Hall, Lyndhurst Road,
London, NW3 5NG
020 7426 5100
info@airstudios.com
www.airstudios.com
Contact: Garry Williams. Music and film scoring, post production

Arqiva
Crawley Court, Crawley,
Winchester SO21 2QA
01962 823434
press.office@arqiva.com
www.arqiva.com
CEO: Tom Bennie. Formerly NTL Broadcast

Ascent Media
1 Stephen Street, London W1T 1AL
020 7691 6000
www.ascentmedia.co.uk
Studio manager: Tony Shepherd

APTN
The Interchange, Oval Road,
Camden Lock, London NW1 7DZ
020 7482 7580
aptnbookings@ap.org
www.aptn.com
Studio manager: James Lewis

Ardmore Studios
Herbert Road, Bray,
Co Wicklow, Ireland
00 353 1 286 2971
kevin@ardmore.ie
www.ardmore.ie
MD: Kevin Moriarty

BBC Elstree Centre
Clarendon Road, Borehamwood,
Herts WD6 1JF
020 8228 7102
www.bbc.co.uk
Senior facility manager: Sue Spree

BBC TV Centre Studios
Wood Lane, Shepherds Bush,
London W12 7RJ
020 8743 8000
bbcresources@bbc.co.uk
www.bbcresources.co.uk
Principal facilities manager: Keith Clark

Bray Studios
Down Place, Water Oakley,
Windsor, Berks SL4 5UG
01628 622111
www.brayfilmstudios.com
General manager: Nathan Hendricks

Broadley Productions
Broadley House, 48 Broadley
Terrace, London NW1 6LG
020 7725 5858
markfrench@broadley.tv
www.broadley.tv
MD and studio manager: Mark French

Canalot Production Studios
222 Kensal Road, London W10 5BN
020 8960 8580
eliza.davis@workspacegroup.co.uk
www.workspacegroup.co.uk
*Studio manager: Barbara
Achemphong*

Capital Studios
13 Wandsworth Plain,
London SW18 1ET
020 8877 1234
bobbi.johnstone
    @capitalstudios.com
www.capitalstudios.co.uk
Studio manager: Bobbi Johnstone

Central Studios
Location House, 5 Dove Lane,
Bristol BS2 9HP
0117 955 4777
info@centralstudios.co.uk
www.centralstudios.co.uk
Studio manager: Dave Garbe

Centre Stage
8-10 Colebrook Place,
London N1 8HZ
020 7288 4599
saul@centrestagestudios.co.uk
www.centrestagestudios.co.uk
*MD: Saul Barrington; studio manager:
Toby Gair*

**CTS and Lansdowne Recording
Studios**
Lansdowne House, Lansdowne
Road, London W11 3LP
020 8846 9444
info@cts-lansdowne.co.uk
www.cts-lansdowne.co.uk
Studio manager: Chris Dibble

Desisti Lighting (UK)
15 Old Market Street, Thetford,
Norfolk IP24 2EQ
01842 752909
info@desisti.co.uk
www.desisti.co.uk
Director: John Reay-Young

Ealing Studios
Ealing Green, London W5 5EP
020 8567 6655
info@ealingstudios.com
www.ealingstudios.com
Studio manager: Jeremy Pelzer

East Side Studios
40A River Road, Barking,
Essex IG11 0DW
020 8507 7572
info@eastsidestudios.com
www.eastsidestudios.com
Studio manager: Susan Noy

Elstree Film Studios
Shenley Road, Borehamwood,
Herts WD6 1JG
020 8953 1600
info@elstreefilmstudios.co.uk
www.elstreefilmstudios.co.uk
Directors: Eden Lee

Enfys
Unit 31 Portanmoor Road,
East Moors, Cardiff,
South Glamorgan CF2 5HB, Wales
029 2049 9988
mail@enfys.tv
www.enfys.tv
Studio manager: Sarah-Jane Salmon

Fountain TV Studios
128 Wembley Park Drive,
Wembley, Middlesex HA9 8HQ
020 8900 5800
everyone@ftv.co.uk
www.ftv.co.uk
Studio manager: Tony Edwards

Greenford Studios
5-11 Taunton Road,
Metropolitan Centre, Greenford,
Middlesex UB6 8UQ
020 8575 7300
studios@panavision.co.uk
www.panavision.co.uk
Studio manager: Kate Tufano

Handstand Productions
13 Hope Street, Liverpool L1 9BH
0151 708 7441
info@handstand-uk.com
www.handstand-uk.com
*Director producers: Han Duijvendak,
Nick Stanley*

Holborn Studios
49/50 Eagle Wharf Road,
London N1 7ED
020 7490 4099
studiomanager@
    holborn-studios.com
www.holborn-studios.co.uk
Studio manager: Billy McCartney

The Hospital
24 Endell Street, Covent Garden,
London WC2H 9HQ
020 7170 9112
studio@thehospital.co.uk
www.thehospital.co.uk
Studio manager: Anne Marie Phelan

IAC
Moorside Road, Winchester,
Hampshire S23 7US
01962 873000
info@iacl.co.uk
www.iacl.co.uk
Studio manager: Ian Rich

ICA Theatre
The Mall, London SW1Y 5AH
020 7930 0493
info@ica.org.uk
www.ica.org.uk
Technical director: Lee Curran

Island Studios
9-11 Alliance Road, Acton,
London W3 0RA
020 8956 5600
info@islandstudios.net
www.islandstudios.net
MD and studio manager: Steve Guidici

London Studios
London Television Centre,
Upper Ground Floor,
London SE1 9LT
020 7737 8888
sales@londonstudios.co.uk
www.londonstudios.co.uk
*MD: Debbie Hills; head of sales:
Kathy Schulz*

Maidstone Studios
New Cut Road, Vinters Park,
Maidstone, Kent ME14 5NZ
01622 691111
info@maidstonestudios.com
www.maidstonestudios.com
*MD: Geoff Miles; liaison manager:
Denise Buckland*

Metro Imaging
76 Clerkenwell Road,
London EC1M 5TN
020 7865 0000
info@metroimaging.co.uk
www.metroimaging.co.uk
Studio manager: Steve Jackson

Millbank Studios
4 Millbank, London SW1P 3JA
020 7233 2020
production@itv.co.uk
www.millbank-studios.co.uk
*Production manager:
Caroline Bloomfield*

Millennium Studios
5 Elstree Way, Borehamwood,
Herts WD6 1SF
020 8236 1400
info@millenniumstudios.co.uk
www.millenniumstudios.co.uk
*MD: Ronan Willson; studio manager:
Toni Cullip*

Molinare Studios
34 Fouberts Place, London W1F 7PX
020 7478 7000
bookings@molinare.co.uk
www.molinare.co.uk
Studio manager: Mick Harley

Park Royal Studios
1 Barretts Green Road,
London NW10 7AE
020 8965 9778
info@parkroyalstudios.com
www.parkroyalstudios.com
*Studio manager: Francois van de
Langkruis*

Phaebus Communications
The Brewery Tower,
The Deva Centre, Trinity Way,
Manchester M3 7BF
0161 605 9999
solutions@phaebus.co.uk
www.phaebus.co.uk
Studio manager: Steve Bettridge

Pinewood Studios
Pinewood Road, Iver Heath,
Bucks SL0 0NH
01753 651700
info@pinewoodgroup.com
www.pinewoodgroup.com
Studio manager: Peter Hicks

**Production House NI/ Stage
Services North**
Unit 5, Prince Regent
Retail Park, Prince Regent Road,
Belfast BT5 6QP
028 9079 8999
info@productionhouse.net
Studio manager: Neil Lewis

RC Film & TV Set Construction
Unit C11 Dundonald Enterprise
Park, Carrowreagh Road,
Dundonald BT16 1QT,
Northern Ireland
028 9055 7557
MD: Russell Fulton

Riverside Studios
Crisp Road, Hammersmith,
London W6 9RL
020 8237 1000
info@riversidestudios.co.uk
www.riversidestudios.co.uk
*Centre manager: Alex Cotterill, Artistic
director: William Burrett-Coutts*

Sands Film Studios
Grices Wharf, 119 Rotherhithe
Street, London SE16 4NF
020 7231 2209
OStockman@sandsfilms.co.uk
www.sandsfilms.co.uk
MD: Olivier Stockman

Shepperton Studios
Studios Road, Shepperton,
Middlesex TW17 0QD
01932 562611
info@pinewoodgroup.com
www.pinewoodgroup.com
Studio manager: David Godfrey

Studio
Cabul Road, London SW11 2PR
020 7228 5228
thestudio@filmed.com
www.the-studio.co.uk
Studio manager: Gemma Masters

Sumners
Suite 401, Barclay House,
35 Whitworth Street West,
Manchester M1 5NG
0161 228 0330
andy@sumners.co.uk
www.sumners.co.uk
*MDs: Janet Sumner, Andy Sumner;
technical manager: Brian Hardman;
facilities manager: Nicola Stanou*

Technicolor Network Services
Chiswick Park, Building 12,
566 Chiswick High Road,
London W4 5AN
020 8100 1000
www.technicolor.com
Facilities manager: Marco Bellini

Teddington Studios
Broom Road, Teddington,
Middlesex TW11 9NT
020 8977 3252
info@teddington.tv
www.teddington.co.uk
Studio manager: Ray Gearing

The Worx
10 Heathmans Road, Fulham,
London SW6 4TJ
020 7371 9777
enquiries@theworx.co.uk
www.theworx.co.uk
MDs: Jackie Mallory, Jonathan Mallory

Twickenham Studios
The Barons, St Margarets,
Twickenham, Middlesex TW1 2AW
020 8607 8888
caroline@twickenhamstudios.com
www.twickenhamstudios.com
Studio manager: Caroline Tipple

VFX Company
Dukes Island Studios, Dukes Road,
London W3 0SL
020 8956 5674
info@thevfxco.co.uk
www.thevfxco.co.uk
*Operations manager: Digna Nigoumi;
producer: Rob Delicata*

Waterfall Studios
2 Silver Road, Wood Lane,
London W12 7SG
020 8746 2000
enquiries@waterfall-studios.com
www.waterfall-studios.com
Studio manager: Ann Fairclough

Post-production

3sixtymedia
Quay Street, Manchester M60 9EA
0161 839 0360
enquiry@3sixtymedia.com
www.the-manchester-studios.tv
*Independent. Effects and virtual reality.
Post-production manager: John Mariner*
• *Island at War; Tonight with Trevor
MacDonald; Blue Murder; Vincent;
Coronation Street*

4x4
First Floor, 21 Ormeau Avenue,
Belfast BT2 8HD
028 9027 1950
4@4x4post.com
www.4x4post.com
*Independent. Effects; graphics;
commercials; audio. Directors: Katy
Jackson; Paula Campbell; Alan Perry;
Jonathan Featherstone*
• *Disability commercials; BTNI
commercial; Just for a Laugh*

422 Manchester
4th Floor, South Central,
11 Peter Street, Manchester M2 5QR
0161 839 6080
production@422.tv
www.422.tv
*Animation, graphics, commercials,
special effects and audio. Production
director: Richard Wallwork*
• *Vimto; Pingu; Mastermind;
A Question of Sport*

422 South
St John's Court, Whiteladies Road,
Bristol BS8 2QY
0117 946 7222
debbiet@422.com
www.422.tv
*Factual television and animation,
digital effects, commercials
production. Production director:
Andy Davies-Coward*
• *The British Isles – A Natural History;
Journey of Life; Royal British Legion*

Ascent Media Camden
13 Hawley Crescent,
London NW1 8NP
020 7284 7900
www.ascent-media.co.uk
*Nine other sites. Film processing
laboratory; video; tape; DVD*
• *Poirot; Auf Wiedersehen Pet; Hustle*

Anvil
Denham Media Park,
North Orbital Road, Denham,
Uxbridge, Middlesex UB9 5HL
020 8799 0555
mike.anscombe@thomson.net
www.anvilpost.com
*Audio. Part of Technicolor (Thomson
Group). Studio manager: Mike Anscombe*
• *The Brief; Ultimate Force; Midsomer
Murders; Like Father, Like Son; Doc
Martin; Auf Wiedersehen Pet; Heartless*

Arena P3
74 Newman Street, London W1T 3EL
020 7436 4360
edit@arenap3.tv
www.arenap3.tv
Part of 2D video facilities. Effects;
audio; documentaries; comedy.
MD: Juliet Gonsales
• *Bo' Selecta!; Trouble at Top;*
  Scambusters; Brassed-Off Britain

Arion Communications
Global House, Denham Media
Park, North Orbital Road,
Denham, Uxbridge,
Middlesex UB9 5HL
01895 834484
sales@arion.co.uk
www.arion.co.uk
Independent. Telecine; DVD
duplication; editing. MD: Neil Mockler
• *Hitchhiker's Guide to the Galaxy;*
  Basic Instinct 2; Sahara

Barcud Derwen
Cibyn, Caernarfon,
Gwynedd LL55 2BD
01286 684300
Cardiff 029 2061 1515
info@barcudderwen.com
www.barcudderwen.com
Drama, graphics. MD: Tudor Roberts
• *Celebrity Poker; Tracy Beaker series;*
  Mountains and Man

Blue
58 Old Compton Street,
London W1D 4UF
020 7437 2626
info@bluepp.co.uk
www.bluepp.co.uk
VTR Group. Special effects; graphics;
commercial; audio. MD: Simon Briggs
• *Equator; My New Home; Britain's*
  Biggest Spenders; Hellman's
  commercial

Capital FX
3rd Floor, 20 Dering Street,
London W1S 1AJ
020 7493 9998
mark.allen@capital-fx.co.uk
www.capital-fx.co.uk
Independent. Special effects; graphics;
taped film transfer. MD: Mark Allen
• *Harry Potter; Troy; Lord of the Rings*

Cine Wessex
Westway House,
19 St Thomas Street, Winchester,
Hampshire SO23 9HJ
01962 865454
info@cinewessex.co.uk
www.cinewessex.co.uk
Independent. Editing; camera kit and
crew hire; 2D and 3D graphics; VHS,
CD and DVD. Facilities director:
Joe Conman
• *City Gardener; Mappin Murder;*
  Room for Improvement

Clear Cut Pictures
1 Springvale Terrace,
London W14 0AE
020 7605 1700
info@clearcutpictures.com
www.clearcutpictures.com
Sister company Clear Cut Hires.
Graphics and digital rostrum;
video and sound. MD: Jo Beighton
• *Crimewatch; Horizon; Money*
  Programme

The Club Post Couture
35 Bedfordbury, Covent Garden,
London WC2 4DU
020 7759 7100
www.theclubpc.co.uk
Independent. Editing; graphic design;
audio; Avid online/offline; duplication.
MD: Bill Cullen
• *Bum Fights; VTV programme for the*
  Deaf; The Curse of Reality TV; Spooks
  interactive; Little Britain interactive;
  Industrial Revelations

Component
2nd Floor, 5 Berners Mews,
London W1T 3AJ
020 7631 4477
mike@component.co.uk
www.component.co.uk
Independent. Pure graphics. Director:
Mike Kenny
• *Hell's Kitchen; Destination D-Day;*
  Without Prejudice; SAS Jungle; Clive
  Anderson Now; Crimewatch; Wogan
  Now and Then; Ron Manager

Computamatch
117 Wardour Street,
London W1F 0NU
020 7287 1316
edl@computamatch.com
www.ascent-media.co.uk
Part of Ascent Group. Film negative
cutting service. MD: Marilyn Sommer
• *5 Children and It; Guinness; Levi's*

Computer Film Services
66b Unit, York Road, Weybridge,
Surrey KT13 9DY
01932 850034
enquiries@computerfilm.com
www.computerfilm.com
Independent. Digital disc recorders
and post-production systems.
Director: Peter Holland

Concrete
34–35 Dean Street,
London W1D 4PR
020 7439 9080
bookings@concretepost.co.uk
www.concretepost.co.uk
Independent. Audio; graphics;
on/offline editing; sound; MD:
Dave Thompson
• *Brassed off Britain; Blag; Celebrity*
  Penthouse; Car Booty; Monty Don
  Project (BBC)

Crow TV
Shepherds Building East,
Richmond Way, London W14 0DQ
020 7471 7970
jocelyn@crowtv.com
www.crowtv.com
Independent. Graphics; editing for
television; pogle colour grade; online/
offline editing; audio. MD: Jocelyn
Buckley
• *Vincent, The Full Story; South Bank*
  Show; The Challenge; Mediterranean
  Tales

Cut and Run
Cinema House, 93 Wardour Street,
London W1F 0UD
020 7432 9696
editorsuk@cutandrun.co.uk
www.cutandrun.co.uk
Independent. Offline editing. MD:
Simon Gosling
• *Commercials: Castrol; Rimmel;*
  Diet Coke; UPS; Lynx

DB Dubbing
4 St Pauls Road, Clifton, Bristol,
Avon BS8 1LT
0117 904 8210
miles@dbdubbing.tv
Independent. Audio. MD: Miles Harris
• *Secret Nature; Built for the Kill;*
  Eden Project

De Lane Lea
75 Dean Street, London W1D 3PU
020 7432 3800
info@delanelea.com
www.delanelea.com
Part of Ascent group. Sound for post-
production TV and film. Chief
operating officer: Hugh Penalt-Jones
• *Cold Mountain; Harry Potter, the*
  Prisoner of Azkaban; Two Brothers;
  Bond: Casino Royale; Children of
  Man; United 93

DGP
Portland House, 12–13 Greek
Street, London W1D 4DL
020 7734 4501
mail@dgpsoho.co.uk
www.dgpsoho.co.uk
Independent. Editing; graphics; DVD;
authoring. MD: Julian Day
• *Murder City; Yahoo; Friends; The*
  Last Samurai; Lord of the Rings:
  Return of the King; Six Feet Under

DVA Associates
7/8 Campbell Court, Bramley,
Tadley, Hampshire RG26 5EG
01256 882032
info@dva.co.uk
www.dva.co.uk
Independent digital media agency.
Graphics; audio; DVD; commercials.
MD: Barrie Gibson
• *SAS Survival Secrets; Life of David*
  Kelly; Goalrush for Meridian

Evolutions Television
5 Berners Street, London W1T 3LF
020 7580 3333
bookings@evolutionstelevision.com
www.evolutionstelevision.com
Independent. Graphics;
documentaries; commercials; audio.
MD: Simon Kanjee
* *Top of the Pops titles; Jump London;*
  Other People's Houses; Top Gear;
  MTV The Lick; MTV Pimp My Ride

The Farm Group
13 Soho Square, London W1D 3QF
020 7437 6677
info@farmgroup.tv
www.farmgroup.tv
Partner with Home, The Shed and
Uncle. Recently purchased Metro
Broadcast. Online/offline editing;
audio dubbing; grading and editing inc
HD; crewing and equipment rental;
audio and video restoration; DVD
production; webcasting; duplications
and standards conversion. MDs: Nicky
Sargent, Vikki Dunn
* *Dunkirk; Friday night with Jonathan*
  Ross; One Life; X-Factor; EPKs for
  Mr Bean; Rugby World Cup promo;
  NHK various programmes

Films at 59
59 Cotham Hill, Bristol,
Avon BS6 6JR
0117 906 4300
info@filmsat59.com
www.filmsat59.com
Independent. Audio; high definition;
equipment hire; online/offline
dubbing. MD: Gina Lee Fucci
* *Teachers; Big Cat Diary; Building the*
  Dream

Final Cut
55-57 Great Marlborough Street,
London W1F 7JX
020 7556 6300
michelle_c@finalcut-uk.com
www.finalcut-edit.com
Offline editing. Producer: Michelle
Corney
* *Commercials: Sony PlayStation;*
  Mountain; Mercedes "movement";
  Nike

Finishing Post
10, Gilt Way, Giltbrook,
Nottingham, Notts NG16 2GN
0115 945 8800
info@finishing-post.co.uk
www.finishing-post.co.uk
Independent. Graphics; editing; CD/
DVD authoring. MD: Mark Harwood
* *Commercials: Jaguar; Peugeot; Heart*
  of the Country; Carlton Country

Framestore CFC
9 Noel Street, London W1F 8GH
020 7208 2600
info@framestore-cfc.com
www.framestore-cfc.com
Independent. Effects; computer
generated commercials; films.
Chief executive: William Sergeant
* *Thunderbirds; Walking with Sea*
  Monsters

Frontier Post
67 Wells Street, London W1T 3PZ
020 7291 9191
info@frontierpost.co.uk
www.frontierpost.co.uk
Independent. Graphics; audio; online/
offline grading. MD: Neil Hatton
* *Property Dreams; Howard Goodall's*
  20th Century Greats; Pagans of the
  Roman Empire

Fusion Broadcast
26 College Gardens,
Belfast BT9 6BS
028 9066 6664
sales@fusionbroadcast.co.uk
www.fusionbroadcast.co.uk
Independent. Crew supplying.
MD: John Morriffey
* *BBC Northern Ireland; BBC Network*

Future Post Production
25 Noel Street, London W1F 8GX
020 7434 6655
info@futurefilmgroup.com
www.futurefilmgroup.com
Part of Future Films Group. Sound;
two Dolby mix studios. MDs: Tim Levy,
Stephen Margolis
* *King Arthur; Exorcist, The Beginning;*
  Harry Potter 3

Glassworks
33-34 Great Pulteney Street,
London W1F 9NP
020 7434 1182
nina@glassworks.co.uk
www.glassworks.co.uk
Independent. Special effects; animation;
all online. MD: Hector Macleod
* *Dream Keeper; Bjork's All is Full of*
  Love; Sprite commercials

Goldcrest Post-Production
1 Lexington Street, 36-44 Brewer
Street, London W1F 9LX
020 7437 7972
mail@goldcrestpost.co.uk
www.goldcrestpost.co.uk
Independent. Sound editing
MD: Keith Williams
* *Cold Mountain; Lord of the Rings,*
  Two Towers; Girl with a Pearl Earring

Golden Square
11 Golden Square, London W1F 9JB
020 7300 3555
info@goldensq.com
www.goldensq.com
Independent. Commercials; special
effects. MD: Phil Gillies
* *Campari; Tomb Raiders; Volkswagen*

Hackenbacker Audio Post
Production
10 Bateman Street,
London W1D 4AQ
020 7734 1324
reception@hackenbacker.com
www.hackenbacker.com
Independent. Audio; sound effects;
films; trailers. MDs: Julian Slater,
Nigel Heath
* *Shaun of the Dead; Girl with a Pearl*
  Earring; Spooks; Hot Fuzz

Hireworks
Pinewood Studios, Pinewood
Road, Iver Heath, Bucks SL0 0NH
0845 257 0500
info@hireworks.tv
www.hireworks.tv
Dry hire post-production equipment
Directors: Mark Cox, Lawrie Read,
Phil Kent
* *Celeb Deck; Glastonbury festival;*
  Liquid News; United 93; After
  Thomas; Miss Potter

Home Post Productions
12-13 Richmond Buildings, Soho,
London W1D 3HG
020 7292 0200
info@homepost.co.uk
www.farmgroup.tv
Part of Farm Group. Graphics; audio;
effects; commercials. MDs: Nicky
Sargent, Vikki Dunn
* *Dunkirk; Friday Night with Jonathan*
  Ross; One Life

Lime
4th Floor, Epatra House, 58-60
Berners Street, London W1T 3NQ
020 7637 3210
james@limepost.co.uk
www.limepost.co.uk
Part of M2 Group. 3D animation; 2D
effects; storyboarding; direction;
studio shooting; graphics. Producer:
Debbie Clark
* *Troy; Q Channel Broadcasting;*
  Waking the Dead; Silent Witness;
  Airwick Sponsorship Campaign;
  MTV; Discovery Channel

Lip Sync Post
123 Wardour Street,
London W1F 0UU
020 7534 9123
info@lipsyncpost.co.uk
www.lipsync.co.uk
Independent. Sound; graphics; editing;
5.1 Dolby ex mixing. MD: Norman Merry
* *Silent Witness; Touch the Void;*
  Trolleywood; Severage; Highland
  of 5; Creep

Liquid TV
1-2 Portland Mews,
London W1F 8JE
020 7437 2623
info@liquid.co.uk
www.liquid.co.uk
Independent. Title branding; special
effects. MD: Asra Alikhan
* *Restoration; Film 2004; Horizon; Troy*

Lola
14-16 Great Portland Street,
London W1W 8BL
020 7907 7878
info@lola-post.com
www.lola-post.com
Independent. Visualeffects;
commercials; films and TV. MDs:
Grahame Andrew, Rob Harvey
* *Troy; 5 Children and It; Ancient*
  Egyptians

M2 Television
Ingestre Court, Ingestre Place,
London W1F 0JL
020 7343 6543
info@m2tv.com
www.m2tv.com
Edit; visual; audio. MD: Tom Jones
• *Revenge; Human Mind;*
  Bodysnatchers, Jane Eyre, Extras

The Machine Room
54–58 Wardour Street,
London W1D 4JQ
020 7734 3433
info@themachineroom.co.uk
www.themachineroom.co.uk
Part of VTR Group. Online editing;
telecine suites; DVD; teramix machine;
archive restoration department.
MD: Luci Weir
• *Love, Actually; Bad Girls; Footballers*
  Wives

Maidstone
New Cut Road, Vintners Park,
Maidstone Kent
01622 684428
sales@maidstonestudios.com
www.maidstonestudios.com
Independent. Edit. Studios hire.
General Manager Kenton Oxley
• *Reeves and Mortimer*

Mediahouse
Hogarth Business Park,
3 Burlington Lane, London W4 2TH
020 8233 5400
info@mediahouse.tv
www.mediahouse.tv
IMG Media Group. Video; graphics;
DVD; transmission studio. Head of
post-production: Karen Mullins
• *Bremner, Bird and Fortune; Planet's*
  Funniest Animals

Men-from-Mars
Unit 6, Walpole Court, Ealing
Green, London W5 5ED
020 8280 9000
info@men-from-mars.com
www.men-from-mars.com
Part of Barcud Derwen. Visual effects
for film and TV. Creative director:
Philip Attfield; production director:
Simon Frame
• *Gladiatress; Chasing Liberty; Jekyll*
  and Hyde; Hamburg Cell; Sons of the
  Wind; De-Lovely; Trial and
  Retribution: Blue Eiderdown

The Mill
40–41 Great Marlborough Street,
London W1F 7JQ
020 7287 4041
info@mill.co.uk
www.mill.co.uk
Independent. Commercials; 3d
animation; edition. MD: Pat Joseph
• *Commercials: Mercedes; Honda; O2*

MGB Facilities
Capital House, Sheepscar Court,
Meanwood Road, Leeds, West
Yorkshire LS7 2BB
0113 243 6868
contact@mgbtv.co.uk
www.mgbtv.co.uk
Independent. Graphics; commercials;
DVD; animation. MD: Mike Gaunt
• *Hasbro commercial; Brazilian*
  Football; DFS Furniture

Molinare
34 Fouberts Place, London W1F 7PX
020 7478 7000
bookings@molinare.co.uk
www.molinare.co.uk
Independent. Graphics; DVD; audio.
MD: Mark Foligno
• *Faking It; Make Me Honest; Poirot*

Moving Picture Company
127 Wardour Street,
London W1F 0NL
020 7434 3100
mpc@moving-picture.com
www.moving-picture.com
Independent. Commercials; effects;
animation; editing. MD: David Jeffers
• *Troy; Dunkirk; Guinness moth*
  commercial, Live Earth, Harry Potter 5

The Sanctuary
6–7 Great Pulteney Street,
London W1F 9NA
020 7434 4133
sales@oasistv.co.uk
www.thesanctuary.tv..co.uk
Independent. Audio; editing; graphics;
duplication. MD: Daniel Stracey,
Maryan Kennedy
• *State of Play; The Young Visitors;*
  May 33rd

Outpost Facilities
Pinewood Studios,
Pinewood Road, Iver,
Buckinghamshire SL0 0NH
01753 630770
charlie@outpostfacilities.co.uk
www.outpostfacilities.co.uk
Independent. Commercials; films;
broadcast; TV. MD: Nigel Gourley
• *My Family; Everything I Know About*
  Men; Teletubbies Everywhere;
  Scrapheap Challenge; Wild Thing I
  Love You

Pepper
14 Greek Street, London, W1D 4DP
020 7836 1188
mailuf@pepperpost.tv
www.pepperpost.tv
Independent. Effects; graphics; dramas.
MDs: Patrick Holzen; Shane Warden
• *Dirty War; Midsomer Murders; White*
  Noise; Spooks; The Sally Lockheart
  Mysteries; Cracker; Prime Evil

Phaebus Communications Group
The Brewery Tower,
The Deva Centre, Trinity Way,
Manchester M3 7BF
0161 605 9999
info@phaebus.co.uk
www.phaebus.co.uk
Two branches. DVD; authoring;
TV production. MD: Steve Bettridge
• *BBC channel idents; Andy Pandy;*
  Thomas Cook conference events

Pink House
33 West Park Clifton, Bristol,
Avon BS8 2LX
0117 923 7087
reception@pinkhousepp.com
www.filmsat59.com
Part of Films at 59. Broadcast; audio;
pictures; effects; commercials.
MD: Anita Nandwani
• *Building the Dream; Big Cook Little*
  Cook; Animal Camera

Prime Focus
37 Dean St, London W1D 4PT
020 7734 5557
reception@primefocus.com
www.primefocusworld.com
Sister company Final Cut. Visual
effects, commercials and films.
Head of production: Pierre Fletcher
• *28 Days Later; BBC Talking Head*
  preview; Millions

Prime Focus London
37 Dean Street, London W12 4PT
020 7565 1000
info@primefocusworld.co.uk
www.primefocusworld.com
Part of Prime Focus World. Telecine;
online editing; special effects; 3D and
2D graphics; animation. MD: Simon
Huhtala
• *Direct Line sponsorship; BBC*
  Bitesize; Hell's Kitchen promotion

Red Vision
Cambos House, 3 Canal Street,
Manchester M1 3HE
0161 907 3764
London 020 7419 2010
Bristol 0117 946 6633
info@redvision.co.uk
www.redvision.co.uk
Computer graphics for film and TV.
MD: David Mousley
• *Touching the Void; D-Day: Men and*
  Machines

Resolution
26 Darblay Street, London W1F 8EL
020 7749 9300
London 020 7437 1336
info@resolution.tv
www.resolution.tv
Broadcast; commercials;
offline/online; audio; graphics. MD:
Mike Saunders
• *Big Brother; Top Gear; Fame Academy*

Rushes

66 Old Compton Street,
London W1D 4UH
020 7437 8676
info@rushes.co.uk
www.rushes.co.uk
*Part of Ascent media. Effects; telecine
for commercial video. MD: Joyce Capper*
• *Commercials: Hewlett Packard;
Offspring; Ford Mondeo (Tom and
Jerry)*

Savalas

Film City Glasgow, 11 Merryland
St, Glasgow G51 2QG
0141 440 6700
linda@savalas.co.uk
www.savalas.co.uk
*Independent. Music production;
audio; sound design. MDs: Giles Lamb;
Michael MacKinnon; Karl Henderson*
• *Magdalene Sisters; Relocation,
Relocation, Relocation; Sea of Souls;
Russian Revolution; Asylum;
American Cousins*

2nd Sense Broadcast

Studio 2000, Elstree Way
Borehamwood, Herts WD6 1SF
020 8236 1133
info@2ndsense.co.uk
www.2ndsense.co.uk
Independent. Audio. MD: Wendy Hewitt
• *Top of the Pops 2; Chuckle Vision;
East Enders Revealed*

Skaramoosh

9-15 Neal Street,
London WC2H 9PW
020 7379 9966
reception@skaramoosh.co.uk
www.skaramoosh.com
*Independent. Audio; Video. MD:
Wendy Hewitt*
• *Strictly Come Dancing; Football
Factory; Naked Science*

Soho Images

8-14 Meard Street,
London W1F 0EQ
020 7437 0831
info@sohoimages.com
www.sohoimages.com
*Independent. Effects; graphic design;
animation. MD: Daniel Slight*
• *Murder in Mind; Bloody Sunday;
Mrs Brown*

Sound Monsters

70 Grafton Way, London W1T 5DT
020 7387 3230
info@soundmonsters.com
www.soundmonsters.com
*Independent. Audio; sound; transfer;
animation. MD: Cliff Jones*
• *Death in Gaza; State of Texas; Real
Great Escapes*

St Anne's Post

20 St Anne's Court,
London W1F 0BH
020 7155 1500
info@saintannespost.co.uk
www.saintannespost.co.uk
*Part of Ascent Group. Audio; editing;
telecine. MD: Keith Williams*
• *Brothers Grimm; Alfie; Night Detective*

Stream

61 Charlotte Street,
London W1T 4PF
020 7208 1567
info@streamdm.co.uk
www.streamdm.co.uk
*Part of Ascent Group. DVD; design
compression; authoring facility.
MD: Paul Kind*
• *The Office; Where We're Calling
From; My Big Fat Greek Wedding*

Strongroom

120-124 Curtain Road,
London EC2A 3SQ
020 7426 5100
nina@strongroom.com
www.strongroom.tv
*Part of Strongroom Studios. Audio post
production for DVD, television and film.
Post-production manager: Sally Drury*
• *New World War; Holiday Exchange;
Pepsi ident; Shaun of the Dead; The
Stone Roses; Little Britain*

Suite

28 Newman Street,
London W1T 1PR
020 7636 4488
shelley@suitetv.co.uk
www.suitetv.co.uk
*Independent. Editing for TV.
MD: Shelley Fox*
• *The Office; Swiss Toni; The Lenny
Henry Show; Extras 2; Virgin Diaries
(MTV); Rob Brydon's Annually
Retentive; Randomist; Catherine Tate*

Sumners

Suite 401, Berkeley House,
35 Whitworth Street West,
Manchester M1 5NG
0161 228 0330
janet@sumners.co.uk
www.sumners.co.uk
*Independent. Online/offline; graphics;
very reality studio. MDs: Janet
Sumner, Andrew Sumner*
• *Best Sitcoms; Songs of Praise; Bank
of Mum and Dad*

Television Set

22 Newman Street,
London W1T 1PH
020 7637 3322
terry.bettles@tvsetgroup.co.uk
www.thetelevisionset.co.uk
*2 branches. Restoration of old archives
for reuse; audio; grading; telecine. MD:
Terry Bettles*
• *D-Day plus 60; Poirot remastering;
Let it Be*

Television Services International

10 Grape Street, London WC2H 8TG
020 7419 1400
enquiries@tsibroadcast.com
www.tsibroadcast.com
*Independent. Ingest transcoding,
content storage and delivery, format
edit: TV, wed TV, TX, VAD. MD:
Nick Doff*
• *Ali G; My New Best Friend;
Who Rules the Roost?*

Top Banana

The Studio, Broome, Stourbridge,
West Midlands DY9 0HA
01562 700404
info@top-b.com
www.top-b.com
*Independent. Animation; DVD;
duplication; effects; graphics.
MDs: Nick Terry; Richard Bridge*
• *Sindy; Jellies; Butt Ugly Martians*

Todd-ao creative services

13 Hawley Crescent,
London NW1 8NP
020 7284 7900
schedule@todd-ao.co.uk
www.todd-ao.co.uk
*Part of Ascent Group. Telecine grading;
negative film processing; video dailies;
offline/online editing. Technical
manager: Dick Knapman*
• *Monarch of the Glen; Canterbury
Tales; Taggart*

Videosonics

68a Delancey Street,
London NW1 7RY
020 7209 0209
info@videosonics.com
www.videosonics.com
*Independent. Audio. MD: Denis
Weinreich*
• *Young Adam; Bright Young Things;
Sexy Beast; Alien Vs Predator;
Glastonbury; White Noise*

Wild Tracks Audio Studio

2nd Floor, 55 Greek Street,
London W1D 3DT
020 7734 6331
bookings@wildtracks.co.uk
www.wildtracks.co.uk
*Independent. Audio. MD: Graham
Pickford*
• *Canon; Bob the Builder; Pingu*

Yellow Moon

30 Shaw Road, Holywood,
County Down BT18 9HX
028 9042 1826
general@yellowmoon.net
www.yellowmoon.net
Independent. Editing. MD: Greg Darby
• *Citizen Alec; Christine's Children;
Sven-Goran Eriksson*

Film and music libraries

BBC Birmingham, Information & Archives
The Mailbox, Birmingham B1 1RF
0121 567 6767
www.bbc.co.uk
Music, news requests, productions

BFI National Film and TV Archives
Kingshill Way, Berkhamsted,
Herts HP4 3TP
01442 876301
darren.long@bfi.org.uk
www.bfi.org.uk
Large collection from 1895 to the present day

East Anglian Film Archive
The Archive Centre, Martineau Lane, Norwich NR1 2DQ
01603 592664
eafa@uea.ac.uk
www.eafa.org.uk
Moving images relating to the region of East Anglia

Film and Video Archive, Imperial War Museum
All Saints Annexe, Austral Street,
London SE11 4SL
020 7416 5290/1
film@iwm.org.uk
www.iwm.org.uk
Images of conflict – 1914 to the present day

Film Institute of Ireland/ Irish Film Archive
6 Eustace Street, Temple Bar,
Dublin 2
00 353 1 679 5744
info@irishfilm.ie
www.irishfilm.ie
Films worldwide. Every Irish film ever made

GMTV Library Sales
London TV Centre, Upper Ground,
London SE1 9TT
020 7827 7363/6
librarysales@gm.tv
www.gm.tv
News, showbiz, lifestyle and travel stories and stock shots from 1993 onwards

Huntley Film Archive
22 Islington Green, London N1 8DU
020 7226 9260
films@huntleyarchives.com
www.huntleyarchives.com
Rare and vintage documentary film from 1895

Images Of War
31a Regents Park Road,
London NW1 7TL
020 7267 9198
derek@warfootage.com
www.warfootage.com
Images of war archive. 1900 to first Gulf war

ITN Archive
200 Grays Inn Road,
London WC1X 8XZ
020 7833 3000
uksales@itnsource.com
www.itnsource.com
More than 780,000 hours of news and feature material

ITV Central
Gas Street, Birmingham B1 2JT
0121 643 9898
www.itv.com

JW Media Music
10–11 Great Turnstile,
London WC1V 7JU
020 7681 8900
info@jwmediamusic.co.uk
www.jwmediamusic.com
Music production and publishing

Media Archive for Central England
1 Salisbury Road, University of Leicester, Leicester LE1 7RQ
0116 252 5066
macearchive@le.ac.uk
www.macearchive.org
East and West Midlands moving image heritage

National Screen and Sound Archive of Wales
Aberystwyth, Ceredigion SY23 3BU
01970 632828
agssc@llgc.org.uk
http://screenandsound.llgc.org.uk
Film archive for Wales

North West Film Archive
Minshull House,
47–49 Chorlton Street,
Manchester M1 3EU
0161 247 3097
n.w.filmarchive@mmu.ac.uk
www.nwfa.mmu.ac.uk
The north-west, 1897 to present day

Northern Region Film and Television Archive
School of Arts & Media,
University of Teesside,
Middlesbrough TS1 3BA
01642 384015
enquiries@nrfta.org.uk
www.nrfta.org.uk
Public sector moving image archive serving County Durham, Northumberland, Tees Valley and Tyne & Wear

Pathé Pictures
14–17 Market Place,
London W1W 8AR
020 7323 5151
www.pathe.co.uk
Worldwide images and film distribution

Royal Television Society, Library & Archive
020 7822 2810
info@rts.org.uk
www.rts.org.uk
Archive TV pictures, award ceremonies and monthly dinners

Scottish Screen Archive
39–41 Montrose Avenue,
Hillington Park, Glasgow G52 4LA
0845 366 4600
ssaenquiries@nls.uk
www.scottish-screen.com
Scotland since the 1890s

South East Film & Video Archive
University of Brighton, Grand Parade, Brighton BN2 0JY
01273 643213
screenarchive@brighton.ac.uk
www.brighton.ac.uk/screenarchive
The south-east: Kent, Surrey, East and West Sussex, Brighton & Hove and Medway

South West Film and Television Archive
Melville Building, Royal William Yard, Stonehouse,
Plymouth PL1 3RP
01752 202650
info@tswfta.co.uk
www.tswfta.co.uk
The south-west from 1890 to the present day

Wessex Film and Sound Archive
Hampshire Record Office,
Sussex Street, Winchester SO23 8TH
01962 847742
david.lee@hants.gov.uk
www.hants.gov.uk
/record-office/film
Central southern England. Film records 1897 to the present day, sound records 1890 to the present day

Wiener Library
4 Devonshire Street,
London W1W 5BH
020 7636 7247
info@wienerlibrary.co.uk
www.wienerlibrary.co.uk
Modern Jewish history

Yorkshire Film Archive
York Lord St John College,
Mayors Walk, York YO31 7EX
01904 876550
info@yorkshirefilmarchive.com
www.yorkshirefilmarchive.com
Moving images of the Yorkshire region

TV & film training and support

BBC Training and development: Broadcast Training
0870 122 0216
training@bbc.co.uk
www.bbctraining.com
All strands of broadcast training within the BBC

Birds Eye View
020 7704 6500/9435
rosiestrang@birds-eye-view.co.uk
www.birds-eye-view.co.uk
Emerging female film-makers

Film Education
020 7851 9450
postbox@filmeducation.org
www.filmeducation.org

First Film Foundation
info@firstfilm.co.uk
www.firstfilm.co.uk
*Training for new film writers,
producers and directors*

FT2 — Film and Television Freelance Training
020 7407 0344
info@ft2.org.uk
www.ft2.org.uk
Training for new broadcast freelancers

New Producers Alliance (NPA)
020 7613 0440
queries@npa.org.uk
www.npa.org.uk
Training and support for film-makers

Shooting People
contact@shootingpeople.org
www.shootingpeople.org
*Online network for independent
filmmakers to exchange information
and ideas*

Skillset: The Sector Skills Council for the Audio Visual Industries
020 7520 5757
info@skillset.org
www.skillset.org
*Owned by broadcast industry; accredits
courses, publishes handbooks and runs
online Skills Set Careers service*

Women in Film and TV
020 7287 1400
info@wftv.org.uk
www.wftv.org.uk
*Membership association open to women
with at least one year's professional
experience in the television, film and/or
digital media industries*

» See also page 406

Trade press

Advance Production News
020 8305 6905
www.crimsonuk.com
*Monthly. Listings for production
companies. Owner: Crimson
Communications. Editor: Alan Williams*

Broadband TV News
01223 464359
jclover@broadbandtvnews.com
www.broadbandtvnews.com
*Free weekly and daily emails and
subscription newsletters. Editor,
international edition: Julian Clover*

Broadcast
020 7505 8000
broadcastnews@emap.com
www.broadcastnow.co.uk
*Weekly. TV and radio industry. Owner:
Emap Media. Editor: Lisa Campbell;
news: Chris Curtis; features editor
and deputy: Emily Booth; chief sub:
Angus Walker*

Cable & Satellite Europe
020 7017 5533
www.telecoms.com
*10pa. Owner: Informa Media and
Telecoms*

Cable & Satellite International
020 7562 2400
neil.howman@cable-satellite.com
www.cable-satellite.com
*6pa. Owner: Perspective Publishing.
Editor: Goran Nastic*

Channel 21 International magazine
020 7729 7460
press@c21media.net
www.c21media.net
*10pa. Owner: C21 Media. Editor-in-
chief: David Jenkinson; editor:
Ed Waller*

Commonwealth Broadcaster
020 7583 5550
cba@cba.org.uk
www.cba.org.uk
*Quarterly of the Commonwealth
Broadcasting Association, trains
journalists in developing
Commonwealth nations.
Secretary-general: Elizabeth Smith*

Contacts — The Spotlight Casting Directories
020 7437 7631
info@spotlight.com
www.spotlight.com
*Annual. Contacts for stage, film, TV
and radio. Editor: Kate Poynton*

Crewfinder
028 9079 7902
mail@adleader.co.uk
www.crewfinderwales.co.uk
*Annual. Wales's film, TV and video
directory. Owner: Adleader
Publications. Proprietor: Stan Mairs*

Digital Spy
nwilkes@digitalspy.co.uk
www.digitalspy.co.uk
Web. Digital TV. Editor: Neil Wilkes

FilmBang
0141 334 2456
info@filmbang.com
www.filmbang.com
*Annual. Scotland's film and video
directory. Editor: Marianne Mellin*

FutureMedia
020 7729 7460
press@c21media.net
www.c21media.net
*10pa. Owner: C21 Media. Editor-
in-chief: David Jenkinson; editor:
Jonathan Webdale*

IBE
01895 421111
editor@ibeweb.com
www.ibeweb.com
*12pa. International broadcast
engineering. Owner: BPL Business
Media. Editor: Neil Nixon*

Kemps Film, TV, Video Handbook (UK edition)
01342 335861
kemps@reedinfo.co.uk
www.kftv.com
*Annual. Guide to international
production. Owner: Reed Business
Information. Editorial contact:
Pat Huson*

The Knowledge
020 8973 3400
orders@hollis-publishing.com
www.hollis-publishing.com
*Annual, June. Production directory.
Owner: Hollis Publishing. Editorial
contact: Louise Baynes*

Line Up
01483 575450
editor@lineup.biz
www.lineup.biz
*6pa. Journal of the Institute of
Broadcast Sound. Owner: Line Up
Publications. Editor: Hugh Robjohns*

Multichannel News
00 1 646 746 6590
www.multichannel.com
*Weekly. Owner: Reed Business
Information. Executive editor/content:
Kent Gibbons; news: Mike Reynolds;
copy chief: Michael Demenchuk*

Pact
020 7067 4367
enquiries@pact.co.uk
www.pact.co.uk
*Monthly. Magazine for independent
producers and film professionals*

Pro Sound News Europe
020 7921 8319
david.robinson@cmpi.biz
www.prosoundnewseurope.com
*12pa. Audio industry. Owner: CMP
Information. Editor: David Robinson;
managing editor: Sharon Lock*

The Production Guide
020 7017 3500
theproductionguide@emap.com
www.productionguideonline.com
*Annual. Information on production.
Owner: Emap Media. Editor: Mei Mei
Rogers*

Satellite Finance
020 7963 7680
monika.gora@telecomfinance.com
www.satellitefinance.com
*11pa. Finance journal for executives.
Owner: The Press Association. Editor:
Ed Ansell*

Stage Screen and Radio
020 7346 0900
editor@stagescreenandradio.org.uk
www.bectu.org.uk
*10pa. Magazine of broadcasting union
Bectu. Editor: Ruby Ali*

Televisual
020 3008 5781
tim@televisual.co.uk
www.televisual.com
*Monthly. Trade magazine for TV.
Owner: Televisual Media UK. Editor:
Tim Dams; news editor: Jonathan
Creamer*

TV International
020 7017 5533
telecoms.enquiries@informa.com
www.telecoms.com
*Fortnightly and daily. International
TV listings. Owner: Informa Media and
Telecoms*

TBI (Television Business International)
020 7017 5533
telecoms.enquiries@informa.com
www.telecoms.com
Annual. Directory of businesses.
Owner: Informa Media and Telecoms

TV Technology and Production
01480 461555
www.imaspub.com
6pa. Broadcasting and production technology. Owner: IMAS Publishing UK. Editor: Mark Hallinger

TVB Europe
01732 364422
tvbeurope@scope.ie
www.tvbeurope.com
Monthly. Broadcasting innovation and technology. Owner: CMP Information. Editor-in-chief: Fergal Ringrose

VLV Bulletin
01474 352835
info@vlv.org.uk
www.vlv.org.uk
Quarterly magazine of Voice of the Listener and Viewer. Advocates citizen and consumer interests in broadcasting. Editor: Jocelyn Hay

Zerb
01822 614405
cfox@urbanfox.com
www.gtc.org.uk
2pa. For camera operators. Owner: The Deeson Group. Editor: Christina Fox

» *Consumer film and TV magazines see page 87*

Events

Bafta Awards
195 Piccadilly, London W1J 9LN
020 7734 0022
www.bafta.org
Film, TV and interactive industries

MediaGuardian Edinburgh International Television Festival
117 Farringdon Road,
London EC1R 3BX
020 7278 9515
www.mgeitf.co.uk
TV and film associations

TV & film associations

Association of Motion Picture Sound
28 Knox Street, London W1H 1FS
020 7723 6727
admin@amps.net
www.amps.net
Film and TV sound technicians

Bafta (British Academy of Film and Television Arts)
195 Piccadilly, London W1J 9LN
020 7734 0022
www.bafta.org
Awards, training and education

Barb (Broadcasters' Audience Research Board)
020 7529 5531
enquiries@barb.co.uk
www.barb.co.uk
Industry-owned audience data
Press: 020 7591 9610

Bectu (Broadcasting, Entertainment, Cinematograph and Theatre Union)
373–377 Clapham Road,
London SW9 9BT
020 7346 0900
info@bectu.org.uk
www.bectu.org.uk
Union for broadcasting, entertainment and theatre

BKSTS — The Moving Image Society
Pinewood Studios, Iver Heath,
Bucks SL0 0NH
01753 656656
Info@bksts.com
www.bksts.com
Film foundation, TV and digital tech, foundation sound for film and video, broadcasting engineering

British Board of Film Classification
3 Soho Square, London W1D 3HD
020 7440 1570
contact_the_bbfc@bbfc.co.uk
www.bbfc.co.uk

British Film Institute
21 Stephen Street, London W1T 1LN
020 7255 1444
publishing@bfi.org.uk
www.bfi.org.uk
Education, exhibitions and resources

British Universities Film & Video Council
77 Wells Street, London W1T 3QJ
020 7393 1500
ask@bufvc.ac.uk
www.bufvc.ac.uk
To promote the use of media within higher education

British Video Association
167 Great Portland Street,
London W1W 5PE
020 7436 0041
general@bva.org.uk
www.bva.org.uk
Represents the interests of publishers and rights owners of pre-recorded home entertainment on video

Broadcasting Press Guild
Tiverton, The Ridge, Woking,
Surrey GU22 7EQ
01483 764895
torin.douglas@bbc.co.uk
Promotes professional interests of journalists who write or broadcast about the media

Cinema and Television Benevolent Fund
22 Golden Square, London W1F 9AD
020 7437 6567
info@ctbf.co.uk
www.ctbf.co.uk
Trade charity

Drama Association of Wales
The Old Library Building,
Singleton Road, Splott, Cardiff
CF24 2ET
029 2045 2200
aled.daw@virgin.net
www.amdram.co.uk

DigiTAG (Digital Terrestrial Television Action Group)
17a Ancienne Route, CH-1218
Grand Saconnex, Geneva,
Switzerland
00 41 22 717 2735
projectoffice@digitag.org
www.digitag.org
Not-for-profit international association

Digital Television Group
7 Old Lodge Place, St Margarets,
Twickenham TW1 1RQ
020 8891 1830
www.dtg.org.uk
International industry-led consortium.
Director general: Marcus Coleman

Digital Video Broadcasting Project (DVB)
Project Office, 17a Ancienne
Route, CH-1218 Grand Saconnex,
Geneva, Switzerland
00 41 22 717 2714
dvb@dvb.org
www.dvb.org
Not-for-profit international association

Directors' Guild of Great Britain
4 Windmill Street, London W1T 2HZ
020 7580 9131
guild@dggb.org
www.dggb.org

Documentary Film-makers Group
225a Brecknock Road,
London N19 5AA
020 7428 0882
info@dfglondon.com
www.dfglondon.com

Equity
Guild House, Upper St Martins
Lane, London WC2H 9EG
020 7379 6000
info@equity.org.uk
www.equity.org.uk
Actors' union

Federation of Entertainment Unions
1 Highfield, Twyford,
Nr Winchester,
Hampshire SO21 1QR
01962 713134
harris.s@btconnect.com

Film Archive Forum
c/o British Universities Film &
Video Council, 77 Wells Street,
London W1T 3QJ
020 7393 1508
luke@bufvc.ac.uk
www.bufvc.ac.uk/faf

Film Distributors' Association
www.launchingfilms.com
Trade body representing theatrical film distributors in the UK

Focal International
Pentax House, South Hill Avenue,
South Harrow HA2 0DU
020 8423 5853
info@focalint.org
www.focalint.org
Trade association for libraries and researchers

Guild of British Camera Technicians
c/o Panavision (UK), Metropolitan Centre, Bristol Road, Greenford, Middlesex UB6 8GD
020 8813 1999
admin@gbct.org
www.gbct.org

Guild of Television Cameramen
01822 614405
chairman@gtc.org.uk
www.gtc.org.uk

Guild of Vision Mixers
www.guildofvisionmixers.org.uk

Institute of Broadcast Sound
PO Box 932, Guildford GU4 7WW
01483 575450
info@ibs.org.uk
www.ibs.org.uk

International Federation of Film Archives (FIAF)
1 Rue Defacqz, B-1000 Brussels, Belgium
00 322 538 3065
info@fiafnet.org
www.fiafnet.org

International Visual Communication Association (IVCA)
19 Pepper Street, Glengall Bridge, London E14 9RP
020 7512 0571
info@ivca.org
www.ivca.org
Promotes corporate visual communication

MCPS and PRS Alliance
29–33 Berners Street,
London W1T 3AB
020 7580 5544
www.mcps-prs-alliance.co.uk
Collects and distributes music royalties

NaSTA (National Student Television Association)
nasta@warwicktv.co.uk
www.nasta.org.uk
Student-run TV stations

National Film Theatre
Belvedere Road, South Bank, Waterloo, London SE1 8XT
020 7928 3535
nft@bfi.org.uk
www.bfi.org.uk

Office of Communications (Ofcom)
Riverside House, 2A Southwark Bridge Road, London SE1 9HA
020 7981 3000
www.ofcom.org.uk
Press: 020 7981 3033,
mediaoffice@ofcom.org.uk

Pact (Producers Alliance for Cinema and Television)
Procter House, 1 Procter Street, London WC1V 6DW
020 7067 4367
enquiries@pact.co.uk
www.pact.co.uk
Trade association for independent production companies

The Picture Research Association
c/o 1 Willow Court, off Willow Street, London EC2A 4QB
chair@picture-research.org.uk
www.picture-research.org.uk

Production Guild
N&P Complex,
Pinewood Studios, Iver Heath, Buckinghamshire SL0 0NH
01753 651767
patrick@productionguild.com
www.productionguild.com

Production Managers Association
Ealing Studios, Ealing Green, Ealing, London W5 5EP
020 8758 8699
pma@pma.org.uk
www.pma.org.uk

Professional Lighting and Sound Association — Plasa
38 St Leonards Road,
Eastbourne BN21 3UT
01323 410335
www.plasa.org

Royal Television Society
5th Floor, Kildare House,
3 Dorset Rise, London EC4Y 8EN
020 7822 2810
info@rts.org.uk
www.rts.org.uk
Membership and events organisation

The Satellite & Cable Broadcasters Group
29 Harley Street, London W1G 9QR
07968 125959
info@scbg.org.uk
www.scbg.org.uk
The trade association for satellite and cable programme providers

Sgrin, Media Agency for Wales
33–35 West Bute St, Cardiff Bay, Cardiff CF10 5LH
029 2033 3300
sgrin@sgrin.co.uk
www.sgrin.co.uk
Film agency for Wales

Voice of the Listener and Viewer (VLV)
101 King's Drive, Gravesend, Kent DA12 5BQ
01474 352835
info@vlv.org.uk
www.vlv.org.uk
Independent, non-profit society working to ensure independence, quality and diversity in broadcasting

UK Film Council
10 Little Portland Street,
London W1W 7JG
020 7861 7861
info@ukfilmcouncil.org.uk
www.ukfilmcouncil.org.uk
Promotes UK as a production centre

UK Post
47 Beak Street, London W1F 9SE
020 7734 6060
info@ukpost.org.uk
www.ukpost.org.uk
Trade body charged with representing the post-production and special effects sector at home and internationally

Writernet
Cabin V, Clarendon Buildings,
25 Horsell Road, Highbury,
London N5 1XL
020 7609 7474
info@writernet.org.uk
www.writernet.org.uk
Information and guidance for playwrights and performance writers

Radio

Paul Robinson

While the television industry shot itself in the foot with apparently limitless deception and sharp practice climaxing at the self-flagellation at the Edinburgh TV festival, radio quietly got on with it in 2007. The BBC's domination of creativity and audience ratings only took a knock when BBC 6 Music was caught suggesting that recorded listener calls on the Liz Kershaw weekend breakfast show were live. The controller, Lesley Douglas, acted swiftly with both Kershaw and the station editor, Ric Blaxill, leaving immediately. Although not quite the high-profile loss of BBC1's controller, Peter Fincham, over the RDF-produced trailer of The Queen, it was an uncharacteristically brutal exit for an executive with history at Radio 1, Capital and Top of the Pops.

Phil Riley, the former chief executive of Chrysalis Radio who stepped down in July probably also felt bruised. Galaxy and Heart have both been significant commercial radio success stories, built up from scratch by Riley and his boss, Richard Huntingford, (now chairman of Virgin Radio). The industry rated Chrysalis as a well-managed "pure radio play" company, but in the past year the group has failed to add new stations and paid the ultimate price by being absorbed into Global Radio — a new radio vehicle headed by Charles Allen, the ex ITV chief executive. Global also attracted Richard Park, the eponymous radio consultant who was instrumental in keeping Capital ahead in London for so many years and who, working with Andria Vidler, the head of Magic, put the Capital DJ Neil Fox on the breakfast show and took Magic to number-one rated commercial radio station in London, a position it will hold into 2008.

Breakfast Magic with DJ Neil Fox

Ralph Bernard, the chief executive of GCap Media, smartly stole Fru Hazlitt from Virgin Radio to add her multiplatform experience and completed Virgin's misery when Paul Jackson, her number two, jumped ship to become managing director of Capital Radio. And the former MD of Capital and chief executive of ITV Richard Eyre joined GCap as chairman.

Over at the BBC, Jenny Abramsky continued to lead BBC Radio with passion and energy and without any changes at the top of the five FM/AM networks, although Andy Parfitt successfully became the longest-serving controller of Radio 1. If his reign ends soon, his legacy will be to have nursed the station to rude health, in empathy with its primarily 15-24 target audience, yet still with public service at its heart. The Today programme celebrated its 50th in October,

Murdo MacLeod

Today veteran John Humphrys

and Radios 1, 2, 3 and 4 all got to 40 on September 30 without too much middle-age spread. Radio 4 has enjoyed another strong year, with landmark programming including Justin Webb's Death to America and The Reunion: Brighton Bomb. Radio 3 had another strong Proms season, and although its weekly audience reach, at just over 2 million, is modest and apparently incapable of growing, its (at times) challenging musical repertoire, drama and arts provides an essential complement to Classic FM.

Radio 2 continued to be the UK's most listened-to station and consolidated its strong weekday line of Wogan, Bruce, Vine, Wright and Evans. Oddly – having won a Sony Gold in April – Mark Radcliffe's weekday late-evening show was axed and he was teamed up with Stuart Maconie mid evening: a partnership that fails to bring out the best in either broadcaster. The late evening on Radio 2 is now a clutter, with an admirably broad range of shows from documentary to Simon Mayo, with whom it is impossible to make a regular appointment.

Commercial radio made strides in 2007 to get audiences and advertisers to reappraise its programming across the local networks, and scored a notable success with the second UK Music Week. Spearheaded by the industry trade body, RadioCentre, under the editorial direction of Bethan Davies the initiative kicked off with a Stereophonics concert across the Contemporary Hit Radio Network (CHR) of 120 stations. The event in May saw live sessions

National listening figures, period ending Jun 2007

	Survey period (months)	Reach (m)	Reach (%)	Share (%)
Top 20 stations/networks				
BBC Radio 2	3	13.1	26	15.6
BBC Radio 1	3	10.9	22	10.3
BBC Radio 4	3	9.5	19	11.2
BBC Radio FIVE LIVE (inc Sports Extra)	3	6.1	12	4.5
Classic FM	3	5.7	11	4.0
Total Magic*	3	3.4	7	2.4
Total Heart (UK)*	6	3.3	6	2.3
Total Kiss Network*	6	2.9	6	1.6
Galaxy Network (UK)*	6	2.6	5	1.8
Total Virgin Radio	6	2.5	5	1.5
talkSPORT (Talk Radio)	3	2.4	5	1.8
Total Smooth Radio*	3	2.3	5	2.0
BBC Radio 3	3	1.8	4	1.1
Total Real Radio*	6	1.6	3	1.7
Total Kerrang!*	3	1.5	3	0.7
The Hits	3	1.3	3	0.5
BBC World Service	3	1.3	3	0.7
Total XFM (UK)*	6	1.2	2	0.7
Total Capital Gold UK*	6	0.9	2	0.6
Smash Hits Radio	3	0.9	2	0.3
ALL BBC	3	33.2	66	54.3
All BBC network radio	3	29.4	58	44.5
BBC local/regional	3	9.9	20	9.8
ALL COMMERCIAL	3	32.0	64	43.5
All national commercial	3	14.1	28	11.2
All local commercial	3	25.8	51	32.3

*Total networks

Source: RAJAR Ltd / Ipsos MORI / RSMB

on commercial radio in peak lunchtime slots from artists such as Amy Winehouse, Paolo Nutini, Mika and Travis and took in the pop, dance, rock and gold networks, embracing in total over 250 local commercial stations across the UK. For the first time in recent memory it was a show of confidence musically – a genre hitherto dominated by the BBC, whose Radio 1 Big Weekend in Preston and Glastonbury festival outside broadcasts were highlights.

New kids on the block also made their mark in 2007. Aside from a new radio group in Global, Gaydar Radio won top digital station at both the Sonys and Arqivas and Channel 4 proved it was serious about radio. In June it beat a consortium led by the transmission provider National Grid Wireless to secure a 12-year licence for the second national digital multiplex. In the process, Channel 4 committed to launch three new branded national stations including a rival to BBC Radio 4, with a particular goal to create a contemporary alternative to the Today programme. Other content partners brought into the Channel 4 Radio family included the Walt Disney Company, Virgin Radio and Sky, whose goal is to launch (with Global Radio) a rolling 24/7 national radio news service as a sister to Sky News. UTV Radio, also a partner, pledged to recreate Talk Radio, the network opinion and debate phone-in station that disappeared on analogue AM when Kelvin MacKenzie acquired the network from CLT (RTL Group) and converted it to TalkSport. The multiplex won't launch for many months, but will do so into a market in which digital radio is thriving and commercial radio is ahead of the BBC on audience share. The Q3 2007 Rajar audience figures put digital listening at a record high of 16.8% of all commercial listening across all platforms and with commercial radio taking a 63% share of all listening to digital-only services.

The final word goes to the BBC's digital Asian Network, which this year made a name for itself as the sound of Asian Britain and demonstrated in superb style how radio can transport you anywhere with its evocative commemoration of the 60th anniversary of India and Pakistan's partition.

● Paul Robinson is the managing director of Kidsco

Awards

Sony Awards 2007

- *Station of the year:* Classic FM
- *Station of the year, audience more than 1 million:* Radio City 96.7
- *Station of the year, audience 300,000 to 1 million:* BBC Radio Derby
- *Station of the year, audience less than 300,000:* Isle of Wight Radio
- *Station of the year, digital terrestrial:* GaydarRadio
- *Breakfast show award:* The Today Programme (BBC Radio News for Radio 4)
- *Entertainment award:* The Chris Evans Show (BBC Radio 2)
- *Music broadcaster of the year:* Colin Murray (BBC Radio 1)
- *Speech programme of the year:* The Reunion (Whistledown Productions for BBC Radio 4)
- *Music radio personality of the year:* Chris Evans (BBC Radio 2)
- *News and current affairs programme of the year:* Five Live Breakfast (BBC Radio News for Five Live)

Top 20 local/regional stations by reach, period ending June 2007

	Survey period (months)	Region	Total survey area	Reach (m)	Reach (%)	Share (%)
Magic 105.4	3	London	10,782	1,963	18	6.2
Heart 106.2 FM	3	London	10,782	1,810	17	6.2
95.8 Capital Radio	3	London	10,782	1,519	14	4.1
Kiss 100 FM	3	London	10,782	1,515	14	4.5
Galaxy Yorkshire	6	Yorkshire	4,320	933	22	8.7
BBC Radio Scotland	3	Scotland	4,267	909	21	8.0
100.7 Heart FM	6	Birmingham	3,520	776	22	8.6
Real Radio (Scotland)	6	Scotland	2,615	771	29	18.6
Century FM (North West)	3	Manchester	5,236	718	14	5.5
LBC 97.3	3	London	10,782	637	6	3.1
Smooth Radio (North West)	3	Manchester	5,355	622	12	5.7
BBC Radio Ulster	3	Ulster	1,391	619	44	22.0
XFM 104.9	3	London	10,782	617	6	2.0
Clyde 1 FM	6	Glasgow	1,824	586	32	14.7
Key 103 (Manchester)	6	Manchester	2,362	502	21	7.7
Smooth Radio (London)	3	London	10,782	502	5	1.4
Choice FM London	3	London	10,782	500	5	1.6
BBC Radio Wales	3	Wales	2,466	480	19	11.4
Galaxy North East	6	North East	2,174	479	22	8.8
Century FM (North East)	6	North East	2,198	474	22	8.5
Smooth Radio (West Midlands)	6	West Midlands	3,520	463	13	8.1
All local commercial radio	3		50,334	25,791	51	32.3
BBC local/regional radio	3		50,334	9,889	20	9.8

Source: RAJAR Ltd / Ipsos MORI / RSMB

Digital multiplex licence-holders

Holder	Owners	Multiplexes number	location
NATIONAL			
BBC	Public	1	85% of the country
Digital One	GCap Media and Arqiva	1	85% of the country
Total national		2	
LOCAL AND REGIONAL*			
Arqiva	Macquarie Communications Infrastructure Group	1	Ayr
CE Digital Ltd	GCap Media, Emap Digital Radio	3	London, Birmingham, Manchester
Digital Radio Group London	GCap Media, Carphone Warehouse, UTV, SMG	1	London
Emap Digital Radio	Emap Radio	12	Central Lancashire, Dundee & Perth, Edinburgh, Glasgow, Humberside, Inverness, Leeds, Liverpool, Northern Ireland, South Yorkshire, Teeside, Tyne & Wear
MXR	Chrysalis Radio, GCap Media, Guardian Media Group, UBC and Ford	5	The North-East, North-West, Wales & Severn Estuary, West Midlands, Yorkshire (all regional)
Now Digital	GCap Media	18	Bournemouth, Bristol & Bath, Cambridge, Cardiff & Newport, Coventry, Exeter & Torbay, Kent, Leicester, Norwich, Nottingham, Peterborough, Plymouth & Cornwall, Reading & Basingstoke, Southend & Chelmsford, South Hampshire, Sussex Coast, Swindon & West Wiltshire, and Wolverhampton, Shrewsbury & Telford
Switchdigital	UTV Radio	3	London and Aberdeen (local), central Scotland (regional)
UTV-Emap Digital	UTV Radio, Emap Digital Radio	3	Swansea, Stoke on Trent, Bradford & Huddersfield
Total local and regional		46	

*Local licences unless stated

Source: DRDB

At the end of 2007, Fru Hazlitt was named the new chief executive of GCap Media, marking a new era for the troubled radio giant. She gave her first interview to MediaGuardian.co.uk's Chris Tryhorn and laid out a new plan for the commercial radio sector.

》》 Mediaguardian.co.uk December 20 2007

Hazlitt: More radio consolidation would be a 'distraction'

Chris Tryhorn

GCap Media's new chief executive, Fru Hazlitt, has told the commercial radio industry to stop being distracted by further attempts at consolidation and to end its obsession with the BBC.

Hazlitt said her priority was to grow the power and reach of GCap's brands, which include Classic FM, Capital 95.8 and Xfm, across a range of media outlets including broadband.

"It's not so much about size, it's about brands and brand behaviour," she told MediaGuardian on her first day in the job.

"We need to demonstrate more than we have to date the quality of our brands. We don't need the distraction [of consolidation]. I think we will be serving our investors better if we are building growth within our own stable."

GCap's chairman, Richard Eyre, agreed that the company — formed from the 2005 merger of GWR and Capital Radio — was in no hurry to launch a new wave of radio consolidation.

"From the board's perspective we have a lot of unfulfilled potential," he said. "The point at which consolidation becomes inevitable is where companies feel their assets have been squeezed as far as they can possibly be squeezed.

"Making sure the cost base is the right size is an important part of our strategy, but we have a strategy beyond that."

The radio industry was gearing up from a fresh round of consolidation earlier in the year when new entrant Global Radio, chaired by Charles Allen, snapped up Chrysalis Radio, and Emap put its radio stations up for sale.

But now that Emap's radio assets have ended up with German magazine group H Bauer, the scope for further tie-ups appears limited.

Hazlitt also said commercial bosses needed to stop obsessing about the BBC, which scored a record 13.9 percentage point lead over the commercial sector in the first quarter of 2007.

"The industry needs to stop distracting itself by worrying about the BBC to actually use what it has got — because there's a lot of good stuff in it — to

build growth and to demonstrate leadership," she said.

"I think the distraction has come from all this acquisition and thinking who we can acquire next. And we've missed some tricks — we've missed the fact that our audience are trying to interact with us online.

"The best thing about that model is that we are growing our revenues online as we are growing audiences. We have a business model that looks very exciting.

"We have beaten the BBC for years in the past — we know how to beat the BBC and there are masses of stations that beat the BBC in their areas. We should focus on our core objectives and let the BBC focus on theirs."

Eyre said Hazlitt's appointment owed much to her experience at online giant Yahoo!, where she rose to be managing director in the UK and Ireland, before leaving to join Virgin Radio in 2005.

"The broadband opportunity is a big one which we feel has not been fully seized by any of the regular groups yet, and the right kind of person needs to be able to make the company really sing in those areas," Eyre said.

Hazlitt was picked from a shortlist of eight candidates, three of whom were internal contenders. Since May, she has been an executive director at GCap and its managing director in London, and previously worked at Capital Radio between 1993 and 1999.

Radio

Radio contacts

BBC radio

Broadcasting House,
Portland Place,
London W1A 1AA
020 7580 4468

Director of audio and music:
Jenny Abramsky, 020 7765 4561

Head of radio news:
Stephen Mitchell

Head of radio current affairs:
Nicola Meyrick, 020 8752 6251

*Controller of multi-platform and
interactive, future media and
technology*
Mark Friend, 020 7765 2545

*Controller of production, factual, radio
drama, TV music entertainment live
events and classical music TV*
Graham Ellis, 020 7765 4455

Press
Head of press and publicity, BBC radio:
Sue Lynas, 020 7765 4630

Nations and regions (Head of English regions):
Gareth Lloyd, 0121 567 6209

Digital radio:
Jamie Austin, 020 7765 0426

Regional press offices
London: 020 7765 5994
Birmingham: 0121 567 6274
Bristol: 0117 974 2130
Manchester: 0161 244 4888
Leeds: 0113 224 7152
Newcastle: 0191 244 1296

》 See also separate press contacts

● Radio stations

BBC Radio 1/1xtra
Yalding House,
152-156 Great Portland Street,
London W1N 6AJ
www.bbc.co.uk/radio1
www.bbc.co.uk/1xtra
*Controller: Andy Parfitt; head
of mainstream programmes: Ben
Cooper, 020 7765 2236; head of music:
George Ergatoudis; head of music
development: Ian Parkinson,
020 7765 0365; breakfast show: Chris
Moyles (Radio 1), Rampage (1xtra)*
Press: Sarah O'Connell,
020 7765 1030

BBC Radio 2
Western House,
99 Great Portland Street,
London W1A 1AA
www.bbc.co.uk/radio2
*Controller: Lesley Douglas, 020 7765
3493; managing editor: Antony
Bellekom, 020 7765 4612; editor,
mainstream programmes: Phil Hughes,
020 7765 4159; editor, specialist
programmes: Dave Barber, 0121 432
9854; breakfast show: Terry Wogan*
Press: Hester Nevill,
020 7765 5712

BBC Radio 3
Broadcasting House, Portland
Place, London W1A 1AA
www.bbc.co.uk/radio3
*Controller: Roger Wright, 020 7765 2523;
head of speech programmes: Abigail
Appleton, 020 7765 3277; head of
music programming: John Evans, 020
7765 0481; controller, Proms, live
events and TV classical music:
Nicholas Kenyon, 020 7765 4928*
Press: Clare Fisher, 020 7765 5887

BBC Radio 4
Broadcasting House, Portland
Place, London W1A 1AA
www.bbc.co.uk/radio4
*Controller: Mark Damazer, 020 7765
3836; network manager: Denis Nowlan,
020 7765 4615; head of radio drama:
Alison Hindell, 020 7557 1006; editor,
entertainment: Caroline Raphael, 020
7765 1870; editor, drama: Jeremy
Howe 020 7765 4505; editor, general
factual: Jane Ellison (features) 020
7765 0631; editor, specialist factual:
Andrew Caspari, 020 7765 2660*
Press: Sian Davis, 020 8576 1865

BBC Radio Five Live &
Five Live Sports Extra
Television Centre, Wood Lane,
London W12 7RJ
www.bbc.co.uk/fivelive
*Head of radio sport: Gordon Turnbull,
020 8225 6206; head of news,
Radio Five Live: Mat Morris, 020 8624
8946; managing editor: Moz Dee,
020 8624 8948*
Press: Andy Bate, 020 8576 1694

BBC 6 Music
Western House,
99 Great Portland Street,
London W1A 1AA
020 7765 3493
www.bbc.co.uk/6music
*Controller: Lesley Douglas, 020 7765
3493; head of programmes: Ric Blaxill;
breakfast show: Shaun Keavney; see
also Radio 2 contacts*

BBC Asian Network
St. Nicholas Circle,
Leicester LE1 3SH
0116 251 6688
www.bbc.co.uk/asiannetwork
*Controller: Andy Parfitt; breakfast:
Sonia Deol*
Press: Andy Bate, 020 8576 1694

BBC World Service
Bush House, Strand,
London WC2B 4PH
020 7557 2941
www.bbc.co.uk/worldservice
*Director: Nigel Chapman, Director of
Global News: Richard Sambrook*

Today programme
Room 5601, Stage 6,
Television Centre, Wood Lane,
London W12 7RJ
www.bbc.co.uk/radio4/today
*Editor: Ceri Thomas; presenters:
John Humphrys, James Naughtie,
Ed Stourton, Sarah Montague,
Carolyn Quinn; comms manager:
Naomi Luland, 020 8576 8367*
Press: 020 8576 8928

● Nations and regions

BBC Radio Scotland
Pacific Quay,
Glasgow G15 1BE
0141 339 8844
scottishplanning@bbc.co.uk
www.bbc.co.uk/scotland
*92-95 FM; 810 AM.
Controller: Ken MacQuarrie*

BBC Radio Nan Gaidheal
52 Church Street, Stornoway,
Isle of Lewis HS1 2LS
01851 705000
feedback@bbc.co.uk
www.bbc.co.uk/scotlandalba/radio
*103-105 FM. Editor: Marion MacKinnon;
news editor: Norman Campbell*

BBC Radio Wales/Cymru
Broadcasting House, Llandaff,
Cardiff CF5 2YQ
0870 010 0110
radiowales@bbc.co.uk
www.bbc.co.uk/radiowales
*93-104 FM. Managing editor: Sali
Collins; head of news: Geoff Williams;
breakfast show: Richard Evans/Felicity
Evans/Rhun Ap Iorwerth/Jo Kiernan/
Sarah Dickens*

BBC Radio Ulster
Broadcasting House,
Belfast BT2 8HQ
028 9033 8000
radioulster@bbc.co.uk
www.bbc.co.uk/radioulster
*92-95.4 FM. Head of radio:
Susan Lovell; editor of music:
Declan McGovern; head of news:
Kathleen Carragher*

BBC Radio Foyle
Northland Road, Derry,
Londonderry BT48 7GD
028 7137 8600
radiofoyle@bbc.co.uk
www.bbc.co.uk/radiofoyle
*93.1 FM; 792 AM. Head of radio:
Paul McCauley*

● BBC local radio

BBC Radio Berkshire
PO Box 1044, Reading RG4 8FH
0118 946 4200
berkshireonline@bbc.co.uk
www.bbc.co.uk/berkshire
*94.6 FM; 95.4 FM; 104.1 FM; 104.4
FM. Editor: Lizz Loxam; breakfast
show: Andrew Peach*

BBC Radio Bristol and Somerset Sound
PO Box 194, Bristol BS99 7QT
01179 741111
radio.bristol@bbc.co.uk
www.bbc.co.uk/radiobristol and
www.bbc.co.uk/bristol
*95.5, 94.9 FM; 1548, 1566 AM.
Managing editor, Bristol: Tim
Pemberton; assistant editors: Dawn
Trevett (Bristol), Simon Clifford
(Somerset Sound); breakfast show:
Nigel Dando/ Rachael Burden*

BBC Radio Cambridgeshire
PO Box 96, 104 Hills Road,
Cambridge CB2 1LD
01223 259696
cambs@bbc.co.uk
www.bbc.co.uk/cambridgeshire
*96 FM; 95.7 FM. News editor: Alison
Daws; managing editor: Jason Horton;
breakfast show: Steve Richardson*

BBC Radio Cleveland
PO Box 95FM, Newport Road,
Middlesbrough TS1 5DG
01642 225211
bbcradiocleveland@bbc.co.uk
www.bbc.co.uk/tees
*95 FM. Managing editor: Matthew
Barraclough; news editor: Peter Harris;
breakfast show: Matthew Davies*

BBC Radio Cornwall
Phoenix Wharf, Truro,
Cornwall TR1 1UA
01872 275421
radio.cornwall@bbc.co.uk
www.bbc.co.uk/cornwall
*103.9 FM; 95.2 FM. Managing editor:
Pauline Causey; news editor: Ed
Goodrich; breakfast show: Pam Spriggs
and James Churchfield*

BBC Radio Cumbria
Annetwell Street, Carlisle CA3 8BB
01228 592444
cumbria@bbc.co.uk
www.bbc.co.uk/radiocumbria
*95.6 FM; 96.1 FM; 104.1 FM.
Managing editor: Nigel Dyson; news
editor: Tom Stight; breakfast show:
Gordon Swindlehurst*

BBC Radio Derby
PO Box 104.5, Derby DE1 3HL
01332 361111
radio.derby@bbc.co.uk
www.bbc.co.uk/radioderby
*1116 AM; 104.5 FM; 95.3 FM; 96FM.
Managing editor: Simon Cornes; news
editor: John Atkin; breakfast show:
Shane O'Connor*

BBC Radio Devon
PO Box 1034, Plymouth PL3 5BD
01752 260323
devon.online@bbc.co.uk
www.bbc.co.uk/devon
*103.4 FM. Managing editor: Robert
Wallis; news editor: Emma Clements;
breakfast show: Michael Chequer*

BBC Essex
198 New London Road,
Chelmsford, Essex CM2 9XB
01245 616000
essex@bbc.co.uk
www.bbc.co.uk/essex
*103.5 FM; 95.3 FM; 765 AM; 1530 AM;
729 AM. Managing editor: Gerald
Maine, news editor: Alison Hodgkins-
Brown; breakfast show: Etholle George
and John Hayes*

BBC Radio Gloucestershire
London Road, Gloucester GL1 1SW
01452 308585
radio.gloucestershire@bbc.co.uk
www.bbc.co.uk/gloucestershire
*104.7 FM; 1413 AM. Managing editor:
Mark Hurrell; news editor: Graham
Day; breakfast show: Mark Cummings*

BBC Radio Guernsey
Bulwer Avenue, St Sampsons,
Guernsey GY2 4LA
01481 200600
radio.guernsey@bbc.co.uk
www.bbc.co.uk/guernsey
*93.2 FM; 1116 AM. Managing editor:
David Martin; news editors: Simon
Alexander and Kay Longlay; breakfast
show: Adrian Gidney*

BBC Hereford and Worcester
Hylton Road, Worcester WR2 5WW
01905 748485
bbchw@bbc.co.uk
www.bbc.co.uk/worcester or
www.bbc.co.uk/hereford
*104 FM; 104.6 FM; 94.7 FM.
Managing editor: James Coghill; news
editor: Jo Baldwin; breakfast show:
Howard Bentham*

BBC Radio Humberside
Queens Court, Queens Gardens,
Hull HU1 3RP
01482 323232
radio.humberside@bbc.co.uk
www.bbc.co.uk/humber
*95.9 FM; 1485 AM. Managing editor:
Simon Pattern; news editor: Polly
Fortune; breakfast show: Andy Comfort*

BBC Radio Jersey
18 Parade Road, St Helier,
Jersey JE2 3PL
01534 837228
jersey@bbc.co.uk
www.bbc.co.uk/jersey
*88.8 FM. Managing editor: Denzil
Dudley; news editor: Matthew Price;
breakfast show: John Uphoff*

BBC Radio Kent
The Great Hall,
Mount Pleasant Road,
Tunbridge Wells, Kent TN1 1QQ
01892 670000
radio.kent@bbc.co.uk
www.bbc.co.uk/kent
*96.7 FM; 97.6 FM; 104.2 FM.
Managing editor: Paul Leaper; news
editor: Peter Stewart; breakfast show:
John Warnett*

BBC Radio Lancashire and BBC Open Centre
26 Darwen Street, Blackburn,
Lancs BB2 2EA
01254 262411
radio.lancashire@bbc.co.uk
www.bbc.co.uk/lancashire
*95.5 FM. Managing editor: John
Clayton; news editor: Chris Rider;
breakfast show: Alison Butterworth*

BBC Radio Leeds
Broadcasting Centre,
2 St Peters Square, Leeds LS9 8AH
0113 244 2131
radio.leeds@bbc.co.uk
www.bbc.co.uk/leeds
*92.4 FM. Managing editor: Phil
Roberts; news editor: Andy Evans;
breakfast show: Andrew Edwards and
Georgie Spanswick*

BBC Radio Leicester
9 St Nicholas Place,
Leicester LE1 5LB
0116 251 6688
leicester@bbc.co.uk
www.bbc.co.uk/leicester
*104.9 FM. Managing editor: Kate
Squire; breakfast show: Ben Jackson*

contacts **Radio**

BBC Radio Lincolnshire
Radion Building, Newport,
Lincoln LN1 3XY
01522 511411
radio.lincolnshire@bbc.co.uk
www.bbc.co.uk/lincolnshire
94.9 FM; 1368 FM; 104 FM. Managing editor: Charlie Partridge; news editor: Andy Farrant; breakfast show: Rod Whiting

BBC London 94.9
35 Marylebone High Street,
London W1U 4AA
020 7224 2424
yourlondon@bbc.co.uk
www.bbc.co.uk/london
94.9 FM. Managing editor: David Robey; breakfast show: Danny Baker

BBC Radio Manchester
PO Box 951, Oxford Road,
Manchester M60 1SD
0161 200 2000
manchester.online@bbc.co.uk
www.bbc.co.uk/manchester
95.1 FM; 104.6 FM. Managing editor: John Ryan; news editor: Mark Elliott; breakfast show: Eamonn O'Neall and Dianne Oxburry

BBC Radio Merseyside and BBC Open Centre
PO Box 95.8, 31 College Lane,
Liverpool L69 1ZJ
0151 708 5500
radio.merseyside@bbc.co.uk
www.bbc.co.uk/liverpool
95.8 FM. Managing editor: Mike Ord; news editor: Andy Ball; breakfast show: Tony Snell

BBC Radio Newcastle
Broadcasting Centre,
Barrack Road,
Newcastle upon Tyne NE99 1RN
0191 232 4141
radio.newcastle@bbc.co.uk
www.bbc.co.uk/england
/radionewcastle
95.4 FM. Managing editor: Andrew Robson; news editor: Rick Martin; breakfast show: Mike Parr

BBC Radio Norfolk
The Forum, Millennium Plain,
Norwich NR2 1BH
01603 617411
radionorfolk@bbc.co.uk
www.bbc.co.uk/norfolk
104.4 FM; 95.1 FM; 855 AM; 873 AM. Managing editor: David Clayton; news editor: Sarah Kings; breakfast show: Stephen Bumfrey

BBC Radio Northampton
Broadcasting House, Abington
Street, Northampton NN1 2BH
01604 239100
northampton@bbc.co.uk
www.bbc.co.uk/northamptonshire
104.2, 103.6 FM. Managing editor: Laura Moss; news editor: Laura Cook; breakfast show: Anna Murby

BBC Radio Nottingham
London Road,
Nottingham NG2 4UU
0115 955 0500
radio.nottingham@bbc.co.uk
www.bbc.co.uk/nottingham
103.8 FM. Managing editor: Sophie Stewart; news editor: Aeneas Rotsos; breakfast show: Andy Whittaker

BBC Radio Oxford
269 Banbury Road,
Oxford OX2 7DW
01865 311444
oxford@bbc.co.uk
www.bbc.co.uk/radiooxford
95.2 FM. Managing editor: Steve Taschini; news editor: Mike Day

BBC Radio Sheffield and BBC Open Centre
54 Shoreham Street,
Sheffield S1 4RS
0114 273 1177
radio.sheffield@bbc.co.uk
www.bbc.co.uk/england
/radiosheffield
88.6 FM. Managing editor: Gary Keown; news editor: Emma Gilliam; breakfast show: Toby Foster

BBC Radio Shropshire
2–4 Boscobel Drive,
Shrewsbury SY1 3TT
01743 248484
radio.shropshire@bbc.co.uk
www.bbc.co.uk/shropshire
96 FM; 95.7 FM. Managing editor: Tim Beach; news editor: Sharon Simcock; breakfast show: Eric Smith

BBC Radio Solent
Broadcasting House, Havelock
Road, Southampton SO14 7PW
023 8063 1311
radio.solent@bbc.co.uk
www.bbc.co.uk/radiosolent
96.1 FM. Managing editor: Mia Costello; breakfast show: Julian Clegg

BBC Southern Counties Radio
Broadcasting Centre,
Guildford GU2 7AP
01483 306306
southern.counties@bbc.co.uk
www.bbc.co.uk/southerncounties
104–104.8 FM; 95–95.3 FM. Managing editor: Mike Hapgood; news editor: Mark Carter; breakfast show: Sarah Gorrell, Ed Douglas, John Radford

BBC Radio Stoke and BBC Open Centre
Cheapside, Hanley,
Stoke on Trent ST1 1JJ
01782 208080
radio.stoke@bbc.co.uk
www.bbc.co.uk/stoke
94.6 FM. Managing editor: Sue Owen

BBC Radio Suffolk
Broadcasting House, St Matthew's
Street, Ipswich, Suffolk IP1 3EP
01473 250000
radiosuffolk@bbc.co.uk
www.bbc.co.uk/suffolk
105.5 FM; 104.5 FM; 103 FM. Managing editor: Peter Cook; news editor: Lis Henderson; breakfast show: Mark Murphy

BBC Radio Swindon
PO Box 1234, Swindon SN1 3RW
01793 513626
radio.swindon@bbc.co.uk
www.bbc.co.uk/wiltshire
103.6 FM. Managing editor: Tony Worgan; news editor: Kirsty Ward and Jillian Moody; breakfast show: Mark O'Donnell

BBC Three Counties Radio
BBC 3CR Hastings Street, Luton,
Bedfordshire LU1 5XL
01582 637400
3cr@bbc.co.uk
www.bbc.co.uk/threecounties
95.5 FM; 104.5 FM; 103 FM. Managing editor: Angus Moorat; breakfast show: Roberto Perrone and Catherine Boyle

BBC Radio Wiltshire
Prospect Place, Swindon,
Wiltshire SN1 3RW
01793 513626
radio.wiltshire@bbc.co.uk
www.bbc.co.uk/wiltshire
103.6 FM. Managing editor: Tony Worgan; news editor: Kirsty Ward and Jillian Moody; breakfast show: Tory Maurice and Matthew Smith

BBC WM (Birmingham)
The Mailbox, Birmingham B1 1RF
0121 567 6000
birmingham@bbc.co.uk
www.bbc.co.uk/birmingham or
www.bbc.co.uk/blackcountry
95.6 FM. Managing editor: Keith Beech; news editor: Raj Ford; breakfast show: Adrian Goldberg

BBC WM (Coventry)
1 Holt Court, Greyfriars Road,
Coventry CV1 2WR
024 7655 1000
coventry@bbc.co.uk
warwickshire@bbc.co.uk
www.bbc.co.uk/coventry
103.7 FM; 94.8 FM; 104 FM. Managing editor: David Clargo; breakfast show: Annie Othen

BBC North Yorkshire — Radio York
20 Bootham Row, York YO30 7BR
01904 641351
northyorkshire.news@bbc.co.uk
www.bbc.co.uk/northyorkshire
1260 AM; 666 AM; 104.3 FM; 103.7 FM; 95.5 FM. Managing editor: Matt Youdale; news editor: Anna Evans; breakfast show: Allan Watkiss, Anna Wallace

● Resources

BBC Radio Resources
Brock House, 19 Langham Street,
London W1A 1AA
020 7765 3208
radio.resources@bbc.co.uk
www.bbcradioresources.com
*Senior operations manager: Martin
Hollister; controller operations and
technology: Miles Hosking;
communications and marketing
manager: Holly Senior*

Event Services
Room 112 Brock House,
19 Langham Street,
London W1A 1AA
020 7765 5100
rr-events-team@bbc.co.uk
www.bbcradioresources.com
*Events manager: Mark Diamond;
events assistant: Joanne Wye,
020 7765 2375*

Outside Broadcasts
Room 112 Brock House,
19 Langham Street,
London W1A 1AA
020 7765 4888
duncan.smith@bbc.co.uk
www.bbcradioresources.com
*Operations manager: Will Garrett;
radio outside broadcasts manager:
Duncan Smith*

● Studios

Birmingham Studios
The Mailbox, Birmingham B1 1RF
0121 567 6767
www.bbc.co.uk/birmingham
*Operations co-ordinator: Liz Treacher;
facilities manager: Caroline Smith*

Bristol Broadcasting House
Whiteladies Road, Bristol BS8 2LR
0117 973 2211
www.bbc.co.uk/bristol
*Radio operations planner:
Maria Clutterbuck; sound manager:
Iain Hunter*

Broadcasting House Studios
Brock House, 19 Langham Street,
London W1A 1AA
020 8743 8000
*www.bbc.co.uk; senior operations
manager: Martin Hollister*

Maida Vale Studios
1-129 Delaware Road,
London W9 2LG
020 7765 2091
www.bbc.co.uk
Facilities manager: John Hakrow

Manchester Studios
New Broadcasting House,
PO Box 27, Oxford Road,
Manchester M60 1SJ
0161 244 4607
www.bbc.co.uk
*Operations co-ordinator:
Alison Turner; operations manager:
Richard Savage*

Commercial radio

Commercial Radio Companies Association
77 Shaftesbury Avenue,
London W1D 5DU
020 7306 2603
info@crca.co.uk
www.crca.co.uk
*Chief executive: Paul Brown; research
and communications manager: Alison
Winter*

● Main commercial radio groups

CN Group
Dalston Road, Carlisle,
Cumbria CA2 5UA
01228 612600
news@
  cumbrian-newspapers.co.uk
www.cumbria-online.co.uk
*Chief executive: Robin Burgess;
managing director: Christopher Bisco;
deputy managing director: Terry Hall*

Chrysalis Radio Group
The Chrysalis Building,
13 Bramley Road, London W10 6SP
020 7221 2213
info@chrysalis.com
www.chrysalis.com
*Chief executives: Richard Huntingford
(whole group), Phil Riley (radio)*

Classic Gold Digital
Network Centre, Chiltern Road,
Dunstable LU6 1HQ
01582 676200
www.classicgolddigital.com
*Managing director: John Baish;
programme controller: Stewart Davies*

GCap Media
30 Leicester Square,
London WC2H 7LA
020 7766 6000
www.gcapmedia.com
*Chief executive: Ralph Bernard; director
of communications: Jane Wilson*

Lincs FM
Witham Park, Waterside South,
Lincoln LN5 7JN
01522 549900
enquiries@lincsfm.co.uk
www.lincsfm.co.uk
*Chief executive: Michael Betton; director
of operations and press: Keith Briggs*

SMG
Pacific Quay, Glasgow G51 1PE
0141 300 3300
www.smg.plc.uk
Acting chief executive: Rob Woodford

Tindle Radio Holdings
Ground Floor, Radio House, Orion
Court, Great Blakenham IP6 0LW
01473 836100
info@tindleradio.com
www.tindleradio.com
*Chief executive: Kevin Stewart; deputy
chief executive: David Lovell; group
programme controller: Mark Franklin*

UKRD Group
Carn Brea Studios, Barncoose
Industrial Estate , Redruth,
Cornwall TR15 3RQ
01209 310435
enquiries@ukrd.co.uk
www.ukrd.com
*Chairman: Trevor Smallwood; chief
executive: William Rogers; group
programme director: Phil Angell*

The Wireless Group
18 Hatfields, London SE1 8DJ
020 7959 7900
www.thewirelessgroup.net
Chief executive: Scott Taunton

● National commercial digital radio

Digital One
30 Leicester Square,
London WC2H 7LA
020 7288 4600
info@digitalone.co.uk
www.ukdigitalradio.com
*Joint venture backed by GCap
and Arqiva. Chief executive:
Quentin Howard*

Freeview
DTV Services Ltd, PO Box 7630,
Mansfield MG18 4YL
020 7792 7412
www.freeview.co.uk
*Five shareholders: BBC, National Grid
Wireless, BSkyB, ITV and Channel 4*

● Stations on AM, DAB* and Freeview

The Arrow
Chrysalis Group, 1 The Square, 111 Broad Street, Birmingham, West Midlands B15 1AS
0121 695 0000
paul.fairburn@chrysalis.com
www.thearrow.co.uk
Rock. DAB; Freeview. Managing director: Paul Fairburn; programme director: Alan Caruther

Choice FM
GCap Media, 30 Leicester Square, London WC2H 7LA
020 7766 6810
info@choicefm.com
www.choicefm.com
Hip-hop and R&B. DAB; 107.1FM. Managing director: Ivor Etienne. Studio: 0870 202 7000

Classic FM
GCap Media, 30 Leicester Square, London WC2H 7LA
020 7343 9000
enquiries@classicfm.co.uk
www.classicfm.com
Classical music. DAB; 99.9-102 FM. Managing Director: Darren Henley; managing editor: Giles Pearman Studio: 0870 070 2969

Core
GCap Media, 30 Leicester Square, London WC2H 7LA
020 7766 6000
fresh@corefreshhits.com
www.corefreshhits.com
Pop, dance and R&B. DAB; Sky; cable; internet. Programme contoller: Bern Leckie; digital content manager: Nick Piggott

Gaydar Radio
Q Soft Consulting, 6th Floor, Queens House, 2 Holly Road, Twickenham TW1 4EG
020 8744 1287
contact@gaydarradio.com
www.gaydarradio.com
Funky house, dance, diva-led house. DAB; Sky; internet. Managing director: Henry Badenhorst; programme controller: Robin Crowley

Heart 106.2
Chrysalis Group, The Chrysalis Building, 13 Bramley Road, London W10 6SP
020 7468 1062
firstname.lastname@ heart1062.co.uk
www.heart1062.co.uk
Feel Good, 106.2 FM. Programme controller: Mark Browning; head of news: Jonathan Richards; breakfast show: Jamie Theakston and Harriet Scott

Heat
Emap Performance Network, Mappin House, 4 Winsley Street, London W1W 8HF
020 7436 1515
www.heatradio.co.uk
Adult contemporary. DAB; Freeview. Development director: Steve Parkinson; programme controller: Robert De'Video

The Hits
Emap Performance Network, Castle Quay, Castlefield, Manchester M15 4PR
0161 288 5000
studio@thehitsradio.com
www.thehitsradio.com
Contemporary music. DAB in Greater London; Freeview; Sky. Station manager: Jamie Wood; programme controller: Anthony Gay

Smooth Radio
Guardian Media Group, 26–27 Castlereagh Street, London W1H 5DL
020 7706 4100
studio@jazzfm.com
www.jazzfm.com
Over 45s. DAB in central Scotland, Greater London, south Wales and Severn estuary; Freeview; 102.2FM in West Midlands. Managing director: Andy Carter; programme controller: Gavin McCoy. Studio: 0844 415 8181

Kerrang!
Emap Performance Network, Kerrang! House, 20 Lionel Street, Birmingham B3 1AQ
0845 053 1052
brendan.moffett@emap.com
http://digital.kerrangradio.co.uk
Rock. Freeview; Sky; cable. Programme director: Andrew Jefferies; managing director: Adrian Serle. Studio: 0845 345 1022

Kiss
Emap Performance Network, Mappin House, 4 Winsley Street, London W1W 8HF
020 7436 1515
feedback@kissonline.co.uk
www.kiss100.com
Rhythmic. DAB; Freeview; Sky; 100 FM in Greater London. Managing director: Steve Parkinson; programme director: Andy Roberts. Studio: 020 7617 9100. Studio: 0845 688 0908

Magic
Emap Performance Network, Mappin House, 4 Winsley Street, London W1W 8HF
020 7975 8100
studio@magicradio.com
www.magic1054.co.uk
Mellow Music. Freeview; Sky; cable. Managing director: Andria Vidler; programme director: Adrian Stewart

Mojo
Emap Performance Network, Mappin House, 4 Winsley Street, London W1W 8HF
020 7436 1515
studio@mojo4music.com
www.mojo4music.com
All Genres. Freeview. Chairman: Dee Ford; Programme director: Robert De'Video. Studio: 020 7436 1054

Oneword Radio
50 Lisson Street, London NW1 5DF
020 7453 1600
info@oneword.co.uk
www.oneword.co.uk
Contemporary music and speech. DAB; Freeview; Sky; internet. Managing director: Simon Blackmore

Planet Rock
30 Leicester Square, London WC2H 7LA
020 7766 6000
joinus@planetrock.com
www.planetrock.com
Classic radio. DAB. Station director: Mark Lee; Executive producer: Trevor White

Premier Christian Radio
Premier Media Group, 22 Chapter Street, London SW1P 4NP
020 7316 1300
enquiries@premier.org.uk
www.premier.org.uk
Contemporary Christian music. Freeview; Sky; cable; 1305, 1332, 1413 AM. Managing director: Peter Kerridge; programme controller: Charmaine Noble-Mclean

Q Radio
Emap Performance Network, Mappin House, 4 Winsley Street, London W1W 8HF
020 7436 1515
brendan.moffett@emap.com
www.q4music.com
Contemporary music. Freeview; Sky; cable. Programme director: Robert De'Video

Smash! Hits
Emap Performance Network, Mappin House, 4 Winsley Street, London W1W 8HF
0161 288 5000
brendan.moffett@emap.com
www.smashhits.net
Chart hits. Freeview; Sky; cable. Programme director: Anthony Gay

TalkSport
The Wireless Group, 18 Hatfields, London SE1 8DJ
020 7959 7800
www.talksport.net
Talk, sport and current affairs. Digital One; 1107, 1053, 1089 AM. Managing director: Scott Taunton; programme director: Bill Ridley. Studio: 0870 420 2020

* only those stations with widespread urban coverage

Virgin Radio
SMG, No 1 Golden Square,
London W1F 9DJ
020 7434 1215
reception@virginradio.co.uk
studio@virginradio.co.uk
www.virginradio.co.uk
Rock. Digital One; Sky; 1197, 1215, 1233, 1242, 1260 AM. Head of production: Mark Bingham; Chief Executive: Paul Jackson

XFM
GCap Media, 30 Leicester Square,
London WC2H 7LA
020 7054 8000
www.xfm.co.uk
Alternative music. DAB; Sky; cable; internet; 104.9 FM. Managing director: Nick Davidson; programme controller: Andy McPherson. Studio: 0871 222 1049; 0870 730 1215

Yarr Radio
Sunrise Radio, Sunrise Radio House, Merrick Road, Southall, Middlesex UB2 4AU
020 843 5313 CHK
info@yarrradio.com
www.yarrradio.com
Asian music. DAB; Sky; internet. Station manager: Ajmer Grewel; chief executive: Avtar Lit. Studio: 020 8574 6262

● News services

ITN Radio
200 Grays Inn Road,
London WC1X 8XZ
020 7430 4090
radio@itn.co.uk
www.itn.co.uk
Managing director: John Perkins; editor: Jon Godel. Newsdesk: 020 7430 4814

Independent Radio News (IRN)
200 Grays Inn Road,
London WC1X 8XZ
020 7430 4090
irn@itn.co.uk
news@irn.co.uk
www.irn.co.uk
Managing director: John Perkins; editor: Jon Godel. Newsdesk: 020 7430 4814

● Commercial local radio: England

95.8 Capital FM
30 Leicester Square,
London WC2H 7LA
020 7766 6000
info@capitalradio.com
www.capitalfm.com
Pop. Greater London. 95.8 FM. Owner: GCap Media. Managing director: Scott Muller; news editor: Matthew Schofield; breakfast show: Johnny Vaughan

107.3 Time FM
2-6 Basildon Road, Abbey Road,
London SE2 OEW
020 8311 3112
www.timefm.com
All-time favourites. South-east London. 106.8, 107.3 FM. Owner: Sunrise Media Group. Station managing director: Mike Huston; news editor: Nigel Goodge; breakfast show: Jonathan Miles

Capital Gold (1548)
30 Leicester Square,
London WC2H 7LA
020 7054 8000
info@capitalradio.com
www.capitalgold.com
Hits of the 60s, 70s and 80s. Greater London. 1548 AM. Owner: GCap Media. Programme director: Andy Turner; head of news: Simon Cliffe; breakfast show: Mick Browne

Choice 107.1 FM
30 Leicester Square,
London WC2H 7LA
020 7054 8000
info@choicefm.com
www.choicefm.com
R&B. North London. 107.1 FM. Owner: GCap Media. Managing director: Ivor Etienne; news editor: Pam Joseph; breakfast show: George Kay

Club Asia
Asia House, 227-247 Gascoigne Road, Barking, Essex IG11 7LN
020 8594 6662
info@clubasiaonline.com
www.clubasiaonline.com
Asians 15-45 Greater London. 972 AM. Independent. Managing director: Ash Kavia; creative director: John Ogden; breakfast show: Jas "The Man" and the Breakfast Clan

Easy Radio
Radio House, Merrick Road,
Southall, Middlesex UB2 4AU
020 8843 5341
info@easy1035.com
www.easy1035.com
Easy listening. Greater London. 1035 AM. Owner: Easy Radio. Programme controller: Paul Owens; breakfast show: Ron Brown

Heart 106.2
The Chrysalis Building,
Bramley Road, London W10 6SP
020 7468 1062
www.heart1062.co.uk
Adult contemporary. Greater London. 106.2 FM. Owner: Chrysalis Radio. Programme controller: Mark Browning; head of news: Jonathan Richards; breakfast show: Jamie Theakston and Harriet Scott

Kiss 100
Mappin House, 4 Winsley Street,
London W1W 8HF
020 7975 8100
firstname.lastname@kiss100.com
www.kiss100.com
Rhythmic. Greater London. 100 FM. Managing director: Steve Parkinson; programme director: Andy Roberts; breakfast show: James Merritt

LBC 97.3 FM
The Chrysalis Building,
Bramley Road, London W10 6SP
020 7314 7300
firstname.lastname@lbc.co.uk
www.lbc.co.uk
Talk radio. Greater London. 97.3 FM. Owner: Chrysalis. Managing director: David Lloyd; programme controller: Scott Solder; head of news: Jonathan Richards; breakfast show: Nick Ferrari

LBC News 1152 AM
The Chrysalis Building,
Bramley Road, London W10 6SP
020 7314 7300
newsroom@lbc.co.uk
www.lbc.co.uk
News. Greater London. 1152 AM. Owner: Chrysalis. Editorial director: Jonathan Richards

London Greek Radio
437 High Road, London N12 OAP
020 8349 6950
sales@lgr.co.uk
www.lgr.co.uk
Greek music. North London. 103.3 FM. Independent. Programme controller and head of news: G Gregoriou; breakfast show: Soula Viola Ri

London Turkish Radio LTR
185B High Road, Wood Green,
London N22 6BA
020 8881 0606
info@londontv.org
www.londonturkishradio.org
Turkish and English music. North London. 1584 AM. Independent. Programme controller: Metin Sak, managing director: Erkan Pastirmacioglu; breakfast show: Fatos Sarman

Magic 105.4 FM
Mappin House, 4 Winsley Street,
London W1W 8HF
020 7955 1054
firstname.lastname@emap.com
www.magic1054.co.uk
Soft melodic. Freeview; Sky; cable. Managing director: Andria Vidler; programme director: Richard Park; breakfast show: Gary Vincent

contacts **Radio**

Premier Christian Radio
22 Chapter Street,
London SW1P 4NP
020 7316 1300
premier@premier.org.uk
www.premier.org.uk
*Contemporary Christian music.
Freeview; Sky; cable; 1305, 1332,
1413 AM. Managing director: Peter
Kerridge; programme controller:
Charmaine Noble-Mclean;*

Smooth FM 102.2
26–27 Castlereagh Street,
London W1H 5DL
020 7706 4100
jazzinfo@jazzfm.com
www.jazzfm.com
*Soul, jazz and R&B. DAB in central
Scotland, Greater London, south
Wales and Severn estuary; Freeview;
102.2 FM in West Midlands. Managing
director: Roy Bennett; programme
director: Mark Walker; breakfast
show: David Prever*

Spectrum Radio
4 Ingate Place, Battersea,
London SW8 3NS
020 7627 4433
name@spectrumradio.net
www.spectrumradio.net
*Multi-ethnic. Greater London. 558 AM.
Independent. General manager: Paul
Hogan; managing director: Toby Aldrich*

Sunrise Radio
Sunrise House, Bridge Road,
Southall, Middlesex UB2 4AU
020 8574 6666
Reception@sunriseradio.com
www.sunriseradio.com
*Asian music. Greater London. 1458
AM. Independent. Chief executive:
Avtar Lit; news editor: David Landau;
breakfast show: Tony Patti*

Virgin 105.8
1 Golden Square, London W1F 9DJ
020 7434 1215
reception@virginradio.co.uk
www.virginradio.co.uk
*Rock. Greater London. 105.8 FM.
Owner: SMG. Programme director:
Paul Jackson; head of news:
Andrew Bailey; breakfast show:
Christian O'Connell*

Xfm
30 Leicester Square,
London WC2H 7LA
020 7054 8000
info@xfm.co.uk
www.xfm.co.uk
*Alternative music. Greater London.
104.9 FM. Owner: GCap Media.
Managing director: Nick Davidson;
programme controller: Andy Ashton;
news centre: Chris Smith*

2-Ten FM
PO Box 2020, Calcot, Reading,
Berkshire RG31 7FG
0118 945 4400
tim.parker@creation.com
www.musicradio.com
*All types of music. Reading,
Basingstoke, Newbury and Andover.
103.4 FM; 97 FM; 102.9 FM. Owner:
GCap Media. Programme controller:
Tim Parker; head of news: Peter Cook;
breakfast show: Foxy and Tom*

96.4 The Eagle
Dolphin House, North Street,
Guildford GU1 4AA
01483 300964
onair@964eagle.co.uk
www.964eagle.co.uk
*Adult contemporary. Guildford.
96.4 FM, 1566AM. Owner: UKRD
Group. Managing director: Valeria
Handley; programme director: Peter
Gordon; head of news: Rob Harris;
breakfast show: Peter Gordon*

103.2 Power FM
Radio House,
Whittle Avenue, Segensworth,
West Fareham PO15 5SH
01489 589911
info@powerfm.co.uk
www.powerfm.com
*20 years to up-to-date pop. South
Hampshire. 103.2 FM. Owner: GCap
Media. Programme director: Jason
Walkerden; head of news: Alison Law;
breakfast show: Dan Morrissey*

107.4 The Quay
Flagship Studios PO Box 1074,
Portsmouth PO2 8YG
023 9236 4141
mail@quayradio.com
www.quayradio.com
*Pop. Portsmouth. 107.4 FM. Owner:
Radio Investments. Programme
controller and breakfast show:
Sam Matterface*

107.5 Sovereign Radio
14 St Mary's Walk, Hailsham,
East Sussex BN27 1AF
01323 442700
info@1075sovereignradio.co.uk
www.1075sovereignradio.co.uk
*Music. Eastbourne. 107.5 FM. Owner:
Local Radio Company. Programme
Controller: Nigel Ansell; Sales
manager: Karen Dyball; breakfast
show: Simon Rose.*

107.6 Kestrel FM
Paddington House, Festival Place,
Basingstoke RG21 7LJ
01256 694000
studio@kestrelfm.com
www.kestrelfm.com
*70s, 80s, 90s and today. Basingstoke.
107.6 FM. Owner: Tindle Group director:
Paul Allen; programme manager: Mark
Watson; head of news: Kevin Gover;
breakfast show: Mark Watson*

107.8 Arrow FM
Priory Meadow Centre,
Hastings, East Sussex TN34 1PJ
01424 461177
info@arrowfm.co.uk
www.arrowfm.co.uk
*Adult contemporary. Hastings. 107.8
FM. Local Radio Company.
Programme controller: Mike Buxton;
head of news: Vicky Jones; breakfast
show: Andy Knight*

107.8 Radio Jackie
The Old Post Office 110–112,
Tolworth Broadway, Surbiton,
Surrey KT6 7JD
020 8288 1300
info@radiojackie.com
www.radiojackie.com
*Family Oriented. South West London
and Surrey. 107.8 FM. Independent.
Managing director: Peter Stremes;
programme controller: Dave Owen;
head of news: Rod Bradbury; breakfast
show: Neil Long*

Bright 106.4
The Market Place Shopping Centre,
Burgess Hill, West Sussex RH15 9NP
01444 248127
reception@bright1064.com
www.bright1064.com
*70s, 80s, 90s and latest. West Sussex,
Surrey and East Sussex. 106.4 FM.
Independent. Managing director:
Allan Moulds; head of news: Philip
Keeler; breakfast show: Scott Bailey*

Capital Gold (1170 and 1557)
Radio House, Whittle Avenue,
Segensworth West, Farnham,
Hampshire PO15 5SH
01489 589911
info@capitalgold.com
www.capitalgold.com
*Hits of the 70s and 80s and today.
South Hampshire. 1557 AM; 1170 AM.
Owner: GCap Media. Programme
director: Andy Turner; head of
news: Alison Law; breakfast show:
David Jensen*

Capital Gold (1242 and 603)
Radio House, John Wilson Business
Park, Whitstable, Kent CT5 3QX
01227 772004
info@capitalgold.co.uk
www.capitalgold.com
*Hits of the 60s, 70s and 80s.
Maidstone, Medway and East Kent.
603 AM; 1242 AM. Owner: GCap
Media. Programme director: Nicola
Everitt; head of news: Clare Martin;
breakfast show: Ali and James*

Capital Gold (1323 and 945)
Radio House, PO Box 2000,
Brighton BN41 2SS
020 7766 6000
info@capitalgold.co.uk
www.capitalgold.com
*Hits of the 60s, 70s and 80s.
Maidstone, Medway and East Kent.
603 AM; 1242 AM. Owner: GCap
Media. Programme director: Andy
Turner; head of news: Clare Martin;
breakfast show: David Jensen*

Classic Gold 1431 and 1485

The Chase, Calcot,
Reading RG31 7RB
0118 945 4400
enquiries@classicgolddigital.com
www.classicgolddigital.com
*80s, 90s and modern. Reading,
Basingstoke and Andover. 1431 AM;
1485 AM. Owner: gcap. Network head
of programmes: Bill Overton and Paul
Baker; head of news: Suzie Southgate*

Classic Gold (1521)

The Stanley Centre, Kelvin Way,
Crawley, West Sussex RH10 9SE
01293 519161
studio@musicradio.com
www.musicradio.co.uk
*60s and 70s. Reigate and Crawley. 1521
AM. Owner: Classic Gold Digital. Sales
team leader: Amanda Masters; network
head of programmes: Bill Overton and
Paul Baker; head of news: Gareth
Davies; breakfast show: Tony Blackburn*

County Sound Radio 1566 AM

Dolphin House North Street,
Guildford GU1 4AA
01483 300964
onair@countysound.co.uk
www.ukrd.com
*Adult contemporary. Guildford. 1566
AM. Owner: UKRD Group. Managing
director: Paul Marcus; programme
director: Peter Gordon; head of news:
Rob Harris; breakfast show: Dave Johns*

CTR 105.6 FM

6-8 Mill Street,
Maidstone ME15 6XH
01622 662500
enq@ctrfm.com
www.ctrfm.com
*Adult contemporary. Maidstone.
105.6 FM. Kent Messenger Group.
Managing director: Geraldine
Allinson; breakfast show: Ant Payne*

Delta FM

Tindle House, High Street,
Bordon, Hants GU35 0AY
01420 473473
studio@deltaradio.co.uk
www.deltaradio.co.uk
*Yesterday and today. Alton,
Hampshire. 101.6 FM; 102 FM;
97.1 FM; 101.8 FM. Owner: Tindle
Newspapers. Managing director:
David Way; sales manager: Jan
Ashley; head of news: Lorna O'Keefe;
breakfast show: Stuart Clark*

FM 103 Horizon

14 Vincent Avenue Crownhill,
Milton Keynes MK8 0AB
01908 269111
reception@horizon.musicradio.com
www.musicradio.com
*80s, 90s and today. Milton Keynes.
103.3 FM. Owner: GCap Media.
Programme controller: Trevor Marshall;
breakfast show: Gareth James*

Invicta FM

Radio House, John Wilson Business
Park, Whitstable, Kent CT5 3QX
01227 772004
info@invictaradio.co.uk
www.invictafm.com
*Pop. Maidstone, Medway and East
Kent. 95.9 FM; 102.8 FM; 96.1 FM; 97
FM; 103.1 FM. Owner: GCap Media.
Programme controller: Craig Body,
head of news: Nicola Everitt; breakfast
show: The Morning Zoo*

Isle of Wight Radio

Dodnor Park, Newport,
Isle of Wight PO30 5XE
01983 822557
admin@iwradio.co.uk
www.iwradio.co.uk
*Adult contemporary and pop. Isle
of Wight. 102 FM; 107 FM. Owner:
The Local Radio Company, Programme
controller: Andy Shier; head of
news: Duncan Smith; breakfast show:
Andy Shier*

Juice 107.2

170 North Street, Brighton BN1 1EA
01273 386107
info@juicebrighton.com
www.juicebrighton.com
*Commercial dance. Brighton. 107.2 FM.
Owner: Brighton & Hove Ltd. Managing
director: Matthew Bashford;
programme controller: Sam Walker;
head of news: Graham Levitt;
breakfast show: Terry Garoghan*

Kick FM

The Studios, 42 Bone Lane,
Newbury, Berkshire RG14 5SD
01635 841600
mail@kickfm.com
www.kickfm.com
*Adult contemporary. Newbury. 105.6
FM; 107.4 FM. Owner: Tindle Group.
Managing director: John Baker; head
of news: Phil Spray; programme
controller: James O'Neill; breakfast
show: Chris Rose and Charlotte Butt*

Kmfm for Canterbury

9 St George's Place, Canterbury,
Kent CT1 1UU
01227 475950
reception@kmfm.co.uk
www.kmfm.co.uk
*Adult contemporary. Canterbury.
106 FM. Owner: KM Radio. Group
programme controller: Spencer Cork;
head of news: Anthony Masters;
breakfast show: Spencer James*

Kmfm for Folkestone and Dover

93-95 Sandgate Road,
Folkestone, Kent CT20 2BQ
01303 220303
Scork@kmfm.co.uk
www.kmfm.co.uk
*60s, 70s, 80s and 90s. Dover and
Folkestone. 106.8 FM; 96.4 FM.
Owner: KM Radio. Group programme
controller: Spencer Cork; head of sales:
Suzanne Fitzsimons; breakfast show:
Johnny Lewis*

Kmfm for Medway

Medway House, Ginsbury Close,
Sir Thomas Longley Road,
Strood ME2 4DU
pcarter@kmfm.co.uk
www.kmfm.co.uk
*Adult contemporary. Medway Towns.
100.4 FM; 107.9 FM. Owner: KM
Radio. Group programme controller:
Steve Fountain; breakfast show:
Richard Walters*

Kmfm for Thanet

181-183 Northdown Road,
Cliftonville, Kent CT9 2PA
01843 220222
initialsurname@kmgroup.co.uk
www.kmfm.co.uk
*Classic hits from 70s and current.
Thanet. 107.2 FM. Owner: KM Radio.
Group programme controller: Steve
Fountain; head of news: Anthony
Masters; breakfast show: Tim Stewart*

Kmfm for West Kent

1 East Street, Tonbridge,
Kent TN9 1AR
01732 369200
tunbridgestudio@kmfm.co.uk
www.kmfm.co.uk
*Adult contemporary. Tunbridge Wells
and Sevenoaks. 96.2 FM; 101.6 FM.
Owner: KM Radio. Group programme
controller: Steve Fountain; head of
news: Anthony Masters; breakfast
show: Neil Faraday*

Mercury FM

The Stanley Centre, Kelvin Way,
Crawley, West Sussex RH10 9SE
01293 519161
studio@musicradio.com
www.musicradio.com
*60s and 70s. Reigate and Crawley.
97.5 FM; 102.7 FM. Owner: GCap
Media. Programme controller: Andrew
Dancey; head of news: Gareth Davies;
breakfast show: Paul Bunker*

Mix 96

Friars Square Studios, 11 Bourbon
Street, Aylesbury HP20 2PZ
01296 399396
info@mix96.co.uk
www.mix96.co.uk
*60s to present day. Aylesbury.
96.2 FM. Owner: Local Radio
Company. Station manager: Lydia
Flack; programme controller: Matt
Faulkner; head of news: Andrew
Carter; breakfast show: Rory and Di*

Mix 107 FM

PO Box 1107, High Wycombe,
Buckinghamshire HP13 6EE
01494 446611
sales@mix107.co.uk
www.mix107.co.uk
*Adult contemporary. South Bucks.
107.4 FM. Owner: Local radio
Company. Programme director:
Andy Muir; head of news: Hilary
Cogan; breakfast show: Big Fun
Breakfast with Andy H and Steve*

Ocean FM

Radio House,
Whittle Avenue, Segensworth,
West Fareham PO15 5SH
01489 589911
info@oceanfm.co.uk
www.oceanfm.com
*70s, 80s and 90s. South Hampshire.
96.7 FM; 97.5 FM. Owner: GCap
Media. Programme controller: Richard
Wilkinson; head of news: Alison Law;
breakfast show: Richard Williams*

Reading 107 FM

Radio House, Madejski Stadium,
Reading, Berkshire RG2 0FN
0118 986 2555
firstname@reading107fm.com
www.reading107fm.com
*Beatles to Bangles. Reading. 107 FM.
Independent. Managing director: Jeff
Lee; programme controller: Robert
Kenny; sales commercial director: Sue
Reynolds; breakfast show: Neale James*

Southern FM

Radio House, PO Box 2000,
Brighton BN41 2SS
01273 430111
news@southernfm.co.uk
www.southernfm.com
*Pop. Brighton, Eastbourne and
Hastings. 103.5 FM; 96.9 FM; 102.4
FM; 102 FM. Owner: GCap Media.
Sales director: Lorraine Wynn;
programme controller: Tony Aldridge;
news editor: Laurence King; breakfast
show: Danny & Nicky in the Morning*

Spirit FM

9-10 Dukes Court, Bognor Road,
Chichester PO19 8FX
01243 773600
info@spiritfm.net
www.spiritfm.net
*Easy listening. Chichester, Bognor Regis,
Littlehampton. 102.3 FM; 96.6 FM,
106.6 FM. Independent. Managing
director: John Oates, programme
controller: Paul Williams; head of
news: Ian Crouch; breakfast show:
Paul Williams*

Splash FM

Guildbourne Centre, Worthing,
West Sussex BN11 1LZ
01903 233005
mail@splashfm.com
www.splashfm.com
*60s, 70s, 80s, 90s and today.
Worthing. 107.7 FM. Independent.
Managing director: David Atkey;
programme controller: Simon Osborne;
news editor: Kerry Worman; breakfast
show: Dave Hunt*

Time 107.5

Lambourne House, 7 Western
Road, Romford, Essex RM1 3LD
01708 731643
info@timefm.com
www.timefm.com
*Soul. Romford, Barking and
Dagenham. 107.5 FM. Owner: Sunrise
Radio. Managing director: Neil
Romain; programme director: Mark
Dover; breakfast show: Mike Porter*

Wave 105 FM

5 Manor Court, Barnes Wallis
Road, Segensworth East,
Fareham, Hampshire PO15 5TH
01489 481057
martin.ball@wave105.com
www.wave105.com
*70s, 80s and 90s hits. Solent. 105.2 FM;
105.8 FM. Owner: Emap. Managing
director: Martin Ball; programme
controller: Dave Shearer; head of
news: Jason Beck; breakfast show:
Steve Power*

Win 107.2

PO Box 107,
The Brooks Shopping Centre,
Winchester, Hampshire SO23 8FT
01962 841071
jo@winfm.co.uk
www.winfm.co.uk
*Adult contemporary. Winchester.
107.2 FM. Owner: Tindle Group.
Station manager: Phil Marriott; head
of news: Kevin Gover; breakfast show:
Phil Marriott*

SOUTH-WEST

2CR FM

5-7 Southcote Road,
Bournemouth, Dorset BH1 3LR
01202 234900
newsbournemouth@creation.com
www.musicradio.com
*80 and 90s and chart music.
Bournemouth and Hampshire. 102.3
FM. Owner: GCap Media. Programme
controller: Lucinda Holman; sales
director: Jane Suttie; breakfast show:
Chris Wright*

97 FM Plymouth Sound

Earl's Acre, Plymouth PL3 4HX
01752 275600
mail@plymouthsound
.musicradio.com
www.musicradio.com
*80s, 90s and today. Plymouth. 97 FM;
96.6 FM. Owner: GCap Media.
Programme controller: Martin Mills,
head of news: Michaela Richards;
breakfast show: Morning Crew*

97.4 Vale FM

Longmead Studios, Shaftesbury,
Dorset SP7 8QQ
01747 855711
studio@valefm.co.uk
www.valefm.co.uk
*Adult contemporary. Shaftesbury.
97.4 FM; 96.6 FM. Owner: Local Radio
Company. Programme controller:
Dave Webster; head of news:
Maria Greenwood; breakfast show:
Cameron Smith*

104.7 Island FM

12 Westerbrook, St Sampsons,
Guernsey GY2 4QQ
01481 242000
firstname@islandfm.guernsey.net
www.islandfm.guernsey.net
*Chart music. Rock show in evenings.
Guernsey. 104.7 FM; 93.7 FM. Owner:
Tindle Radio. Programme controller:
Tim Manns; head of news: Andy
Richards; breakfast show: Richard
Harding*

107.5 3TR FM

Riverside Studios, Boreham Mill,
Bishopstow, Warminster BA12 9HQ
01985 211111
admin@3trfm.com
www.3trfm.com
*Classics. Warminster. 107.5 FM.
Owner: Local Radio Company.
Managing director: Ceri Hurfod Jones;
sales manager: Will Brougham; head
of news: Tessa Bickers; breakfast show:
Jono & Tess*

Bath FM

Station House, Ashley Avenue,
Lower Weston, Bath BA1 3DS
01225 471571
news@bath.fm
www.bath.fm
*Adult contemporary. Bath. 107.9 FM.
Independent. Managing director:
Jo Woods; programme controller:
Tim Lewis; head of news: John
Watson; breakfast show: Ian Dore*

Quay West

Royal Clarence House,
York Buildings High Street,
Bridgwater TA6 3AT
01278 727701
studio@bcrfm.co.uk
www.quaywestfm.net
*Music from last four decades.
Bridgwater. 107.4 FM. Radio
Broadcasting Limited; station manger:
David Englefield; breakfast show:
Drew Haddon*

Channel 103 FM

6 Tunnell Street,
St Helier, Jersey JE2 4LU
01534 888103
firstname@channel103.com
www.channel103.com
*Broad mix of pop and rock. Jersey.
103.7 FM. Owner: Tindle Radio.
Managing director: Linda Burnham;
programme controller: Tim Manns;
head of news: Christina Ghidona;
breakfast show: Peter Mac*

Classic Gold 666/954

Hawthorn House, Exeter Business
Park, Exeter EX1 3QS
01392 444444
*Classic Hits. Exeter, Torbay. 954 AM;
Owner: Classic Gold Digital. Head of
programmes: Stuart Davies; head of
news: Michelle Horsley; breakfast
show: Tony Blackburn*

Classic Gold 774
Bridge Studios, Eastgate Centre, Gloucester GL1 1SS
01452 572400
www.classicgolddigital.com
Various sounds. Gloucester, Cheltenham. 774 AM. Owner: Classic Gold Digital. head of programmes: Bill Overton; breakfast show: Tony Blackburn

Classic Gold 828
5 Southcote Road, Bournemouth, Dorset BH1 3LR
01202 234900
newsbournemouth@creation.com
www.classicgolddigital.com
Popular music. Bournemouth. 828 AM. Owner: Classic Gold Digital. Head of programmes: Paul Baker; breakfast show: Tony Blackburn

Classic Gold 936/1161 AM
1st Floor, Chiseldon House Stonehill Green Westlea, Swindon, Wiltshire SN5 7HB
01793 663000
reception@musicradio.com
www.musicradio.com
Popular music. Swindon. 936 AM; 1161 AM. Owner: Classic Gold Digital. Managing director: Neil Cooper; head of programming: Paul Kaye; breakfast show: Tony Blackburn

Classic Gold 1152 AM
Earl's Acre, Plymouth PL3 4HX
01752 275600
www.classicgolddigital.com
70s, 80s and 90s. Plymouth. 1152 AM. Owner: Classic Gold Digital. Head of programmes: Paul Baker; head of news: Daryl Jenner; breakfast show: Tony Blackburn

Classic Gold 1260
One Passage Street, Bristol BS99 7SN
0117 984 3200
admin@classicgolddigital.com
www.classicgolddigital.com
Chart Music. Bristol and Bath. 1260 AM. Owner: Classic Gold Digital. Head of programmes: Paul Andrews; head of news: Cormac Macmahon; breakfast show: Bush and Troy

Fire 107.6FM
The Picture House, 307 Holdenhurst Road, Bournemouth BH8 8BX
01202 318100
firstname@fire1076.com
www.fire1076.com
Rhythmic and contemporary. Bournemouth and Poole. 107.6 FM. Owner: The Local Radio Company. Station manager: Joanna Bishop; head of news: Marie Horner; breakfast show: Dave, Marie and Josh

FOX FM
Brush House, Pony Road, Oxford OX4 2XR
01865 871000
reception@foxfm.co.uk
www.foxfm.co.uk
Adult contemporary. Oxford and Banbury. 102.6 FM; 97.4 FM. Owner: GCap. Programme controller: Jon O'Neill; head of news: Giselle Ruskin; breakfast show: Debbie & Adam

Gemini FM
Hawthorn House, Exeter Business Park, Exeter EX1 3QS
01392 444444
gemini@geminifm.musicradio.com
www.musicradio.com
Top 40. Exeter, Torbay. 97 FM; 103 FM; 96.4 FM. Owner: GCap; Content Director: Dirk Anthony; head of news: Michelle Horsley; breakfast show: Matt & Charlie

GWR FM and Classic Gold Digital
PO Box 2000, One Passage Street, Bristol BS99 7SN
0117 984 3200
reception@musicradio.com
www.musicradio.com
70s, 80s and 90s and today. Swindon and west Wiltshire. 102.2 FM; 96.5 FM; 97.2 FM. Owner: GCap Media. Programme controller: Paul Andrew; head of news: Cormac MacMahon; breakfast show: Join Paulina and Russ

GWR FM (Bath)
PO Box 2000, One Passage Street, Bristol BS99 7SN
0117 984 3200
reception@gwrfm.musicradio.com
www.musicradio.com
Chart music. Bristol and Bath. 103 FM. Owner: GCap Media. Content director: Dirk Anthony; programme controller: Paul Andrew; head of news: Cormac MacMahon; breakfast show: Paulina and Russ

GWR FM (Bristol)
PO Box 2000, One Passage Street, Bristol BS99 7SN
0117 984 3200
reception@gwrfm.musicradio.com
www.musicradio.com
Chart music. Bristol and Bath. 103 FM; 96.3 FM. Owner: GCap Media. Managing director: Dirk Anthony; programme controller: Paul Andrew; head of news: Cormac MacMahon; breakfast show: Tony and Michaela

Ivel FM
The Studios, Middle Street, Yeovil, Somerset BA20 1DJ
reception: 01935 848488
all@ivelfm.co.uk
www.ivelfm.co.uk
60s, 70s, 80s to present day. Yeovil. 105.6 FM, 106.6 FM. Owner: Local Radio Company. Programme controller: Steve Carpenter; heads of news: Robbie Lane; breakfast show: Steve Carpenter

Lantern FM
2b Lauder Lane, Roundswell Business Park, Barnstaple EX31 3TA
01271 342342
paul.hopper@gcapmedia.com
www.musicradio.com
Late 90s to present day. Barnstaple. 97.3 FM; 96.2 FM. Owner: GCap Media. Sales director: Francis Falagan; programme controller: Paul Hopper; head of news: Tim Pryor; breakfast show: Hopps and Chapple

Orchard FM
Haygrove House, Taunton, Somerset TA3 7BT
01823 338448
orchardfm@musicradio.com
www.musicradio.com
Top 40. Yeovil and Taunton. 102.6 FM; 97.1 FM; 96.5 FM. Owner: GCap Media. Programme controller: Jon White; journalists: Nicola Maxey and Darren Bevan; breakfast show: Ian and Laura

Passion 107.9
270 Woodstock Road, Oxford OX2 7NW
01865 315980
info@passion1079.com
www.passion1079.com
Dance and pop. Oxford. 107.9 FM. Owner: Absolute Radio. Programme controller and station manager: Ian Walker; breakfast show: Darren Lee

Pirate FM
Carn Brea Studios, Wilson Way, Redruth, Cornwall TR15 3XX
01209 314400
enquiries@piratefm.co.uk
www.piratefm.co.uk
60s to today. Cornwall and west Devon. 102.2 FM; 102.8 FM. Owner: UKRD Group. Managing director: Beverley Warne; programme director: Bob McCreadie; head of news: Tristan Hunkin; breakfast show: Bob McCreadie

Severn Sound
Bridge Studios, Eastgate Centre, Gloucester GL1 1SS
01452 572400
www.musicradio.com
80s to today. Gloucester and Cheltenham. 103 FM; 102.4 FM. Owner: GCap Media. Programme controller: Marcus Langreiter; sales manager: Lorraine Milkins; breakfast show: Shaun Tilley

South Hams Radio
Unit 1G, South Hams Business Park, Churchstow, Kingsbridge, Devon TQ7 3QH
01548 854595
reception@southhamsradio.com
www.southhamsradio.com
Adult contemporary. South Hams. 101.9 FM; 100.8 FM; 100.5 FM; 101.2 FM. Owner: GCap Media. head of news: Steph Wright; breakfast show: Graham Russell

Traditional media

Spire FM
City Hall Studios, Malthouse Lane,
Salisbury, Wiltshire SP2 7QQ
01722 416644
info@spirefm.co.uk
www.spirefm.co.uk
*Chart hits. South Wilts, West Hams
and Salisbury. 102 FM. Owner: Local
Radio Company. station manager:
Karen Bosley; programme controller:
Stuart McGinley; breakfast show:
Chris Ewington*

Star 107.2
Bristol Evening Post Building,
Temple Way, Bristol BS99 7HD
0117 910 6600
www.starbristol.co.uk
*Adult contemporary and soul. Bristol.
107.2 FM. Owner: UKRD Group. Station
manager: Sue Brooks; head of news:
Martin Jones; breakfast show: JP*

Star 107.5
Cheltenham Film Studios, 1st Floor,
West Suite, Arle Court, Hatherley
Lane, Cheltenham GL51 6PN
01242 699555
studio@star1075.co.uk
www.star1075.co.uk
*70s, 80s and 90s and greatest hits.
Stroud. 107.3 FM; 107.9 FM. Owner:
UKRD Group. Head of sales: Junie
Lewis; programme manager: Brody
Swain; head of news: Nelly Bird;
breakfast show: Brody Swain*

Star 107.7 FM
11 Beaconsfield Road,
Weston Super Mare BS23 1YE
01934 624455
name@star1077.co.uk
www.star1077.co.uk
*70s, 80s and 90s popular music. North
Somerset. 107.7 FM. Owner: UKRD
Group. Programme controller: Ian
Downs; head of news: Will Jordan;
breakfast show: Ian Downs*

Kiss 101
26 Baldwin Street, Bristol BS1 1SE
0117 901 0101
info@vibe101.co.uk
www.vibe101.co.uk
*Dance and R&B. South Wales and
Severn estuary. 97.2 FM; 101 FM.
Owner: Emap. Managing director:
Susanna Cole; programme controller:
Nathan Thomson; breakfast show:
Matt Rogers and Caroline Cook*

Wessex FM
Radio House, Trinity Street,
Dorchester DT1 1DJ
01305 250333
admin@wessexfm.com
www.wessexfm.com
*Hits of 60s, 70s, 80s. Weymouth and
Dorchester. 97.2 FM; 96 FM. Owner:
Local Radio Company. Station
manager: Steve Bulley; head of news:
Maria Greenwood; breakfast show:
Jason Herbert*

96.9 Chiltern FM
5, Abbey Court, Fraser Road,
Priory Business Park, Bedford,
Bedfordshire MK44 3WH
01234 272400
firstname.surname@
  musicradio.com
www.musicradio.com
*80s, 90s to today. Bedford. 96.9 FM.
Owner: GCap Media. Sales manager:
Sharon Rush; programme controller:
Stuart Davies; head of news: Huw
James; breakfast show: Andy Gelder*

97.6 Chiltern FM
Chiltern Road, Dunstable,
Bedfordshire LU6 1HQ
01582 676200
firstname.surname@
  musicradio.co.uk
www.musicradio.com
*Easy listening. Hertfordshire,
Bedfordshire, Buckinghamshire. 97.6
FM. Owner: GCap Media. Programme
director: Stuart Davies; programme
controller: Paul Holmes; head of news:
Huw James; breakfast show: Gareth
Wesley*

102.7 Hereward FM
PO Box 225 Queensgate Centre,
Peterborough PE1 1XJ
01733 460460
firstname.surname@
  gcapmedia.com
www.musicradio.com
*Adult contemporary. Greater
Peterborough. 102.7 FM. Owner: GCap
Media. Programme controller: Tom
Haynes; head of news: Erin Mitchell;
breakfast show: Kev Lawrence*

103.4 The Beach
PO Box 103.4, Lowestoft,
Suffolk NR32 2TL
0845 345 1035
103.4@thebeach.co.uk
www.thebeach.co.uk
*Chart past and present. Great Yarmouth
and Lowestoft. 103.4 FM. Owner: Tindle
Radio. Managing director: David Blake;
news editor: Ross Hutchinson; breakfast
show: Paul Carter*

Broadland 102
St George's Plain, 47–49 Colgate,
Norwich NR3 1DB
01603 630621
firstname.surname@
  gcapmedia.com
www.musicradio.com
*80s, 90s and today. Norfolk and north
Suffolk. 102.4 FM. Owner: GCap
Media. Programme controller: Steve
Martin; head of news: Harry Mitchell;
breakfast show: Rob and Chrissie*

Classic Gold 792/828
Chiltern Road, Dunstable,
Beds LU6 1HQ
01582 676200
firstname.surname@
  classicgolddigital.com
www.classicgolddigital.com
*60s to modern. Luton, Bedford. 792
AM; 828 AM. Owner: GCap/Classic
Gold Digital. Programme controller:
Paul Holmes; head of news: Huw
James; breakfast show: Tony
Blackburn and Laura Pittson*

Classic Gold 1332 AM
PO Box 225, Queensgate Centre,
Peterborough PE1 1XJ
01733 460460
firstname.surname@
  classicgolddigital.com
www.classicgolddigital.com
*Classic hits. Peterborough. 1332 AM.
Owner: GCap/Classic Gold Digital.
Programme controller: Bill Overton;
head of news: Erin Mitchell; breakfast
show: Tony Blackburn*

Classic Gold Amber
St George's Plain,
47–49 Colgate, Norwich NR3 1DB
01603 630621
firstname.surname@
  classicgolddigital.com
www.classicgolddigital.com
*80s, 90s and today. Norwich. 1152 AM.
Owner: GCap Media/Classic Gold
Digital. Programme controller: Paul
Baker; sales centre manager: Rod
Walker; breakfast show: Tony Blackburn*

Classic Gold Amber 1152
Alpha Business Park, 6–12 White
House Road, Ipswich IP1 5LT
01473 461000
firstname.surname@
  classicgolddigital.com
www.classicgolddigital.com
*70s and 80s. Ipswich and Bury St
Edmunds. 1251 AM; 1170 AM. Owner:
GCap/Classic Gold Digital. Programme
controller: Bill Overton; breakfast
show: Tony Blackburn*

Classic Gold Breeze
Radio House, 31 Glebe Road,
Stanford, Essex CN1 1QG
01245 524500
firstname.surname@
  classicgolddigital.com
www.classicgolddigital.com
*Classic 60s, 70s, 80s. Southend and
Chelmsford. 1359 AM; 1431 AM.
Owner: GCap/Classic Gold Digital.
Programme controller: Paul Baker;
breakfast show: Tony Blackburn*

Dream 100 FM
Northgate House, St Peter's
Street, Colchester, Essex CO1 1HT
01206 764466
info@dream100.com
www.dream100.com
*70s to today. North Essex and south
Suffolk. 100.2 FM. Owner: Tindle
Radio. Managing director: Jamie
Brodie; programme controller: David
Rees; head of news: Rachel Whitehead;
breakfast show: Chris Sturgess*

Dream 107.7

Unit 12, Bentlalls Shopping Centre, Haybridge, Malton, Essex CM3 4GP
0845 365 1078
firstname.surname@dream107.com
www.dream107.com
Adult contemporary. Chelmsford. 107.7 FM. Owner: Tindle Radio. Managing director: Jamie Brodie; programme controller, head of news and breakfast show: Paul Lovett

Essex FM

Radio House, 31 Glebe Road, Stanford, Essex CN1 1QG
01245 524500
firstname.surname@ gcapmedia.com
www.musicradio.com
Adult contemporary. Chelmsford. 107.7 FM. Owner: GCap Group. Managing director: Bob Norman; programme controller and head of news: Chris Coppon breakfast show: Martin and Su

Fen Radio 107.5 FM

5 Church Mews, Wisbech, Cambridgeshire PE13 1HL
01945 467107
studio@fenradio.co.uk
www.fenradio.co.uk
70s to today. Fenland. 107.1 FM; 107.5 FM. Owner: UKRD Group. Station manager and programme director: Mark Pryke; programme manager: Richard Grant; sales director: Pam Lawton; breakfast show: Joe Rudd

Hertbeat FM

The Pump House, Knebworth Park, Hertford, Hertfordshire SG3 6HQ
01438 810900
info@hertbeat.com
www.hertbeat.com
80s/90s, specialist programmes weekend. Hertfordshire. 106.9 FM; 106.7 FM. Independent. Station manager: Brett Harley; programme controller: Steve Folland; news editor: Ruth Gibbon; breakfast show: Steve Folland

KL.FM 96.7

18 Blackfriars Street, Kings Lynn, Norfolk PE30 1NN
01553 772777
admin@klfm967.co.uk
www.klfm967.co.uk
Best of past 30 years. Kings Lynn and west Norfolk. 96.7 FM. Owner: UKRD Group. Managing director: William Rogers; station manager: Mark Pryke; programme controller: Simon Rowe; head of news: Gary Phillips; breakfast show: Simon Roe

Lite FM

2nd Floor, 5 Church Street, Peterborough PE1 1XB
01733 898106
info@lite1068.com
www.lite1068.com
Adult contemporary. Peterborough. 106.8 FM. Owner: Forward Media Group. Managing director: David Myatt

North Norfolk Radio

The Studio, Breck Farm, Stody, Norfolk NR24 2ER
01263 860808
info@northnorfolkradio.com
www.northnorfolkradio.com
Adult contemporary. North Norfolk. 103.2 FM; 96.2 FM. Owner: Tindle Radio. Programme controller: Tom Kay; head of news: Jen Dale

Q103 FM

Enterprise House, The Vision Park, Chivers Way, Histon, Cambridgeshire CB4 9WW
01223 235255
firstname.surname@ gcapmedia.com
www.musicradio.com
Mix of today. Cambridge and Newmarket. 103 FM. Owner: GCap Media. Area programme controller: James Keen; sales director: Sharon Rush; head of news: Katie Burnett; breakfast show: Charlie and Helen

SGR Colchester

Abbey Gate Two, 9 Whitewell Road, Colchester CO2 7DE
01206 575859
sgrcolchester@musicradio.com
www.musicradio.com
80s, 90s and today. Colchester. 96.1 FM. Owner: GCap Media. Programme controller: Jonathon Hemmings; sales director: Julie Bennet; head of news: Charlotte Saker; senior presenter: Paul Morris; breakfast show: Louise and Graham

SGR FM

Alpha Business Park, 6-12 White House Road, Ipswich, Suffolk IP1 5LT
01473 461000
firstname.surname@ gcapmedia.com
www.sgrfm.co.uk
80s, 90s and current hits. Suffolk. 96.4 FM; 97.1 FM. Owner: GCap Media. Programme controller: Dan Thorpe; head of news: Sonia Clarke

Star 107.9

20 Mercers Row, Cambridge CB5 8HY
01223 305107
admin@star107.co.uk
www.star1079.co.uk
Mainstream adult contemporary. Cambridge and Ely. 107.1 FM, 107.9 FM. Owner: UKRD Group. Programme controller: Mark Peters; head of news: Emma Owen; breakfast show: Mark Peters

Ten 17

Latton Bush Centre, Southern Way, Harlow, Essex CM18 7BB
01279 431017
firstname.surname@ musicradio.com
www.musicradio.com
Pop. East Herts, west Essex. 101.7 FM. Owner: GCap Media. Programme director: Freddie Scherer; news editor: Jessica Shiddell; breakfast show: Neil Grayson

Kiss FM

Reflection House, The Anderson Centre, Olding Road, Bury St Edmunds IP33 3TA
01284 715300
general@vibefm.co.uk
www.vibefm.co.uk
Dance and R&B. East of England. 105-108 FM. Owner: Emap. Managing director and programme controller: Steve Parkinson; news editors: Dawn Ferguson and Neil Didsbury; breakfast show: Stuart Grant

Watford's Mercury 96.6

Unit 5, The Metro Centre, Dwight Road, Watford WD18 9UP
01923 205470
firstname.surname@ hertsmercury.co.uk
www.hertsmercury.co.uk
Popular music. St Albans and Watford. 96.6 FM. Independent. Programme controller: Tank Montana; head of news: Daniel Freedman; breakfast show: Laura and Steve

EAST MIDLANDS

96 Trent FM

Level 6, Chapel Quarter, Maid Marian Way, MG1 6JR
0115 873 1500
firstname.surname@ musicradio.com
www.musicradio.com
All types of music. Nottinghamshire. 96 FM. Owner: GCap Media. Programme controller: Chris Pegg; head of news: Lewis Scrimshaw; breakfast show: Jo and Twiggy

102.8 RAM FM

35-36 Irongate, Derby DE1 3GA
01332 205599
ramfm@musicradio.com
www.ramfm.co.uk
All current pop music. Derby. 102.8 FM. Owner: GCap Media. Programme controller: James Daniels; head of news: Anna Taylor; breakfast show: Deano and Pete

107 Oak FM

7 Waldron Court, Prince William Road, Loughborough, Leicestershire LE11 5GD
01509 211711
studio@oak107.co.uk
www.oak107.co.uk
60s to today. Charnwood and north-west Leicestershire. 107 FM. Owner: CN Group. Station manager: Eddie Startup; programme manager: Gavin Sanways; breakfast show: Gavin Sanways

Touch FM
5-6 Aldergate, Tamworth,
Staffordshire B79 7DJ
01827 318000
studio@cnradio.co.uk
www.touchtbl.co.uk
80s, 90s and today. South-east Staffordshire. 101.6 FM; 102.4 FM. Owner: CN Group. Managing director: Rupert Alison; programme manager: Dave James; head of news: Mike Thomas; breakfast show: Dave James

Classic Gold 1557
Northamptonshire,
19-21 St Edmunds Road,
Northampton NN1 5DT
01604 795600
firstname.surname@
   classicgolddigital.com
www.classicgolddigital.com
Classic music. Northampton. 1557 AM. Owner: GCap/Classic Gold Digital. Programme controller: Colin Patterson; head of news: Richard Purvis; breakfast show: Tony Blackburn

Classic Hits
PO Box 262, Worcester WR6 5ZE
01432 360246
officemanager@classichits.co.uk
www.classichits.co.uk
Last four or five decades of hits. Hereford and Worcester. 954 AM; 1530 AM. Owner: Murfin Media International. Managing director: Muff Murfin; head of news: Andrew Currie; breakfast show: Paul Smith

Classic Gold GEM
Level 6, Chapel Quarter,
Maid Marian Way, MG1 6JR
0115 873 1500
firstname.surname@
   musicradio.com
www.musicradio.com
All types of music. Nottinghamshire. 96 FM. Owner: GCap Media. Programme controller: Chris Pegg; head of news: Lewis Scrimshaw;

Connect FM
Second Floor, 5 Church Street,
Peterborough, PE1 1XB
0844 800 1769
info@connectfm.com
www.connectfm.com
70s, 80s and 90s and today. Kettering, Corby. 107.4 FM; 97.2 FM. Owner: Forward Media Group. Group managing director: David Myatt; programme manager: Russ Down; head of news: Russ Down; breakfast show: Ian Sharpe

Fosseway Radio
PO Box 107, Hinckley,
Leicestershire LE10 1WR
01455 614151
studios@fossewayradio.co.uk
www.fossewayradio.co.uk
70s, 80s and 90s and hits of today. Hinckley, Nuneaton. 107.9 FM. Owner: Lincs FM. Chief executive: Michael Betton; programme manager: Ian Ison; head of news: James Wall; breakfast show: Julien Saunders

Heart 106 FM
City Link, Nottingham NG2 4NG
0115 910 6100
news@heart106.com
www.heart106.com
80s, 90s and contemporary. East Midlands. 106 FM. Owner: Chrysalis; Managing Director: Chris Jones; breakfast show: Sam and Amy

Leicester Sound
6 Dominus Way, Meridian Business
Park, Leicester LE19 1RP
0116 256 1300
www.musicradio.com
90s and today. Leicester. 105.4 FM. Owner: GCap Media. Programme controller: Simon Ritchie; head of sales: Bina Chauhan; head of news: Hayley Brewer; breakfast show: Rae and Kev

Lincs FM
Witham Park, Waterside South,
Lincoln LN5 7JN
01522 549900
enquiries@lincsfm.co.uk
www.lincsfm.co.uk
Pop. Lincoln. 102.2 FM; 97.6 FM; 96.7 FM. Owner: Lincs FM. Chief executive: Michael Betton; programme manager: Katie Trinder; news editor: Shaun Dunderdale; breakfast show: John Marshall

Mansfield 103.2
The Media Suite,
4 Brunts Business Centre,
Samuel Brunts Way, Mansfield,
Nottinghamshire NG18 2AH
01623 646666
info@mansfield103.co.uk
www.mansfield103.co.uk
70s, 80s and 90s and present day. Mansfield and District. 103.2 FM. Independent. Managing director: Tony Delahunty; programme director: Ian Watkins; head of news: Ian Watkins; breakfast show: John Tannen

Northants 96
19-21 St Edmunds Road,
Northampton NN1 5DY
01604 795600
firstname.surname@
   gcapmedia.com
www.northants96.co.uk
Pop. Northampton. 96.6 FM. Owner: GCap Media. Programme controller: Colin Patterson; head of news: Richard Purvis; breakfast show: Jagger and Woody

Peak 107 FM
Radio House, Foxwood Road,
Chesterfield S41 9RF
01246 269107
info@peak107.com
www.peakfm.net
50/50 music mix. Chesterfield, north Derbyshire, south Sheffield and Peak District. 102 FM; 107.4 FM. Owner: UTV. Group programme controller: Chris Buckley; head of news: Naz Premji; breakfast show: Sean Goldsmith and Becky Measures

Rutland Radio
40 Melton Road, Oakham,
Rutland LE15 6AY
01572 757868
enquiries@rutlandradio.co.uk
www.rutlandradio.co.uk
Last 40 years' hits. Rutland and Stamford. 97.4 FM; 107.2 FM. Owner: Lincs FM. Station manager: Rob Persani; breakfast show: Rob Persani

Sabras Radio
Sabras Sound, Radio House,
63 Melton Road, Leicester LE4 6PN
0116 261 0666
neal@sabrasradio.com
www.sabrasradio.com
Asian music. Leicester. 1260d AM. Independent. Managing director and programme controller: Don Kotak; breakfast show: Alpa

Smooth 106.6 FM
Alder Court, Riverside Business
Park, Nottingham NG2 1RX
0115 986 1066
reception@saga1066fm.co.uk
www.saga1066fm.co.uk
Easy listening from past six decades. East Midlands. 106.6 FM. Owner: Guardian Media Group. Managing director: Phil Dixon; programme director: Paul Robey; head of news: Colin Palmer; breakfast show: Gary Burton

Signal 1
Stoke Road, Stoke on Trent ST4 2SR
01782 441300
info@signalradio.com
www.signal1.co.uk
Pop music. Stoke on Trent. 96.4 FM; 102.6 FM; 96.9 FM. Owner: The Wireless Group. Group programme director: Kevin Howard; managing director: Chris Hurst; head of news: Paul Sheldon; breakfast show: Andy Golding and Louise Stone

Signal Two
Stoke Road, Stoke on Trent ST4 2SR
01782 441300
info@signalradio.com
www.signal2.co.uk
Pop music. Stoke on Trent. 1170 AM. Owner: The Wireless Group. ILR group programme: Kevin Howard; managing director: Chris Hurst; head of news: Paul Sheldon; breakfast show: Andy Golding and Louise Stone

Trax FM
PO Box 444, Worksop,
Nottinghamshire S80 1HR
01909 500611
enquiries@traxfm.co.uk
www.traxfm.co.uk
Adult contemporary. Bassetlaw. 107.9 FM. Owner: Lincs FM. Programme controller: Nick Hancock; head of news: Tina Masters; breakfast show: Nick Hancock

96.4 FM BRMB
Nine Brindleyplace, 4 Ooozells Square, Birmingham B1 2DJ
0121 566 5200
info@brmb.co.uk
www.brmb.co.uk
Chart music. Birmingham. 96.4 FM. Owner: GCap Media. Commercial controller: Jane Davis; programme controller: Adam Bridge; breakfast show: The Big Brum Breakfast

100.7 Heart FM
1 The Square, 111 Broad Street, Birmingham B15 1AS
0121 695 0000
news@heartfm.co.uk
www.heartfm.co.uk
Easy listening. West Midlands. 100.7 FM. Owner: Chrysalis Radio. Station manager: Sunita Wright; programme director: Luis Clark; head of news: Dave McMullan; breakfast show: Ed James

107.1 Rugby FM
Dunsmore Business Centre, Spring Street, Rugby CV21 3HH
01788 541100
studio@rugbyfm.co.uk
www.rugbyfm.co.uk
60s, 70s, 80s and 90s and to date. Rugby. 107.1 FM. Owner: CN group. Sales director: Nathalie Toner; head of news: Daniel Bruce; breakfast show: Carl Hartley

107.4 Telford FM
Shropshire Star, Waterloo Road, Ketley, Telford TF1 5HU
01952 280011
staff@telfordfm.co.uk
www.telfordfm.co.uk
Easy listening. Telford. 107.4 FM. Independent. Programme director: Pete Wagstaff; breakfast show: Paul Shuttleworth

107.7 The Wolf
2nd Floor, Mander House, Wolverhampton WV1 3NB
01902 571070
firstname@thewolf.co.uk
www.thewolf.co.uk
50/50 mix of yesterday and today. Wolverhampton. 107.7 FM. Owner: UTV. Group programme director: John Dash; breakfast show: Dickie Dodd

Beacon FM
267 Tettenhall Road, Wolverhampton WV6 0DE
01902 461300
firstname.surname@creation.com
www.musicradio.com
Popular mix. Wolverhampton. 97.2 FM; 103.1 FM. Owner: GCap Media. Programme director: Darrell Woodman; head of news: Shauna McCarthy; breakfast show: Jo Jesmond and Fresh

Touch FM 102
The Guard House Studios, Banbury Road, Stratford-upon-Avon CV37 7HX
01789 262636
info@thebear.co.uk
www.thebear.co.uk
Classic and current hits. Stratford-upon-Avon. 102 FM. Owner: CN Group. Station director: Mark Wright; programme controller: Steve Hyden; head of news: Daniel Bruce; breakfast show: Tony Morrell and Louisa Allen

Capital Gold (1152)
30 Leicester Square, London WC2H 7LA
020 7766 6000
info@capitalgold.co.uk
www.capitalgold.com
Hits of the 60s, 70s and 80s. Birmingham. 1152 AM. Owner: GCap Media. Programme director: Andy Turner; head of news: Justin King; breakfast show: Tom Ross

Classic Gold 1359
Hertford Place, Coventry CV1 3TT
024 7686 8200
firstname.surname@classicgolddigital.com
www.classicgolddigital.com
70s, 80s and 90s. Coventry. 1359 AM. Owner: GCap/Classic Gold Digital. Programme controller: Mike Zeller; breakfast show: Ant and Helen

Classic Gold WABC
267 Tettenhall Road, Wolverhampton WV6 0DE
01902 461300
firstname.surname@classicgolddigital.com
www.classicalgolddigital.com
Classic 80s, 90s onward. Wolverhampton. 990 AM; 1017 AM. Owner: GCap, Classic Gold Digital. Programme controller: Darrell Woodman; head of news: Adam Edward; breakfast show: Tony Blackburn

Galaxy 102.2
1 The Square, 111 Broad Street, Birmingham B15 1AS
0121 695 0000
galaxy1022@galaxy1022.co.uk
www.galaxy1022.co.uk
Easy listening. Birmingham. 102.2 FM. Owner: Chrysalis Radio. Managing director: Paul Fairburn; programme director: Neil Greenslade; head of news: Chris Kowalik; breakfast show: Dave Clark

Touch FM 96
Watch Close, Spon Street, Coventry CV1 3LN
024 7652 5656
firstname.lastname@cnradio.co.uk
www.intouchfm.co.uk
Pop and Dance. Coventry. 96.2 FM. Owner: CN Group. Sales director: Mark Wright; programme manager: Don Douglas; head of news: Daniel Bruce

Mercia FM
Hertford Place, Coventry CV1 3TT
024 7686 8200
merciafm@musicradio.com
www.musicradio.com
80s, 90s and modern. Coventry. 102.9 FM; 97 FM. Owner: GCap Media. Programme controller: Mike Zeller; head of news: Tony Attwater; breakfast show: Ant and Helen

Radio XL 1296 AM
KMS House, Bradford Street, Birmingham B12 0JD
0121 753 5353
arun@radioxl.net
www.radioxl.net
Indian and Asian mixes. Birmingham. 1296 AM. Independent. Managing director: Arun Bajaj; programme director: Sukjoinder Ghataore; breakfast show: Tej

Smooth 105.7 FM
3rd Floor, Crown House, Beaufort Court, 123 Hagley Road, Edgbaston B16 8LD
0121 452 1057
onair@saga1057fm.co.uk
www.saga1057fm.co.uk
40s onwards. West Midlands. 105.7 FM. Owner: Guardian Media Group. Managing director: Phil Dickson; programme director: Paul Robey; news editor: Colin Palmer; breakfast show: Mike Wyer

Wyvern FM
1st Floor, Kirkham House, Worcester WR3 7NS
01905 612212
wyvern.news1@gcapmedia.com
www.musicradio.com
Pop music. Hereford and Worcester. 102.8 FM; 97.6 FM; 96.7 FM. Owner: GCap Media. Programme controller: Mark Watts; head of news: Vicki Breakwell; breakfast show: Lee Stone

Alpha 103.2
Radio House, 11 Woodland Road, Darlington Co., Durham DL3 7BJ
01325 255552
studio@alphafm.co.uk
www.alphafm.co.uk
Classic hits from last 30 years. Darlington. 103.2 FM. Owner: Local Radio Company. Station manager: Peter Grant; head of news: Jonathon Kearsley; breakfast show: Tim West

Century FM
Church Street, Gateshead NE8 2YY
0191 490 3600
info@centuryfm.co.uk
www.100centuryfm.com
80s, 90s and today. North-east England. 96.2 FM; 96.4 FM; 100.7 FM; 101.8 FM. Owner: Guardian Media Group. Programme controller: Paul Smith; head of news: Myles Ashby; breakfast show: Scott and Lisa

Galaxy 105-106

Kingfisher Way, Silverlink Business Park, Tyne and Wear NE28 9NX
0191 206 8000
matt.mcclure@galaxy1056.co.uk
www.galaxy1056.co.uk
Dance and R&B. North-east England. 105.3 FM; 105.6 FM; 105.8 FM; 106.4 FM. Owner: Chrysalis Radio. Programme director: Richard Spencer; Journalist: Kevin McGreth; breakfast show: Steve and Karen

Magic 1152

55 Degrees North, Pilgrim Street. Newcastle upon Tyne NE1 6BS
0191 230 6100
paul.chantler@metroandmagic.com
www.magic1152.co.uk
Classic 60s and 70s. Tyne and Wear. 1152 AM. Owner: Emap Performance Network. Managing director: Sally Aitchison; programme director: Trevor James; breakfast show: Steve Colman

Magic 1170

Radio House,
Yales Crescent, Thornaby,
Stockton-on-Tees TS17 6AA
01642 888222
www.tfmradio.co.uk
Adult contemporary. Teesside. 1170 AM. Owner: Emap Performance Network. Managing director: Sally Aitchison; programme director: Chris Rick; head of news: Hayley Brewer; breakfast show: Alan Roth

Metro Radio

Longrigg, Swalwell,
Newcastle upon Tyne NE99 1BB
0191 230 6100
paul.chantler@metroandmagic.com
www.magic1152.co.uk
Adult contemporary and chart. Tyne and Wear. 97.1 FM. Owner: Emap Performance Network. Managing director: Sally Aitchison; programme director: Trevor James; breakfast show: Tony Horn

Sun FM

PO Box 1034, Sunderland SR5 2YL
0191 548 1034
progs@sun-fm.com
www.sun-fm.com
Adult contemporary. Sunderland. 103.4 FM. Owner: Local Radio Company. Brand controller: Helen Edmundson; head of news: Stephen McCabe; breakfast show: Simon Grundy

TFM

Radio House,
Yales Crescent, Thornaby,
Stockton-on-Tees TS17 6AA
01642 888222
www.tfmradio.co.uk
Adult contemporary. Teesside. 96.6 FM. Owner: Emap Performance Network. Managing director: Sally Aitchison; programme director: Chris Rick; head of news: Hayley Brewer; breakfast show: Graham Mack

96.3 Radio Aire

51 Burley Road, Leeds LS3 1LR
0113 283 5500
firstname.lastname@radioaire.com
www.radioaire.co.uk
Adult contemporary. Leeds. 96.3 FM. Owner: Emap Performance Network. Managing director: Alexis Thompson; programme director: Stuart Baldwin; head of news: Alice Bailey; breakfast show: Simon Logan

96.9 Viking FM

The Boat House, Commercial Road, Hull HU1 2SG
01482 325141
reception@vikingfm.co.uk
www.vikingfm.co.uk
Variety. Hull. 96.9 FM. Owner: Emap Performance Network. Programme director: Craig Beck; head of news: Jo Taylor; breakfast show: Sam and Mark

97.2 Stray FM

The Hamlet, Hornbeam Park Avenue, Harrogate HG2 8RE
01423 522972
mail@strayfm.com
www.strayfm.com
60s and 70s. Harrogate. 97.2 FM. Owner: Local Radio Company. Managing director: Sarah Barry; programme director: Chris Bell; head of news: Patrick Dunlop; breakfast show: Chris Bell

Classic Gold 1278/1530 AM

Pennine House, Forster Square, Bradford, West Yorkshire BD1 5NE
01274 203040
general@pulse.co.uk
www.pulse.co.uk
Oldies. Bradford, Halifax and Huddersfield. 1278 AM; 1530 AM. Owner: The Wireless Group. ILR group programme director: Mark Brow; managing director: Tony Wilkinson; head of news: Stephanie Otty; breakfast show: Tony Blackburn and Laura Pittson

Compass FM

26a Wellowgate, Grimsby DN32 ORA
01472 346666
enquiries@compassfm.co.uk
www.compassfm.co.uk
Easy listening. Grimsby. 96.4 FM. Owner: Lincs FM. Station Manager: Richard Lyon; head of news: Shaun Dunderdale; breakfast show: Richard Lyon

Dearne FM

PO Box 458, Barnsley S71 1XP
01226 321733
enquiries@dearnefm.co.uk
www.dearnefm.co.uk
60s, 70s, 80s and 90s and current hits. Barnsley. 97.1 FM; 102 FM. Owner: Lincs FM Group. Programme controller: Matt Jones; head of news: James Marriott; breakfast show: James Brandon

Fresh Radio

Firth Mill, Firth Street, Skipton, North Yorkshire BD23 2PT
01756 799991
info@freshradio.co.uk
www.freshradio.co.uk
Adult contemporary. Yorkshire Dales with Skipton. 1431 AM; 1413 AM; 936 AM. Independent. Managing director: Dave Parker; head of news: James Wilson; breakfast show: Nick Bewes

Galaxy 105

Joseph's Well, Hannover Walk, off Park Lane, Leeds LS3 1AB
0113 213 0105
mail@galaxy105.co.uk
www.galaxy105.co.uk
Dance and R&B. Yorkshire. 105.8 FM; 105.6 FM; 105.1 FM; 105.6 FM; DAB; Sky; cable. Owner: Chrysalis Radio. Managing director: Martin Healy; head of news and programme director: Mike Cass; breakfast show: Hirsty, Danny and JoJo

Hallam FM

Radio House, 900 Herries Road, Sheffield S6 1RH
0114 209 1000
Programmes@hallamfm.co.uk
www.hallamfm.co.uk
All types of music. South Yorkshire. 102.9 FM; 103.4 FM; 97.4 FM. Owner: Emap Performance Network. Managing director: Esther Morton; head of news and programming: Simon Monk; breakfast show: Big John Breakfast Show

Home 107.9

The Old Stableblock, Lockwood Park, Huddersfield HD1 3UR
01484 321107
info@home1079.com
www.home1079.com
Pop from past three decades. Huddersfield. 107.9 FM. Owner: Local Radio Company. Programme controller: Chris Bell; sales director: Susie Sweeny; head of news: Emma Clark; breakfast show: Paul Clark

Magic 828

51 Burley Road, Leeds LS3 1LR
0113 283 5500
firstname.lastname@radioaire.com
www.radioaire.co.uk
Adult contemporary. Leeds. 96.3 FM. Owner: Emap Performance Network. Managing director: Alexis Thompson; programme director: Stuart Baldwin; head of news: Alice Bailey; breakfast show: Simon Logan

Magic 1161 AM

The Boat House, Commercial Road, Hull HU1 2SG
01482 325141
reception@magic1161.co.uk
www.magic1161.co.uk
Variety. Hull, Humberside and East Yorkshire 96.9 FM. Owner: Emap Performance Network. Programme director: Craig Beck; head of news: Jo Taylor; breakfast show: Sam and Mark

97.2 Magic AM
Radio House, 900 Herries Road,
Sheffield S6 1RH
0114 209 1000
Programmes@hallamfm.co.uk
www.hallamfm.co.uk
*All types of music. South Yorkshire.
102.9 FM; 103.4 FM; 97.4 FM. Owner:
Emap Performance Network.
Managing director: Esther Morton;
head of news and programming: Simon
Monk; breakfast show: Big John
Breakfast Show*

Minster FM
PO Box 123, Dunnington,
York YO19 5ZX
01904 488888
general@minsterfm.com
www.minsterfm.com
*Past few decades. York. 104.7 FM;
102.3 FM. Owner: Local Radio
Company. Commercial station
manager: Rachel Barker; programme
controller: David Green; head of news:
Tracey Gee; breakfast show: Brooksy*

The Pulse
Pennine House, Forster Square,
Bradford, West Yorkshire BD1 5NE
01274 203040
general@pulse.co.uk
www.pulse.co.uk
*Oldies. Bradford, Huddersfield and
Halifax. 102.5 FM; 97.5 FM. Owner:
UTV. programme director: Mark Brow;
managing director: Tony Wilkinson;
head of news: Stephanie Otty;
breakfast show: Jackie and Steve*

Real Radio (Yorkshire)
Sterling Court, Capitol Park,
Leeds WF3 1EL
0113 238 1114
info@realradiofm.com
www.realradiofm.com
*90s and popular. South and West
Yorkshire. 107.6 FM; 106.2 FM; 107.7
FM. Owner: Guardian Media Group
Radio. Managing director: Steve South;
programme director: Tony Mackenzie;
head of news: Justin Lockwood;
breakfast show: Daryl Denham*

Ridings FM
01924 367177
enquiries@ridingsfm.co.uk
www.ridingsfm.co.uk
*Popular music. Wakefield. 106.8 FM.
Owner: Lincs FM. programme controller:
John Tulson; head of news: Holly Emery;
breakfast show: Kev Wilson*

Sunrise FM
55 Leeds Road, Bradford BD1 5AF
01274 735043
usha@sunriseradio.fm
www.sunriseradio.fm
*Asian music. Bradford. 103.2 FM.
Independent. Managing director and
programme controller: Usha Parmar;
head of news: Gail Papworth;
breakfast show: Gail and Sadiah*

Trax FM
5 Sidings Court, White Rose Way,
Doncaster DN4 5GW
01302 341166
events@traxfm.co.uk
www.traxfm.co.uk
*All sorts. Doncaster. 107.1 FM. Owner:
Lincs FM. Programme controller: Rob
Wagstaff; sales manager: Peggy
Watson; head of news: Tina Master;
breakfast show: Mick Hancock*

Yorkshire Coast Radio
PO Box 962, Scarborough,
North Yorkshire YO11 3ZP
01723 581700
studio@yorkshirecoastradio.com
www.yorkshirecoastradio.com
*Chart hits. Bridlington, Scarborough,
Whitby. 96.2 FM; 102.4 FM. Owner:
Local Radio Company. Station manager
and programme controller: Chris
Sigsworth; head of news: Rhiannon
Wynell; breakfast show: Ben Fry*

Yorkshire Coast Radio
The Old Harbour Master's Office,
Harbour Road, Bridlington,
East Yorkshire YO15 2NR
01723 581700
enquiries@yorkshirecoastradio.com
www.yorkshirecoastradio.com
*Adult contemporary. Bridlington.
102.4 FM. Owner: local radio
company. Commercial and brand
manager: Chris Sigsworth; sales
director: Peter Bilsborough; breakfast
show: Greg Dukeson*

NORTH-WEST

2BR
Imex Lomeshaye Business Village,
Nelson, Lancashire BB9 7DR
01282 690000
info@2br.co.uk
www.2br.co.uk
*70s to current. Burnley. 99.8 FM.
Owner: Local Radio Company.
Breakfast show: Brendan Kearney*

96.2 The Revolution
PO Box 962, Oldham OL1 3JF
0161 621 6500
info@therevolution.uk.com
www.revolutiononline.co.uk
*Classic and chart hits. Oldham. 96.2
FM. Owners: UKRD; Hirst Kidd &
Rennie. Station manager: Jackie
Sulkowski; programme controller and
head of news: Phil Mackenzie;
breakfast show: John Warburton*

97.4 Rock FM
PO Box 974, Preston PR1 1YE
01772 477700
firstname.lastname@rockfm.co.uk
www.rockfm.co.uk
*Adult contemporary. Preston and
Blackpool. 97.4 FM. Owner: Emap
Performance Network. Programme
director: Anthony Gay; head of news:
Clare Hannah; breakfast show: Adam
Catterall*

100.4 Smooth FM
8 Exchange Quay,
Manchester M5 3EJ
0161 877 1004
jazzinfo@jazzfm.com
www.jazzfm.com
*Smooth and R&B. North-west England.
100.4 FM. Owner: Guardian Media
Group Radio. Managing director: Roy
Bennett; programming director: Steve
Collins; head of music: Derek Webster;
breakfast show: Chris Best*

102.4 Wish FM
Orrell Lodge, Orrell Road, Orrell,
Wigan WN5 8HJ
01942 761024
studio@wish_fm.com
www.wishfm.net
*80s, 90s, up to date. Wigan. 102.4 FM.
Owner: UTV. Programme manager:
Jo Heuston; head of news: Stuart
Arrowsmith; breakfast show:
Chris Milow*

106.7 FM The Rocket
Paramount Studios, Paramount
Business Park, Wilson Road,
Liverpool, Merseyside L36 6AW
Reception: 0151 480 5488
Studio: 0845 051 1067
www.kcr1067.com
*60s to modern. Knowsley. 106.7 FM.
Owner: Independant. Managing
director: Ray Ferguson; programme
controller: Ray Ferguson; head of
news: John Donnelly; breakfast show:
John Cooper*

106.9 Silk FM
Radio House, Bridge Street,
Macclesfield, Cheshire SK11 6DJ
01625 268000
mail@silkfm.com
www.silkfm.com
*Adult contemporary. Macclesfield.
106.9 FM. Owner: local radio.
Programme manager: Andy Bailey;
head of news: Rebecca Wood;
breakfast show: Andy Bailey*

107.2 Wire FM
Warrington Business Park,
Long Lane, Warrington WA2 8TX
01925 445545
info@wirefm.com
www.wirefm.com
*Adult contemporary. Warrington.
107.2 FM. Owner: UTV; head of news:
Mark Bell; breakfast show: Dominic
Walker and Lou Taylor*

Asian Sound Radio
Globe House, Southall Street,
Manchester M3 1LG
0161 288 1000
info@asiansoundradio.co.uk
www.asiansoundradio.com
*Asian hip-hop. East Lancashire. 963
AM; 1377 AM. Independent. Managing
director and programme director:
Shujat Ali; head of news: Farrukh
Humayun*

The Bay
PO Box 969, St Georges Quay,
Lancaster LA1 3LD
01524 848747
information@thebay.fm
www.thebay.fm
*Adult contemporary. Morecambe Bay,
South Lakes, Cumbria. 102.3 FM; 96.9
FM; 103.2 FM. Station director: bill
johnston; programme controller: Phil
Rodgers; head of news: Peter Storry;
breakfast show: Darren and Lorna*

Century 105 FM
Laser House,
Waterfront Quay, Salford Quays,
Manchester M50 3XW
0161 886 8800
info1054@centuryfm.co.uk
www.1054centuryfm.com
*Pop. North-west England. 105.4 FM.
Owner: Guardian Media Group.
Managing director: Roy Bennet; Brand
programme director: Sarah Carter;
head of news: James Rea; breakfast
show: Paul Salt*

Classic Gold Marcher 1260 AM
The Studios, Mold Road,
Wrexham LL11 4AF
01978 752202
firstname.surname@classicgolddi
gital.com
www.classicgolddigital.com
*Classical music. Wrexham and Chester.
1260 AM. Owner: GCap/Classic Gold
Digital. Programme controller: Lisa
Marrey; head of news: Elina Cavanagh;
breakfast show: Tony Blackburn*

Dee 106.3
2 Chantry Court, Chester CH1 4QN
01244 391000
info@dee1063.com
www.dee1063.com
*Adult contemporary. Chester. 106.3
FM. Independent. Station manager:
Steph Roberts; head of news: Mike
Baker; breakfast show: Gavin and Irene*

Dune FM
The Power Station, Victoria Way,
Southport PR8 1RR
01704 502500
studio@dunefm.co.uk
www.dunefm.co.uk
*Adult contemporary. Southport. 107.9
FM. Owner: Local Radio Company.
Programme controller: John Storey;
head of news: Neil Newton; breakfast
show: John Storey*

Galaxy 102
5th Floor, The Triangle, Hanging
Ditch, Manchester M4 3TR
0161 279 0300
mail@galaxy102.co.uk
www.galaxy102.co.uk
*Dance and R&B. Manchester. 102 FM.
Owner: Chrysalis Radio. Managing
director: Martyn Healey; programme
director: Mike Cass; breakfast show:
Rob Ellis*

Imagine FM
Regent House, Heaton Lane,
Stockport SK4 1BX
0161 609 1400
info@imaginefm.com
www.imaginefm.co.uk
*Hits 70s to 90s and today. Stockport.
104.9 FM. Owner: UTV. Head of news
and programme controller: Paul
Willett; breakfast show: Martin Emery*

Juice 107.6
27 Fleet Street, Liverpool L1 4AR
0151 707 3107
mail@juiceliverpool.com
www.juice.fm
*R&B. Liverpool. 107.6 FM. Owner:
UTV. Managing director: Ian Fowler
programme director: Gary Burgess;
head of news: Catherine Davies;
breakfast show: Simon Greening*

Key 103
Castle Quay, Castlefield,
Manchester M15 4PR
0161 288 5000
first.name@key103.co.uk
www.key103.com
*Mainstream. Manchester. 103 FM.
Owner: Emap Performance Network.
Managing director: Michelle Surrell;
programme director: Gary Stein; head
of news: John Pickford; breakfast
show: Mike Toolan*

Lakeland Radio
Lakeland Food Park,
Plumgarths, Crook Road, Kendal,
Cumbria LA8 8QJ
01539 737380
info@lakelandradio.co.uk
www.lakelandradio.co.uk
*60s to modern. Kendal and
Windermere. 100.8 FM; 100.1 FM.
CN group. head of music: Steven Bell;
breakfast show: Simon Yaxley*

Magic 999
St Pauls Square, Preston PR1 1YE
01772 477700
name.surname@magic999.co.uk
www.magic999.co.uk
*Adult contemporary. Preston and
Blackpool. 999 AM. Owner: Emap
Performance Network. Programme
director: Anthony Gay; head of news:
Clare Hannah; breakfast show: Rob
Charles*

Magic 1152
Castle Quay, Castlefield,
Manchester M15 4PR
0161 288 5000
firstname.lastname@
magicradio.com
www.manchestersmagic.co.uk
*80s, 90s. Manchester. 1152 AM. Owner:
Emap Performance Network.
Managing director: Michelle Surrel;
programme director: Gary Stein; head
of news: John Pickford; breakfast
show: Macdonald snd Maguire*

Magic 1548
St Johns Beacon, 1 Houghton
Street, Liverpool L1 1RL
0151 472 6800
firstname@magic1548.com
www.radiocity.co.uk
*Adult contemporary. Liverpool.
1548 AM. Owner: Emap Performance
Network. programme director:
Richard Maddock; head of news: Steve
Hothersell; breakfast show: Phil Easton*

Marcher Sound
The Studios, Mold Road,
Gwersyllt, Nr Wrexham LL11 4AF
01978 752202
firstname.surname@
gcapmedia.com
www.mymfm.co.uk
*Pop music. Wrexham and Chester.
103.4 FM. Owner: GCap Media.
Managing director: Sarah Smithard;
programme controller: Lisa Marrey;
head of news: Elina Cavanagh;
breakfast show: Jamie and Bec*

Radio City 96.7
St Johns Beacon, 1 Houghton
Street, Liverpool L1 1RL
0151 472 6800
firstname@magic1548.com
www.radiocity.co.uk
*Adult contemporary. Liverpool. 1548
AM. Owner: Emap Performance
Network. programme director: Richard
Maddock; head of news: Steve
Hothersell; breakfast show: Phil Easton*

Tower FM
The Mill, Brownlow Way,
Bolton BL1 2RA
01204 387000
info@towerfm.co.uk
www.towerfm.co.uk
*Traditional music. Bolton and Bury.
107.4 FM. Owner: UTV. programme
director: Brian Paige; head of news:
Sophie Hubberstey; breakfast show:
Vicks and Martin*

Wave FM
965 Mowbray Drive, Blackpool,
Lancashire FY3 7JR
01253 304965
wave@thewavefm.co.uk
www.wave965.com
*Chart and retro. Blackpool. 96.5 FM.
Owner: UTV. Group managing
director: Scott Taunton; Station
director: Helen Bowden; breakfast
show: Roy and Gemma*

Wirral's Buzz FM
Pacific Road Arts Centre, Pacific
Road, Birkenhead CH41 1LJ
0151 650 1700
sarah.smithard@musicradio.com
www.musicradio.com
*Chart 80s and 90s. Wirral. 97.1 FM.
Owner: GCap media. Programme
controller: Lisa Marrey; head of news:
Elina Cavanagh; breakfast show: Amy
and Jeff*

● Commercial local radio: Wales

96.4 FM The Wave
PO Box 964, Swansea SA4 3AB
01792 511964
info@thewave.co.uk
www.thewave.co.uk
Chart hits. Swansea. 96.4 FM. Owner: UTV. ILR Programme director: Steve Barnes; station manager: Carrie Mosley; head of news: Emma Thomas; breakfast show: Badger and Emma

Bridge FM
PO Box 1063, Bridgend CF35 6WF
0845 890 4000
firstname.surname@bridge.fm
www.bridge.fm
Adult contemporary. Bridgend. 106.3 FM. Owner: Town and Country broadcasting. Managing director: Martin Mumford; programme controller: Andy Griffiths; head of news: Sam Burson; breakfast show: Lee Jukes

Champion FM
Llys y Dderwen Parc Menai,
Bangor LL57 4BN
01248 673400
sarah.smithard@musicradio.com
www.musicradio.com
Modern music. Caenafon. 103 FM. Owner: GCap Media. Managing director: Clive Douthwaite; Area programme controller: Steve Simms; head of news: Sean Pritchard; breakfast show: Kevin Bach

Coast FM
PO Box 963, Bangor LL57 4ZR
01248 673400
firstname.surname@
    musicradio.com
www.coastfm.co.uk
Modern music. North Wales coast. 96.3 FM. Owner: GCap Media. Managing director: Clive Douthwaite; programme controller: Steve Simms; head of news: Sean Pritchard; breakfast show: Craig Pilling

Radio Ceredigion
Yr Hen Ysgol Gymraeg,
Aberystwyth, Ceredigion SY23 1LF
01970 627999
admin@ceredigionfmf9.co.uk
www.ceredigionradio.co.uk
Adult contemporary Welsh. Ceredigion. 97.4 FM; 103.3 FM; 96.6 FM. Independent. Programme controller: Mark Simon; head of news: Bylam Williams; breakfast show: Thomo

Radio Maldwyn
The Studios, The Park, Newtown,
Powys SY16 2NZ
01686 623555
radio.maldwyn@ukonline.co.uk
www.magic756.net
Adult contemporary. Montgomeryshire. 756 AM. Owner: Murfin Media International. Managing director, operations director and programme controller: Austin Powell; head of news: Andrew Curry; breakfast show: Mark Edwards

Radio Pembrokeshire
Unit 14 The Old School Estate,
Station Road, Narbarth,
Pembrokeshire SA67 7DU
01834 869384
enquiries@radiopembrokeshire.com
www.radiopembrokeshire.com
Adult contemporary rock. Pembrokeshire, West Carmarthenshire. 102.5 FM. town and country. programme controller: Ed Goddard; head of news: Sam Burson; breakfast show: Ben Stone

Real Radio (South Wales)
Unit 1, Ty-Nant Court, Ty-Nant Road
Morganstown, Cardiff CF15 8LW
029 2031 5100
info@realradiofm.com
www.realradiofm.com
70s to modern. South Wales regional. 105.9 FM; 106 FM; 105.2 FM; 105.4 FM. Owner: Guardian Media Group Radio. Programme director: Ricky Durkin; head of news: Gareth Setter; breakfast show: Bobby McVay

Red Dragon FM & Capital Gold
Atlantic Wharf,
Cardiff Bay CF10 4DJ
029 2066 2066
firstname.lastname@
    reddragonfm.co.uk
www.reddragonfm.co.uk
Chart music. Cardiff and Newport. 103.2 FM; 97.4 FM. Owner: GCap Media. Programme controller: Mark Ryan; head of news: David Grundy; breakfast show: Jason Mel

Sunshine 855
Unit 11, Burway Trading Estate,
Bromfield Road, Ludlow,
Shropshire SY8 1EN
01584 873795
sunshine855@ukonline.co.uk
www.sunshine855.com
Adult contemporary. Ludlow. 855 AM. Owner: laser broadcasting. Operations director and programme controller: Stewart Linnel MBE; head of news: John Hyde; breakfast show: John Hyde

Swansea Sound
Victoria Road, Gowerton,
Swansea SA4 3AB
01792 511170
info@swanseasound.co.uk
www.swanseasound.co.uk
Chart hits. Swansea. 1170 AM. Owner: UTV. Station manager: Carrie Mosley; head of news: Emma Thomas; head of music: Andy Miles; breakfast show: Kevin Johns

Valleys Radio
Festival Park Victoria, Beech
Grove, Ebbw Vale NP23 8XW
01495 301116
admin@valleysradio.co.uk
www.valleysradio.co.uk
Adult contemporary. Heads of south Wales valleys. 1116 AM; 999 AM. Owner: UTV. Managing director: Chris Hurst; head of news: Emma Thomas; breakfast show: Tony Peters

● Commercial local radio: Scotland

96.3 Rock Radio
Real Radio, Glasgow Business Park,
Glasgow G69 6GA
0141 781 1011
sales@q-fm.com
www.q96.net
All types. Paisley. 96.3 FM. Owner: Guardian Group Media. Managing director: Billy Anderson; head of news: Heather Cane; breakfast show: Kieran Elliot

Argyll FM
27-29 Longrow, Campbeltown,
Argyll PA28 6ER
01586 551800
argyllradio@hotmail.com
www.argyllfm.co.uk
Adult contemporary. Kintyre, Islay and Jura. 107.7 FM; 107.1 FM; 106.5 FM. Independent. Managing director: Colin Middleton; programme controller: Kenny Johnson; head of news: Ian Henderson; breakfast show: Bill Young

Beat 106
Four Winds Pavilion,
Pacific Quay, Glasgow G51 1EB
0141 566 6106
info@beat106.com
www.beat106.com
Dance. Central Scotland. 106.1 FM; 105.7 FM. Owner: GCap Media. Programme controller: Owen Ryan; news editor: Louise Robertson; breakfast show: Julian Sinclair

Central FM
201 High Street, Falkirk FK1 1DU
01324 611164
mail@centralfm.co.uk
www.centralfm.co.uk
Hits and memories. Stirling and Falkirk. 103.1 FM. Owner: Local Radio Company. Programme controller: Gary Muricroft; head of news: Tadek Kopszywa; breakfast show: Malky Brow

Clan FM
Radio House, Rowantree Avenue,
Newhouse Ind. Estate,
Newhouses, Lanarkshire ML1 5RX
01698 733107
reception@clanfm.com
www.clanfm.com
Adult contemporary. North Lanarkshire. 107.9 FM; 107.5 FM. Owner: Kingdom Group. Station manager: Janis Melville; programme controller: Darren Stenhouse; breakfast show: David Ross; head of news: Andrew Thompson

Clyde 1 FM
Clydebank Business Park,
Glasgow G81 2RX
0141 565 2200
info@clyde1.com
www.clyde1.com
Pop. Glasgow. 97 FM; 103.3 FM; 102.5 FM. Owner: Emap Performance Network. Managing director: Paul Cooney; programme controller: Paul Saunders; head of news: Paul Saunders; breakfast show: George Bowie

contacts **Radio**

Forth One

Forth House, Forth Street,
Edinburgh EH1 3LE
0131 556 9255
info@forthone.com
www.forthone.com
*Adult contemporary. Edinburgh. 97.6
FM; 102.2 FM; 97.3 FM. Owner: Emap
Performance Network. Managing
director: Cathy Kirk; programme
director: Luke McCullough; head of
news: Paul Robertson; breakfast show:
Andy Douglas and Joe Mclaren*

Forth Two

Forth House, Forth Street,
Edinburgh EH1 3LE
0131 556 9255
info@forth2.com
www.forth2.com
*60s, 70s, 80s, 90s and today.
Edinburgh. 1548 AM. Owner: Emap
Performance Network. Managing
director: Cathy Kirk; programme
director: Luke McCullough; head of
news: Paul Robertson; breakfast show:
Bob Malcolm*

Heartland FM

Atholl Curling Rink, Lower Oakfield
Pitlochry, Perthshire PH16 5HQ
01796 474040
mailbox@heartlandfm.co.uk
www.heartlandfm.co.uk
*Classic hits. Pitlochry and Aberfeldy.
97.5 FM; 102.7 FM. Independent.
Programme controller: Peter Ramsden;
head of news: Margaret Stevenson;
breakfast show: Bruce P*

Isles FM

PO Box 333, Stornoway,
Isle of Lewis HS1 2PU
01851 703333
studio@isles.fm
www.isles.fm
*Adult contemporary. Western Isles.
103 FM. Independent. Director of
operations: David Morrison; head
of news: Peggy McNeill.*

Kingdom FM

Haig House, Haig Business Park
Markinch, Fife KY7 6AQ
01592 753753
info@kingdomfm.co.uk
www.kingdomfm.co.uk
*Across-the-board mix. Fife. 95.2 FM;
105.4 FM; 96.6 FM; 106.3 FM; 96.1
FM. Independent. Managing director:
Kevin Brady; programme director:
Darren Stenhouse; head of news: Alan
Smith; breakfast show: Mickey Gavin*

Lochbroom FM

Radio House, Mill Street,
Ullapool, Ross-shire IV26 2UN
01854 613131
radio@lochbroomfm.co.uk
www.lochbroomfm.co.uk
*Adult contemporary. Ullapool. 96.8 FM;
102.2 FM. Independent. Chairman:
Walley Beale; programme controller
and breakfast show: Simon Calder*

Moray Firth Radio (MFR)

Scorguie Place, Inverness IV3 8UJ
01463 224433
mfr@mfr.co.uk
www.mfr.co.uk
*Contemporary and chart. Inverness.
96.6 FM; 96.7 FM; 97.4 FM; 102.5 FM;
102.8 FM. Owner: Emap Performance
Network. Managing director:
Gary Gallagher; head of news: Claire
Riley; breakfast show: Nicky Marr and
Gino Connti*

NECR

The Shed, School Road, Kintore,
Aberdeenshire AB51 0UX
01467 632909
necrradio102.1fmsales@
supanet.com
www.necrfm.co.uk
*Recent hits and classic gold and
specialist country, Irish and Scottish.
Inverurie. 102.1 FM; 102.6 FM; 97.1
FM; 103.2 FM; 101.9 FM; 106.4FM.
Independent. Managing director: Colin
Strong; programme controller: John
Dean; head of news: John Dean;
breakfast show: John Dean*

Nevis Radio

Ben Nevis Estate, Claggan,
Fort William PH33 6PR
01397 700007
studio@nevisradio.co.uk
www.nevisradio.co.uk
*Daily chart music. Evening specialist.
Fort William and parts of Lochaber.
96.6 FM; 102.4 FM; 97 FM; 102.3 FM.
Independent. Head of news, station
manager and programme controller:
Willie Cameron; breakfast show:
David Ogg*

Northsound One

Abbotswell Road, West Tullos,
Aberdeen AB12 3AJ
01224 337000
northsound@srh.co.uk
www.northsound1.co.uk
*Modern music. Aberdeen and north-
east Scotland. 96.9 FM; 97.6 FM; 103
FM. Owner: Emap Performance
Network. Managing director: Ken
Massie; programme controller: Chris
Thomson; head of news: Sarah
Campbell; breakfast show: Greigsy*

Northsound Two

Abbotswell Road, West Tullos,
Aberdeen AB12 3AJ
01224 337000
northsound@srh.co.uk
www.northsound2.co.uk
*Modern music. Aberdeen and north-east
Scotland. 1035 AM. Owner: Emap
Performance Network. Managing
director: Ken Massie; programme
controller: Chris Thomson; head of news:
Sarah Campbell; breakfast show: Greigsy*

Oban FM

132 George Street, Oban,
Argyll PA34 5NT
01631 570057
obanfmradio@btconnect.com
www.obanfm.tk
*Gaelic to modern pop. Oban. 103.3 FM.
Independent. Station manager:
Laura Johnston; programme director:
Doug Carmichael; head of news:
Coll McDougall*

Radio Borders

Tweedside Park, Galashiels TD1 3TD
01896 759444
programming@radioborders.com
www.radioborders.com
*Hits and memories. Borders. 96.8 FM;
103.1 FM; 103.4 FM; 97.5 FM. Owner:
Emap Performance Network.
Programme controller: Keith Clarkson;
head of news: Louise Smith; breakfast
show: Keith Clarkson*

Real Radio (Scotland)

PO Box 101, Parkway Court,
Glasgow Business Park,
Glasgow G69 6GA
0141 781 1011
contact.name@realradiofm.com
www.realradiofm.com
*Wide variety. Central Scotland. 100.3
FM; 101.1 FM. Owner: Guardian Media
Group Radio. Managing director: Billy
Anderson; programme director: Jay
Crawford; head of news: Heather
Kane; breakfast show: Robin Galloway*

River FM

Stadium House,
Alderstone Road, Livingstone,
West Lothian EH54 7DN
01506 410411
office@river-fm.com
www.river-fm.com
*Adult contemporary and charts. West
Lothian. 107.7 FM; 103.4 FM. Owner:
Kingdon Radio Group. Programme
controller: Donny Hughes; sales
director: Wahida Wilson; breakfast
show: James Russell*

RNA FM

Radio North Angus, Arbroath
Infirmary, Rosemount Road,
Arbroath, Angus DD11 2AT
01241 879660
info@radionorthangus.co.uk
www.radionorthangus.co.uk
*Classic/Scottish and pop. Arbroath,
Carnoustie. 96.6 FM. Independent.
Managing director and head of news:
Malcolm Finlayson*

SIBC

Market Street, Lerwick,
Shetland ZE1 0JN
01595 695299
info@sibc.co.uk
www.sibc.co.uk
*Rock and pop. Shetland. 96.2 FM;
102.2 FM. Independent. Managing
director and programme controller:
Inga Walterson; head of news: Ian
Anderson*

South West Sound
Unit 40, The Loreburne Centre,
High Street, Dumfries DG1 2BD
01387 250999
firstname.lastname@
  southwestsound.co.uk
www.southwestsound.co.uk
*Chart music. Dumfries and Galloway.
96.5 FM; 97 FM; 103 FM. Owner:
Emap Performance Network.
Managing director: Fiona Blackwood;
programme director: Alan Toomey;
head of news: Ross Nixon; breakfast
show: Tommy Jardine*

Tay AM
6 North Isla Street, Dundee DD3 7JQ
01382 200800
tayam@radiotay.co.uk
www.radiotay.co.uk
*Various music. Dundee and Perth.
1584 AM; 1161 AM. Owner: Emap
Performance Network. Managing
director and programme director: Ally
Ballingall; head of news: Amanda
Mezzullo; breakfast show: Grant Reed*

Tay FM
6 North Isla Street, Dundee DD3 7JQ
01382 200800
tayam@radiotay.co.uk
www.radiotay.co.uk
*Various music. Dundee and Perth.
102.8 FM; 96.4 FM. Owner: Scottish
Radio Holdings. Managing director
and programme director: Ally
Ballingall; head of news: Amanda
Mezzullo; breakfast show: Grant Reed*

Two Lochs Radio
Gairloch, Rossshire IV21 2BQ
0870 741 4657
info@2lr.co.uk
www.2lr.co.uk
*Broad mix and Scottish Gaelic.
Gairloch and Loch Ewe. 106.6 FM.
Independent. Programme director:
Colin Pickering; chairman and station
manager: Alex Gray*

Wave 102
8 South Tay Street, Dundee DD1 1PA
01382 900102
studio@wave102.co.uk
www.wave102.co.uk
*80s, 90s and today. Dundee. 102 FM.
Owner: UTV; programme controller:
Peter Mac; head of news: Mandy
Carter; breakfast show: Peter Mac*

Waves Radio Peterhead
7 Blackhouse Circle,
Peterhead AB42 1BW
01779 491012
waves@radiophd.freeserve.co.uk
www.wavesfm.com
*Current and classic. Peterhead. 101.2
FM. Independent. Managing director
and chairman: Norman Spence; head of
news: Glenn Moir; program controller:
Kenny King; breakfast show: Kenny King*

West FM
Radio House, 54a Holmston Road,
Ayr KA7 3BE
01292 283662
info@westfm.co.uk
www.westfm.co.uk
*Wide variety including music. Ayr.
97.5FM; 96.7 FM. Owner: Emap
Performance Network. Managing
director: Brenda Ritchie; programme
director: Alan Toomey; head of news:
Rob Waller; breakfast show: Alan
Shaw*

West Sound AM
Radio House, 54a Holmston Road,
Ayr KA7 3BE
01292 283662
info@westsound.co.uk
www.westsound.co.uk
*Wide variety of music. Ayr. 1035 AM.
Owner: Scottish Radio Holdings.
Managing director: Sheena Borthwick;
programme director: Alan Toomey;
head of news: Ian Wilson; breakfast
show: Kenny Campbell*

Your Radio
Pioneer Park Studios, Unit 1-3,
80 Castlegreen Street,
Dumbarton G82 1JB
01389 734422
info@yourradio.com
www.yourradiocom
*Popular music. Dumbarton. 103 FM;
106.9 FM. Independent. Station
manager: Susan Dignon; programme
controller: Dave Ross; head of news:
Gary Pews; breakfast show: Dave Ross*

● Commercial local radio: Northern Ireland

Cool FM
PO Box 974, Belfast BT1 1RT
028 9181 7181
music@coolfm.co.uk
www.coolfm.co.uk
*Pop. Northern Ireland. 97.4 FM.
Owner: Emap Performance Network.
Managing director: Mark McHaffey;
head of news: Bob Huggins; breakfast
show: Pete Snodden*

Downtown Radio
Newtownards, Co Down,
Northern Ireland BT23 4ES
028 9181 5555
Programmes@downtown.co.uk
www.downtown.co.uk
*Adult contemporary. Northern
Ireland. 97.1 FM; 103.1 FM; 103.4 FM;
102.4 FM; 1026 AM; 96.6 FM; 102.3 FM;
96.4 FM. Owner: Emap Performance
Network. Programme controller: Henry
Ownes; head of news: Bob Huggins;
breakfast show: Dougie Marshall*

Six FM
2c Park Avenue, Burn Road,
Cookstown BT80 8AH
028 8675 8696
firstnamelastname@
  midfm106fm.co.uk
www.mid106fm.co.uk
*80s, 90s mix. Mid-Ulster. 106 FM.
Owner: Northern Media. Station
director: Robert Walsh; news manager:
James Devril; breakfast show:
Earl Doherty*

Q101
42A Market Street, Omagh,
Co. Tyrone BT78 1EH
028 8224 5777
Manager@q101west.fm
www.q101west.fm
*Chart and pop. Omagh and
Enniskillen. 101.2 FM. Owner:
Northern Media. Programme
controller: Robert Walsh; head of
news: Catrina Louchral; breakfast
show: Brian Gallagher*

Q102
The Riverview Suite,
87 Rossdowney Road, Waterside,
Londonderry BT47 5SU
028 7134 4449
Manager@q102.fm
www.q102.fm
*70s to today. Londonderry. 102.9 FM.
Owner: Northern Media. Managing
director and programme controller:
David Austin; head of news: Jimmy
Cadden; breakfast show: Greg Park*

Q97.2 Causeway Coast Radio
24 Cloyfin Road, Coleraine,
Co Londonderry BT52 2NU
028 7035 9100
Manager@q972.fm
www.q972.fm
*Adult contemporary. Coleraine. 97.2
FM. Owner: Northern Media.
Programme controller: Robert Walsh;
head of news: Damien McGinley;
breakfast show: Barrie Owler*

Minor stations*

Adventist World Radio
01344 401401
www.awr.org
*Community and religious programmes.
Satellite. Programme director: Ray Allen*

Amrit Bani
020 8606 9292
info@amritbaniradio.com
www.amritbani.com
*Religious Asian broadcasting. Digital.
Operational director: Mr. G Singh*

Apna Radio
www.apnaradio.com
*Punjabi, Hindi and Pakistani music.
Internet*

Asian Gold
020 8571 7200
info@sukhsagarradio.com
www.sukhsagarradio.com
*Ethnic Asian. Digital. Chief executive
director: Zorawar Gakhal*

* stations available in UK only on cable, satellite or internet, or on a small number of local DAB licences

Bloomberg Radio
020 7330 7575
ecoleman4@bloomberg.net
www.bloomberg.co.uk
Financial news. 1130 AM. Radio editor:
Eric Coleman

Calvary Chapel Radio
020 8466 5365
07779 507032
ccradio@btconnect.com
www.calvarychapelradio.co.uk
Christian radio. Sky. Managing
director: Brian Brodersen; programme
controller: Alison Johnstone-White

Club Asia
020 8594 6662
info@clubasiaonline.com
www.clubasiaonline.com
Asians 15-45. 963 AM, 972 AM.
Programme controller: Ruckshama Ali

Easy Radio
0845 612 8040
info@easy1035.com
www.easy1035.com
DAB. Programme controller: Paul Owens

ETBC London
www.etbclondon.com
Tamil language

Family Radio
00 1 800 543 1495
www.familyradio.com
Christian gospel. Internet

HCJB World Radio
01274 721810
info@hcjb.org.uk
www.hcjb.org
Religious. International shortwave

Holiday FM
www.holidayfmradio.co.uk
Gran Canaria, Lanzarote, Tenerife,
Costa del Sol, Ibiza, Costa Blanca

Kool AM
020 8373 1075
pfmnews@email.com
www.koolam.co.uk
Harlow. 1134 AM. Programme
controller: Joe Bone

Laser Radio
01342 327842
laser@ukmail.com
www.laserradio.net
Baltic sea area and Scandinavia. 9290
AM. Managing director: Andrew Yeates

Music Choice
020 3107 0300
www.musicchoice.co.uk
Non-stop music compilation channels.
Sky; internet. CEO: Margo Daly

NPR Worldwide
(National Public Radio)
00 1 202 513 2000
www.npr.org/worldwide
Vice president, communications:
Andi Sporkin

Panjab Radio
020 8848 8877
info@panjabradio.co.uk
www.panjabradio.co.uk
DAB and internet

Radio Caroline
020 8340 3831
info@radiocaroline.co.uk
www.radiocaroline.co.uk
Album rock music. Sky and internet.
Programme controller and station
manager: Peter Moore

Radio France Internationale (RFI)
00 33 1 5640 1212
www.rfi.fr
France's "World Service". Internet

Radio Telefis Eireann
00 353 1 208 3111
info@rte.ie
www.rte.ie
Ireland's public service broadcaster.
Managing director: Adrian Moynes

Real Radio
029 2031 5100
ricky.durkin@realradiofm.com
www.realradiofm.com
60s to present day. 105-106 FM.
Managing director: Andy Carter;
programme director: Ricky Durkin

Spectrum Digital 1
020 7627 4433
enquiries@spectrumradio.net
www.spectrumradio.net
Multi-ethnic. 558 AM. General manager:
Paul Hogan

Sunrise Radio
020 8574 6666
reception@sunriseradio.com
www.sunriseradio.com
Asian. 1458 AM. Managing director:
Tony Lit; programme controller:
Tony Patti

Premier
020 7316 1300
www.premier.org
African and Caribbean churches.
Sky and internet

TBC Radio
07817 063682
info@tbcuk.com
www.tbcuk.com
Political analysis, news, Asian music.
Satellite. Station director: V Ramarag

TotalRock
info@totalrock.com
www.totalrock.com
Rock and metal. Sky and internet.
Editorial contact: Malcolm Dome

Trans World Radio UK
0161 923 0270
web@twr.org.uk
www.twr.org.uk
Christian music. Sky and internet;
1467 AM Saturday and Sunday
11.15pm; short-wave 9.87 MHz and
11.865 MHz each morning. Chief
executive: Russell Farnworth

Voice of America
00 1 202 203 4000
publicaffairs@voa.gov
www.voanews.com
News, information, educational and
cultural programming. Satellite

WorldSpace UK
020 7896 4160
ukservice@worldspace.com
www.worldspace.com
Music, news. Satellite. Senior
vice-president: Safia Safwat

Community radio

7 Waves
0151 691 1595
pauline.murphy@merseymail.com
www.7waves.co.uk
Leasowe, Wirral. Project coordinator:
Pauline Murphy

209 Radio
01223 488418
getinvolved@209radio.co.uk
www.209radio.co.uk
Cambridge. Station manager:
Karl Hartland

ACE Consortium
info@ace-consortium.net
Nottingham.
Secretary: Kelbert Henriques

Aldershot Garrison FM
01748 830050
hq@garrisonradio.com
www.army.mod.uk/garrisonradio
Programme director: John McCray

Alive in the Spirit of Plymouth FM
01752 242262
chris@cornerstonevision.com
Programme manager:
Christopher Girdler

ALL FM
0161 248 6888
alex@allfm.org
www.allfm.org
Manchester. Station manager:
Alex Green

Angel Radio Havant
023 9248 1988,
angelradio@37.com
Managing Director: Tony Smith

Angel Radio Isle of Wight
01983 246810
angelradioiw@hotmail.com
Contact: Chris Gutteridge

Asian Star
07841 918434
sbba1@yahoo.co.uk
Slough. Station manager: Sbba Siddique

BCB
01274 771677
info@bcbradio.co.uk
www.bcb.yorks.com
Bradford. Director: Mary Dowson;
broadcast manager: Jonathan Pinfield

Betar Bangla
020 7729 4333
betarbangla@btconnect.com
London. Chief executive and director:
Golam Mohammed Chowdhury

Bexley Community Media
Association
01322 447767
info@bcma.biz
www.bcma.biz
Chief executive: Andrew Sayers

Branch FM
01924 454750
studio@branchfm.co.uk
Dewsbury. Station Manager:
Stephen Hodgson

Bristol Community FM
0560 1126659
phil@bcfm.org.uk
www.bcfm.org.uk
Station manager: Phil Gibbons

BRFM
01795 876045
office@brfm.net
www.brfm.net
Isles of Sheppey. Station manager:
Danny Lawrence

Burst FM (Bristol University)
0117 954 5777
info@burstradio.org.uk
www.burstradio.org.uk
Station manager: Martin MacLachlan

Cambridge University Radio
01223 501004.
sm@cur1350.co.uk
www.cur1350.co.uk
Station manager: Michael Brooks

Canalside Community Radio FM
01625 576689
nick@ccr-fm.co.uk
www.ccr-fm.co.uk
Bollington, Macclesfield. Programme
controller and coordinator: Nick Wright

Carillon Radio
01509 564433
carillonradio@aol.com
Loughborough. Station manager:
Jon Sketchley

Castledown Radio
01264 791929
studio@castledownradio.info
www.castledownradio.info
Ludgershall, Wiltshire. Project
manager: Baz Reilly

Catterick Garrison FM
01748 830050
hq@garrisonradio.com
www.army.mod.uk/garrisonradio/
Programme director: John McCray

Cheshire FM
01606 737844
info@cheshirefm.com
www.cheshirefm.com
Northwich. Managing Director:
David Duffy

Chesterfield Broadcasting
Network
01246 851150
info@trustfm.co.uk
Station director: Ivan Spenceley

Colchester Garrison Radio
01206 782589
colchester@garrisonradio.com
www.garrisonradio.com
Managing director: Mark Page

Crescent Radio
01706 340786
faheem@myself.com
www.crescentradio.net
Rochdale. Contact: Faheem Chishti

Cross Rhythms City Radio
0870 011 8008
jonathan.bellamy@
  crossrhythms.co.uk
www.crossrhythms.co.uk
Stoke on Trent (Hanley). General
manager: Jon Bellamy

Cross Rhythms Teesside
joel.hauxwell@gmail.com
www.crossrhythmsteesside.co.uk
Stockton on Tees. General manager:
Joel Hauxwell

Demo FM
020 8655 7209
gracembailey@yahoo.co.uk
London. Record producer:
Charles Bailey

Desi Radio
020 8574 9591
info@desiradio.org.uk
www.desiradio.org.uk
West London. Manager: Amarjit Khera

Drystone Radio
01535 635392
drystoneradio@fsmail.net
www.drystoneradio.co.uk
Yorkshire Dales. Director: David Adams

Express FM
023 9282 2112
studio@expressfm.com
www.expressfm.com
South Hampshire. Managing director:
Cheryl Buggy

Focus FM Radio
info@focusradio.com
www.focusradio.com
Bristol. Director: Theo Stephenson

Forest FM
01202 820003
vwradio@aol.com
www.forestfm.co.uk or
www.forestfm.com
Verwood Dorset. Managing director:
Steve Saville

Forest of Dean Community Radio
01594 820722
contactus@fodradio.org
www.fodradio.org
Cinderford, Glos. Director:
Martin Harrison

Future Radio
01603 250505
info@nr5project.co.uk
www.futurefmradio.co.uk
Norwich. Radio manager:
Tom Buckham

Generation Radio Clapham Park
020 8623 9419
studio@generationradio.co.uk
www.generationradio.co.uk
London. Programme director:
Andy Sayers

Gloucester FM
01452 546400
admin@gloucesterfm.com
www.gloucesterfm.com
Chairman: Derrick Francis

Harborough FM
01858 464666
barry.badger@harboroughfm.co.uk
www.hfm.freeservers.com
Market Harborough. Station manager:
Barry Badger

Hayes Community Radio
020 8573 7992
office@hayesfm.org
www.hayesfm.org
Operations manager: Surish Sharma

Hope FM
01202 780396
jblaircrawford@aol.com
www.hopefm.com
Bournemouth. Executive director:
Blair Crawford

Indian Muslim Welfare Society
01924 500555
info@imws.org.uk
Batley. Centre manager: Mr Muza Kazi

Ipswich Community Radio
01473 418022
info@icrfm.co.uk
www.icrfm.co.uk
Station co-ordinator: Nick Greenland

Life FM
020 8963 0935
bryan@lifefm.org.uk
www.lifefm.org.uk
London. Project director:
Bryan Anderson

Link FM
0845 273 2228
dave.butler@haveringbep.co.uk
www.linkfm.net
Romford. Managing director:
Dave Butler

Lionheart Radio
01665 602244
studio@lionheartradio.co.uk
www.lionheartradio.co.uk
Alnwick, Northumberland. Station
Director: George Millar

Lune Valley Radio
01524 271294
paul@lakelandtoday.com
Kirby Lonsdale. Contact:
Paul Broadbent

New Style Radio 98.7 FM
0121 456 3826
newstyle@acmccentre.co.uk
www.newstyleradio.co.uk
Birmingham. Chairman: Wesley Hall

NuSound Radio
07909 998927
tari.sian@nusoundradio.com
www.nusoundradio.com
Ilford. Project director: Tari Sian

Pendle Community Radio
01282 723455
info@mwfuk.org
www.mwfuk.org
Manager: Sagheer Akhtar

Phoenix FM (Essex)
01277 849929
studio@phoenixfm.com
www.phoenixfm.com
Brentwood and Billericay.
Station manager: Paul Golder

Phoenix FM (Halifax)
01422 365923
sales@phoenixfm.co.uk
www.phoenixfm.co.uk
Director: Anna Lombardi

Pure Radio
0161 474 5961
info@pureradio.org.uk
www.pureradio.org.uk
Stockport. Radio project officer:
Dave Stearn

Raaj Radio
0116 2756212
infor@raajradio.co.uk
www.raajradio.co.uk
Leicester. Chief executive: Dr CPS Johal

Radio Barnsley
01226 216319
richodr@blueyonder.co.uk
www.ymcaradiobarnsley.co.uk
Barnsley. Training manager:
Dave Richardson

Radio CD (Radio Cultural Diversity)
01865 766032
jwoodman@doctors.org.uk
www.radiocd.org
Oxford. Programme director:
Dr Woodman

Radio Faza 91.1 FM
0115 844 0052
radiofaza@hotmail.com
www.radiofaza.org.uk
Nottingham. Marketing manager:
Javed Mirza

Radio Faza FM/Karimia Institute
0115 841 5807
bmccnottingham@hotmail.com
www.karimia.com
Nottingham. Director: Dr Musharaf
Hussain

Radio Hartlepool
01429 275222
jason@radiohartlepool.co.uk
www.radiohartlepool.co.uk
Managing director: Jason Anderson

Radio Reverb
01273 323040
info@earshot.org.uk
www.radioreverb.com
Brighton. Chair of the Board: Karen Cass

Radio Scilly
01720 423417
radioscilly@aol.com
www.radioscilly.co.uk
Studio manager: Peter Hobson

Radio Teesdale
01833 696750
alastair@teesdaleenterprise.co.uk
Station Manager: Peter Dickson

Radio Verulam
07711 286488
studio@radioverulam.com
www.radioverulam.com
St Albans and Hemel Hempstead.
Station manager: Phil Richards

Redbridge Radio
07814 450586
Director: Tony Bowmer

Resonance FM
020 7403 1922
info@resonancefm.com
www.resonancefm.com
London. Station managers: Richard
Thomas and Chris Weaver

Seaside Radio
01964 611427
lyz@seasideradio.org
Withernsea, E Yorks. Project manager:
Lyz Turner

Shalom FM
07000 245638
shalomfm@hotmail.com
www.shalomfm.com
London. Director: Richard Brian Ford

Sheffield Live
0114 2814082
sangita@thedrum.org.uk
Sheffield. Project leader:
Sangita Basudev

Siren FM
01522 886001
brudd@lincoln.ac.uk
Lincoln. Board Member: Bryan Rudd

Skyline Community Radio
01489 799008
webmaster@
  skylinecommunityradio.co.uk
www.skylinecommunityradio.co.uk
Southampton. Managing director:
David Algate

Sound Radio
info@soundradio.info
www.soundradio.org.uk
East London. Contact: Lol Gellor

Stourbridge Radio Group
01902 696425
info@stourbridgeradio.com
www.stourbridgeradio.com
Chairman and chief executive:
Dr Paul Collins

Sussex Surrey Radio
01737 644259
info@susyradio.com
www.susyradio.com
Redhill and Reigate. Contact:
Colin Pearse

Takeover Radio
0116 299 9600
sharon@takeoverradio.com
www.takeoverradio.com
Leicester. Director: Paul Quilter

Tameside Community Radio
0161 408 2036
info@tamesideradio.com
www.tamesideradio.com
Managing Director: Simon Walker

Tidworth Bulford Garrison FM
hq@garrisonradio.com
www.army.mod.uk/garrisonradio
Programme director: John McCray

Tyneside Community Broadcast
0191 240 1025
admin@cbit.org.uk
www.cbit.org.uk
Newcastle. Manager: Elaine Parker

Unity Radio 24
023 8023 3239
kelly@unity101.org
www.unity24.org
Southampton. Project manager:
Ram Kalyan ("Kelly")

Voice of Africa Radio
020 7059 0035
info@voiceofafricaradio.com
www.voiceofafricaradio.com
London. Project manager: Space Clottey

Walsall FM
pw004t5791@blueyonder.co.uk
Contact: Pam Weaver

Wayland Community Radio
01760 441161
wayland.radio@tesco.net
Watton, Norfolk. Project manager:
David Hatherly

West Hull Community Radio (WHCR FM)
07711 117042
contact@whcrfm.com
www.whcrfm.com
Contact: John Harding

Wetherby Community Radio Group
bobpreedy@yahoo.co.uk
Contact: RE Preedy

Wharfedale FM
01943 463502
nigelfrancis@btinternet.com
Otley, Leeds. Chairman: Nigel Francis

Wirral Christian Media
0151 643 1696
office@flamefmwirral.org.uk
www.flamefmwirral.org.uk
Manager: Norman Polden

Wolverhampton Community Radio Training
01902 572260
whitehousep@wolvcoll.ac.uk
www.wcrfm.com
Chairman: Peter Whitehouse

Wythenshawe FM
0161 237 5454
phil@radioregen.org
www.radioregen.org
Director: Phil Korbel

Youth Community Media
0845 226 1246
chris@youthcommunitymedia.org.uk
www.youthcommunitymedia.org.uk
Worcester. Station Manager: Chris Fox

● Wales

Afan FM
07791 375999
craig@afanfm.co.uk
www.afanfm.co.uk
Port Talbot. Station manager:
Craig Williams

Beats FM
029 2064 0500
john.lenney@immtech.co.uk
www.immtech.co.uk
Cardiff. Director: John Lenny

BRFM
01495 313003
studio@brfm.co.uk
www.brfm.co.uk
Blaenau Gwent. Station manager:
Chris Lewis

Calon FM
01978 293373
mail@nadira.co.uk
www.newi.ac.uk
Wrexham. Head of communications,
technology and environment: Nadira
Tudor (07765 276880)

GTFM
01443 406111
news@gtfm.co.uk
www.gtfm.co.uk
Pontypridd. Station manager:
Terry Mann

Toradio
tormedia@softhome.net
www.tormedia.info/toradio.htm
Torfaen. Contact: Alan Fossey

● Scotland

Awaz FM
0141 420 6666
info@awazfm.co.uk
www.awazfm.co.uk
Glasgow. Directory: Javed Sattar

Black Diamond FM
0131 271 3711
admin@midlothianradio.org.uk
www.midlothianradio.org.uk
Edinburgh. Chairman: John Ritchie

Celtic Music
info@celticmusicradio.org.uk
www.celticmusicradio.org.uk
Glasgow. Directors: Robert McWilliam

East End Broadcast
0141 550 3954
Glasgow. Chief executive:
David McDermot

Edinburgh Garrison FM
01748 830050
hq@garrisonradio.com
www.army.mod.uk/garrisonradio/
Programme director: John McCray

Leith FM
0131 553 5304
info@leithmediaworks.com
www.leithmediaworks.co.uk
Edinburgh. Contact: Sandy Campbell

Ness Community Radio
01463 731740
colin.macphail@virgin.net
Inverness. Admin director:
Colin MacPhail

Radio Asia Scotland
Radioasiascotland@hotmail.com
Glasgow. Contact: Mohammed Nasar
Moughal

Revival Radio
01236 823810
info@revivalradio.org.uk
www.revivalradio.org.uk
Cumbernauld. Chairman: Ian Dunlop

RNIB Scotland VIP ON AIR
0141 334 5530
ross.macfayien@viponair.com
www.viponair.com
Glasgow. Station manager:
Ross Macfayien

Station House Media Unit
01224 487174
info@shmu.org.uk
www.shmu.org.uk
Aberdeen. Co-ordinator: Murray Dawson

Superstation Orkney
info@thesuperstation.co.uk
www.thesuperstation.co.uk
Contact: Dave Miller

● Northern Ireland

BFBS – Lisburn
01494 878702
www.bfbs.com
Controller: Mr. Foster

Down FM
028 4461 5815
ian.mccormick@edifhe.ac.uk
www.edifhe.ac.uk
Downpatrick. Head of information
and design: Ian McCormick

Féile FM
028 9024 2002
emma@feilebelfast.com
www.feilebelfast.com
Belfast. Station manager: Emma Mullen

Raidió Fáilte
028 9020 8040
mary@aislingghear.tv
Belfast. Contact:
Máire Uí Mhaoilchiaráin

Hospital, student and sporting event radio

1287 AM Insanity
01784 414267
studio@su.rhul.ac.uk
www.insanityradio.com
Egham. Student radio. 1287 AM.
Station manager: Chris Jackson-Jones

1503 AM Radio Diamonds
01933 652000
press.office@rd-fc.co.uk
Matchday service for Rushden and
Diamonds FC. 1503 AM. Director:
Keith Cousins

B-1000
www.brunel.ac.uk
Uxbridge. Brunel University. 999 AM

Bailrigg FM
01524 593902
station.manager@bailriggfm.co.uk
www.bailriggfm.co.uk
Lancaster University. 87.7 FM. Station
manager: Sara Bury

Basildon Hospital Radio
01268 282828
studios@bhr1287.net
www.bhr1287.net
1287 AM. Chairman: Alan Newman

Bedrock AM
0870 199 3692
www.musicinhospital.org.uk
Romford. Oldchurch Hospital. 846 AM

BFBS
01494 878701
adminofficer@bfbs.com
www.bfbs.com
Chalfont St Peter. Forces radio.
Northern Ireland only. 1287 AM.
Radio controller: Charles Foster

Big Blue
gary@bigbluedigital.co.uk
Chelsea. Matchday service. 96.3 FM.
Contact: Gary Taphouse

Blast 1386
0118 967 5068
blast1386@reading-college.ac.uk
www.blast1386.com
Reading. Student radio. 1386 AM;
internet. Station manager: Bob Goertz

Bridge FM
01382 496333
info@bridgefm.org.uk
www.bridgefm.org.uk
Dundee. Hospital, Tayside. 87.7 FM.
Presenter: Barry Hampton; station
manager: Bob McNally

C4 Radio
01227 782510
c4radio@cant.ac.uk
Canterbury. Christchurch College. 999
AM. Station manager: Lucy Drury

Canterbury Hospital Radio
01227 864161
www.chradio.org.uk
Canterbury. 945 AM. Studio manager:
Martin Pauley

Canterbury Student Radio
01227 824703
www.csrfm.com
University of Kent. 1350 AM. Liz Nicholson

Cardiff Stadium Radio
01264 369369
paul.forsyth@sounddec.com
www.sounddeck.com
Cardiff. Rugby referee match commentary. Sales director: Paul Forsyth

Carillon Radio
01509 564433
carillonradio@aol.com
Loughborough. Loughborough Hospital, Coalville Hospital. 1386 AM

Carlett Radio
0151 551 7777
enquiries@wmc.ac.uk
Wirral Metropolitan College. 1287 AM

Chichester Hospital Radio
01243 788122 x3000
studio@chr1431.org.uk
www.chr1431.org.uk
St Richard's Hospital. 1431 AM. Presenter: Mark Hughes

City Hospital Radio
01442 262222
Hemel Hempstead. St Albans City Hospital. 1350 AM; 1287AM. Chairman: Neil O'Hara

Crush
01707 501004
uhsu.comms@herts.ac.uk
http://uhsu.herts.ac.uk
/media/crush/
Hatfield. University of Hertfordshire. 1278 AM. Sabbatical Officer: Alex Salmon

CUR
01223 569509
studio@cur1350.co.uk
www.cur1350.co.uk
Cambridge. Churchill College, University of Cambridge. 1350 AM. Station manager: Michael Brooks

D:One
01332 590500
http://done.udsu.co.uk/
Derby. University of Derby. 1278 AM. Station manager: Richard Green

Dorton Radio Station
01732 592500
karen.campbell@rlsb.org.uk
www.rlsb.org.uk
Sevenoaks. Dorton College. 1350 AM. Station manager: Karen Campbell

Frequency
01772 894895
www.yourunion.co.uk
Preston. University of Central Lancashire. 1350 AM. Station manager: Emma Syer

GU2
01483 689311
studio@gu2.co.uk
www.gu2.co.uk
Guildford. Student. 1350 AM. Head of Creative: Tom Knight

Hospital Radio Basingstoke
01256 313521
mail@hrbasingstoke.co.uk
www.hrbasingstoke.co.uk
945 AM. Programme controller: Neil Ogden

Hospital Radio Crawley
01293 534859
1287 AM

Hospital Radio Plymouth
01752 763441
www.hospitalradioplymouth.org.uk
87.7 FM. Station Manager: Bob Smith

Hospital Radio Pulse
01527 512048
studio@hospitalradiopulse.com
www.hospitalradiopulse.com
Redditch. 1350 AM. Programme controller: Ian Barstow

Hospital Radio Reading
0118 322 8505
requests@
    hospitalradioreading.co.uk
www.hospitalradioreading.org.uk
Royal Berkshire and Battle Hospitals. 945 AM. Programme controller: Stephen Ham

Hospital Radio Rossendale
01706 233334
945 AM. Contact: David S Foster

Hospital Radio Yare
01493 842613
jean@birchwell.co.uk
www.radioyare.com
Great Yarmouth. James Paget, Northgate, Lowestoft hospitals. 1350 AM. Chairman: Jean Thorpe; programme controller: Phil Marshall

IC Radio
020 7594 8100
info@icradio.com
www.icradio.com
South Kensington. Imperial College halls of residence. 999 AM. Station manager: Mike Jones

Jam 1575
01482 466999
email@jam1575.com
www.jam1575.com
Hull. Hull University. 1575 AM. Station manager: Oliver Tripp

Junction 11
0118 378 4152
studio@1287am.com
www.1287am.com
Reading. Reading University. 1287 AM. Station manager: Dave Wiley

Kendal Radio
01539 795420
Info@kendalhospitalradio.com
www.kendalhospitalradio.org.uk
Hospital radio. Chairman: John Fulstow

Kingstown Radio
01482 327711
onair@kingstownradio.com
www.kingstownradio.co.uk
Hull. Hull hospital radio. 1350 AM. Station manager: Nick Palmer

Kool AM
020 8373 1075
pfmnews@email.com
www.koolam.co.uk
Edmonton. 1134 AM. Programme controller: Joe Bone

Livewire
01603 592512
manager@livewire1350.com
www.livewire1350.com
Norwich. UEA students. 1350 AM. Station Manager Paul Tuttnall

Loughborough Campus Radio
01509 635050
studio@lcr1350.co.uk
www.lcr1350.co.uk
Loughborough. Student radio. 1350 AM. Head of media: Lucy Pritchard; station manager: Oliver Folkerd

Mid-Downs Hospital Radio
01444 441350
studio@ndr.org.uk
Haywards Heath. Hospital radio. 1350 AM. Station manager: Alan French

Nerve Radio
Jhawkins@bournemouth.ac.uk
www.nervemedia.net
Bournemouth. Bournemouth University. 87.7 FM. Web manager: Jason Hawkins

Nevill Hall Sound
01873 858633
info@nevillhallsound
www.nevillhallsound.com
Abergavenny. Nevill Hall Hospital. 1287 AM. Station manager: Deborah Bowing

Newbold Radio
01344 454607 x324
www.newbold.ac.uk
Binfield. Newbold College. 1350 AM

Oakwell 1575 AM
enquiries@oakwell1575am.co.uk
www.oakwell1575am.co.uk
Barnsley. Matchday service for Barnsley FC. 1575 AM. Station manager: Dave Parker

Palace Radio 1278 AM
020 8653 5796
info@palaceradio.net
www.palaceradio.net
London. Matchday service for Crystal Palace FC. 1278 AM. Station Manager: Jerry Clark

Portsmouth Hospital Broadcasting
www.qaradio.co.uk
Queen Alexandra Hospital and St Mary's Hospital. 945 AM. Station manager: Barrie Swann

Radio Air3
01786 467179
stationmanager@airthrey.co.uk
http://susaonline.org.uk
Sterling. Student, music, politics. 1350 AM. Station manager: Matt Ludlow

Radio Branwen
01766 781911
radiobranwen@yahoo.co.uk
Harlech. Student, music. 87.7 FM.
Station manager: Trevor Andrews

Radio Brockley
020 8954 6591
studio@radiobrockley.org
www.radiobrockley.org
London. Stanmore's Royal National.
Orthopaedic Hospital. 999 AM

Radio Bronglais
01970 635363
office@radiobronglais.co.uk
www.radiobronglais.co.uk
Aberystwyth. Bronglais General
Hospital. 87.8 FM. Station manager:
Martin Oakes

Radio Cavell
info@radiocavell1350.org.uk
www.radiocavell1350.org.uk
Royal Oldham Hospital. 1350 AM.
Broadcasting manager: Phil Edmunds

Radio Glangwili
01267 227504
Carmarthen. West Wales General
Hospital. 87.7 FM

Radio Heatherwood
01344 625818
www.radioheatherwood.org.uk
Ascot. Heatherwood Hospital. 999 AM.
Station manager: Dave Smith

Radio Hotspot
01473 326287
www.royalhospitalschool.org
Ipswich. The Royal Hospital School.
1287 AM. Manager: Don Topley

Radio Lonsdale
01229 877877
studio@radiolonsdale.co.uk
www.radiolonsdale.co.uk
Hospital. 87.7 FM. Station manager:
Julian Ackred

Radio Nightingale
01709 304244
Admin@radionightingale.org.uk
www.radionightingale.org.uk
Rotherham District General Hospital.
1350 AM

Radio North Angus
01382 424095
info@radionorthangus.co.uk
www.radionorthangus.co.uk
Arbroath Infirmary and Brechin
Infirmary. 96.6 FM, 87.7 FM.
Managing director: Malcolm Finlayson

Radio North Tees
01642 624337
info@radionorthtees.com
www.radionorthtees.com
Stockton on Tees. Hospital radio.
Station manager: Elliot Kennedy

Radio Northwick Park
020 8869 3959
info@radionorthwickpark.org
www.radionorthwickpark.org
North-west London. Hospital radio.
Programme controller: Matt Blank

Radio Reading
0118 322 6560
www.hospitalradioreading.org.uk
Aberdeen. Royal Aberdeen Children's
Hospital. 945 AM

Radio Redhill
01737 768511
studio@radioredhill.co.uk
www.radioredhill.co.uk
East Surrey Hospital. 1287 AM.
Station manager: Nigel Gray

Radio Rovers
01254 261413
touchline@radiorovers.com
www.gjmedia.co.uk/rrovers
Blackburn. Blackburn Rovers
matchday service. 1404 AM.
Station manager: Alan Yardley

Radio Tyneside
0191 273 6970
info@radiotyneside.co.uk
www.radiotyneside.co.uk
Newcastle General Hospital. 1575 AM

Radio Warwick
024 7657 3077
studio@radio.warwick.ac.uk
www.radio.warwick.ac.uk
Warwick. Student radio. 1251 AM.
Station manager: Matt Rebeiro

Radio West Suffolk
01284 713403
peteowen1350@hotmail.com
www.radiowestsuffolk.co.uk
Bury St Edmunds. West Suffolk
Hospital. 1350 AM. Vice chairman:
P Owen

Radio Wexham
01753 570033
Wexham Park Hospital. 945 AM

Radio Ysbyty Glan Clwyd
01745 584229
Conway. Glan Clwyd District General
Hospital. 1287 AM. Manager:
Morag Jelly

Ram Air
01274 233269
studio@ramair.co.uk
www.ramair.co.uk
Bradford. University of Bradford. 1350
AM. Station manager: Ben Nunney

Range Radio
0161 861 9727
studio@rangeradio.co.uk
www.rangeradio.co.uk
Manchester. Student radio. 1350 AM.
Station manager: Martin Bryant

Red
red@essex.ac.uk
www.essexstudent.com
/media/redradio
Colchester. Student radio. 1404 AM.
Station manager: Shruti Budhia

RK1 FM
01691 773671
singletonr@moretonhall.com
www.moretonhall.org
/radio_report.html
Oswestry. Moreton Hall Educational
Trust. 87.7 AM. Head of science:
Richard Singleton

Rookwood Sound Hospital Radio
029 2031 3796
chief@rookwoodsound.co.uk
www.rookwoodsound.co.uk
Llandaff. Rookwood Hospital. 945 AM.
Programme controller: Matthew
Morrissey

The Saint 107.8 FM
023 8033 0300
studio@saintsfc.co.uk
www.saintsfc.co.uk
Adult contemporary, Southampton FC.
Southampton. 107.8 FM. Independent.
Programme controller, station director
and breakfast show: Stewart Dennis

Sports! Link-fm
01225 835553
info@sportslinkfm.com
www.sportslinkfm.com
Live sports commentary. 87.7 to 105
FM. Managing director: Peter Downey

SNCR
0115 914 6467
Nottingham. South Nottingham
College. 1278 AM

Southside Hospital Broadcasting
01642 854742
info@southsideradio.com
www.southsideradio.com
James Cook University Hospital.
Contact: Alex Lewczuk

Stoke Mandeville Hospital Radio
01296 331575
info@smhr.co.uk
www.smhr.co.uk
1575 AM

Storm FM
01248 383235
admin@stormfm.com
www.stormfm.com
Bangor. University of Wales Bangor.
87.7 FM. Manager: Mike Walsh

Storm Radio
01206 500700
storm@colchsfc.ac.uk
www.colchsfc.ac.uk
Colchester. Student radio. 999 AM.
Station manager: Shirley Hart

Subcity Radio
0141 341 6219
manager@subcity.org
www.subcity.org
Glasgow. Student radio. 1350 AM.
Station manager: Shaun Murphy

Surge
023 8059 1287
office@surgeradio.co.uk,
studio@surgeradio.co.uk
www.surgeradio.co.uk
University of Southampton. 1287 AM.
Station manager: Stewart Davies;
programme controller: James Panner;
head of music: Chrissie Jackson

Trust AM
01909 502909
studio@trustam.com
www.trustam.com
Doncaster. Doncaster and Bassetlaw
Foundation Trust group of hospitals.
1278 AM. Programme controllers:
Steve Roberts and Andy Morton

Tunbridge Wells Hospital Radio
01892 528528
info@hrtw.org.uk
www.hrtw.org.uk
Kent and Sussex, Pembury and Tonbridge Cottage hospitals. 1350 AM. Programme controller: Chris Manser

UCA
01292 886358
Marcus.Bowman@paisley.ac.uk
www.ucaradio.paisley.ac.uk
Ayr. University campus, Ayr. 87.7 FM; DAB. Station manager: Marcus Bowman

University Radio Falmer
01273 678999
exec@urfonline.com
www.urfonline.com
Falmer. University of Sussex and Brighton University Falmer Campus. 1431 AM. Station manager: Daniel Parslow

University Radio York
01904 433840
ury@ury.york.ac.uk
http://ury.york.ac.uk
York. Student radio. 1350 AM. Programme controller: Matt Wareham

URB
01225 386611
studio@bath.ac.uk
www.1449urb.com
Bath. Student radio. 1449 AM.

URF
01273 678999
exec@urfonline.com
www.urfonline.com
Brighton. Student radio. 1431 AM. Station manager: Jonathan Pascoe

URN
0115 846 8722
manager@urn1350.net
www.urn1350.net
Nottingham. University of Nottingham. 1350 AM. Station manager: Mike Young; head of music: Tom Aldridge

Viva AM
01925 722298
head@penketh.warrington.sch.uk
www.penkethhigh.com
/vivaradio.htm
Warrington. Penketh High School. 1386 AM. Programme controller: Jonathan Kay

VRN
01592 268530
www.classicvrn.org.uk
Kirkaldy. Victoria Hospital, Kirkaldy. 1287 AM. Station Manager: Colin Johnson

WCR AM
01902 572260
training@wcr1350.co.uk
www.wcr1350.co.uk
Wolverhampton. College radio. 1350 AM. Manager: Steve Morris

Withybush FM
01437 773564
studio@withybushfm.co.uk
www.withybushfm.co.uk
Withybush Hospital. 87.7 FM. Station manager: Hilary Raymond

Xpression
01392 263568
stationmanager@Xpressionfm.com
www.Xpressionfm.com
Exeter. Student radio. 87.7 FM. Station manager: Chloe Aust

Xtreme
01792 295989
studio@xtremeradio.info
www.xtremeradio.info
Swansea. Student radio. 1431 AM. Station Manager: Bindha Singh

Radio associations

Association for International Broadcasting
PO Box 141, Cranbrook TN17 9AJ
020 7993 2557
info@aib.org.uk
www.aib.org.uk
Trade organisation

Broadcasting Press Guild
Tiverton, The Ridge, Woking, Surrey GU22 7EQ
01483 764895
torin.douglas@bbc.co.uk
Promotes interests of journalists who write or broadcast about the media

Commercial Radio Companies Association
The Radiocentre, 77 Shaftesbury Avenue, London W1D 5DU
020 7306 2603
info@radiocentre.org
www.radiocentre.org

Creators' Rights Alliance
British Music House, 26 Berners Street, London W1T 3LR
020 7436 7296
info@creatorsrights.org
www.creatorsrights.org.uk
Campaigns to protect creators' rights; operates in all media areas

Digital Radio Development Bureau (DRDB)
The Radiocentre, 77 Shaftesbury Avenue, London W1D 5DU
020 7306 2630
info@drdb.org
www.drdb.org
Trade body; funded and supported by BBC and commercial radio multiplex operators

Musicians Union
60–62 Clapham Road, London SW9 0JJ
020 7840 5534
london@musiciansunion.org.uk
www.musiciansunion.org.uk

Office of Communications (Ofcom)
Riverside House, 2A Southwark Bridge Road, London SE1 9HA
020 7981 3000
mediaoffice@ofcom.org.uk
www.ofcom.org.uk
Broadcasting super-regulator

Performing Rights Society
29–33 Berners Street, London W1T 3AB
020 7580 5544
mediaquery@
mcps-prs-alliance.co.uk
www.prs.co.uk
Collects and distributes royalties
Press: 020 7306 4803

Rad10
rad10@rad10.com
www.rad10.com
Free training resource for radio volunteers looking at going professional; offers advice for community radio groups

Radio Joint Audience Research (Rajar)
Paramount House, 162–170 Wardour St, London W1F 8ZX
020 7292 9040
info@rajar.co.uk
www.rajar.co.uk
Audience measurement office. Wholly owned by the Commercial Radio Companies Association and the BBC

The Radio Academy
5 Market Place, London W1W 8AE
020 3205 0150
info@radioacademy.org
www.radioacademy.org
Professional body for radio; aims to promote excellence and a greater understanding of the medium

Voice of the Listener and Viewer (VLV)
101 King's Drive, Gravesend, Kent DA12 5BQ
01474 352835
info@vlv.org.uk
www.vlv.org.uk
Independent, non-profit society working to ensure independence, quality and diversity in broadcasting

Women's Radio Group
27 Bath Road, London W4 1LJ
020 8995 5442
wrg@zelo.demon.co.uk
www.womeninradio.org.uk
Training and networking charity

World Radio Network
PO Box 1212, London SW8 2ZF
020 7896 9000
email@wrn.org
www.wrn.org
Home to series of global radio networks; hosts transmission services for world's leading broadcasters

Radio trade press

Advance Production News
Crimson Communications,
211a Station House,
Greenwich Commercial Centre,
49 Greenwich High Road,
London SE10 8JL
020 8305 6905
www.crimsonuk.com
Monthly. List all TV programmes and films about to be made. Editor: Alan Williams

Audio Media
IMAS Publishing UK, Atlantica
House, 11 Station Road, St Ives,
Cambs PE27 5BH
01480 461555
p.mac@audiomedia.com
j.miller@audiomedia.com
www.audiomedia.com
Monthly. Professional audio. Editor: Paul Mac; news: Jonathan Miller;

Broadcast
Emap Media, 33–39 Bowling
Green Lane, London EC1R 0DA
020 7505 8000
admin@broadcastnow.co.uk
www.broadcastnow.co.uk
Weekly. TV and radio industry. Editor: Conor Dignam; news: Chris Curtis; features and deputy editor: Emily Booth; chief sub: Angus Walker

Commonwealth Broadcaster
Commonwealth Broadcasting
Association, 17 Fleet Street,
London EC4Y 1AA
020 7583 5550
cba@cba.org.uk
www.cba.org.uk
Quarterly. Editor: Elizabeth Smith

**Contacts — The Spotlight Casting
Directories**
The Spotlight, 7 Leicester Place,
London WC2H 7RJ
020 7437 7631
info@spotlight.com
www.spotlight.com
Annual. Contacts for stage, film, TV and radio. Editor: Kate Poynton

Line Up
Line Up Publications,
The Hawthornes, 4 Conference
Grove, Crowle WR7 4SF
01905 381725
editor@lineup.biz
www.lineup.biz
Bi-monthly. Journal of the Institute of Broadcast Sound. Editor: Hugh Robjohns

Pro Sound News Europe
CMP Information, Ludgate House,
245 Blackfriars Road,
London SE1 9UY
020 7921 8319
david.robinson@cmpi.biz
www.prosoundnewseurope.com
12pa. Audio industry. Owner: CMP Information. Editor: David Robinson;

QSheet
10 Northburgh Street,
London EC1V 0AT
020 7253 8888
www.qsheet.com
Monthly. Support material for presenters and producers. Editor: John Reynolds; features and interviews: Nik Harta; art direction and design: Dominic Philcox

Radcom
Radio Society of Great Britain,
Lambda House, Cranbourne Road,
Potters Bar EN6 3JE
0870 904 7373
radcom@rsgb.org.uk
www.rsgb.org
Monthly. Radio enthusiasts

Radio Magazine
Crown House, 25 High Street,
Rothwell, Northants NN14 6AD
01536 418558
name@theradiomagazine.co.uk
www.theradiomagazine.co.uk
Weekly. Radio news for industry. Editor: Paul Boon; features and assistant editor: Collette Hillier; advertising and technical manager: Daniel Hailstone

Stage Screen and Radio
Bectu, 373–377 Clapham Road,
London SW9 9BT
020 7346 0900
jturner@bectu.org.uk
www.bectu.org.uk
10pa. Broadcasting union. Editor: Janice Turner

VLV Bulletin
Voice of the Listener and Viewer,
101 Kings Drive,
Gravesend DA12 5BQ
01474 352835
info@vlv.org.uk
www.vlv.org.uk
Quarterly. Advocates citizen and consumer interests in broadcasting. Editor: Jocelyn Hay

Global media

Janine Gibson

Dow Jones is another piece in the
global media jigsaw for Rupert Murdoch

Our discussions of the global media landscape tend, inevitably, to focus on the English-speaking world. We then, again inevitably, narrow in even further to obsess over the bits of it owned and operated by one Rupert Murdoch. Last year, though, something happened overseas with more impact on the UK market than Murdoch buying the Wall Street Journal, which he did of course and more of that later.

More impact than a deal to purchase a newspaper for $5.6bn, 67% above its market value and bucking every industry trend? Well, perhaps a bunch of screenwriters in Los Angeles and New York might have started a movement that could make that deal look puny.

The Writers Guild of America strike, which began in late October, should never have happened. Oh, they threaten to strike with every contract negotiation, went the received wisdom. They never actually do. Not since the strike of 1988, which cost $500m and lasted 22 weeks. And that was 20 years ago. In real (today's) money? Phew.

As production shut down on pretty much every talkshow, drama and scripted comedy on broadcast television, the movie industry also began to grind to a halt as the writers dug in. The reason it's so significant comes from what it tells us about the production business. Writers use the internet too and they see their employers (the networks in the case of the TV industry) shifting their programmes online, sometimes only hours after their first airing and sometimes (in the case of "webisodes" of very popular shows) in advance. This whole new broadcast window is significant because it can run forever – that is, you or I can call up this stuff, on demand, as often as we want, indefinitely, and the writers get no "residual" payments (the royalties they get for every play of their show on broadcast television).

Having been finessed out of a good deal on DVD sales (currently they receive around 4 cents from a $20 DVD purchase), the writers want their cut of the future. Their opponents round the negotiating table, the AMTP (Alliance of Motion Picture and Television Producers) say the internet is used only for promotional purposes and makes no money, so how can they possibly give the writers a cut.

As a position, it stretches belief. Particularly as US networks (Fox, NBC and Viacom, owner of several cable franchises as well as CBS) are launching advertiser-funded, online-only video sites to rival

Global media

YouTube, as well as fighting to have their copyrighted work removed from the Google-owned network.

But the AMTP is fighting with reason. First the writers, then the directors' guild and then the actors' guild will want a piece of the action. That's without the support staff and the US Teamsters union, which seems to control everything that actually gets a production made, from lighting to transport.

With UK writers already warned not to provide "scab" writing support to US producers and stars of small and large screen lending their support and seemingly endless supplies of baked goods to the pickets, the dispute has already led those who create the content to reassess their worth.

Writers have begun to talk publicly about finding "alternative funding models" for their work. And that means moving outside broadcast media. When social network platforms such as Bebo and MySpace are commissioning series and Google is offering producers a cut of in-video ads inserted into YouTube channels, suddenly the traditional networks aren't quite the cartel they think they are. Think it's all a storm in a teacup? Look at the 10 short films made with top ranking Hollywood actors and distributed via the internet that topped all the viral video charts. Check out the strike blogs that proliferated from the teams of "pencils down" staff of America's most bankable shows: Letterman, the Daily Show and Tonight with Jay Leno.

By December, a strike that was never supposed to happen had been under way for three weeks and, though talks had re-opened, a watershed had passed. The talent has cottoned on to the internet.

But the moguls haven't quite had it yet. Murdoch may have sent his key lieutenant, the News Corp chief executive, Peter Chernin, into the AMTP negotiations, but he was hands-on in the deal to buy Dow Jones, owners of the Wall Street Journal, in a classic Murdoch manoeuvre. In the face of utter hostility from the owners – the Bancroft family – and public condemnation from the liberal establishment, he overbid, divided and yes, ruled. As he prepared to take control on December 13, it was already clear from his public pronouncements that he was going to import his own team, drop the pay wall around WSJ's subscription-only web offering and positively relished the opportunity to take on the New York Times.

But the domestic battles aside, the value of Dow Jones to Murdoch might lie in his long-held Asian ambitions, as Katie Allen wrote in the Guardian in July 2007.

"Media experts at PricewaterhouseCoopers expect Asia Pacific to be the fastest growing region for the sector over the next five years. Against a backdrop of strong economic growth, they predict spending in the media and entertainment markets will rise to $470bn in 2011 from $297bn in 2006.

'We are going to see a lot of market entry-type activity in the course of the next two to three years,' says Marcel Fenez, the Hong Kong-based managing partner at PwC's global entertainment and media practice. 'In terms of segments of news, financial news has always been important in Asia, probably disproportionately important. Financial news is a driver, and that applies across the entire region.'

Murdoch has made no secret of his ambition to grab a bigger slice of the Asian media markets. He has owned the Star TV business there for more than a decade, and recently embarked on a joint venture with India's Tata group to create the Indian satellite TV service Tata Sky.

Buying Dow Jones fills in another piece of the Asian – and the global – puzzle for News Corp. The acquisition brings on board the 30-year-old Wall Street Journal Asia, including its 15 bureaus across the region, nine printing plants and the resources of more than 200 Dow Jones Newswires reporters in Asia. He also gets Chinese WSJ.com, a Chinese-language online business news service, launched in 2002."

All true. But the gems of this deal were in the details. One dynasty (the Bancrofts) v another fledgling version (the Murdochs) and the peculiarities of both, exposed to the world. The most revealing episodes of the entire takeover battle – apparently so resisted by the Bancroft family – were those that exposed how little, when it came down to it, they actually cared for the future of the organisation. As the crucial votes were counted and it emerged that the last stand was nothing more than a PR exercise, the vital detail was that the Bancrofts had hung out for Murdoch to pay ... their legal fees. And then, months afterwards, the much shouted-about position on the board of News Corp to guarantee the WSJ's future? Handed to the 27-year-old Natalie Bancroft, an opera singer.

Global media

Traditional media

Murdoch and meddling

Janine Gibson

The new Wall Street Journal owner's urge to tinker brings both threat and opportunity for rivals.

It seemed to be a nail-biter, though it turns out not to have been close at all. Many of the conscientious objectors among the Bancroft clan, effective owners of the Wall Street Journal, were simply hoping for a bigger offer. Now the family can shuffle off the global media-proprietor stage in anguish over its decision to sell to Rupert Murdoch; the deep ethical anguish that is abated only by $5.6bn, plus legal and banking fees paid.

Tempting as it is to sneer at the Bancrofts or even be a tiny bit disappointed in them, it's not really on. The media industry is dying on its feet, isn't it? Murdoch's offer priced Dow Jones at 67% above its market value. Compare it, say, to the £125m that Sir Alan Sugar got for his "digital future" set-top box company this week (also from Murdoch).

The truth is that the value in Dow Jones lies in its digital operations – its successful subscription-only website and wire services which supply business news round the world and, crucially, to Wall Street. There are plenty of players in online financial news, but no one player dominates among the FTs, Bloombergs and Reuters. There are obvious inroads to be made.

Whether they're obvious enough to justify the price tag is arguable. Murdoch paid a sum that no one else was prepared to for Dow Jones, but he will stick with it and no one else bets the farm quite like Murdoch.

And for him there's an X-factor. Call it a spiritual urge to challenge what he sees as the instinctive liberal bias of the establishment media. Especially when there's a significant business opportunity in such a mission. Think of the New York Times as the CNN of this particular battle and the Wall Street Journal as Fox – fair and balanced – News. The inexorable rise of the latter forced CNN into abandoning its traditions and shifting into more opinionated coverage, trying at times to out-rightwing Fox.

The fear expressed by Bancrofts and leader writers alike in the US is that the Murdoch-backed WSJ will team up with Fox News, the tabloid New York Post and the proposed Fox Business Channel to create some sort of multi-platform, rightwing, fire-breathing dragon. Add to this Murdoch's express ambition to take on the Financial Times in Europe and Asia. Now it's a global behemoth of rightwing financial news terror, conquering territories with its control of business information and mis-reporting stories according to the proprietor's whim.

We know that Murdoch can't resist meddling in the coverage of his newspapers because we have the expert witness of Andrew Neil testifying. Also, because we can see it most days in the Sun or the Times. We also know that meddling is nothing like as straightforward as a direct order – that it's in the appointing of staff who know what the proprietor likes or believe what he believes. That bias can be as subtle in what we don't report as what we do. Bad news story about Beijing? Just put it in brief at the bottom of page 54. It's not so much publishing a glowing book about the Chinese government, as it is suppressing a negative one. You do what Fox News does when faced with bad news from Iraq. You don't spin it, you just ignore it.

Here's the rub though. If you abandon the traditions of impartial, broad, financial reporting that have taken the WSJ to the second-highest circulation in the US, then the market will abandon you. It's a busy market, filled with potential rivals, from the Financial Times to Bloomberg to Reuters and the New York Times. And for each of them the deal represents opportunity as well as threat.

Because if Murdoch can't resist fiddling, then the rest move in. You might not be able to win over the business audience by appealing to its left-leaning conscience or innate liberal bias. But you can certainly appeal to its need to know everything all the time. Knowledge is wealth-creation.

David Montgomery, once boss of the Mirror Group, ended 2007 as head of one of Europe's major newspaper groups. Whether the staff are quite so happy about his acquisition of over 300 European titles, is another matter, as Helen Pidd found out.

» **MediaGuardian**   November 19 2007

First we take Berlin
Helen Pidd

David Montgomery's Mecom now owns over 300 European titles, but the staff are in uproar.

It is often said that David Montgomery is a very thin man with a very thick skin. But quite how lead-lined his ego is only really becomes apparent when you watch him calmly face several hundred angry German journalists who dislike him and everything he stands for.

There is no huffing, no puffing, no hint of a blush. His swept-back almost-mullet remains unruffled. He greets their sarcastic insults with a wry smile and responds to criticisms about his controversial management plans by claiming, straight-faced, that he wants to "liberate" them from the "hum-drum" side of journalism. Hum-drum things, incidentally, such as subediting – but we will come back to that.

Last Thursday in Berlin, a sceptical audience assembled in front of the former Mirror Group boss. The crowd included staff from various media organisations owned by Berliner Verlag – the publishing company bought out by Montgomery's European newspaper group Mecom over the past two years.

The crowd included journalists from the former east German newspapers Berliner Zeitung and Berliner Kurier, Time Out-style listings magazine Tip, weekly freesheet Abendblatt, web-only paper Netzeitung and also, via a conference call, Hamburg's biggest-selling tabloid, the Hamburger Morgenpost. This group were particularly anxious: their 35-year-old editor Matthias Onken had quit the previous week. Unconfirmed rumours claimed he resigned in protest at the cuts Mecom wanted him to make.

The first time Montgomery had faced this testy crowd, back in 2005 when Mecom became the first foreign company to own a stake in a German newspaper group, many were wearing T-shirts bearing the uncompromising message: "You're not welcome." This after Berliner Zeitung staff tried to print an entirely blank edition in protest at their new, Montgomery-installed editor – they only failed when said editor noticed a lack of copy

at 5pm and made them put out an emergency 12-page paper. No one managed to stop the editor of the Berliner Kurier tabloid printing a picture of Montgomery upside down alongside the frontpage headline "nein".

Last week's tense meeting was just one on a whistlestop tour that Montgomery is currently taking around Europe. The reason? To try to quell the fears of the 11,000-strong workforce he has gained with unprecedented speed since 2005, when Mecom began with £48m of private equity from a dozen top-drawer investors. Now the group is the size of Trinity Mirror or Daily Mail and General Trust, on course to a turnover of £948m this year.

It is quite astonishing how busy he has been in two years. Studying the map on the Mecom website feels like being in a hopeless game of Risk where Montgomery has annexed half the board: already he owns more than 300 titles in Norway, the Netherlands, Denmark, Germany, Poland and Ukraine. And he is not done yet. Every week comes a new rumour about a fresh Mecom takeover target – currently Germany is worrying about him buying FT Deutschland and the Guardian-esque national Süddeutsche Zeitung.

Montgomery happily confirms his interest in both. "We are always interested in examining assets that are in our segment, but I am not going

Sarah Lee

Global media

to comment on specific assets," he tells the Guardian. "What I will say is that what we look for is newspapers with a high level of subscribers and generally, but not exclusively, regional newspapers."

Montgomery, then, seems well on the way to taking Europe – and Europe doesn't like it. The Norwegian unions complain he has broken promises not to sack workers or merge companies, the Danes moan he wasted valuable funds on an ill-advised freesheet war to the detriment of the rest of his Danish portfolio. The Poles say he has cut costs too brutally and compromised editorial independence by cosying up to the outgoing Kaczynski government in order to purchase the 49% of Rzeczpospolita, an important Polish national paper, he does not already own.

But the Germans perhaps oppose Montgomery most of all. As Klaus Raab, media editor of the left-leaning Tageszeitung, puts it, "The fact is that German journalists like Montgomery about as much as they like athlete's foot."

"Mister Montgomery," began one senior female journalist from the Berliner Zeitung at the meeting last week, the politeness in her salutation not necessarily matched by her following question. She began by listing the various awards won by her newspaper recently, stressing how hard she and her colleagues worked. Then came the kick to the crotch: "But you can't read our newspaper. You don't speak German, you speak business-talk. We might as well be writing in Chinese for all you can understand. So how are we supposed to believe you respect what we do and aren't just interested in what you can make from us?"

Through his translator, Montgomery responded. After a quick defence of his O-level in German, the 59-year-old said he was well aware of the star talent lurking in the Berliner Zeitung. What he wanted to do was "better disseminate it". Simply using content on one medium was "bankrupt" as a financial model, he said.

And here is one key pillar of Mecom's European strategy: the notion that all journalists have to be able to work across different media. "I want Mecom to become a pure creative content business where our journalists provide stories for many different platforms," said Montgomery. This idea may be old hat to Brits but it is a big step in Germany, where two of the biggest newspapers, the Frankfurter Allgemeine Zeitung and the Süddeutsche Zeitung, still don't even put all of their copy online.

The German journalists at Thursday's summit all seemed broadly in favour of different media – but asked if they were going to be given the money and investment to do it. After some to-ing and fro-ing, Montgomery eventually said: "Our guarantee is that we will make the investment if you will come to the party. I need your full-blooded commitment". He also promised, to hoots of laughter, that this tranformation would be a liberating experience. When asked how exactly, he said he wanted to eliminate the unnecessary barriers between the journalist and the reader, such as the "restrictive paraphernalia" of the subediting process which can too often slow down the distribution of news.

One Montgomery idea that German journalists show no signs of warming to is giving Berliner Zeitung's editor Josef Depenbrock a second job, as commercial director of BV Deutsche Zeitungsholding. To put that into perspective, it's not unlike Alan Rusbridger taking over Carolyn McCall's position as chief executive of Guardian Media Group while remaining editor of the Guardian.

Montgomery says this will not compromise editorial independence or integrity. "Journalists have to be aware that their wages are paid for by people buying the paper and also by advertisers," he tells the Guardian. They have to make their journalism attractive to advertisers, he adds.

"There has been some mischief-making in the press suggesting that journalism is tainted by commerce, but I have not heard a single complaint about the Berliner Zeitung's journalism since we took over. We have never asked them to do puff pieces for advertisers and that wouldn't be tolerated."

Which brings us to the big worry of all Mecom workers who have read about Montomery's reputation – a cold-blooded cost cutter whose complete lack of personal warmth causes the temperature in the room to drop as soon as he walks into it. He may say his priority isn't cutting journalistic jobs, but many journalists were sceptical. They know that the Daily Mirror editor had been summoned to Claridge's by Montgomery, then head of the Mirror Group, and sacked, 48 hours after assuming his job was safe. They have read Amanda Platell's New Statesman article written in 1999 in which she said, "For him, truth and falsehood were apparently neutral categories, to be used according to the tactical needs of the moment."

According to Kjetil Haanes, vice president of Norway's national union of journalists, since Mecom paid ?900m (£644) for the big northern European media group Orkla in 2006, more than 20% of the workforce have left – either sacked or resigning in protest at their new owner's cost-cutting tactics.

Montgomery admits a significant number of staff have left the group. "But most of them have been in middle management and administration.

They left the business because they were perceived as not making enough of a difference to the publishing business," he tells the Guardian, adding that he had brought a lot more women into senior management. This is not a new Monty tactic: at Today he assembled a team of bright young women including Platell, who came to be known as the "red jacket brigade".

Orkla also operated in Poland, Ukraine and Denmark. Mecom got off to a particularly rocky start in the latter country, spending €40-50m launching Dato, a freesheet which closed within six months after getting into a bloody and costly war with two other media groups.

Another problem has been a mass exodus of talent. "Since July 2006, 20 out of 30 top managers have left. Some voluntarily, some forced," says one Danish media observer, who did not want to be named. "Montgomery doesn't seem to fully understand the Danish media market, and he has fired or scared away many of the people that could have helped him understand it. It has got so bad the group's top titles are facing recruitment difficulties right now."

These departures have included the editor-in-chief of Berlingske Tidende, the leading national daily quality newspaper in Denmark, and, perhaps most spectacularly, the newly appointed chief financial officer, Per Madsen. He quit before even sitting at his desk in September this year, apparently having had a change of heart. One reason cited for these departures is a dislike of being controlled from London. In Poland things aren't looking much better. Numerous ex-Orkla employees have been sacked since Mecom took over, and costs are being savagely cut. Grzegorz Gauden was the most high-profile victim – the editor-in-chief of Rzeczpospolita, a national newspaper equivalent to the FT, until September 2006. When Mecom inherited 51% of shares from Orkla, he was sacked.

Gauden believes he was sacked for political reasons. He was unpopular with the outgoing Kaczynski government, whom Mecom needed to keep sweet. The state owned the remaining 49% of Rezeczpospolita, and Kaczynski's Law and Justice Party seemed prepared to sell the state share to Mecom – for a price. Gauden thinks his departure was part of the proposed deal, which with the recent change in Polish government now looks unlikely to go through.

"Yes, it's probably fair to say the outgoing editor was unpopular with the Polish government," says a Mecom spokeswoman in response. "But the choice of editor is Mecom's, not the government's, and is made purely for editorial and commercial reasons."

"Mecom were brutal to me," Gauden says now. "And Montgomery is a strange man. I was in the same room as him twice before I was sacked, and he never even bothered to say hello to me. He is so cold." Sound familiar?

From the Mirror to Mecom

Mecom was born in March 2005 when David Montgomery, along with City brokers Numis, approached top investors for money to start the business. They began by accepting the relatively low sum of £48m from a dozen top-notch establishments, which provided them with the cash they needed to start their shopping spree. The group's first purchase was a stake in the German publishing company the Berliner Verlag, and its most recent, 86.5% of Koninklijke Wegener NV, the largest publisher of regional newspapers and free door-to-door papers in the Netherlands. Although group revenues for 2007 are projected to be £948m (up from £804m in 2006), Mecom has huge debts: ABN Amro estimates the company's net debt will be around £502m by the end of the year.

Global media contacts

Global media contacts

Bertelsmann
Carl-Bertelsmann-Strasse 270,
33311 Gütersloh, Germany
00 49 5241 800
info@bertelsmann.de
www.bertelsmann.com
Press: 00 49 5241 802 466
andreas.grassemeyer@
  bertelsmann.com

Clear Channel
200 East Basse Road, San
Antonio, TX 78209, USA
00 1 210 822 2828
www.clearchannel.com
Press:
lisacdollinger@clearchannel.com

ComCast
1500 Market Street, Philadelphia,
PA 19102, USA
00 1 866 281 2100
www.comcast.com

Gannett
7950 Jones Branch Drive,
McLean VA 22107, USA
00 1 703 854 6000
www.gannett.com
Press: tjconnel@gannett.com

Newsquest Media Group
58 Church Street, Weybridge,
Surrey KT13 8DP
01932 821212
enquiries@newsquestmedia.co.uk
www.newsquestmedia.co.uk

General Electric/NBC
3135 Easton Turnpike,
Fairfield CT 06828, USA
00 1 203 373 2211
www.ge.com/en
Press: gary.sheffer@ge.com

News Corporation
1211 Avenue of Americas, 8th
Floor, New York, NY 10036, USA
00 1 212 852 7000
www.newscorp.com
Press: abutcher@newscorp.com

Sony
550 Madison Avenue, New York,
NY 10022, USA
00 1 212 833 8000
www.sony.com; www.sony.co.uk
Press: press@eu.sony.com

Time Warner
1 Time Warner Centre,
58th and 8th Avenue, New York,
NY 10019, USA
00 1 212 484 8000
www.timewarner.com

Viacom
1515 Broadway, New York,
NY 10036, USA
00 1 212 258 6000
www.viacom.com
Press: press@viacom.com

Vivendi Universal
42 avenue de Friedland,
75008 Paris Cedex 08, France
00 33 1 7171 1000
New York: 00 1 212 572 7000
www.vivendi.com
Press: 00 33 1 7171 1180

Walt Disney
500 South Buena Vista Street,
Burbank, CA 91521-9722, USA
00 1 818 560 1000
www.disney.go.com
Press: kim.kerscher@dig.com

Global news outlets

● Ireland

Connacht Tribune
15 Market Street, Galway, Ireland
00 353 91 536222
www.connacht-tribune.ie
*Weekly. Editor: John Cunningham;
Sentinel editor: Brendon Carol; head of
production: Declan Maguire*

Cork Evening Echo
Academy Street, Cork, Ireland
00 353 21 480 2142
www.eveningecho.ie
*Daily. Editor: Maurice Gubbins; news:
Emma Connolly; features: John Dolan*

Evening Herald
27-32 Talbot Street,
Dublin 1, Ireland
00 353 1 705 5333
www.independent.ie
*Daily. Editor: Stephen Rea; news:
Philip Maloy; features: Dave Lawlor*

Irish Mail on Sunday
3rd Floor, Embassy House,
Herbert Park Lane, Ballsbridge,
Dublin 4, Ireland
00 353 1 637 5800
*Sunday. Editor: Ted Verity; news:
Paul Drury; features: Aileen Doherty;
head of production: Ciaran O'Tuama*

Irish Daily Star
62a Terenure Road North,
Terenure, Dublin 6W, Ireland
00 353 1 490 1228
www.thestar.ie
*Daily. Editor: Gerard Colon; news:
Michael O'Cain; features: Danny Smyth*

Irish Examiner
Academy Street, Cork, Ireland
00 353 21 427 2722
www.examiner.ie
*Daily. Editor: Tim Vaughan; news:
John O'Mahoney; features: Fionnuala
Quinlan*

Irish Independent
27-32 Talbot Street,
Dublin 1, Ireland
00 353 1 705 5333
www.independent.ie
*Daily. Editor: Gerry O'Regan; news:
Philip Dunne; features: Peter Carvosso*

Irish Times
PO Box 74, 24-28 Tara Street,
Dublin 2, Ireland
00 353 1 675 8000
www.ireland.com
*Daily. Editor: Geraldine Kennedy;
news: John Maher; features: Shelia
Wayman*

Kerryman
Clash, Tralee,
County Kerry, Ireland
00 353 66 714 5560
www.kerryman.ie
*Weekly. Editor: Declan Malone; news:
Diedre Walsh; features: Marisa Reidy*

Leinster Leader
18/19 South Main Street, Naas,
County Kildare, Ireland
00 353 45 897302
www.leinsterleader.ie
*Weekly. Editor: John Whelan; features:
Sylvia Pownall*

Limerick Leader
54 O'Connell Street,
Limerick, Ireland
00 353 61 214503/6
www.limerickleader.ie
*Weekly. Editor: Alan English;
news: Eugene Phelan*

Limerick Post
Town Hall Centre, Rutland Street,
Limerick, Ireland
00 353 61 413322
www.limerickpost.ie
*Weekly. Editor: Billy Ryan; news: Clare
Doyle; features: Rose Rush*

RTÉ
New Library Building, Donnybrook,
Dublin 4, Ireland
00 353 1 208 3111
info@rte.ie
www.rte.ie
*Irish national broadcaster.
Commissioning editors: drama: Jane
Gogan; factual: Kevin Dawson;
entertainment: Kevin Linehan; Fair
City (soap): Tara O'Brian; young
people: Sheila DeCourcy; daytime and
lifestyle: Grainne McAleer; regional:
Ray McCarthy; Irish language,
multiculture and entertainment:
Mairead Ninuadhain – all
firstname.lastname@rte.ie*
Press: 00 353 1 208 3434

Sunday Business Post
80 Harcourt Street,
Dublin 2, Ireland
00 353 1 602 6000
www.thepost.ie
Sunday. Editor: Cliff Taylor; news: Gavin Daley; features: Fiona Neff; head of production: Tom McHale

Sunday Independent
27–32 Talbot Street,
Dublin 1, Ireland
00 353 1 705 5333
www.independent.ie
Sunday. Editor: Angus Faning; news: Willy Kealy; features: Anne Harris

Sunday Tribune
15 Lower Baggot Street,
Dublin 2, Ireland
00 353 1 631 4300
www.tribune.ie
Sunday. Editor: Noirin Hegarty; deputy editor: Diarmuid Doyle; news: Olivia Doyle; features: Lise Hand; head of production: Paul Howe

Sunday World
27–32 Talbot Street,
Dublin 1, Ireland
00 353 1 884 9000
www.sundayworld.com
Sunday. Editor: Colm McGinty; news: John Donlon; features: Eamon Dillon; head of production: John Noonan

TG4
Baile na hAbhann,
Co na Gaillimhe, Ireland
00 353 91 505050
www.tg4.ie
Irish-language broadcaster. Director of television: Alan Esslemont

---

● Other Europe

Corriere della Sera
28 via Solferino,
Milano 20121, Italy
00 39 026 339
www.corriere.it
Italian daily. Editor: Paulo Mieli

Cyprus Mail
24 Vassiliou Voulgaroctonou Street, PO Box 21144, 1502
Nicosia, Cyprus
00 357 22 818 585
editor@cyprus-mail.com
www.cyprus-mail.com
English-language daily (not Mondays). Editor: Kosta Pavlowitch

Deutsche Welle
Public Broadcasting Service,
Kurt-Schumacher-Str. 3, 53113
Bonn, Germany
00 49 228 429 0
www.dw-world.de
German broadcaster. European focus. Editor: Erik Bettermann

Diario de Noticias
Altzutzate 8, Polígono Industrial
Areta, HUARTE-PAMPLONA,
Portugal
00 351 948 33 25 33
dnot@dn.pt
www.noticiasdenavarra.com
Portuguese daily. Editor: Pablo Munoz

EuroNews
BP 161, 60 Chemin de Mouilles,
69131 Lyon Ecully, France
00 33 4 7218 8000
info@euronews.net
www.euronews.net
Pan-European TV news

Le Figaro
37 rue du Louvre,
75002 Paris, France
00 33 1 4221 6200
www.lefigaro.fr
Rightwing quality daily. Editor in chief: Philippe Mathon

Frankfurter Allgemeine Zeitung
Hellerhofstraße 2-4, 60327
Frankfurt am Main, Germany
00 49 069 75910
info@faz.net
www.faz.net
Right-leaning daily. Online editor: Kai N. Pritzsche

Gazeta Wyborcza
Szewska, 5, 31009 Krakow,
Poland
00 48 12 629 5000
www.gazeta.pl
Poland's most popular daily

International Herald Tribune
6 bis, rue des Graviers,
92521 Neuilly Cedex, France
00 33 1 4143 9322
iht@iht.com
www.iht.com
Editor: Michael Oreskes

Kathimerini
D Falireos & E Makariou St 2,
185–47 N Faliron, Piraeus, Greece
00 30 210 480 8000
editor@ekathimerini.com
www.ekathimerini.com
English-language daily, supplement to the International Herald Tribune. Editor: Nikos Konstandaras

Libération
11, rue Béranger,
75154 Paris Cedex 03, France
00 33 1 42 76 17 89
www.libe.com
Left-leaning quality daily. Editor: Renaud Dély

Le Monde
80 Boulevard Auguste Blanqui,
75013 Paris, France
00 33 1 5728 2000
mediateur@lemonde.fr
www.lemonde.fr
France's bestselling quality daily of record. Evenings. Editor: Eric Fottorino

Moscow Times
Ulitsa Vyborgskaya 3, Bldg 1,
127018 Moscow, Russia
00 7 495 234 3223
editors@themoscowtimes.com
www.moscowtimes.ru
Respected English-language daily. Editor: Andrew McChesney

El Mundo
Calle Pradillo, 42,
28002 Madrid, Spain
00 34 91 586 48 00
cartas.director@elmundo.es
www.elmundo.es
Progressive Spanish daily. Editor: Pedro Ramirez

El País
Miguel Yuste 40,
28037 Madrid, Spain
00 34 91 337 8200
redaccion@prisacom.com
www.elpais.es
Spain's biggest daily paper. Editor: Jesus Ceberio

Prague Post
Stepanska 20, Prague 1,
110 00, Czech Republic
00 420 2 9633 4400
info@praguepost.com
www.praguepost.com
The Czech Republic's best English-language daily. Editor: Frank Kuznik

Radio France Internationale
116, avenue du President
Kennedy, Paris 75016, France
00 33 1 5640 1212
www.rfi.fr
France's "World Service"

Radio Netherlands
Box 222, 1200 JG Hilversum,
The Netherlands
00 31 35 672 4211
letters@rnw.nl
www.radionetherlands.nl
Holland's best English-language news service

La Repubblica
Piazza Indipendenza, 11/b,
Rome 00185, Italy
00 39 06 49821
larepubblica@repubblica.it
www.repubblica.it
Liberal Rome-based daily. In Italian. Editor: Ezio Maruo

Der Standard
Herrengasse 19-21,
A-1010 Wien, Austria
00 43 1 53 170
chefredaktion@derstandard.at
www.derstandard.at
In German. Liberal daily. Editor: Oscar Bronnir

Süddeutsche Zeitung
Sendlinger Strasse 8, 80331
München, Germany
00 49 89 21830
redaktion@sueddeutsche.de
www.sueddeutsche.de
In German. Major Munich-based paper. Broadly liberal. Editor: Hans Werner Kilz

De Telegraaf
30 Basisweg, 1043 Amsterdam,
The Netherlands
00 31 20 585 9111
redactie-i@telegraaf.nl
www.telegraaf.nl
In Dutch. Holland's largest national daily. Editor: Ef Bos

● Middle East

Al-Ahram
Galaa St., Cairo, Egypt
00 20 2578 6441
weeklyeditor@ahram.org.eg
http://weekly.ahram.org.eg
Editor-in-chief: Assam El-Kersh; web editor: Amira Howeidy

Al-Jazeera
PO Box 23127, Doha, Qatar
00 974 438 2777
info@aljazeera.net.qa
www.english.aljazeera.net
Arabic and now English language satellite channel, based in Qatar

Aljazeera Publishing
London, UK
www.aljazeera.com

Daily Star
Marine Tower 6th floor,
Rue de La Ste Famille, Gemaizeh,
Achrafieh, Beirut, Lebanon
00 961 1 587277
www.dailystar.com.lb
Lebanese daily. Publisher: Mr Hanna Anbar

Ha'aretz
21 Schocken St, PO Box 233,
Tel Aviv 61001, Israel
00 972 3 512 1212/1204
contact@haaretz.co.il
www.haaretzdaily.com/
English edition of Israel's moderate national daily, published in Tel Aviv, supplement to the International Herald Tribune. Editor: David Landau

Jerusalem Post
Jerusalem Post Building, PO Box
81, Jerusalem 91000, Israel
00 972 2531 5666
eedition@jpostmail.com
www.jpost.com
Conservative English-language daily. Editor: David Horovitz

Jordan Times
Jordan Press Foundation,
PO Box 6710, Queen Rania Al
Abdullah Street, Amman, Jordan
00 962 6 560 0800
jotimes@jpf.com.jo
www.jordantimes.com
Jordan's only English-language daily. Editor: Samir Barhoum

Middle East Times
PO Box 16137, 2086 Acropolis,
Nicosia, Cyprus
00 357 22 45 47 57
editor@middleeastimes.net
www.metimes.com
Quality English-language weekly, based in Cyprus. Editor: Claude Salhani

● US and Canada

CBS Television Network
51 W 52nd St, NY 10019, USA
00 1 212 975 4321
www.cbs.com
News network

CNN
100 International Blvd, Atlanta,
GA 30303, USA
00 1 404 827 1500
www.cnn.com
News network

International Herald Tribune
6 bis, rue des Graviers,
92521 Neuilly Cedex, France
00 33 1 4143 9322
iht@iht.com
www.iht.com
International daily, owned by the New York Times. Editor: Michael Oreskes

LA Times
202 W 1st St, Los Angeles,
CA 90012, USA
00 1 213 237 5000
www.latimes.com
Biggest west-coast daily. Editor: Jim O'Shea

NBC
30 Rockefeller Plaza, New York,
NY 10112, USA
00 1 212 664 4444
www.nbc.com
News network

New York Times
229 West 43rd Street, New York,
New York 10036, USA
00 1 212 556 1234
editorial@nytimes.com
www.nytimes.com
National paper of record. Editor: Andrew Rosenthal

Wall St Journal
200 Liberty Street, New York,
NY 10281, USA
00 1 212 416 2000
wsj.ltrs@wsj.com
www.wsj.com
Conservative financial daily. Editor: Marcus Brauchli

Wall St Journal Europe
87 Boulevard Brand Whitlock,
1200 Brussels, Belgium
00 32 2 741 1211
www.europesubs.wsj.com
Global business news for Europe. Editor: Frederick Kempe

Washington Post
1150 15th Street NW, Washington,
DC 20071, USA
00 1 202 334 6000
www.washingtonpost.com
The New York Times' main rival. Editor: Leonard Downie

● Canada

Toronto Globe and Mail
444 Front Street West, Toronto,
Ontario M5V 2S9, Canada
00 1 416 585 5000
newsroom@GlobeAndMail.ca
www.theglobeandmail.com
Quality daily, Canada. Editor: Angus Frame

● Africa

Daily Mail and Guardian
PO Box 91667, Auckland Park,
Johannesburg 2006, South Africa
00 27 11 250 7300
editoronline@mg.co.za
www.mg.co.za
South African daily. Editor: Ferial Haffejee

Daily Nation
Nation Centre, Kimathi Street,
Nairobi, Kenya
00 254 20 320 88 000
www.nationmedia.com/dailynation
Kenya's biggest daily paper. Editor: Joseph Odindo

Daily News
PO Box 47549, Greyville 4023,
South Africa
00 27 31 308 2911
pather@nn.independent.co.za
www.dailynews.co.za
Daily independent paper. Editor: Dennis Pather

The East African
Kenya
00 254 20 540 633
comments@nationaudio.com
www.nationaudio.com/eastafrican

East African Standard
I&M Bank Tower, Kenyatta Ave,
PO Box 30080, 00100 GPO,
Nairobi, Kenya
00 254 20 322 2111
editorial@eastandard.net
www.eastandard.net
Editor: Chaacha Mwita

Le Matin
1 Rud Birchir Attar, Algiers, Algeria
00 213 216 706 85
In French. Moderate, secular paper. Editor: Mohamed Benchicou

Monitor, Uganda
Plot 29-35, 8th Street,
Industrial Area (PO Box 12141),
Kampala, Uganda
00 256 41 232 367
info@monitor.co.ug
www.monitor.co.ug
Major independent daily. Editor: Peter Mwesige

SABC
Private Bag X1, Auckland Park,
2006, South Africa
00 27 11 714 6300
feedback@sabcnews.com
www.sabcnews.com
South African broadcaster

Sunday Times (South Africa)
2nd floor, Johnnic Publishing
House, 4 Biermann Avenue,
Rosebank, 2196, South Africa
00 27 11 280 3000
suntimes@sundaytimes.co.za
www.sundaytimes.co.za

● Asia

Asahi Shimbun
5-3-2 Tsukiji 5, Chuo-ku, Tokyo,
104-8011, Japan
00 81 3545 0131
www.asahi.com/english
Japanese daily. English edition sold as
supplement to the International
Herald Tribune.

Dawn
Haroon House,
Dr Ziauddin Ahmed Road,
Karachi 74200, Pakistan
00 92 21 111 444 777
webmaster@dawn.com
www.dawn.com
English-language daily of record.
Editor: Abbas Nasir

Hindustan Times
Hindustan Times House,
18-20, Kasturba Gandhi Marg,
New Delhi-110001, India
00 91 11 23361234
salil@hindustantimes.com
www.hindustantimes.com
Editor: Shailesh Shekhar

Jakarta Post
Jl. Palmerah Selatan 15,
Jakarta 10270, Indonesia
00 62 21 5300476
editorial@thejakartapost.com
www.thejakartapost.com
Editor: Endy M Bayuni

JoongAng Ilbo
7, Sunhwa-dong, Jung-gu,
Seoul 100-759, Korea
00 82 2 751 9215
iht@joongang.co.kr
http://joongangdaily.joins.com
Korean daily. Editor: A Lin Neumann

South China Morning Post
16F Somerset House, Taikoo Place,
979 King's Road, Quarry Bay,
Hong Kong
00 852 2565 2222
peter.dedi@scmp.com
www.scmp.com
English-language daily. Editor: CK Lau

Star News Asia
8th Floor, One Harbourfront,
18 Tak Fung Street, Hunghom,
Kowloon, Hong Kong
00 852 2621 8888
www.startv.com/starnewsasia

Straits Times
1000 Toa Payoh North,
News Centre, Singapore 31944
00 65 6319 5397
STI@sph.com.sg
www.straitstimes.asia1.com.sg
Singapore's most widely circulated
English-language paper: close ties to
the government. Editor: Patrick Daniel

Taipei Times
14F, NO. 399, Ruiguang Rd., Neihu
District, Taipei City 11492, Taiwan
00 886 2 2656 1000
inquiries@taipeitimes.com
www.taipeitimes.com

● Latin America and Caribbean

O Estado de Sao Paulo
Av. Eng. Caetano, Alvares, 55,
São Paulo, Brazil
00 55 11 3856 2122
atende@estado.com.br
www.estado.estadao.com.br
Editor: Roberto Gazzi

El Mercurio
Avda. Santa Maria 5542, Vitacura,
Santiago Province, Chile
00 56 2330 1111
www.elmercurio.cl
Daily. Editor: Christian Zegers Ariztia

La Nacion
Bouchard 551, 1106, Buenos Aires,
Argentina
00 54 11 4319 1600
cescribano@lanacion.com.ar
www.lanacion.com.ar
Conservative Argentine daily.
Editor: Alejandro Dominguez.

El Tiempo
Terra Networks Colombia,
Diagonal 97 No. 17-60 Oficina
402, Bogotá, Colombia
00 57 160 29898
www.eltiempo.com
Editor: Roberto Pombo

El Universal
Burcarlini 8, Colony Centre,
Mexico City, Mexico
00 52 55 5709 1313/6917
enrique.cardenas@
    eluniversal.com.mx
www.el-universal.com.mx
Editor: Enrique Cárdenas

● Caribbean

Jamaica Gleaner
7 North Street, PO Box 40,
Kingston, Jamaica
00 1 876 922 3400
feedback@jamaica-gleaner.com
www.jamaica-gleaner.com
Editor: Garfield Grandison

● Pacific

ABS-CBN (Philippines)
Manila, Phillipines
00 63 2 924 4101
newsfeedback@abs-cbn.com
www.abs-cbnnews.com
News network

The Age, Melbourne
250 Spencer Street, Melbourne
3000, Australia
00 61 3 9600 4211
inquiries@theage.com.au
www.theage.com.au
Editor: Andrew Jaspan

New Zealand Herald
PO Box 32, Auckland,
New Zealand
00 64 9 379 5050
www.nzherald.co.nz
Editor: Tim Murphy

Sydney Morning Herald
201 Sussex St, GPO Box 506,
Sydney NSW 2001, Australia
00 61 2 9282 2833
newsdesk@smh.com.au
www.smh.com.au
Quality daily. Editor: Alan Oakley

Global journalism bodies

**Association of European
Journalists, British section**
40 Bruce Road, London E3 3HL
020 8981 4691
aejuk@btopenworld.com
www.aej-uk.org

**AMARC (World Association of
Community Broadcasters)**
705 Bourget Street, Suite 100,
Montreal, Quebec,
H4C 2M6, Canada
00 1 514 982 0351
amarc@amarc.org
www.amarc.org

Article XIX
6-8 Amwell Street,
London EC1R 1UQ
020 7278 9292
info@article19.org
www.article19.org
Combats censorship

Committee to Protect Journalists
330 7th Avenue 11th Floor,
New York NY 10001, USA
00 1 212 465 1004
info@cpj.org
www.cpj.org
Independent, non-profit body
defending right of journalists to report
without fear of reprisal

**Foreign Press Association
in London**
11 Carlton House Terrace,
London SW1Y 5AJ
020 7930 0445
reception@foreign-press.org.uk
www.foreign-press.org.uk

**Institute for War and Peace
Reporting**
48 Grays Inn Road,
London WC1X 8LT
020 7831 1030
yigal@iwpr.net
www.iwpr.net
Training in conflict areas

contacts **Global media**

211

International Centre for Journalists
1616 H Street NW, Third Floor,
Washington DC 20006, USA
00 1 202 737 3700
www.icfj.org
Training in media ethics, investigative reporting and support through www.ijnet.org and international exchanges

International Consortium of Investigative Journalists
910 17th Street, NW, 7th Floor,
Washington, DC 20006, USA
00 1 202 466 1300
www.publicintegrity.org/icij

International Federation of Journalists
IPC-Residence Palace, Bloc C,
Rue de la Loi 155,
B-1040 Brussels, Belgium
00 32 2 235 2200
ifj@ifj.org
www.ifj.org

International Federation of the Periodical Press
Queens House,
55–56 Lincoln's Inn Fields,
London WC2A 3LJ
020 7404 4169
info@fipp.com
www.fipp.com
Works for benefit of magazine publishers worldwide

International Freedom of Expression
555 Richmond St W, Suite 1101, PO Box 407, Toronto, Ontario, Canada M5V 3B1
00 1 416 515 9622
ifex@ifex.org
www.ifex.org

International News Safety Institute
Residence Palace, Block C,
International Press Centre,
155 Rue de la Loi,
1040 Brussels, Belgium
00 32 2 235 2201
info@newssafety.com
www.newssafety.com
Safety network for journalists in conflict zones

International Press Institute
Spiegelgasse 2,
A-1010 Vienna, Austria
00 43 1 512 90 11
ipi@freemedia.at
www.freemedia.at
Network of editors, executives and senior journalists

International Women's Media Foundation
1625 K Street NW, Suite 1275,
Washington, DC 20006, USA
00 1 202 496 1992
info@iwmf.org
www.iwmf.org
Assists women into news media

InterNews
1640 Rhode Island Avenue NW,
7th Floor,
Washington DC 20036, USA
00 1 202 833 5740
info@ internews.org
www.internews.org
News around the world

InterWorld Radio
Panos Institute, 9 White Lion Street, London N1 9PD
020 7239 7633
anna.egan@panos.org.uk
www.interworldradio.net
Global network for radio stations and journalism

Overseas Press and Media Association
OPMA Secretariat, 15 Magrath Avenue, Cambridge CB4 3AH
01223 512631
membership@opma.co.uk
www.opma.co.uk

Panos London
9 White Lion Street, London N1 9PD
020 7278 1111
info@panos.org.uk
www.panos.org.uk
Journalism in developing countries

Reporters Sans Frontières
5 Rue Geoffroy-Marie,
75009 Paris, France
00 33 1 4483 8484
rsf@rsf.org
www.rsf.org
Reporters without borders – freedom of the press

World Association of Newspapers
7 Rue Geoffroy St. Hilaire,
75005 Paris, France
00 33 1 4742 8500
www.wan-press.org
Senior newsroom editors' forum

World Press Freedom Committee
11690-C Sunrise Valley Drive,
Reston, VA 20191, USA
00 1 703 715 9811
freepress@wpfc.org
www.wpfc.org

World Press Photo
Jacob Obrechtstraat 26, 1071 KM Amsterdam, The Netherlands
00 31 20 676 6096
office@worldpressphoto.nl
www.worldpressphoto.nl

Global media trade press

The Fourth Estate
00 61 416 178 908
michael@walsh.net
www.fourthestate.com
Website and weekly newsletter. Editor: Mike Walsh. Digital technology and media

MediaChannel
575 8th Avenue, 2200, New York,
NY 10018, USA
00 1 212 246 0202
editor@mediachannel.org
www.mediachannel.org
Website. Executive director: Timothy Karr; executive editor: Danny Schechter

Middle East Media Guide
PO Box 72280, Dubai, UAE
00 971 50 553 0209
editor@middleeastmediaguide.com
www.middleeastmediaguide.com
Annual. Editor: Ben Smalley

Online Journalism Review
3502 Watt Way, Los Angeles,
CA 90089, USA
00 1 213 740 0948
rniles@usc.edu
www.ojr.org
Website. Editor: Larry Pryor

PR Week
Haymarket Professional Publications, 174 Hammersmith Road, London W6 7JP
020 8267 4429
prweek@haynet.com
www.prweek.com
Weekly. Editor-in-chief: Kate Nicholas; editor: Ravi Chandiramani

World Press Freedom Review
IPI Headquarters, Spiegelgasse 2,
A-1010 Vienna, Austria
00 43 1 512 90 11
ipi@freemedia.at
www.freemedia.at/wpfr/world_m.htm
Website. Director: Johann P Fritz

Global media bodies

Association for International Broadcasting
PO Box 990, London SE3 9XL
020 8297 3993
info@aib.org.uk
www.aib.org.uk
Market intelligence, representation, contacts and other services

Association for Progressive Communications
PO Box 29755, Melville 2109, South Africa
00 27 11 726 1692
webeditor@apc.org
www.apc.org
Internet and ICTs for social justice and development

APC secretariat
Presidio Building 1012, Torney Avenue, PO Box 29904, San Francisco, CA 94129, USA

Committee of Concerned Journalists (CCJ)
Project for Excellence in Journalism, 1850 K St, NW Suite 850, Washington, DC 20006, USA
001 202 293 7394
mail@journalism.org
www.journalism.org
Initiative by journalists to clarify and raise the standards of American journalism

European Audio-Visual Observatory
76, allee de la Robertsau, 67000 Strasbourg, France
00 33 388 144400
obs@obs.coe.int
www.obs.coe.int
European media observatory. Operates within framework of Council of Europe

European Broadcasting Union
17A, Ancienne Route, CH-1218 Grand-Saconnex, Switzerland
00 41 22 717 2111
ebu@ebu.ch
www.ebu.ch/en/index.php
Professional association of national broadcasters

International Advertising Association
521 Fifth Avenue, Suite 1807, New York, NY 10175, USA
00 1 212 557 1133
iaa@iaaglobal.org
www.iaaglobal.org
Advocates consumer and advertiser free choice

International Center for Journalists (ICFJ)
1616 H Street, NW, Third Floor, Washington, DC 20006, USA
00 1 202 737 3700
editor@icfj.org
www.icfj.org
Aims to help journalists and raise standards, esp in places with little tradition of a free press

International Classified Media Association (ICMA)
ICMA Head Office, Koggestraat 9H, 1012 TA Amsterdam, The Netherlands
00 31 20 638 2336
info@icmaonline.org
www.icmaonline.org
Represents major publishers

International Communications Forum
24 Greencoat Place, London SW1P 1RD
020 7798 6010
icforum@yahoo.co.uk
www.icforum.org
Goodwill network

International Institute of Communications
Regent House, 24–25 Nutford Place, London W1H 5YN
020 7323 9622
enquiries@iicom.org
www.iicom.org
Industry, government and academic forum

International Newspaper Marketing Association
10300 North Central Expressway, Suite 467, Dallas, Texas 75231, USA
00 1 214 373 9111
www.inma.org

International Press Institute (IPI)
Spiegelgasse 2, A-1010 Vienna, Austria
00 43 1 512 90 11
ipi@freemedia.at
www.freemedia.at
Global network of editors, media executives and leading journalists. Supports press freedom, free flow of information, and improved journalism standards

International Public Relations Association
1, Dunley Hill Court, Ranmore Common, Dorking, Surrey RH5 6SX
01483 280130
iprasec@btconnect.com
www.ipra.org
Network of PR pioneers

International Publishers Association
Ave de Miremont 3, 1206 Geneva, Switzerland
00 41 22 346 3018
secretariat@ipa-uie.org
www.ipa-uie.org
NGO with consultative status to UN

International Telecommunication Union
Place des Nations, CH-1211 Geneva 20, Switzerland
00 41 22 730 51 11
itumail@itu.int
www.itu.int
UN body for coordination of global telecom services

International Webcasting Association
4206 F Technology Court, Chantilly, VA 20151, USA
info@webcasters.org
www.webcasters.org

World Associations of Newspapers (WAN)
7 Rue Geoffroy St. Hilaire, 75005 Paris, France
00 33 1 4742 8500
contact_us@wan.asso.fr
www.wan-press.org
Defends press freedom and economic independence of newspapers

World Federation of Advertisers
120, Avenue Louise, 1050 Brussels, Belgium
00 32 2 502 57 40
www.wfanet.org

World Summit on the Information Society
Executive Secretariat, Place des Nations, 1211 Geneva 20, Switzerland
00 41 22 730 60 48
wsis@itu.int
www.itu.int/wsis

contacts **Global media**

Film

Andrew Pulver

Harry Potter... the highest-grossing film franchise

Warner Bros. Pictures

There's no stopping the bespectacled schoolboy wizard: at the time of writing, Harry Potter and the Order of the Phoenix is – by some distance – the biggest film of the year in the UK. It's the fifth in the Potter series, and its £49.4m at the UK box office means that so far JK Rowling's creation has relieved Britons of more than £260m. And the films on an upswing too: Phoenix has taken a little bit more than 2005's Goblet of Fire (£48.6m), which itself did a bit better than the lowest-performing of the cycle, 2004's Prisoner of Azkaban at £46.1m. But that's chickenfeed compared with the US, where the Potter has smashed the billion-dollar mark: the total for the five movies stands at $1.4bn (£686m). Quite how the producing studio, Warner Bros, will replace this cash flow after the projected 2010 release of the last Potter film, The Deathly Hallows, remains to be seen. And will Disney's Narnia series, the only remotely comparable multi-book franchise, post similar figures? The second film, Prince Caspian, won't be out until next year – a three-year gap that risks losing the momentum of the opening instalment.

Nevertheless, British box-office analysts are happy with the audience figures for 2007 so far: as of November the total figure is £781.7m, a 13% increase on last year. A glance at the stats shows that June 2007 was a particularly significant month, with the release of Fantastic Four: The Rise of the Silver Surfer and Shrek the Third boosting the totals by 52% compared with a year earlier. But the continuing prosperity of the British box office still shows a worrying dependency on sequels: six of the top 10 films of the year are the second or third helpings of already successful movies – and a further two (The Simpsons Movie and Transformers) are spin-offs of already-massive products. The Pixar film Ratatouille is the biggest grossing "original" movie of the year here; only another cartoon, Bee Movie, has a realistic chance of dislodging it. Will sequels do the business next year? There's no Shrek or Pirates of the Caribbean to shore up the figures, but there is a new Harry Potter (The Half Blood Prince), a fourth Indiana Jones, another Batman film (The Dark Knight), the second Narnia and Hellboy movies, and another go at The Incredible Hulk. Aside from Potter, it's hard to see a massive release that will shoulder the burden of Hollywood's rather shaky grip on its finances.

The end of the year saw the American film industry buckle from two different assaults. Firstly, the writers' strike, whose knock-on

Film

effects eventually hit the movie industry by forcing the postponement of the Angels & Demons shoot, and precipitating Brad Pitt's exit from the thriller State of Play just as it began filming (he cited script problems that strike action rendered unfixable). And secondly, stalling DVD sales, which meant that studio estimates of income have been overinflated, leading to the spectacular losses of around $1.6bn (£777m) announced in the trade press in mid-November. But US cinemas are posting figures that are similarly optimistic to Britain's: a 4.8% rise year-on-year from 2006 — the current total is $8.41bn (£4.08bn). And US exports are still ruling the roost: Pirates of the Caribbean: At World's End is the most successful release of 2007, with a worldwide take of $961m (£467.01m). The next 44 movies in the world box-office chart are American too: at number 46, the highest non-US movie is the biopic of Edith Piaf, La Vie en Rose, with $80.5m (£39.12).

But figures don't tell the whole story. Arguably the phenomenon of the year was the sudden ascension of Judd Apatow and Seth Rogen to the throne of Hollywood comedy kings. Apatow had worked as a writer-producer on the acclaimed sitcoms The Larry Sanders Show and Freaks & Geeks, and had made an admired but hardly spectacular movie debut in 2005 with The 40 Year Old Virgin. Rogen was even more unlikely: an out-of-shape Canadian who had been part of the F&G ensemble, and whom Apatow had given a part in Virgin. But Knocked Up was an unexpected summer hit, and was the springboard for Rogen's own writing debut, the teen comedy Superbad — which, like Knocked Up, also went past the $100m box-office mark in the US. The Apatow-Rogen axis is now Hollywood's hottest, with a flurry of upcoming projects: Pineapple Express, Walk Hard: The Dewey Cox Story, Zack and Miri Make a Porno and Drillbit Taylor all bearing their imprint.

In the UK, the nearest equivalent, in terms of elevation into the cinematic stratosphere, was the ascension of Scottish actor James McAvoy. McAvoy was known to TV audiences for his role in Shameless, but the film world, if they knew him at all, had only his roles in the unexceptional Inside I'm Dancing and Starter for 10 to go on. In January 2007 UK audiences saw him in The Last King of Scotland (resulting in a Bafta nomination), and in September opposite Keira Knightley in Atonement. As performances, they couldn't have been more different and, like Daniel Day-Lewis 20 years before, appeared to consecrate him as an actor's actor for a new generation.

Elsewhere in British cinema it was a good year for the independents, with the photographer Anton Corbijn making a huge impact with Control, his biopic of Ian Curtis, and Shane Meadows securing much praise for his skinhead drama This Is England. But it was two British films backed in Hollywood — Hot Fuzz, Simon Pegg and Nick Frost's follow-up to Shaun of the Dead, and Mr Bean's Holiday, directed by Steve "League of Gentlemen's Apocalypse" Bendelack — that proved most popular in their country of origin, both taking over £20m at the UK box office. The Oscars also saw recognition for British cinema: most obviously for Helen Mirren's best actress award for The Queen, but also in its counterpart male award: Forest Whitaker playing Idi Amin in the aforementioned Last King of Scotland.

More significantly, perhaps, the Oscars provided the Academy's long-withheld recognition for Martin Scorsese: his film The Departed won four awards, including best director. (Scorsese had already been nominated, and lost, five times, for Raging Bull, The Last Temptation of Christ, Goodfellas, Gangs of New York and The Aviator.) And it also helped trigger the non-English-language cinema story of the year: by giving The Lives of Others the best foreign film award, the Oscars set the film about communist-era East Germany on the path of unlikely worldwide success. A renewed cinematic interest in the former Soviet bloc was sealed by the award of the Cannes Palme d'Or to a hitherto-unknown Romanian director, Cristian Mungiu, for his 80s-set abortion drama 4 Months, 3 Weeks and 2 Days, which excavated life under Ceausescu with chilling honesty.

Cannes also saw the premiere of Quentin Tarantino's Death Proof, one half of an exploitation-cinema homage with Robert Rodriguez (whose film, Planet Terror, was conspicuously not selected). Death Proof, however, prompted a critical storm over "torture porn", a horror sub-genre that Tarantino had endorsed by executive-producing Hostel and its sequel, the best-known exponents of the ultraviolent style of film-making. Taking the moral high ground, though, 2007 also saw American cinema coming to grips with the Middle East wars, with a string of productions – The Kingdom, Lions for Lambs, In the Valley of Elah, Grace Is Gone, Redacted – all seeking to ask questions about US involvement there.

Digital cinema – in both expensive and inexpensive forms – continued to make inroads into the mainstream. Europe's most advanced digital multiplexes were opened by Odeon – both with 18 screens – in February 2007 at Hatfield in Hertfordshire and Surrey Quays, London. At the other end of the cinema spectrum the paragon of the arthouse, David Lynch, released his first digital feature, Inland Empire, and told journalists he had turned his back on celluloid. The Film Council and the BBC sponsored a summer season of classic films, including The Dam Busters, Brief Encounter and Billy Liar, released to cinemas in a digital format to coincide with a TV series on the history of British film. And the low-budget world found a new inspiration as the US "mumblecore" scene – with films such as The Puffy Chair, Funny Ha Ha, and Hannah Takes the Stairs – finally secured British screenings.

But 2007 also marked the end of an era. Two giants of European film-making, Ingmar Bergman and Michelangelo Antonioni, died on the same day, July 30, aged 89 and 94 respectively. The film world has changed almost beyond recognition since their glory days in the 1950s and 60s, but they remain two of the most significant directors ever to have worked in the medium. They will be remembered.

● Andrew Pulver is film editor at the Guardian

Film

Awards

Baftas 2007

- *Best film:* The Queen
- *Best director:* Paul Greengrass for United 93
- *Best actor:* Forest Whitaker for The Last King of Scotland
- *Best actress:* Helen Mirren for The Queen
- *Best supporting actor:* Alan Arkin for Little Miss Sunshine
- *Best supporting actress:* Jennifer Hudson for Dreamgirls
- *Best original screenplay:* Michael Arndt for Little Miss Sunshine
- *Best adapted screenplay:* Peter Morgan/Jeremy Brock for The Last King of Scotland
- *Best foreign film:* Pan's Labyrinth

Oscars 2007

- *Best picture:* The Departed
- *Best director:* Martin Scorsese for The Departed
- *Best actor:* Forest Whitaker for The Last King of Scotland
- *Best actress:* Helen Mirren for The Queen
- *Best supporting actor:* Alan Arkin for Little Miss Sunshine
- *Best supporting actress:* Jennifer Hudson for Dreamgirls
- *Best original screenplay:* Michael Arndt for Little Miss Sunshine
- *Best adapted screenplay:* William Monahan for The Departed
- *Best foreign language film:* The Lives of Others (Germany)
- *Best animated film:* Happy Feet

Cannes 2007

- *Palme d'Or:* 4 luni, 3 saptamini si 2 zile / 4 Months, 3 Weeks, and 2 Days by Cristian Mungiu
- *Grand Prix:* Mogari no mori / The Mourning Forest by Naomi Kawase

Top 20 UK films released in the UK and Ireland, 2006

	Title	Country of origin	Box office gross £m	Distributor
1	Casino Royale*	UK/USA/Cze	55.48	Sony
2	The Da Vinci Code	UK/USA	30.42	Sony
3	Flushed Away*	UK/USA	11.13	Paramount
4	The Queen*	UK/Fra/Ita	9.00	Pathé
5	Stormbreaker	UK/Ger/USA	6.79	Entertainment
6	Children of Men	UK/USA	4.86	Universal
7	The History Boys	UK	4.22	20th Century Fox
8	The Wind that Shakes the Barley	UK/Ger/Ita/Spa/Ire	3.91	Pathé
9	V for Vendetta	UK/USA/Ger	3.58	Warner Bros
10	United 93	UK/Fra/USA	2.90	UIP
11	Match Point	UK/USA/Lux	2.47	Icon
12	It's A Boy Girl Thing	UK/Can	2.42	Icon
13	Derailed	UK/USA	2.30	Buena Vista
14	Alien Autopsy	UK	2.18	Warner Bros.
15	Confetti	UK	2.09	20th Century Fox
16	An American Haunting	UK/USA	2.02	Lions Gate
17	Severance	UK/Hun/IoM	1.72	Pathé
18	Basic Instinct 2: Risk Addiction	UK/USA/Ger/Spa	1.16	Entertainment
19	A Cock and Bull Story	UK	1.10	Lions Gate
20	Breaking and Entering	UK/USA	0.97	Buena Vista

Box office gross = cumulative total up to March 4 2007
* Film was still being exhibited on March 4 2007

Source: Nielsen EDI, RSU

Dumb and dumber

Joe Queenan

This summer's big hit, Knocked Up, is the latest in a new genre of romantic comedies in which an unappealing hero gets together with a gorgeous, successful woman. The critics loved it – but if this offensive, misogynist nonsense is the future of cinema then we're in deep trouble, argues Joe Queenan.

The new romantic comedy model, as defined by this summer's blockbuster hit Knocked Up, was the subject of a recent New Yorker article by the esteemed film critic David Denby. Though conceding that today's romcoms lack the sophistication and the witty heroines of the Cary Grant-Katharine Hepburn vehicles of the 1930s and 40s, Denby was pretty positive about today's "slacker-striver" romances, as he calls them, in which some grizzled slob with no ambition lands the gorgeous, together gal. And he positively adored Knocked Up, in which the aforementioned slob actually impregnates the gorgeous gal on a one-night stand. It is "one of the key movies of the era", he wrote, "filled with the messages and rages of life in 2007".

Denby is far from the only serious critic to have fallen for Knocked Up. The Guardian's Peter Bradshaw, for example, described it as "the sweetest, funniest, gentlest thing I have seen in such a long time", and "the best film of the summer".

Thus, even though Knocked Up – like The 40 Year Old Virgin and all its other kin – focuses on immature, misogynist, porn-obsessed male losers who revel in one another's smelly, unhygienic company, there are apparently insights and laughs aplenty to be found in this tale of a loser ultimately saved by the love of a good woman – a good woman, naturally, endowed with a stunning rack.

There is, of course, another way of looking at this subject: that the new genre of romantic comedies are not really upbeat, coming-of-age motion pictures about young male schmucks who are saved by the love of a good woman, but heart-rending tragedies about beautiful young women

Top 20 films released in the UK and Ireland, 2006			
Title	**Country of origin**	**Box office gross £m**	**Distributor**
1 Casino Royale*	UK/USA/Cze	55.48	Sony
2 Pirates of the Caribbean: Dead Man's Chest	USA	52.52	Buena Vista
3 The Da Vinci Code	UK/USA	30.42	Sony
4 Ice Age II	USA	29.6	20th Century Fox
5 Borat	USA	24.11	20th Century Fox
6 Night at the Museum*	USA	20.77	20th Century Fox
7 X-Men 3	USA	19.22	20th Century Fox
8 Happy Feet*	Aus/USA	18.86	Warner Bros.
9 Cars	USA	16.45	Buena Vista
10 Superman Returns	USA/Aus	16.12	Warner Bros.
11 Mission Impossible 3	USA	15.45	UIP
12 The Devil Wears Prada	USA	14.02	20th Century Fox
13 Chicken Little	USA	13.51	Buena Vista
14 Over the Hedge	USA	13.22	UIP
15 The Departed*	USA	12.8	Entertainment
16 The Holiday	USA	12.34	Universal
17 Flushed Away*	UK/USA	11.13	Paramount
18 The Break Up	USA	10.38	UIP
19 Walk the Line	USA	10.36	20th Century Fox
20 Brokeback Mountain	USA	10.08	Entertainment

Box office gross = cumulative total up to March 4 2007   * Film was still being exhibited on March 4 2007   Source: Nielsen EDI, RSU
UK Film Council Statistical yearbook UK admissions and box office gross

Film

who are doomed to spend the rest of their lives with juvenile, not especially good-looking dorks. This is the premise of There's Something About Mary, the film that arguably spawned the genre, pairing the charismatic Cameron Diaz with the gnomish Ben Stiller, and a raft of other modern movies. What distinguishes these films from High Fidelity, another motion picture about the excruciating process of putting one's pathetic male friends into cold storage and getting serious about a romantic liaison – and sometimes blamed for having kickstarted the genre – is that John Cusack is not a loser dork. At least his long-suffering girlfriend gets something out of the relationship. Denby and a host of critics may have found Knocked Up "raucously funny"; I think women need to start their own film industry: this one isn't working.

It is anybody's guess what the female protagonist gets out of the relationship with Seth Rogen in Knocked Up. This is the latest film from Hollywood's current saviour Judd Apatow (The 40 Year Old Virgin, Talledega Nights, Anchorman). Knocked Up stars Rogen, who wrote the script with Apatow, as an overweight, unemployed stoner who hits the big time, romance-wise, when he accidentally gets blonde bombshell Katherine Heigl pregnant. Knocked Up made quite an impression when it was released in the US, not only with the public (mostly young males) but with critics – who are almost all male – ostensibly because it was not explicitly idiotic like Talledega Nights or Anchorman, and because it purported to make a larger point. The point it purports to make is that men do not grow up until they have children, and maybe not even then. This will probably not come as a complete surprise to most of the women on this planet.

The other point that Knocked Up seems to make is that women, even the ones who work in television, exist for no other reason than to help men grow up, if necessary by having babies. As Denby notes, this is an idea that has been kicking around since the early Renaissance, when Dante Alighieri frantically sought salvation through the ministrations of his beloved Beatrice: men need women to inspire them to the loftiest creative and moral heights; otherwise they will fail miserably. But unlike Rogen, at least Dante had a job.

Knocked Up is a less jokey film than The 40 Year Old Virgin (a film which made me wonder: would they have made this film if the hero was a woman? Answer: not in a million years). In Knocked Up, Rogen plays a pudgy, penniless 23-year-old stoner slob living in an LA pigsty with a quartet of fellow slobs. The five little pigs have spent months devising a website that will inform other morons at precisely what point in a film female nudity

occurs. One night Rogen meets a beautiful young woman (Heigl) at a singles bar no bouncer worth his salt would have ever admitted him into.

The woman gets blind drunk, drags him home, and sleeps with her condomless beau. We never find out why; nobody could be drunk enough not to realise what a schmuck he is, not even an entertainment reporter. So far, this is a generic male fantasy: jobless dink has one-night-stand with gorgeous blonde woman, and hopes she will call him back, though not seriously expecting this to happen. To be fair, loser slobs do, sometimes, get to sleep with gorgeous women in real life. But usually they are 60 years old and run hedge funds, not websites tracking cinema nudity. And they are never stoners.

Rogen's fantasy ceases to be stereotypically joyous when Heigl discovers that she is pregnant. Amazingly, neither party ever seriously considers the highly attractive option of abortion, which may be a sign that the anti-abortion movement is gathering strength in Hollywood, or may simply result from a realisation that abortion makes a poor subject for a comedy (puking and watching women on the toilet is fine, though). Or it may simply be a sign that feminism is dead. The film now moves in an excruciatingly predictable direction, as Rogen gradually realises that he will have to shape up and do the right thing and be a do-right-man for his do-right, if somewhat dim, woman. Along the way, there are a lot of jokes about bodily functions, a lot of dialogue that is explicitly contemptuous of women, and a lot of profanity. This is a film for teenage boys who dream of growing up to be teenage men.

Knocked Up goes where few films have dared to not go before. The boy-who-will-not-grow-up theme is the same dramatic linchpin used in The Break-Up and Shaun of the Dead. So is the blonde-who-hopes-her-boyfriend-will-one-day-come-to-his-senses. Of all the films in this genre, Shaun of the Dead is the most amusing, because the boys-who-can't-let-go-of-the-male-bonding-thing takes a back seat to the zombies-are-destroying-Albion plot line. The Break-Up, starring Vince Vaughn and Jennifer Aniston, takes a similar tack, with Aniston assuming the role of the zombie that must be destroyed if Chicago, civilisation or her boyfriend are to survive. The clueless, accessorial blonde girlfriend has been a staple of comedies for years, though Heigl, with her infuriating Lisa Kudrow Acting School mannerisms, brings a new level of vacuity to the genre.

Where is all this leading? It's leading to a future so dark that women will look back on the decade that brought them The Runaway Bride, Notting Hill, My Best Friend's Wedding and My Big Fat Greek Wedding as a golden age. Infatuated by

Apatow's success, Hollywood has turned over the keys to the industry to the 40-year-old producer/director/screenwriter, whose upcoming projects include a film about high-school losers (Superbad), a film about a stoner who witnesses a murder (The Pineapple Express), a film about a sad little man who just broke up with his girlfriend (Forgetting Sarah Marshall), and a film about a Mossad agent who fakes his own death so that he can become a hair stylist. Thus, the situation today is very much like back in the days when John Belushi, Dan Aykroyd, Chevy Chase and the rest of the Saturday Night Live alumni turned out third-rate movies faster than anyone could possibly see them, and dominated screen comedy until Robin Williams came along to make things worse.

Anyone out there who finds Apatow's films amateurish, derivative, juvenile and offensive to women is simply out of luck. Like the satanic alumni of Saturday Night Live, Apatow and his posse never stop working, everything they pitch gets enthusiastically greenlighted, and until one of these films bombs, the public is going to be seeing an awful lot of his work. When Apatow made The 40 Year Old Virgin, there was much rejoicing in the land, because people were thrilled that someone was once again making "sophisticated" romantic comedies instead of the usual moronic Adam Sandler fare. Well, Sandler is the star of Apatow's upcoming Don't Mess With The Zohan. The dark ages are back. Not that they ever left.

Film

Film contacts

Hollywood studios

Buena Vista Motion Pictures Group
500 S. Buena Vista Street,
Burbank, CA 91521
00 1 818 955 6600
http://bventertainment.go.com
Owned by Disney. President: Nina Jacobson

Icon Productions
808 Wilshire Blvd, 4th Fl,
Santa Monica, CA 90401
00 1 310 434 7300
www.iconmovies.net
Partner: Mel Gibson; partner and president: Bruce Davey

MGM Pictures
10250 Constellation Blvd,
Los Angeles, CA 90067
00 1 310 449 3000
www.mgm.com
Chairman and CEO: Alex Yemenidjian

Miramax Films
161 Avenue of the Americas,
New York, NY 10013
001 917 606 5500
www.miramax.com
Owned by Disney.

Sony Pictures Entertainment
10202 W Washington Blvd,
Culver City, CA 90232
00 1 310 244 4000
www.sonypictures.com
Chairman and CEO: Michael Lynton

Touchstone Television Productions
500 S Buena Vista St,
Burbank, CA 91521
00 1 818 560 1000
http://touchstone.movies.go.com
Owned by Disney. President: Mark Pedowitz

Twentieth Century Fox Film Corporation
10201 West Pico Blvd, Los
Angeles, CA 90035
00 1 310 369 1000
www.fox.com
Co-chairmen: Jim Gianopulos, Tom Rothman

Universal Studios
100 Universal City Plaza,
Universal City, CA 91608
00 1 818 777 1000
www.universalstudios.com
President and COO: Ron Meyer

Warner Bros Entertainment
4000 Warner Blvd, Burbank,
CA 91522
00 1 818 954 6000
www.warnerbros.com
Chairman and CEO: Barry M. Meyer

Major animators and special effects studios

Aardman Animations
Gas Ferry Rd, Bristol BS1 6UN
0117 984 8485
www.aardman.com

Bolexbrothers
Unit 6, Brunel Lock Development,
Smeaton Road, Cumberland Basin,
Bristol BS1 6SE
0117 985 8000
www.bolexbrothers.co.uk

DreamWorks Animation SKG
1000 Flower St, Glendale,
CA 91201
00 1 818 695 5000
www.pdi.com

Industrial Light & Magic
www.ilm.com

Pixar Animation Studios
1200 Park Ave, Emeryville,
CA 94608
00 1 510 922 3000
www.pixar.com

UK film companies

Amber Films
5&9 Side, Newcastle NE1 3JE
0191 232 2000
www.amber-online.com

Bard Entertainments
7 Denmark Street,
London WC2H 8LZ
020 7240 7144
office@bardentertainments.co.uk
www.bardentertainments.co.uk

BBC Films
Grafton House, 379 Euston Road,
London NW1 3AU
020 7765 0251
www.bbc.co.uk/bbcfilms

Capitol Films
Bridge House, 2nd Floor, 63-65
North Wharf Road, London W2 1LA
020 7298 6200
films@capitolfilms.com
www.capitolfilms.com

Celador Films
39 Long Acre, London WC2E 9LG
020 7845 6800
www.celador.co.uk/films.php

Company Pictures
Suffolk House, 1-8 Whitfield
Place, London W1T 5JU
020 7380 3900
enquiries@companypictures.co.uk
www.companypictures.co.uk
MDs: Charlie Pattinson, George Faber

Dan Films
32 Maple Street, London W1T 6HB
020 7916 4771
enquiries@danfilms.com
www.danfilms.com

Ecosse Films
Brigade House, 8 Parsons Green,
London SW6 4TN
020 7371 0290
info@ecossefilms.com
www.ecossefilms.com
MD: Douglas Rae

Focus Films
Focus Films, The Rotunda Studios,
r/o 116-118 Finchley Road,
London NW3 5HT
020 7435 9004
focus@focusfilms.co.uk
www.focusfilms.co.uk

Ipso Facto Films
1 Pink Lane,
Newcastle upon Tyne NE1 5DW
0191 230 2585
info@ipsofactofilms.com
www.ipsofactofilms.com

Merchant Ivory Productions
46 Lexington Street,
London W1F 0LP
020 7437 1200
contact@merchantivory.com
www.merchantivory.com

Pathé
Kent House, 14-17 Market Place,
Great Titchfield Street,
London W1N 8AR
020 7323 5151
www.pathedistribution.com

Picture Palace Productions
13 Egbert Street, London NW1 8LJ
020 7586 8763
www.picturepalace.com

Qwerty Films
2nd Floor, 42-44 Beak Street.
London W1F 9RH
020 7440 5920
info@qwertyfilms.com

Ruby Films
26 Lloyd Baker Street,
London WC1X 9AW
020 7833 9990

Scion Films
18 Soho Square, London W1D 3QL
020 7025 8003
info@scionfilms.com
www.scionfilms.com

Sigma Films
Film City Glasgow, Summertown
Road, Glasgow G51 2LY
0141 445 0400
latenights@sigmafilms.com
www.sigmafilms.com

Vertigo Films
The Big Room Studios,
77 Fortress Road, London NW5 1AG
020 7428 7555
mail@vertigofilms.com
www.vertigofilms.com
Press: press@vertigofilms.com

Working Title Films
Oxford House, 76 Oxford Street,
London W1D 1BS
020 7307 3000
www.workingtitlefilms.com

TV & film independent production companies

» see TV, page 147

Post-production

» see TV, page 158

TV and film studios

» see TV, page 156

UK distributors

20th Century Fox
Twentieth Century House,
31-32 Soho Square,
London W1D 3AP
020 7437 7766
www.fox.co.uk

Arrow Films
Orchard Villa, Porters Park Drive,
Shenley WD7 9DS
01923 858306
alex@arrowfilms.co.uk
www.arrowfilms.co.uk

Artificial Eye
14 King Street, London WC2E 8HR
020 7240 5353
info@artificial-eye.com
www.artificial-eye.com

Blue Dolphin Films
40 Langham Street,
London W1W 7AS
020 7255 2494
info@bluedolphinfilms.com
www.bluedolphinfilms.com

Buena Vista International UK/ Filmfactory
3 Queen Caroline Street,
London W6 9PE
020 8222 1000
feedback@thefilmfactory.co.uk
www.thefilmfactory.co.uk

CineFile
12 Sunbury Place,
Edinburgh EH4 3BY
0131 225 6191
info@cinefile.co.uk
www.cinefile.co.uk

Columbia TriStar UK
25 Golden Square, London W1F 9LU
020 7533 1000
www.sonypictures.co.uk

Dogwoof Pictures
Second floor, 1A Neals Yard,
Covent Garden, London WC2H 9DP
020 7395 1217
info@dogwoofpictures.com
www.dogwoofpictures.com

Entertainment Film Distributors
108-110 Jermyn Street,
London SW1Y 6HB
020 7930 7744

Eros International
customerservice1@
   erosmultimedia.net
www.erosentertainment.com

Feature Film Company
19 Heddon Street,
London W1B 4BG
020 7851 6500
www.contentfilm.com

Granada International
The London Television Centre,
Upper Ground, London SE1 9LT
020 7491 1441
int.info@granadamedia.com
www.carltonint.co.uk

Icon Film Distribution
Solar House, 915 High Road,
North Finchley, London N12 82J
020 8492 6300
reception@
   icon-entertainment.co.uk
www.iconmovies.co.uk

Lionsgate Films
Ariel House, 74A Charlotte Street,
London W1T 4QJ
020 7299 8800
info@lionsgatefilms.co.uk
www.lionsgatefilms.co.uk

Metrodome
Royalty House, 3rd Floor, 72-74
Dean Street, London W1D 3SG
020 7153 4421
www.metrodomegroup.com

Momentum Pictures
184-192 Drummond Street,
London NW1 3HB
020 7391 6900
info@momentumpictures.co.uk
www.momentumpictures.co.uk

Optimum Releasing
22 Newman Street,
London W1T 1PH
020 7637 5403
info@optimumreleasing.com
www.optimumreleasing.com

Pathé Distribution
Kent House, 14-17 Market Place,
Great Titchfield Street,
London W1W 8AR
020 7323 5151
www.pathe.co.uk

Tartan Films Distribution
Royalty House, 72-74 Dean Street,
London W1D 3SG
020 7494 1400
www.tartanfilms.com

UGC Films UK
34 Bloomsbury Street,
London WC1B 3QJ
020 7631 4683

United International Pictures
UIP House, 45 Beadon Road,
Hammersmith, London W6 0EG
020 8741 9041
enquiries@uip.com
www.uip.com

Warner Bros
98 Theobalds Road,
London WC1X 8WB
020 7984 5000
www.warnerbros.com

Film commissions

UK Film Council
10 Little Portland Street,
London W1W 7JG
020 7861 7861
info@ukfilmcouncil.org.uk
www.ukfilmcouncil.org.uk
The government-backed strategic agency working to stimulate a successful UK film industry and culture
Press: 020 7861 7508

Bath Film Office
01225 477711
bath_filmoffice@bathnes.gov.uk
www.visitbath.co.uk

Screen West Midlands
0121 265 7120
info@screenwm.co.uk
www.screenwm.co.uk

Eastern Screen
01603 767077
locations@screeneast.com
www.easternscreen.com

Edinburgh Film Focus
0131 622 7337
info@edinfilm.com
www.edinfilm.com

EM Media
0115 934 9090
info@em-media.org.uk
www.em-media.org.uk

European Film Communication
00 39 067 290 5757
info@europeanfilm
   communication.com
www.europeanfilm
   communication.com

Glasgow Film Office
0141 287 0424
info@glasgowfilm.com
www.glasgowfilm.org.uk

Isle of Man Film Commission
01624 687173
iomfilm@dti.gov.im
www.isleofmanfilm.com

Northern Ireland Screen
028 9023 2444
info@northernirelandscreen.co.uk
www.northernirelandscreen.co.uk

contacts **Film**

Scottish Highlands and Islands Film Commission
01463 710221
trish@scotfilm.org
www.scotfilm.org

Scottish Screen
0141 302 1700
info@scottishscreen.com
www.scottishscreen.com

Wales Screen Commission
0800 849 8848
enquiry@
walesscreencommission.co.uk
www.walesscreencommission.co.uk

Regional agencies

East Midlands: EM Media
0115 934 9090
info@em-media.org.uk
www.em-media.org.uk

East: Screen East
01603 776920
info@screeneast.co.uk
www.screeneast.co.uk

Film London
020 7613 7676
info@filmlondon.org.uk
www.filmlondon.org.uk
Strategic agency for film and media in London, to act as catalyst for film-making in London

North-east: Northern Film and Media
0191 269 9200
www.northernmedia.org

North-west: North West Vision
0870 609 4481
info@northwestvision.co.uk
www.northwestvision.co.uk

Screen Yorkshire
0113 294 4410
info@screenyorkshire.co.uk
www.screenyorkshire.co.uk

South-east (not London): Screen South
01303 259777
info@screensouth.org
www.screensouth.org

South-west: South West Screen
0117 952 9977
info@swscreen.co.uk
www.swscreen.co.uk

West Midlands: Screen West Midlands
0121 265 7120
info@screenwm.co.uk
www.screenwm.co.uk

TV & film training and support

» *see TV, page 163*

Trade Press

Advance Production News
020 8305 6905
www.crimsonuk.com
Monthly. Owner: Crimson Communications. Editor: Alan Williams

British Film Magazine
020 7636 7455
terence@britishfilmmagazine.com
www.britishfilmmagazine.com
Independently owned. Editor: Terence Doyle

Channel 21 International magazine
020 7729 7460
press@c21media.net
www.c21media.net
10pa. Owner: C21 Media. Editor-in-chief: David Jenkinson; editor: Ed Waller

Contacts — The Spotlight Casting Directories
020 7437 7631
info@spotlight.com
www.spotlight.com
Annual. Contacts for stage, film, TV and radio. Editor: Kate Poynton

Crewfinder
028 9079 7902
mail@adleader.co.uk
www.crewfinderwales.co.uk
Annual. Wales's film, TV and video directory. Owner: Adleader Publications. Proprietor: Stan Mairs

FilmBang
0141 334 2456
info@filmbang.com
www.filmbang.com
Annual. Scotland's film and video directory. Editor: Marianne Mellin

The Hollywood Reporter
020 7420 6000
Daily. Hollywood trade paper. UK bureau chief: Stuart Kemp

IBE
01342 717459
info@bpl-business.com
www.ibeweb.com
6pa. International broadcast engineering. Owner: BPL Business Media. Editor: Neil Nixon

Kemps Film, TV, Video Handbook (UK edition)
01342 335861
kemps@reedinfo.co.uk
www.kftv.com
Annual. Guide to international production. Owner: Reed Business Information. Editorial contact: Pay Hewsone

The Knowledge
020 8973 3444
knowledge@
hollis-publishing.com
www.theknowledgeonline.com
Annual. Production directory. Owner: Hollis Publishing. Editorial contact: Louise Baynes

Pact Directory of Independent Producers
020 8977 7711
www.pact.co.uk
Online Directory

Pro Sound News Europe
020 7921 8319
david.robinson@cmpi.biz
www.prosoundnewseurope.com
12pa. Audio industry. Owner: CMP Information. Editor: David Robinson; managing editor: Anthony Lord

The Production Guide
020 7505 8000
info@theproductionguide.co.uk
www.theproductionguide.co.uk
Owner: Emap

Screen Digest
020 7424 2820
sales@screendigest.com
www.screendigest.com
Monthly. Editor: David Fisher; chief analyst: Ben Keen

Screen International
020 7505 8080
screeninternational@emap.com
www.screendaily.com
Weekly. News service for global film industry. Owner: Emap Media. Editor-in-chief: Colin Brown; editor: Michael Gubbins

Stage Screen and Radio
020 7346 0900
janice@stagescreenandradio.org.uk
www.bectu.org.uk
10pa. Magazine of broadcasting union Bectu. Editor: Janice Turner

VLV Bulletin
01474 352835
info@vlv.org.uk
www.vlv.org.uk
Quarterly magazine of Voice of the Listener and Viewer. Advocates citizen and consumer interests in broadcasting. Editor: Jocelyn Hay

Zerb
01822 614405
admin@gtc.org.uk
www.gtc.org.uk
2pa. For camera operators. Managing Editors: Christina Fox; Alison Chapman

Consumer film and TV magazines

>> *see page 87*

Events

Bafta Awards
195 Piccadilly, London W1J 9LN
020 7734 0022
www.bafta.org
Film, TV and interactive industries

British Independent Film Awards
81 Berwick Street,
London W1F 8TW
020 7287 3833
info@bifa.org.uk
www.bifa.org.uk

Cannes Film Festival
3, rue Amélie 75007 Paris, France
00 33 1 53 59 61 00
festival@festival-cannes.fr
www.festival-cannes.org

London Film Festival
British Film Institute,
Belvedere Road, South Bank,
London SE1 8XT
020 7815 1322
www.lff.org.uk

Raindance Film Festival
81 Berwick Street,
London W1F 8TW
020 7287 3833
info@raindance.co.uk
www.raindance.co.uk

TV & film associations

>> *see TV, page 165*

contacts **Film**

225

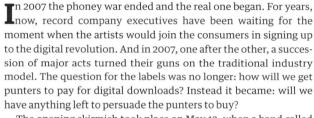

Music

Michael Hann

In 2007 the phoney war ended and the real one began. For years, now, record company executives have been waiting for the moment when the artists would join the consumers in signing up to the digital revolution. And in 2007, one after the other, a succession of major acts turned their guns on the traditional industry model. The question for the labels was no longer: how will we get punters to pay for digital downloads? Instead it became: will we have anything left to persuade the punters to buy?

The opening skirmish took place on May 13, when a band called the Crimea made their second album available as a free download. The Crimea had been dropped by Warner after their debut failed to set the world on fire to the required degree. But they'd had the support necessary to get their name known and build a fanbase, so when the free download was announced it was widely reported, and nearly 70,000 fans took advantage. The free downloads translated into ticket sales for shows, too, and the Crimea found themselves making more money than they had when they were still signed.

Strong fanbase... The Crimea

But the Crimea? It's not exactly Top Chart Star Revolutionises Music, is it? No. But that was to come.

In July, Prince announced that his latest album would be given its first release as a giveaway with the Mail on Sunday. And those attending any of his 21 nights at the O2 centre in London would also be given a free copy. Prince isn't the commercial force he was when Purple Rain was selling 20m copies worldwide – his last album, 3121, sold just 80,000 in the UK – but this was the first time one of the canonical names in pop, and one with commercial power (albeit based now on his performance at the concert box office), had renounced the highways of the industry, presumably sure that the £300,000 the Mail on Sunday were reputedly paying would be more than he would see in royalties from the UK. The reaction was volcanic. Sony, unsurprisingly, announced that it was pulling the new album from its release schedules, while a spokesman for record shops warned: "The Artist Formerly Known as Prince should know that with behaviour like this he will soon be the Artist Formerly Available in Record Stores."

But we were yet to get the real shocker, the one that had bloggers the world over proclaiming: "At last! Our music is free! Down with The Man!" That came in the first week of October, when, in quick succession, came bulletins from the Charlatans and Radiohead. The former said their next album, when they got round to it, would be available for free download. The latter – and this was the real big news – said they'd have a new album ready in a couple of weeks. Oh, and anyone who wanted it could pay as much or as little as they wanted. It turned out that more than half of all listeners decided Radiohead probably already had more money than they knew what to do with, what with being one of the world's biggest bands, and decided to pay nothing.

And so the music pages, papers and websites were filled with fevered speculation: was this the end of the record label? And was it good bloody riddance? Possibly. And no.

The common thread running through 2007's digital leaps was that they all involved established acts. Even the Crimea had a couple of years suckling at the corporate teat before going it alone. In short, these were all acts who 1) already had a fanbase; 2) already had name recognition within the music media; 3) were already familiar with how to manouevre situations to their advantage. Undoubtedly they will be copied. There will be scores of major acts who would be desperately keen to be free of major-label politics (especially if they espouse politics of their own) and cut the middleman out. Will we see Coldplay go this route? Very possibly. REM? Surely. U2? Maybe. But they will do so because they can do for themselves all the things record labels can do. They've got the stature and financial muscle to generate press coverage, record in their own time and tour how they want.

Imagine instead that you are a member of a young band. You're good, but you're playing to no more than 30 people in the back of a pub. You've got a MySpace presence, and you've had a couple of thousand downloads from that. What you need at this point is not to record, at your own expense, an album that you give away for free. First, you can't afford to. Second, even if you could, no one is going to know you've done so, because there's no record label shouting the odds on your behalf to the public, the media, TV and radio. The smaller you are, the harder it is to go it alone. Having a Radiohead or a Coldplay is what enables major record labels to take punts on other bands. Once the bankers are taken away, what will subsidise the signing of unknown bands? The situation is even bleaker for the bedroom labels that help guarantee the health of pop music by releasing records out of love, sometimes discovering significant talents along the way: why invest your savings in something that people are beginning to expect you to provide for free?

It's oddly comparable to the aftermath of the Bosman ruling in football, when clubs suddenly realised the possibility of developing players and then losing them for nothing at the end of their contract.

In an age of dwindling record sales, the labels have been doing their best to find new ways to generate revenue. The latest is the so-called 360-degree deal, whereby an artist is signed for a larger advance than they might previously have expected, but in return the label gets a cut of touring and merchandising revenue as well. The hardcore punk band Gallows benefited from this in the spring, signing to Warner for a reported £1m. It seemed a staggering sum for a band who would surely not recoup on sales – until the ferocious

Madonna parts company with Warner

loyalty of their live fanbase was factored in. But even this new model for record companies was turned against them in October, when Madonna announced she was leaving Warner, her label throughout her career, and signing a $120m deal with the concert promoter Live Nation. The promoter – one of the behemoths of live music – would release three albums, promote the singer's tours, and get slices of the ancillary revenue. One could see Madonna's logic: if the people who put out records want money from tours, why not let people who know how to put on tours put out the records, given that the real money-spinner is live performance?

Everything's changing, for sure. But everything has been changing for years now. And, truth be told, there is still no consensus on what picture will emerge. All we have are fragments that fit into the puzzle in different places. But every fragment suggests dark times ahead for the old model of music.

● Michael Hann is the Guardian's film and music editor

Awards

Brit awards 2007
- *British album:* Arctic Monkeys – Whatever People Say I Am, That's What I'm Not
- *British group:* Arctic Monkeys
- *British male solo artist:* James Morrison
- *British female solo artist:* Amy Winehouse
- *International album:* The Killers – Sam's Town
- *International group:* The Killers
- *International male solo artist:* Justin Timberlake
- *International female solo artist:* Nelly Furtado
- *Outstanding contribution to music:* Oasis

Nationwide Mercury music prize 2006
- Klaxons – Myths of the Near future

Q awards 2007
- *Best Album:* Amy Winehouse – Back to Black
- *Best Live Act:* Muse
- *Best new act:* The Enemy
- *Best track:* Manic Street Preachers – Your Love Alone is Not Enough
- *Best video:* Kaiser Chiefs, Ruby

MTV Europe music awards 2007
- *Best group:* Linkin Park
- *Best album:* Nelly Furtado – Loose
- *Best solo:* Avril Lavigne
- *Video star:* Justice – D.A.N.C.E.

Gramophone awards 2007
- *Best orchestral:* London Symphony Orchestra/Valery Gergiev – Prokofiev Complete Symphonies
- *Best chamber:* Pavel Haas Quartet – Haas and Janácek String Quartets
- *Best instrumental:* Steven Isserlis – Bach Cello Suites
- *Best solo vocal:* Jonas Kaufmann; Helmut Deutsch – R.Strauss Lieder
- *Best historic archive:* Bayreuth Festival Opera/Joseph Keilberth – Wagner Götterdämmerung
- *Best contemporary:* BBC Symphony Orchestra/Oliver Knussen – Julian Anderson Alhambra Fantasy

Music

Top 20 albums 2006

1	Eyes Open	Snow Patrol
2	Beautiful World	Take That
3	Ta-dah	Scissor Sisters
4	Whatever People Say I Am That's What I'm Not	Arctic Monkeys
5	Inside In/Inside Out	Kooks
6	Razorlight	Razorlight
7	Now That's What I Call Music 65	Various Artists
8	Stop The Clocks	Oasis
9	The Love Album	Westlife
10	I'm Not Dead	Pink
11	Undiscovered	James Morrison
12	In Between Dreams	Jack Johnson
13	Sam's Town	Killers
14	Now That's What I Call Music 64	Various Artists
15	Corinne Bailey Rae	Corinne Bailey Rae
16	Under The Iron Sea	Keane
17	Stadium Arcadium	Red Hot Chili Peppers
18	The Sound Of — The Greatest Hits	Girls Aloud
19	Love	Beatles
20	Twenty Five	George Michael

Top 10 downloads 2006

1	Crazy	Gnarls Barkley
2	I Don't Feel Like Dancin'	Scissor Sisters
3	Hips Don't Lie	Shakira featuring Wyclef Jean
4	Chasing Cars	Snow Patrol
5	Maneater	Nelly Furtado
6	Sexyback	Justin Timberlake
7	A Moment Like This	Leona Lewis
8	From Paris To Berlin	Infernal
9	No Tomorrow	Orson
10	America	Razorlight

Top 10 singles 2006

1	Crazy	Gnarls Barkley
2	A Moment Like This	Leona Lewis
3	Hips Don't Lie	Shakira featuring Wyclef Jean
4	I Don't Feel Like Dancin'	Scissor Sisters
5	I Wish I Was A Punk Rocker	Sandi Thom
6	From Paris To Berlin	Infernal
7	Maneater	Nelly Furtado
8	Patience	Take That
9	SOS	Rihanna
10	Sexyback	Justin Timberlake

Source: OCC/BPI

A major shake-up at EMI looks set to bring massive changes for the music industry

»» The Guardian   January 12 2008

EMI in crisis: Radiohead quit, Robbie Williams on strike — and now 1,000 jobs cut

Julia Finch, Owen Gibson and Alex Needham

Artists lose patience with management at once iconic record label following private equity takeover.

It was never going to be an easy relationship: hard-nosed City financiers and businessmen working alongside songwriters and musicians.

The men in suits reckon that working together they can revitalise EMI, the struggling group which has been a key part of the British pop industry for more than 40 years. It is the label behind the Beatles, Queen, Pink Floyd, David Bowie and more recently Radiohead, Coldplay, Kylie and Robbie Williams.

But just six months after Terra Firma, a private equity group, acquired the label for £3.2bn, the signs are not good: Radiohead have quit, describing the new regime as like "a confused bull in a china shop" and this week Williams has gone on strike, refusing to deliver his new album. Kylie and Coldplay are said to be considering their options and Tony Wadsworth, the man in charge of the UK arm, has been ousted after 25 years. Now it is understood that 1,000 EMI staff are to lose their jobs.

A look at 2007's biggest-selling albums puts EMI's woes in stark terms. The top 100 features a mere six from the label — and three are compilations of old material by Cliff Richard, Phil Collins and the Spice Girls. EMI's highest-placed album is only the 26th biggest seller of the year — Lily Allen's Alright, Still, which came out in 2006. Overall,

2007 saw EMI's share of the albums market fall 2.5 percentage points to 15.4%.

Williams's strike is more bad news. While Rudebox, released last Christmas, performed relatively poorly, his new album is being recorded with Guy Chambers, who co-wrote his biggest hits, and Mark Ronson, who produced much of Amy Winehouse's Back to Black, which was 2007's best-selling album.

Tim Clark, of IE Management, which represents Williams, said the singer would not release another EMI record until the management's plans became clearer. "We're led to believe there is going to be a new and wholesale cutback in staff. Tony Wadsworth has left, we understand other long-serving employees will be leaving too. We won't deliver an album to a company where we don't know what their structure will be or how they will handle things."

Next week Terra Firma is to say how it intends to turn EMI into a lean, mean music machine. Its plans focus on "efficiencies" — those job cuts. A source close to the private equity group said: "Workers need to spend more time servicing their artists and less time going to whizzy parties and travelling the world."

Terra Firma is run by Guy Hands, 48, a one-time bond trader who is not exactly rock and roll. William Hague was best man at his wedding.

Over his career he has acquired businesses ranging from pub companies to railway rolling stock leasing. He bought thousands of Ministry of Defence homes and controls the Odeon and UCI cinema chains. Since buying EMI — which he intends to turn around and sell for far more than he paid within about five years — he has called in several other traditional business executives with no music experience to help with the task. Post Office chairman Allan Leighton has become an adviser, as has former BBC director-general Lord Birt and former BAA airports boss Mike Clasper.

The bands and their management are far from impressed. As Radiohead's manager, Bryce Edge, said: "When you're dealing with creative talent, there's a lot of risk-taking that goes on. That's where Terra Firma is going to struggle."

Hands has uncovered all sorts of costs he has

Dan Chung

Music

never seen before, from multi-million-pound "hand out and hope" advances to artists to a £20,000-a-month bill for candles. He is said to have been astonished by EMI's £200,000-a-year spend to keep its Hammersmith head office in flowers and fruit. Seasoned industry executives, however, know that "fruit and flowers" is shorthand for artists' partying requirements.

But this isn't just a flabby, badly run business which Hands will easily be able to lick into shape. The entire industry has been battered first by piracy and now by legitimate downloads which, while g fast, are not offsetting the fall in CD sales. The big moneyspinner is now touring, which labels generally do not get a slice of − although EMI is said to want in on the act.

At the same time, the artists are becoming more powerful. The internet has given them more control. Clark said: "There really are other people, very good people, that can do the finances, do the press, market, promote and so on − and do it hugely competitively."

Artists also want to control their back catalogue and if they are unhappy can walk out − as Radiohead have done. As singer Thom Yorke explained on the band's website: "What we wanted was some control over our work and how it was used in the future by them − that seemed reasonable to us, as we cared about it a great deal. Mr Hands was not interested. So neither were we."

One EMI executive said Hands is still convinced that he can turn EMI around, but needs to get rid

of entrenched interests, like Wadsworth. And not everyone thinks he will fail, or that the end of the major label is nigh. EMI's Lily Allen has attacked Radiohead, which allowed fans to pay what they liked for a download of their latest album, for "devaluing music" and Pet Shop Boys' Neil Tennant said he had no interest in marketing and distribution: "I just don't want to be in that business. I'd rather complain to EMI if it goes wrong."

Peter Ruppert, who runs music consultancy Entertainment Media Research, said Hands could turn EMI around by treating it like an independent label but sticking to strict business rules: "In the past it was about who had the biggest chequebook but it's really about who works the smartest at it and who can make the music business work, and work for the artist."

New EMI owner Guy Hands

Music contacts

Record labels

679 Recordings
020 7284 5780
www.679recordings.com

Ace Records
020 8453 1311
www.acerecords.co.uk

Additive Records
020 7605 5000
www.additiverecords.com
Owner: EMI Group

All Around the World
01254 264120
info@aatw.com
www.aatw.com

Aqwa Records
www.aqwa.com

Arista Records
020 7384 7500
www.arista.com
Owner: Sony BMG

Asylum Records
asylum2006@gmail.com
www.asylumrecords.com
Owner: Warner Music Group

Atlantic Records Group
020 7938 5500
www.atlanticrecords.com
Owner: Warner Music Group
Press: 020 7938 5566

At Large
020 7605 5000
Owner: EMI Group
Press: 020 7605 5317

Audiorec
020 8204 5000
info@audiorec.co.uk
www.audiorec.co.uk

B Unique Records
info@b-uniquerecords.com
www.b-uniquerecords.com

Bad Boy
020 7938 5500
www.badboyonline.com
Owner: Warner Music Group

Baroque Records
024 7636 1001
info@baroquerecords.co.uk
www.baroquerecords.co.uk

Beggars Group
020 8870 9912
beggars@beggars.com
www.beggars.com

Benbecula Records
2006@benbecula.com
www.benbecula.com

BMG Classics
020 7384 7500
www.bmgclassics.com
Owner: Sony BMG

Chandos Records
01206 225200
enquiries@chandos.net
www.chandos.net

Chemikal Underground
0141 550 1919
www.chemikal.co.uk

Cherry Red
020 8740 4110
infonet@cherryred.co.uk
www.cherryred.co.uk

Columbia Records
020 7384 7500
www.columbiarecords.com
Owner: Sony BMG

Cooking Vinyl
020 8600 9200
info@cookingvinyl.com
www.cookingvinyl.com

Definite Records
020 8959 0468
Info@definiterecords.net
www.definiterecords.net

Detour Records
01730 815422
detour@btinternet.com
www.detour-records.co.uk

Domino
020 8875 1390
enquiries@dominorecordco.com
www.dominorecordco.com

Earache
020 7240 5002
talita@earache.com
www.earache.com

Echo
020 7229 1616
info@echo.co.uk
www.echo.co.uk

Elektra
020 7938 5500
www.atlanticrecords.com
Owner: Warner Music Group
Press: 020 7938 5566

EMI Records UK
020 7605 5000
www.emirecords.co.uk
Owner: EMI Group
Press: 020 7605 5317

Epic Records
020 7384 7500
www.epicrecords.com
Owner: Sony BMG

FatCat Records
01273 747433
info@fat-cat.co.uk
www.fat-cat.co.uk

Fierce Panda
ellie@fiercepanda.co.uk
www.fiercepanda.co.uk

Forever Heavenly
020 7494 2998
www.heavenly100.com
Press: 020 7833 9303

Geffen Records
020 7471 5400
www.geffen.com
Owner: Universal Music Group

Gorgeous Music
020 7724 2635
davix@gorgeousmusic.net
www.gorgeousmusic.net

Gut
020 7266 0777
www.gutrecords.com

Heavenly Records
020 7494 2998
www.heavenly100.com
Owner: EMI Group
Press: 020 7833 9303

Hyperion Records
020 8318 1234
info@hyperion-records.co.uk
www.hyperion-records.co.uk

Independiente
020 8747 8111
www.independiente.co.uk

Interscope Geffen A&M
020 7471 5400
www.interscope.com
Owner: Universal Music Group

Def Jam Music
020 7471 5333
www.islanddefjam.com
Owner: Universal Music Group

J Records
020 7384 7500
www.jrecords.com
Owner: Sony BMG

Jeepster
0845 126 0621
info@jeepster.co.uk
www.jeepster.co.uk

Jive Records
020 7384 7500
www.jiverecords.com
Owner: Sony BMG

LaFace Records
020 7384 7500
www.laface.com
Owner: Sony BMG

Lava Records
020 7938 5500
www.lavarecords.com
Owner: Warner Music Group
Press: 020 7938 5566

Legacy Recordings
020 7384 7500
www.legacyrecordings.com
Owner: Sony BMG

Locoz Records
01622 890611
mail@locozrecords.com
www.locozrecords.com

Lost Highway Records
020 7471 5333
www.losthighwayrecords.com
Owner: Universal Music Group

Matador Records
020 8875 6200
natalie@matadorrecords.com
www.matadorrecords.com

Maverick Records
020 7368 2500
www.maverick.com
Owner: Warner Music Group

MCA
020 7471 5300
www.umgnashville.com
Owner: Universal Music Group

Mercury
020 7471 5333
www.umgnashville.com
Owner: Universal Music Group

Mi5 Recordings UK
07976 131145
0151 907 2935
info@mi5recordings.co.uk
www.mi5recordings.co.uk

Mighty Atom Productions
01792 367992
dave@mightyatom.co.uk
www.mightyatom.co.uk

Ministry of Sound
0870 060 0010
arnie@ministryofsound.com
www.ministryofsound.com

Motown Records
020 7471 5300
www.motown.com
Owner: Universal Music Group

Mute Records
020 8964 2001
info@mute.co.uk
www.mute.com
Owner: EMI Group

Nil By Mouth Records
0121 689 0370
info@nil-by-mouth.co.uk
www.nil-by-mouth.co.uk

Nonesuch Records
020 7368 3536
nonesuch.uk@warnermusic.com
www.nonesuch-uk.com
Owner: Warner Music Group

One Little Indian
020 8772 7600
info@indian.co.uk
www.indian.co.uk

Opera Rara
020 7613 2858
info@opera-rara.com
www.opera-rara.com

Parlophone
020 7605 5000
www.parlophone.co.uk
Owner: EMI Group
Press: 020 7605 5437

Polydor
020 7471 5400
www.polydor.co.uk
Owner: Universal Music Group

Positiva
020 7605 5157
www.positivarecords.com
Owner: EMI Group
Press: 020 7324 6155

Provident Music Group
01323 431574
www.providentmusic.com
Owner: Sony BMG

RCA Records
020 7384 7500
www.rcarecords.com
Owner: Sony BMG

Real World
020 7605 5000
www.realworld.on.net
Owner: EMI Group
Press: 020 7605 5895

Reprise Records
020 7761 6000
www.repriserec.com
Owner: Warner Music Group

Riverrun Records
01767 651146
riverrunltd@aol.com
www.rvrcd.co.uk

Rough Trade Records
020 8960 9888
Olly.parker@roughtraderecords
www.roughtraderecords.com

Sanctuary Classics
020 7300 1888
info@sanctuaryclassics.com
www.sanctuaryclassics.com

Sanctuary Music Group
020 7602 6351
www.sanctuaryrecords.co.uk

Seriously Groovy
020 7439 1947
info@seriouslygroovy.com
www.seriouslygroovy.com

Sire Records
020 7761 6000
www.sirerecords.com
Owner: Warner Music Group

Skint Records
mail@skint.net
www.skint.net

So So Def Records
020 7384 7500
www.soso-def.com
Owner: Sony BMG

Solarise Records
info@solariserecords.com
www.solariserecords.com

Sony Classical
020 7384 7500
www.sonyclassical.com
Owner: Sony BMG

Sony Wonder
www.sonywonder.com

Thirdwave Records
info@thirdwavemusic.com
www.thirdwavemusic.com

Topic Records
020 7263 1240
tony.engle@topicrecords.co.uk
www.topicrecords.co.uk

Universal Classics
020 7471 5000
www.iclassics.com
Owner: Universal Music Group

Universal Records
020 7471 5000
www.universalrecords.com
Owner: Universal Music Group

V2
020 7471 3000
www.v2music.com

Verity Records
020 7384 7500
www.verityrecords.com
Owner: Sony BMG

Verve Music Group
020 7471 5000
publicity@vervemusicgroup.com
www.vervemusicgroup.com
Owner: Universal Music Group

Virgin Records UK
020 8964 6000
www.the-raft.com
Owner: EMI Group
Press: 020 8964 6241

Visible Noise
020 7792 9791
julie@visiblenoise.com
www.visiblenoise.com
Press: matt@bluelight.co.uk

Wall of Sound
info@wallofsound.net
www.wallofsound.net
020 8324 2500

Warner Bros Records
020 7761 6000
www.wbr.com
Owner: Warner Music Group

Warner Jazz
020 7368 2500
www.warnerjazz.co.uk
Owner: Warner Music Group
Press: 020 7368 2542

Warner Music International
020 7368 2500
www.wmg.com
Owner: Warner Music Group

Zomba
020 7835 5200

Music publishers

Big Life
020 7554 2100
reception@
biglifemanagement.com
www.biglifemanagement.com

BMG Music Publishing
020 7835 5200
intl.coregeneral@bmg.com
www.bmgmusicsearch.com

Bucks Music
020 7221 4275
info@bucksmusicgroup.co.uk
www.bucksmusicgroup.com

Carlin Music
020 7734 3251
www.carlinmusic.com

Chrysalis Music Publishing
020 7221 2213
info@chrysalismusic.co.uk
www.chrysalismusic.co.uk

EMI Music Publishing
020 7434 2131
www.emimusicpub.com

Independent Music Group
020 8523 9000
erich@
independentmusicgroup.com
www.independentmusicgroup.com

Kobalt Music Group
020 7401 5500
sales@kobaltmusic.com
www.kobaltmusic.com

Memory Lane Music Group
020 8523 8888
www.memorylanemusicgroup.com

Notting Hill
020 7243 2921
info@nottinghillmusic.com
www.nottinghillmusic.com

Sanctuary Music Publishing
020 7602 6351
info@sanctuarygroup.com
www.sanctuarygroup.com

Sony Music Publishing
020 7911 8200
www.sonymusic.co.uk

Universal Music Publishing
020 8752 2600
inbox.publishing@umusic.com
www.universalmusicpublishing
.com

Warner Chappell UK
020 8563 5800
www.warnerchappell.co.uk

Sheet music publishers

Associated Board of the Royal Schools of Music Publishing
020 7636 5400
publishing@abrsm.ac.uk
www.abrsmpublishing.com

Boosey & Hawkes Music Publishers
020 7054 7200
marketing.uk@boosey.com
www.boosey.com

Brass Wind Publications
01572 737409
info@brasswindpublications.co.uk
www.brasswindpublications.co.uk

Breitkopf & Härtel
01303 870037
www.breitkopf.com

Faber Music
020 7833 7900
information@fabermusic.com
www.fabermusic.com

Music Sales
020 7612 7400
music@musicsales.co.uk
www.musicsales.com

Oxford University Press
01865 353699
music.enquiry.uk@oup.com
www.oup.co.uk

Peters Edition
020 7553 4000
www.editionpeters.com

Stainer & Bell
020 8343 3303
post@stainer.co.uk
www.stainer.co.uk

United Music Publishers
01992 703110
info@ump.co.uk
www.ump.co.uk

Universal Edition
020 7439 6678
uelondon@universaledition.com
www.universaledition.com

Production music companies

AKM Music
01926 864068
akm@akmmusic.co.uk
www.akmmusic.co.uk

Amphonic Music
01883 627306
www.amphonic.com

Audio Network
01787 477277
office@audiolicense.net
www.audiolicense.net

Burning Petals
0870 749 1117
enquiries@burning-petals.com
www.burning-petals.co.uk

Extreme Music
020 7485 0111
www.extrememusic.com

KPM Music
020 7412 9111
kpm@kpm.co.uk
www.playkpm.com

Mediatracks
01254 691197
info@mediatracks.co.uk
www.mediatracks.co.uk

Music House
020 7412 9111
enquiries@musichouse.co.uk
www.musichouse.co.uk

Primrose Music
020 8946 7808
www.primrosemusic.com

West One Music
020 7907 1500
info@westonemusic.com
www.westonemusic.com

Digital distributors

Amazon
020 8636 9200
www.amazon.co.uk
Free downloadable tracks from high-profile artists
Press: 020 8636 9280

Artist Direct
www.artistdirect.com
Free downloadable tracks from high-profile artists

Connect
00 1 212 833 8000
service@connect-europe.com
www.connect-europe.com
Sony site, with music from all major labels and many indies
Press: 01932 816417

eMusic
00 1 212 201 9240
www.emusic.com
Subscription-based service
Press: 00 1 212 561 7454
pr@emusic.com

Epitonic
00 1 212 320 3624
www.epitonic.com

Insound
00 1 212 777 8056
www.insound.com/mp3
Free indie MP3s

Intomusic.co.uk
020 8676 4850
info@intomusic.co.uk
www.intomusic.co.uk
Independent and alternative music

iTunes UK
0800 039 1010
www.apple.com/uk/itunes
Apple's digital jukebox and music store
Press:
appleuk.pr@euro.apple.com

Mperia.com
00 1 650 388 3000
www.mperia.com
Press: pr@bitpass.com

Napster
www.napster.co.uk
Subscription service
Press: media@napster.co.uk

OD2/Loudeye
0117 910 0150
info@ondemanddistribution.com
www.ondemanddistribution.com
*Handles distribution for Big Noise
Music, Freeserve Music Club, MSN UK,
MTV UK. MyCokeMusic.com and
Tiscali Music Club*

Playlouder
site@playlouder.com
www.playlouder.com
UK music site
Press: media@playlouder.com

Ricall
020 7592 1710
www.ricall.com
*Music research and licencing network
for professional buyers and sellers of
music*

Streets Online
digital@streetsonline.co.uk
www.streetsonline.co.uk
Owned by Woolworths

Trax2Burn
01202 315333
www.trax2burn.com
*Three house music labels: End
Recordings, Underwater and Southern
Fried*

Vitaminic.com
00 1 415 781 7670
info@vitaminic.com
www.vitaminic.com
Pan-European site

Wippit
0870 737 1100
info@wippit.com
www.wippit.com
Specialises in independent label artists

Recording studios

**Association of Professional
Recording Services (APRS)**
PO Box 22, Totnes TQ9 7YZ
01803 868600
info@aprs.co.uk
www.aprs.co.uk

MEMBERS OF APRS

Abbey Road Studios
3 Abbey Road, London NW8 9AY
020 7266 7000
info@abbeyroad.com
www.abbeyroad.com
Studio manager: Colette Barber

Air Edel Studios
18 Rodmarton Street,
London W1U 8BJ
020 7486 6466
trevor.best@air-edel.co.uk
www.air-edel.co.uk
Studio manager: Trevor Best

Air Studios
Lyndhurst Hall, Lyndhurst Road,
London NW3 5NG
020 7794 0660
information@airstudios.com
www.airstudios.com
Contact: Alison Burton

British Grove Studios
20 British Grove, Chiswick,
London W4 2NL
020 8741 8941
davidstewart@
  britishgrovestudios.com
www.britishgrovestudios.com
Studio manager: David Stewart

Classic Sound
5 Falcon Park, Neasden Lane,
London NW10 1RZ
020 8208 8100
classicsound@dial.pipex.com
www.classicsound.net
Director: Neil Hutchinson

The Dairy
43-45 Tunstall Road,
London SW9 8BZ
020 7738 7777
info@thedairy.co.uk
www.thedairy.co.uk
Studio manager: Emily Taylor

ICC Studios
4 Regency Mews, Silverdale Road,
Eastbourne, Sussex BN20 7AB
01323 643341/2
info@iccstudios.co.uk
www.iccstudios.co.uk
Technical director: Helmut Kaufman

ICE PR
Unit 5, Acklam Workshops,
10 Acklam Road, London W10 5QZ
020 8968 2222
info@ice-pr.com
www.ice-pr.com
MD: Jason Price

Iguana Studio
Unit 1, 88a Acre Lane,
London SW2 5QN
020 7924 0496
info@iguanastudio.co.uk
www.iguanastudio.co.uk
Director: Andrea Terrano

Jacobs Studio
Ridgeway House, Dippenhall,
Nr Farnham, Surrey GU10 5EE
01503 250812
andy@jacobs-studios.co.uk
www.jacobs-studios.co.uk
MD: Andy Fernbach

Keynote Studios
Green Lane, Burghfield Bridge,
Burghfield, Reading RG30 3XN
0118 959 9944
keynotestudios@btconnect.co.uk
www.keynotestudios.co.uk
Owner and partner: Noel Newton

Konk Recording Studio
84-86 Tottenham Lane,
London N8 7EE
020 8340 7873
linda@konkstudios.com
Studio manager: Sarah Lockwood

Lansdowne Recording Studios
CTS-Lansdowne Recording
Studios, P.O. Box 47189
London, W6 6DA
020 8846 9444
info@cts-lansdowne.co.uk
www.cts-lansdowne.co.uk
CEO: Adrian Kerridge

Metropolis
The Powerhouse, 70 Chiswick
High Road, London W4 1SY
020 8742 1111
studios@metropolis-group.co.uk
www.metropolis-group.co.uk
Studio bookings: Alison Hussey

Parr Street Studios
33-45 Parr Street, Liverpool L1 4JN
0151 707 1050
info@parrstreet.co.uk
www.parrstreet.co.uk

Phoenix Sound
Pinewood Studios,
Pinewood Road, Iver Heath,
Buckinghamshire SL0 0NH
01753 785495
info@phoenixsound.net
www.phoenixsound.net
Studio Manager: Peter Fielder

RAK Recording Studios
42-48 Charlbert Street,
St John's Wood, London NW8 7BU
020 7586 2012
trisha@rakstudios.co.uk
www.rakstudios.co.uk
Studio manager: Trisha Wegg

Real World Studios
Box Mill, Mill Lane, Box,
Corsham, Wiltshire SN13 8PL
01225 743188
studios@realworld.co.uk
www.realworld.co.uk
Studio manager: Owen Leech

Rockfield Studios
Amberley Court, Rockfield Road,
Monmouth NP25 5ST
01600 712449
lisaward@rockfieldstudios.com
www.rockfieldstudios.com
Director: Kingsley Ward

Roundhouse Recording Studios
91 Saffron Hill, London EC1N 8PT
020 7404 3333
roundhouse@stardiamond.com
www.stardiamond.com/roundhouse
Contact: Lisa Gunther

Sain
Llandwrog, Caernarfon,
Gwynedd LL54 5TG
01286 831111
eryl@sainwales.com
www.sainwales.com
Studio manager: Eryl Davies

Townhouse Studios
150 Goldhawk Road,
London W12 8HH
020 8932 3200
julie.bateman@
    sanctuarygroup.com
www.sanctuarygroup.com
Managing Directors: Al Stein

Sawmills Studio
Golant, Fowey, Cornwall PL23 1LW
01726 833338
ruth@sawmills.co.uk
www.sawmills.co.uk
Studio manager: Ruth Taylor

Soho Recording Studios
Basement, The Heals Building,
22-24 Torrington Place,
London WC1E 7HJ
020 7419 2444
dominic@sohostudios.co.uk
www.sohostudios.co.uk
Manager: Dominic Sanders

Sound Recording Technology
Edison Road, St Ives,
Cambridgeshire PE27 3LF
London: 020 8446 3218
Cambridge: 01480 461880
srt@btinternet.com
www.soundrecordingtechnology
    .co.uk
MD: Sarah Pownall

Sphere Studios
2 Shuttleworth Road, Battersea,
London SW11 3EA
020 7326 9450
inform@spherestudios.com
www.spherestudios.com
MD: Francesco Camelli

Strongroom Studios
120-124 Curtain Road,
London EC2A 3SQ
020 7426 5100
mix@strongroom.com
www.strongroom.com
MD: Richard Boote

Promoters

Barfly
49 Chalk Farm Road,
London NW1 8AN
020 7691 4244
london.info@barflyclub.com
www.barflyclub.com
*Clubs based in Aberdeen, Camden
London, West End London,
Birmingham, Brighton, Cardiff,
Liverpool, Glasgow and York*

Club Fandango
131 Aberdeen Centre, 22-24
Highbury Grove, London N5 2EA
everyone@clubfandango.co.uk
www.clubfandango.co.uk
*Venues in London, Brighton, Bristol,
Manchester and Glasgow.
Wolverhampton, Southampton,
Northampton and Huddersfield. London
venues include Dublin Castle, The
Borderline (with BMI) & the Bull & Gate*

Mean Fiddler Music Group
Head office, 16 High Street,
Harlesden, London NW10 4LX
020 8961 5490
www.meanfiddler.com
*Astoria, Jazz Cafe, Borderline, The
Forum and Glastonbury festival*

Music venues

» *see page 347*

Events

All Tomorrow's Parties
020 7733 8009
ken@hermana.co.uk
www.atpfestival.com
*Three-day festival held over two
consecutive weekends*

Bampton Classical Opera
01993 851876
Holcot House, Market Square,
Bampton, Oxfordshire OX18 2JJ
mail@bamptonopera.org
www.bamptonopera.org
Lively and accessible opera productions

BBC Proms
020 7589 8212
proms@bbc.co.uk
www.bbc.co.uk/proms
Press: 020 7765 5575

Belladrum Tartan Heart
Phoineas House, Belladrum
Estate, By Beauly, Inverness-shire
IV4 7BA, Scotland
01463 741366
info@tartanheartfestival.co.uk
www.tartanheartfestival.co.uk

Benicassim
http://fiberfib.com/en/festival
    /the-festival
*Indie, electronica and pop festival on
the beach*

Bestival
Get Involved Ltd, The Studio,
131c Salusbury Road,
London NW6 6RG
020 8962 8040
clare@getinvolvedltd.com
www.bestival.net
"Boutique" 3-day festival

Big Chill
Chillfest ltd, PO Box 52707,
London EC2P 2WE
info@bigchill.net
www.bigchill.net
Dance music

Cambridge Folk Festival
The Cambridge Corn Exchange,
3 Parsons Court, Wheeler Street,
Cambridge CB2 3QE
01223 457555
folkfest@cambridge.gov.uk
www.cambridgefolkfestival.co.uk

Camden Crawl
www.thecamdencrawl.com
The London version of SXSW

Carling Weekend
(Reading, Leeds)
Mean Fiddler, 16 High Street,
Harlseden, London NW10 4LX
020 8961 5490
www.meanfiddler.com

Creamfields
Cream Group, Nation,
Wolstenholme Square, 1-3 Parr
Street, Dursebury, Holton
0151 707 1309
info@cream.co.uk
www.cream.co.uk

D:percussion
www.dpercussion.com
Manchester's free music festival

Deeply Vale
www.deeplyvale.com
*Plans for a revival of the original
1970s festival*

Dot to Dot Festival
www.dottodotfestival.co.uk
Nottingham city based festival

Download
www.downloadfestival.co.uk

Get Loaded
020 7247 4121
stix@turnmills.co.uk
www.get-loaded.co.uk
Touring indie/dance crossover festival

Give it a Name
info@giveitaname.co.uk
www.giveitaname.co.uk

Glade
sarah@leylinepromotions.com
www.gladefestival.com
Electronic dance music

Glastonbury Festival
28 Northload Street,
Glastonbury, Somerset BA6 9JJ
01458 834596
office@glastonburyfestivals.co.uk
www.glastonburyfestivals.co.uk

contacts **Music**

Global Gathering
www.globalgathering.co.uk
Dance music

Glyndebourne Festival
Glyndebourne Productions,
Glyndebourne, Lewes
01273 812321
info@glyndebourne.com
www.glyndebourne.com

Great Escape
www.escapegreat.com
Brighton venues

Green Man Festival
020 7733 8009
info@thegreenmanfestival.co.uk
www.thegreenmanfestival.co.uk
Folk and folktronica
Press: ken@hermana.co.uk

Guilfest
54 Haydon Place, Guildford,
Surrey GU1 4NE
info@guilfest.co.uk
www.guilfest.co.uk
Family-friendly festival

HI:FI
info@hififestival.com
www.hififestival.com
*Aiming to bridge the gap between
dance and rock music*

Homelands Festival
Mean Fiddler, 16 High Street,
Harlesden, London NW10 4LX
020 8961 5490
www.welovehomelands.com

Hyde Park Calling
access@getlive.co.uk
www.hydeparkcalling.co.uk
Two-day festival in Hyde Park

Isle of Wight Festival
info@isleofwightfestival.org
www.isleofwightfestival.org

Latitude
020 7792 9400
0121 224 7453
charlie@presscounsel.com
margaret@fmguk.com
www.latitudefestival.co.uk/home
*Music festival with poetry, comedy,
film, theatre, books*
Press: Press Counsel, 5-7 Vernon
Yard, off Portobello Road,
London W11 2DX

London Calling
020 8232 1606
andy.center@ithacamedia.co.uk
www.londoncalling2007.com
*International exhibition for artists,
managers, labels, service providers,
brands*

The London Fleadh
Mean Fiddler, 16 High Street,
Harlesden, London NW10 4LX
020 8961 5490
www.meanfiddler.com

Middlesbroughmusiclive
01642 247755
phil@tenfeettall.co.uk
www.middlesbroughmusiclive
.co.uk
City-based festival

O2 Wireless
www.wirelessfestival.co.uk
Free festival in Hyde Park

Rock-Ness
Unit 2, Broomfield Holiday Park,
West Lane, Ullapool IV26 2UT,
Scotland
01463 238660
info@rockness.co.uk
www.rockness.co.uk
Dance music festival on Lock Ness

Summer Sundae
De Montfort Hall, Granville Road,
Leicester LE1 7RU
0116 233 3113
dmh.office@leicester.gov.uk
www.summersundae.co.uk
Press: 020 7833 9303
julie@9pr.co.uk

SXSW
Cill Ruan, 7 Ard na Croise, Thurles,
County Tipperary, Ireland
00 353 5042 6488
una@sxsw.com
www.sxsw.com
International showcase

Tapestry Goes West
Tapestry, PO Box 45580,
London NW1 9UN
07887 924950
info@tapestrygoeswest.com
www.tapestrygoeswest.com
*Indie-folk festival featuring a medieval
village and jousting display*

TDK Cross Central
Cross Central Events, King's Cross
Freight Depot, York Way,
London N1 0UZ
020 7833 9944
claire@crosscentral.co.uk
www.crosscentral.co.uk

Tin Pan Alley
info@tinpanalleyfestival.co.uk
www.tinpanalleyfestival.co.uk
*Takes place on Denmark Street, in
association with Shelter*

T in the Park
www.tinthepark.com
Press: Liana Mellotte
0141 204 7970

V Festival
www.vfestival.com
Press: vfestival@cakemedia.com

Womad
Womad Press Department,
Millside, Mill Lane, Box,
Wiltshire SN13 8PN
01225 743481
info@womad.org
www.womad.org
World music

Orchestras

BBC National Orchestra of Wales
BBC Wales, Broadcasting House,
Cardiff CF5 2YQ
0800 052 1812
now@bbc.co.uk
www.bbc.co.uk/wales/now

BBC Philharmonic
New Broadcasting House,
Oxford Road, Manchester M60 1SJ
0161 244 4001
philharmonic@bbc.co.uk
www.bbc.co.uk/orchestras
/philharmonic

**BBC Scottish Symphony
Orchestra**
BBC Scotland, Broadcasting
House, Queen Margaret Drive,
Glasgow G12 8DG
0141 338 2606
bbcsso@bbc.co.uk
www.bbc.co.uk/scotland/musicsc
otland/bbcsso/concerts

English Symphony Orchestra
1 Stockwood Business Park,
Stockwood, Redditch B96 6SX
01386 791044
info@eso.co.uk
www.eso.co.uk

London Philharmonic Orchestra
89 Albert Embankment,
London SE1 7TP
020 7840 4200
admin@lpo.org.uk
www.lpo.co.uk

London Symphony Orchestra
Barbican Centre, Silk Street,
London EC2Y 8DS
020 7588 1116
admin@lso.co.uk
www.lso.co.uk

Royal Philharmonic Orchestra
16 Clerkenwell Green,
London EC1R 0QT
020 7608 8800
info@rpo.co.uk
www.rpo.co.uk

Royal Scottish National Orchestra
73 Claremont Street,
Glasgow G3 7JB
0141 226 3868
www.rsno.org.uk

Music schools

Birmingham Conservatoire
Paradise Place, Birmingham B3 3HG
0121 331 5901/5902
conservatoire@uce.ac.uk
www.conservatoire.uce.ac.uk

Leeds College of Music
3 Quarry Hill, Leeds LS2 7PD
0113 222 3400
enquiries@lcm.ac.uk
www.lcm.ac.uk

Royal Academy of Music
Marylebone Road,
London NW1 5HT
020 7873 7373
www.ram.ac.uk

Royal College of Music
Prince Consort Road,
London SW7 2BS
020 7589 3643
info@rcm.ac.uk
www.rcm.ac.uk

Royal Northern College of Music
124 Oxford Road,
Manchester M13 9RD
0161 907 5200
info@rncm.ac.uk
www.rncm.ac.uk

Royal Scottish Academy of Music and Drama
100 Renfrew Street,
Glasgow G2 3DB
0141 332 4101
www.rsamd.ac.uk

Royal Welsh College of Music and Drama
Castle Grounds, Cathays Park,
Cardiff CF10 3ER
029 2034 2854
music.admissions@rwcmd.ac.uk
www.rwcmd.ac.uk
Press: Press@rwcmd.ac.uk

Trinity College of Music
King Charles Court, Old Royal
Naval College, Greenwich,
London SE10 9JF
020 8305 4444
info@tcm.ac.uk
www.tcm.ac.uk

Major record companies

EMI Group
27 Wrights Lane, London W8 5SW
020 7795 7000
www.emimusic.co.uk
• *Labels: Additive Records, EMI Records, Heavenly Records, Mute Records, Parlophone, Positiva Records, Real World, Virgin Records UK*
Press: Amanda Conroy
020 7795 7529

Sony BMG Music Entertainment
550 Madison Ave, New York,
NY 10022-3211, USA
00 1 212 833 8000
www.sonybmg.com
CEO: Andrew Lack
• *Labels: Arista, BMG Classics, Columbia, Epic, J Records, Jive Records, LaFace Records, Legacy Recordings, Provident Music Group, RCA Records, Sony Classical, Sony Music UK, Sony Wonder, So So Def, Verity*
Press: 00 1 212 833 5047

Sony Music Entertainment (UK)
Bedford House, 69–79 Fulham
High Street, London SW6 3JW
020 7384 7500
www.sonymusic.co.uk
Corporate Press: 020 7384 7725

Universal Music Group
2220 Colorado Avenue, Santa
Monica, CA 90404, USA
00 1 310 865 5000
http://new.umusic.com
Chairman and CEO: Jorgen Larsen
• *Labels: Geffen, Island, Lost Highway, MCA, Mercury, Motown Records, Polydor, Universal Classics, Verve Music Group*

Universal Music International
8 St James's Square,
London SW1Y 4JU
020 7747 4000
Corporate Press, UK:
020 7471 5385
corporate press, international:
020 7747 4216

Warner Music Group
75 Rockefeller Plaza, New York,
NY 10019, USA
00 1 212 275 2000
www.wmg.com
Chairman and CEO, Warner Music Group: Edgar Bronfman Jr; chairman and CEO, US recorded music, Warner Music Group US: Lyor Cohen; chairman and CEO, Warner Music International: Patrick Vien
• *Labels: Asylum, Atlantic, Bad Boy, Cordless, East West, Elektra, Lava, Maverick, Nonesuch, Perfect Game, Reprise, Rhino, Sire, Warner Bros. and Word*
Press:
mediainquiries@wmg.com

UK office
28 Kensington Church Street,
London W8 4EP
020 7368 2500
www.warnermusic.co.uk
Press: 020 7761 6000

Music TV shows

The Album Chart Show
3DD Entertainment Limited
190 Camden High Street,
London NW1 8QP
020 7428 1800
http://3ddgroup.com
Executive producer: Andrew Higgie
andrew.higgie@3DDgroup.com

Guerilla Gig Live
Somethin' Else
Units 1–4, 1a Old Nichol Street,
London E2 7HR
020 7250 5500
info@somethinelse.com
Executive producer: Jez Nelson

Later...With Jools Holland
3DD Entertainment Limited
190 Camden High Street,
London NW1 8QP
020 7428 1800
http://3ddgroup.com
Producers: Mark Cooper, Alison Howe

Transmission with T Mobile
At It Productions,
60–70 Salusbury Road,
London NW6 6NU
020 7644 0000
www.atitproductions.com
Series producer: Sophie Johnson

Music websites

● Online magazines and networks

Alternate Music Press
aussie450@lycos.com
www.alternatemusicpress.com
Publication with music archive.
Editor: Ben Kettlewell

CMU music network
chris@unlimitedmedia.co.uk
caro@unlimitedmedia.co.uk
www.cmumusicnetwork.co.uk/default
Information network linking grassroots music and mainstream music.

Cool Hunting
001 917 415 3937
josh@coolhunting.com
www.coolhunting.com/music.php
Music industry intelligence.
Editor-in-chief: Josh Rubin

Drownedinsound
editor@drownedinsound.com
www.drownedinsound.com
New music. Editor: Sean Adams

fiveeight
020 7837 1347
tim@fruktmusic.com
www.fiveeight.net
Providing coverage and strategic insight into the music industry. Editor: Eamonn Forde

Fly
020 8749 3255
damian@fly.co.uk
www.fly.co.uk/fly
World music. Editor: Damian Rafferty

Pitchfork Media
ryan@pitchforkmedia.com
www.pitchforkmedia.com
New music. Associate editor: Ryan Schreiber

Playlouder
site@playlouder.com
www.playlouder.com
New music. Directors: Jim Gottlieb and Paul Hitchman

contacts **Music**

239

Popjustice
020 7352 9444
contact@popjustice.com
www.popjustice.com
*Internet equivalent to Smash Hits
magazine. Founder: Peter Robinson*

Popmatters
editor@popmatters.com
http://popmatters.com
*Cultural critique. Music editor:
Sarah Zupko*

Stylus Magazine
todd_burns@stylusmagazine.com
http://stylusmagazine.com
New music. Editor-in-chief: Todd Burns

● Music archives

Classical Archives
001 650 330 8050
www.classicalarchives.com
*Archived classical music. Website
founder: Pierre Schwob*

Classical Source
www.classicalsource.com
*Classical music resource site (reviews,
directory of links to other sources).
Managing director: Chris Caspell*

Dimeadozen
www.dimeadozen.org
*Audio archive. Downloadable live gigs
and demo tracks*

Last.fm
www.last.fm
Music discovery/cataloguing project

Pandora
www.pandora.com
*Music discovery/cataloguing project.
Director of communications: Michelle
Husak*

Rock's backpages
020 7589 2433
www.rocksbackpages.com
*Library of rock music journalism
from the 1950s onwards. Contact:
Tony Keys, tony@rocksbackpages.com*

YouTube
http://youtube.com
Video sharing

● Blogs

Fluxblog
perpetua@gmail.com
www.fluxblog.org
Music journalism blog

The Hype Machine
http://hype.non-standard.net
Audio blog (mp3)

Largehearted Boy
http://blog.largeheartedboy.com
*Music journalism blog with free
downloads*

Stereogum
info@stereogum.com
www.stereogum.com
Music journalism blog

Music press

Audience
020 7486 7007
info@audience.uk.com
www.audience.uk.com
*Monthly. For live international
contemporary music industry. Owner:
Audience Media. Managing editor:
Stephen Parker; sales manager: Brij
Gosai*

Billboard
020 7420 6000
www.billboard.com
*Weekly magazine and daily email.
Owner: Nielson Company. Executive
Editor: Tom Ferguson; news: Lars
Brandle*

Five Eight
020 7837 1347
eamonn@fiveeight.net
www.fiveeight.net
*Monthly magazine and daily email.
Editor: Eamonn Forde*

Gramophone
020 8267 5136
www.gramophone.co.uk
*Monthly. Owner: Haymarket.
Editor: James Inverne*

Kerrang!
020 7182 8000
www.kerrang.com
*Weekly. Owner: Bauer. Editor:
Paul Brannigan*

Mojo
020 7436 1515
www.mojo4music.com
*Monthly. Owner: Bauer. Editor:
Phil Alexander*

Music Industry News Network
00 1 718 278 0662
editor@mi2n.com
www.mi2n.com
*News aggregator. Editor-in-chief:
Eric de Fontenay*

Music Week
020 7921 8390
martin@musicweek.com
www.musicweek.com
*Weekly. Owner: CMP Information.
Editor: Martin Talbot; news: Paul
Williams; features: Adam Webb; chief
sub: Dougal Baird; online editor:
Nicola Slade*

MusicAlly
020 7490 5444
mail@musically.com
www.musically.com
*Fortnightly plus bulletins. Owner:
Digital music. Editor: Paul Brindley;
features: Toby Lewis*

Musician
020 7840 5531
info@musiciansunion.org.uk
www.musiciansunion.org.uk
Quarterly. Editor: Keith Ames

NME
020 3148 5000
www.nme.com
*Weekly. Owner: IPC Media.
Editor: Conor McNicholas*

Q
020 7182 8000
www.q4music.com
*Monthly. Owner: Bauer.
Editor: Paul Rees*

Record of the Day
020 8520 2130
info@recordoftheday.com
www.recordoftheday.com
*Daily newsletter. Editor: Nicola Slade;
music editor: James Foley*

»» *More consumer music magazines
see page 87*

Associations

Association of British Orchestras
20 Rupert Street,
London W1D 6DF
020 7287 0333
info@abo.org.uk
www.abo.org.uk

Association of Independent Music
Lamb House, Church Street,
London W4 2PD
020 8994 5599
www.musicindie.org

Association of Professional Recording Services
PO Box 22, Totnes TQ9 7YZ
01803 868600
info@aprs.co.uk
www.aprs.co.uk

British Academy of Composers and Songwriters
British Music House, 25–27
Berners Street, London W1T 3LR
020 7636 2929
info@britishacademy.com
www.britishacademy.com

Entertainment Retailers Association
Colonnade House, 1st Floor,
2 Westover Road, Bournemouth,
Dorset BH1 2BY
01202 292063
www.bard.org

British Music Information Centre
1st Floor, Lincoln House,
75 Westminster Bridge Road,
London SE1 7HS
020 7928 1902
info@bmic.co.uk
www.bmic.co.uk

British Music Rights
British Music House, 26 Berners
Street, London W1T 3LR
020 7306 4446
britishmusic@bmr.org
www.bmr.org

British Phonographic Industry
Riverside Building, County Hall,
Westminster Bridge Road,
London SE1 7JA
020 7803 1300
research@bpi.co.uk
www.bpi.co.uk

IFPI
54 Regent Street, London W1B 5RE
020 7878 7900
info@ifpi.org
www.ifpi.org
Represents music industry worldwide

**Incorporated Society
of Musicians**
10 Stratford Place, London W1C 1AA
020 7629 4413
membership@ism.org
www.ism.org

**Independent Music Companies
Association**
70 Codenberg, 1000 Brussels,
Belgium
0032 2 503 3138
European indie label association

**Mechanical-Copyright
Protection Society**
Copyright House, 29-33 Berners
Street, London W1T 3AB
020 7580 5544
www.mcps.co.uk

Music Industries Association
Ivy Cottage Offices, Finch's Yard,
Eastwick Road, Great Bookham,
Surrey KT23 4BA
01372 750600
enquiries@mia.org.uk
www.mia.org.uk

Music Publishers Association
6th Floor, British Music House,
26 Berners Street,
London W1T 3LR
020 7580 0126
info@mpaonline.org.uk
www.mpaonline.org.uk

Musicians Union
www.musiciansunion.org.uk
Regional offices:
London
33 Palfrey Place, London SW8 1PE
020 7840 5504
london@musiciansunion.org.uk
East and South-east England
1a Fentiman Road, London SW8 1LD
020 7840 5537
eastsoutheast@
    musiciansunion.org.uk
Midlands
Benson House, Lombard Street,
Birmingham B12 0QN
0121 622 3870
birmingham@
    musiciansunion.org.uk
North of England
40 Canal Street,
Manchester M1 3WD
0161 236 1764
manchester@
    musiciansunion.org.uk

Scotland and Northern Ireland
1 Woodside Terrace,
Glasgow G3 7UY
0141 341 2960
glasgow@musiciansunion.org.uk
Wales and South-west England
199 Newport Road,
Cardiff CF24 1AJ
029 2045 6585
cardiff@musiciansunion.org.uk

Official UK Charts Company
4th Floor,
58/59 Great Marlborough Street,
London W1F 7JY
020 7478 8500
lucy@theofficialcharts.com
www.theofficialcharts.com

Performing Rights Society
Copyright House, 29-33 Berners
Street, London W1T 3AB
020 7580 5544
www.prs.co.uk

Phonographic Performance
PPL, 1 Upper James Street,
London W1F 9DE
020 7534 1000

**Producers and Composers of
Applied Music**
01886 884204
bobfromer@onetel.com
www.pcam.co.uk

New world order

Alan Rusbridger

Since a free press first evolved, we have derived our authority from a feeling — a sense, a pretence — that journalism is, if not infallible, something close to it. We speak of ourselves as being interested in the truth, the real truth. We're truth seekers, we're truth tellers, we tell truth to power.

As a marketing proposition, it had its merits, even if the claim has probably always been treated with some scepticism — and is increasingly so today. Some journalists have always been a bit uneasy with this narrative of what we do. They know that "the truth" is a troublesome concept. As Walter Lippman wrote as long ago as 1922, "If we assume ... that news and truth are two words for the same thing we shall, I believe, arrive nowhere."

Here's not the place for arguments about the desirability, or possibility, of objective journalism: we could be here all week and not agree. But if "the truth" were so easily obtainable on the day — with rolling news, within the hour — then there would be no need for historians. As journalists, we're doing well if we confine ourselves to being truthful about what we know, which is often (through no fault of our own) fairly circumscribed. We're doing better if we're also truthful about what we don't know. We should always be uneasy at grandiose boasts that we're revealing The Truth.

This is especially so the more news organisations have moved away from the role of being simple, relatively passive reporters. Once upon a time news reporters would sit at the back of public meetings, or in parliamentary press galleries, and produce a higher form of stenography. We saw our role as recorders, independent witnesses. We may wonder, looking back through yellowing newspaper files, at the public's appetite for all that verbatim reporting of speeches and meetings. But those newspapers sold in very large quantities.

In time that function became either partly surplus to requirement — newer technologies came along — or else too costly or else too irrelevant. It's a mantra now that people are too "time-poor" to read yards of text about parliamentary debates or, indeed, virtually anything. People still make speeches, but we report them less and less. We collude with politicians in producing and publishing bites.

The trend over many years now — at least in Britain, but, I think more broadly — has been for shorter articles, more features, more opinion, more commentary, more campaigning, more about the personal and emotional life. Many journalists are not content with sitting back and being passive witnesses. They want to be players.

There was virtually no debate in Britain when, two or three years ago, the editor of one of our five main national quality papers said he now thought of his title as a viewspaper rather a newspaper. This was simply an interesting variant on an established theme. Viewspaper? Newspaper? Take your choice.

But it's perhaps inevitable that, the more you move from reporting to advocacy, campaigning and persuasion, the more people will question you. Any force in society that attempts to exert active strong influence can't be surprised to find people wanting to question everything from your motives to your methods.

In other words, handing down tablets of stone and telling people "this is how it is" is a less persuasive proposition than it once was. It's laborious to recite the numerous surveys of trust that show that journalists are not invariably regarded as dealers of the unclouded truth. The message these surveys convey is not necessarily that people think we're despicable people who make it all up (though they may believe that about some journalists on some papers). I think it's rather that the public at large have a rather more honest assessment of what journalism is than we give them credit for. In other words, I think such surveys capture a rather sophisticated sense of what we do – which in the privacy of the newsroom, or the pub, we know ourselves, but which we think we're keeping secret from everyone else.

This pretence is no longer sustainable because:

> Readers, users – call them what you will – now have real-time access to much of the information that was once our exclusive preserve. By that I mean that the traditional news media were, on the day, the only source of information. A speech, a debate, a report, a scientific paper – most people had few independent ways of verifying a newspaper or broadcast account, certainly on the day it was published or broadcast. Now a huge amount of information is simultaneously released on official websites, enabling millions of people to check your version of events against the original.

What does that mean? It means that inquiring, suspicious or specialist readers will swiftly be able to test your journalism for accuracy or bias. Of course, we still have sources of information not available to just anyone. But today there are millions of fact-checkers out there. Millions of them have their own blogs or websites. So we can refuse systematically to correct or clarify our journalism, but we would be foolish to imagine that it will therefore go uncorrected or unclarified. It will: all that will happen is that it will take place elsewhere.

And, of course, that will still happen even if you do have your own processes in place. The question editors have to face is: is it not a bit uncomfortable knowing that your failings may be revealed and widely discussed elsewhere, with not a word appearing in your own newspaper or on your own channel? Which is the road to building trust – engaging or ignoring?

The second reason why the tablet-of-stone era journalism is over is that, increasingly, the people on whom we report will not simply publish material so that people can consume it in an unmediated form: they will go further and actively use these new channels of communication to question us, if not actively discredit us. A recent example was the so-called video-ambushing of a BBC reporter who lost his cool, to put it mildly, while interviewing a leading scientologist. The Church of Scientology published the clip on YouTube in advance of the BBC Panorama programme itself.

Now imagine someone issuing a full transcript of an interview that appeared to show highly selective or misleading use of quotes on the part of a newspaper. Such situations happen already and will occur more and more frequently, leaving editors to ponder how to respond: will they do so via press offices or PR campaigns — to try and win a battle of spin? Or is there a virtue in greater transparency and independent examination in our own papers and publishing platforms? In this case the BBC responded by posting its own version of an interview with the Scientologist over whom John Sweeney lost his temper. The producer of Panorama also appeared on the BBC's own news programme to talk about both the programme and the outburst.

How happy would editors be to publish all on record source material for all stories and all interviews on the web?

What all this points to is a new age in which the old model — we pushed the stuff out and took little notice of the response — is over. You would have to be a very unobservant journalist these days not to see that the entrails of mainstream journalism are picked over by millions of bloggers. At the last count, Technorati claimed to be monitoring 71 million [this rose to 110m in December] individual weblogs — on an hourly basis.

In a sense this is comforting: it shows that what we do — and what we write — still matters and continues to stir up emotions, debate and controversies. And it will be increasingly odd if raging discussions about newspapers exist purely in a digital space, with not a word of it being allowed into print.

But, in a sense I think this is all rather old-fashioned debate because, in truth, the debate *is* raging out there in a way that many mainstream journalists have not quite yet appreciated. At times it feels more like a cacophony than a debate, it's true. But various technological and economic forces are bearing down on what we do so forcefully and, frankly, so fast, that the very nature of journalism is being challenged in fundamental ways that have yet to filter back into more conventional print-focused newsrooms.

As with all these developments, so-called old media has a decision to make — whether to stand aloof from them and basically say "that's not what we do." Or else to try it out on the basis that it might, indeed, not be what we do, but there are some things we can learn from it, or that might affect us. And of course there is a third possibility: that we try it out and decide that that's exactly what we should be doing.

Let's have a whistle-stop look at the sorts of things going on out there that might be called journalism, though often not as it's conventionally been understood.

In the world out there — the digital world without legacy assets and costs and infrastructures — there is a huge energy around networks of people, usually not highly paid media professionals, but amateurs, or groups of amateurs directed by professionals, seeking new ways of disseminating, aggregating and assessing information. No one has yet found a satisfactory name for it, so "citizen journalism", or "networked publishing" has to do for the time being.

You might group the experiments into four different types: hyperlocal; user-generated news sites; user-generated comment or discussion sites; crowdsourcing.

Actually, most so-called "citizen journalism" sites exhibit a combination of characteristics that make it hard to group them into strictly defined categories.

Many sites allow their users to comment on articles written by professional journalists. This is not really citizen journalism, which is more about the citizen actually writing the story, or contributing to its content, or – at the very least – being able to influence which stories are displayed on the site.

The first trend is towards "hyperlocal". These are online news sites – often the internet version of a local paper – that contain user-generated content produced by local residents. The advantage is that they often report on topics that conventional newspapers tend to ignore. "Hyperlocal" news sites tend to focus on one community but, as is the case with the BBC's Action Network, can be a collective of local stories/concerns generated by non-professional users on a nationwide scale.

Traditional media companies have not stood idly by as these revolutionary experiments take place and gather speed. Some managements may be motivated by cost, some by fear of losing market and advertising. Some, I think, are genuinely excited by the journalistic possibilities and the competitive advantage that can come from involving so-called citizen reporters.

An obvious example is CNN's I-Reports, which allow citizen journalists to submit their stories, video, audio and pictures to the site.

Submissions are also considered for CNN Exchange, a new area of CNN's online focusing exclusively on user-submitted content.

Then there is Newsvine, which incorporates news aggregation, social networking, citizen journalism, blogging, user ratings and online discussions. The main page gives a clear overview of all the news submitted from the Associated Press and the Newsvine users, along with buttons to vote and comment on stories.

User-generated comment sites technically include most individual blogs. One of the most popular examples of a collaborative blog is the Dailykos, which has between 14 million and 24 million visits a month. Founded in 2002, it was one of the first such sites to allow users to vote on content. Finally, there are the new experiments in so-called "crowdsourcing" – a word describing the attempt to tap into the collective mind of the public in order to further journalistic aims.

It tests the principle – fairly widely advanced by web theorists - that some people in the audience know more than even the smartest reporters and editors.

Crowdsourcing can either involve transferring editorial control to the citizens (eg by asking them to conduct an interview that will form part of a larger article) or not (eg by signing up members of the public as "sources" who can tip off professional reporters).

Public Insight Journalism is an attempt by Minnesota Public Radio to plug into the public's knowledge. To date more than 24,000 people have volunteered to become a "public source" for MPR. Through surveys and email, they share information with the station. The network is growing by around 1,000 sources a month. MPR reporters have used the network for stories on crime in Minneapolis, obstacles faced by women entrepreneurs, advances in green architecture, rising middle-class insecurity, and religion at the office.

Another example is Assignment Zero, an attempt by New York University's Jay Rosen to create an open-platform reporting tool.

Its aim is to bring together professional writers and editors with citizen journalists to collaborate on reporting and writing about the rise of crowdsourcing on the web.

The site's "Newsroom" comprises the Assignment Desk, where contributors can learn about what has been covered and pick up an assignment; the Exchange, where people can talk through the story and offer new ideas; and the Scoop, where the editor comments on the day's developments.

These are just a few snapshots of some of the things that are going on in the digital sphere as people – some journalists, some non-journalists – try to investigate new forms of reporting.

What they all have in common is a more level playing field between journalists (where they are involved at all) and readers; a blurring of the distinction between publisher and recipient; more transparency; more collaboration; more give and take. The sense of editorial content being produced behind high castle walls is quite foreign to this new world.

Now, of course, there are all the obvious objections to much of that: most of them centre on matters of trust. How can you evaluate the work of amateurs, some of them anonymous, very few of them with any kind of journalistic training? How could anyone place trust in this kind of journalism?

Well, one answer is that this one of the main questions they're grappling with themselves – hence experiments in teaming up professional journalists with material derived from this huge potential pool of sources. Hence experiments in searching for more and more sophisticated ranking systems, so that the so-called wisdom of crowds can serve as a method for sorting out journalistic wheat from chaff.

These experiments are in their infancy and of course sceptics, not to mention net-enthusiasts, don't find it difficult to pick holes in what's going on. Those of us working in established news organisations can derive some comfort from what we know about the value of traditional journalism at its best and in the trust invested in our brands.

But we know this too: trust has to be re-earned all the time. It's emphatically not a one-off thing that, once earned, exists in perpetuity. And – sorry to labour this point again – most opinion surveys don't stand out for the trust readers and viewers place in many forms of mainstream media.

Which I hope brings me back to these established news organisations and how they continue to keep the trust that is essential for them to compete in a world in which many of the other aspects of what they do can be done as well, or better, or faster, or more interactively, elsewhere.

In a 24/7 world – which is what we're all moving to – it has to begin with a searching examination of what journalism is. This is a debate that must surely be happening in all newspapers that are trying to dip any kind of a toe into the digital world.

Let's try a few things conventional journalism is not:

It's not about delivering the truth, the whole truth and nothing but the truth. No one believes that any more if they ever did.

It's not an infallible way of ascertaining what is going wrong around us.

It's not defined by an arbitrary moment in the 24-hour clock to suit the historic schedules of print plants, distribution chains and wholesale delivery.

It's rarely something about which we, as journalists, have exclusive knowledge of, or access, to.

It is something more fluid ... a much more iterative thing than the tablet of stone. It is about us saying "this is how it seems to us; it's not the definitive word on the subject by any means; some of you will know more about this; we can collaborate to try and get closer to the truth on this story; this is how you can contribute."

Those who have heard me speak before may have heard me quote a passage from a speech the Washington Post columnist David Broder made nearly 30 years ago:

> "I would like to see us say over and over until the point has been made ... that the newspaper that drops on your doorstep is a partial, hasty, incomplete, inevitably somewhat flawed and inaccurate rendering of some of the things we heard about in the past 24 hours ... distorted despite our best efforts to eliminate gross bias by the very process of compression that makes it possible for you ... to read it in about an hour. If we labelled the paper accurately then we would immediately add: But it's the best we could do under the circumstances, and we will be back tomorrow with a corrected updated version ..."

I first read that as a reporter in Washington in 1987 and it still strikes me as the best description of what a newspaper is. And is, even more so today. The greater the speed required of us in the digital world – and speed does matter, but never at the expense of accuracy or fairness or anything that would imperil trust – the more we should be honest about the tentative nature of what is possible.

Journalism becomes a never-ending organic business of placing material in the public domain, of adding to it, clarifying it, correcting it, adding something here, subtracting something there, editing, contextualising, analysing, responding. Everything we do will be more contestable, more open to challenge and alternative interpretation.

It throws up big questions about the nature of the record we thus create. There is no longer just a file of once-a-day papers accessible in bound volumes in public libraries, but a record that is simultaneously permanent and, potentially, permanently changing. How do you record and capture all those changes? When we publish something that's wrong is it better to mend it invisibly so that the mistake is removed from the permanent record, or is it more important to record or capture the fact of the untrue publication as well as the correction or clarification?

These are enormous conceptual shifts in what we do. They are difficult to work out, enormously difficult to manage and involving quite painful re-engineering of traditional workforces and re-allocation of resources.

The question is: how will big mainstream news organisations with a foot — sometimes awkwardly — in each camp cope with these issues? How will they negotiate the apparent contrast between the moated castle of the old world, where even a readers' editor or ombudsman seems a step too far, with the wide open spaces of the new world?

On the Guardian we've recently hired four moderators to help deal with the tidal wave of user-generated comment our Comment Is Free site now gets. We've hired a head of communities and user experience to help us devise strategies and implementation for developing user interaction on the site. Her job is also to sit between the editorial, technical and commercial wings of the operation to represent the "user" when we're making decisions about content or applications. And, of course, we still have a readers' editor. It's sometimes an awkward place to be, involving real-time mediation, examination and explanation. It's not to be confused with customer relations, yet in most news organisations, it's the best we offer. Increasingly, the readers' editor on the Guardian helps us think about what it is we do: she would be failing in her job if she weren't frequently ahead of us, if only because you can see things more clearly from a distance.

I don't think ombudsmen are a panacea to all the challenges this new digital age is throwing up. But — to return to my starting point — I think a refusal to have some kind of independent system embedded within news organisations, as we all come under more and more intense scrutiny, looks increasingly odd.

● Alan Rusbridger is the editor of the Guardian. This is an edited extract from a speech he gave to the Organisation of News Ombudsmen in 2007

Digital media

Digital media

Jeff Jarvis

Facebook founder Mark Zuckerberg

Never mind websites. Forget page views. They're so 2006. 2007 was the year of Facebook.

The social site, started in 2004 to organise college communities, was finally opened to the rest of us, and in the spring, it was discovered en masse by media wonks (like me), who forced acquaintances into joining, using the evangelistic fervor of recent cult converts. Then, in May, Facebook opened up to developers, who now were able to add applications to the service; already, they've built 5,000. And in October, Microsoft beat Google to invest in the company at a valuation of $15bn.

Worth it? I'd say yes. Facebook has 50 million active users (each worth $300, according to Microsoft's maths, v $500 a year for a newspaper reader, according to Deutsche Bank). They are joined by 200,000 more daily, all of whom spend an average of 20 minutes every day inside.

But far more valuable than that is the realisation of Facebook as a platform, on top of which we users organise our communities, and on top of which those developers are building venture-backed companies. The Facebook analytics firm Adanomics tracks the supposed value of these applications, pegging the most popular, Top Friends, with 20m installations, at $28m. My own teenaged son wrote a Courses app valued at $94,000. I hope he'll soon support me in my retirement.

Facebook is answering the question every company should be asking: What would Google do? Google built a platform that enables others to build businesses; now so has Facebook. Indeed, the 23-year-old Facebook founder Mark Zuckerberg's ambition is to build nothing less than the Google of people.

Yahoo would have been wise to have asked that question — WWGD? — years ago. Instead, it made itself into a classic, albeit digital, media company during six years under the leadership of its CEO Terry Semel, a former Hollywood studio boss. That strategy ran out of gas and in June, Yahoo fired Semel. Its co-founder Jerry Yang took over and is now hinting at his new strategy: Yahoo as a platform.

At the same time, Yahoo's traffic numbers have been falling, but that's not because of dwindling popularity. It's because Yahoo's pages, like those of many sites now, are built on newer technologies — Flash, Ajax — which embed more content and functionality into a single view, reducing the clicks a user makes. That is why the tracking service Nielsen decided this year to stop counting page views, which had been the universal measure of web popularity (but page views are now, remember, so 2006).

Measuring the web is being further complicated by the explosive (and perhaps faddish) growth last year of widgets: exportable modules of content and programming that are easy to add to a blog or MySpace page – YouTube videos, for example. Indeed, TV networks are counting on such open distribution. NBC and Fox announced a new service to air their shows online; CBS began executing an "audience-network" strategy to have viewers share shows; and the BBC and Sky released new players. Yet at the same time, Viacom was suing YouTube parent Google for enabling piracy. All this reveals only that the very architecture of media distribution on the web is still very much in development.

But the business model of internet media is becoming clearer.

Google, Yahoo, Microsoft, and AOL have been in a race in recent months to buy advertising technologies – DoubleClick, aQuantive, Right Media, Tacoda – and no wonder, as it is apparent that the web will be supported by little more than adverts and ego. In September, the New York Times ended its quixotic attempt to charge for content, TimesSelect, when it concluded that getting traffic and ads via Google search was a better business. This only fuelled speculation that once Rupert Murdoch took over the Wall Street Journal, he would shut its tollbooth. The Economist has jumped its pay wall. That would leave only FT.com trying to charge readers online as it does in print. So much for circulation revenue. All online is a freesheet.

So if advertising is the lifeblood of the internet – and thus the future of all media – who controls it? Who wins? Who else? Google. By one calculation, it now has 40% market share of online advertising and that share is growing faster than the industry itself.

So the constant calculation in media minds is whether Google is friend or enemy – as if there's really a choice. Belgian newspapers won a suit against GoogleNews to take down their headlines, but by May, they had relented and allowed their news to return to Google. In a little-heralded but still significant shift, Google that same month included current and archived headlines, videos, and photos in its reconstituted "universal search" results, giving new attention to media other than plain old web pages (which – need more proof? – are so 2006).

Online ad spend, at constant (2000) prices		
Year	Spend £m	Market share %
2006	1,834	10.6
2005	1,272	7.2
2004	784	4.5
2003	448	2.7
2002	192	1.2
2001	164	1
2000	153	0.9
1999	51	0.3
1998	20	0.1
1997	8	0.1

Source: WARC/ Advertising Association

Digital media

Google also became a publisher itself. In August, it licensed and now serves complete wire-service articles. This only worried the newspapers that used to get that traffic. And it's not as if newspapers don't have enough to worry about. While in the UK the national brands keep up their playground squabbling over who's biggest online, in the US, newspapers should be so lucky. Tribune Company is going private, Belo and Scripps are hiving off their underperforming newspaper divisions, and every month, the industry's finances get worse.

Where does Google go next? This year's rumour is that it will release a phone or mobile operating system, overshadowing the launch of Apple's everywhere-computer, the iPhone. Media will finally and truly go mobile. For a preview of that, look no farther than the June US launch of the iPhone, where fanatics queuing overnight broadcast the scene live from webcams and wireless laptops and published about it in new microblogging platforms: Twitter, Pownce, and status updates on, yes, Facebook.

There's Facebook again. But note the one player that emerges in all of 2007's developments: Google. This may have been Facebook's year. But so far, it is still Google's century.

● Jeff Jarvis is a Media Guardian columnist, and writes the BuzzMachine blog

2007 ... the year of the Apple iPhone

Awards

Webby

- *Best copy/writing:*   HowStuffWorks **www.howstuffworks.com**
- *Blog — business:*   DealBook **www.nytimes.com/dealbook**
- *Blog — culture/personal:*   we make money not art **www.we-make-money-not-art.com**
- *Blog — political:*   Truthdig **www.truthdig.com**
- *Community:*   Flickr **www.flickr.com**
- *Guides/ratings/reviews:*   Yelp **http://yelp.com**
- *Magazine:*   MediaStorm **http://mediastorm.org**
- *Movie and film:*   Pan's Labyrinth **www.panslabyrinth.com**
- *Music:*   Last.fm **www.last.fm**
- *News:*   BBC News **www.bbc.co.uk/news**
- *Newspaper:*   Guardian Unlimited **www.guardian.co.uk**
- *Politics:*   OpenSecrets **www.OpenSecrets.org**
- *Radio:*   BBC Radio 1 **www.bbc.co.uk/radio1**
- *Telecommunications:*   Black Label Series No.1 Chocolate Micro
  http://chocolate.lgmobile.com/uk/en/product/blacklabel.html
- *TV:*   Current TV **www.current.tv**

Bafta Games Awards 2007

- *Best game:*   Bioshock
- *Action and adventure:*   Crackdown
- *Strategy and simulation:*   Wii Sports
- *Multiplayer:*   Wii Sports
- *Sports:*   Wii Sports
- *Technical achievement:*   God of War 2
- *Artistic achievement:*   Okami

Journalism, we are constantly being told, is changing faster than ever before. The range of technological innovations now in our hands is growing all the time, as well as simultaneously getting cheaper. The result is that all sorts of tools are accessible to grunt journalists that were beyond their reach a few years ago.

These changes, wherever they appear, scare some and excite others. And no surprise: after all, as Charles Darwin said, "It is not the strongest of the species that survives, nor the most intelligent, but rather the one most responsive to change". That might sound like a clarion call or simply contentious, but without a shadow of a doubt this shift is radically altering the way some of us are working.

As a technology reporter at the Guardian, much of my day involves trawling the web for stories and leads, or talking to innovators, researchers and bloggers. I'm primarily employed to write for the Guardian's printed news pages, but unfettered access to fresh technologies has meant we are now involved in a number of new areas.

The web is now — and should be — an integral part of what journalists (in any medium) do. But while it might be at the centre of all this perceived change, it's been a core element of the journalist's repertoire for a long time. In fact, it is now such a fundamental part of the toolkit — for research, investigation, people-finding and so on — that it is difficult to imagine life without it.

But some other tools I use might not be so familiar. My RSS reader — like the wire services of the web — keeps track of thousands of websites for me. Elsewhere Twitter, a group text-messaging tool, lets me talk to readers and contacts very directly. Services such as Google Docs allow me to share information with sources, while the photo-sharing website Flickr lets us find interesting pictures from readers and experts.

These are all hugely popular online services, not crazy hi-tech backwaters — and even though some of them might seem cutting-edge, the truth is that they become mainstream very quickly.

If that sounds far-fetched, then you just have to look at the way websites such as Facebook have exploded to see how quickly something can turn from a niche service to a useful professional tool.

To supplement the closing gap between writing for the web and writing for print, we're increasingly using audio (including a weekly podcast that is listened to by thousands of people) and branching out into video where it is appropriate.

All of these projects have involved learning new skills — I can now operate a sound mixing desk, and do some basic video editing, for example — but it's not all about entirely new technology.

Most of us already carry a camera built into our mobile phone, and an increasing number of people tote a voice recorder or a video camera too (particularly in our spare time). Of course, nobody is suggesting that a snapped mobile picture will ever take the place of the professional photojournalist — but if you get the chance to record an event as it happens, any newshound who suggested otherwise would need putting down.

And those used to the nimble newspaper kitbag, consisting of little more than a pen and paper, needn't worry about lugging around a huge amount of gear — being flexible doesn't mean you'll be weighed down. We now carry small, broadcast-quality audio recorders that not only help us tape interviews for our own purposes, but also make them available for download directly from the website.

Regardless of how easy it is to collect this material, however, it's time-consuming to process it. Even if you're lightning-fast, editing audio takes substantially longer than text, and editing video takes longer still. But, just as reporters should know the essential mechanics of newsprint production, we'll all be expected to know the basics of multimedia working (even if we don't use them every day). That's why we now have a team of audio producers — who help put together the Guardian's weekly podcast shows and one-off downloads — and an expanding video crew, who do the hard work with cameras and editing footage.

It's conceivable that some media owners might try to make its workers do everything, but after a couple of experiments with working across all media simultaneously — including a massive conference in the US and a conveniently timed visit to South Korea during a nuclear crisis — it has become clear to me that producing audio and video alongside text for print and web deadlines is simply too time-consuming to be useful.

Solo journalism of this sort relies on meticulous planning and great support, and as such is best suited to special projects or one-off events.

Kevin Sites, the former CNN correspondent and Yahoo journalist, remains a fantastic example of what you can do in the field if you have the right experience and equipment — but even he gets help.

In fact, looking at the sort of work pioneered by Sites is a little like viewing a magic eye picture: stare too closely and you'll be bombarded by concerns that the future of journalism is a corpus of reporters who are jacks of all trades, but masters of none.

Actually, it turns out that the answer is already in front of us: the model is the exactly the same as the ones we already experience in the business — a reporter isn't usually expected to edit or lay out their own stories, but it's useful if they have the

Digital media

ability to pitch in where necessary.

This experimental attitude, and openness to learning, has meant there are a few crucial lessons I have learned already (even if I am not good enough to follow them myself).

Technically, try to take every opportunity you can, but be efficient and economic. For each minute you can save through judicious filming or recording, you're saving five minutes later on – get what you need and nothing more.

This is important because, while speed is incredibly important (and in our 24-hour news culture, we are addicted to the concept of "breaking news") quality is still what determines whether somebody trusts you and comes back for more. Resist the temptation to use the web as a dumping ground, because if you do it badly then somebody else will have a better version. Get something wrong, and you'll need to make it right. It's better to spend half an hour making sure you have things correct than to waste an extra day dealing with an avalanche of complaints.

That's not the same as only releasing perfect work, however: the web is a work in progress and so there is always the chance for revision and expansion. Be flexible.

Learn to think broadly about what you are doing, and who is looking at your work. Remember, despite your experience, you may not always be the best arbiter of the story. A good example of this would be when we ran an interview with a leading technologist: I'd written the best mainstream news story we could get, but we supported it by putting the full interview online. In fact, a subtle detail of the interview turned out to be of interest to a significant minority of readers – with the result that the Q&A proved more popular than the original story because it got picked up by a wide spread of niche publications.

It's hard to say what the tools of journalism will be in a decade, but given what we're learning now, the chances are that they'll be recognisable. From our current position, the pace of change might seem fast, but really this is just catch-up time for a news industry that only goes through one revolution in every generation.

Tom Coates, a technologist who has worked for the BBC and Yahoo, put it well when he described the panic inside many media businesses.

"My sense of these media organisations that use this argument of incredibly rapid technology change is that they're screaming that they're being pursued by a snail and yet they cannot get away," he wrote. "The problem being that the snail's been moving closer for the last 20 years and they just weren't paying attention."

It's an apposite description because, beyond all the jargon, the fact is that the basic bread and butter of journalism isn't actually changing: it's about getting to the facts and telling a good story.

We might be doing things that are new to us, but if that means you can do your job better – by making your work more accurate and more engaging – then it seems to me like there's very little to lose. Right now digital journalism might feel like an immense change, but for us, as for Darwin, change is what makes us better.

● Bobbie Johnson is technology correspondent at the Guardian

How I work | **Jemima Kiss**

While the news industry faces daily challenges in how it distributes and funds its content, journalists are also adapting their working practices to keep up with a new and very different information landscape.

Writing about the changes in the industry, the influence of new technologies and new practices, has made me more aware of and perhaps more inspired by these changes than most. More than any other news sector, the technology industry is dominated by small but very noisy expert blogs, from those who obsessively follow developments with Apple's mobile phone to former entrepreneurs and venture capitalists who report the minutiae of the start-up world.

In this arena, reports are based on well-informed hunches or carefully extracted leaks, just as they are often are in an old-school newsroom. Keeping up with all this means monitoring blogs and comments on story threads, in combination with news releases and news stories on mainstream sites.

A good chunk of my job involves monitoring and filtering an enormous amount of information. Fortunately there are some very clever tools that help me do this.

Traditional news wires are almost entirely redundant for my job; my day revolves around my RSS newsreader, which waves a flag at me every time a new story is published on any of the 70+ sources I follow. These sources range from the official BBC and BT press office feeds to the Wall Street Journal technology, the gadget blog Engadget and the indispensable aggregated feed Techmeme.

I bunch feeds together by subject and by priority, so when I do my main trawl of the day I prioritise the best, and only look through the more niche or quirky ones if I have time. The feeds don't display stories more than 48 hours old but still – if I'm behind on a bad day that can mean 1,300 headlines to skim through. The closest analogy is of standing on a hill furiously grabbing at the hundreds of dandelion seeds that are drifting past.

I use the bookmarking site Del.icio.us to list all the stories worthy of note. Del.icio.us lists the link, headline and a short description of each story on one page and will even automatically paste a day's links into a blog for me.

There'll be a further barrage of news releases and tips coming in through email, by phone from PRs and contacts, and sometimes tips through contacts on Twitter, the group messaging service, and social nets such as Facebook.

I'm constantly weighing up how much time I assign to each story according to its weight and its subject. Some will take most of the day to work into a news story, depending how long it takes to get extra information or pin down interviewees, and other stories worth noting I'll just summarise on the blog and link to the original source. Writing on the blog gives me more flexibility over a story; it's easier to write in a more chatty way to describe the atmosphere when you meet someone. Clearly that's not suitable for every subject, but trade coverage doesn't have to be dry.

Some stories are more juicy and bloggable because they involve a contentious subject; as our blogs editor, Kevin Anderson, once pointed out, a sensible rule of thumb for blogging is to aim to start a conversation or to reflect one. That's a different objective to that of a conventional news story, which is often more of a conclusion than a beginning.

It has taken mainstream news sites a long time to become comfortable with linking to other news sites. But the view of linking as helping out rivals is very outdated; users will go to another site anyway if they want to, and will appreciate you more if you help them find new information and aggregate the stories they want to find, wherever they might live. That becomes another reason for them to visit your site – and besides, including links on your site helps to improve your search engine ranking. Think of it as putting the web in world wide web.

It's a scary world, blogging. Fellow bloggers, and particularly commenters, can be ferocious. To blog properly, you have to put yourself out there – you have to blog as a personality and not as a faceless entity. Being seen as a real person reduces the troll count (slightly) – similarly the worst comments will come from people who have made sure their identity is disguised. But dealing with comments by nurturing discussion threads, answering questions and (dare I say it) openly correcting any mistakes is part of the job of blogging.

Seeding stories is another task for any blogger. Once you've put your stories out there, you need to do what you can to make them spread and grow. That means going to other sites and joining in relevant discussions on comment threads, planting the seeds of your site as you go. It's not an exact science and it can't be done methodically – it simply requires a near-obsessive fascination with the area you cover and the compulsion to have your fingers in as many relevant pies as possible. That invariably means skipping through your RSS feeds before breakfast, while you scatter crumbs into your keyboard at lunch and just one last check before bedtime.

Blogging is very far from being an easy option, but once you're inside the conversation it's the only place to be.

However, at the end of the day I always tuck the newspaper under my arm and do the crossword on the tube. That ritual's not changing any time soon.

● Jemima Kiss is a new media reporter at the Guardian

Top 10 sites by average monthly UK unique audience

	Name	Average monthly UK unique audience (m)		% change
		Oct 07–Nov 07	Oct 06–Nov 06	
1	Google	27.9	24.0	16%
2	MSN/Windows Live	21.8	20.8	5%
3	Microsoft	17.1	18.1	-5%
4	Yahoo!	16.7	16.4	2%
5	BBC	16.5	15.5	7%
6	eBay	14.9	14.7	1%
7	Amazon	12.6	10.5	20%
8	YouTube	10.4	5.7	81%
9	Apple	9.9	10.5	-6%
10	Wikipedia	9.5	6.7	41%

Source: Nielsen Online

I basically live with one foot in the internet, so there are some sites always open in my laptop browser. Gmail is my main email, as it's easy to sort, search through and archive. In fact, the usability of Google applications means I can use Google Docs to share documents, collaborative writing projects or things that I've started but want to pick up at a later date, knowing I can get at it from anywhere. I know one should never trust Wikipedia blindly, but it's a damn good place to start. IMDB too, if only because the question "Oooh, what's that bloke been in?" is never far from my lips, whatever's on the screen.

Through Flickr I store and share my pictures with friends, family and random others. Twitter is an addiction; posing the simple question "What are you doing?", and with 140 characters to reply, it's a lesson in brevity — I can fire off ideas or observations from text or instant messenger programmes to come back to later, but also keep up with a small group of friends who also use it. Tumblr goes back to the original meaning of weblog: it's a very quick and attractive way to keep a "log" of pictures, videos and links while wandering around the web. A mini multimedia blog, a scrapbook, if you like. Being on Facebook seems to be obligatory at the moment, though the larger it gets and the more people from different areas of my life congregate on there, the less I'm inclined to use it.

I love the way that internet writers interact with TV, in terms of instant reviews, intelligent conversation, live blogging and recaps. At the moment it's something US bloggers are better at than homegrown ones, unfortunately, but that will change. Television Without Pity and South Dakota Dark are great collaborative sites that generate a lot of good quality material every day, Televisionary is a one-man show, but impressively detailed and thorough, and Project Rungay provides an unofficial companion to one franchise with a strong editorial voice. Behind the Sofa is a pretty good example of this being done in the UK — although in that case the one show in collaborative discussion is Doctor Who, and it sometimes gets a little geeky, even for me.

Having had my own personal blog for a few years, I belong to a strong community of British personal and humorous blogs. I use Google Reader as my feed-reader to keep up with them all — again, the interface makes different blogs easy to sort into folders, search and archive. Favourites are far too many to name, but I tend to prefer strong, funny writers to themed or genre blogs. There's also a lot of room for experimentation under the safe cloak of anonymity and also for character-based blogging — Jonny Billericay's Private Secret Diary being a particularly brilliant example of the latter. Naked Blog and A Woman of Experience have strong personality-driven blogs, frequently updated, whereas No Kids Yet and Pandemian are infrequent but extremely talented writers, and always worth waiting for. For humour, Non-Working Monkey, Kitchentable and Smaller Than Life are three naturally funny people being witty in an observational way. Petite Anglaise is an engaging writer whose story of single-motherhood in Paris will soon be published in book form, while, closer to home, Diamond Geezer is a meticulously researched, lovingly crafted blog celebrating the writer's obsession with London. And of course, my own site is great. But I would say that. I'm a blogger.

● Anna Pickard is Guardian Unlimited's multimedia reporter

Top 10 current events & global news sites in the UK

	Name	Average monthly UK unique audience (m) Dec 06–Nov 07
1	BBC News	7.2
2	Yahoo! News	2.8
3	Guardian Unlimited	2.6
4	The Sun	1.9
5	Telegraph	1.8
6	Times Online	1.8
7	Google News	1.6
8	AOL News	1.4
9	Daily Mail	1.2
10	MSN News & Weather	1.0

Top 10 entertainment sites in the UK

	Name	Average monthly UK unique audience (m) Dec 06–Nov 07
1	BBC	16.1
2	Real Network	8.9
3	YouTube	8.3
4	iTunes	5.8
5	Sky	4.6
6	Lycos Europe Movie	3.2
7	The National Lottery	2.8
8	Channel 4	2.5
9	Gorilla Nation Media	2.4
10	eBay Sports	2.3

Top 10 sports sites in the UK

	Name	Average monthly UK unique audience (m) Dec 06–Nov 07
1	BBC Sport	4.9
2	eBay Sports	2.3
3	Sky Sports	1.8
4	Premium TV	1.6
5	Yahoo! Sports	0.9
6	ESPN	0.7
7	AOL Sports	0.7
8	WWE	0.5
9	premierleague.com	0.5
10	Mandm Direct	0.5

Top 10 mass merchandiser sites in the UK

	Name	Average monthly UK unique audience (m) Dec 06–Nov 07
1	Amazon	10.6
2	Tesco	5.2
3	eBay Stores	4.6
4	Argos	4.4
5	Play.com	2.8
6	John Lewis	1.7
7	Currys	1.6
8	ASDA	1.4
9	COMET	1.4
10	Woolworths UK	1.2

Source: Nielsen Online

Digital media contacts

In this section we provide details of some of the key companies involved in the digital sector, online publishers, digital media agencies and associations.

Main search engines/ portals

AltaVista
Overture Services, Inc. Pasadena, USA: 001 626 685 5601
www.altavista.co.uk

Ask
London: 020 7400 2222
infogeneral@ask.com
www.ask.com
Press: 020 7400 2222

Blinkx
London: 020 8906 6857
San Francisco, USA: 001 415 615 1514
info@blinkx.com
www.blinkx.com
Video search engine including audio, video, viral and TV content

Exalead
Scotland: 01698 404630
Paris: 00 33 155 352 621
contact@exalead.com
www.exalead.co.uk
Metasearch

Excite UK
Rome, Italy: 00 39 06 570231
bberger@staff.excite.it
www.excite.co.uk
Press: 00 39 06 5702 3208

Google UK
European HQ:
Dublin 04, Ireland
UK sales office:
London: 020 7031 3000
UK@google.com
www.google.co.uk
Press: 020 7031 3130

Hotbot
London: 020 7462 9200
Germany: 00 49 180 530 2037
ukcustomercare@ lycos-europe.com
www.hotbot.com
Metasearch

Icerocket
Dallas, USA: 001 214 658 7161
www.icerocket.com
Blog searcher

Kelkoo UK
sales@kelkoo.co.uk
www.kelkoo.co.uk
Shopping search engine owned by Yahoo!
Press: press@kelkoo.co.uk

Lycos UK
London: 020 7462 9200
www.lycos.co.uk
Press: ukpressoffice@ lycos-europe.com

ma.gnolia
San Francisco, USA: 001 415 364 0070
contact@ma.gnolia.com
http://ma.gnolia.com
Bookmark search engine

Mahalo
Santa Monica, USA: 001 310 593 6150
contact@mahalo.com
www.mahalo.com

MSN
London: 0870 601 0100
www.msn.co.uk
Press: 0870 207 7377
ukprteam@microsoft.com

Newsnow
London: 020 7471 0400
www.newsnow.co.uk
News feeds and internet press cuttings services

Plum
San Francisco, USA: 001 415 738 0724
info@plum.com
www.plum.com
Sharing and bookmarking service

Technorati
San Francisco, USA: 001 415 896 3000
partners@technorati.com
www.technorati.com
Blog searcher

Yahoo! UK
London: 020 7131 1000
www.yahoo.co.uk

Main software publishers

10Tacle Studios AG
Darmstadt, Germany: 00 49 6151 397 380
contact@10tacle.com
www.10tacle.com
Games production and development

2Simple Software Ltd
London: 020 8203 1781
info@2simple.com
www.2simple.com
Educational software provider for primary schools

Activision UK
Uxbridge: 020 3060 1000
Santa Monica, USA: 001 310 255 2000
www.activision.com
Games software

Adobe
Uxbridge: 020 8606 1100
www.adobe.co.uk
Design and publishing software

Advisory Unit:
Computers in Education
Hatfield: 01707 281102
www.advisory-unit.org.uk
Supplier of geographical and ICT products and training for schools

Apple Computer UK
Uxbridge: 020 8218 1000
www.apple.com/uk
Computer hardware/software
Press: appleuk.pr@euro.apple.com

Atari UK
London: 020 8222 9700
www.uk.atari.co.uk
Games

Autodesk Ltd
Farnborough: 01252 456600
www.autodesk.co.uk

AVG
0871 223 8902
sales@avgvirusfree.co.uk
www.avgvirusfree.co.uk
Anti-virus reseller

Azzurri Communications
Newbury: 01635 520360
info@azzu.co.uk
www.azzurricommunications.com
Telecoms and IT solutions

Birchfield Interactive Plc
Cardiff: 0800 915 6616
www.birchfield.co.uk
Producer of educational software

Boardworks Ltd
Oxford: 0870 350 5560
support@boardworks.co.uk
www.boardworks.co.uk
Educational resources for teachers using interactive whiteboards and projector

Cambridge-Hitachi
Cambridge: 01223 325013
info@cambridge-hitachi.com
www.cambridge-hitachi.com
Literacy and mathematics software for primary and secondary schools

Capita Children's Services
Bedford: 01234 838080
sales@capita-cs.co.uk
www.capita-cs.co.uk
Supplier of information management systems to schools and local authorities

CD Team
Oxfordshire: 01491 636373
info@cdteam.co.uk
www.cdteam.co.uk
Data storage, duplication and protection services

CentreSoft
Birmingham: 0121 625 3388
sales@centresoft.co.uk
www.centresoft.co.uk
Distributor of computer and video games in the UK

Channel4 Learning
Wetherby: 0870 124 6444
www.channel4learning.net
Content aimed at formal educational institutions and the home market

CNet Networks
London: 020 7903 6800
San Francisco, USA:
    001 415 344 2000
www.cnetnetworks.com

Codemasters
Southam: 01926 814132
www.codemasters.co.uk
Games
Press: press@codemasters.co.uk

Crick Software Ltd
Northampton: 01604 671691
info@cricksoft.com
www.cricksoft.com
Educational software

D3Publisher of Europe Ltd
info@d3p.co.uk
www.d3p.co.uk
Games development and publication

Denton Wilde Sapte
London: 020 7242 1212
info@dentonwildesapte.com
www.dentonwildesapte.com

Disney Interactive Studios formerly Buena Vista Games
London: 020 8222 1000
http://disney.go.com
    /disneyinteractivestudios
Games publisher

Don Johnston Special Needs Ltd
Warrington: 01925 256500
info@donjohnston.co.uk
www.donjohnston.co.uk
Professional services and materials for teachers of special needs pupils

Economatics Education Ltd
Sheffield: 0114 281 3311
education@economatics.co.uk
www.economatics-education.co.uk
Developer and supplier of equipment, software and teaching materials for the primary and secondary education sectors

EducationCity.com
Leicestershire: 0870 350 1860
info@educationcity.com
www.educationcity.com
Online teaching and learning resource

Eidos Interactive
Wimbledon: 020 8636 3000
plc@eidos.co.uk
www.eidos.co.uk
Games

Electronic Arts
Chertsey, Surrey
www.electronicarts.co.uk
Independent developer and publisher of interactive entertainment software
Press: 01932 450000

Empire Interactive Europe Ltd
London: 020 8343 7337
cssales@empire.co.uk
www.empireinteractive.com

Encyclopaedia Britannica (UK) Ltd
London: 020 7500 7800
enquiries@britannica.co.uk
www.britannica.co.uk
Learning and knowledge products

Fisher-Marriott Software
Woodbridge: 01394 387050
contact@fishermarriott.com
www.fishermarriott.com
Educational software developer

Focus Multimedia
Rugeley: 01889 570156
info@focusmm.co.uk
www.focusmm.co.uk
CD-ROMS, software and graphics

Free Radical Design
www.frd.co.uk
Video games developer

Future Publishing
Bath: 01225 442244
www.futurenet.co.uk
Produces special interest consumer magazines, websites and events

Granada Learning
London: 0845 602 1937
info@granada-learning.com
www.granada-learning.com
Educational multimedia company
Press:
www.granada-learning.com

Grid Learning Ltd
www.thegrid.org.uk
Online resources for Hertfordshire schools

Harcourt Education
Oxford: 01865 888000
enquiries@harcourt.co.uk
www.harcourt.co.uk
Publisher of books and e-learning materials for schools

IBM Lotus
Portsmouth: 023 9256 1000
www.lotus.co.uk, www.ibm.com
Office software

Imparo
Chichester: 01243 815820
info@imparo.com
www.imparo.com
Interactive educational products for home and classroom

Indigo Learning Ltd
St Ives: 01480 354335
paul@indigolearning.com
www.indigolearning.com
Software publisher

Intent Media
Hertford: 01992 535646
mcv@intentmedia.co.uk
www.intentmedia.co.uk
Producer of specialist trade magazines

Intuit
Twyford: 0845 606 2161
www.intuitshop.co.uk
Business and finance help

Just Flight Ltd
Huntingdon: 01480 377450
scott@justflight.com
www.justflight.com
Developer and publisher of flight and train simulation products for home PCs

Koei Ltd
Letchworth Garden City:
    01462 476130
www.koei.co.uk
Information service about latest games and release dates
Press: will@koei.co.uk

Konami Digital Entertainment GmbH
www.konami-europe.com
Digital entertainment products

Linux
Ogdensburg, NY 13669 USA:
    001 315 393 1202
www.linux.org.uk
Free operating system
Press: pr@linux.org

Logotron Ltd
Cambridge: 01223 425558
info@logo.com
www.logo.com
Publisher of creative and constructivist educational software for schools

LucasArts
www.lucasarts.com
Publisher and developer of interactive entertainment software

Macrovision UK
Maidenhead: 0870 871 1111
info@macrovision.co.uk
www.macrovision.com
Provider of content protection, digital rights management, and software licensing solutions

Majesco Europe Ltd
Edison, USA: 001 732 225 8910
www.majescoentertainment.com
Provider of digital entertainment content and products

Manches LLP
London: 020 7404 4433
manches@manches.com
www.manches.com
Media legal advice

Mercury Games Ltd
London: 020 7833 3524
jayne.curtis@mercurygames.com
www.mercurygames.com
Computer and video game publisher

Microsoft UK
Reading: 0870 601 0100
www.microsoft.com/uk
Software house
Press: 0870 207 7377
ukprteam@microsoft.com

McAfee UK
Slough: 01753 217500
www.mcafee.com
Anti-virus

Midas Interactive Entertainment Ltd
www.midasinteractive.com
Provider of digital entertainment content and products

Midway Games Ltd
London: 020 7382 7720
Chicago, USA: 001 773 961 2222
www.midway.com
Developer and publisher of interactive entertainment software

Namco Bandai Games Europe SAS
London: 020 7484 3350
nbge_info@
  namcobandaigames.co.uk
www.namco.co.uk
Japanese video games developer

Nimbus Manufacturing
Gwent: 01633 465175
pedwards@nimbuscd.com
www.nimbuscd.com

Nintendo UK Ltd
www.nintendo-europe.com
Press:
prenquiries@nintendo.co.uk

Oxygen Software
Moscow, Russia:
  0117 495 102 9278
support@oxygensoftware.com
www.oxygensoftware.com
Software developer

RealNetworks
London: 020 7618 4000
www.real.co.uk
Audio and video
Press: real@axicom.com

REM (Rickitt Educational Media) Ltd
Langport: 01458 254700
info@r-e-m.co.uk
www.r-e-m.co.uk
Web site provides a single source for educational software

Resource Education
Derby: 0870 777 0247
ws4@resourcekt.co.uk
www.resourcekt.co.uk
Educational software

RM plc
Abingdon: 0845 070 0300
www.rm.com
Provides ICT software, infrastructure and services

Roxio Incorporated
0844 448 5500
www.roxio.co.uk
Provider of consumer digital media creation applications

Saitek Plc
Bristol: 01454 451900
info@saitek.com
www.saitek.com
Designer and manufacturer of consumer electronic products for multimedia gaming

Sci/Eidos Ltd
London: 020 8636 3000
www.eidosinteractive.co.uk
Developer and publisher of entertainment software

Sega Europe Ltd
Brentford: 020 8995 3399
www.sega-europe.com

Serco Learning Solutions
Derby: 0845 688 8400
enquiries@sercolearning.com
www.sercolearningsolutions.com
Provides schools with effective solutions to management and learning needs

Sherston Publishing Group
Wiltshire: 01666 843200
sales@sherston.co.uk
www.sherston.com
Educational software for primary schools

Sibelius Software Ltd
London: 0800 458 3111
infoUK@sibelius.com
www.sibelius.com
Software for writing, teaching and publishing music

Soft Teach Educational
Wiltshire: 01985 840329
tony@soft-teach.co.uk
www.soft-teach.co.uk
Publisher and distributor of educational software for primary schools

Softease
Derbyshire: 01335 343421
sales@softease.com
www.softease.com
Educational software developer of applications for use in schools across the curriculum

Sony Computer Entertainment Europe
www.scee.com
Sales, marketing, distribution and software development for PlayStation®

Sony DADC
Salzburg, Austria:
  00 43 624 688 0555
www.sonydadc.com
Solution and technology provider for the entertainment, education and information industries

Sony Online Europe (SOE Europe Ltd)
0870 511 1999
www.sony.co.uk
Press: press@eu.sony.com

Sparrowhawk & Heald Ltd
St Ives: 01480 354340
nick@sparrowhawkandheald.co.uk
www.sparrowhawkandheald.co.uk
Educational multimedia consultancy specialising in digital content

The Stationery Office Ltd
Norwich: 01603 622211
customer.services@tso.co.uk
www.tso.co.uk
Managed print and publishing services for public and private sector clients

Symantec UK
Reading: 0870 243 1080
www.symantec.co.uk
Information security provider
Press: 0118 943 6846

TAG Learning Ltd
Kent: 01474 357350
sales@taglearning.com
www.taglearning.com
Supplier and developer of ICT software and tools for home and school education

Take 2 Interactive Software
Windsor: 01753 496600
www.take2games.co.uk
Publisher, developer and distributor of interactive entertainment software, hardware and accessories

Tecmo
Torrance, USA: 001 310 944 5005
info@tecmoinc.com
www.tecmogames.com

THQ International Ltd
Cobham: 0870 608 0047
eursupport@thq.com.
www.thq-games.com
Developer and publisher of interactive entertainment software

Ubisoft Entertainment Ltd
Surrey: 01932 578000
www.ubi.com

Vivendi Universal Interactive Publishing UK Ltd
Reading: 0871 075 2621
www.sierra.com
Global developer, publisher and distributor of multi-platform interactive entertainment

Warner Home Video
ukcustomer.enquiries@
  warnerbros.com
www.warnerbros.co.uk

White Space (Wordshark) Ltd
London: 020 8748 5927
tigg@wordshark.co.uk
www.numbershark.co.uk
Computer programs to help with basic literacy and numeracy

Widgit Software
Cambridge: 01223 425558
info@widgit.com
www.widgit.com
Educational software focusing on improving communication and literacy

contacts **Digital media**

Technical and design firms

Abacus e-media
London: 020 7297 5200
info@abacusemedia.com
www.abacusemedia.com
A leading online developer

Automattic
San Francisco, USA:
001 832 875 4078
m@mullenweg.com
http://automattic.com

BlueBridge Technologies Group
tothetop@bbridgetech.com
www.bbridgetech.com
Photo sharing site

Fortune Cookie Ltd
London: 0870 736 1000
hello@fortunecookie.co.uk
www.fortunecookie.co.uk
Website designer

Fresh Media Group
London: 020 7078 8430
info@freshmediagroup.com
www.freshmediagroup.com

ICO Solutions
Cheltenham: 0800 019 9860
info@icosolutions.com
www.icosolutions.com
Professional web services

Madgex
Brighton: 01273 775100
info@madgex.com
www.madgex.com
Provider of job boards, CMS and social networking systems

Monomo Ltd
London: 020 7033 0268
intouch@monomo.com
www.monomo.co.uk
Creative design consultancy

On-Idle
London: 020 8980 8960
info@on-idle.com
www.on-idle.com
Graphic design, interface design, content management systems, websites, interactive tools and corporate branding solutions

Savvis
Berkshire: 0118 322 6000
emea-sales@savvis.net
www.savvis.net
Digital content management, hosting, network and security service

Segala
Surrey: 01483 572866
Dublin: 00 353 1 293 1966
info@segala.com
www.segala.com
Specialist in web accessibility and mobile web standards compliance

Skinkers
London: 020 7579 8350
enquiries@skinkers.com
www.skinkers.com
Information broadcast technology

Yospace
Staines: 01784 466388
feedback@yospace.com
www.yospace.com
Provider of user-generated video gallery for mobile handsets

Main ISPs

Alcatel Telecom UK
Paris, France: 00 33 1 4075 1010
www.alcatel-lucent.com
Communication technologies and related services

Allcomm
Wolverhampton: 0845 850 6106
www.allcomm.co.uk
Communications agency

Andrews & Arnold
Bracknell: 0333 340 0000
http://aaisp.net.uk

AOL UK
London: 020 7348 8000
www.aol.co.uk
Press: ukmediaoffice@aol.com

Be Unlimited
www.bethere.co.uk
Internet service

Boltblue
help@boltblue.com
www.boltblue.com
Mobile internet portal

Brightview
London: 0870 160 0079
www.brightview.com

British Telecom
London: 020 7356 5000
www.bt.com
Press: 020 7356 5000

Bulldog Broadband
0800 404 8151
www.bulldogbroadband.com
Broadband provider

Bytel Ltd
Belfast: 028 9045 6111
info@bytel.net.uk
www.bytel.net.uk
Internet and network service provider

C2 Internet
Nantwich: 0845 658 0020
info@c2internet.net
www.c2internet.net
Business internet service provider

Cable & Wireless UK
London: 020 7315 4000
www.cw.com
International communications company

Cisco Systems
San Jose, USA: 001 408 526 4000
www.cisco.com
Hardware, software, and service offerings to create internet solutions that make networks possible

Claranet UK
London: 020 7685 8310
info@clara.net
www.clara.net
Press: 020 7685 8019

Community Internet
Kidlington, Oxfordshire:
01865 856170
info@ci-net.com
www.ci-net.com
Broadband provider

DataComms Europe
Croydon: 020 7101 0223
sales@dcomms.co.uk
www.dcomms.co.uk
Broadband services

Datanet
Hampshire: 0845 130 6010
Info@datanet.co.uk
www.datanet.co.uk
Internet protocol solutions provider

Demon
London: 0800 027 5848
netsales@demon.net
www.demon.net

Easynet
London: 020 7900 4444
enquiries.uk@uk.easynet.net
www.easynet.net
Press: 0870 770 4767

Eclipse Internet
Hull: 01392 333334
www.eclipse.net.uk
Broadband provider

EFH Broadband
www.efhbroadband.com
Broadband provider

Elite UK Serve
Portsmouth: 0870 741 5898
sales@eliteukserve.net
www.eliteserve.net

Entanet
Telford: 0870 770 9588
www.enta.net
Press: 0870 770 9635

Exa Networks
Bingley: 0845 145 1234
info@exa-networks.co.uk
www.exa-networks.co.uk

Freedom 2 Surf
Stoke Mandeville: 0870 242 3758
www.freedom2surf.net
Press: press@freedom2surf.net

Global Internet
London: 0844 395 0603
www.globalnet.co.uk

Griffin Internet
Derby: 0870 804 0804
john.dawson@griffin.com
www.griffin.com
IT services company

HomeChoice
Stevenage: 0845 678 3333
enquiries@homechoice.co.uk
www.homechoice.co.uk

Hotchilli Internet
London: 0870 255 5555
www.hotchilli.com
Internet provider and telecom services

Houxou.com
Hertfordshire: 0870 742 5398
support@houxou.com
www.houxou.com

IDnet
Letchworth: 01462 476555
contactus@idnet.net
www.idnet.net

Internet Central
Stoke-on-Trent: 01782 667788
www.internet-central.net

Internet for Business
Aberdeen: 0800 027 0110/
01224 333300
info@ifb.net
www.ifb.net
Independent internet service provider

Inweb Networks
Surrey: 01784 494400
info@inweb.co.uk
www.inweb.co.uk
Data and telecommunications provider

Karoo
Hull: 01482 602444
www.karoo.co.uk

KeConnect Internet
Ipswich: 0845 050 6050
sales@keconnect.co.uk
www.keconnect.co.uk

Kingston Communications
Hull: 01482 602711
corporate.communications@
kcom.com
www.kcom.com
Communication solutions

London Web
London: 020 8349 4500
contactus@londonweb.net
www.londonweb.net
Communications agency

Lumison
Edinburgh: 0845 119 9900
www.lumison.net

Madasafish/Freenetname
London: 0844 395 0830
care@madasafish.com
www.madasafish.com

Merula Limited
St Neots: 01480 222940
www.merula.net

Mistral Internet
Hull: 0870 493 6300
info@mistral.net
www.mistral.net
Service-based communications company
Press: marketing@mistral.net

Namesco (NDO)
Worcester: 0845 363 3630
www.names.co.uk

Netservices Plc
Manchester: 0870 753 0900
info@netservicesplc.com
www.netservicesplc.com
Integrated networking, voice and converged solutions

NewNet
Fareham,: 01329 226722
info@newnet.co.uk
www.newnet.co.uk
Telecommunications services

Nildram
Stoke Mandeville: 0870 160 8600
info@nildram.net
www.nildram.net
Press: 01629 826942

Onyx Internet
Middlesborough: 0845 771 5715
www.onyx-group.net

One.Tel
London: 0845 818 8000
www.onetel.co.uk

Orange Broadband
London: 0870 373 5605
www.orange.co.uk
Press: 0870 373 5517

Pipex
Welwyn Garden City:
0845 077 2537
www.pipex.co.uk

PlusNet Technologies
Sheffield: 0845 140 0200
www.plus.net.uk

Powernet
Milton Keynes: 01908 605188
info@powernet.co.uk
www.powernet.co.uk
Internet service and solutions provider

Prodigy Networks
enquiries@prodigynet.co.uk
www.prodigynet.co.uk
Telecommunications and internet provider

SAQ Net
Hayling Island: 0870 737 7700
enquiries@saqnet.co.uk
www.saq.co.uk

Scotland Online
Dundee: 01382 429000
reception@scotlandonline.co.uk
www.scotlandonline.co.uk

Scotnet
Inverness: 0845 270 0010
sales@scotnet.co.uk
www.scotnet.co.uk

Sky Broadband
0870 551 5515
www.sky.com

Skymarket
Surrey: 0800 321 7788
sales@ skymarket.co.uk
www.skymarket.co.uk

Star
0800 138 4443
www.star.net.uk
Business internet service provider

Supanet
Burnley: 01282 681111
sales@internexusgroup.co.uk
www.supanet.com

Surfanytime
Hamilton: 0870 141 7113
www.surfanytime.co.uk

Talk-101
Warrington: 0845 310 1010
www.talkinternet.co.uk

TalkTalk Broadband
London: 020 8896 5000
www.talktalk.co.uk
Press: pressoffice@cpw.co.uk

Telecomplete
Manchester: 0845 456 1116
enquiries@telecomplete.co.uk
www.telecomplete.co.uk

Tesco Telecoms
www.tesco.com/telecoms

Timewarp
Speke, Merseyside: 0870 838 0700
info@timewarp.co.uk
www.timewarp.co.uk
Broadband provider for business

Tiscali UK
London: 020 7087 2000
www.tiscali.co.uk

Topletter
Ipswich: 0870 235 1271
www.topletter.com
Press: marketing@topletter.com

Total Web Solutions
Stockport: 0870 787 9888
www.totalwebsolutions.com
Broadband for business

Twang.net
Newbury: 01635 239000
info@twang.net
www.twang.net
Business communications provider

UK Online
0800 053 2222
www.ukonline.net
Press: linda.harris@ukonline.net

UKFast.net
Manchester: 0845 458 4545
www.ukfast.net

UTV Internet
Belfast: 0845 247 0000
www.utvinternet.com

Verizon/MCI
www.mci.com
Communication and technology agency

Virgin Media
London: 01256 752000
www.virginmedia.com
Press: 01256 752670

Vispa Internet
Altrincham: 0870 1624 888
info@vispa.net
www.vispa.co.uk

Vodafone
Newbury: 0700 050 0100
www.vodafone.co.uk

Waitrose.com
0800 013 2282
custserve@waitrose.com
www.waitrose.com
/internetaccessfromwaitrose

Wanadoo/Freeserve
London: 0870 376 8888
www.orange.co.uk
Communications service company

Yahoo! UK
London: 020 7808 4000
agency@uk.yahoo-inc.com
www.yahoo.co.uk

Zen Internet
www.zen.co.uk
Press: 0845 058 9002
pr@zen.co.uk

Main telecom companies

3
Maidenhead: 0845 603 8333
www.three.co.uk

British Telecom
London: 020 7356 5000
www.bt.com
Press: 020 7356 5000

Cable and Wireless
London: 020 7315 4000
www.cw.com

Colt Communications
London: 020 7390 3900
info@colt.net
www.colt.net/uk/en

Coms
London: 020 7148 3000
info@coms.com
www.coms.com
Press: techteam@midnight.co.uk

Hutchison 3G UK
London: 0870 733 0333
www.three.co.uk
Press: 0845 603 8333

Kingston Communications
Kingston upon Hull:
01482 602000
www.kcom.com
Press: 01482 602711

O2
Slough: 0113 272 2000
www.o2.com
Press: 01753 628402

Orange
London: 0870 373 1500
www.orange.co.uk
Press: 020 7984 2000

Talk Talk
London: 0870 444 1820
pressoffice@cpw.co.uk
www.talktalk.co.uk

Thus
Glasgow: 0800 027 5848
www.thus.net

T-Mobile (UK)
Hatfield: 01707 315000
www.t-mobile.co.uk
Press: 07017 150150

Verizon Business
Reading: 0118 905 5000
pressoffice_uk@lists.mci.com
www.verizonbusiness.com
Press: ukpressoffice@
verizonbusiness.com

Virgin Media
London: 01256 752000
www.virginmedia.com
Press: 01256 752670

Virgin Mobile
www.virginmobile.com

Vodafone
Newbury: 0700 050 0100
www.vodafone.co.uk
Press: 0845 444 4466/
01635 673939

News online

BBC News.co.uk
London: 020 8743 8000
www.bbc.co.uk

Belfast Telegraph
Belfast: 028 9026 4000
www.belfasttelegraph.co.uk

FT.com
London: 020 7873 3000
joanna.manning-cooper@ft.com
www.ft.com
Press: 020 7873 4447

Guardian Unlimited
London: 020 7278 2332
editor@guardianunlimited.co.uk
www.guardian.co.uk
Press: 020 7239 9818

The Independent
London: 020 7005 2000
www.independent.co.uk

ITV News
editor@itn.co.uk
www.itv.com/news

NewsTrust
www.newstrust.net

Online Mirror
London: 020 7293 3000
mirrornews@mgn.co.uk
www.mirror.co.uk
Press: 020 7293 3222

Orange
Leeds: 0113 367 4600
simon.glover@orange.co.uk
www.orange.co.uk

Reuters
London: 020 7250 1122
www.uk.reuters.com
Press: 020 7542 7457

The Scotsman
Edinburgh: 0131 620 8620
enquiries@scotsman.com
www.scotsman.com
Press: 0131 620 8507

Sky News
Isleworth: 0870 240 3000
www.sky.com/skynews

The Sun Online
London: 020 7782 4000
corporate.info@the-sun.co.uk
www.thesun.co.uk

Telegraph Online
London: 020 7538 3235
corporateaffairs@telegraph.co.uk
www.telegraph.co.uk

The Times
London: 020 7782 5000
online.editor@thetimes.co.uk
www.timesonline.co.uk

The Wall Street Journal
New York, USA: 001 212 416 2000
www.wsj.com

News blogsites and community reporting

Buzzfeed
info@buzzfeed.com
http://buzzfeed.com
The hottest buzz on the web

Epolitix
London: 020 7091 7630
info@epolitix.com
www.epolitix.com
UK politics news website

Eurek Alert!
Washington, DC, USA:
001 202 326 6716
webmaster@eurekalert.org
www.eurekalert.org
Science news

Huffington Post
info@huffingtonpost.com
www.huffingtonpost.com
News and opinion website

Newsvine
www.newsvine.com
News online

Now Public
contact@nowpublic.com
www.nowpublic.com
Participatory news service

Politics.co.uk
www.politics.co.uk
Politics news website

Sphere
www.sphere.com
News blog site

Spot-On
San Francisco, USA:
001 415 771 7133
Editor@spot-on.com
www.spot-on.com
News online

Digital media

Online publishers

CNET Networks
London: 020 7903 6800
San Francisco, USA:
  001 415 344 2000
ukmarketing@cnet.com
www.cnetnetworks.com
Interactive media company
Press: publicrelations@cnet.com

CTO Media
London: 07974 581357
online@camden.tv
www.camden.tv
*Londons first web-based community
television station*

Dazeddigital.com
London: 020 7336 0766
dazed@dazedgroup.com
www.dazeddigital.com
*Extended features from Dazed &
Confused magazine with an online
community for rising talent*
Press: johanna@dazedgroup.com

Future Publishing
Bath: 01225 442244
UK media relations manager:
  wguyatt@futurenet.co.uk
Communications executive:
  lymayew@futurenet.co.uk
www.futureplc.com
Magazine publisher

Gawker Media
choire@gawker.com
www.gawker.com
Parent company of several blogs

Handbag.com
editor@handbag.com
www.handbag.com
Women's consumer site

Magicalia Digital
01689 899200
feedback@magicalia.com
www.magicalia.com
Media publishing group

Motley Fool UK
London: 020 7297 8181
ukwebfool@fool.co.uk
www.fool.co.uk
Personal finance

MyVillage
London: 020 7792 0624
info@myvillage.co.uk
www.myvillage.co.uk
Leisure guide

Petite Personal Shopper
Aberystwyth: 07779 084573
yasmin@petitepersonalshopper.com
www.petitepersonalshopper.com
*Fashion magazine website aimed at the
petite market*

Popbitch
hello@popbitch.com
www.popbitch.com
Celeb gossip email and forum

Rapnews.co.uk
editorial@rapnews.co.uk
www.rapnews.co.uk
*The leading online resource for hiphop
culture and rap music*

Redactive Media Group
London: 020 7880 6200
info@redactive.co.uk
www.redactive.co.uk
Magazine publisher

Salon.com
San Francisco, USA:
  001 415 645 9200
www.salon.com
US online magazine

Shinymedia.com
0845 052 3405
info@shinymedia.com
www.shinymedia.com
Commercial blog publisher

Six Apart
San Francisco, USA:
  001 415 344 0056
jane@sixapart.com
www.sixapart.com
Web communication

Slate
New York, USA: 001 212 445 5330
www.slate.com
US online magazine
Press: press@slate.com

Teamtalk Media
www.teamtalk.com
Football news

Upmystreet.com
London: 020 7802 2992
content@upmystreet.com
www.upmystreet.com
Local information
Press: pr@upmystreet.com

Vice Magazine
London: 020 7749 7828
aaron@viceuk.com
www.viceland.com
*Online publisher: culture, news,
fashion, music, humour*

Wikipedia
St Petersburg, USA:
  001 727 231 0101
Press@wikimedia.org
www.wikipedia.org
User-edited encyclopaedia
Press: 001 727 231 0101

YourKindaTV.com
London: 020 7096 0802
contact@yourkindatv.com
www.yourkindatv.com
*Online news and views which combines
user submitted content with
professionally produced content.*
Press: 020 7612 1155

New media agencies

3T Productions
0161 492 1400
queries@3t.co.uk
www.3t.co.uk

Agency.com
020 7964 8200
info.london@agency.com
www.agency.com

Agency Republic
020 7942 0000
chat@agencyrepublic.com
www.agencyrepublic.com/home.asp

AKQA
020 7780 4786
info@akqa.com
www.akqa.com

Altogether Digital
London: 020 7689 1200
Edinburgh: 0131 243 2553
hello@dcinteract.com
www.dcinteract.com

Amaze
0870 240 1700
generalenquiries@amaze.com
www.amaze.com

APCO Online
London: 020 7526 3600
Washington, D.C. USA:
  001 202 778 100
london@worldwide.com
information@apcoworldwide.com
www.apcoworldwide.com
Communication consultancy

Arc Worldwide
020 7751 1662
jim.mullen@arcww.com
www.arcww.com
Digital marketing solutions

Avenue A-Razorfish
020 7907 4545
info@avenuea-razorfish.com
www.avenuea-razorfish.com

Babel Media
01273 764100
info@babelmedia.com
www.babelmedia.com

Bentley Designs Ltd (bd2)
01942 234900
enquiries@bd2.co.uk
www.bd2.co.uk
*Design, marketing and development
professionals*

Big Picture Advertising
020 7240 6582
simon@bigpictureadvertising.co.uk
www.bigpictureadvertising.co.uk

Bostock and Pollitt
020 7379 6709
info@bostockandpollitt.com
www.bostockandpollitt.com

Brand Republic
020 8267 5000
brand.republic@haymarket.com.
www.brandrepublic.com
*News site covering online advertising,
marketing, media and PR sectors*

buzzobjects
07906 292373
info@buzzobjects.com
www.buzzobjects.com

Carlson Digital
020 8875 0875
www.carlsonmarketing.co.uk

Cimex Media Ltd
020 7324 7780
info@cimex.com
www.cimex.com
Consultancy through to digital design,
technical and content services

Clock Ltd
01923 261166
info@clock.co.uk
www.clock.co.uk
Online marketing

CMW Interactive
020 7224 4050
david.smith@cmwinteractive.com
www.cmwinteractive.com

Codegent Ltd
020 7720 4040
info@codegent.com
www.codegent.com
Digital communications and online
marketing

Complete
020 7383 5300
general@complete.co.uk
www.complete.co.uk

Conchango
01784 222222
talktous@conchango.com
www.conchango.com

Craik Jones Digital
020 7734 1650
digital@craikjones.co.uk
www.digital.craikjones.co.uk

cScape
020 7689 8800
m.daniels@cscape.com
www.cscape.com

Custom Communication
07949 830256
info@customcommunication.co.uk
www.customcommunication.co.uk
Online contract publishing/social
media strategies

Dare Digital
020 7299 3000
us@daredigital.com
www.daredigital.com

Deal Group Media
020 7691 1880
www.dgm-uk.com

De-Construct
020 7684 8444
info@de-construct.com
www.de-construct.com

Detica
01483 442000
info@detica.com
www.detica.com

Digit
020 7377 4000
info@digitlondon.com
www.digitlondon.com

Digital TMW
020 7349 4000
info@tmw.co.uk
www.tmw.co.uk

Digitas
020 7874 9400
info@digitas.com
www.digitas.com

DoubleClick
New York, USA: 001 212 271 2542
www.doubleclick.com
Digital media agency
Press:
publicrelations@doubleclick.net

Draft London
020 3048 0000
john.minnec@draftlondon.com
www.draftlondon.com

DVA
01256 882032
info@dva.co.uk
www.dva.co.uk

E3 Media
0117 902 1333
info@e3media.co.uk
www.e3media.co.uk

EHS Brann
020 7017 1000
firstname.lastname@ehs.co.uk
www.ehs.co.uk

Euro RSCG Interaction UK
020 7240 4111
info-interaction@eurorscg.com
www.eurorscginteraction.co.uk

Flare Creative
020 8334 2190
contactme@flarecreative.com
www.flarecreative.com
Digital agency

Freestyle New Media Group
01926 652832
info@fsnm.co.uk
www.fsnm.co.uk

Gizmodo
http://uk.gizmodo.com/
An online review dedicated to gadgets,
gizmos, and cutting-edge consumer
electronics

Global Beach
020 7384 1188
info@globalbeach.com
www.globalbeach.com

Glue London
020 7739 2345
www.gluelondon.com

Good Technology
020 7343 3700
firstname.surname@wearegt.com
www.wearegt.com

Grand Union
020 7908 0700
info@thegrandunion.com
www.thegrandunion.com
Digital agency

Green Cathedral
01223 266400
info@greencathedral.com
www.greencathedral.com
Integrated digital marketing agency

Greenlight
020 7253 7000
rfi@greenlight.co.uk
www.greenlight.co.uk
Search engine marketing company

GT Network
020 7299 7000
info@gtnetwork.com
www.gtnetwork.com

Gurus
023 8023 1219
info@gurumedia.net
www.gurumedia.net

Haygarth Direct
020 8971 3300
stephen.m@haygarth.co.uk
www.haygarth.co.uk

The Hub Communications
020 3008 6260
www.thehub.co.uk

Interesource New Media
020 7613 8200
www.interesource.com

Ioko365
01904 438000
info@ioko.com
www.ioko.com

IR Group
020 7436 3140
mark.hill@the-group.net
www.the-group.net

IS Solutions
01932 893333
www.issolutions.co.uk

iTouch
020 7613 6000
info@itouch.co.uk
www.itouch.co.uk

Lateral
020 7613 4449
www.lateral.net

Latitude Group Ltd
01925 413513
office@latitudegroup.com
www. latitudegroupcom

Lawton eMarketing
023 8082 8522
steve.sponder@lawton.co.uk
www.lawtonemarketing.com

LBI International
020 7446 7500
info.uk@lbi.com
www.lbicon.com/en
Europe-wide digital media agency
incorporating LBIcon, Wheel, Lost
Boys, MetDesign, Starring, Escador,
FramFab and Aspect. Amsterdam/
Stockholm HQ

Lightmaker Group
Tunbridge Wells: 01892 615015
Manchester: 0161 834 9889
sales@lightmaker.com
www.lightmaker.com
matt.farrar@lightmaker.com

Louter Productions
0121 443 2835/07916 152215
fabrice.millet@
    louterproductions.com
www.louterproductions.com
*Audio visual solutions for the
charitable/art sector*

Madgex
01273 775100
info@madgex.com
www.madgex.com
*Works with B2B publishers to develop
their online titles, drive web traffic and
increase revenue*

Magic Lantern Productions
020 7738 9911
info@magiclantern.co.uk
www.magiclantern.co.uk
Digital consultancy agency

McCann-i
01625 822200
info@mccann-i.com
www.mccann-i.com

M-Corp
01425 477766
enquiries@m-corp.com
www.m-corp.com

MediaVest IP
020 7190 8000
firstname.lastname@
    smvgroup.com
www.mediavest.co.uk

Metia
020 7959 5400
info@metia.com
www.metia.com

MitchellConnerSearson Group
020 7420 7991
london@choosemcs.co.uk
www.mitchellconnersearson.com

Netstore
0870 300 6400
www.netstore.co.uk

New Media Age
020 7970 4848
www.nma.co.uk
*Site covers the business of interactive
media: the internet, wireless internet
and interactive TV*

Ogilvy Interactive
020 7345 3000
www.ogilvy.com

Poulters
0113 383 4200
enquiries@poulters.com
www.poulters.com

Profero
020 7387 2000
contact@profero.com
www.profero.com

Proximity London
020 7298 1000
info@proximitylondon.com
www.proximitylondon.com

Rathergood
07796 487538
joel@rathergood.com
www.rathergood.com
Animations, songs, commercials

Reading Room
020 7025 1800
info@readingroom.com
www.readingroom.com

Realise
020 7743 7150
www.realise.com

Recreate Solutions
020 8233 2916
contactus@recreatesolutions.com
www.recreatesolutions.com

Redbee Media
020 8008 0080
www.redbeemedia.com

Redskin
020 7636 8262
info@redskinmarketing.com
www.redskinmarketing.com

The Register
020 7153 4480
enquiries@theregister.co.uk
www.theregister.co.uk
Technology news online

Rufus Leonard
020 7404 4490
enquiries@rufusleonard.com
www.rufusleonard.com

Sapient
020 7786 4500
eu_sales@sapient.com
www.sapient.co.uk

Sift Group
0117 915 9600
service@sift.co.uk
www.sift.co.uk

Souk Digital
020 7420 7880
firstname.surname@
    soukcomms.com
www.soukcomms.co.uk

Spinnaker
0844 477 9448
www.up-spinnaker.co.uk
*Business-focused websites, digital
marketing campaigns and direct online
sales*

Syzygy UK
020 3206 4000
london@syzygy.net
www.syzygy.net

Tangozebra
020 7183 9300
info@tangozebra.com
www.tangozebra.com

TBG
020 7428 6650
info@tbglondon.com
www.tbglondon.com
*Full service digital marketing agency
that provides creative, strategy, media
planning and technology services*

TBWA\GGT
020 7440 1100
info@tequila-uk.com
www.tequila-uk.com

TechCrunch
www.techcrunch.com
*A weblog dedicated to profiling and
reviewing new internet products and
companies*

Them
020 8392 6868
talktous@themlondon.com
www.themlondon.com

Tribal DDB
020 7258 4500
www.tribalddb.com

TVF Medical Communications
020 7837 3000
firstname.lastname@tvf.co.uk
www.tvfcommunications.com

twentysix London
020 7535 9800
info@twentysixlondon.com
www.twentysixlondon.com

urbandevcorp
07906 292373
info@urbandevcorp.com
www.urbandevcorp.com

Web Technology Group
020 7339 8600
info@webtechnologygroup.co.uk
www.webtechnologygroup.co.uk

WIN
01494 750500
businessdevelopment@winplc.com
www.winplc.com

XM London
020 7724 7228
xminfo@ccgxm.com
www.xmlondon.co.uk

Digital media planning and buying

Ad 2 One
020 7401 0222
info@ad2onegroup.com
www.ad2-one.co.uk
*Digital sales and marketing group of
companies*

AdLink
Montabaur, Germany:
    00 49 260 296 2000
www.adlink.net
Digital marketing solutions

All Response Media
020 7017 1450
enquiries@allresponsemedia.com
www.allresponsemedia.com
www.digit-all.co.uk

Arnold Interactive
Boston, USA: 001 617 587 8000
NewYork, USA: 001 212 463 1000
Washington DC, USA:
001 703 288 7300
www.arnoldworldwide.com
Advertising/marketing company

Carat Interactive
020 7430 6320
reception@carat.com
www.carat.com

Code Computer Love
0161 276 2080
info@codecomputerlove.com
www.computerlove.co.uk
Digital communications agency

Dare Digital
020 7299 3001
us@daredigital.com
www.daredigital.com
Interactive marketing agency

eType
020 7436 6726
www.etype-europe.com
Online advertising sales house

Cheeze
01473 236892
info@cheeze.com
www.cheeze.com

i-level
020 7340 2700
www.i-level.com

Isobar UK
020 7405 1050
info@isobarcommunications.com
www.isobarcommunications.com

MediaCom North
0161 839 6600
johnmarshall@mediacomnorth.com
www.mediacomnorth.com

MediaVest
020 7190 8000
ecombe@uk.starcomww.com
www.mediavest.co.uk

Milton Bayer
0870 751 0690
www.miltonbayer.com
Creative marketing agency

Moving Brands
020 7739 7700
info@movingbrands.com
www.movingbrands.com

Outrider
001 314 209 1005
contact.us@outrider.com
www.outrider.com

PHDiQ
020 7446 0555
callen@phd.co.uk
www.phd.co.uk

Profero
020 7387 2000
contact@profero.com
www.profero.co.uk

Quantum
020 7287 8768
info@quantum-media.co.uk
www.quantum-media.co.uk

Skive
020 7637 2704
yo@skive.co.uk
www.skivecreative.com
*Digital strategy design and production
company*

Steak Media
020 7420 3500
www.steakmedia.co.uk
Digital marketing agency

Swamp
0113 230 4000
contact@swamp.co.uk
www.swampme.com
Digital marketing agency

Starcom Digital
020 7190 8000
ecombe@uk.starcomww.com
www.starcomww.co.uk

TBG
020 7428 6650
info@tbglondon.com
www.tbglondon.com
*Full service digital marketing agency
that provides creative, strategy, media
planning and technology services*

Tequila
Pyrmont, Australia:
00 61 2 8584 5500
tim@tequila.com.au
www.tequila.com.au
Digital marketing agency

Tribal DDB
020 7258 4500
www.tribalddb.com

Unique Digital Marketing
020 7354 6566
mark@unique-digital.co.uk
www.unique-digital.co.uk

Zed
01923 815913
design@zed.co.uk
www.zed.co.uk

New media trade press

3G Mobile
Informa Telecoms & Media
020 7017 5615
telecoms.enquiries@informa.com
www.informatm.com
*Fortnightly. Editor: Julian Bright; news
and features: Nick Lane; chief sub:
Charles Gordon*

Computer Weekly
Reed Business Information
020 8652 3500
editorial@computerweekly.com
www.computerweekly.com
*Weekly. Editor: Hooman Bassirian;
news and features: Mike Simons;
production: Stuart Nissen*

Computing
VNU Business Publications
020 7316 9000
help@vnuservices.co.uk
www.computing.co.uk
*Weekly. Editor: Bryan Glick; news,
features and production: Catrina Attard*

EI magazine
Ark Publishing
020 8785 2700
publishing@arkgroup.com
www.eimagazine.com
*Monthly. Deputy editor: Kate Clifton;
features and production: Emma
Palfreyman*

Gamesindustry.biz
Eurogamer Network Ltd
01273 382521
contact@gamesindustry.biz
www.gamesindustry.biz
Daily. Editor: Phil Elliott

Informa Telecoms & Media
Informa Telecoms & Media
020 7017 4800
Kathryn.Bushnell@informa.com
www.arcgroup.com
Strategic research reports

IT Europa
IT BPL
01895 454458
contact@ITEuropa.com
www.iteuropa.com
20pa. Editor: John Garratt

IT Week
VNU Business Publications
020 7316 9000
itweek_letters@vnu.co.uk
www.itweek.co.uk
*Weekly. Editor: Madeline Bennett;
news, features and production:
Matthew Bush*

Journalism.co.uk
Mousetrap Media, 68 Middle
Street, Brighton BN1 1AL
01273 384293
info@journalism.co.uk
www.journalism.co.uk
*Website editor/publisher: John
Thompson; news reporter: Oliver Luft;
sales/marketing manager: Louise Walter;
production manager: Clare Fisher*

MCV
Intent Media
01992 535646
www.mcvuk.com
Weekly. Editor: Neil Long

.net
Future Publishing Ltd
01225 442244
mailus@netmag.co.uk
www.netmag.co.uk
Monthly. Editor: Dan Oliver

NetImperative
020 8535 7565
editorial@netimperative.com
www.netimperative.com
*Email and online news service,
daily and weekly newsletters. Editor:
Mike Butcher*

New Media Age
Centaur Media
020 7970 4000
www.nma.co.uk
*Weekly. Editor-in-chief: Michael
Nutely; deputy and features: Nic
Howell; production: George Stewart*

Online Journalism Review
Annenberg School of Journalism
001 213 740 3914
rniles@usc.edu
www.ojr.org
Online. Publisher: Geoffrey Cowan; editor: Robert Niles

The Online Reporter
Rider Research
01280 820560
info@newsriderresearch.com
www.riderresearch.com
Weekly. Editor: Charles Hall

The Register
020 7462 7744
news@theregister.co.uk
www.theregister.co.uk
Website. UK Editorial director: Drew Cullen; editor: Joe Fay

Revolution
Haymarket Business Publications
020 8267 4947
revolution.ads@haynet.com
www.brandrepublic.com/revolution
Monthly. Editor: Phillip Buxton; news: Emma Rigby; features: Alicia Buller; art editor: David Grant; production: Vic Johnstone

Telemedia Magazine
0870 732 7327
info@worldtelemedia.co.uk
www.worldtelemedia.co.uk
/wtmag.htm
Quarterly. Publisher: Toby Padgham; editor: Paul Skeldon

VNUnet.com
VNU Publications
020 7316 9000
newseditor@vnunet.com
www.vnunet.com
Online. Editor: Robert Jacques

Web User
IPC Media
020 3148 4327
www.webuser.co.uk
Fortnightly. Editor: Claire Woffenden

Wired
001 415 276 8400
www.wired.com
Monthly. General manager: Kourosh Karimkhany; managing editor: Leander Kahney; editor-in-chief: Evan Hansen; copy chief: Tony Long

ZDNet UK and Silicon.com
CNet Networks
020 7903 6800
www.cnet.com
Online. Editors: site: Matt Loney, news: Richard Thurston, executive: Andrew Donoghue

Internet associations

ABC electronic
01442 870800
info@abce.org.uk
www.abce.org.uk

Association of Freelance Internet Designers
a.carson@uku.co.uk
www.afid.net

Association of Online Publishers (AOP)
020 7404 4166
www.ukaop.org.uk
info@ukaop.org.uk

British Interactive Media Association
01277 658107
info@bima.co.uk
www.bima.co.uk

British Internet Publishers Alliance (BIPA)
01865 310732
angela.mills@wade.uk.net
www.bipa.co.uk

British Web Design and Marketing Association
020 8204 2474
info@ukwda.org
www.ukwda.org

Entertainment and Leisure Software Publishers Association
020 7534 0580
info@elspa.com
www.elspa.com
Trade association for games industry

HTML Writers Guild/International Webmasters Association
help@iwanet.org
www.hwg.org
Training body for web designers

The Independent Games Developers Association (Tiga)
0845 094 1095
info@tiga.org
www.tiga.org

Internet Advertising Bureau
020 7886 8282
info@iabuk.net
www.iabuk.net

Internet Corporation for Assigned Names and Numbers (ICANN)
001 310 823 9358
icann@icann.org
www.icann.org

Internet Service Providers Association
0870 050 0710
pressoffice@ispa.org.uk
www.ispa.org.uk

Internet Watch Foundation
01223 237700
media@iwf.org.uk
www.iwf.org.uk
Operates hotline for public to report inadvertent exposure to illegal internet content

London Internet Exchange (Linx)
info@linx.net
www.linx.net
Press: 01733 207700

Online News Association (ONA)
New York, USA:
001 646 290 7900
lschwab@journalists.org
www.journalists.org
Supports the rights of online journalists

UK Podcasters Association (UK PA)
0870 919 2807
yours@ukpodcasters.org.uk
www.ukpodcasters.org.uk
A non-profit organisation set up to protect its members' rights and promote podcasting

Networking conferences

Chinwag
London: 0870 730 7313
help@chinwag.com
www.chinwag.com
Provides an online community, jobs board and live events for digital media practitioners

First Tuesday
London: 0870 899 8066
info@firsttuesday.org.uk
www.firsttuesday.co.uk
For established technology entrepreneurs and companies seeking venture capital, investors and related service providers

Internet People
http://internetpeeps.com/blog
A London-based community for the internet startup sector

Media Bistro
New York, USA: 001 212 929 2588
www.mediabistro.com
Web community for media professionals

New Media Knowledge
London: 020 7911 5000
nmk@nmk.co.uk
www.nmk.co.uk
A knowledge-sharing hub for businesses and individuals working in digital media

Second Chance Tuesday
www.theglasshouse.net
/content/sctlondon

Research sites

10 Downing Street
www.number-10.gov.uk
Prime Minister's Office website

ABC electronic (ABCe)
01442 870800
info@abce.org.uk
www.abce.org.uk
Providing third party independent verification and certification for data related to electronic media

AlphaGalileo
020 7812 0670
alphagalileo@alphagalileo.org
http://alphagalileo.org
Internet based resource for European news

Boing Boing
http://boingboing.net
Directory/blog site

Boo.com
00 353 1 498 0700
Press@boo.com
www.boo.com
Online travel site

ComScore
020 7099 1760
Reston, USA: 001 703 438 2000
worldpress@comscore.com
www.comscore.com
Providing global internet ratings

Conservative Home
tim@conservativehome.com
http://conservativehome.blogs
.com

Highbeam Research
Chicago, USA: 001 312 782 3900
www.highbeam.com
Magazine and newspaper archive, online library and research tool

Hitwise
London: 020 7378 3600
New York, USA: 001 212 380 2900
www.hitwise.co.uk
Insights to online marketing

Infobel
Brussels, Belgium:
00 32 2 379 2940
www.infobel.com
Telephone and business directory electronic publisher

Labour Home
020 8133 5247
support@labourhome.org
www.labourhome.org

Liberal Democrats Home
020 7222 7999
info@libdems.org.uk
www.libdems.org.uk
Provides information on Liberal Democrat policy and activity

Martindale's The Reference Desk
www.martindalecenter.com
International art, business, science and technology reference centre

One Look
Hilton Head Island, USA:
001 843 363 2667
www.onelook.com
Search engine for words and phrases linked to the world's online dictionaries

Project Gutenberg
help@pglaf.org
www.gutenberg.org
Downloadable ebooks

The Public Whip
www.publicwhip.org.uk
An independent, non-governmental project to help the public watch MPs

Theyworkforyou.com
07811 082158
team@mysociety.org
www.theyworkforyou.com
Comments on Parliament and representatives in Parliament

Unruly Media
07974 328052
scott@unrulymedia.com
www.viralvideochart.com
Social media intelligence and viral marketing services

Wikipedia
07733 223584
St. Petersburg, USA:
001 727 231 0101
wp@davidgerard.co.uk
dgerard@gmail.com
www.wikipedia.org
User-edited encyclopedia

Social networking sites and online communities

bebo
020 7478 0300
sarah@bebo.com
www.bebo.com
Social networking site

Facebook
Palo Alto, USA: 001 650 853 1300
info@facebook.com
www.facebook.com
A social utility that enables people to communicate and share information across the digital platform

Flickr
flickr-pr@yahoo-inc.com
http://flickr.com
Online photo management and sharing application

friendster.com
San Francisco, USA:
001 415 618 0074
help@friendster.com
www.friendster.com
Online social network
Press: press@friendster.com

habbo
020 7288 6175
info.uk@sulake.com
www.habbo.com
Virtual community for teenagers

hi5
San Francisco, USA:
001 415 404 6094
www.hi5.com
Social community

Isporty
www.isporty.com
Sport based social utility

Linkedin.com
www.linkedin.com
Social community
Press: press@linkedin.com

Maple Story
www.maplestory.com
Press: press@mapleeurope.com

Meetro
http://meetro.com
Social messenger

MySociety
07811 082158
team@mysociety.org
www.mysociety.org
Project which helps build websites for community use

Myspace
www.myspace.com
Online community

Netlog
www.netlog.com
Social community

Orkut — Google's social network
www.orkut.com
Social community

Photobucket
http://photobucket.com
Online photo management and sharing application

Picasa
http://picasa.google.com
Online photo management and sharing application

The Second Life
San Francisco, USA:
001 415 243 9000
contact@lindenlab.com
http://secondlife.com

The Sims
http://thesims.ea.com

TrustedPlaces
020 7239 4920
info@trustedplaces.com
http://trustedplaces.com
Community site for people to review places they have experienced in their daily lives

Twitter
San Francisco, USA:
001 866 924 2008
support@twitter.com
http://twitter.com
Communication platform connecting SMS, IM, and the web

World of Warcraft
www.worldofwarcraft.com

Zooomr
San Francisco, USA:
001 415 205 3611
zfeedback@bbridgetech.com
www.zooomr.com
Photo sharing site

Online radio and music sites

Accuradio
Chicago, USA: 001 312 527 3879
feedback@accuradio.com
www.accuradio.com

BlogTalkRadio
Lakewood, USA: 001 330 439 4711
www.blogtalkradio.com
Free, live social radio broadcasting network
Press@blogtalkradio.com

Kazaa
www.kazaa.com
Download music, movies games and software
Press: sharman@iicpr.com

Last.fm
020 7780 7080
office@last.fm
www.last.fm

Music Station
020 8600 0580
info@omnifone.com
www.omnifone.com

Radio Handi
San Jose, USA: 001 888 825 0800
www.radiohandi.com

Shoutcast
www.shoutcast.com
Free internet radio

Online video and tv sites

BitTorrent
San Francisco, USA:
001 415 568 9007
info@bittorrent.com
www.bittorrent.com
Content delivery service

Brightcove
London: 020 7812 7244
Cambridge, USA:
001 617 500 4947
www.brightcove.com
Internet TV service
Press: press@revver.com

Current TV UK
info@uk.current.com
http://uk.current.com
Global television network
Press: pressUK@uk.current.com

Joost
020 7240 9702
london@joost.com
www.joost.com
Free TV

Livestation
www.livestation.com

Mediaroom (Microsoft TV)
London: 020 7067 0500
Redmond, USA: 001 425 882 8080
www.microsoft.com/tv
Internet TV service
Press (UK): mstvemea@
webershandwick.com

Permission TV
Waltham, USA: 001 781 419 9700
info@permissiontv.com
www.permissiontv.com
Video host

RealNetworks
Seattle, USA: 001 206 674 2700
public_relations@real.com
www.realnetworks.com
Digital entertainment media services and software

Revver
http://one.revver.com
Video sharing network

Sumo TV
info@sumo.tv
www.sumo.tv

Tape It Off the Internet, or Tiot
www.tapeitofftheinternet.com

VBS (Vice Broadcasting System)
020 7749 7828
aaron@viceuk.com
www.vbs.tv
Online TV

Video Jug
020 7749 6850
www.videojug.com
Library of factual content online

Vuze
Palo Alto, USA: 001 650 963 4799
info@azureus-inc.com
www.vuze.com
Internet TV service

YourKindaTV
contact@yourkindatv.com
www.yourkindatv.com
Video host

YouTube
www.youtube.com
Online video

Podcasting sites

Talk Shoe
Wexford, USA: 001 724 935 8255
info@talkshoe.com
www.talkshoe.com
Live interactive podcasts and audioblogs

Waxxi
001 805 705 7357
hello@waxxi.us
www.waxxi.us
Interactive podcasting site
Press: press@waxxi.us

Personal bookmarking

del.icio.us
corporate@del.icio.us
http://del.icio.us
Social bookmarking website

Netvibes
www.netvibes.com
Personal bookmarking
Press: nsavage@mantra-pr.com

Rememble
07809 375312
Press: gavin@rememble.com
www.rememble.com

Events

Austin Game Developers Conference
Austin, USA: 001 415 947 6135
www.austingdc.net
Game developers conference

British Academy Video Games Awards
020 7734 0022
kellys@bafta.org
www.bavga.co.uk
British academy video awards

Chinwag Live
0870 730 7313
live@chinwag.com
http://live.chinwag.com
Events on trends in the digital media and marketing industry

Develop Conference and Expo
020 7405 4500
www.develop-conference.com
Conference and exposition for the games developer
Press: charlotte@bastion.co.uk

Edinburgh Interactive Festival
01462 456780
www.edinburghinteractive
festival.com
Interactive festival
Press: laura.west@bhpr.co.uk

First Tuesday
0870 899 8066
info@firsttuesday.org.uk
www.firsttuesday.co.uk
Professional networking forum for established technology entrepreneurs and companies
Press: press@firsttuesday.org.uk

Futures
0151 709 1566
elaine@designinit.org.uk
www.futuresnetwork.org.uk
Events for designers working in the communications field

Games Convention
Germany: 00 49 341 678 8280
info@leipziger-messe.de
www.gc-germany.com
Gaming trade fair

Golden Joystick Awards
020 7042 4055
lisa.mccabe@futurenet.co.uk
www.goldenjoystick.com
Gaming ceremony

Le Web 3
www.leweb3.com
*Europe's forum for web innovators,
entrepreneurs and bloggers to debate
issues*

London Games Festival
020 7534 0584
info@londongamesfestival.com
www.londongamesfestival.co.uk
Games festival
Press : 020 7307 3100

RetailVision Europe
01784 268404
www.retailvision.com/europe
*Where new PC and consumer
electronics products are unveiled*

The TopCoder Open
Glastonbury, USA:
  001 860 633 5540
service@topcoder.com
www.topcoder.com
Programming competition
Press: jmckeown@topcoder.com

Virtual Worlds Forum Europe
020 7813 2376
contact@virtualeconomicforum
.com
http://virtualworldsforum.com
European virtual worlds conference

Web Wednesdays
07939 064338
hello@webwednesdays.com
www.webwednesdays.com
*A networking event created specifically
for internet entrepreneurs*

Webby Awards
New York, USA: 001 212 675 3555
jcollins@webbyawards.com
www.webbyawards.com
Awards for excellence on the internet
Press: 001 212 627 8098

Advertising, PR and media law

Advertising

Simon Marquis

A chastened man ... Jonathan Durden

Perhaps it shouldn't surprise anyone that advertising, whose stock in trade is creativity, has a pretty colourful life itself – except that much of what actually happens in advertising you couldn't make up.

This has been another vintage year of the unexpected, the incredible, the brilliant and the downright crazy. What never changes from year to year is the sheer energy of the business, its restlessness and its indomitable conviction that there is always a better idea just around the corner.

Top of the "stranger than fiction" category in 2007 was the saga of Jonathan Durden. For years heralded as one of the smartest brains in media planning and a partner in a highly acclaimed media agency, in May he announced his intention to join the creative agency Miles Calcraft Briginshaw Duffy. Nothing very odd about that but within weeks he had turned up in – of all places – the Big Brother house. What, astonished colleagues and friends asked, had possessed him? His stay in the house was brief, but perhaps not brief enough: one Sunday newspaper unearthed some particularly lurid stories about him. Miles Calcraft maintained a discreet silence. Durden emerged a wiser, chastened man. A close second was the ribald libel case involving Sir Martin Sorrell and some former employees that, sensibly for all, settled out of court and in a remarkable twist, Saatchi, the agency that helped Margaret Thatcher to power in 1979, was appointed by Labour to help with the 2007 general election that never was.

The ad world had its usual share of comings and goings. Christine Walker retired from the successful agency she founded and has yet to declare her next move. Rupert Howell, the man behind the famous Tango ad campaign, has resurfaced as the new head of all things commercial at ITV. Andrew Harrison, ex-Rowntrees marketer, has taken up the reins at RadioCentre, while David Pattison (an erstwhile partner of Durden) also quit his old company for a senior role at the digital agency i-Level. A number of clients made the move to agency jobs too, including Alan Rutherford, media supremo at Unilever, switching to Publicis-owned Digitas, and Sony's David Patton taking his first chance agency-side with Grey.

One or two agency founders have made themselves rich – the smartest deal of the year award goes to Clemmow Hornby Inge, who sold just under 50% of the company to WPP for £30m. In spite – or

Awards

perhaps because of – the relentless growth of the agency super-networks, there is always a new trio of bright sparks who decide to risk their houses and sanity and start an agency. Top managers James Murphy, Ben Priest and David Golding at London's Y&R announced mid-year that they were going it alone, as did three media experts, Phil Nunn, Simon Timlett and Amy Lennox, who have decided to called themselves Trinity rather than do the usual thing and put their names above the door. Somewhat surprisingly, given his impeccable track record, Chris Ingram, one of the pioneers of the media agency, admitted his new venture, Ingram, had not delivered what it promised and was up for sale.

Advertising came under renewed scrutiny and attack in 2007. Advertisers and agencies rather take for granted their right to advertise, leaving the frontline defence of this freedom to a small, poorly funded organisation, the Advertising Association. Early in the year, a new, feisty chief executive took the helm. Baroness Buscombe, a Conservative life peer and lawyer by background, saw advertising as indivisible from other forms of free expression and – more than that – a positive force for good in society, providing consumers with information to make choices between brands and services, and a strong driver of economic prosperity.

However, not everyone agrees with this point of view. Advertising, by its nature, is conspicuous, and so is an easy target for campaigners of all hues. As the commotion about childhood obesity mounts, there has been a growing call for limitations on the advertising of sweets, crisps, fizzy drinks and even cheese. The health secretary, Alan Johnson, has joined the throng by asking for tougher advertising controls. The fact that there is little evidence to suggest that restricting advertising of these products will have any discernible effect on the problem of obesity has done little to dampen

Top 20 UK creative agencies 2006	
Rank/Agency	Ad spend (m)
1 Abbott Mead Vickers BBDO	407.1
2 JWT London	349.8
3 McCann-Erickson Advertising	292.2
4 M&C Saatchi	255.4
5 Publicis	249.8
6 Rainey Kelly Campbell Roalfe/Y&R	222.2
7 Bartle Bogle Hegarty (BBH)	212.5
8 Ogilvy & Mather	208.8
9 DDB London	202.1
10 Leo Burnett	181.5
11 Saatchi & Saatchi	174.5
12 Euro RSCG London	163.5
13 Grey Worldwide	159.8
14 Mother	159.3
15 Delaney Lund Knox Warren & Partners	145.4
16 Clemmow Hornby Inge Ltd	137.8
17 WCRS	134.1
18 TBWA London	131.4
19 Lowe	99.1
20 Vallance Carruthers Coleman Priest	79.3

Source: Nielsen Media Research © Tables cannot be republished without prior written permission from Nielsen Media Research.

Top 20 UK media buying agencies 2006	
Rank/Agency	Ad spend (m)
1 Mediacom Holdings	883.2
2 OMD	777.9
3 Mindshare Media UK	732.3
4 Starcom UK Group	654.2
5 Carat	608.0
6 Zenithoptimedia	577.4
7 Initiative Media London	371.9
8 Walker Media	252.3
9 Mediaedge:CIA	233.1
10 PHD	231.4
11 Universal McCann UK	228.9
12 Vizeum UK	151.5
13 Brilliant Media	117.4
14 Mediavest (Manchester)	114.3
15 Media Planning Group	89.5
16 Mediaedge:CIA Manchester	81.2
17 Feather Brooksbank	68.1
18 Zed Media	66.9
19 Booth Lockett Makin	57.2
20 John Ayling & Associates	52.0

Source: Nielsen Media Research © Tables cannot be republished without prior written permission from Nielsen Media Research.

Advertising, PR and media law

calls for further curbs. In the autumn, yet another health "problem" bubbled to the surface: that of "hazardous drinking" amongst the middle classes. Industry observers are predicting demands for further advertising restrictions in this category and there are mutterings that "cars will be next".

Buscombe is now making a plea for proper financial backing of the Advertising Association so that clear and rational arguments can be advanced for the positive role advertising can play. She wants it to be seen as part of the solution to society's ills and concerns and not one of its causes.

Advertising is also about advertisements and 2007 clocked up a decent tally of the inspired and the great. Honda deservedly maintained its winning form with the awards juries and was pronounced Advertiser of the Year 2007 at the Cannes Advertising festival. It also won coveted D&AD awards – the pinnacle of creative approbation.

The Cannes Grand Prix went, however, to "Evolution" a viral campaign for Dove soap, created by Ogilvy & Mather Toronto, now paid the ultimate compliment of a spoof version featuring not a beautiful woman but a bloke transformed by booze, fags and burgers. All eyes were on a campaign from Fallon London for Cadbury's Dairy Milk, featuring a gorilla and a famous Phil Collins drum performance. Don't ask why and how this works, but it does. My 13-year-old son has pronounced that and the new Sony Walkman commercial (also by Fallon) the coolest things on television. The agency will be dusting down its shelves in anticipation of a clutch of prizes in 2008.

Finally, one of the most talented creative directors in the business was knighted in 2007. Arise Sir John Hegarty. That's pretty cool too.

⬤ Simon Marquis is an advertising industry consultant

ASA rulings

Banned

⬤ **November 2007** Shell Europe Oil Products Ltd was told it had made misleading claims with the wording of an advertisement. The advert featured the words "We use our waste CO2 to grow flowers, and our waste sulphur to make super-strong concrete". The wording of the advertisement implied that Shell uses all of its waste CO2 to grow flowers, whereas in actual fact it uses a significantly smaller proportion. The ASA ruled that the advertisement was likely to be misleading.

⬤ **July 2007** The ASA upheld complaints over an interactive internet ad for BMW's new Mini range. The advertisement included the words "Floor it" next to a graphic of an acceleration pedal. When viewers clicked the pedal, the car was seen to accelerate and the more the viewer clicked, the faster the car went. Complaints were made that the advert was

irresponsible, by encouraging excessive speeding. The ASA agreed that the ad "made speed and acceleration the predominant message", thus encouraging dangerous speeding.

⬤ **March 2007** Cadbury Trebor Bassett Services ran numerous advertisements for its Trident chewing gum. The various adverts depicted a black man, a white middle-aged woman and a white man speaking in rhyme with strong Caribbean accents and exaggerated mannerisms. A total of 519 complaints from viewers argued that the adverts were offensive and racist because many thought that they "showed offensive stereotypes and ridiculed black or Caribbean people and their culture". Cadbury responded with evidence that it had carried out consumer research before the advertisements were produced that had found that the majority of people surveyed favoured the humour of the campaign. While the ASA acknowledged this, it was also keen to highlight the 1 in 5 respondents who found the ads offensive. The complaints were upheld.

● **January 2007** Dolce & Gabbana featured two ads in magazine supplements from the Times and the Daily Telegraph. The first image showed two men brandishing knives in a violent manner towards another man, with a fourth man wounded on the floor. The second advert featured a woman holding a knife, with a wound to her chest. More than 160 complainants, including Mothers Against Murder and Aggression, registered their displeasure with the ASA. Taking note of recent knife-related crimes, the ASA upheld the view that the advert was irresponsible, as it was seen to be "condoning and glorifying knife-related violence".

Allowed

● **November 2007** Danone UK Ltd ran a TV advertisement for Danone Activia, and claimed that "After 14 days, 82% of people with digestive discomfort said they felt better". Primarily it claimed to assist with a "bloated feeling". Despite receiving complaints from the Medicines and Healthcare products Regulatory Agency over its medical claims, Danone provided valid evidence. The ASA decided not to uphold the complaints, as Danone was only claiming to relieve the feeling of bloatedness and digestive discomfort (regular symptoms of a healthy digestion), not to treat digestive disorders.

● **October 2007** The ASA received more than 30 complaints when the NHS ran a TV advert as part of its "Smoke-Free.co.uk" campaign. The advert showed a woman lighting a cigarette at a wedding reception, and highlighted the dangers of second-hand smoke. The voiceover stated that second-hand smoke "attacks vital organs of everyone who breathes it, increasing their chances of heart disease by a quarter, even if they've never smoked". Various viewers felt the advert was offensive to smokers and others, including Imperial Tobacco Ltd, argued that the information was misleading. The Department of Health challenged the complaints with scientific evidence demonstrating that second-hand smoke can increase the risk of heart disease and argued that

the advert did not focus on the actual smokers but on the smoke instead. The ASA dismissed complaints that the advert was offensive, stating that it "concentrated solely on the issue of second-hand smoke's impact on the health of smokers and non-smokers" and therefore would not be seen as offensive to smokers.

● **July 2007** H&M Hennes Ltd released an advert for a new range of clothes designed by Madonna. The advert featured Madonna interviewing a woman, who in one particular shot was escorted by two men into another room and undressed and redressed in more fashionable clothes. A number of viewers complained that the advert seem to represent a young girl being forced to disrobe by two men and therefore was offensive to show publicly. H&M expressed its disappointment that the advert had been perceived in such a way, stating that it was meant to target women of all ages interested in fashion, not just teenagers. The company was also keen to point out that an ex-kids restriction (which means it was kept away from programmes specifically made for children) had been given before airing the advert. The ASA did not uphold the complaints that the advert was offensive and threatening. It considered that the quick change of clothes could be seen to be replicating the outfit changes that take place in catwalk fashion.

● **April 2007** A TV ad by Walkers Snack Foods Ltd for Comic Relief advertisement had various celebrities dressing up as schoolchildren and wearing a pair of large false ears. The only "pupil" not wearing the false ears was Gary Lineker, who was grabbed by the teacher and dragged out of the classroom whilst the other pupils laughed at him. A number of viewers complained that it could be seen to be encouraging bullying and also could discriminate against those who did have big ears. On behalf of Walkers, Abbot Mead Vickers BBDO responded that the intention had been to produce a fun advert for Comic Relief and to raise money for several good causes. It was also argued that Gary Lineker's ears had always been a humorous aspect of previous Walkers adverts and thus the Comic Relief advert was merely keeping in line with this. Despite the ASA recognising the seriousness of bullying, the complaints were not upheld, as it was agreed the advert would be seen as a joke and typical of other Comic Relief sketches.

The Fallon agency had an extraordinary 2007. In a year when the industry was distracted by online revenues and credit crunches, the creativity of this London shop was consistent and well rewarded, with the Cadbury Gorilla ad named favourite of the year. Stephen Armstrong profiled them for MediaGuardian in October, just as the latest Sony Bravia ad was about to launch.

Loads of balls and an explosion of creativity

Stephen Armstrong

Every now and then an advert comes along that, for reasons almost impossible to define, grabs the zeitgeist by the throat. Coke's I'd Like To Teach The World To Sing, say, or the Levi's Launderette ad or Tango's Slap. Last week, Australia's Channel 9 News showed the full 90 seconds of a British ad that had never appeared in an Aussie commercial break, describing it as "the ad the whole world's talking about".

If you haven't seen it, it's incredibly simple to describe but almost impossible to understand. A man in a gorilla suit sits at a drum kit as Phil Collins's Coming In The Air Tonight wafts towards its thunderous mid-point. Collins's trademark drum roll clatters down, and gorilla suit thwacks his toms with unholy glee then settles back to pound along, lip twitching and shoulders shaking, with obvious content. And that is it. It's for Cadbury's Dairy Milk and its 28 different postings on YouTube have – since the ad was launched at the end of August – garnered roughly 10m views. It has already been spoofed with a toy gorilla as well as remixed with a 50 Cent and a Bonnie Tyler track. It is simple, bonkers and funny and – although it may commit the crime of resurrecting Collins's career – it seems to have tickled half the planet's funny bone.

The agency behind the ad is Fallon, officially the offshoot of a US agency but staffed and run entirely from London. Although it has been going for almost 10 years, it is the past three in which there has been an explosion of creativity.

"Sometimes, the very best agencies produce one belting ad a year," says Campaign's deputy editor Francesca Newland. "We've already had the Skoda Cake ad and Cadbury Gorilla from Fallon this year, and its next Sony work is breaking shortly. The agency has hit a creative stride that is rarely seen these days."

As a result, the agency is trampling all over the current vogue for carefully honed adland theories of success – like Disruption, as posited by Jean-Marie Dru, president and CEO of TBWA worldwide, or 360-degree brand stewardship, the mantra of Ogilvy. When I discuss this with the Fallon partners in their Soho offices, behind what seems to be the door to a flat above a shop, their only theory appears to be – avoid theories at all costs.

"All our ads happen so differently that I'd be worried about calling it a process," says client director Chris Willingham. "If you take Disruption, that sounds a bit like someone saying – we've done that five times and it worked, so let's make it into a theory."

"We've had a couple of dips in the last 10 years, and they've usually come when we've started to develop a house style," agrees Richard Flintham, founding partner and executive creative director. "House style can be destructive. Success can mean looking at what you've done and trying to work out why – but maybe you just did it." Although someone else in advertising has already claimed "just do it" as a slogan, it applies to Fallon's breakthrough moment – the Sony Bravia TV commercial known affectionately as Balls.

The agency started in 1998 when the talk of the ad world was St Luke's, the co-operatively run hotshop. Mr Fallon himself is a short man from Minneapolis who had set up in WC1 without a single client to see if he could hustle in the UK market. A successful campaign for Skoda in 2001 was a landmark. "We went from kids crying in showrooms when they found their parents were thinking of buying a Skoda to 60,000 cars a year," says chairman Laurence Green – but the industry still thought of Fallon as something of a one-trick pony.

Early Sony work had been respectable, with the agency switching the slogan from Saatchi's vague "Go Create" to the touchy feely "You make it a Sony". At the end of 2004, however, it suggested to the client that it hurl a million coloured balls down a hill in San Francisco to launch the Bravia colour TV. "The idea had to go all the way back to Tokyo and there were a lot of people asking – "but where's the actual product? Why are we doing this?" Green explains. "We had to back the idea all the way through." When it came to the shoot, they could only get 250,000 balls made in time, and toyed with the idea of adding them digitally. "But in the end, we decided they would all be real balls – do it for real. That became our mantra; go and do the damn thing for real," Green adds.

Which is how they inadvertently realised how the internet could save advertising. "The idea that we were throwing these balls down a hill and having 50 students on roller skates with brooms clear them throughout the day over a three-day shoot caught the imagination of the people of San Francisco," says Flintham. "It's the most wired city in the world. They all turned up with cameras and were sending stuff shooting around the world. At the end of our first day, our creative director Juan Cabral got an email from his friend in Argentina showing footage of what he'd been doing that day."

Initially, the agency panicked. The rules of advertising are clear – you keep your powder dry at all times. Never let anyone know what your ad is like and only reveal it when fully complete at the sales conference. With Balls, however, some 15 million people had seen parts of the ad before Fallon had finished editing the final version. Although it has never been shown on US TV, it often comes high in consumer surveys of America's favourite advertising. Indeed, if you type "advert" into Google, the Bravia ad is still the first listing you get.

"We'd been saying digital is here but we were only half listening," Green explains. "But from the moment we turned over the first camera the consumer was involved and it suddenly became really obvious."

As a result, the likes of Malcolm Poynton, executive creative director at Ogilvy London and Mark Roalfe, chairman of RKCR/Y&R, are eager to praise Fallon. "The market is so confused and so many ads are complicated arguments, but Fallon just make feeling good part of their creative strategy," says Roalfe.

"When they launched, I think I was critical of their work, but since Juan joined he's added a Latin American element that stops them being too British," Poynton adds. In other parts of the industry, however, people aren't so generous. "It's like the industry melting down over Gorilla," Flintham shakes his head. "Lots of agencies, especially planners, are going – 'what's it got to do with chocolate?' Lots of people hate it. I can't see why you'd hate it. We sat around, thought – what does chocolate make you feel like? And can everybody please be 12 again ..."

This week, the next Bravia ad is launched, featuring stop-frame animation of colourful Plasticine bunnies running around New York – there are already websites showing footage of the shoot.

With most agencies still getting to grips with the multimedia world, Fallon's argument is that you just have to be very entertaining and the medium may do the rest for you. "It's the most amazing time to work in our business since ITV was switched on," Green says. "It's astonishing what you can do. Some people are running away and others, like us, are running towards it thinking how much fun we can have."

Total advertising expenditure, by media sector (£m)					
	2002	2003	2004	2005	2006
National newspapers	1,930	1,902	1,974	1,912	1,914
Regional newspapers	2,878	2,962	3,132	2,994	2,782
Consumer magazines	785	784	819	827	812
Business and professional	1,088	1,048	1,082	1,064	1,016
Directories	990	1,029	1,075	1,131	1,174
Press production costs	643	634	660	652	647
Total press	**8,314**	**8,359**	**8,742**	**8,581**	**8,346**
Television	4,341	4,378	4,653	4,820	4,594
Direct mail	2,378	2,467	2,469	2,371	2,322
Outdoor & transport	816	914	986	1,043	1,084
Radio	547	584	606	579	534
Cinema	180	180	192	188	188
Internet	197	465	825	1,367	2,016
Total	**16,772**	17,348	18,472	18,948	19,083

Note: TV, outdoor, radio, cinema and direct mail data include production costs. Internet excludes production costs. Press production costs are shown separately.
Source: WARC/Advertising Association

Advertising contacts

Global supergroups

Aegis
43–45 Portman Square,
London W1H 6LY
020 7070 7700
www.aegisplc.com

Aegis Media/Carat
Parker Tower, 43–49 Parker Street,
London WC2B 5PS
020 7430 6000
www.carat.co.uk
Carat MD: Neil Jones; head of marketing: Nick Gracie; head of PR: Joe Rudkin

Grey Global
777 Third Avenue, New York,
NY 10017, USA
001 212 546 2000
www.grey.com
Bought by WPP in 2005. CEO: Jim Heekin

Grey London
The Johnson Building, 77 Hatton Garden, London EC1N 8JS
020 3037 3000
www.grey.co.uk
Chairman: David Alberts; MD: Chris Hirst; deputy chairman and head of business development: Nicola Mendelsohn; head of PR: Julian Douglas 020 7413 2317

Havas
2 Allée de Longchamp,
92281 Suresnes Cedex, France
00 33 1 58 47 90 00
www.havas.com
Chairman and CEO: Alain de Pouzilhac; corporate communications: Lorella Gessa, 00 33 1 5847 9036

Interpublic
1114 Avenue of the Americas,
New York, NY 10036, USA
00 1 212 704 1200
www.interpublic.com
Chairman and CEO: Michael Roth; senior vice-president and director of corporate communications: Philippe Krakowsky, pkrakowsky@interpublic.com

Omnicom
437 Madison Avenue, New York,
NY 10022, USA
001 212 415 3600
publicaffairs@omnicomgroup.com
www.omnicomgroup.com
President and CEO: John D Wren

Publicis
133 Avenue des Champs Elysées,
75008 Paris, France
00 33 1 4443 7000
contact@publicis.com
www.publicis.com

WPP
27 Farm Street, London W1J 5RJ
020 7408 2204
enquiries@wpp.com
www.wpp.com
CEO: Sir Martin Sorrell; group communications director: Feona McEwan

Advertising agencies

1576 Advertising
0131 473 1576
www.1576.co.uk
Independent

Abbott Mead Vickers BBDO
020 7616 3500
www.amvbbdo.com
Owner: Omnicom

AGA
020 7330 8888
www.aga.co.uk
Independent

AKA
020 7836 4747
www.akauk.com
Independent

Arc Worldwide
020 7751 1662
www.arcww.co.uk
Edinburgh: 0131 556 0115
Owner: Publicis

Archibald Ingall Stretton
020 7467 6100
www.archibaldingallstretton.com
40% owned by Havas

ARM Direct
020 7224 3040
www.arm-direct.co.uk
Independent

Artavia Advertising
01271 323333
www.artavia.co.uk
Barnstaple: 01271 323333
Bournemouth: 01202 293999
Exeter: 01392 495529
Manchester: 0161 833 1000
Skipton: 01756 701640
Truro: 01872 223585
Owner: Accord Holdings

Attinger Jack
01225 758222
www.aja.co.uk
Independent

AWA
0161 968 6900
www.awa.uk.net
Independent

Barkers Scotland
0141 248 5030
www.barkersscotland.co.uk
Edinburgh: 0131 229 7493
Owner: Barkers

Barrington Johnson Lorains
0161 831 7141
www.bjl.co.uk
Independent

Bartle Bogle Hegarty
020 7734 1677
www.bartleboglehegarty.com
Milton Keynes: 01908 326888
Majority owned by employees, minority stake held by Leo Burnett

BDH\TBWA
0161 908 8600
www.bdhtbwa.co.uk
Owner: Omnicom

Beechwood
020 7439 4142
www.beechwood.com
Independent

Bespoke Communications
020 7436 0266
www.bespokecommunications.com
Independent

Big Communications
0116 299 1144
www.bigcommunications.co.uk
Member of the Mission Marketing Group plc

Blac
020 7379 7799
www.blacagency.com
Independent

Black & White Advertising
0191 493 2493
www.blackandwhite.uk.net
Independent

Bray Leino
01598 760700
www.brayleino.co.uk
Independent

The Bridge
0141 552 8384
www.thebridgeuk.com
Independent

Burkitt DDB
020 7258 3979
www.ddblondon.com
Owner: Omnicom

Camp Chipperfield Hill Murray
020 7881 3200
www.cchm.co.uk
Owner: Hill Murry

Carter Gosling
01225 465415
www.cartergosling.co.uk
Independent

cdp-travissully
020 7437 4224
www.cdp-travissully.com
Owner: Dentsu

Charterhouse Advertising & Marketing
0161 848 9050
www.charterhouse-advertising.co.uk
Independent

Cheetham Bell JWT
0161 832 8884
www.cheethambelljwt.com
Owner: WPP

Chemistry Communications
020 7736 5355
www.chemistrygroup.co.uk
Independent

Chick Smith Trott
020 7907 1200
www.cstadvertising.com
Independent

Clark McKay and Walpole
020 7927 3600
www.cmw-uk.com

Claydon Heeley Jones Mason
020 7924 3000
www.claydonheeley.com
Owner: Omnicom

Clayton Graham Advertising
0141 221 3700
www.claytongraham.co.uk
Independent

Clear Marketing Communications
0161 448 8008
www.clearmarketing.co.uk
Independent

Clemmow Hornby Inge
020 7462 8500
www.chiadvertising.com
Independent

Curious
0141 204 5665
www.coltas.com
Independent

Connectpoint Advertising
0161 817 4200
www.connectpoint.co.uk
Independent

Craik Jones Watson Mitchell Voelkel
020 7734 1650
www.craikjones.co.uk
Owner: Abbott Mead Vickers

Cravens Advertising
0191 232 6683
www.cravens.co.uk
Leeds: 0113 384 6030
Independent

CWA Creative
0116 232 7400
www.cwa.co.uk
Christchurch: 01202 482288
Independent

Da Costa & Co
020 7916 3791
www.dacosta.co.uk
Independent

David Gent Creative
01706 220388
www.davidgentcreative.com
Saffron Walden: 01799 502662
Independent

Delaney Lund Knox Warren & Partners
020 7836 3474
www.dlkw.co.uk
Independent

Dewynters
020 7321 0488
www.dewynters.com
Independent

DFGW
020 7632 5200
www.dfgw.com
Independent

Dig For Fire
0114 281 1200
www.digforfire.co.uk
Independent

DKA Creative
020 7467 7300
www.dka.uk.com
Independent

Doner Cardwell Hawkins
020 7734 0511
www.doner.co.uk
Part of Doner

Draft London
020 3048 0000
www.draftworldwide.com
Part of Draft Worldwide

Eardrum
020 7287 2211
www.eardrum.com
Independent

EHS Brann
020 7017 1000
www.ehsbrann.com
Cirencester: 01285 644744
Part-owned by Euro RSCG

Euro RSCG
020 7017 1000
www.eurorscg.co.uk
Owner: Havas

Factor 3
01242 254242
www.factor3.co.uk
Independent

Fallon
020 7494 9120
www.fallon.co.uk
Owner: Publicis

Farm Communications
020 7428 8200
www.creativebrief.com
Independent

FCB Group
020 7947 8000
www.london.fcb.com
Owner: Interpublic

FEREF
020 7292 6300
www.feref.com
Independent

Fox Kalomaski
020 7691 8090
www.foxkalomaski.co.uk
Independent

Being
028 9055 7700
www.beingonline.co.uk
Independent

Genesis Advertising
028 9031 3344
www.genesis-advertising.co.uk
Independent

Gillett & Bevan
0161 228 0023
www.gillett-bevan.com
Independent

Girardot
020 7360 7800
www.girardot.co.uk
Independent

Golley Slater & Partners
020 7255 6400
www.golleyslater.com
Birmingham: 0121 454 2323
Independent

Goode International
01491 873323
www.goode.co.uk
Independent

Harrison Troughton Wunderman
020 7611 6333
www.htw.wunderman.com
Owner: WPP

HDM Agency
020 7420 8020
www.hdmagency.co.uk
Independent

Hooper Galton
020 7494 6300
www.hoopergalton.co.uk
Independent

Huet & Co
0161 835 3100
www.huet.co.uk
Independent

IAS Smarts
0131 555 0425
www.iassmarts.com
Belfast: 028 9039 5500
Birmingham: 0121 456 3199
Edinburgh: 0131 555 0425
London: 020 7535 9900
Manchester: 01625 578578
Owner: Incepta

ICG
01772 679383
www.icgonline.co.uk
Independent

Ideas Eurobrand
020 7738 1900
www.ideaseurobrand.com
Independent

Inferno
020 7292 7070
www.inferno-group.com
Independent

JDA
0113 290 4290
www.jda.co.uk
Warrington: 01925 638899
Independent

Joshua Agency
020 7453 7900
www.joshua-agency.co.uk
Owner: Grey Global

JWT
020 7656 7000
www.jwt.com
Owner: WPP

Kaleidoscope Advertising Design & Marketing
0151 707 2220
www.kadm.co.uk
Independent

Karmarama
020 7612 1777
www.karmarama.com
Independent

Kastner & Partners
020 7689 6989
www.kastnernetwork.co.uk
Independent

Lavery Rowe
020 7378 1780
www.laveryrowe.com
Birmingham: 0121 212 2230
Independent

Lawton Communications
023 8082 8500
www.lawton.co.uk
Independent

Leagas Delaney
020 7758 1758
www.leagasdelaney.com
Independent

Leith Agency
www.leith.co.uk
Edinburgh: 0131 561 8600
Owner: Cello

Leo Burnett
020 7751 1800
www.leoburnett.co.uk
Owner: Publicis

Levy McCallum
028 9031 9220
www.levymccallum.co.uk
Belfast: 028 9031 9220
Edinburgh: 0131 225 9733
Glasgow: 0141 248 7977
Independent

Lowe London
020 7584 5033
www.loweworldwide.com
Owner: Interpublic

M&C Saatchi
020 7543 4500
www.mcsaatchi.com
Independent

Maher Bird Associates
020 7309 7200
www.mba.co.uk
Owner: Omnicom

Marr Associates
01828 632800
www.marr.co.uk
Independent

Martin Tait Redheads
0191 232 1926
www.mtra.co.uk
Independent

Masius
020 7307 9170
www.masius.com
Owner: Publicis

Matters Media
020 7224 6030
Independent

McCann Erickson
020 7837 3737
www.mccann.co.uk
Birmingham: 0121 713 3500
Bristol: 0117 921 1764
Manchester: 01625 822200
Owner: Interpublic

Mediaedge:cia
020 7803 2000
www.mecglobal.com
Independent

Merle
0141 242 1800
www.merleagency.com
Independent

Miles Calcraft Briginshaw Duffy
020 7073 6900
www.mcbd.co.uk
Independent

Mortimer Whittaker O'Sullivan
020 7379 8844
www.mwo.co.uk
Independent

Mostly Media
01935 478238
www.mostlymedia.co.uk
Independent

Mother
020 7012 1999
www.motherlondon.com
Independent

Mustoes
020 7379 9999
www.mustoes.co.uk
Independent

Nexus/H UK
01892 517777
www.nexus-h.co.uk
Independent

Nitro
020 7292 5999
www.nitro-group.com
Independent

Oakbase
01244 391391
www.oakbase.co.uk
Independent

Ogilvy & Mather
020 7345 3000
www.ogilvy.com
Owner: WPP

Ogilvy Primary Contact
020 7468 6900
www.primary.co.uk
Owner: WPP

Palmer Hargreaves Wallis Tomlinson
01926 452525
www.ph-wt.com
London: 020 7713 0999
Independent

Peacock Productions
020 7580 8868
www.peacockdesign.com
Independent

CCH and Ping Communications
020 7881 3200
www.cchandping.com
Independent

Poulter Partners
0113 285 6500
www.poulters.com
Independent

Proximity Media
020 7298 1000
www.proximitylondon.com
Owner: Omnicom

Publicis
020 7935 4426
www.publicis.co.uk
Owner: Publicis

Publicity Bureau
01302 730303
www.publicitybureau.co.uk
Independent

Purity
020 7420 7900
www.puritylondon.com
Independent

Quiet Storm
020 7907 1140
www.quietstorm.co.uk
Independent

Radford Advertising & Marketing
0161 832 8807
www.radfordnet.com
Independent

Radioville
020 7534 5999
www.radioville.co.uk
Independent

Rainey Kelly Campbell Roalfe/Y&R
020 77611 6569
www.rkcryr.com
Owner: Young & Rubicam

Rapier
020 7369 8000
www.rapieruk.com
Independent

Raw Media
01305 259444
www.rawmedia.co.uk
Independent

Rhythmm
0117 942 9786
www.rhythmm.co.uk
Independent

Robson Brown
0191 232 2443
www.robson-brown.co.uk
Manchester: 0161 601 4900
Independent

RPM3
020 7434 4343
www.rpm3.co.uk
Independent

Saatchi & Saatchi
020 7636 5060
www.saatchi-saatchi.com
Owner: Publicis

Scholz & Friends London
020 7961 4000
www.s-f.com
Owner: S&F Holding GmbH

Sheppard Day Associates
020 7821 2222
www.sheppard-day.com
Independent

SHOP
020 7307 9840
www.shopopen.co.uk
Independent

Smarter Communications
020 7257 2600
www.smartercomms.com
Independent. Includes Senior King

Sold Out Advertising
020 7704 0409
www.soldout.co.uk
Independent

Space City Productions
020 7371 4000
www.spacecity.co.uk
Independent

SPS Advertising
01392 464545
Independent

St Luke's Communications
020 7380 8888
www.stlukes.co.uk
Cooperative

TBA
020 7380 0953
www.tbaplc.co.uk
Independent

Team Saatchi
020 7436 6636
www.teamsaatchi.co.uk
Owner: Publicis

Tequila\London
020 7440 1100
www.tequila-uk.com
Owner: Omnicom

Tequila\Manchester
0161 908 8100
www.tequilamanchester.com
Owner: Omnicom

UK Advertising & Marketing Services
01322 228899
www.ukams.co.uk
Independent

Union Advertising Agency
0131 625 6000
www.union.co.uk
Leeds: 0113 266 6050
Independent

Vallance Carruthers Coleman Priest
020 7592 9331
www.vccp.com
Independent

WAA
0121 321 1411
www.waa.co.uk
London: 020 7758 2871
Independent

The Walker Agency
01202 414200
www.thewalkeragency.co.uk
Independent

Ware Anthony Rust
01223 566212
www.war.uk.com
Independent

WARL
020 7400 0900
www.warl.com
Independent

WCRS
020 7806 5000
www.wcrs.com
Owner: Engine

WFCA Integrated
01892 511085
www.wfca.co.uk
Independent

Wieden & Kennedy
020 7194 7000
www.wklondon.com
Independent

Windmill Partnership
020 7371 2868
www.windmillpartnership.com
Independent

WWAV Rapp Collins
020 8735 8000
www.wwavrc.co.uk
Edinburgh: 0131 553 9444
Owner: Omnicom

Wyatt International
0121 454 8181
www.wyattinternational.com
Independent

Young & Rubicam EMEA
020 7387 9366
www.yandr.com
Owner: WPP

Young Phillips
01202 298969
Independent

ZenithOptimedia UK
020 7961 1000
www.zenithoptimedia.com
Owner: Publicis

Media agencies

All Response Media
020 7017 1450
www.allresponsemedia.com
Leeds: 0113 394 4660
Owner: Havas

AMS Media
020 7843 6900
www.amsgroup.co.uk
Independent

Attinger Jack
01225 758222
www.aja.co.uk
Independent

BJK&E Media
020 7025 3900
www.bjke.co.uk
Owner: WPP

BLM Media
020 7437 1317
www.blm.co.uk
Independent

Bray Leino
01598 760700
www.brayleino.co.uk
Independent

Brilliant Media
0113 394 0000
www.brilliantmedia.co.uk
Manchester: 0161 214 7222
Independent

Bygraves Bushell Valladares & Sheldon
020 7734 4445
www.bbvs.co.uk
Independent

Carat
020 7430 6000
www.carat.com
Owner: Aegis

Equinox Communications
020 7864 1950
www.equinoxcomm.co.uk
Owner: Zenith Optimedia

Feather Brooksbank
0131 555 2554
www.featherbrooksbank.co.uk
Glasgow: 0141 332 3382
Manchester: 0161 834 9793
Owner: Aegis

Initiative Media London
020 7663 7000
www.initiative.co.uk
Owner: Interpublic

John Ayling & Associates
020 7439 6070
Independent

Lavery Rowe Advertising
020 7378 1780
www.laveryrowe.com
Independent

Manning Gottlieb OMD
020 7470 5300
www.mgomd.com
Owner: Omnicom

Advertising, PR and media law

Matters Media
020 7224 6030
Independent

Media Campaign Services
020 7389 0800
www.mediacampaign.co.uk
Independent

Media Planning
020 7393 9000
www.mpg.com
Owner: Havas

Mediability
0161 925 6979
www.mediability.co.uk
Independent

MediaCom
020 7874 5500
www.mediacomuk.com
Owner: WPP

MediaCom North
0161 839 6600
www.mediacomnorth.com
Owner: WPP

MediaCom Scotland
0131 555 1500
Owner: WPP

Mediaedge:cia
020 7803 2000
www.mediaedgecia.com
Manchester: 0161 930 9000
Owner: WPP

MediaVest
020 7190 8000
www.mediavest.co.uk
Manchester: 0161 211 8032
Owner: Publicis

MediaVision Manchester
0161 228 3909
www.mvmediagroup.co.uk
Owner: Publicis

Michaelides and Bednash
020 7468 1168
www.michaelidesandbednash.com
Independent

MindShare
020 7969 4040
www.mindshareworld.com
Owner: WPP

MRM Partners UK
020 7837 3737
www.mrmpworldwide.com
Owner: Interpublic

Naked
020 7336 8084
www.nakedcomms.com
Independent

OMD
020 7893 4893
www.omd.com
Owner: Omnicom

Outdoor Connection
020 7544 4680
www.outdoorconnection.co.uk
Owner: Omnicom

PHD
020 7446 0555
www.phd.co.uk
Manchester: 0161 237 7900
Owner: Omnicom

Rathbone Media
0870 830 1850
www.rathmedia.com
Independent

Robson Brown
0191 232 2443
www.robson-brown.co.uk
Manchester: 0161 877 2004
Independent

Starcom UK
020 7453 4444
www.smvgroup.com
London: 020 7190 8000
Owner: Publicis

Total Media Group
020 7937 3793
www.totalmedia.co.uk
Warwick: 01926 840011
Independent

Vizeum UK
020 7379 9000
www.vizeum.co.uk
Owner: Aegis

Walker Media
020 7447 7500
www.walkermedia.com
Part-owner: M&C Saatchi

Wallace Barnaby
01481 726052
www.wallacebarnaby.com
Jersey: 01534 759807
Independent

WWAV Rapp Collins
020 8735 8000
www.wwavrc.co.uk
Edinburgh: 0131 553 9444
Owner: Omnicom

Zed Media
020 7961 3501
www.zedmedia.co.uk
Owner: Publicis

Outdoor media

Clear Channel UK
020 7478 2200
www.clearchannel.co.uk
Independent

JC Decaux
020 7298 8000
www.jcdecaux.co.uk
Birmingham: 0121 423 3777
Glasgow: 0141 891 8100
Manchester: 0161 873 8800
Independent

Primesight
020 7882 1200
www.primesight.co.uk
Erith: 01322 342028
Owner: SMG

Titan
020 7838 4000
020 7838 4055, Sally Henly
www.titanoutdoor.co.uk
Birmingham: 0121 567 2970
Dublin: 00 353 1 29 5233
Glasgow: 0141 779 5250
Leeds: 0113 244 2761
Liverpool: 0151 236 5353
Independent

Viacom Outdoor
020 7482 3000
www.viacom-outdoor.co.uk
Belfast: 028 9032 2333
Birmingham: 0121 788 5250
Bristol: 0117 964 9927
Dublin: 00 353 1669 4500
Edinburgh: 0131 555 1515
Glasgow: 0141 552 5259
Leeds: 0113 242 2294
Manchester: 0161 877 7414
Owner: Viacom

New media agencies

» see page 267

Direct and promotional marketing

141 Worldwide
020 7706 2306
www.141ww.com
Owner: WPP

Arc Worldwide
020 7751 1662
www.arcww.co.uk
Owner: Publicis

BD-NTWK
020 7749 5500
www.bd-ntwk.com
Glasgow: 0141 567 8000
Independent

Billington Cartmell
020 7471 1900
www.bcl.co.uk
Independent

Carlson Marketing
020 8875 0875
www.carlson-europe.com
Bristol: 01454 618811
Northampton: 01604 886000
Independent

Clark McKay and Walpole
020 7927 3600
www.cmw-uk.com
Independent

Claydon Heeley Jones Mason
020 7924 3000
www.chjm.com
Owner: Omnicom

Craik Jones Watson Mitchell Voelkel
020 7734 1650
www.craikjones.co.uk
Owner: Omnicom

Dialogue Marketing
020 8783 3100
www.dialmkg.com
Owner: WPP

Dig For Fire
0114 281 1200
www.digforfire.co.uk
Independent

Draft London
020 3048 0000
www.draftworldwide.com
Part of Draft Worldwide

dunnhumby
020 8832 9222
www.dunnhumby.com
Part-owner: Tesco

EHS Brann
01285 644744
www.ehsbrann.com
London: 020 7017 1000
Part-owner: Euro RSCG

Euro RSCG KLP
020 7017 1000
www.klp.co.uk
Owner: Euro RSCG

Euro RSCG Skybridge
020 8661 8201
www.eurorscgskybridge.com
Owner: Havas

SBG and Finex Communications
020 7326 9191
www.digitalanddirect.co.uk
Owner: Incepta

Geoff Howe
020 8941 7575
www.geoffhowe.com
Independent

GHA
01903 885672
www.g-h-a.co.uk
Independent

Harrison Troughton Wunderman
020 7611 6333
www.htw.wunderman.com
Owner: WPP

Haygarth
020 8971 3300
www.haygarth.co.uk
Independent

Iris
020 7654 7900
www.irisnation.com
Manchester: 0161 830 4750
Independent

Joshua Agency
020 7453 7900
www.joshua-agency.co.uk
Owner: Grey Global

Marketing Store
020 7745 2100
www.themarketingstore.com
Birmingham: 0121 384 9000
Leeds: 0113 246 8266
Owner: Harvey

OgilvyOne
020 7345 3000
www.ogilvy.com
Owner: WPP

Partners Andrews Aldridge
020 7478 2100
www.andrewsaldridge.com
Independent

Red Cell Response
020 7150 3400
www.redcellresponse.com
Owner: WPP

Proximity Media
020 7298 1000
www.proximitylondon.com
Owner: Omnicom

Rapier
020 7369 8000
www.rapieruk.com
Independent

RMG Connect
020 7656 7310
www.rmgconnect.com
Owner: WPP

SMP
01892 548282
www.smp.uk.com
Independent

TDA
01242 633111
www.tdaltd.com
Independent

Tequila\London
020 7440 1100
www.tequila-uk.com
Owner: Omnicom

Tequila\Manchester
0161 908 8100
www.tequilamanchester.com
Owner: Omnicom

Tullo Marshall Warren
020 7349 4000
www.tmw.co.uk
Independent

Souk Response
020 7349 4000
www.soukcommunications.com
Independent

WWAV Rapp Collins
020 8735 8000
www.wwavrc.co.uk
Edinburgh: 0131 553 9444
Owner: Omnicom

Trade press

Advertising Age
001 212 210 0100
editor@adage.com
www.adage.com
*Weekly. Owner: Crain
Communications. Publishing and
editorial director: David Klein;
editor: Scott Donaton*

Brand Strategy
020 7970 4000
ruth.mortimer@centaur.co.uk
www.brandstrategy.co.uk
*Monthly. Owner: Centaur.
Editor: Ruth Mortimer*

Campaign
020 8267 4683
campaign@haynet.com
www.brandrepublic.com
*Weekly. Owner: Haymarket. Editor:
Claire Beale; news: Francesca Newland;
features: Larissa Bannister; production:
Michael Porter*

Cream
020 7613 9700
www.csquared.cc
*Quarterly. Creative media.
Editor: Alastair Ray*

Creative Review
020 7970 4000
patrick.burgoyne@centaur.co.uk
www.creativereview.co.uk
*Monthly. Owner: Centaur. Editor:
Patrick Burgoyne; deputy editor:
Paula Carson*

Design Week
020 7292 3704
lyndark@centaur.co.uk
www.designweek.co.uk
*Weekly. Owner: Centaur.
Editor: Lynda Relph-Knight;*

Mad.co.uk
020 7970 4000
stuart.aitken@centaur.co.uk
www.mad.co.uk
*Online magazine. Owner: Centaur.
Editor: Branwell Johnson; news:
Arif Durrani*

Marketing
020 8267 5000
marketing@haynet.com
www.brandrepublic.com
*Weekly. Owner: Haymarket. Editor:
Craig Smith; news: Ben Carter;
features: Drew Barrand; production
manager: Emma Lawton*

Marketing Direct
020 8267 5000
noelle.mcelhatton@haynet.com
www.mxdirect.co.uk
*Monthly. Owner: Haymarket.
Editor: Noelle McElhatton; features:
Melanie May*

Marketing Week
020 7970 4000
mw.editorial@centaur.co.uk
www.marketing-week.co.uk
*Weekly. Owner: Centaur. Editor: Stuart
Smith; deputy and news: Sonoo Singh*

Media Week
020 8267 5000
mwnewsdesk@haynet.com
www.mediaweek.co.uk
*Weekly. Owner: Haymarket. Editor:
Steve Barrett; news: Ellen Bennett;
features editor: Julia Martin;
production: Glenys Trevor*

New Media Age
020 7970 4000
mike.nutley@centaur.co.uk
www.nma.co.uk
*Weekly. Owner: Centaur. Editor:
Mike Nutley; news: Justin Pearse*

Shots
020 7505 8000
lyndy.stout@shots.net
www.shots.net
International advertising. 6pa. Owner: Emap Communications. Editor: Lyndy Stout; assistant editor: Danny Edwards

Advertising Associations

Advertising Association
7th Floor North, Artillery House,
11–19 Artillery Row,
London SW1P 1RT
020 7340 1100
aa@adassoc.org.uk
www.adassoc.org.uk
Press:
jim.rothwell@adassoc.org.uk

Advertising Standards Authority
Mid City Place, 71 High Holborn,
London WC1V 6QT
020 7492 2222
enquiries@asa.org.uk
www.asa.org.uk

Chartered Institute of Marketing
Moor Hall, Cookham,
Maidenhead, Berkshire SL6 9QH
01628 427500
info@cim.co.uk
www.cim.co.uk

Committee of Advertising Practice
Mid City Place, 71 High Holborn,
London WC1V 6QT
020 7492 2222
enquiries@cap.org.uk
www.cap.org.uk
Press: press@cap.org.uk

Direct Marketing Association
DMA House, 70 Margaret Street,
London W1W 8SS
020 7291 3300
info@dma.org.uk
www.dma.org.uk

Incorporated Society of British Advertisers
Langham House, 1b Portland Place, London W1B 1PN
020 7291 9020
Media@isba.org.uk
www.isba.org.uk

Institute of Practitioners in Advertising
44 Belgrave Square,
London SW1X 8QS
020 7235 7020
info@ipa.co.uk
www.ipa.co.uk

International Advertising Association
521 Fifth Avenue, Suite 1807,
New York, NY 10175 USA
001 212 557 1133
iaa@iaaglobal.org
www.iaaglobal.org

Internet Advertising Bureau
Ingram House,
13–15 John Adam Street,
London WC2N 6LU
info@iabuk.net
www.iabuk.net
Press: 020 7886 8282

Market Research Society
15 Northburgh Street,
London EC1V 0JR
020 7490 4911
info@mrs.org.uk
www.mrs.org.uk

Nielsen/NetRatings
77 St John Street,
London EC1M 4AN
020 7014 0590
info@netratings.com
www.netratings.com
Press: 020 7014 0597

Outdoor Advertising Association of Great Britain
Summit House, 27 Sale Place,
London W2 1YR
020 7973 0315
enquiries@oaa.org.uk
www.oaa.org.uk

World Federation of Advertisers
120 Avenue Louise,
1050 Brussels, Belgium
00 32 2 502 5740
info@wfanet.org
www.wfanet.org

Public relations

Julian Henry

Former BP chairman Sir John Browne

Oh how the mighty are fallen. The sudden resignation of Sir John Browne as chairman of BP in May this year after lying about his private life is a reminder that none of us are untouchable, and that even the most powerful business executives can slip upon a PR banana skin. He joins Britney Spears, ITV game shows, Bernard Matthews turkeys and the 2012 Olympic logo, all of which have taken a beating from the press in 2007 after PR problems of one sort or another.

In the publicity business the truth is a precious commodity, and though it may be uncertified by anyone other than God as he stands in judgment at the Gates of Heaven, the PR industry's continued expansion has demonstrated how marketing people are mostly interested in creating their own robust version of events.

The story that generated more newspaper coverage than any other is the unfortunate case of Madeleine McCann. A relentless publicity campaign has made Maddy's face famous around the world, but it has failed to dispel the mood of suspicion and finger-pointing that has arisen as conflicting versions of events have been offered up into the public arena.

Perhaps Kate and Gerry McCann started off blindly hoping their problems would somehow be solved by wrapping the tragedy up and handing it on a plate to the media. This story has a huge commercial value because it is a well-cast and real-life human drama. Journalists have not been shy in promoting the most intimate aspects of the affair to their readers and the McCanns are now deemed fair game because they chose to publicise their case so energetically.

The problem with launching a publicity campaign like this is that you cannot simply turn down the heat when you feel like it. By submitting their case to the public they have unwittingly relinquished any right of control over what conclusions may be drawn and any belated attempt to rescue their privacy, dignity and perceived innocence is almost certainly doomed until definitive evidence of what happened that night becomes available.

In the industry, we call this kind of job "crisis PR". It's an unfortunate category, bunching together natural disasters, plummeting stock on the world markets and terrorist attacks. But crisis PR also brings out the best in natural communicators.

When a Virgin train crashed in February Richard Branson's response was typical of the old media pro he has become. He jumped in his chopper, flew to the site and talked passionately to reporters to remind us that a) his trains were strong and well made

b) the train driver was a hero and c) Virgin Trains don't crash very often. It was a textbook example of how to restore public confidence at a key moment. Anyone doubting the impact of negative PR should go to Newcastle and talk to the people at Northern Rock.

You might call this kind of work "defence of reputation" and it is here, at the corporate end of the publicity business, where the real money is to be found. When the City PR firm Financial Dynamics sold its agency for a cool £139m to a US management consultancy at the end of 2006, it was a defining moment, and effectively put into context the sale of more glamorous but significantly less valuable agencies such as Freuds, Jackie Cooper, Lynne Franks and others, which had gone to market for a trifling £10m or so in previous years.

The most obvious PR success of the year in media land is Facebook. It didn't need an agency for the launch because, like the best pyramid selling or viral marketing, it relied on word of mouth and the desire that young people have to show off. Facebook appointed its first PR agency, Bite PR, in the summer in a hotly contested pitch battle involving 12 competing agencies.

Facebook makes it easy for brands and corporations to talk to millions of 16- to 24-year-olds with a new sense of intimacy, and social networking has taken on a faddish appeal as various opportunists and chancers jump on the bandwagon. These fast-growing online companies that create miniature worlds – Facebook, Second Life, RuneScape, MySpace – have usurped the telecoms companies, handset-makers, games console companies and software designers as the new playgrounds for adventurous marketeers in our industry.

They are powerful today because they reflect the zeitgeist, and illuminate a behaviour change in the mass market that is an advertiser's dream: they cluster audiences from around the world around lifestyle choices. We all want one of these companies on our books because they bring with them access to new marketing techniques, audience research and a global perspective that allows you to foresee trends.

However, the new ground being broken here requires legislation and regulation as well as raising corporate PR issues involving copyrighted material, privacy, marketing to minors, censorship and other areas that will keep both the legal and PR professions busy for years to come.

Perhaps the BBC's difficulties in 2007 might have been resolved less painfully if the organisation had been at the centre of an easily mobilised social network. Unlike Facebook or Microsoft, for example, the BBC is a part of the fabric of British life, with millions of stakeholders who are quite happy to pay their licence fees. It's a pity this audience was not called on to contribute to the debate around Peter Fincham's departure, as they may have provided a perspective to illustrate how media organisations are prone to over-react in an attempt to appear politically correct.

With this backdrop of self-examination and paranoia, perhaps it's not surprising that the PR business is beginning to look more confident and respectable. Fleet Street is withering, the big advertising agencies are struggling to reinvent themselves and the TV industry has been caught duping its audience. The coming year should be a great time for PR professionals to show themselves as both reputable and inspiring.

● Julian Henry is the chairman of Henry's House PR Agency

Perhaps the greatest PR turnaround of 2007 was that of the Conservative party. Little wonder, with a former PR at the helm in David Cameron. But how much was a former tabloid editor responsible? MediaGuardian's PR commentator Julian Henry revealed all during conference season

»› MediaGuardian   September 24 2007

Coulson's Tory party conference test

Julian Henry

Journalism and public relations go together like chalk and cheese. The best journalists are those dedicated to the disclosure of the truth. They are answerable ultimately to their readers, and they try to avoid the influence of vested interest. Us PR people on the other hand . . .

Most UK PR companies are beholden to corporations that sell stuff such as healthcare, food or financial services. And business is booming. Agency fees are up over 20% a year, according to PR Week. So with newspapers shedding jobs it is understandable that some hacks might look to switch industries.

Perhaps the most high-profile case in recent times came in May when ex-News of the World editor Andy Coulson was unveiled as director of communication and planning for the Conservative party. Appointing a journalist – however eminent – into a challenging PR job is a risk. And it illustrates how one specific area of communication – the daily news media and specifically the Murdoch press – has become critical to the thinking of the Conservatives.

Like the solid professional he is, Coulson has wasted no time in getting stuck in. A number of conspicuous puff pieces in the News of the World, the Sun, the Telegraph and other dailies have appeared. He has a desk at Westminster alongside David Cameron, shadow chancellor George Osborne and director of strategy Steve Hilton. And news filters out through Coulson's showbiz pals that he joins Cameron at shadow cabinet meetings, and is privy to the strategic moves, much as Alastair Campbell was during the early Blair years.

But it was different then. Campbell and Peter Mandelson re-invented the way that politicians marketed themselves by launching an obsessive and brutal assault on daily media outlets. Campbell in particular used his skill as a former hack to out-negotiate Fleet Street at its own game. This can only complicate Coulson's mission, as he will need to persuade us that what we are seeing is real, as well as communicating a sense of cohesion, unity and purpose within the party.

Having said that, the main aim of improving the Conservatives' profile is achievable as he creates publicity for Cameron's highly campaignable ideas. But Coulson will need both a bulletproof vest and an invisibility cloak if he is going to survive sniper fire from old-school Conservatives who resent his position. A high-profile spin doctor is an easy target for those wanting to create problems.

The other battle he faces requires the help of Steve Hilton, the canny ex-advertising executive now widely credited with plotting Cameron's ascent over the past two or three years. Hilton is a key man for the future of the Tories, though you sense that his partnership with Coulson, dynamic and hard hitting as it may be, might lack grassroots support within the party, and this may be the cause of the recent problems with Michael Ancram and others.

Devising a route into the heart of the party to inspire traditionalists and modernisers will be the true test of the duo's strategic talents. The 300,000 members of the party are a key asset. They cannot be treated as a database or as newspaper readers. They need to be involved, unified and motivated, as they were when Cameron first took over as leader.

You can expect the new Tory PR machine to start to reveal their hand at the Conservative party conference, which starts on Sunday in Blackpool. They will have to be wary, though.

A few years ago our PR agency staged a stunt there on behalf of Ikea. The organisers had chosen

Martin Argles

Public relations

Ikea furniture for delegates to sit on. We arranged for a photographer to snap an unsuspecting Margaret Thatcher reclining on a modish Ikea sofa, and then cheekily announced that she and her Tory team had ditched traditional British values in favour of a modern pro-European design thanks to her endorsement of Sweden's No 1 furniture retailer. The story made the front of the Times, ran in the Daily Mail and the Sun, and triggered a debate on Newsnight; the people at Ikea were delighted. That's the kind of ambushing that goes on.

Those who question whether journalists make decent PRs can point to the story of Amanda Platell, who, in 1999, was the editor of a Sunday paper. She was sacked and then became the PR chief for Conservative leader William Hague. When she resigned two years later it was revealed that she'd kept a video diary, which was broadcast on C4 to the rage of party members. She later renounced all links to the Conservatives and said the party's image was "vicious, self-interested, ruthless and above all nasty". I am sure that the Coulson story will end differently.

PR disasters

● **November 2007** Taking her own lead, Heather Mills appeared on GMTV expressing her anguish about the way in which she had been treated by the press over her separation with Paul McCartney. Miss Mills gave in to her frustration by ranting about her mistreatment on the morning TV show, stating that she had been suicidal and very depressed. The PR consultant Mark Borkowski was keen to point out that all the television appearance did was "to provide more ammunition for the following day's papers — coverage that continued to gnaw away at her fragile self-esteem".

● **November 2007** A computer disc containing the personal information of more than 15,000 Standard Life customers was lost as it was sent to the company's headquarters in Edinburgh. According to HM Revenue and Customs, discs containing personal taxpayer information are routinely sent to insurance companies. However, it took five weeks after the incident for customers to receive a letter warning them that they could be at risk of fraud and should be "vigilant". Many customers argued that the delay in notification only made the situation worse.

● **August 2007** The manufacturing company Johnson & Johnson filed a lawsuit against the American Red Cross, claiming that the logo of the Red Cross was its own trademark. The American Red Cross fought back, branding the lawsuit "obscene", and arguing that the two companies had been co-existing for many years without any dispute. Johnson & Johnson argued that the American Red Cross had

gone beyond its traditional use of the logo by introducing new products such as first aid kits and toothbrushes, which subsequently competed with similar products by Johnson & Johnson. However, the American Red Cross was keen to point out that the Red Cross has become a well-known symbol of international aid and disaster relief for both the charity and manufacturing company.

● **March 2007** The BBC was forced to apologise to viewers when it was revealed that Blue Peter deceived its viewers by faking the results of a competition. The show had faced technical problems that prevented viewers from getting through to the studio and had asked a visiting child to pose as the winning caller. Despite the BBC not making any profit from the failed calls, Ofcom, the broadcasting watchdog, decided the BBC had made a serious error of judgment and fined it £50,000.

● **February 2007** Cadbury Schweppes came up with a promotional campaign for Dr Pepper that consisted of hiding a coin worth $10,000 in a graveyard and then enticing customers to find it with the chance to win up to $1m. The drinks company was forced to apologise for the stunt after the graveyard was closed after fears that potential "treasure" hunters would destroy more than 5,000 graves, including those of some of America's revolutionary heroes. According to Cadbury Schweppes, none of the graves were destroyed and the coin had been removed. Despite this, the local authorities still viewed the stunt as "disrespectful".

Advertising, PR and media law

PR coups

● **July 2007** A clear PR success for promoters of The Simpsons Movie, who pulled out all the strings when it came to creating ideas for promoting the film. The campaign began in the US, with a clever stunt to find the "home of the Simpsons". More than 20 American towns called Springfield were invited to enter a competition to become the host of The Simpsons Movie premiere. The towns had to produce a video demonstrating their enthusiasm to be the winning town. In addition, promoters recreated the Kwik-E-Mart by transforming 7-11 stores. In the UK, a large painted outline of Homer Simpson appeared on the hillside next to the Cerne Abbas giant in Dorset. According to Mark Borkowski, the PR team had proved that "great stunts do generate coverage and do work".

● **June 2007** As a result of An Inconvenient Truth the former vice president Al Gore, along with the Intergovernmental Panel on Climate Change, were awarded the Nobel Peace prize. The Academy award-winning documentary film focused on climate change and in particular global warming. A percentage of the profits were donated to assist the Alliance for Climate Protection. The PR team behind the film were also named PR professionals of the year for their successful efforts to promote climate change.

● **June 2007** The makers of a Dutch reality TV show, The Big Donor Show, sparked a whirlwind of controversy after the show was discovered to be a hoax. The programme was to show a terminally ill woman choosing which contestant would receive her kidneys when she dies. However, it was revealed that the show was invented in order to raise awareness of organ donation in the Netherlands. Mark Borkowski stated that "if there are various charities and health organisations linked up to this hoax then it is indeed a very clever publicity stunt".

● **March 2007** Moving beyond the coffee, Starbucks extended its role with a new record company, Hear Music. For years the coffee chain has been selling music in its stores and has also signed deals to distribute previously unreleased tracks by artists such as Alanis Morrisette and Bob Dylan. With the formation of the new record label, the store can now sign new and already established artists.

3 x 1 Public Relations
Glasgow
0141 221 0707
info@3x1.com
www.3x1.com

AD Communications
Esher, Surrey
01372 464470
rallen@adcomms.co.uk
www.adcomms.co.uk

APR Communications
London
020 7351 2227
arobson@aprcommunications.com
www.aprcommunications.com

AS Biss & Co
London
020 7340 6200
tellmemore@asbiss.com
www.asbiss.com

Ashley Communications
Rickmansworth, Hertfordshire
01923 779547
info@ashleycomms.com
www.ashleycomms.com

Attenborough Saffron
London
020 7067 1597
info@attenborough.net
www.attenborough.net

August One
London
020 8846 8300
enquiries@augustone.com
www.augustone.com

Automotive PR
London
020 7494 8050
info@automotivepr.com
www.automotivepr.com

AxiCom
London
020 8392 4050
jtanner@axicom.com
www.axicom.com

B2B Communications
Chessington, Surrey
020 8974 2404
enquiries@
 b2bcommunications.co.uk
www.b2bcommunications.co.uk

Band & Brown Communications
London
020 7419 7000
info@bbpr.com
www.bbpr.com

Barkers Scotland
Glasgow
0141 248 5030
ckelly@barkers-scot.com
www.barkersscotland.co.uk

Barrett Dixon Bell
Altrincham, Cheshire
0161 925 4700
info@bdb.co.uk
www.bdb.co.uk

Beattie Communications
London
020 7053 6000
info@beattiegroup.com
www.beattiegroup.com
Birmingham: 0121 698 8625
Edinburgh: 0131 220 8269
Falkirk: 01324 602550
Glasgow: 01698 787878
Manchester: 0161 935 8334

Bell Pottinger Public Affairs
London
020 7861 2400
pbingle@bell-pottinger.co.uk
www.bppa.co.uk

Bell Pottinger Public Relations
London
020 7861 3800
info@bell-pottinger.co.uk
www.bell-pottinger.co.uk

Berkeley PR International
Reading
0118 988 2992
enquiries@berkeleypr.co.uk
www.berkeleypr.co.uk
Bristol: 01454 203595
Derbyshire: 01629 826942

BGB & Associates
London
020 7902 2990
pr@bgb.co.uk
www.bgb.co.uk

The Big Partnership
Glasgow
0141 333 9585
info@bigpartnership.co.uk
www.bigpartnership.co.uk
Aberdeen: 01224 571414
Edinburgh: 0131 558 3111

Biosector 2
London
020 7632 1960
www.biosector2.com

Bite Communications
London
020 8741 1123
moreUK@bitepr.com
www.bitepr.com

BMB
Luton
01582 725454
reception@bmb.uk.com
www.bmb.uk.com

Brahm PR
Leeds
0113 230 4000
www.brahm.com

Brands2Life
London
020 7592 1200
info@brands2life.com
www.brands2life.com

Brave PR
London
020 7802 8111
charlotte.a@bravepr.com
www.bravepr.com

Bray Leino
Bristol
0117 973 1173
info@brayleino.co.uk
www.brayleino.co.uk

Brazen
Manchester
0161 923 4994
nina@brazenpr.com
www.brazenpr.com

The Bright Consultancy
Solihull, West Midlands
0121 711 5000
pr@bright-consultancy.co.uk
www.bright-consultancy.co.uk

Broadgate
London
020 7726 6111
contact@bgate.co.uk
www.bgate.co.uk

Brower Lewis Pelham PR
London
020 7259 1550
www.prco.com

Brunswick
London
020 7404 5959
info@brunswickgroup.com
www.brunswickgroup.com

Buchanan Communications
London
020 7466 5000
www.buchanan.uk.com
Leeds: 01943 883990

Buffalo Communications
London
020 7292 8680
info@buffalo.co.uk
www.buffalo.co.uk

Burson-Marsteller
London
020 7831 6262
bm-london_reception@uk.bm.com
www.bm.com

Camargue
London
020 7636 7366
www.camarguepr.com
Birmingham: 0121 616 5920
Cheltenham: 01242 577277

Camron PR
London
020 7420 1700
genevieve@camron.co.uk
www.camron.co.uk

Capital MS&L
London
020 7307 5330
steffan.williams@capitalmsl.com
www.capitalmsl.co.uk

Capitalize
London
020 7940 1700
info@capitalize.co.uk
www.capitalize.co.uk

Carat
London
020 7430 6000
nick.gracie@carat.com
www.carat.co.uk

Carrot Communications
London
020 7386 4860
kate.hartley@carrotcomms.co.uk
www.carrotcomms.co.uk

Chameleon PR
London
020 7680 5500
www.chameleonpr.com

Cherton Enterprise
Belfast
028 9065 4007
robin.guthrie@cherton.co.uk
www.cherton.co.uk

CIB Communications
Leatherhead, Surrey
01372 371800
gavint@cibcommunications.co.uk
www.cibcommunications.co.uk

Citigate Communications
London
020 7282 2880
Birmingham: 0121 236 7532

Citigate Dewe Rogerson
London
020 7638 9571
perri.taylor@citigatedr.co.uk
www.citigatedr.co.uk

Citypress PR
Manchester
0161 606 0260
www.citypress.co.uk

Clareville Communications
London
020 7736 4022
mail@clareville.co.uk
www.clareville.co.uk

**Clear Communication
Consultancy & Training**
London
020 7432 2500
clear@clearco.co.uk
www.clearco.co.uk

Cohesive Communications
London
020 7470 8777
www.cohesive.uk.com
Chepstow: 01291 626200

Cohn & Wolfe
London
020 7331 5300
jonathan_shore@cohnwolfe.com
www.cohnwolfe.com

Colette Hill Associates
London
020 7622 8252
cha@chapr.co.uk
www.chapr.co.uk

College Hill
London
020 7457 2020
pr@collegehill.com
www.collegehill.com

Colman Getty PR
London
020 7631 2666
pr@colmangetty.co.uk
www.colmangetty.co.uk
Edinburgh: 0131 558 8851

The Communication Group
London
020 7630 1411
enquiries@
   thecommunicationgroup.co.uk
www.thecommunicationgroup.co.uk

Communique PR
Manchester
0161 228 6677
www.communiquepr.co.uk
London: 020 7300 6300

Companycare Communications
Reading
0118 920 7650
www.companycare.com

Consolidated Communications
London
020 7287 2087
sarahr@consol.co.uk
www.consol.co.uk

Corixa Communications
Bristol
0117 949 3394
www.corixa.co.uk

Cow Communications
London
020 7684 6969
dirk.singer@cowpr.com
www.cowpr.com

Cubitt Consulting
London
020 7367 5100
www.cubitt.com

Darwall Smith Associates
London
020 7553 3700
gill@dsapr.co.uk
www.dsapr.co.uk

Dialogue Agency
Twickenham
020 8607 0340
enquiry@dialogueagency.com
www.dialogueagency.com

DTW
London
office@dtw.co.uk
www.dtw.co.uk
Guisborough, Cleveland:
   01287 610404

Edelman
London
020 7344 1200
london@edelman.com
www.edelman.co.uk

Edson Evers
Stafford
01785 255146
www.edsonevers.com

**EHPR (Elizabeth Hindmarch
Public Relations)**
Windsor, Berkshire
01753 842017
info@ehpr.co.uk
www.ehpr.co.uk

EML
Kingston-upon-Thames, Surrey
020 8408 8000
info@eml.com
www.eml.com

Eulogy!
London
020 7927 9999
pr@eulogy.co.uk
www.eulogy.co.uk

Euro RSCG Riley
London
020 7022 4000
www.eurorscg-riley.co.uk

Financial Dynamics
London
020 7831 3113
amy.hewitt@fd.com
www.fd.com

Finsbury PR
London
020 7251 3801
info@finsbury.com
www.finsbury.com

Firefly Communications
London
020 7386 1400
claire.walker@fireflycomms.com
www.fireflycomms.com

Fishburn Hedges
London
020 7839 4321
info@fishburn-hedges.com
www.fishburn-hedges.co.uk

Flagship Consulting
London
020 7886 8440
info@flagshipconsulting.co.uk
www.flagshipconsulting.co.uk

Fleishman-Hillard (UK)
London
020 7306 9000
www.fleishman.co.uk
Dublin: 00 353 1 618 8444
Edinburgh: 0131 226 2162

Focus PR
London
020 7432 9432
vision@focuspr.co.uk
www.focuspr.co.uk

Four Communications
London
0870 444 4568
info@fourcommunications.com
www.fourcommunications.com

Fox Parrack Singapour
London
020 7851 7750
dfox@foxps.com
www.foxps.com

Freshwater Marketing Communications
Cardiff
029 2054 5370
info@freshwater-uk.com
www.freshwater-uk.com
Birmingham: 0121 633 7775
Bristol: 0117 317 8135
Glasgow: 0141 229 4050
London: 020 7432 2507

Freud Communications
London
020 3003 6300
www.freud.com

Galliard Healthcare Communications
London
020 7663 2250
www.galliardhealth.com

Garnett Keeler Marketing Communications
Surbiton, Surrey
020 8399 1184
pr@garnett-keeler.com
www.garnett-keeler.com

GCI London
London
020 7072 4000
info@gciuk.com
www.gciuk.com

Geronimo Communications
Leeds
0113 306 0000
welcome@
geronimocommunications.com
www.geronimocommunications
.com
Bury St Edmunds: 01284 768935
London: 020 7299 8740
Nottingham: 0115 934 7340

GolinHarris
London
020 7067 0600
www.golinharris.com

Golley Slater PR
London
020 7240 9920
www.golleyslater.com
Bangor: 01248 672636
Birmingham: 0121 384 9700
Bristol: 0117 917 5710
Cardiff: 029 2038 8621
Cirencester: 01285 741111
Edinburgh: 0131 272 2733
Leeds: 01943 484848
Manchester: 0161 832 7178
Newcastle: 0191 245 9020

Good Relations
London
020 7861 3030
afossey@goodrelations.co.uk
www.goodrelations.co.uk

Gough Allen Stanley
Bromsgrove, Worcs
01527 579555
info@gough.co.uk
www.gough.co.uk

Grant Butler Coomber
London
020 8322 1922
www.gbc.co.uk

Grayling
London
020 7255 1100
info@uk.grayling.com
www.grayling.com

Great Circle Communications
Edinburgh
0131 225 4646
info@greatcircle.co.uk
www.greatcircle.co.uk

Green Issues Communications
London
020 7152 4022
www.greenissues.com
Cardiff: 029 2050 4050
Manchester: 0161 209 3850
Reading: 0118 959 1211

Hallmark Public Relations
Winchester
01962 718720
inspired@hallmarkpr.com
www.hallmarkpr.com

Halogen PR
London
020 7087 3260
www.halogenuk.com

Harrison Cowley
London
020 7404 6777
info@harrisoncowley.com
www.harrisoncowley.com
Birmingham: 0121 237 7532
Bristol: 0117 929 2311
Cardiff: 029 2034 4717
Edinburgh: 0131 226 2363
Leeds: 0113 237 0777
Manchester: 0161 839 5666
Southampton: 023 8033 7237

Haslimann Taylor
Birmingham
0121 355 3446
bron@haslimanntaylor.com
www.haslimanntaylor.com

Haygarth
London
020 8971 3300
stephen.m@haygarth.co.uk
www.haygarth.co.uk

Henry's House
London
020 7291 3000
www.henryshouse.com

Hill & Knowlton
London
020 7413 3000
wfick@hillandknowlton.com
www.hillandknowlton.co.uk

Hills Balfour Synergy
London
020 7367 0900
info@hillsbalfoursynergy.com
www.hillsbalfoursynergy.com

The Hoffman Agency
London
020 7470 8762
lhoffman@hoffman.com
www.hoffman.com

Hotwire PR
London
020 7608 2500
kristin.syltevik@hotwirepr.com
www.hotwirepr.com

Houston Associates
London
020 8778 1900
info@houston-associates.com
www.houston-associates.com

IAS Smarts
Edinburgh
0131 555 0425
www.iassmarts.com
Belfast: 028 9039 5500
Birmingham 0121 456 3199
Glasgow: 0141 222 2040
Manchester: 01625 434343
London: 020 7535 9900

Publicasity
Hemel Hempstead
01442 261199
pr@publicasity.co.uk
www.publicasity.co.uk
London: 020 7632 2400

The Ideas Network
London
020 7351 4719
enquiries@ideasnetwork.co.uk
www.ideasnetwork.co.uk

The Impact Agency
London
020 7580 1770
mail@impactagency.co.uk
www.theimpactagency.com

Insight Marketing & Communications
London
020 7861 3999
info@insightmkt.com
www.insightmkt.com
Heathrow: 020 8564 6398
Manchester: 01625 500800

The ITPR Group
Chertsey, Surrey
01932 578800
www.itpr.co.uk

Jackie Cooper PR
London
020 7208 7208
Info@jcpr.com
www.jcpr.com

JBP Public Relations
Bristol
0117 907 3400
www.jbp.co.uk

Johnson King
London
020 7357 7799
mikek@johnsonking.co.uk
www.johnsonking.com

Kaizo
London
020 3043 4151
crispin.manners@kaizo.net
www.kaizo.net

Kavanagh Communications
Guildford
01483 238840
anne@
    kavanaghcommunications.com
www.kavanaghcommunications.com

Keene Public Affairs Consultants
London
020 7287 0652
kpac@keenepa.co.uk
www.keenepa.co.uk

Kelso Consulting
London
020 7388 8886
pr@kelsopr.com
www.kelsopr.com

Kenyon Fraser
Liverpool
0151 706 9966
richardk@kenyons.co.uk
www.kenyons.co.uk

Kestrel WorldCom
London
020 8789 2587
kestrel@kestrelcomms.co.uk
www.kestrelworldcom.com

Ketchum
London
020 7611 3500
david.gallagher@ketchum.com
www.ketchum.com

Kinross & Render
London
020 7592 3105
sr@kinrossrender.com
www.kinrossrender.com

Kysen PR
London
020 7323 3230
www.kysenpr.co.uk

Lansons Communications
London
020 7490 8828
pr@lansons.com
www.lansons.com

Lawson Dodd
London
020 7535 1355
iam@lawsondodd.co.uk
www.lawsondodd.co.uk

Leader Communications
Warwickshire
01564 796200
ms@leader.co.uk
www.leader.co.uk

Lewis PR
London
020 7802 2626
kathp@lewispr.com
www.lewispr.com

Lexis Public Relations
London
020 7908 6488
www.lexispr.com

Lighthouse PR
London
020 7494 6577
www.lighthousepr.com

London Communications Agency
London
020 7612 8480
lca@londoncommunications.co.uk
www.londoncommunications.co.uk

M: Communications
London
020 7153 1530
info@mcomgroup.com
www.mcomgroup.com

Manning Selvage & Lee
London
020 7878 3000
results@mslpr.co.uk
www.mslpr.co.uk

Mantra Public Relations
London
020 7438 4910
dsmith@mantra-pr.com
www.mantra-pr.com

Market Engineering
Banbury, Oxon
01295 277050
www.marketengineering.co.uk

Mary Rahman PR
London
020 7749 1136
www.mr-pr.com

Mason Williams
0845 0941 007
info@mason-williams.com
www.mason-williams.co.uk

McCann Erickson Public Relations
Solihull
0121 713 3500
brendan.callaghan@
    europe.mccann.com
www.mccann.com

McCluskey International
London
020 8237 7979
info@mccluskey.co.uk
www.mccluskeyinternational.co.uk

Media Strategy
London
020 7400 4480
clewington@mediastrategy.co.uk
www.mediastrategy.co.uk

Medicom Group
Hampton Court, Surrey
020 8481 8100
enquiries@medicomgroup.com
www.medicomgroup.com

MediTech Media
London
020 7398 0500
info@meditech.co.uk
www.meditech-media.com
Manchester: 0161 236 2367

Midas PR
London
020 7584 7474
info@midaspr.co.uk
www.midaspr.co.uk

Midnight Communications
Brighton
01273 666200
enquiries@midnight.co.uk
www.midnight.co.uk

Mulberry Marketing Communications
London
020 7928 7676
info@mulberrymc.com
www.mulberrymc.com

Munro & Forster Communications
London
020 7815 3900
www.munroforster.com

Neesham PR
Wendover, Buckinghamshire
01296 628180
admin@neesham.co.uk
www.neesham.co.uk

Nelson Bostock Communications
London
020 7229 4400
info@nelsonbostock.com
www.nelsonbostock.com

Nexus Communications Group
London
020 7808 9808
www.nexuspr.com

NorthBank Communications
Congleton
01260 296500
info@
    northbankcommunications.com
www.northbankcommunications
    .com
London: 020 7268 3002

Northern Lights
Harrogate
01423 562400
mail@northernlightspr.com
www.northernlightspr.com

Ogilvy Public Relations
London
020 7309 1000
www.ogilvypr.com

Pagoda PR
Edinburgh
0131 556 0770
info@pagodapr.com
www.pagodapr.com
Belfast: 028 9032 8291

Parkgreen Communications
London
020 7851 7480
info@parkgreenmedia.com
www.parkgreenmedia.com

Partners Group
York
01904 610077
postbox@partners-group.co.uk
www.partners-group.co.uk

Pegasus PR
Worthing, West Sussex
01903 821550
info@pegasuspr.co.uk
www.pegasuspr.co.uk

Penrose Financial
London
020 7786 4888
pr@penrose.co.uk
www.penrose.co.uk

PFPR Communications
Maidstone, Kent
01622 691361
info@pfpr.com
www.pfpr.com

Phipps Public Relations
London
020 7759 7400
askus@phippspr.co.uk
www.phippspr.com

Pinnacle Marketing Communications
Pinner, Middlesex
020 8869 9339
simon@pinnaclemarcom.com
www.pinnacle-marketing.com

Piranhakid
London
020 7973 5938
www.piranhakid.com

Pleon
London
020 7479 5656
www.pleon.com

Porter Novelli
London
020 7853 2222
www.porternovelli.com
Banbury: 01295 224400
Edinburgh: 0131 470 3400

Portfolio Communications
London
020 7240 6959
www.portfoliocomms.com

Portland PR
London
020 7404 5344
info@portlandpr.co.uk
www.portlandpr.co.uk

Positive Profile
London
020 7489 2028
henryg@positiveprofile.com
www.positiveprofile.com

PPS Group
London
020 7629 7377
www.ppsgroup.co.uk
Birmingham: 0121 200 0813
Bristol: 0145 427 5630
Edinburgh: 0131 226 1951
Manchester: 0161 832 2139

Prowse & Co
Leatherhead, Surrey
01372 363386
reception@prowse.co.uk
www.prowse.co.uk

Ptarmigan Consultants
Leeds
0113 242 1155
www.ptarmiganpr.co.uk

Public Relations Consultants Association
London
020 7233 6026
pressoffice@prca.org.uk
www.prca.org.uk

Purple PR
London
020 7439 9888
enquiries@purplepr.com
www.purplepr.com

QuayWest Communications
Coggeshall, Essex
01376 563156
s.morrison@quay-west.co.uk
www.quay-west.co.uk

Radiator PR
London
020 7404 8264
www.radiatorpr.com

Rainier PR
London
020 7494 6570
rainier@rainierpr.co.uk
www.rainierpr.co.uk
Cambridge: 01359 250641

The Red Consultancy
London
020 7025 6500
red@redconsultancy.com
www.redconsultancy.com

Red Door Communications
London
020 8392 8040
info@rdcomms.com
www.rdcomms.com

Regester Larkin
London
020 7831 3839
enquiries@regesterlarkin.com
www.regesterlarkin.com

Republic
London
020 7379 5000
www.republicpr.com

Resolute Communications
London
020 7357 8187
info@resolutecommunications.com
www.resolutecommunications.com

Revolver Communications
Leeds
0113 287 0123
enquiries@revolvercomms.com
www.revolvercomms.com

Richard Lewis Communications
Southampton
01962 771111
info@crossculture.com
www.crossculture.com

Ruder Finn UK
London
020 7462 8900
mail@ruderfinn.co.uk
www.ruderfinn.com

Salt
London
020 8870 6777
info@saltlondon.com
www.saltlondon.com

Seal Communications
Birmingham
0121 200 0780
www.sealcommunications.co.uk
London: 020 7935 4030

Shine Communications
London
020 7553 3333
brilliance@shinecom.com
www.shinecom.com

Shire Health Group
London
020 7108 6400
matt.degruchy@
    shirehealthlondon.com
www.shirehealthlondon.com

Six Degrees
Marlow, Buckinghamshire
01628 480280
mail@sixdegreespr.com
www.sixdegreespr.com

Spark Marketing Communications
London
020 7436 0420
info@sparkcomms.co.uk
www.sparkcomms.co.uk

Spinoza Kennedy Vesey Public Relations
Manchester
0161 838 7770
www.skvpr.co.uk

Spreckley Partners
London
020 7388 9988
info@spreckley.co.uk
www.spreckley.co.uk

Staniforth
London
020 7573 7480
urgent@staniforth.co.uk
www.staniforth.co.uk
Manchester: 0161 919 8495

Starfish Communications
London
020 7031 8145
fearfield@star-fish.net
www.star-fish.net

Storm Communications
London
020 7240 2444
info@stormcom.co.uk
www.stormcom.co.uk
Beaconsfield: 01494 670444

StrategicAlliance International
Old Amersham, Bucks
01494 434434
nicholasf@strategicpr.net
www.strategicpr.net

Target Public Relations
Cheltenham
01242 633100
www.targetgroup.co.uk

Taylor Alden
London
020 8543 3866
pr@tayloralden.co.uk
www.tayloralden.com
Newbury: 01635 521103

Taylor Herring
London
020 8206 5151
james@taylorherring.com
www.taylorherring.com

TBWA UK Group
London
020 7573 6666
www.tbwa-london.com

Text 100
London
020 8846 0700
stacey.hinds@text100.co.uk
www.text100.com

Trimedia
London
020 7025 7500
www.trimediagroup.com

Twelve Consultancy
London
020 7631 0737
graham@twelvepr.co.uk
www.twelvepr.co.uk

Warman Group
Birmingham
0800 138 4443
enquiries@warmangroup.com
www.warmangroup.com

Weber Shandwick
London
020 7067 0000
enquiriesuk@webershandwick.co.uk
www.webershandwick.co.uk

Westbury Communications
London
020 7751 9170
www.westburycom.co.uk

Whiteoaks Consultancy
Farnham, Surrey
01252 727313
comms@whiteoaks.co.uk
www.whiteoaks.co.uk

Wild Card PR
London
020 7355 0655
deck@wildcardpr.co.uk
www.wildcard.co.uk

William Murray PR
London
020 8256 1360
www.williammurraypr.co.uk

Willoughby PR
Birmingham
0121 456 3004
angelah@willoughby-pr.co.uk
www.willoughby-pr.co.uk

Metia
London
020 3100 3500
www.metia.com

Wyatt International
Birmingham
0121 454 8181
info@wyattinternational.com
www.wyattinternational.com

Yellow Door Creative Marketing
London
020 7580 0707
www.yellow-door.co.uk

PR trade press

Hollis UK Public Relations Annual
020 8973 3400
orders@hollis-pr.co.uk
www.hollis-pr.com
Annual. Press and PR contacts. Owner: Hollis Publishing. Editor: Sarah Hughes

PR Week
020 8267 4429
prweek@haynet.com
Weekly. Owner: Haymarket. Editor: Danny Rogers; deputy news: David Singleton; features: Alex Black; sub: Will Stanbridge

Associations

Association of Public Relations Consultants
Willow House, Willow Place,
London SW1P 1JH
020 7233 6026
info@prca.org.uk
www.prca.org.uk

British Association of Communicators in Business
GA2 Oak House,
Woodlands Business Park,
Breckland, Linford Wood West,
Milton Keynes MK14 6EY
01908 313755
enquiries@cib.uk.com
www.cib.uk.com
Professional body for internal and corporate communications staff

Chartered Institute of Public Relations
32, St James's Square,
London SW1Y 4JR
020 7766 3333
info@cipr.co.uk
www.cipr.co.uk

Public relations

contacts

Media law

Jerry Bridge-Butler

England fly-half Jonny Wilkinson

It was reported after England's triumph in the 2003 rugby World Cup that Jonny Wilkinson was going to patent his famous pre-kick stance. Whatever you might think about the England fly-half's remarkable talents, obtaining such a patent would have proved beyond even his skills. This widely reported story was pure fallacy, as it is simply not possible to patent a kicking technique, nor something that is already known. This story was of interest because it was yet another example of the media's general ignorance when it comes to intellectual property.

Intellectual property, or IP for short, is a catch-all term for various legal rights to ideas, names and creative work. The different forms of IP include patents, trademarks and copyright. Patents protect new inventions, such as bagless vacuum cleaners, from being unfairly copied. They are only available for new inventions that achieve a "technical effect", and kicking a ball through a big H doesn't count as technical. A trademark is any sign that differentiates one trader's goods from those of another, and a trademark registration allows traders to stop others using their signs (usually names or logos). Copyright is completely separate from both these things, and is the most misunderstood and misrepresented form of IP. This is a cause for concern, because copyright protects written works, and if journalists can't get their facts straight when reporting on copyright, then what chance have they got when it comes to protecting their own?

When journalists all worked for large publishing companies, this issue was simply one for the lawyers to deal with, but in this digital age, internet bloggers and MySpace jockeys can find themselves woefully exposed. Copyright protects artistic works from being unfairly copied. It was primarily devised to protect literature, music, drama and visual art, but the modern version actually protects almost anything that requires some effort to create, including such diverse things as computer code and the layout of a newspaper or magazine. A journalist's written work is certainly covered, whether it be on paper or online.

But wait: copyright has a few catches. The first, and the one that causes all the confusion, is that copyright only protects the actual form of a work, and not the ideas behind it. The easiest way to see this in action is in newspapers. If one paper published a story copied word for word from another newspaper, then there would be a clear breach of copyright, because the exact "form" of the original work was copied.

However, the first newspaper is perfectly entitled to copy the idea of that story from the other newspaper, and provided the author uses their own words, there is no breach of copyright. This is because the "form" of the work has not been copied. Even the most casual Fleet Street observer can see this type of copying every day. The key thing to remember is that the copyright in your work is only infringed by the unauthorised use of your actual words or pictures, not by copying your ideas.

In the pre-digital era, copyright infringement was rare because the copying of another's written words required the considerable effort of writing them all out again, or actually stealing the written document. It would have been pretty obvious that such actions were scurrilous, and as such they were only carried out by the unscrupulous. With the advent of digital publishing, however, and the rather miraculous concept of copy and paste, the opportunity to infringe copyright is only a few tempting keystrokes away. As such, it's now more important than ever to have some basic knowledge of copyright.

Publications own the copyright in their employees' work, so if you work for such an organisation and find your work has been copied you should immediately inform the editor, and it becomes their problem. If you are one of the increasing number of writers who publish themselves online, then you have no choice but to address the problem yourself. Copyright is a statutory right, which means artistic works automatically benefit from its protection, and you do not have to take any action to acquire the right. However, if you want to enforce it, it is important to establish that you created the work first, so you should keep dated copies of your work. It may be possible to do this electronically, but it would only be worth it if the validity of such dating could not be questioned in court. Alternatively, there are organisations with which you can deposit your work for this purpose, such as the UK-based Anti Copying In Design, details of which can be found at www.acid.uk.com, along with all sorts of other useful information on copyright. The UK Intellectual Property Office may also offer a similar service in the future, as it seeks to better serve the needs of creative artists.

If you find that your copyright has been breached, start off with a polite email. If the infringer won't cooperate, seek the advice of an intellectual property attorney.

The Chartered Institute of Patent Attorneys website at www.cipa.org.uk, has information, contact details for IP attorneys, and a dedicated press officer to answer press enquires about patents. Visit the Institute of Trade Mark Attorneys website at www.itma.org.uk for information about trademarks and trademark attorneys.

● Jerry Bridge-Butler is a fellow of the Chartered Institute of Patent Attorneys, and a partner at G. F. Redfern & Co

Law and the Media

● **December 2007** The former Socialist MSP Tommy Sheridan was arrested and charged with perjury in relation to his previous libel trial against the News of the World. In 2006, Sheridan sued the newspaper over claims that he had cheated on his wife in drug-fuelled orgies at a swingers' cub in Manchester. New developments came after claims suggested that Sheridan had lied under oath in the trial, after which he had walked away with £200,000 in damages. During the 23-day trial, 11 members of the Scottish Socialist party gave evidence that Sheridan had admitted during a meeting to attending the swingers' club, but four other members denied such allegations. Sheridan was detained and questioned by police in Edinburgh and continues to maintain his innocence.

● **November 2007** Nicole Kidman sued the Telegraph over allegations that her "favourite perfume" was not the one she had been paid to promote. Kidman stood to lose a multi-million pound deal with Chanel after the Telegraph's Spy column reported she had been using a fragrance by Jo Malone during the premiere of her latest movie, and was seen "dabbing it on whenever she had a moment". The article also alleged that Chanel was "unhappy" and that Kidman had breached her contract. A statement on behalf of Kidman stated that the allegations were "entirely untrue" and "grossly defamatory". The Telegraph Media Group accepted that the allegations were in fact untrue and agreed to pay Kidman her legal costs and "substantial" damages.

● **October 2007** Good news for investigative journalism. The court of appeal upheld Graeme McLagan's "Reynolds defence", in which a journalist can claim the right to publish material that serves the public interest. In 2006, McLagan had lost a defamation case against Michael Charman, a police officer, who claimed that information found in McLagan's book Bent Coppers labelled him as corrupt. The appellate court reversed the initial ruling and held that "exposing police corruption is obviously in the public interest". This was the first time the "Reynolds defence" had been applied and had succeeded in the publication of a book.

● **July 2007** The social networking website Facebook faced legal action from three Harvard graduates, who accused its founder, Mark Zuckerberg, of stealing key elements from their site, ConnectU, and using them to form Facebook. The Harvard graduates claim that Zuckerberg had agreed to write a computer code for their Harvard Connection project — a site that aimed to create a network for the university's students and alumni. However, according to the trio, Zuckerberg had stalled and used their ideas to set up Facebook. The accusations suggested that Zuckerberg was guilty of fraud, copyright infringement and misappropriation of trade secrets. Zuckerberg denies all charges and refuses to spend much time worrying about this issue. Facebook's lawyers asked for the case to be thrown out on the basis that ConnectU's "broad brush allegations" were "unsupported by evidence". According to US District Judge Douglas Woodlock, "dorm room chitchat does not make a contract". The case continues.

● **February 2007** In a landmark defeat, two brothers and members of the British National Party, Christopher and Barry Roberts, lost their libel case against the anti-fascist Searchlight magazine in relation to an article published in 2003. The article reported on a letter that highlighted the internal feuds within the BNP's London region between supporters of the BNP leader, Nick Griffin, and his predecessor, John Tyndall. Searchlight reported that a letter issued by two Tyndall supporters accused Christopher Roberts of stealing money from a BNP rally and only returning it after threats that he would be reported to the police. There were also accusations that he and his brother had threatened to "kidnap, torture and kill" their opponents and their families. Lord Justice Ward held that the nature of Searchlight's report was one of "neutral reportage", meaning that they were reporting the allegations without adopting or endorsing them. The appeal court held that Searchlight was conducting responsible journalism and agreed that it was in the public interest to report such findings.

Media law

A landmark case finally ended in 2007. The battle over Michael Douglas and Catherine Zeta-Jones's wedding photographs ended up having very little to do with who was hiding behind the wedding cake and everything to do with privacy laws, created via the backdoor

>> **MediaGuardian**   May 7 2007

Privacy gets the OK

Hugh Tomlinson and Dan Tench

The outline of a privacy law is emerging in the wake of OK!'s victory over Hello! and Lord Browne's attempts to silence his former partner

It took nearly seven years, but the tussle between OK! and Hello! over unauthorised photographs of the wedding of Catherine Zeta-Jones and Michael Douglas finally drew to a close last week. When it was launched, the case represented the first test of whether the then newly enacted human rights legislation would lead to a new law of privacy in Britain. Now that it has concluded, clear outlines of that privacy law are emerging.

Traditionally English law did not recognise a right of privacy. Sixteen years ago when the 'Allo 'Allo actor Gorden Kaye brought an action over an intrusive and unauthorised "interview" conducted with him in a hospital bedroom, the courts said firmly that there was no law of privacy in the UK.

But in 2000 the Human Rights Act came into force, enshrining in law a citizen's right to respect for a "private and family life". The courts were quick to use this new right to grant effective privacy protection in a number of cases. And over the past six months, court decisions have taken in many important privacy issues, from private journals to adultery, from surreptitious photographs to "kiss and tell".

Last week's conclusion of the celebrity magazine battle, coupled with the attempts by the BP chief executive Lord Browne to prevent former lover Jeff Chevalier telling all to the Mail on Sunday, show how far privacy law has developed in the intervening period.

Things really began to change in 2000 when an unauthorised photographer infiltrated the Douglas/Zeta-Jones wedding. His surreptitious snaps were transmitted to Hello!, enabling it to spoil OK!'s expensive exclusive on the same event. The courts accepted that the privacy of the Douglases had been infringed by the unauthorised pictures, and the couple were awarded modest damages for distress.

But in the end, the real issue in the Douglas case was about the buying and selling of "privacy rights". Having sold the right to publish wedding photographs to one celebrity magazine, were the couple and OK! entitled to prevent Hello! from publishing photographs of the same event? The court of appeal decided that OK! had no claim for the revenue lost as a result of the Hello! "spoiler", but last week the House of Lords reversed this, saying that Hello! owed a direct obligation in confidence to OK! and allowed the loss – valued at £1m – to be recovered. The act of being a celebrity or running a celebrity magazine was held to be a "lawful trade", and traders in such commodities are entitled to protection over the commercial value of their business.

The Lord Browne case involved more intimate matters. Most of the media attention focused on the lie which Lord Browne told the court and which led to his downfall. But this made little difference to the result. The courts engaged in careful analysis of the extent to which a person can expect conversations with friends and lovers to remain confidential, and decided Lord Browne was entitled to the protection of privacy for the private expression of views about his colleagues and communications about business matters to a sexual partner.

Entitled to protection ... Catherine Zeta-Jones and Michael Douglas

MurdoMacleod

An injunction was, however, refused in relation to some items of information concerning BP which shareholders and colleagues had a proper interest in knowing. The court was not concerned about the truth or falsity of the allegations by Chevalier but whether there was a proper interest in disclosing them.

The court of appeal permitted the publication of only the "bare fact" of the past relationship between Lord Browne and Chevalier on the basis that, without mention of it, the publication of the "public interest" material would not make sense.

Both these cases show how far privacy law has moved since the Gorden Kaye case. The basic outline of this law can now be summarised in five points:

1. The law will protect information which is "obviously private" or where there is a reasonable expectation of privacy.

The question is deceptively simple: was there a reasonable expectation that the information will remain private? The approach is flexible. The court looks at the nature of the information, the form in which it is conveyed as well as the relationship between the person disclosing and the person making the claim. Sometimes information is obviously private, such as the contents of Prince Charles' private travel journals. Information about sexual or financial matters will also obviously be protected as would be the kind of "revelations" in most tabloid "kiss and tell" stories.

2. The law will protect potentially private information even if it is false.

Many newspaper stories about private life are a heady mixture of the true and the made up. It has often been argued that no privacy can lie in false information. However, it was established in a case brought by Canadian folk singer Loreena McKennitt that "the truth or falsity of the information is an irrelevant inquiry in deciding whether the information is entitled to be protected". A made up story about a person's intimate life is just as objectionable as a true one.

3. The availability of information to others is no longer decisive.

The fact that the information has previously been made known to others does not always mean that it is no longer private. The fact that information is known to friends or work colleagues does not mean that a newspaper is free to publish to the whole world. Even prior publication in the media is only one factor in considering whether

information merits future protection. Particularly in the case of photographs, the court may prevent a republication of something which has already been widely distributed. Most starkly in the Douglas case, even though OK! had published pictures of the wedding, it still enjoyed confidentiality in other pictures of the wedding even though it would be hard to identify any real additional information in these further pictures not already published.

4. Publication of private information can be justified in the public interest.

The public interest is not the same as what the public is interested in. There is no real public interest in the publication of "vapid tittle-tattle about the activities of footballers' wives and girlfriends". The court looks at the balance between the right to privacy (under article 8 of the European Convention on Human Rights) and the right to freedom of expression (under article 10). Neither takes priority. The nature of the private information and the "type of expression" are taken into account – publications which contribute to a "debate of general interest" are likely to be permitted. Those which contribute only to public entertainment are likely to be restrained.

5. Everything depends on context, circumstances and impression.

Privacy cases are decided not on the basis of strict rules but on the facts. In this, different judges can take radically different views in relation to the same set of facts. It is striking that in both the Douglas case and the celebrated privacy case brought by Naomi Campbell, of the nine judges which heard each case as it went from trial, through the court of appeal to the House of Lords, five opposed the privacy complaint and four supported it. In each case three of the four were in the House of Lords, so the claims succeeded. So while the legal principles are becoming clearer, a consensus among the judiciary as to what is and what is not an invasion of privacy in any particular case remains elusive.

These five points provide a rough guide to the new territory of privacy. Under the influence of human rights case law from Strasbourg we are moving slowly but inescapably towards the stricter privacy protection of French or Italian law. With each decision, the new law is becoming clearer and more robust. The law of privacy has finally come of age.

● Hugh Tomlinson QC is a barrister at Matrix chambers. Dan Tench is a media partner at Olswang solicitors

Media law

Media law firms

Akin Gump Strauss Hauer and Feld
Citypoint, Level 32,
One Ropemaker Street,
London EC2Y 9AW
020 7012 9600
londoninfo@akingump.com
www.akingump.com
IP; licensing; finance; media infringement (esp digital music online); defamation; employment inc credit disputes, contracts, confirmation of minors' contracts

Allen and Overy
One Bishops Square,
London E1 6AO
020 3088 0000
claire.meeghan@allenovery.com
www.allenovery.com
IP; finance; regulatory and antitrust. For IT, publishing, film, video, radio and TV, programming, live performance, music, sports, ads and PR

Arnold and Porter (UK)
Tower 42, 25 Old Broad Street,
London EC2N 1HQ
020 7786 6100
www.arnoldporter.com
Patents, trademarks, copyright and trade secrets

Ashurst
Broadwalk House, 5 Appold Street, London EC2A 2HA
020 7638 1111
enquiries@ashurst.com
www.ashurst.com
Commercial agreements, transactions and litigation; acquisitions, disposals, mergers; advice on European and UK law, licensing, regulation esp pan-European broadcasting; regulators, governments, broadcasters, producers, telecoms, multiplex and satellite operators; specialist film practice

Baily Gibson
30 High Street, High Wycombe,
Buckinghamshire HP11 2AG
01494 442661
Beaconsfield: 01494 672661
wycombe@bailygibson.co.uk
www.bailygibson.co.uk
E-commerce; IP

Baker and McKenzie
100 New Bridge Street,
London EC4V 6JA
020 7919 1000
info@bakernet.com
www.bakernet.com
E-commerce; IT licensing; broadcast media regulation inc pay-per-view contracts, digital copyright, convergence of media and network technologies

Beachcroft
100 Fetter Lane, London EC4A 1BN
020 7242 1011
Birmingham: 0121 698 5200
Bristol: 0117 918 2000
Manchester: 0161 934 3000
Leeds: 0113 251 4700
Winchester: 01962 705500
info@beachcroft.co.uk
www.beachcroft.co.uk
Interactive commerce and new media inc branding; data protection and privacy; franchising; IP; IT

Beale and Company
Garrick House, 27–32 King Street,
Covent Garden, London WC2E 8JB
020 7240 3474
Dublin: 00 353 1428 3450
reception@beale-law.com
www.beale-law.com
IT inc software, hardware supply and retail; e-commerce; internet; web design; database licensing

Berwin Leighton Paisner
Adelaide House, London Bridge,
London EC4R 9HA
020 7760 1000
media@blplaw.com
www.blplaw.com

Bird and Bird
90 Fetter Lane, London EC4A 1JP
020 7415 6000
london@twobirds.com
www.twobirds.com
IP; IT; broadcasting; film finance; advertising; sponsorship; film production; music; publishing

Blake Lapthorn Linnell
Watchmaker Court,
33 St John's Lane,
London EC1M 4DB
020 7405 2000
Oxford: 01865 248607
Southampton: 023 8063 1823
Fareham: 01489 579990
Portsmouth: 023 9222 1122
info@bllaw.co.uk
www.bllaw.co.uk
IP; IT

BM Nyman and Co
181 Creighton Avenue,
London N2 9BN
020 8365 3060
bernie.nyman@iname.com
www.bmnyman.co.uk
Publishing law; copyright; defamation; contracts

Bournemouth Media School
Talbot Campus, Fern Barrow,
Poole, Dorset BH12 5BB
01202 965360
eforbes@bournemouth.ac.uk
http://media.bournemouth.ac.uk
Media law consultancy to press, broadcast, film and creative industries.
See also careers and training, p. 380

Briffa
Business Design Centre, Upper Street, Islington, London N1 0QH
020 7288 6003
info@briffa.com
www.briffa.com
IP inc brand protection; personality rights in sport; rights for ad industry and designers

Brightley Commercial
Lower Landrine, Mitchell,
Newquay, Cornwall TR8 5BB
01872 519087
robert@brightley.com
www.brightley.com
Commercial/company law; contracts; IP; music business agreements

Bristows
3 Lincoln's Inn Fields,
London WC2A 3AA
020 7400 8000
info@bristows.com
www.bristows.com
IP and media law inc publishing, ads and marketing. Defamation; sponsorship and merchandising; TV distribution; privacy; competition law

Campbell Hooper
35 Old Queen Street,
London SW1H 9JD
020 7222 9070
ch@campbellhooper.com
www.campbellhooper.com
IP; commercial and media dispute resolutions; defamation and media management; theatre; merchandising and sponsorship; advertising and marketing law; brand and domain name management; ICT; e-commerce; software licensing; data protection; licensing agreements

Capital Law Commercial
One Caspian Point, Caspian Way,
Cardiff CF10 4DQ
0870 224 1819
www.capitallaw.co.uk
Formerly Palser Grossman. IP

Carter-Ruck
International Press Centre,
76 Shoe Lane, London EC4A 3JB
020 7353 5005
lawyers@carter-ruck.com
www.carter-ruck.com
Defamation; human rights; IP; employment law

Charles Lucas and Marshall
Eastcott House, 4 High Street,
Swindon SN1 3EP
01793 511055
Newbury: 01635 521212
Wantage: 01235 771234
Hungerford: 01488 682506
www.clmsolicitors.co.uk
IT

Advertising, PR and media law

Charles Russell
8-10 New Fetter Lane,
London EC4A 1RS
020 7203 5000
Guildford: 01483 252525
Cheltenham: 01242 221122
enquiry@cr-law.co.uk
www.charlesrussell.co.uk
*Telecoms, IT, e-commerce, competition
and regulatory law specialists. Data
protection team; internet law;
entertainment work for film, TV,
literary and music sectors inc
reputation management and IP*

Clarke Willmott
Burlington House, Botleigh
Grange Business Park, Hedge End,
Southampton SO30 2DF
023 8062 4400
Birmingham: 0121 236 0076
Bristol: 0117 941 6600
Taunton: 01823 442266
info@clarkewillmott.com
www.clarkewillmott.com

Clifford Chance
10 Upper Bank Street, Canary
Wharf, London E14 5JJ
020 7006 1000
info@cliffordchance.com
www.cliffordchance.com
*Full IP service: patents, trademarks,
copyright, design, trade secrets and
unfair competition*

Clifford Miller
Burnhill Business Centre,
50 Burnhill Road, Beckenham,
Kent BR3 3LA
020 8663 0044
generalmail@ntlworld.com
www.cliffordmiller.com
IP; competition (anti-trust); IT law

Clintons
55 Drury Lane, Covent Garden,
London WC2B 5RZ
020 7379 6080
info@clintons.co.uk
www.clintons.co.uk
*Film and TV: finance; development; IP;
production; catalogue acquisition and
disposal; distribution and exploitation;
rights clearance. Radio: contracts;
digital exploitation; IP; licence
agreements; licence applications;
regulation. Talent agencies: contracts
and individual freelance broadcast and
bi-media service agreements.
Publishing: contracts, libel, disputes,
rights exploitation*

Cobbetts
Ship Canal House, King Street,
Manchester M2 4WB
0845 404 2404 (also offices in
Birmingham and Leeds)
enquiries@cobbetts.co.uk
www.cobbetts.co.uk
*Software development, outsourcing,
data protection, distance selling and
ad regulations; defamation; IP; ICT;
experience in gaming, music publishing
and events, interactive TV, new media,
film and TV*

Collins Long
24 Pepper Street, London SE1 0EB
020 7401 9800
info@collinslong.com
www.collinslong.com
*Contracts; litigation; development;
production; financing; distribution;
film; music and tv*

Collyer-Bristow
4 Bedford Row, London WC1R 4DF
020 7242 7363
cblaw@collyerbristow.com
www.collyerbristow.com
*IP; IT and e-commerce; artists and
managers, composers and publishers,
record producers and distributors,
scriptwriters, film producers, actors
and performers*

Couchman Harrington Associates
20-22 Bedford Row, London
WC1R 4EB
020 7611 9660
enquiries@
    couchmanharrington.com
www.chass.co.uk
Sports law, IP and broadcasting

Courts and Co
15 Wimpole Street,
London W1G 9SY
020 7637 1651
law@courtsandco.com
www.courtsandco.com
*IP inc electronic delivery of AV
material; UK trademarks, community
trademarks and Madrid Protocol
applications; members of International
Trademark Association; classical music
contracts – recording, film and video*

Covington and Burling – Registered Foreign Lawyers and Solicitors – London
265 Strand, London WC2R 1BH
020 7067 2000
www.cov.com
*IP and data protection; broadcasting,
telecoms, multichannel video
distribution, PCS/cellular*

Cripps Harries Hall
Wallside House,
12 Mount Ephraim Road,
Tunbridge Wells, Kent TN1 1EG
01892 515121
reception@crippslaw.com
www.crippslaw.co.uk
*IP; technology; copyright and other
media rights; defamation, libel and
slander*

Cumberland Ellis (incorporating Barth and Partners)
Atrium Court, 15 Jockey's Fields,
London WC1R 4QR
020 7242 0422
contact@cumberlandellis.com
www.cep-law.co.uk
*Specialist sports law team advising on
issues such as sponsorship, licensing
agreements and media rights; IP;
specialist charity law team advising on
issues including commercial activities
and contracts, donations,
constitutions and dispute resolutions*

Davenport Lyons
30 Old Burlington Street,
London W1S 3NL
020 7468 2600
dl@davenportlyons.com
www.davenportlyons.com
*Specialist areas: defamation; film
and TV; music; IP; publishing; ads; IT,
e-commerce, interactive and new
media; sport*

David Price Solicitors and Advocates
21 Fleet Street, London EC4Y 1AA
020 7353 9999
enquiries@lawyers-media.com
www.lawyers-media.com
*Defamation (libel and slander), breach
of confidence and privacy, contempt
and copyright, pre-publication advice,
internet defamation*

Dean Marsh and Co
1892 Building, 54 Kingsway Place,
Sans Walk, London EC1R 0LU
020 7553 4400
info@deanmarsh.com
www.deanmarsh.com
Music and entertainment

Denton Wilde Sapte
1 Fleet Place, London, EC4M 7WS
020 7242 1212
info@dentonwildesapte.com
www.dentonwildesapte.com
*IP; services for ads and marketing,
broadcasting, IT, live performance,
music, publishing, sponsorship, sport
and telecoms; film and TV production,
film financing*

Dickinson Dees
St Ann's Wharf, 112 Quayside,
Newcastle Upon Tyne NE99 1SB
0844 984 1500
law@dickinson-dees.com
www.dickinson-dees.com
IT and e-commerce

DLA Piper Rudnick Gray Cary
3 Noble Street, London EC2V 7EE
0870 011 1111
(also offices in Birmingham,
Liverpool, Manchester, Leeds,
Sheffield, Edinburgh, Glasgow)
info@dlapiper.com
www.dlapiper.com
*Defamation, confidentiality and
privacy, digital media, data protection
and freedom of information,
publishing, gaming, contractual, IT.
Clients include Time Warner Book
Group, ITV plc, Thomson and IPC*

DMA Legal
4th Foor, 15-16 New Burlington
Street, London W1S 3BJ
020 7534 5850
info@dmalegal.com
www.dmalegal.com
*IP, defamation, contracts, licensing,
distribution, multimedia agreements,
royalty arrangements*

DMH Stallard
100 Queens Road, Brighton,
East Sussex BN1 3YB
01273 329833
Gatwick: 01293 605000
London: 020 7423 1000
enquiries@dmhstallard.com
www.dmhstallard.com
*Technology, media and telecoms;
charities and public sector*

Dorsey and Whitney
21 Wilson Street, London EC2M 2TD
020 7588 0800
london@dorsey.com
www.dorsey.com
IP litigation

DWF
5 Castle Street, Liverpool,
Merseyside L2 4XE
0151 907 3000
Manchester: 0161 603 5000
enquiries@dwf.co.uk
www.dwf.co.uk
IP; contracts

Dyer Burdett and Co
64 West Street, Havant,
Hampshire PO9 1PA
023 9249 2472
mail@dyerburdett.com
www.dyerburdett.com
*IP; sport; TV, radio, film and theatre
production and licensing*

Edwin Coe
2 Stone Buildings,
London WC2A 3TH
020 7691 4000
law@edwincoe.com
www.edwincoe.com
IP

Eversheds
Senator House,
85 Queen Victoria Street,
London EC4V 4JL
020 7919 4500
Birmingham: 0121 232 1000
Cambridge: 01223 443666
Ipswich: 01473 284428
Leeds: 0113 243 0391
Manchester: 0161 831 8000
Cardiff: 029 2047 1147
Newcastle: 0191 241 6000
Norwich: 01603 272727
Nottingham: 0115 950 7000
www.eversheds.com
*E-commerce, IT; music, TV and related
areas; IP*

Farrer and Co
66 Lincoln's Inn Fields,
London WC2A 3LH
020 7242 2022
enquiries@farrer.co.uk
www.farrer.co.uk
IP and media law

Fasken Martineau Stringer Saul
17 Hanover Square,
London W1S 1HU
020 7917 8500
info@stringersaul.co.uk
www.fasken.co.uk
IP; IT and internet; publishing

Ferdinand Kelly
21 Bennetts Hill, Birmingham,
West Midlands B2 5QP
0121 643 5228
pm@ferdinandkelly.co.uk
www.ferdinandkelly.co.uk
E-commerce, franchising, IT, IP

Field Fisher Waterhouse
35 Vine Street, London EC3N 2AA
020 7861 4000
info@ffw.com
www.ffw.com
*Services to broadcasters and
publishers esp licensing book and
magazine publishing rights in TV
programmes; IP*

Finers Stephens Innocent
179 Great Portland Street,
London W1W 5LS
020 7323 4000
enquiries@fsilaw.co.uk
www.fsilaw.com
*Specialist areas: ads and sales
promotion; anti-counterfeiting;
copyright; cultural property;
defamation; design rights; IT and
e-commerce; obscenity; publishing;
sports law; trademark and brand
management; visual arts; photo
agencies and libraries; TV and film*

Fladgate Fielder
25 North Row, London W1K 6DJ
020 7323 4747
fladgate@fladgate.com
www.fladgate.com
IP, IT and sports law

Foot Anstey
21 Derrys Cross, Plymouth,
Devon PL1 2SW
01752 675000
Exeter: 01392 411221
Taunton: 01823 337151
info@foot-ansteys.co.uk
www.foot-ansteys.co.uk
*Specialist media, commercial, and
employment advice to newspapers,
publishers and ISPs*

Freshfields Bruckhaus Deringer
65 Fleet Street, London EC4Y 1HS
020 7936 4000
www.freshfields.com
*IP; IT; specialist telecoms, media and
technology (TMT) group*

Gamlins
31-37 Russell Road, Rhyl,
Denbighshire LL18 3DB
01745 343500
gamlins@gamlins.co.uk
www.gamlins.co.uk
IP

George Davies
Fountain Court, 68 Fountain Street,
Manchester, Lancashire M2 2FB
0161 236 8992
mail@georgedavies.co.uk
www.georgedavies.co.uk
*IP, contracts and franchising; also
sports personalities and major
sporting bodies*

Gersten and Nixon
National House, 60-66 Wardour
Street, London W1F 0TA
020 7439 3961
law@gernix.co.uk
www.gernix.co.uk
*All aspects of media and
entertainment law*

Goodman Derrick
90 Fetter Lane, London EC4A 1PT
020 7404 0606
law@gdlaw.co.uk
www.gdlaw.co.uk
*Media law: disputes and litigation;
contracts and documentation;
programme clearance; regulatory
advice. Film: banking, securitisation;
distribution, writer and talent
contracts; mergers and acquisitions;
sponsorship and merchandising
agreements; script clearance*

Gray and Co
Habib House, 3rd Floor,
9 Stevenson Square,
Piccadilly, Greater Manchester,
Lancashire M1 1DB
0161 237 3360
*Entertainment industry in Manchester
and north-west esp. music and record
companies, film and TV contracts and
finance, sport*

Greenwoods Solicitors
Monkstone House,
City Road, Peterborough,
Cambridgeshire PE1 1JE
01733 887700
www.greenwoods.co.uk
*IP; e-commerce and IT; property and
planning issues for production
companies; corporate and commercial
law*

Grundberg Mocatta Rakison
Imperial House, 15-19 Kingsway,
London WC2B 6UN
020 7632 1600
post@gmrlaw.com
www.gmrlaw.com
IP

H2O Law
40-43 Chancery Lane,
London WC2A 1JQ
020 7405 4700
enquiries@h2o-law.com
www.h2o-law.com
*Art and photography: advise artists
and photographers on IP, contracts
and licensing; Publishing: manages
authors rights, advises on contract and
dispute issues, IP and libel vetting*

Halliwells
St James's Court, Brown Street,
Manchester M2 2JF
0870 365 8000
(also offices in Liverpool, London
and Sheffield)
info@halliwells.com
www.halliwells.com
*Services to music and sports
industries; IP; financing*

Hamlins
Roxburghe House,
273–287 Regent Street,
London W1B 2AD
020 7355 6000
enquiries@hamlins.co.uk
www.hamlins.co.uk
IP and copyright

Hammonds
7 Devonshire Square,
Cutlers Gardens, London EC2M 4YH
0870 839 0000
enquiries@hammonds.com
www.hammonds.com
ICT, e-commerce, data protection, media, sport and entertainment

Harbottle and Lewis
Hanover House, 14 Hanover
Square, London W1S 1HP
020 7667 5000
www.harbottle.com
All areas inc film, TV, broadcasting, IT, sport, music, publishing, fashion, advertising, marketing and theatre; IP, defamation, employment, property, immigration, finance, tax and admin

Haynes Phillips
113–117 Farringdon Road,
London EC1R 3BX
020 7843 1820
hello@haynesphillips.com
www.haynesphillips.com
IP; music: contracts, rights, licensing, management, merchandising, music publishing, videos

HBJ Gateley Wareing
One Eleven Edmund Street,
Birmingham B3 2HJ
0121 234 0000
Nottingham: 0115 983 8200
Leicester: 0116 285 9000
info@hbj-gw.com
www.gateleywareing.co.uk
IP, esp in computers and software; technology sector: trademarks, patents, e-commerce, databases and rights

Herbert Smith
Exchange House, Primrose Street,
London EC2A 2HS
020 7374 8000
contact@herbertsmith.com
www.herbertsmith.com
Litigation, competition, corporate, IP, piracy, copyright and defamation; TV and radio, IT, books and publishing, media, music, ads and marketing

Hewitsons
Shakespeare House,
42 Newmarket Road, Cambridge,
Cambridgeshire CB5 8EP
01223 461155
Northampton: 01604 233233
Saffron Walden: 01799 522471
mail@hewitsons.com
www.hewitsons.com
IP; IT inc internet, e-commerce, ICT

Hextalls
28 Leman Street, London E1 8ER
020 7488 1424
info@hextalls.com
www.hextalls.com
Telecoms, media and technology dept serving music, entertainment, publishing and telecoms sector

Hill Dickinson
Pearl Assurance House,
2 Derby Square, Liverpool L2 9XL
0151 236 5400
London: 020 7203 9033
Manchester: 0161 817 7200
Chester: 01244 896600
law@hilldickinson.com
www.hilldickinson.com
Broadcasting, theatre and film; e-commerce; endorsement, merchandising and sponsorship; IT; libel and slander; publishing; sports law

HLW
Commercial House,
Commercial Street, Sheffield,
South Yorkshire S1 2AT
0114 276 5555
info@hlwlaw.co.uk
www.hlwlaw.co.uk
IP

Holme Roberts and Owen
12-20 Camomile Street, 9th Floor,
London EC3A 7PJ
020 7015 0520
www.hro.com
IP; film, telecoms, sport and entertainment

Howard Kennedy
Harcourt House, 19 Cavendish
Square, London W1A 2AW
020 7636 1616
enquiries@howardkennedy.com
www.howardkennedy.com
IP; film, TV, music, theatre, sports

Howell-Jones Partnership
75 Surbiton Road,
Kingston upon Thames,
Surrey KT1 2AF
020 8549 5186
kingston@hjplaw.co.uk
www.hjplaw.co.uk
IP

Humphreys and Co
14 King Street, Bristol BS1 4EF
0117 929 2662
lawyers@humphreys.co.uk
www.humphreys.co.uk
IP; sports contracts; IT; also advises artists, publishers, writers, managers and record companies in music and entertainment industries

Ingram Winter Green
Bedford House, 21A John Street,
London WC1N 2BL
020 7845 7400
back-chat@iwg.co.uk
www.iwg.co.uk
E-business and IT; clients in TV, print media, film, radio, music, printing and ad industries; film finance, syndication, distribution, regulation and broadcasting complaints

Kemp Little
Cheapside House, 138 Cheapside,
London EC2V 6BJ
020 7600 8080
amanda.millar@kemplittle.com
www.kemplittle.com
IP; IT and telecoms regulation

Kent Jones and Done
Churchill House,
Regent Road, Stoke-On-Trent,
Staffordshire ST1 3RQ
01782 202020
mail@kjd.co.uk
www.kjd.co.uk
IT, e-commerce, technology licensing, trademarks and copyright, entertainment

Kimbells
Power House, Harrison Close,
Knowlhill, Milton Keynes MK5 8PA
01908 668555
www.kimbells.com
IT and IP

Kirkland and Ellis International
30 St Mary Axe, London EC3A 8AF
020 7469 2000
info@kirkland.com
www.kirkland.com
IP inc transactions and litigation relating to internet and e-commerce

**Kirkpatrick and Lockhart
Nicholson Graham**
110 Cannon Street,
London EC4N 6AR
020 7648 9000
mbennett@klng.com
www.klng.com
IP; IT and technologies

Kuit Steinart Levy
3 St Marys Parsonage,
Manchester, Lancashire M3 2RD
0161 832 3434
ksllaw@kuits.com
www.kuits.com
Licensing and brand acquisitions; sports merchandising; e-commerce

Latham and Watkins
11th Floor, 99 Bishopsgate,
London EC2M 3XF
020 7710 1000
owen.williams@lw.com
www.lw.com
IP and technology; acquisition, financing, licensing and dispute resolution

Lawdit Solicitors
No 1 Brunswick Place,
Southampton SO15 2AN
023 8023 5979
info@lawdit.co.uk
www.lawdit.co.uk
IP inc domain names, data protection, e-commerce, IT contracts, media law, trademarks and websites

Laytons
Carmelite, 50 Victoria Embankment,
Blackfriars, London EC4Y 0LS
020 7842 8000
Guildford: 01483 407000
Manchester: 0161 834 2100
london@laytons.com
www.laytons.com
*Company, Commercial, IP, IT and
related UK and EU competition law*

Leathes Prior
74 The Close, Norwich,
Norfolk NR1 4DR
01603 610911
info@leathesprior.co.uk
www.leathesprior.co.uk
*IP inc counterfeiting, domain names,
passing-off and trade libel; data
protection; employment; e-commerce
and IT*

Lee and Thompson
Greengarden House,
15-22 St Christophers Place,
London W1U 1NL
020 7935 4665
mail@leeandthompson.com
www.leeandthompson.com
*All aspects of media work covered
(contracts, business structures, IP,
litigation etc) esp in the fields of music,
film and television (finance and
production), sport and celebrity
representation*

Lennox Bywater
9 Limes Avenue, London NW7 3NY
020 8906 1206
lennox.bywater@virgin.net
www.lennoxbywater.com

Sports law

Leonard Lowy and Co
500 Chiswick High Road,
London W4 5RG
020 8956 2785
leonard@leonardlowy.co.uk
www.leonardlowy.co.uk
Music industry

Lester Aldridge
Russell House, Oxford Road,
Bournemouth, Dorset BH8 8EX
01202 786161
info@LA-law.com
www.lesteraldridge.com
IP

Lewis Silkin
5 Chancery Lane, Clifford's Inn,
London EC4A 1BL
020 7074 8000
info@lewissilkin.com
www.lewissilkin.com
Media brands and technology

Linklaters
One Silk Street, London EC2Y 8HQ
020 7456 2000
rupert.winlaw@linklaters.com
www.linklaters.com
*IP; IT and comms law – inc telecoms
and satellites; broadcasting;
e-commerce and internet; outsourcing;
data protection*

Lovells
Atlantic House, Holborn Viaduct,
London EC1A 2FG
020 7296 2000
information@lovells.com
www.lovells.com
IP; technology, media and telecoms

Macfarlanes
10 Norwich Street,
London EC4A 1BD
020 7831 9222
penny.rutterford@macfarlanes.com
www.macfarlanes.com
*IP; IT; e-commerce; advertising and
marketing*

Maclay Murray and Spens
151 St Vincent Street,
Glasgow G2 5NJ
0141 248 5011
London: 020 7002 8500
Edinburgh: 0131 226 5196
Aberdeen: 01224 356130
magnus.swanson@mms.co.uk
www.mms.co.uk
*IP; technology (software, electronics
and engineering), film and media,
internet and e-commerce*

Magrath and Co
66/67 Newman Street,
London W1T 3EQ
020 7495 3003
admin@magrath.co.uk
www.magrath.co.uk
*IP; agreements for recording artists
and recording companies, actors,
sports people, TV and filmmakers*

Manches
Aldwych House, 81 Aldwych,
London WC2B 4RP
020 7404 4433
manches@manches.com
www.manches.com
*IT, IP, internet, publishing and media
inc sponsorship, merchandising,
financing, litigation, defamation, data
protection, ad and sales promotion laws*

Mann and Partners
New Court Chambers,
23-25 Bucks Road, Douglas,
Isle Of Man IM99 2EN
01624 695800
law@mannandpartners.com
www.mannandpartners.com
*Contracts, disputes and general work
for the film industry*

**Marks and Clerk Patent and
Trademark Attorneys**
90 Long Acre, London WC2E 9RA
020 7420 0000
london@marks-clerk.com
www.marks-clerk.com
*Patents; trademarks; copyright;
design; domain names; licensing*

Marks and Clerk Solicitors
90 Long Acre, London WC2E 9RA
020 7420 0250
solicitors@marks-clerk.com
www.marks-clerk.com
IP; IT; publishing

Marriott Harrison
12 Great James Street,
London WC1N 3DR
020 7209 2000
www.marriottharrison.co.uk
*Corporate finance; media/
entertainment; commercial/IT*

Martineau Johnson
1 Colmore Square,
Birmingham B4 6AA
0870 763 2000
lawyers@martjohn.com
www.martineau-johnson.co.uk
*IP; IT inc hardware acquisition,
software licensing, internet and
e-commerce*

McClure Naismith
Equitable House,
47 King William Street,
London EC4R 9AF
020 7929 3770
Edinburgh: 0131 228 4994
Glasgow: 0141 204 2700
london@mcclurenaismith.com
www.mcclurenaismith.com
IP; IT; dispute resolution and litigation

McCormicks
Britannia Chambers,
4 Oxford Place, Leeds,
West Yorkshire LS1 3AX
0113 246 0622
Harrogate: 01423 530630
p.mccormick@mccormicks-
solicitors.com
www.mccormicks-solicitors.com
*IP; defamation and media law;
sponsorship; sports law; rights
management and exploitation;
charity law; general commercial and
corporate law*

McGrigors
5 Old Bailey, London EC4M 7BA
020 7054 2500
enquiries@mcgrigors.com
www.mcgrigors.com
IP

Memery Crystal Solicitors
44 Southampton Buildings,
London WC2A 1AP
020 7242 5905
info@memerycrystal.com
www.memerycrystal.com
*Digital technology inc branding,
software development, licensing
agreements, IP, data protection, rights
protection, litigation, domain name
disputes and internet libel*

MLM
Pendragon House, Fitzalan Court,
Newport Road, Cardiff,
South Glamorgan CF24 0BA
029 2046 2562
enquiries@mlmsolicitors.com
www.mlmsolicitors.com
*IP; IT, technology companies,
TV companies and broadcasters*

Advertising, PR and media law

Moorcrofts
James House, Mere Park,
Dedmere Road, Marlow,
Buckinghamshire SL7 1PB
01628 470000
info@moorcrofts.com
www.moorcrofts.com
*Corporate, IP and regulation. Clients
include RDF, Video Arts and TV Network*

Morgan Cole
Buxton Court, 3 West Way,
Oxford, Oxfordshire OX2 0SZ
01865 262600
Cardiff: 029 2038 5385
Reading: 0118 955 3000
Swansea: 01792 634 634
ian-emery@morgan-cole.com
www.morgan-cole.com
IP

Morrison and Foerster MNP
CityPoint, 1 Ropemaker Street,
London EC2Y 9AW
020 7920 4000
london@mofo.com
www.mofo.com
*IP; new media and technology; telecoms
and other regulation; all aspects of
project and corporate finance*

Myers Fletcher and Gordon
15 Cambridge Court,
210 Shepherds Bush Road,
Hammersmith, London W6 7NJ
020 7610 4433
mfg@mfglon.co.uk
www.mfg-law.com
*Entertainment law, internet,
copyright, appropriation of
personality, IP, dispute litigation*

Nabarro Nathanson
Lacon House, Theobalds Road,
London WC1X 8RW
020 7524 6000
info@nabarro.com
www.nabarro.com
E-commerce, telecoms, IT

Network Law
Asmec Centre, Eagle House,
The Ring, Bracknell,
Berkshire RG12 1HB
0844 544 7727
info@networklaw.org
www.networklaw.org
*National IT IP firm. Clients include
Microsoft and Dell*

New Media Law
102 Dean Street, London W1D 3TQ
020 7734 9777
ian.penman@newmedialaw.biz
www.newmedialaw.biz
*Specialise in media/entertainment
law, including copyright (film, music
and TV) and new media*

Nexus Solicitors
Carlton House, 16–18 Albert
Square, Manchester, Lancashire
M2 5PE
0161 819 4900
help@nexussolicitors.co.uk
www.nexussolicitors.co.uk
*Sports and media inc sponsorship,
endorsement agreements,
merchandising and licensing, football
transfers, event regulation, publishing*

Norton Rose
3 More London Riverside,
London SE1 2AQ
020 7283 6000
www.nortonrose.com
All aspects of media law

Olswang
90 High Holborn,
London WC1V 6XX
020 7067 3000
london@olswang.com
www.olswang.com
*Media communications, technology
and property*

Orchard Brayton Graham
24 Britton Street,
London EC1M 5UA
0870 874 7477
info@orchardlaw.com
www.obglaw.com
*Film, marketing, music, publishing,
TV and radio, IT, internet*

Osborne Clarke
2 Temple Back East, Temple Quay,
Bristol, BS1 6EG
0117 917 3000
www.osborneclarke.com
*IP; IT and telecoms; advertising and
marketing*

Peachey and Co
95 Aldwych, London WC2B 4JF
020 7316 5200
email@peachey.co.uk
www.peachey.co.uk
*Broadcasting; creative media (ads and
marketing); new media; software and
IT services; sport; telecoms*

Penningtons
Bucklersbury House, 83 Cannon
Street, London EC4N 8PE
020 7457 3000
information@penningtons.co.uk
www.penningtons.co.uk
E-business and IP

Pictons
28 Dunstable Road, Luton,
Beds LU1 1DY
01582 870870
marketing@pictons.co.uk
www.pictons.co.uk
Technology IP

Pinsent Masons
Dashwood House, Citypoint,
1 Ropemaker Street,
London EC2Y 9AH
020 7418 7000
Birmingham: 0121 200 1050
Bristol: 0117 924 5678
Edinburgh: 0131 225 0000
Glasgow: 0141 248 4858
Leeds: 0113 244 5000
Manchester: 0161 234 8234
enquiries@pinsentmasons.com
www.pinsentmasons.com
*IP; IT inc resolution of IT and telecoms
disputes*

Putsman Solicitors
Britannia House, 50 Great Charles
Street, Birmingham,
West Midlands B3 2LT
0121 237 3000
www.pwlc.co.uk
*IP etc for TV production, band and
media managers, celeb agents,
publishers, media personalities, signed
bands and artists, casting agents, venues*

Rawlison Butler
Griffin House, 135 High Street,
Crawley, West Sussex RH10 1DQ
01293 527744
info@rawlisonbutler.com
www.rawlisonbutler.com
*IP and brand protection; IT and
e-commerce; data protection; EU and
UK competition law; contracts*

Reed Smith
Beaufort House, 15 Saint Botolphs
Street, London EC3A 7EE
020 7403 2900
www.reedsmith.com
*Pre-publication and pre-broadcast
inc libel, invasion of privacy etc;
non-litigation such as protecting IP,
general corporate, negotiation of
industry-related agreements, labour
and employment, comms regulatory,
and ad branding; media management*

Reid Minty
Moss House, 15–16 Brooks Mews,
London W1K 4DS
020 7318 4444
lawyers@reidminty.co.uk
www.reidminty.co.uk
*Defamation: libel, slander and
malicious falsehood; employment and
litigation*

Reynolds Porter Chamberlain
Tower Bridge House,
St Katharine's Way,
London E1W 1AA
020 3060 6000
enquiries@rpc.co.uk
www.rpc.co.uk
*Content-related issues for press,
publishers, TV*

Richard Howard and Co
45–51 Whitfield Street,
London W1T 4HB
020 7831 4511
richard.howard@
  richardhoward.co.uk
www.richardhoward.tv
*TV, paper and electronic publishing,
multimedia and telecoms; IP*

DWF
6 Winckley Square, Preston PR1 3JJ
01772 556677
Leeds: 0113 243 1555
Manchester: 0161 603 5000
*E-commerce and computer contracts;
IP; confidentiality agreements and
data protection*

Robert Muckle
Norham House,
12 New Bridge Street West,
Newcastle upon Tyne NE1 8AS
0191 232 4402
enquiries@robertmuckle.co.uk
www.robertmuckle.co.uk
IP; IT; dispute resolution

Roiter Zucker
Regent House,
5–7 Broadhurst Gardens,
Swiss Cottage, London NW6 3RZ
020 7328 9111
mail@roiterzucker.co.uk
www.roiterzucker.co.uk
IP and disputes

Rollits
Wilberforce Court, High Street,
Hull, North Humberside HU1 1YJ
01482 323239
info@rollits.com
www.rollits.com
*IP and telecoms; media and
entertainment law; IT/ technology*

Rooks Rider
Challoner House, 19 Clerkenwell
Close, London EC1R 0RR
020 7689 7000
lawyers@rooksrider.co.uk
www.rooksrider.co.uk
IP

Rosenblatt
9–13 St Andrew Street,
London EC4A 3AF
020 7955 0880
info@rosenblatt-law.co.uk
www.rosenblatt-law.co.uk
Defamation and IP

Ross and Craig
12a Upper Berkeley Street,
London W1H 7QE
020 7262 3077
reception@rosscraig.com
www.rosscraig.com
*Co-production arrangements;
IP and copyright; film and TV funding;
rights acquisition; production and
artistes' contracts; defamation; IT and
e-commerce*

Rouse & Co International
11th Floor, Exchange Tower,
1 Harbour Exchange Square,
London E14 9GE
020 7536 4100
Oxford: 01865 318400
rouse@iprights.com
www.iprights.com
*IP services worldwide in TV, film,
entertainment and publishing sectors
inc agreements, rights, licensing and
defence of infringement*

Rowberry Morris
17 Castle Street, Reading,
Berkshire RG1 7SB
0118 958 5611
admin@rowberrymorris.co.uk
www.rowberrymorris.co.uk
*All aspects of media law. Specialist
unit advises new bands and writers*

RT Coopers Solicitors
Telfords Yard, 6/8 The Highway,
London E1W 2BS
020 7488 2985
enquiries@rtcoopers.com
www.rtcoopers.com
*Film, TV, music, IP, copyright,
branding, licensing, publishing etc*

Salans
Millennium Bridge House,
2 Lambeth Hill, London EC4V 4AJ
020 7429 6000
london@salans.com
www.salans.com
IP; IT and communications law

Schillings
Royalty House, 72–74 Dean Street,
London W1D 3TL
020 7453 2500
legal@schillings.co.uk
www.schillings.co.uk
IP and media management

Seddons
5 Portman Square,
London W1H 6NT
020 7725 8000
enquiries@seddons.co.uk
www.seddons.co.uk
Entertainment and music industry

Shepherd And Wedderburn
Condor House, 10 St. Paul's
Churchyard, London EC4M 8AL
020 7429 4900
www.shepwedd.co.uk
*IP and trademark litigation, copyright,
sport law*

Sheridans
Whittington House, Alfred Place,
London WC1E 7EA
020 7079 0100
info@sheridans.co.uk
www.sheridans.co.uk
*Agreements; music, book and
magazine publishing; distribution;
licensing; merchandising; sponsorship;
trademarks and domain names*

Simmons and Simmons
Citypoint, 1 Ropemaker Street,
London EC2Y 9SS
020 7628 2020
enquiries@
    simmons-simmons.com
www.simmons-simmons.com
*IT litigation; technology, media and
telecommunications*

Simons Muirhead and Burton
50 Broadwick Street, Soho,
London W1F 7AG
020 7734 4499
mail@smab.co.uk
www.smab.co.uk
*Film and TV regulatory and
production law; dispute resolution,
copyright and libel advice*

SJ Berwin
10, Queens Street Place,
London EC4R 1BE
020 7111 2222
info@sjberwin.com
www.sjberwin.com
*IP; film, TV and radio work (content
and carriage), music, telecoms, sport,
animation, digital media, e-commerce
and online*

Slaughter and May
One Bunhill Row, London EC1Y 8YY
020 7600 1200
www.slaughterandmay.com
IP; IT; technology, media and telecoms

Spearing Waite
41 Friar Lane, Leicester,
Leicestershire LE1 5RB
0116 262 4225
info@spearingwaite.co.uk
www.spearingwaite.co.uk
Franchising, agency and licensing; IP

Spring Law
40 Craven Street,
London WC2N 5NG
020 7930 4158
tim.perry@springlaw.co.uk
www.springlaw.co.uk
*IP, franchise arrangements,
sponsorship, rights exploitation,
distribution, merchandising, licensing,
marketing, ads and promotions*

Squire Sanders and Dempsey
Tower 42, 25th Floor, 25 Old
Broad Street, London EC2N 1HQ
020 7189 8000
ssdinfo@ssd.com
www.ssd.com
*Communications law inc IP, internet,
licensing, regulatory restructuring,
satellite communications,
broadcasting and cable*

Steeles
Bedford House, 21A John Street,
London WC1N 2BF
020 7421 1720
media@steeleslaw.co.uk
www.steeleslaw.co.uk
*For record labels, agents, managers,
event organisers, artists, publishers,
writers, broadcasters, unions and
professional bodies*

Tarlo Lyons
Watchmaker Court, 33 St John's
Lane, London EC1M 4DB
020 7405 2000
simon.stokes@tarlolyons.com
www.tarlolyons.com
*IP; digital media; IT; data protection;
ads; website development and e-
commerce; information security and
fraud; telecoms*

Taylor Wessing
Carmelite, 50 Victoria Embankment,
London EC4Y 0DX
020 7300 7000
london@taylorwessing.com
www.taylorwessing.com
Patents, copyright and other IP

Teacher Stern Selby
37–41 Bedford Row,
London WC1R 4JH
020 7242 3191
g.shear@tsslaw.com
www.tsslaw.com
*Defamation and reputation
management; IT; IP; internet and e-
commerce; data protection; telecoms
and risk management*

Thompsons
Congress House,
23-28 Great Russell Street,
London WC1B 3LW
0800 783 0266
info@thompsons.law.co.uk
www.thompsons.law.co.uk
*Represents media unions and their
members including NUJ, Bectu and
Amicus*

Thomson Snell and Passmore
3 Lonsdale Gardens,
Tunbridge Wells, Kent TN1 1NX
01892 510000
info@ts-p.co.uk
www.ts-p.co.uk
E-commerce and IP law

TLT Solicitors
Sea Containers House,
20 Upper Ground, Blackfriars
Bridge, London SE1 9LH
020 7620 1311
www.tltsolicitors.com
*IT inc internet and e-commerce; sports
law*

Travers Smith
10 Snow Hill, London EC1A 2AL
020 7295 3000
travers.smith@traverssmith.com
www.traverssmith.com
*IT and e-commerce; media and IP;
contracts*

Truman and Co Solicitors, Truelegal
76 Fore Street, Topsham,
Exeter, Devon EX3 0HQ
01392 879414
info@truelegal.co.uk
www.truelegal.co.uk
*Commercial, media and e-law for
advertising, marketing, PR, web, new
media companies in London and South
West. Anglo German specialist.*

Turner Parkinson
Hollins Chambers,
64a Bridge Street, Manchester,
Lancashire M3 3BA
0161 833 1212
tp@tp.co.uk
www.tp.co.uk
IP; computer contracts and e-commerce

Veale Wasbrough
Orchard Court, Orchard Lane,
Bristol BS1 5WS
0117 925 2020
central@vwl.co.uk
www.vwl.co.uk
*IP esp tech, computer systems and
e-commerce*

Vizards Tweedie
Barnards Inn, 86 Fetter Lane,
London EC4A 1AD
020 7405 1234
www.vizardstweedie.co.uk
Media and IT law

Wake Smith
68 Clarkehouse Road, Sheffield,
South Yorkshire S10 2LJ
0114 266 6660
legal@wake-smith.com
www.wake-smith.co.uk
*Media and entertainment law; global
tech licensing contracts; agency,
distribution and marketing
agreements*

Watson Farley and Williams
15 Appold Street,
London EC2A 2HB
020 7814 8000
info@wfw.com
www.wfw.com
*Telecoms, media and tech: for
operators, regulators, equipment and
maintenance providers, internet
services, content providers, e-
commerce users and developers*

Wiggin
95 Promenade, Cheltenham,
Gloucestershire GL50 1WG
01242 224114
law@wiggin.co.uk
www.wiggin.co.uk
*Broadcast media, telecoms,
e-commerce, advertising, publishing,
gaming, music, IP, content and
regulation*

Wilmer Cutler Pickering Hale and Dorr
Alder Castle House, 10 Noble
Street, London EC2V 7QJ
020 7645 2400
www.wilmerhale.com
*IP; services for telecoms, internet,
e-commerce and software industries*

Wollastons
Brierly Place, New London Road,
Chelmsford, Essex CM2 0AP
01245 211211
enquiries@wollastons.co.uk
www.wollastons.co.uk
*IP inc agreements, licensing,
trademark registration, infringement
of copyright, passing off, breach of
confidence, warranties and liability,
internet trade and portal development*

Wragge and Co
55 Colmore Row,
Birmingham B3 2AS
0870 903 1000
mail@wragge.com
www.wragge.com
*Media business services from content
creation and exploitation to financing
and corporate development. Offices in
London and Brussels*

Wright Hassall Solicitors
9 Clarendon Place, Leamington
Spa, Warwickshire CV34 5QP
01926 886688
email@wrighthassall.co.uk
www.wrighthassall.co.uk
*IP and transactional support to
technology, new media and advertising
clients. Emphasis on branding, design,
merchandising, sponsorship, sales
promotion and all copyright issues.*

Wright, Johnston and Mackenzie
302 St Vincent Street,
Glasgow G2 5RZ
0141 248 3434
Edinburgh: 0131 221 5560
enquiries@wjm.co.uk
www.wjm.co.uk
IP and dispute resolution

Media law journals

ALM
Editor: 001 212 313 9130
efriedlander@amlaw.com
www.ipww.com
*Monthly, plus annual digest issue.
Editor: Pamela Sherrid*
Press: 001 401 848 5494

Media Law and Policy
New York Law School
001 212 431 2163
www.nyls.edu/pages/1572.asp

PA Media Lawyer
020 7963 7000
medialawyer@pa.press.net
www.medialawyer.press.net
Bi-monthly. Editor: Mike Dodd

Copyright associations

Authors' Licensing and Collecting Society (ALCS)
The Writers' House, 13 Haydon
Street, London EC3N 1DB
020 7264 5700
alcs@alcs.co.uk
www.alcs.co.uk
*UK collecting society for writers and
their successors*

British Copyright Council
Copyright House,
29-33 Berners Street,
London W1T 3AB
01986 788122
secretary@britishcopyright.org
Copyright watchdog

Copyright Licensing Agency
Saffron House, 6–10 Kirby Street,
London EC1N 8TS
020 7400 3100
cla@cla.co.uk
www.cla.co.uk
Administers copyrights

contacts

Design and Artists Copyright Society (DACS)
33 Great Sutton Street,
London EC1V 0DX
020 7336 8811
info@dacs.org.uk
www.dacs.org.uk
Copyright and collecting society for visual artists

Federation Against Copyright Theft (FACT)
Unit 7, Victory Business Centre,
Worton Road, Isleworth,
Middlesex TW7 6DB
020 8568 6646
contact@fact-uk.org.uk
www.fact-uk.org.uk
UK film anti-piracy body

Irish Copyright Licensing Agency
25 Denzille Lane, Dublin 2
00 353 1 662 4211
info@icla.ie
www.icla.ie
Ireland's reproduction rights organisation

Mechanical-Copyright Protection Society
29–33 Berners Street,
London W1T 3AB
020 7580 5544
www.mcps.co.uk
Collects and distributes music royalties: record companies, broadcasters, novelties, online

Patent Office
Concept House, Cardiff Road,
Newport NP10 8QQ
0845 950 0505
enquiries@patent.gov.uk
www.patent.gov.uk
Patents, trademarks, design and copyright

Performing Rights Society
29–33 Berners Street,
London W1T 3AB
020 7580 5544
www.prs.co.uk
Collects and distributes music royalties: pubs, clubs, broadcasters, online

Public Lending Right
Richard House, Sorbonne Close,
Stockton-on-Tees TS17 6DA
01642 604699
registrar@plr.uk.com
www.plr.uk.com
Library payment scheme for authors

Publishers Licensing Society
37–41 Gower Street,
London WC1E 6HH
020 7299 7730
pls@pls.org.uk
www.pls.org.uk
Supports Copyright Licensing Agency

UK Copyright Bureau
110 Trafalgar Road, Portslade,
East Sussex BN41 1GS
info@copyrightbureau.co.uk
www.copyrightbureau.co.uk
Copyright service for authors, playwrights, scriptwriters, poets, musicians and associated literary crafts

Writers, Artists and their Copyright Holders (Watch)
David Sutton, Director of Research
Projects, University of Reading
Library, PO Box 223,
Whiteknights, Reading RG6 6AE
0118 931 8783
UK: d.c.sutton@reading.ac.uk
US: rworkman@mail.utexas.edu
www.watch-file.com
Database primarily containing names and addresses of copyright holders and contacts for authors and artists whose archives are housed in libraries in North America and UK

Associations

International Bar Association – Media Law Committee
10th Floor, 1 Stephen Street,
London W1T 1AT
020 7691 6868
member@int-bar.org
www.ibanet.org

Stanhope Centre for Communications Policy Research
Room D329, Social Sciences
Building, Northampton Square,
City University, London EC1V 0HB
020 7040 4566
www.stanhopecentre.org/
Media law and policy forum

Contacts book

Government: **UK government**

Downing Street

Prime Minister's Office
10 Downing Street,
London SW1A 2AA
020 7270 3000
www.number-10.gov.uk
Prime minister: Gordon Brown*
Chief of staff & parliamentary private
secretary: Tom Scholar
Press: 020 7930 4433

Government departments

Cabinet Office
70 Whitehall, London SW1A 2AS
020 7276 3000
www.cabinet-office.gov.uk
Cabinet Office minister: Ed Miliband*
(also Chancellor of the Duchy of
Lancaster)
Parliamentary secretary: Phil Hope
Parliamentary secretary and minister
for the East Midlands: Gillian Merron
Press: 020 7276 1191

Children, Schools and Families
Sanctuary Building, Great Smith
Street, London SW1P 3BT
0870 000 2288
www.dcsf.gov.uk
Children, Schools and Families
secretary: Ed Balls*
Parliamentary under-secretaries:
Kevin Brennan, Lord Adonis
Press: 020 7925 6789

**Communities and Local
Government**
Eland House, Bressendon Place,
London SW1E 5DU
020 7944 4400
www.communities.gov.uk
Communities and local government
secretary: Hazel Blears*
Parliamentary under-secretaries:
Baroness Andrews, Parmjit Dhanda,
Iain Wright

Culture, Media and Sport
2-4 Cockspur Street,
London SW1Y 5DH
020 7211 6200
www.culture.gov.uk
Culture secretary: Andy Burnham*
Minister of state: Margaret Hodge;
parliamentary under-secretary:
Gerry Sutcliffe
Press: 020 7211 6145

Defence
Horseguards Avenue,
London SW1A 2HB
020 7218 9000
www.mod.uk
Defence secretary: Des Browne*
Ministers of state: Bob Ainsworth,
Lord Drayson; parliamentary under-
secretary: Derek Twigg
Press: 020 7218 7907

Environment, Food and Rural Affairs

17 Smith Square, London SW1P 3JR
020 7238 6000
www.defra.gov.uk
Environment secretary: Hilary Benn*
Ministers of state: Lord Rooker, Phil
Woolas; parliamentary under-
secretary: Joan Ruddock;
parliamentary under-secretary and
minister for the South East
Press:
   animal welfare: 020 7238 6044
   environment: 020 7238 6054
   rural affairs: 020 7238 5608
   sustainable farming and food:
      020 7238 6146

Foreign Office
Whitehall, London SW1A 2AH
020 7270 1500
www.fco.gov.uk
Foreign secretary: David Miliband*
Minister of state for Europe: Jim
Murphy; ministers of state: Dr Kim
Howells, Sir Digby Jones, Sir Mark
Malloch Brown; parliamentary under-
secretary: Meg Munn
Press: 020 7008 3100

Health
79 Whitehall, London SW1A 2NS
020 7210 4850
www.dh.gov.uk
Health secretary: Alan Johnson*
Minister of state for reform: Lord
Warner; minister of state: Rosie
Winterton; minister of state for public
health: Caroline Flint; parliamentary
under-secretary of state for care
services: Ivan Lewis
Press: 020 7210 5221

Home Office
Direct Communications Unit,
2 Marsham Street,
London SW1P 4DF
020 7035 3535
www.homeoffice.gov.uk
Home secretary: Jacqui Smith*
Ministers of state: Liam Byrne,
Tony McNulty; parliamentary under-
secretaries: Vernon Coaker, Admiral
Sir Alan West, Meg Hilliar
Press: 020 7035 4381

Innovation, Universities and Skills
1 Victoria Street, London SW1H 0ET
020 7215 5555
www.dius.gov.uk
Innovation, Universities and Skills
secretary: John Denham*
Ministers of state: Bill Rammel,
Ian Pearson; parliamentary
under-secretaries: David Lammy,
Lord Triesman
Press: 020 7925 6789

International Development

1 Palace Street, London SW1E 5HE
020 7023 0000
www.dfid.gov.uk
International development secretary
of state: Douglas Alexander*
Parliamentary under-secretaries: Gareth
Thomas, Shriti Vadera, Shahid Malik
Press: 020 7023 0600

Justice
54 Victoria Street,
London SW1E 6QW
020 7210 8614
www.justice.gov.uk
Secretary of state for Justice and Lord
Chancellor: Jack Straw*
Ministers of state: David Hanson,
Michael Wills; parliamentary under
secretaries: Lord Hunt of King's Heath,
Maria Eagle, Bridget Prentice
Press: 020 7210 8901

Law Officers' Department
9 Buckingham Gate,
London SW1E 6JP
020 7271 2492
www.attorneygeneral.gov.uk
Attorney general: Baroness Scotland*
Solicitor general: Vera Baird
Press: 020 7271 2440

Northern Ireland Office
11 Millbank, London SW1P 4PN
028 9052 0700
www.nio.gov.uk
Northern Ireland secretary of state:
Shaun Woodward*
Minister of state: Paul Goggins
Press: 020 7210 0260/0213

Privy Council
2 Carlton Gardens,
London SW1Y 5AA
020 7210 1033
www.privy-council.org.uk
www.commonsleader.gov.uk
Leader of the Lords and Lord President
of the Council: Baroness Ashton*
Leader of the Commons and Lord
Privy Seal: Harriet Harman*; deputy
leader: Helen Goodman
Press: 020 7210 1092

Scotland Office
Whitehall, London SW1A 2AU
020 7270 6754
www.scotlandoffice.gov.uk
Secretary of state: Des Browne*
Parliamentary under-secretary:
David Cairns
Press: 0131 244 9053

* cabinet members

Business, Enterprise and Regulatory Reform
1 Victoria Street, London SW1H 0ET
020 7215 5000
www.dberr.gov.uk
Trade and industry secretary:
John Hutton*
Ministers of state: Stephen Timms, Sir Digby Jones, Pat McFadden, Michael Wicks, Lord Drayson; parliamentary under-secretary: Gareth Thomas
Press: 020 7215 6403

Transport
76 Marsham Street,
London SW1P 4DR
020 7944 8300
www.dft.gov.uk
Transport secretary: Ruth Kelly*
Minister of state: Rosie Winterton; parliamentary under-secretaries: Jim Fitzpatrick, Tom Harris
Press:
   rail: 020 7944 3108
   roads: 020 7944 3066
   sea and air: 020 7944 3108

Treasury
1 Horse Guards Road,
London SW1A 2HQ
020 7270 4558
www.hm-treasury.gov.uk
Chancellor of the Exchequer:
Alistair Darling*
Chief secretary: Yvette Cooper*; financial secretary: Jane Kennedy; exchequer secretary: Angela Eagle; economic secretary: Kitty Ussher
Press: 020 7270 5238

Wales Office
Whitehall, London SW1A 2ER
020 7270 0534
www.walesoffice.gov.uk
Wales secretary: Paul Murphy*
Parliamentary under-secretary:
Huw Irranca-Davies
Press: 020 7270 0566

Work and Pensions
79 Whitehall, London SW1A 2NS
020 7238 0800
www.dwp.gov.uk
Work and pensions secretary:
James Purnell*
Minister of state: Mike O'Brien; minister of state and minister for Yorkshire and the Humber: Caroline Flint; parliamentary under-secretaries: Anne McGuire, James Plaskitt, Lord McKenzie of Luton; parliamentary under-secretary and minister of state for the East of England: Barbara Follett
Press: 020 7238 0866

* cabinet members

ALSO ATTENDING CABINET:
(Cabinet members not listed at an office or ministry above, or those holding another portfolio)

Lords chief Whip
  Lord Grocott of Telford*
Minister for Women and Labour Party Chair
  Harriet Harman*
PM's Parliamentary private secretaries
  Angela E Smith*, Ian Austin*
Commons chief Whip
  Geoff Hoon*
Olympics minister & minister for London
  Tessa Jowell*
Minister for Housing
  Caroline Flint
Minister for Children
  Beverley Hughes
Minister for Africa, Asia and UN
  Mark Malloch-Brown

● Wales

National Assembly for Wales
Cardiff Bay, Cardiff CF99 1NA
029 2082 5111
www.assemblywales.org
First minister: Rhodri Morgan
Deputy first minister: Ieuan Wyn Jones
Ministers: health and social services: Edwina Hart; education, culture and welsh language: Carwyn Jones; economy and transport: Dr Brian Gibbons; sustainability and rural development: Jane Davidson; social justice and public service delivery: Andrew Davies; budget and business: Jane Hutt
Press: 029 2089 8099

● Scotland

Scottish Executive
St Andrews House,
Edinburgh EH1 3DG
0131 556 8400
www.scotland.gov.uk
First minister: Alex Salmond; Minister for Europe, external affairs and culture: Linda Fabiani; parliamentary business: Bruce Crawford; cabinet secretary for finance and sustainable growth: John Swinney; enterprise, energy and tourism: Jim Mather; transport, infrastructure and climate change: Stewart Stevenson: cabinet secretary for education and lifelong learning: Fiona Hyslop; children and early years: Adam Ingram; schools and skills: Maureen Watt; cabinet secretary for health and wellbeing: Nicola Sturgeon; public health: Shona Robison; communities and sport: Stewart MacAskill; community safety: Fergus Ewing; cabinet secretary for rural affairs and the environment: Richard Lochhead; environment: Michael Russell
Press: 0131 244 2664

● Northern Ireland

Northern Ireland Assembly
(suspended October 2002)
Northern Ireland Executive
(suspended October 2002)

Local and regional government

Local Government Association
020 7664 3131
www.lga.gov.uk
Press: 020 7664 3333
County Councils Network
020 7664 3011
www.countycouncilsnetwork.org.uk
Audit Commission for Local Authorities
020 7828 1212
www.audit-commission.gov.uk
0844 798 2128
Convention of Scottish Local Authorities
0131 474 9200
www.cosla.gov.uk
Press: 0131 474 9205
Improvement and Development Agency
020 7296 6600
www.idea-knowledge.gov.uk
Press: 020 7296 6529
Local Government Ombudsman
0845 602 1983
www.lgo.org.uk
Scottish Public Services Ombudsman
0800 377 7330
www.spso.org.uk
Public Services Ombudsman for Wales
01656 641150
www.ombudsman-wales.org

Professional bodies

Association of Council Secretaries and Solicitors
www.acses.org.uk
Association of Electoral Administrators
0151 281 8246
www.aea-elections.co.uk
Association of Local Authority Chief Executives
www.alace.org.uk

● London

Greater London Authority
020 7983 4000
www.london.gov.uk
Press: 020 7983 6553

**Association of
London Government**
020 7934 9999
www.londoncouncils.gov.uk
daytime: 020 7934 9620/9755

City of London
020 7606 3030
www.cityoflondon.gov.uk
Press: 020 7332 1906

● London boroughs

Barking and Dagenham
020 8592 4500
www.barking-dagenham.gov.uk
Press: 020 8227 2107

Barnet
020 8359 2000
www.barnet.gov.uk
Press: 020 8359 7796

Bexley
020 8303 7777
www.bexley.gov.uk
Press: 020 8294 6222

Brent
020 8937 1234
www.brent.gov.uk
Press: 020 8937 1066

Bromley
020 8464 3333
www.bromley.gov.uk
Press: 020 8313 4415

Camden
020 7278 4444
www.camden.gov.uk
Press: 020 7974 5717

Croydon
020 8686 4433
www.croydon.gov.uk
Press: 020 8760 5644

Ealing
020 8825 5000
www.ealing.gov.uk
Press: 020 8825 8686

Enfield
020 8379 1000
www.enfield.gov.uk
Press: 020 8921 5124

Greenwich
020 8854 8888
www.greenwich.gov.uk
Press: 020 8921 5040

Hackney
020 8356 5000
www.hackney.gov.uk
Press: 020 8356 3736

Hammersmith and Fulham
020 8748 3020
www.lbhf.gov.uk
Press: 020 8753 2164

Haringey
020 8489 0000
www.haringey.gov.uk
Press: 020 8489 2997

Harrow
020 8863 5611
www.harrow.gov.uk
Press: 020 8424 1295

Havering
01708 434343
www.havering.gov.uk
Press: 01708 432005

Hillingdon
01895 250111
www.hillingdon.gov.uk
Press: 01895 250534

Hounslow
020 8583 2000
www.hounslow.gov.uk
Press: 020 8583 2180

Islington
020 7527 2000
www.islington.gov.uk
Press: 020 7527 3376

Kensington and Chelsea
020 7937 5464
www.rbkc.gov.uk
Press: 020 7361 2826

Kingston upon Thames
020 8547 5757
www.kingston.gov.uk
Press: 020 8547 4710

Lambeth
020 7926 1000
www.lambeth.gov.uk
Press: 020 7926 2841

Lewisham
020 8314 6000
www.lewisham.gov.uk
Press: 020 8314 7337

Merton
020 8274 4901
www.merton.gov.uk
Press: 020 7545 4645

Newham
020 8430 2000
www.newham.gov.uk
Press: 020 8430 6892

Redbridge
020 8554 5000
www.redbridge.gov.uk
Press: 020 8708 2151

Richmond upon Thames
020 8891 1411
www.richmond.gov.uk
Press: 020 8891 7766

Southwark
020 7525 5000
www.southwark.gov.uk
Press: 020 7525 7306

Sutton
020 8770 5000
www.sutton.gov.uk
Press: 020 8770 5145

Tower Hamlets
020 7364 5000
www.towerhamlets.gov.uk
Press: 020 7364 4969

Waltham Forest
020 8496 3000
www.lbwf.gov.uk
Press: 020 8496 4855

Wandsworth
020 8871 6000
www.wandsworth.gov.uk
Press: 020 8871 6031

Westminster
020 7641 6000
www.westminster.gov.uk
Press: 020 7641 2259

● County councils

Bedfordshire
01234 363222
www.bedfordshire.gov.uk
Press: 01234 228888

Buckinghamshire
01296 395000
www.buckscc.gov.uk
Press: 01296 382055

Cambridgeshire
01223 717111
www.cambridgeshire.gov.uk
Press: 01223 717612

Cheshire
01244 602424
www.cheshire.gov.uk
Press: 01244 602216

Cornwall
01872 322000
www.cornwall.gov.uk
Press: 01872 322186

Cumbria
01228 606060
www.cumbria.gov.uk
Press: 01228 606365

Derbyshire
0845 605 8058
www.derbyshire.gov.uk
Press: 01629 585035

Devon
01392 382000
www.devon.gov.uk
Press: 01392 382173

Dorset
01305 251000
www.dorsetcc.gov.uk
Press: 01305 224725

Durham
0191 383 3000
www.durham.gov.uk
Press: 0191 383 3373

East Sussex
01273 481000
www.eastsussex.gov.uk
Press: 01273 481570

Essex
08457 430430
www.essexcc.gov.uk
Press: 01245 434979

Gloucestershire
01452 425000
www.gloucestershire.gov.uk
Press: 01452 425226

Hampshire
01962 870500
www.hants.gov.uk
Press: 01962 847666

Herefordshire
01432 260000
www.herefordshire.gov.uk/
Press: 01432 260224

Hertfordshire
01438 737555
www.hertsdirect.org
Press: 01992 555539

Kent
0845 824 7247
www.kent.gov.uk
Press: 01622 694034

Lancashire
0845 053 0000
www.lancashire.gov.uk
Press: 01772 533194

Leicestershire
0116 232 3232
www.leics.gov.uk
Press: 0116 265 6274

Lincolnshire
01522 552222
www.lincolnshire.gov.uk
Press: 01522 782060

Norfolk
0844 800 8020
www.norfolk.gov.uk
Press: 01603 222716

North Yorkshire
01609 780780
www.northyorks.gov.uk
Press: 01609 532206

Northamptonshire
01604 236236
www.northamptonshire.gov.uk
Press: 01604 237200

Northumberland
01670 533000
www.northumberland.gov.uk
Press: 01670 534850

Nottinghamshire
0115 982 3823
www.nottinghamshire.gov.uk
Press: 0115 977 3791

Oxfordshire
01865 792422
www.oxfordshire.gov.uk
Press: 01865 810256

Rutland
01572 722577
www.rutland.gov.uk
Press: 01572 758328

Shropshire
0845 678 9000
www.shropshireonline.gov.uk
Press: 01743 252813

Somerset
0845 345 9166
www.somerset.gov.uk
Press: 01823 355020

Staffordshire
01785 223121
www.staffordshire.gov.uk
Press: 01785 276829

Suffolk
01473 583000
www.suffolkcc.gov.uk
Press: 01473 264397

Surrey
0845 600 9009
www.surreycc.gov.uk
Press: 020 8541 9548

Warwickshire
0845 090 7000
www.warwickshire.gov.uk
Press: 01926 412758

West Sussex
01243 777100
www.westsussex.gov.uk
Press: 01243 777408

Wiltshire
01225 713000
www.wiltshire.gov.uk
Press: 01225 713114

Worcestershire
01905 763763
www.worcestershire.gov.uk
Press: 01905 766642

Isle of Wight
01983 821000
www.iwight.com
Press: 01983 823693

City and district councils

AVON

>> *see Somerset & Avon   page 326*

BEDFORDSHIRE

Bedford
01234 267422
www.bedford.gov.uk
Press: 01234 221622

Luton
01582 546000
www.lutonline.gov.uk

Mid Bedfordshire
0845 230 4040
www.midbeds.gov.uk

South Bedfordshire
01582 472222
www.southbeds.gov.uk

BERKSHIRE

Reading
0118 939 0900
www.reading.gov.uk
Press: 0118 939 0301

Bracknell Forest
01344 352000
www.bracknell-forest.gov.uk

Slough
01753 457111
www.slough.gov.uk

West Berkshire
01635 42400
www.westberks.gov.uk

Windsor and Maidenhead
01628 798888
www.rbwm.gov.uk

Wokingham
0118 974 6000
www.wokingham.gov.uk

BUCKINGHAMSHIRE

Milton Keynes
01908 691691
www.mkweb.co.uk
Press: 01908 252009

Aylesbury Vale
01296 585858
www.aylesburyvaledc.gov.uk

Chiltern
01494 729000
www.chiltern.gov.uk

South Bucks
01895 837200
www.southbucks.gov.uk

Wycombe
01494 461000
www.wycombe.gov.uk

CAMBRIDGESHIRE

Cambridge
01223 457000
www.cambridge.gov.uk

Peterborough
01733 747474
www.peterborough.gov.uk

East Cambridgeshire
01353 665555
www.eastcambs.gov.uk

Fenland
01354 654321
www.fenland.gov.uk

Huntingdonshire
01480 388388
www.huntsdc.gov.uk

South Cambridgeshire
0845 045 0500
www.scambs.gov.uk

CHANNEL ISLANDS

Isles of Scilly
01720 422537
www.scilly.gov.uk
Press: 01720 424043

States of Jersey
01534 445500
www.gov.je
Press: 01534 445500

States of Guernsey
01481 717000
www.gov.gg
Press: 01481 717131

CHESHIRE

Chester
01244 324324
www.chester.gov.uk
Press: 01244 402362

Congleton
01270 274821
www.congleton.gov.uk

Crewe and Nantwich
01270 537777
www.crewe-nantwich.gov.uk

Ellesmere Port and Neston
0151 356 6789
www.ellesmereport-neston
.gov.uk

Halton
0151 424 2061
www.halton.gov.uk

Macclesfield
01625 500500
www.macclesfield.gov.uk

Vale Royal
01606 862862
www.valeroyal.gov.uk

Warrington
01925 444400
www.warrington.gov.uk

CLEVELAND

Hartlepool
01429 266522
www.hartlepool.gov.uk
Press: 01429 523510

Middlesbrough
01642 245432
www.middlesbrough.gov.uk
Press: 01642 729502

Redcar and Cleveland
0845 612 6126
www.redcar-cleveland.gov.uk

CORNWALL

Caradon
01579 341000
www.caradon.gov.uk

Carrick
01872 224400
www.carrick.gov.uk

Kerrier
01209 614000
www.kerrier.gov.uk

North Cornwall
01208 893333
www.ncdc.gov.uk

Penwith
01736 362341
www.penwith.gov.uk

Restormel
01726 223300
www.restormel.gov.uk

COUNTY DURHAM

Durham
0191 383 3000
www.durham.gov.uk
Press: 0191 383 3373

Chester-le-Street
0191 387 1919
www.chester-le-street.gov.uk

Darlington
01325 380651
www.darlington.gov.uk

Derwentside
01207 693693
www.derwentside.gov.uk

Easington
0191 527 0501
www.easington.gov.uk

Sedgefield
01388 816166
www.sedgefield.gov.uk

Teesdale
01833 690000
www.teesdale.gov.uk

Wear Valley
01388 765555
www.wearvalley.gov.uk

CUMBRIA

Carlisle
01228 817000
www.carlisle.gov.uk
Press: 01228 817150

Allerdale
01900 702702
www.allerdale.gov.uk

Barrow-in-Furness
01229 894900
www.barrowbc.gov.uk

Copeland
01946 852585
www.copelandbc.gov.uk

South Lakeland
01539 733333
www.southlakeland.gov.uk

DERBYSHIRE

Derby
01332 293111
www.derby.gov.uk
Press: 01332 256207

Amber Valley
01773 570222
www.ambervalley.gov.uk

Bolsover
01246 242424
www.bolsover.gov.uk

Chesterfield
01246 345345
www.chesterfield.gov.uk

Derbyshire Dales
01629 761100
www.derbyshiredales.gov.uk

Erewash
0115 907 2244
www.erewash.gov.uk

High Peak
0845 129 7777
www.highpeak.gov.uk

North East Derbyshire
01246 231111
www.ne-derbyshire.gov.uk

South Derbyshire
01283 221000
www.south-derbys.gov.uk

DEVON

Exeter
01392 277888
www.exeter.gov.uk
Press: 01392 265103

Plymouth
01752 668000
www.plymouth.gov.uk
Press: 01752 304913

East Devon
01395 516551
www.eastdevon.gov.uk

Mid Devon
01884 255255
www.middevon.gov.uk

North Devon
01271 327711
www.northdevon.gov.uk

South Hams
01803 861234
www.southhams.gov.uk

Teignbridge
01626 361101
www.teignbridge.gov.uk

Torbay
01803 201201
www.torbay.gov.uk

Torridge
01237 428700
www.torridge.gov.uk

West Devon
01822 813600
www.westdevon.gov.uk

DORSET

Bournemouth
01202 451451
www.bournemouth.gov.uk
Press: 01202 454668

Christchurch
01202 495000
www.dorsetforyou.com

East Dorset
01202 886201
www.dorsetforyou.com

North Dorset
01258 454111
www.north-dorset.gov.uk

Poole
01202 633633
www.boroughofpoole.com

Purbeck
01929 556561
www.purbeck.gov.uk

West Dorset
01305 251010
www.dorsetforyou.com

Weymouth and Portland
01305 838000
www.weymouth.gov.uk

EAST SUSSEX

Brighton and Hove
01273 290000
www.brighton-hove.gov.uk
Press: 01273 291040

Eastbourne
01323 410000
www.eastbourne.gov.uk

Hastings
01424 781066
www.hastings.gov.uk

Lewes
01273 471600
www.lewes.gov.uk
Press: 01273 484141

Rother
01424 787878
www.rother.gov.uk

Wealden
01892 653311
www.wealden.gov.uk

ESSEX

Southend-on-Sea
01702 215000
www.southend.gov.uk
Press: 01702 215020

Basildon
01268 533333
www.basildon.gov.uk

Braintree
01376 552525
www.braintree.gov.uk

Brentwood
01277 312500
www.brentwood.gov.uk

Castle Point
01268 882200
www.castlepoint.gov.uk

Chelmsford
01245 606606
www.chelmsford.gov.uk

Colchester
01206 282222
www.colchester.gov.uk

Epping Forest
01992 564000
www.eppingforestdc.gov.uk

Harlow
01279 446655
www.harlow.gov.uk

Maldon
01621 854477
www.maldon.gov.uk

Rochford
01702 546366
www.rochford.gov.uk

Tendring
01255 686868
www.tendringdc.gov.uk

Thurrock
01375 652652
www.thurrock.gov.uk

Uttlesford
01799 510510
www.uttlesford.gov.uk

GLOUCESTERSHIRE

Gloucester
01452 522232
www.gloucester.gov.uk
Press: 01452 396133

Cheltenham
01242 262626
www.cheltenham.gov.uk
Press: 01242 775049

Cotswolds
01285 623000
www.cotswold.gov.uk
Press: 01285 623120

Forest of Dean
01594 810000
www.fdean.gov.uk

South Gloucestershire
01454 868686
www.southglos.gov.uk

Stroud
01453 766321
www.stroud.gov.uk

Tewkesbury
01684 295010
www.tewkesbury.gov.uk

GREATER MANCHESTER

Manchester
0161 234 5000
www.manchester.gov.uk
Press: 0161 234 3534

Bolton
01204 333333
www.bolton.gov.uk

Bury
0161 253 5000
www.bury.gov.uk

Oldham
0161 770 3000
www.oldham.gov.uk

Rochdale
01706 647474
www.rochdale.gov.uk

Salford
0161 794 4711
www.salford.gov.uk

Stockport
0161 480 4949
www.stockport.gov.uk

Tameside
0161 342 8355
www.tameside.gov.uk

Trafford
0161 912 2000
www.trafford.gov.uk

Wigan
01942 244991
www.wiganmbc.gov.uk

HAMPSHIRE

Portsmouth
023 9283 4092
www.portsmouth.gov.uk
Press: 023 9283 4043

Southampton
023 8022 3855
www.southampton.gov.uk
Press: 023 8083 2000

Basingstoke and Deane
01256 844844
www.basingstoke.gov.uk

East Hampshire
01730 266551
www.easthants.gov.uk

Eastleigh
023 8068 8068
www.eastleigh.gov.uk

Fareham
01329 236100
www.fareham.gov.uk

Gosport
023 9258 4242
www.gosport.gov.uk

Hart
01252 622122
www.hart.gov.uk

Havant
023 9247 4174
www.havant.gov.uk

New Forest
023 8028 5000
www.newforest.gov.uk

Rushmoor
01252 398398
www.rushmoor.gov.uk

Test Valley
01264 368000
www.testvalley.gov.uk

Winchester
01962 840222
www.winchester.gov.uk

HERTFORDSHIRE

St Albans
01727 866100
www.stalbans.gov.uk
Press: 01727 819316

Broxbourne
01992 785555
www.broxbourne.gov.uk

Dacorum
01442 228000
www.dacorum.gov.uk

East Hertfordshire
01279 655261
www.eastherts.gov.uk

Hertsmere
020 8207 2277
www.hertsmere.gov.uk

North Hertfordshire
01462 474000
www.north-herts.gov.uk

Stevenage
01438 242242
www.stevenage.gov.uk

Watford
01923 226400
www.watford.gov.uk

Welwyn Hatfield
01707 357000
www.welhat.gov.uk

KENT

Canterbury
01227 862000
www.canterbury.gov.uk
Press: 01227 862050

Ashford
01233 331111
www.ashford.gov.uk

Dartford
01322 343434
www.dartford.gov.uk

Dover
01304 821199
www.dover.gov.uk

Gravesham
01474 337000
www.gravesham.gov.uk

Maidstone
01622 602000
www.digitalmaidstone.co.uk

Medway
01634 306000
www.medway.gov.uk

Sevenoaks
01732 227000
www.sevenoaks.gov.uk

Shepway
01303 850388
www.shepway.gov.uk

Swale
01795 424341
www.swale.gov.uk

Thanet
01843 577000
www.thanet.gov.uk

Tonbridge and Malling
01732 844522
www.tmbc.gov.uk

Tunbridge Wells
01892 526121
www.tunbridgewells.gov.uk

LANCASHIRE

Lancaster
01524 582000
www.lancaster.gov.uk
Press: 01524 582041

Preston
01772 906900
www.preston.gov.uk
Press: 01772 906464

Blackburn with Darwen
01254 585585
www.blackburn.gov.uk
Blackpool
01253 477477
www.blackpool.gov.uk
Burnley
01282 425011
www.burnley.gov.uk
Chorley
01257 515151
www.chorley.gov.uk
Fylde
01253 658658
www.fylde.gov.uk
Hyndburn
01254 388111
www.hyndburnbc.gov.uk
Press: 01254 380108
Pendle
01282 661661
www.pendle.gov.uk
South Ribble
01772 421491
www.south-ribblebc.gov.uk
West Lancashire
01695 577177
www.westlancsdc.gov.uk
Wyre
01253 891000
www.wyrebc.gov.uk

LEICESTERSHIRE

Leicester
0116 254 9922
www.leicester.gov.uk
Press: 0116 252 6081
Blaby
0116 275 0555
www.blaby.gov.uk
Charnwood
01509 263151
www.charnwood.gov.uk
Harborough
01858 828282
www.harborough.gov.uk
Hinckley and Bosworth
01455 238141
www.hinckley-bosworth.gov.uk
Melton
01664 502502
www.melton.gov.uk
North West Leicestershire
01530 454545
www.nwleics.gov.uk
Oadby and Wigston
0116 288 8961
www.oadby-wigston.gov.uk

LINCOLNSHIRE

Lincoln
01522 881188
www.lincoln.gov.uk
Press: 01522 873443
Boston
01205 314200
www.boston.gov.uk
East Lindsey
01507 601111
www.e-lindsey.gov.uk

North East Lincolnshire
01472 313131
www.nelincs.gov.uk
North Kesteven
01529 414155
www.n-kesteven.gov.uk
North Lincolnshire
01724 296296
www.northlincs.gov.uk
South Holland
01775 761161
www.sholland.gov.uk
South Kesteven
01476 406080
www.southkesteven.gov.uk
West Lindsey
01427 676676
www.west-lindsey.gov.uk

MERSEYSIDE

Liverpool
0151 233 3000
www.liverpool.gov.uk
Press: 0151 225 5509
Knowsley
0151 489 6000
www.knowsley.gov.uk
Sefton
0845 140 0845
www.sefton.gov.uk
St Helens
01744 456789
www.sthelens.gov.uk
Wirral
0151 606 2000
www.wirral.gov.uk

NORFOLK

Norwich
01603 212212
www.norwich.gov.uk
Press: 01603 212167/212991
Breckland
01362 656870
www.breckland.gov.uk
Broadland
01603 431133
www.broadland.gov.uk
Great Yarmouth
01493 856100
www.great-yarmouth.gov.uk
King's Lynn and West Norfolk
01553 616200
www.west-norfolk.gov.uk
North Norfolk
01263 513811
www.north-norfolk.gov.uk
South Norfolk
01508 533633
www.south-norfolk.gov.uk

NORTH AND EAST YORKSHIRE

York
01904 551550
www.york.gov.uk
Press: 01904 552005
Craven
01756 700600
www.cravendc.gov.uk

East Riding of Yorkshire
01482 393939
www.eastriding.gov.uk
Hambleton
0845 121 1555
www.hambleton.gov.uk
Harrogate
01423 500600
www.harrogate.gov.uk
Kingston upon Hull
01482 300300
www.hullcc.gov.uk
Richmondshire
01748 829100
www.richmondshire.gov.uk
Ryedale
01653 600666
www.ryedale.gov.uk
Scarborough
01723 232323
www.scarborough.gov.uk
Selby
01757 705101
www.selby.gov.uk
Stockton-on-Tees
01642 393939
www.stockton.gov.uk

NORTHAMPTONSHIRE

Northampton
01604 837837
www.northampton.gov.uk
Corby
01536 464000
www.corby.gov.uk
Daventry
01327 871100
www.daventrydc.gov.uk
East Northamptonshire
01832 742000
www.east-northamptonshire
.gov.uk
Kettering
01536 410333
www.kettering.gov.uk
South Northamptonshire
0845 230 0226
www.southnorthants.gov.uk
Wellingborough
01933 229777
www.wellingborough.gov.uk

NORTHUMBERLAND

Alnwick
01665 510505
www.alnwick.gov.uk
Berwick-upon-Tweed
01289 330044
www.berwick-upon-tweed.gov.uk
Blyth Valley
01670 542000
www.blythvalley.gov.uk
Castle Morpeth
01670 535000
www.castlemorpeth.gov.uk
Tynedale
01434 652121
www.tynedale.gov.uk
Wansbeck
01670 532200
www.wansbeck.gov.uk

NOTTINGHAMSHIRE

Nottingham
0115 915 5555
www.nottinghamcity.gov.uk
Press: 0115 915 4754

Ashfield
01623 450000
www.ashfield-dc.gov.uk

Bassetlaw
01909 533533
www.bassetlaw.gov.uk

Broxtowe
0115 917 7777
www.broxtowe.gov.uk

Gedling
0115 901 3901
www.gedling.gov.uk

Mansfield
01623 463463
www.mansfield.gov.uk

Newark and Sherwood
01636 650000
www.newark-sherwooddc.gov.uk

Rushcliffe
0115 981 9911
www.rushcliffe.gov.uk

OXFORDSHIRE

Oxford
01865 249811
www.oxford.gov.uk
Press: 01865 252096

Cherwell
01295 252535
www.cherwell-dc.gov.uk

South Oxfordshire
01491 823000
www.southoxon.gov.uk

Vale of White Horse
01235 520202
www.whitehorsedc.gov.uk

West Oxfordshire
01993 861000
www.westoxon.gov.uk

SHROPSHIRE

Bridgnorth
01746 713100
www.bridgnorth-dc.gov.uk

North Shropshire
01939 232771
www.northshropshiredc.gov.uk

Oswestry
01691 671111
www.oswestrybc.gov.uk

Shrewsbury and Atcham
01743 281000
www.shrewsbury.gov.uk

South Shropshire
01584 813000
www.southshropshire.gov.uk

Telford & Wrekin
01952 380000
www.telford.gov.uk

SOMERSET AND AVON

Bath and North-east Somerset
01225 477000
www.bathnes.gov.uk

Bristol
0117 922 2000
www.bristol.gov.uk
Press: 0117 922 2650

Mendip
01749 648999
www.mendip.gov.uk

North Somerset
01934 888888
www.n-somerset.gov.uk

Sedgemoor
0845 408 2540
www.sedgemoor.gov.uk

South Somerset
01935 462462
www.southsomerset.gov.uk

Taunton Deane
01823 356356
www.tauntondeane.gov.uk

West Somerset
01643 703704
www.westsomersetonline.gov.uk

SOUTH YORKSHIRE

Doncaster
01302 734444
www.doncaster.gov.uk

Rotherham
01709 382121
www.rotherham.gov.uk

Sheffield
0114 272 6444
www.sheffield.gov.uk
Press: 0114 203 9082

STAFFORDSHIRE

Stoke-on-Trent
01782 234567
www.stoke.gov.uk
Press: 01782 232900

Cannock Chase
01543 462621
www.cannockchasedc.gov.uk

East Staffordshire
01283 508000
www.eaststaffsbc.gov.uk

Lichfield
01543 250011
www.lichfield.gov.uk

Newcastle-under-Lyme
01782 717717
www.newcastle-staffs.gov.uk

South Staffordshire
01902 696000
www.sstaffs.gov.uk

Stafford
01785 619000
www.staffordbc.gov.uk

Staffordshire Moorlands
0845 603 3010
www.staffsmoorlands.gov.uk

Tamworth
01827 709709
www.tamworth.gov.uk

SUFFOLK

Ipswich
01473 432000
www.ipswich.gov.uk
Press: 01473 432031

Babergh
01473 822801
www.babergh.gov.uk

Forest Heath
01638 719000
www.forest-heath.gov.uk

Mid Suffolk
01449 720711
www.midsuffolk.gov.uk

St Edmundsbury
01284 763233
www.stedmundsbury.gov.uk

Suffolk Coastal
01394 383789
www.suffolkcoastal.gov.uk

Waveney
01502 562111
www.waveney.gov.uk

SURREY

Elmbridge
01372 474474
www.elmbridge.gov.uk

Epsom and Ewell
01372 732000
www.epsom-ewell.gov.uk

Guildford
01483 505050
www.guildford.gov.uk

Mole Valley
01306 885001
www.molevalley.gov.uk

Reigate and Banstead
01737 276000
www.reigate-banstead.gov.uk

Runnymede
01932 838383
www.runnymede.gov.uk

Surrey Heath
01276 707100
www.surreyheath.gov.uk

Tandridge
01883 722000
www.tandridgedc.gov.uk

Waverley
01483 523333
www.waverley.gov.uk

Woking
01483 755855
www.woking.gov.uk

TYNE AND WEAR

Newcastle upon Tyne
0191 232 8520
www.newcastle.gov.uk
Press: 0191 211 5057

Gateshead
0191 433 3000
www.gateshead.gov.uk

North Tyneside
0191 200 5000
www.northtyneside.gov.uk

South Tyneside
0191 427 1717
www.southtyneside.info

Sunderland
0191 553 1000
www.sunderland.gov.uk

WARWICKSHIRE

Warwick
01926 450000
www.warwickdc.gov.uk

North Warwickshire
01827 715341
www.northwarks.gov.uk

Nuneaton and Bedworth
024 7637 6376
www.nuneatonandbedworth
.gov.uk

Rugby
01788 533533
www.rugby.gov.uk

Stratford-on-Avon
01789 267575
www.stratford.gov.uk

WEST MIDLANDS

Birmingham
0121 303 9944
www.birmingham.gov.uk
Press: 0121 303 3287

Coventry
024 7683 3333
www.coventry.gov.uk
Press: 024 7683 4848

Dudley
01384 818181
www.dudley.gov.uk

Sandwell
0121 569 2200
www.sandwell.gov.uk

Solihull
0121 704 6000
www.solihull.gov.uk

Walsall
01922 650000
www.walsall.gov.uk

Wolverhampton
01902 551155
www.wolverhampton.gov.uk
Press: 01902 554077

WEST SUSSEX

Adur
01273 263000
www.adur.gov.uk

Arun
01903 737500
www.arun.gov.uk

Mid Sussex
01444 458166
www.midsussex.gov.uk

Chichester
01243 785166
www.chichester.gov.uk

Crawley
01293 438000
www.crawley.gov.uk

Horsham
01403 215100
www.horsham.gov.uk

Worthing
01903 239999
www.worthing.gov.uk

WEST YORKSHIRE

Leeds
0113 234 8080
www.leeds.gov.uk
Press: 0113 247 4328

Bradford
01274 431000
www.bradford.gov.uk

Calderdale
0845 245 6000
www.calderdale.gov.uk

Kirklees
01484 221000
www.kirklees.gov.uk

Wakefield
01924 306090
www.wakefield.gov.uk

WILTSHIRE

Kennet
01380 724911
www.kennet.gov.uk

North Wiltshire
01249 706111
www.northwilts.gov.uk

Salisbury
01722 336272
www.salisbury.gov.uk
Press: 01722 434561

Swindon
01793 463000
www.swindon.gov.uk
Press: 01793 463105

West Wiltshire
01225 776655
www.westwiltshire.gov.uk

WORCESTERSHIRE

Worcester
01905 722233
www.cityofworcester.gov.uk

Bromsgrove
01527 873232
www.bromsgrove.gov.uk

Malvern Hills
01684 862151
www.malvernhills.gov.uk

Redditch
01527 64252
www.redditchbc.gov.uk

Wychavon
01386 565000
www.wychavon.gov.uk

Wyre Forest
01562 732928
www.wyreforestdc.gov.uk

Government offices for the regions

East of England
01223 372500
www.go-east.gov.uk

East Midlands
0115 971 9971

London
020 7217 3328
www.go-london.gov.uk

North-east
0191 201 3300
www.go-ne.gov.uk

North-west
0161 952 4000
www.go-nw.gov.uk

South-east
01483 882255
www.gose.gov.uk

South-west
0117 900 1700
www.gosw.gov.uk

West Midlands
0121 352 5050
www.go-wm.gov.uk

Yorkshire and the Humber
0113 280 0600
www.goyh.gov.uk

Government News Network offices

www.gnn.gov.uk

East
01223 372780

East Midlands
0115 971 2780

London
020 7261 8325

North-east
0191 202 3600

North-west
0161 952 4513

South-east
020 7261 8647

South-west
0117 900 3551

West Midlands
0121 352 5500

Yorkshire and the Humber
0113 341 3170

Scotland
0131 244 9060/1

Wales
0844 800 6823

Regional development agencies

East of England
01223 713900
www.eeda.org.uk
Press: 01223 484624

East Midlands
0115 988 8300
www.emda.org.uk
Press: 0115 988 8375

London
020 7593 8000
www.lda.gov.uk

North-east
0191 229 6200
www.onenortheast.co.uk
Press: 0191 229 6311

North-west
01925 400100
www.nwda.co.uk
Press: 01925 400232

South-east
01483 484200
www.seeda.co.uk
Press: 01483 484216

South-west
01392 214747
www.southwestrda.org.uk
Press: 01392 229567

West Midlands
0121 380 3500
www.advantagewm.co.uk
Press: 0121 503 3228

Yorkshire
0113 394 9600
www.yorkshire-forward.com
Press: 0113 394 9923

Wales

National Assembly for Wales
» *see page 320*

Cardiff
029 2087 2000
www.cardiff.gov.uk
Press: 029 2087 2964

Swansea
01792 636000
www.swansea.gov.uk
Press: 01792 636092

Carmarthenshire
01267 234567
www.carmarthenshire.gov.uk

Ceredigion
01970 617911
www.ceredigion.gov.uk

Denbighshire
01824 706000
www.denbighshire.gov.uk

Flintshire
01352 752121
www.flintshire.gov.uk

Gwynedd
01286 672255
www.gwynedd.gov.uk

Isle of Anglesey
01248 750057
www.ynysmon.gov.uk

Monmouthshire
01633 644644
www.monmouthshire.gov.uk

Newport
01633 656656
www.newport.gov.uk

Pembrokeshire
01437 764551
www.pembrokeshire.gov.uk

Powys
01597 826000
www.powys.gov.uk

● County borough councils

Blaenau Gwent
01495 350555
www.blaenau-gwent.gov.uk

Bridgend
01656 643643
www.bridgend.gov.uk

Caerphilly
01443 815588
www.caerphilly.gov.uk

Conwy
01492 574000
www.conwy.gov.uk

Merthyr Tydfil
01685 725000
www.merthyr.gov.uk

Neath Port Talbot
01639 763333
www.npt.gov.uk

Rhondda Cynon Taff
01443 424000
www.rhondda-cynon-taff.gov.uk

Torfaen
01495 762200
www.torfaen.gov.uk

Vale of Glamorgan
01446 700111
www.valeofglamorgan.gov.uk

Wrexham
01978 292000
www.wrexham.gov.uk

Scotland

Scottish Executive
» *see page 320*

Aberdeen
01224 523406
www.aberdeencity.gov.uk
Press: 01224 522821

Dundee
01382 434000
www.dundeecity.gov.uk
Press: 01382 434500

Edinburgh
0131 200 2000
www.edinburgh.gov.uk
Press: 0131 529 4044

Glasgow
0141 287 2000
www.glasgow.gov.uk
Press: 0141 287 0906

Aberdeenshire
01467 620981
www.aberdeenshire.gov.uk

Angus
0845 277 7778
www.angus.gov.uk

Argyll and Bute
0141 578 8000
www.eastdunbarton.gov.uk

Clackmannanshire
01259 450000
www.clacksweb.org.uk

Dumfries and Galloway
01387 260000
www.dumgal.gov.uk

East Ayrshire
01563 576000
www.east-ayrshire.gov.uk

East Dunbartonshire
0141 578 8000
www.eastdunbarton.gov.uk

East Lothian
01620 827827
www.eastlothian.gov.uk

East Renfrewshire
0141 577 3001
www.eastrenfrewshire.gov.uk

Falkirk
01324 506070
www.falkirk.gov.uk

Fife
01592 414141
www.fifedirect.org.uk

Highland
01463 702000
www.highland.gov.uk

Inverclyde
01475 717171
www.inverclyde.gov.uk

Midlothian
0131 270 7500
www.midlothian.gov.uk

Moray
01343 543451
www.moray.gov.uk

North Ayrshire
0845 603 0590
www.north-ayrshire.gov.uk

North Lanarkshire
01698 332000
www.northlan.gov.uk

Orkney Islands
01856 873535
www.orkney.gov.uk

Perth and Kinross
01738 475000
www.pkc.gov.uk

Renfrewshire
0141 842 5000
www.renfrewshire.gov.uk

Scottish Borders
01835 824000
www.scottishborders.gov.uk

Shetland Islands
01595 693535
www.shetland.gov.uk

South Ayrshire
01292 612000
www.south-ayrshire.gov.uk

South Lanarkshire
01698 454444
www.southlanarkshire.gov.uk

Stirling
0845 277 7000
www.stirling.gov.uk

West Dunbartonshire
01389 737000
www.west-dunbarton.gov.uk

West Lothian
01506 775000
www.westlothian.gov.uk

Western Isles
01851 703773
www.w-isles.gov.uk

Northern Ireland

Belfast
028 9032 0202
www.belfastcity.gov.uk
Press: 028 9027 0221

Lisburn
028 9250 9250
www.lisburncity.gov.uk

ANTRIM

Antrim
028 9446 3113
www.antrim.gov.uk

Ballymena
0845 658 1581
www.ballymena.gov.uk

Ballymoney
028 2766 0200
www.ballymoney.gov.uk

Carrickfergus
028 9335 8000
www.carrickfergus.org

Larne
028 2827 2313
www.larne.gov.uk

Moyle
028 2076 2225
www.moyle-council.org

Newtownabbey
028 9034 0000
www.newtownabbey.gov.uk

ARMAGH

Armagh
028 3752 9600
www.armagh.gov.uk

Craigavon
028 3831 2400
www.craigavon.gov.uk

COUNTY DERRY

Coleraine
028 7034 7034
www.colerainebc.gov.uk

Derry
028 7136 5151
www.derrycity.gov.uk
Press: 028 7137 6504

Limavady
028 7772 2226
www.limavady.gov.uk

Magherafelt
028 7939 7979
www.magherafelt.gov.uk

DOWN

Ards
028 9182 4000
www.ards-council.gov.uk

Banbridge
028 4066 0600
www.banbridge.com

Castlereagh
028 9049 4500
www.castlereagh.gov.uk

Down
028 4461 0800
www.downdc.gov.uk

Newry and Mourne
028 3031 3031
www.newryandmourne.gov.uk

North Down
028 9127 0371
www.northdown.gov.uk

FERMANAGH

Fermanagh
028 6632 5050
www.fermanagh.gov.uk

TYRONE

Cookstown
028 8676 2205
www.cookstown.gov.uk

Dungannon and South Tyrone
028 8772 0300
www.dungannon.gov.uk

Omagh
028 8224 5321
www.omagh.gov.uk

Strabane
028 7138 2204
www.strabanedc.com

Government: **parliament and politics**

Parliaments and assemblies

Parliament
020 7219 3000
www.parliament.uk
Commons information office:
020 7219 4272
Commons press:
020 7219 0898
Lords information office:
020 7219 3107
Journalist dedicated line:
020 7219 0969

National Assembly for Wales
0845 010 5500
www.wales.gov.uk
Press: 029 2089 8099

Scottish Parliament
0131 348 5000
www.scottish.parliament.uk
Press: 0131 348 5000

Main political parties

Labour party
0870 590 0200
www.labour.org.uk
Press: 07659 134974

Conservative party
020 7222 9000
www.conservatives.com
Press: 020 7984 8121

Liberal Democrat party
020 7222 7999
www.libdems.org.uk
Press: 020 7340 4949

Regional parties

● Wales

Plaid Cymru
029 2064 6000
www.plaidcymru.org
Press: 029 2064 6010

Welsh Labour party
029 2087 7700
www.welshlabour.org.uk
Press: 029 2087 7707

Welsh Conservative party
029 2061 6031
www.welshconservatives.com
Press: 029 2089 8395

Welsh Liberal Democrats
029 2031 3400
www.welshlibdems.org.uk
Press: 029 2089 8426

● Scotland

Scottish Conservative party
0131 247 6890
www.scottishconservatives.com
Press: 0131 348 5620

Scottish Green party
0870 077 2207
www.scottishgreens.org.uk
Press: 0131 348 6360

Scottish Labour party
0141 572 6900
www.scottishlabour.org.uk
Press: 0141 572 6905

Scottish Liberal Democrats
0131 337 2314
www.scotlibdems.org.uk
Press: 0131 348 5810

Scottish National party
0131 525 8900
www.snp.org

Scottish Socialist party
www.scottishsocialistparty.org

● Northern Ireland

Alliance party
028 9032 4274
www.allianceparty.org

Democratic Unionist party
028 9047 1155
www.dup.org.uk
Press: 028 9065 4479

Progressive Unionist party
028 9022 5040
www.pup-ni.org.uk

Sinn Féin
00 353 1 872 6100
www.sinnfein.ie

Social Democratic and Labour party
028 9024 7700
www.sdlp.ie
Press: 028 9052 1364

Ulster Unionist party
028 9076 5500
www.uup.org
Press: 028 9076 5521

Minor parties

National party
0870 757 6267
www.bnp.org.uk
Press: 07074 530267

Communist League party
mail@communistleague.org.uk
www.communistleague.org.uk

Communist party of Britain
office@communist-party.org.uk
www.communist-party.org.uk

Cooperative party
020 7367 4150
www.party.coop
Press: 020 7367 4160

English Independence party
020 7278 5221
www.englishindependenceparty
.com

Green party
020 7272 4474
www.greenparty.org.uk
Press: 020 7561 0282

Liberal party
0151 259 5935
www.liberal.org.uk
Separate from the Liberal Democrats

National Front
0121 246 6838
www.natfront.com

Socialist party
020 8988 8777
www.socialistparty.org.uk
Press: 020 8988 8778

Socialist Party of Great Britain
www.worldsocialism.org

UK Independence party
01626 831290
www.ukip.org
Press: 020 7222 9365

Workers Revolutionary party
020 7232 1101
www.wrp.org.uk

Parliamentary and electoral bodies

Electoral Commission
020 7271 0500
www.electoralcommission.org.uk
Press: 07968 791684

Electoral Reform Society
020 7928 1622
www.electoral-reform.org.uk
Press: 07984 644138

Hansard Society
020 7438 1222
www.hansardsociety.org.uk
Press: 020 7438 1225

Parliamentary Counsel
020 7210 2588
www.parliamentary-counsel
.gov.uk
Cabinet Office press office:
020 7276 0317

Thinktanks

Adam Smith Institute
020 7222 4995
www.adamsmith.org
Free market economics

Bow Group
020 7431 6400
www.bowgroup.org
Centre-right

Centre for Economic Policy Research
020 7878 2900
www.cepr.org
European network of research fellows

Centre for Global Energy Studies
020 7235 4334
www.cges.co.uk

Centre for Policy Studies
020 7222 4488
www.cps.org.uk
Established 1974 by Margaret Thatcher and Keith Joseph

Centre for the Study of Financial Innovation
020 7493 0173
www.csfi.org.uk

Centre Forum
020 7340 1160
www.centreforum.org
Independent liberal

Chatham House
020 7957 5700
www.chathamhouse.org.uk

Civitas
020 7799 6677
www.civitas.org.uk
Civil society

Demos
0845 458 5949
www.demos.co.uk
Everyday democracy

Fabian Society
020 7227 4900
www.fabian-society.org.uk
Centre-left

Federal Trust
020 7735 4000
www.fedtrust.co.uk

Foreign Policy Centre
020 7388 6662
www.fpc.org.uk
Established 1998 by Labour government

International Institute for Environment and Development
020 7388 2117
www.iied.org

Institute for European Environmental Policy
020 7799 2244
www.ieep.org.uk

Institute for Global Ethics
020 7486 1954
www.globalethics.org

HLSP Limited. (formerly Institute for Health Sector Development)
020 7253 5064
www.hlspinstitute.org

Institute for Jewish Policy Research
020 7935 8266
www.jpr.org.uk

Institute for Public Policy Research
020 7470 6100
www.ippr.org.uk
Centre-left

International Institute for Strategic Studies
020 7379 7676
www.iiss.org

Institute of Economic Affairs
020 7799 8900
www.iea.org.uk
UK's original free market think tank

Institute of Fiscal Studies
020 7291 4800
www.ifs.org.uk

Institute of Ideas
020 7269 9220
www.instituteofideas.com

New Economics Foundation
020 7820 6300
www.neweconomics.org

New Policy Institute
020 7721 8421
www.npi.org.uk
Progressive think tank

New Politics Network
020 7278 4443
www.new-politics.com
Democracy and participation in politics

Overseas Development Institute
020 7922 0300
www.odi.org.uk

Policy Studies Institute
020 7911 7500
www.psi.org.uk

Politeia
020 7240 5070
www.politeia.co.uk
Role of the state

Scottish Council Foundation
0131 225 4709
www.scottishcouncilfoundation.org

Smith Institute
020 7823 4240
www.smith-institute.org.uk
Social values and economic imperatives

Social Affairs Unit
020 7637 4356
www.socialaffairsunit.org.uk

Social Market Foundation
020 7222 7060
www.smf.co.uk

Alternative and protest

Anarchist Federation
info@ afed.org.uk
www.afed.org.uk

Anti-Nazi League
020 7924 0333
www.anl.org.uk

Big Green Gathering
01458 834629
www.big-green-gathering.com

Campaign Against Racism and Facism (CARF)
020 7837 1450
www.carf.demon.co.uk

Charter 88
0845 450 7210
www.charter88.org.uk

Creative Exchange
020 7065 0980
www.creativexchange.org

Democracy Movement
020 8570 5681
www.democracymovement.org.uk

Freedom Association
0845 833 9626
www.tfa.net

Globalise Resistance
020 7053 2071
www.resist.org.uk

Green Events
020 7424 9100
www.greenevents.co.uk

GreenNet
0845 055 4011
www.gn.apc.org

Indymedia
www.indymedia.org.uk
Network of independent media activists

Love Music Hate Racism
020 7924 0333
www.lmhr.org.uk

OneWorld
020 7239 1400
www.oneworld.net
Anti-globalisation

Peoples' Global Action
www.agp.org

Protest Net
rabble-rouser@protest.net
www.protest.net

Red Star Research
07960 865601
www.red-star-research.org.uk

Revolutionary Communist Group
020 7837 1688
www.revolutionarycommunist.com

Rising Tide
07708 794665
www.risingtide.org.uk

Squall
squall@squall.co.uk
www.squall.co.uk

The Land is Ours
01460 249 204
www.tlio.org.uk
Press: 0117 944 6219

Undercurrents News Network (UNN)
01792 455900
www.undercurrents.org
Alternative news videos

Unite Against Fascism
020 7833 4916
020 7837 4522
www.uaf.org.uk

Urban 75
www.urban75.com

Wombles
wombles@hushmail.com
www.wombles.org.uk
Anarchist and libertarian

Freemasons

Freemasons
grandsecretary@grandlodge.org.uk
www.grandlodge.org.uk

Government: **global politics**

Government departments

Foreign Office
020 7270 1500
www.fco.gov.uk
Press: 020 7008 3100
International Development
020 7023 0000
www.dfid.gov.uk
Press: 020 7023 0600

International

United Nations
001 212 963 1234
www.un.org
Press:
spokesman of the secretary
general: 001 212 963 7160
media accreditation:
001 212 963 6937/34
Regional United Nations Information Centre
00 32 2788 8484
www.unric.org
UN Commission on International Trade Law (UNCITRAL)
00 43 1 26 060 4061
www.uncitral.org
UN Educational, Scientific & Cultural Organisation (Unesco)
00 33 1 4568 1000
www.unesco.org
Press: 00 33 1 4568 1770
UN High Commissioner for Human Rights (UNHCHR)
00 41 22 917 9000
www.ohcr.org
Press: 00 41 22 917 9602
UN High Commissioner for Refugees (UNHCR)
020 7759 8090
00 41 22 739 8502/9242
www.unhcr.org
Press: gbrloea@unhcr.org
UN Relief & Works Agency for Palestinian Refugees (UNRWA)
www.un.org/unrwa
UN World Food Programme
00 39 06 65131
www.wfp.org
Unicef
020 7405 5592
www.unicef.org.uk
Press: 020 7430 0162
International Labour Organisation (ILO)
00 41 22 799 6111
www.ilo.org
Press: 00 41 22 799 7912
International Maritime Organisation (IMO)
020 7735 7611
www.imo.org
Press: 020 7587 3153

International Monetary Fund (IMF)
001 202 623 7000
www.imf.org
Press: 001 202 623 7100
International Whaling Commission
01223 233971
www.iwcoffice.org
Nato
00 32 2 707 72 11
www.nato.int
Press: 00 32 2 707 1399
OneWorld
020 7239 1400
www.oneworld.net
Press: 020 7239 1424
World Bank
001 202 473 1000
www.worldbank.org
UK Press: 020 7930 8511
World Health Organisation (WHO)
00 41 22 791 2111
www.who.int
Press: 00 41 22 791 2222
World Trade Organisation (WTO)
00 41 22 739 5111
www.wto.org
Press: 00 41 22 739 50 07

EU Institutions

European Parliament
London: 020 7227 4300
Edinburgh: 0131 577 7866
www.europarl.europa.eu
European Commission
00 800 6789 1011
www.europa.eu.int/comm/
Press: 00 32 2 296 5745
Committee of the Regions of the European Union
00 32 2 282 2211
www.cor.europa.eu
Press: 00 32 2 546 9393
Council of the European Union
00 32 2 281 6111
http://ue.eu.int
Press: 00 32 2 281 6319
Court of Justice of the European Communities
00 352 43031
www.curia.europa.eu
Press: 00 352 4301 35177
European Central Bank
00 49 69 1 3440
www.ecb.int
Press: 00 49 69 1344 7454/5
European Court of Auditors
00 352 43 984 5410
www.eca.eu.int
Press: 00 352 43 984 5424

European Economic and Social Committee
00 32 2 546 9011
www.esc.eu.int
Press: 00 32 2 546 9011
European Environment Agency
00 45 33 367100
http://org.eea.europa.eu
Press: 00 45 33 367 269
European Investment Bank
00 352 43791
www.eib.org
Press: 00 353 43 79 21 00
The European Ombudsman
00 33 3 8817 2313
www.euro-ombudsman.eu.int
European Police Office
00 31 70 302 5000
www.europol.europa.eu
Press: corporaterelations@
europol.europa.eu
Office for Official Publications of the European Communities
00 352 29291
http://publications.europa.eu
Translation Centre for the Bodies of the European Union
00 352 42 17111
www.cdt.europa.eu
Western European Union
www.weu.int

Other European contacts

Council of Europe
00 33 3 8841 2033
www.coe.int
Press: 00 33 3 8841 2560
Council of European Municipalities and Regions
00 32 2 511 7477
00 33 1 4450 5959
www.ccre.org
Press: 00 32 2 500 0534
European Court of Human Rights
00 33 3 8841 2018
www.echr.coe.int
Press: 00 33 3 9021 4215
European Space Agency
00 33 1 5369 7654
www.esa.int
Press: 00 33 1 5369 7155
European University Institute, Florence
00 39 055 46851
www.iue.it
European Youth Parliament
00 49 30 9700 5095
www.eypuk.org
Organisation for Economic Cooperation and Development
00 33 1 4524 8200
www.oecd.org
Press: 00 33 1 4524 9700

Organisation for Security and Cooperation in Europe
00 43 1 514360
www.osce.org
Press: 00 43 1 514350
Eurocorps
00 33 388 43 20 03
www.eurocorps.net
Press: 00 33 388 43 20 06

Political parties

Confederal Group of the European United Left/Nordic Green Left
00 32 2 284 2683/2686
www.guengl.org
Press: 00 32 475 646628
European Liberal Democrats
00 32 2 237 01 40
www.eldr.org
Greens-European Free Alliance
00 32 2 284 3045
00 33 3 881 75897
00 33 3 881 7 5879
www.greens-efa.org
Press: 00 32 2 284 4683
        00 33 3 8817 4760
Independence/Democracy Group in the European Parliament
ind-dem@europarl.europa.eu
http://indemgroup.org
Group of European People's Party (Christian Democrats) and European Democrats
00 32 2 284 2234
00 33 3 8817 4144
www.epp-ed.org
Press: 00 32 2284 2228
Parliamentary Group of the Party of European Socialists
00 32 2 28 43099
www.socialistgroup.org
Union for Europe of the Nations Group
00 32 2 284 2971
www.uengroup.org
Press: 00 32 2 28 42249

Pro-Europe and anti-Europe lobbies

Bruges Group
020 7287 4414
www.brugesgroup.com
Eurosceptic thinktank
European Movement
020 7820 9965
www.euromove.org.uk
Pro-European
Federation of Small Businesses
01253 336000
www.fsb.org.uk
Powerful anti-euro lobby
Press: 020 7891 8100
The No Campaign
info@no-euro.com
www.nocampaign.com
Pro-Europe, anti-euro
Press: 020 7222 9100

Commonwealth and British international

British Council
020 7389 4268
www.britcouncil.org
Press: 020 7389 4939
Commonwealth Institute
020 7024 9822
www.commonwealth.org.uk
Press: 020 7861 8574
Commonwealth Secretariat
020 7747 6500
www.thecommonwealth.org
Press: 020 7747 6385

British overseas territories

Anguilla
Governor: 001 264 497 2621/2
The most northern of the Caribbean islands
Bermuda
Governor, Hamilton:
        001 441 292 3600
100 small islands, 20 inhabited, 600 miles off North Carolina, USA
British Antarctic Territory
Commissioner, London:
        020 7008 2610
Uninhabited part of Antarctica, including South Orkney and South Shetland islands
British Indian Ocean Territory
Commissioner, London:
        020 7008 2890
Group of Chagos Archipelago islands in central Indian Ocean, south of India
British Virgin Islands
Governor, Tortola:
        001 284 494 2345/2370
Eastern Caribbean group of 46 islands, 11 inhabited, near Anguilla
Cayman Islands
Governor, Georgetown:
        001 345 244 2425
Three tax-free, wealthy islands south of Cuba
Falkland Islands
Governor, Stanley: 00 500 27433
Largest islands in the south Atlantic
Gibraltar
Governor: 00 350 45440
Promontory of southernmost Spain
Montserrat
Governor, Olveston:
        001 664 491 2688/9
East Caribbean volcanic island
Pitcairn Islands
Governor, Auckland:
        00 09 64 366 0186
Eastern group in Pacific, between north New Zealand and Peru. Home of mutineers from HMS Bounty, 1790
St Helena
Governor, Jamestown: 00 290 2555
Island in south Atlantic, 1,100 miles off Angola. Two dependencies

Ascension Island
Administrator: 00 247 7000
700 miles north-west of St Helena
Tristan da Cunha
Administrator: 00 870 764 341 816
Island group 1,850 miles west of Cape Town
South Georgia & Sandwich Islands
Governor, Stanley: 00 500 27433
Scattered islands east and south-east of Cape Horn. South Georgia is military, South Sandwich unhinhabited and volcanic
Turks & Caicos Islands
Governor, Grand Turk:
        001 649 946 2309
30 Caribbean islands, north of Haiti

International aid

ActionAid
020 7561 7561
www.actionaid.org.uk
Press: 020 7561 7614
Baby Milk Action
01223 464420
www.babymilkaction.org
Book Aid International
020 7733 3577
www.bookaid.org
British Leprosy Relief Association
01206 216700
0845 121 2121
www.lepra.org.uk
British Overseas NGOs for Development (Bond)
020 7837 8344
www.bond.org.uk
British Red Cross
0870 170 7000
www.redcross.org.uk
Press: 020 7877 7046/7039
Care International
020 7934 9334
www.careinternational.org.uk
Press: 020 7934 9315
Casa Alianza
00 502 2433 9600
www.casa-alianza.org
Catholic Agency for Overseas Development
020 7733 7900
www.cafod.org.uk
Press: 020 7326 5557
Christian Aid
020 7620 4444
www.christian-aid.org.uk
Press: 020 7523 2421
Christian Vision
0121 522 6087
www.christianvision.com
Church Mission Society
020 7928 8681
www.cms-uk.org
Disasters Emergency Committee
020 7387 0200
www.dec.org.uk
Build Africa
0800 652 6294
www.icrcharity.com

International Committee of Red Cross
00 41 22 734 6001
www.icrc.org
Press: 00 41 22 730 2282

International HIV/Aids Alliance
01273 718900
www.aidsalliance.org

International Rescue Committee
001 212 551 3000
www.theirc.org
Press: 020 7692 2741

Islamic Relief
020 8531 6752
www.islamic-relief.org.uk
Press: 0121 622 0649

Médecins sans Frontières (UK)
020 7404 6600
www.uk.msf.org

Methodist Relief and Development Fund
020 7467 5132
www.mrdf.org.uk

Muslim Aid
020 7377 4200
www.muslimaid.org.uk

Oxfam
01865 473727
www.oxfam.org.uk
Press: 01865 472498

Plan UK
020 7482 9777
www.plan-uk.org

Sightsavers
01444 446600
www.sightsavers.org.uk

Tear Fund
0845 355 8355
www.tearfund.org
Press: 020 8943 7779

Voluntary Services Overseas
020 8780 7200
www.vso.org.uk
Press: 020 8780 7365

WaterAid
020 7793 4500
www.wateraid.org
Press: 020 7793 4793

World Development Movement
020 7820 4900
www.wdm.org.uk

World Emergency Relief
0870 429 2129
www.wer-uk.org

World Vision UK
01908 841000
www.worldvision.org.uk
Press: 01908 244418

Human rights

ActionAid
020 7561 7561
www.actionaid.org.uk
Press: 020 7561 7614

Amnesty International
020 7033 1500
www.amnesty.org.uk
Press: 020 7033 1548

Anti-Slavery
020 7501 8920
www.antislavery.org
Press: 020 7501 8934

Asian Human Rights Commission
00 852 2698 6339
www.ahrchk.net

Association for Civil Rights in Israel
00 9722 652 1218
www.acri.org.il

British Institute of Human Rights
020 7848 1818
www.bihr.org

British Refugee Council
020 7346 6700
www.refugeecouncil.org.uk
Press: 020 7346 1213

Burma Campaign
020 7324 4710
www.burmacampaign.org.uk
Press: 020 7324 4713

Campaign Against Criminalising Communities
020 7586 5892
www.cacc.org.uk

Campaign Against Sanctions on Iraq
info@casi.org.uk
www.casi.org.uk

Campaign Against the Arms Trade
020 7281 0297
www.caat.org.uk

Centre for Research on Globalisation
001 514 425 3814
http://globalresearch.ca

Citizens for Global Solutions
001 202 546 3950
www.globalsolutions.org
Press: 001 202 546 3950

Coalition for the International Criminal Court
001 212 687 2863
00 31 70 363 4484
www.iccnow.org

Concern Worldwide
0800 032 4000
www.concern.net
Press: 00 353 1 417 7700

Derechos Human Rights
00 31 71 798634
www.derechos.org

Eliminate Child Labour in Tobacco
00 41 22 306 1444
www.eclt.org

European Roma Rights Centre
00 36 1 413 2200
http://errc.org

Free Tibet Campaign
020 7324 4605
www.freetibet.org

Gendercide Watch
office@gendercide.org
www.gendercide.org

Global Action to Prevent War
001 212 818 1815
www.globalactionpw.org

Global Fund for Women
001 415 202 7640
www.globalfundforwomen.org
Press: 001 415 202 7640 x338

Human Rights Watch
020 7713 1995
www.hrw.org

International Fellowship of Reconciliation
00 31 72 512 3014
www.ifor.org

International Physicians for the Prevention of Nuclear War
001 617 868 5050
www.ippnw.org

Kurdish Human Rights Project
020 7405 3835
www.khrp.org

Labour Behind the Label
01603 666160
www.labourbehindthelabel.org

One World Action
020 7833 4075
www.oneworldaction.org

Safer World
020 7324 4646
www.saferworld.org.uk
Press: 020 7324 4671

Stop the War Coalition
020 7278 6694
www.stopwar.org.uk
Press: 07939 242229

Transcend
00 40 742 079 716
www.transcend.org

Unrepresented Nations and Peoples Organisation
00 31 70 364 6504
www.unpo.org

War Resistors International
020 7278 4040
info@wri-irg.org
www.wri-irg.org

Womankind Worldwide
020 7549 0360
www.womankind.org.uk

World Commission for Peace and Human Rights Council
00 92 51 411704
www.worphco.cjb.net

World Organization For Human Rights USA
001 202 296 5702
www.humanrightsusa.org

Government: overseas embassies in the UK

Afghanistan
020 7589 8891
www.afghanembassy.co.uk
Albania
020 7828 8897
Algeria
020 7221 7800
Andorra
020 8874 4806
Angola
020 7299 9850
www.angola.org.uk
Antigua and Barbuda
020 7258 0070
www.antigua-barbuda.com
Argentina
020 7318 1300
www.argentine-embassy-uk.org
Armenia
020 7938 5435
Australia
020 7379 4334
www.australia.org.uk
Austria
020 7344 3250
www.austria.org.uk
Azerbaijan
020 7938 3412
www.president.az
Bahamas
020 7408 4488
Bahrain
020 7201 9170
Bangladesh
020 7584 0081
www.bangladeshhighcommission
.org.uk
Barbados
020 7631 4975
Belarus
020 7937 3288
http://belembassy.org/uk
Belgium
020 7470 3700
www.diplobel.org/uk
Belize
020 7723 3603
www.bzhc-lon.co.uk
Bolivia
020 7235 4248
www.embassyofbolivia.co.uk
Bosnia and Herzegovina
020 7373 0867
Botswana
020 7499 0031
Brazil
020 7499 0877
www.brazil.org.uk
Brunei
020 7581 0521
Bulgaria
020 7584 9400
www.bulgarianembassy.org.uk

Burma
020 7499 4340
www.myanmar.com
Burundi
00 32 2 230 45 35
Nearest embassy is in Belgium
Cambodia
020 7483 9063
Cameroon
020 7727 0771
Canada
020 7258 6600
www.dfait-maeci.gc.ca/canada
europa/united_kingdom
Cape Verde
0151 236 0206
Chile
020 7580 6392
China
020 7299 4049
www.chinese-embassy.org.uk
Colombia
020 7589 9177
www.colombianembassy.co.uk
Congo
020 7922 0695
Congo, Democratic Republic of
020 7278 9825
Costa Rica
020 7706 8844
http://costarica.embassy
homepage.com
Croatia
020 7387 2022
Cuba
020 7240 2488
Cyprus
020 7499 8272
Czech Republic
020 7243 1115
www.mzv.cz/london
Denmark
020 7333 0200
www.denmark.org.uk
Dominica, Commonwealth of
020 7370 5194/5
www.dominica.co.uk
Dominican Republic
020 7727 6285
www.serex.gov.do
Ecuador
020 7584 2648
Egypt
020 7499 3304
El Salvador
020 7589 4328
Equatorial Guinea
020 7499 6867
Eritrea
020 7713 0096
Estonia
020 7589 3428
www.estonia.gov.uk

Ethiopia
020 7589 7212-5
www.ethioembassy.org.uk
Fiji
020 7584 3661
Finland
020 7838 6200
www.finemb.org.uk
France
020 7073 1000
www.ambafrance-uk.org
Gabon
020 7823 9986
Gambia, The Republic of
020 7937 6316
Georgia
020 7603 7799
www.geoemb.org.uk
Germany
020 7824 1300
www.german-embassy.org.uk
Ghana
020 7201 5900
www.ghana.embassyhomepage
.com
Greece
020 7229 3850
www.greekembassy.org.uk
Grenada
020 7631 4277
Guatemala
020 7351 3042
Guinea
020 7599 4819
Guinea Bissau
01892 530478
Guyana
020 7229 7684
Holy See
020 8944 7189
Honduras
020 7486 4880
Hungary
020 7201 3440
www.huemblon.org.uk
Iceland
020 7259 3999
www.iceland.org.uk
India
020 7836 8484
www.hcilondon.org
Indonesia
020 7499 7661
www.indonesianembassy.org.uk
Iraq
020 7602 8456
Iran
020 7225 3000
www.iran-embassy.org.uk
Ireland
020 7235 2171
Israel
020 7957 9500
http://london.mfa.gov.il/

Italy
020 7312 2200
www.amblondra.esteri.it

Ivory Coast
020 7201 9601

Jamaica
020 7823 9911
www.jhcuk.com

Japan
020 7465 6500
www.uk.emb-japan.go.jp

Jordan
020 7937 3685
www.jordanembassyuk.org

Kazakhstan
020 7581 4646
www.kazakhstanembassy.org.uk

Kenya
020 7636 2371/5

Kiribati
01873 840375

Korea, DPR (North Korea)
020 8992 4965
www.koreanembassy.org.uk

Korea, Republic of (South Korea)
020 7227 5500
http://korea.embassyhomepage
.com

Kuwait
020 7590 3400
www.kuwaitinfo.org.uk

Kyrgyzstan
020 7935 1462
www.kyrgyz-embassy.org.uk

Latvia
020 7312 0040
www.london.am.gov.lv/en

Lebanon
020 7229 7265

Lesotho
020 7235 5686
www.lesotholondon.org.uk

Liberia
020 7388 5489

Libya
020 7201 8280

Lithuania
020 7486 6401
http://amb.urm.lt/jk

Luxembourg
020 7235 6961

Macedonia
020 7976 0535
www.macedonianembassy.org.uk

Madagascar
020 3008 4550

Malawi
020 8455 5624

Malaysia
020 7235 8033

Maldives
020 7224 2135
www.maldiveshighcommission.org

Malta
020 7292 4800

Mauritania
020 7478 9323

Mauritius
020 7581 0294-8

Mexico
020 7499 8586
www.embamex.co.uk

Moldova
020 8995 6818

Mongolia
020 7937 0150
www.embassyofmongolia.co.uk

Morocco
020 7581 5001

Mozambique
020 7383 3800

Namibia
020 7636 6244

Nauru
01732 746061

Nepal
020 7229 1594
www.nepembassy.org.uk

Netherlands
020 7590 3200
www.netherlands-embassy.org.uk

New Zealand
020 7930 8422
www.nzembassy.com

Nicaragua
020 7938 2373
http://freespace.virgin.net/
emb.ofnicaragua

Nigeria
020 7839 1244
www.nigeriahc.org.uk

Norway
020 7591 5500
www.norway.org.uk

Occupied Palestinian Territories
020 8563 0008

Oman
020 7225 0001

Pakistan
020 7664 9200
www.pakmission-uk.gov.pk

Panama
020 7493 4646

Papua New Guinea
020 7930 0922

Paraguay
020 7610 4180
www.paraguayembassy.co.uk

Peru
020 7838 9223
www.peruembassy-uk.com

Philippines
020 7937 1600
www.philemb.org.uk

Poland
0870 774 2700
www.polishembassy.org.uk

Portugal
020 7235 5331
www.portembassy.gla.ac.uk

Qatar
020 7493 2200

Romania
020 7937 9666
www.roemb.co.uk

Russia
020 7229 2666

Rwanda
020 7224 9832
www.ambarwanda.org.uk

**Saint Christopher and Nevis
(St Kitts and Nevis)**
020 7937 9718

St Lucia
020 7370 7123

St Vincent and the Grenadines
020 7565 2874

Samoa
01303 260541

San Marino
020 7823 4762

Sao Tome and Principe
020 8788 6138

Saudi Arabia
020 7917 3000
www.saudiembassy.org.uk

Senegal
020 7937 7237
www.senegalembassy.co.uk

Serbia
020 7235 9049
www.yugoslavembassy.org.uk

Sierra Leone
020 7404 0140
www.slhc-uk.org.uk

Singapore
020 7235 8315
www.mfa.gov.sg/london

Slovakia
020 7243 0803
www.slovakembassy.co.uk

Slovenia
020 7222 5700
www.gov.si/mzz/dkp/vlo/eng

South Africa
020 7451 7299
www.southafricahouse.com

Spain
020 7235 5555

Sri Lanka
020 7262 1841
www.slhclondon.org

Sudan
020 7839 8080
www.sudan-embassy.co.uk

Suriname
07768 196326
www.honoraryconsul.info

Swaziland
020 7630 6611

Sweden
020 7917 6400
www.swedish-embassy.org.uk

Switzerland
020 7616 6000
www.swissembassy.org.uk

Syria
020 7245 9012
www.syrianembassy.co.uk

Tajikistan
020 7584 5111

Tanzania
020 7569 1470
www.tanzania-online.gov.uk

Thailand
020 7225 5512

Togo
00 33 1 4380 1213
Nearest embassy is in Paris
Tonga
020 7724 5828
Trinidad and Tobago
020 7245 9351
Tunisia
020 7584 8117
Turkey
020 7393 0202
www.turkconsulate-london.com
Turkmenistan
020 7255 1071
Uganda
020 7839 5783
Ukraine
020 7727 6312
www.ukremb.org.uk
United Arab Emirates
020 7581 1281
United States
020 7499 9000
www.usembassy.org.uk
Uruguay
020 7589 8835
Uzbekistan
020 7229 7679
www.uzbekembassy.org
Venezuela
020 7584 4206
www.venezlon.co.uk
Vietnam
020 7937 1912
www.vietnamembassy.org.uk
Yemen
020 7584 6607
www.yemenembassy.org.uk
Zambia
020 7589 6655
www.zhcl.org.uk
Zimbabwe
020 7836 7755
http://zimbabwe.embassy
homepage.com

Government: **overseas diplomatic contacts**

KEY

E   Embassy
HC   High Commission
DHC   Deputy High Commission
CG   Consulate-General
C   Consulate
HonC   Honorary Consulate
VC   Honorary Vice-consulate   *Source: Foreign Office*

Afghanistan
E: Kabul 00 93 70 102: 000
    www.britishembassy.gov.uk/afghanistan

Albania
E: Tirana 00 355 42 34973/4/5   *www.uk.al*

Algeria
E: Algiers 00 213 2123 0068
    www.britishembassy.gov.uk/algeria

Andorra
C: Andorra La Vella 00 376 839 840
    www.ukinspain.com

Angola
E: Luanda 00 244 2 334582/3, 392991, 387681
    www.britishembassy.gov.uk/angola

Antigua and Barbuda
HC: St John's 00 1 268 462 0008/9, 463 0010

Argentina
E: Buenos Aires 00 54 11 4808 2200
    www.britain.org.ar

Armenia
E: Yerevan 00 3741 264301   *www.britishembassy.am*

Australia
HC: Canberra 00 61 2 6270 6666   *www.britaus.net*
CG: Brisbane 00 61 7 3223 3200
CG: Melbourne 00 61 3 9652 1600
CG: Perth 00 61 8 9224 4700
CG: Sydney 00 61 2 9247 7521
C: Darwin 00 61 8 941 6130

Austria
E: Vienna 00 43 1 716 130   *www.britishembassy.at*
C: Bregenz 00 43 5574 78586
C: Graz 00 43 316 8216 1621
C: Innsbruck 00 43 512 588320
C: Salzburg 00 43 662 848133

Azerbaijan
E: Baku 00 99 412 497 5188/89/90
    www.britishembassy.gov.uk/azerbaijan

Bahrain
E: 00 973 574100   *www.ukembassy.gov.bh*

Bangladesh
HC: Dhaka 00 880 2 882 2705
    www.britishhighcommission.gov.uk/bangladesh

Barbados
HC: Bridgetown 00 1 246 430 7800
    www.britishhighcommission.gov.uk/barbados

Belarus
E: Minsk 00 375 172 105920   *www.britain.by*

Belgium
E: Brussels 00 32 2 287 6211
    www.britishembassy.gov.uk/belgium
HC: Antwerp 00 32 3 213 2125
HC: Ghent 00 32 9 235 7221

Belize
HC: Belmopan 00 501 822 2146
    www.britishhighbze.com

Bolivia
E: La Paz 00 591 2 243 3424
    www.britishembassy.gov.uk/bolivia

Bosnia and Herzegovina
E: Sarajevo 00 387 5121 2395
    www.britishembassy.gov.uk/bih

Botswana
HC: Gaborone 00 267 395 2841
    www.britishhighcommission.gov.uk/botswana

Brazil
E: Brasilia 00 55 61 329 2300   *www.uk.org.br*
CG: Rio de Janeiro 00 55 21 2555 9600
CG: São Paulo 00 55 11 3094 2700
    www.gra-bretanha.org.br
C: Belém 00 55 91 222 5074, 223 0990
C: Belo Horizonte 00 31 3261 2072
C: Curitiba 00 55 41 322 1202
C: Fortaleza 00 55 85 242 0888
C: Manáus 00 55 92 613 1819
C: Porto Alegre 00 55 51 3232 1414
C: Rio Grande 00 55 53 233 7700
C: Salvador 00 55 71 243 7399
C: Santos 00 55 13 3211 2300

Brunei
HC: Bandar Seri Begawan 00 673 2 222231/223121
    www.britishhighcommission.gov.uk/brunei

Bulgaria
E: Sofia 00 359 2 933 9222   *www.british-embassy.bg*
C: Varna 00 359 52 665 5555

Burma
E: Rangoon 00 95 1 370863

Burundi
E-liaison: Bujumbura 00 257 827602

Cambodia
E: Phnom Penh 00 855 23 427124, 428295
HC: Sihanoukville 00 855 12 587407
    www.britishembassy.gov.uk/cambodia

Cameroon
HC: Yaoundé 00 237 222 0545/0796   *www.britcam.org*

Canada
HC: Ottawa 00 1 613 237 1530
CG: Montreal 00 1 514 866 5863
CG: Toronto 00 1 416 593 1290
CG: Vancouver 00 1 604 683 4421
C: Halifax/Dartmouth 00 1 902 461 1381
C: St John's 00 1 709 579 2002
C: Winnipeg 00 1 204 896 1380
C: Quebec City 00 1 418 521 3000

Chad
E: Ndjamena 00 237 222 05 45, 07 96

Chile
E: Santiago 00 56 2 370 4100
    www.britishembassy.gov.uk/chile
C: Valparaíso 00 56 32 213063
C: Punta Arenas 00 56 61 211535

China
E: Beijing 00 86 10 5192 4000
    www.uk.cn
CG: Shanghai 00 86 21 6279 7650   *www.uk.cn*
CG: Guangzhou 00 86 20 8314 3000   *www.uk.cn/gz*
CG: Chongqing 00 023 6369 1500
    www.britishcouncil.org.cn

Colombia
E: Bogotá 00 57 1 326 8300   *www.britain.gov.co*
C: Cali 00 57 2 653 6089
C: Medellin 00 57 4 377 9966

Congo, Democratic Republic of
E: Kinshasa 00 243 8171 50761

Costa Rica
E: San José 00 506 258 2025
    www.britishembassycr.com

Croatia
E: Zagreb 00 385 1 600 9100
www.britishembassy.gov.uk/croatia
C: Split 00 385 21 341 464
C: Dubrovnik 00 385 20 324597

Cuba
E: Havana 00 53 7 204 1771
www.britishembassy.gov.uk/cuba

Cyprus
HC: Nicosia 00 357 22 861100 *www.britain.org.cy*

Czech Republic
E: Prague 00 420 2 5740 2111 *www.britain.cz*

Denmark
E: Copenhagen 00 45 3544 5200
www.britishembassy.dk
C: Aabenraa 00 45 7462 3500
C: Aalborg 00 45 9811 3499
C: Aarhus 00 45 8627 3338
C: Esbjerg 00 45 7518 1476
C: Fredericia 00 45 7592 2000
C: Herning 00 45 9627 7300
C: Odense 00 45 6614 4714
C: Torshavn, Faroe Islands 00 45 2 9835 0077

Djibouti
C: Djibouti 00 253 38 5007

Dominica, Commonwealth of
HC: Roseau 00 1 246 430 7800
HONC: Roseau 00 1 767 448 7655

Dominican Republic
E: Santo Domingo 00 1 809 472 7111
C: Puerto Plata 00 1 809 586 4244/8464

Ecuador
E: Quito 00 593 2 2970 800/1
www.britembquito.org.ec
C: Guayaquil 00 593 4 256 0400 x318
C: Galápagos 00 593 5 526157/9

Egypt
E: Cairo 00 20 2 794 0850/2/8
www.britishembassy.gov.uk/egypt
CG: Alexandria 00 20 3 546 7001/2, 522 3717, 522 0507
C: Suez 00 20 62 313872

El Salvador
C: San Salvador 00 503 281 5555
E: Guatemala City 00 502 2367 5425,6,7,8,9

Eritrea
E: Asmara 00 291 1 120145

Estonia
E: Tallinn 00 372 667 4700 *www.britishembassy.ee*

Ethiopia
E: Addis Ababa 00 251 11 661 2354
www.britishembassy.gov.uk/ethiopia

Fiji
HC: Suva 00 679 322 9100
www.britishhighcommission.gov.uk/fiji

Finland
E: Helsinki 00 358 9 2286 5100
www.britishembassy.fi
C: Jyväskylä 00 358 14 446 9211
C: Kotka 00 358 5 234 4281
C: Kuopio 00 358 17 368 1800
C: Åland Islands 00 358 18 13591, 47720
C: Oulu 00 358 83 310 7117
C: Rovaniemi 00 358 16 317831
C: Tampere 00 358 3 256 5701
C: Turku 00 358 2 274 3410
C: Vaasa 00 358 6 282 2000

France
E: Paris 00 33 1 4451 3100
www.amb-grandebretagne.fr
CG: Bordeaux 00 33 5 5722 2110
CG: Lille 00 33 3 2012 8272
CG: Lyon 00 33 4 7277 8170
CG: Marseille 00 33 4 9115 7210
C: Amiens 00 33 3 2272 0848
C: Boulogne-sur-Mer 00 33 3 2187 1680
C: Calais 00 33 3 2196 3376
C: Cayenne, French Guiana 00 594 311034
C: Cherbourg 00 33 2 3378 0183
C: Dunkirk 00 33 3 2866 1198
C: Fort de France, Martinique 00 596 618892
C: Guadeloupe 00 590 825757
C: La Réunion 00 33 2 6234 7576
C: Le Havre 00 33 2 3519 7888
C: Lorient 00 33 6 1732 6310
C: Montpellier 00 33 4 6715 5207
C: Nantes 00 33 2 5172 7260
C: New Caledonia 00 687 273627/282153
C: Papeete, French Polynesia 00 689 706382
C: Saumur 00 33 2 4152 9054
C: St Malo-Dinard 00 33 2 2318 3030
C: Toulouse 00 33 5 6130 3791
C: Tours 00 33 2 4743 5058

Gabon
C: Libreville 00 241 762200/742041

Gambia, The Republic of
HC: Banjul 00 220 449 5133/4
www.britishhighcommission.gov.uk/thegambia

Georgia
E: Tbilisi 00 995 32 274747
www.britishembassy.gov.uk/georgia

Germany
E: Berlin 00 49 30 204570 *www.britischebotschaft.de*
CG: Düsseldorf 00 49 211 94480
www.british-consulate-general.de
CG: Hamburg 00 49 40 448
CG: Munich 00 49 89 211090
CG: Stuttgart 00 49 711 5006342
C: Bremen 00 49 421 590708
C: Hanover 00 49 511 388 3808
C: Kiel 00 49 431 331971
C: Nuremburg 00 49 911 2404 303

Ghana
HC: Accra 00 233 21 701 0650/ 00 233 21 221665
www.britishhighcommission.gov.uk/ghana

Greece
E: Athens 00 30 210 727 2600
www.british-embassy.gr
C: Heraklion (Crete) 00 30 2810 224012
C: Rhodes 00 30 22410 22005
C: Thessaloniki 00 30 2310 278006
VC: Corfu 00 30 26610 30055
VC: Kos 00 30 22420 21549
VC: Patras 00 30 2610 277329
VC: Syros 00 30 22810 82232/88922
VC: Zakynthos 00 30 26950 22906/48030

Grenada
HC: St George's 001 473 440 3536/3222

Guatemala
E: Guatemala City 00 502 2367 5425-9

Guinea
CG: Conakry 00 224 45 5807

Guyana
HC: Georgetown 00 592 22 65881,2,3,4
www.britishhighcommission.gov.uk/guyana

Haiti
C: Port-au-Prince 00 509 257 3969

Holy See
E: Rome 00 39 06 422 04000
www.britishembassy.gov.uk/holysee

Honduras
C: San Pedro Sula 00 504 550 2337
C: Tegucigalpa 00 504 237 6577/0645/0324
E: Guatemala City 00 502 2367 5425,6,7,8,9
Hungary
E: Budapest 00 36 1 266 2888
    www.britishembassy.hu
Iceland
E: Reykjavik 00 354 550 5100
VC: Akureyri 00 354 463 0102
India
HC: New Delhi 00 91 11 2687 2161
    www.britishhighcommission.gov.uk/india
DHC: Chennai 00 91 44 5219 2151
DHC: Kolkata 00 91 33 2288 5172
DHC: Mumbai 00 91 22 6655 2222
Indonesia
E: Jakarta 00 62 21 315 6264
    www.britain-in-indonesia.or.id
C: Medan 00 62 061 661 3476
Iran
E: Tehran 00 98 21 66705011/7
    www.britishembassy.gov.uk/iran
Iraq
E: Baghdad 00 964 0 7901 926 280
    www.britishembassy.gov.uk/iraq
Ireland
E: Dublin 00 353 1 205 3700   *www.britishembassy.ie*
Israel
E: Tel Aviv 00 972 3 725 1222   *www.britemb.org.il*
C: Eilat 00 972 8 634 0810
CG: Tel Aviv 00 972 3 5100166
Italy
E: Rome 00 39 06 4220 0001   *www.britain.it*
CG: Milan 00 39 02 723001
C: Bari 00 39 080 554 3668
C: Cagliari 00 39 070 828628
C: Catania 00 39 095 741330
C: Genoa 00 39 010 5740071
C: Florence 00 39 055 284133
C: Naples 00 39 081 423 8911
C: Palermo 00 39 091 582 533
C: Trieste 00 39 040 347 8303
C: Venice 00 39 041 505 5990
Jamaica
HC: Kingston 00 1 876 510 0700
    www.britishhighcommission.gov.uk/jamaica
C: Montego Bay 00 1 876 999 9693
Japan
E: Tokyo 00 81 3 5211 1100   *www.uknow.or.jp*
HONC: Fukuoka 00 81 92 476 2155
CG: Osaka 00 81 6 6120 5600
C: Nagoya 00 81 52 223 5031
Jerusalem
CG: 00 972 2 541 4100
CG: West Jerusalem 00 972 2 671 7724
Jordan
E: Amman 00 962 6 590 9200   *www.britain.org.jo*
Kazakhstan
E: Astana 00 73172 556200
    www.britishembassy.gov.uk/kazakhstan
Kenya
HC: Nairobi 00 254 20 284 4000
    www.britishhighcommission.gov.uk/kenya
C: Mombasa 00 254 41 313609/220023
Korea (North)
E: Pyongyang 00 850 2 381 7980
Korea (South)
E: Seoul 00 82 2 3210 5500   *www.uk.or.kr*
C: Pusan 00 82 5 1463 4630
Kuwait
E: 00 965 240 3335   *www.britishembassy-kuwait.org*
Kyrgystan
HC: Bishkek 00 996 312 68081

Latvia
E: Riga 00 371 777 4700   *www.britain.lv*
Lebanon
E: Beirut 00 961 1 990400
    www.britishembassy.gov.uk/lebanon
C: Mount Lebanon 00 961 4 723502
C: Tripoli 00 961 4 431320
Liberia
HONC: Freetown 00 231 226056
Libya
E: Tripoli 00 218 21 340 3644/5
    www.britishembassy.gov.uk/libya
Lithuania
E: Vilnius 00 370 5 246 2900   *www.britain.lt*
Luxembourg
E: 00 352 229864   *www.britain.lu*
Macedonia
E: Skopje 00 389 2 3299 299
    www.britishembassy.gov.uk/macedonia
Malawi
HC: Lilongwe 00 265 1 772400
    www.britishhighcommission.gov.uk/malawi
Malaysia
HC: Kuala Lumpur 00 60 3 2170 2200
    www.britain.org.my
Malta
HC: Valletta 00 356 2323 0000
    www.britishhighcommission.gov.uk/malta
Mauritania
HC: Nouakchott 00 222 525 8331
Mauritius
HC: Port Louis 00 230 202 9400
C: Rodrigues 00 230 832 0120
Mexico
E: Mexico City 00 52 55 5 242 8500
    www.britishembassy.gov.uk/mexico
C: Veracruz 00 52 229 931 1285 / 931 0955
Moldova
E: Chisinau 00 3732 2225902
    www.britishembassy.gov.uk/moldova
Monaco
C: 00 377 9350 9954
Mongolia
E: Ulaanbaatar 00 976 11 458133
    www.britishembassy.gov.uk/mongolia
Morocco
E: Rabat 00 212 37 633333   *www.britain.org.ma*
CG: Casablanca 00 212 22 85 74 00
C: Agadir 00 212 48 823401/2
C: Marrakech 00 212 44 435095
C: Tangier 00 212 39 936939/40
Mozambique
HC: Maputo 00 258 21 356 000
    www.britishhighcommission.gov.uk/mozambique
C: Beira 00 258 23 325 997
Namibia
HC: Windhoek 00 264 61 274800
    www.britishhighcommission.gov.uk/namibia
Nepal
E: Kathmandu 00 977 1 441 0583/1281/1590/4588
    www.britishembassy.gov.uk/nepal
Netherlands
E: The Hague 00 31 70 427 0427   *www.britain.nl*
CG: Amsterdam 00 31 20 676 4343
C: Willemstad (Curacao) 00 599 9 747 3322
New Zealand
HC: Wellington 00 64 4 924 2888   *www.britain.org.nz*
CG: Auckland 00 64 9 303 2973
C: Christchurch 00 64 0 337 43367
Nigeria
HC: Abuja 00 234 9 413 2010/2011/3885-7
    www.ukinnigeria.com
DHC: Lagos 00 234 1 261 9531/9537/9541/9543

Norway
E: Oslo 00 47 2313 2700 *www.britain.no*
C: Alesund 00 47 7011 7500
C: Bergen 00 47 5536 7810
C: Bodo 00 47 7556 5800
C: Kristiansand 00 47 3812 2070
C: Stavanger 00 47 5152 9713
C: Tromso 00 47 7762 4500
C: Trondheim 00 47 7360 0200

Oman
E: Muscat 00 968 609000
www.britishembassy.gov.uk/oman

Pakistan
HC: Islamabad 00 92 51 201 2000
www.britishhighcommission.gov.uk/pakistan
DHC: Karachi 00 92 21 582 7000
C: Lahore 00 92 04263 16589/90

Panama
E: Panama City 00 507 269 0866
www.britishembassy.gov.uk/panama

Papua New Guinea
HC: Port Moresby 00 675 325 1677
www.britishhighcommission.gov.uk/papuanewguinea

Paraguay
HONC: Asunción 00 595 21 210 405
E: Buenos Aires 00 54 11 4808 2200
www.britain.org.ar

Peru
E: Lima 00 51 1 617 3000 *www.britemb.org.pe*
C: Arequipa 00 51 54 241 340
C: Cusco 00 51 84 226671/239974
C: Trujillo 00 51 44 245935

Philippines
E: Manila 00 63 2 8580 8700
www.britishembassy.gov.uk/philippines
C: Angeles City 00 63 45 323 4187
C: Cebu 00 63 32 346 0525
C: Olongapo 00 63 47 252 2222

Poland
E: Warsaw 00 48 22 311 0000 *www.britishembassy.pl*
C: Gdansk 00 48 58 341 4365
C: Katowice 00 48 32 206 9801
C: Krakow 00 48 12 421 7030
C: Lodz 00 48 42 631 18 18
C: Lublin 00 48 81 742 0101
C: Poznan 00 48 61 665 8850
C: Szczecin 00 48 91 487 0302
C: Wroclaw 00 48 71 344 8961

Portugal
E: Lisbon 00 351 21 392 4000 *www.uk-embassy.pt*
C: Oporto 00 351 22 618 4789
C: Portimao 00 351 282 490 750
HONC: Azores 00 351 296 628 175

Qatar
E: Doha 00 974 442 1991
www.britishembassy.gov.uk/qatar

Romania
E: Bucharest 00 40 21 201 7200
www.britishembassy.gov.uk/romania

Russia
E: Moscow 00 7 095 956 7200
www.britaininrussia.ru
CG: St Petersburg 00 7 812 320 3200
www.britain.spb.ru

Rwanda
E: Kigali 00 250 584098, 585771, 585773
www.britishembassykigali.org.rw

St Kitts and Nevis
HC: Basseterre 001 268 462 0008/9

St Lucia
HC: Castries 001 758 45 22484/5

St Vincent
HC: Kingstown 001 784 457 1701

Samoa
HC: Apia 00 64 4 924 2888

San Marino
CG: Florence 00 39 055 284133

São Tomé and Principe
C: São Tomé 00 239 12 21026/7

Saudi Arabia
E: Riyadh 00 966 1 488 0077
www.britishembassy.gov.uk/saudiarabia
CG: Jeddah 00 966 2 622 5550

Senegal
E: Dakar 00 221 823 7392/9971
www.britishembassy.gov.uk/senegal

Serbia
E: Belgrade 00 381 11 264 5005
www.britishembassy.gov.uk

Seychelles
HC: Victoria 00 248 283666 *www.bhcvictoria.sc*

Sierra Leone
HC: Freetown 00 232 22 232 961/362/563-5
www.britishhighcommission.gov.uk/sierraleone

Singapore
HC: 00 65 6424 4200 *www.britain.org.sg*
C: Singapore 00 65 6473 1111

Slovakia
E: Bratislava 00 421 2 5998 2000
www.britishembassy.sk

Slovenia
E: Ljubljana 00 386 1 200 3910 *www.british-embassy.si*

Solomon Islands
HC: Honiara 00 677 21705/6

Somalia
E: Mogadishu 00 252 1 20288/9

South Africa
HC: Pretoria 00 27 12 421 7500 *www.britain.org.za*
CG: Cape Town 00 27 21 405 2400
C: Durban 00 27 31 202 6823
C: Port Elizabeth 00 27 41 363 8841

Spain
E: Madrid 00 34 91 700 8200 *www.ukinspain.com*
CG: Barcelona 00 34 93 366 6200
C: Bilbao 00 34 94 415 7600/7711/7722
C: Alicante 00 34 96 521 6022
C: Las Palmas, Canary Islands 00 34 928 262 508
C: Málaga 00 34 95 235 23 00
C: Palma 00 34 971 712445, 712085, 716048, 718501, 712696
C: Santa Cruz de Tenerife, Canary Islands 00 34 922 28 6863/6653
VC: Ibiza 00 34 971 30 1818

Sri Lanka
HC: Colombo 00 94 11 2 437336/43
www.britishhighcommission.gov.uk/srilanka

Sudan
E: Khartoum 00 249 11 777105
www.britishembassy.gov.uk/sudan

Suriname
C: Paramaribo 00 597 402 558/870

Sweden
E: Stockholm 00 46 8 671 3000
www.britishembassy.se

Switzerland
E: Berne 00 41 31 359 7700 *www.britishembassy.ch*
CG: Geneva 00 41 22 918 2400
VC: Basel 00 41 61 483 0977
VC: Lugano 00 41 91 950 0606
VC: Montreux/Vevey 00 41 21 943 3263
VC: Valais 00 41 27 480 3210
VC: Zurich 00 41 1 383 6560

Syria
E: Damascus 00 963 11 373 9241-3/7
C: Aleppo 00 963 21 267 2200

Tajikistan
E: Dushanbe 00 992 372 24 22 21/24 14 77
www.britishembassy.gov.uk/tajikistan

Tanzania
HC: Dar es Salaam 00 255 22 211 0101
www.britishhighcommission.gov.uk/tanzania

Thailand
E: Bangkok 00 66 02 305 8333

Togo
E: Dushanbe 00 233 21 221 665

Trinidad and Tobago
HC: Port of Spain 001 868 6 222748/81234/81068
www.britishhighcommission.gov.uk

Tunisia
E: Tunis 00 216 7110 8700
www.britishembassy.gov.uk/tunisia

Turkey
E: Ankara 00 90 312 455 3344
www.britishembassy.org.tr
VC: Antalya 00 90 242 244 5313
CG: Istanbul 00 90 212 355 5657
C: Bodrum 00 90 252 319 0093/4
C: Izmir 00 90 232 463 5151
C: Marmaris 00 90 252 412 6486

Turkmenistan
E: Ashgabat 00 993 12 363462-4
www.britishembassy.gov.uk/turkmenistan

Uganda
HC: Kampala 00 256 31 312000   *www.britain.or.ug*

Ukraine
E: Kiev 00 380 44 490 3660
www.britemb-ukraine.net

United Arab Emirates
E: Abu Dhabi 00 971 2 610 1100
www.britishembassy.gov.uk/uae
E: Dubai 00 971 4 309 4444

United States
E: Washington 00 1 202 588 6500
www.britainusa.com
CG: Atlanta 00 1 404 954 7700
CG: Boston 00 1 617 245 4500
CG: Chicago 00 1 312 970 3800
CG: Houston 00 1 713 659 6270
CG: Los Angeles 00 1 310 481 0031
CG: New York 00 1 212 745 0200
CG: San Francisco 00 1 415 617 1300
C: Anchorage 00 1 907 786 4848
C: Charlotte 00 1 704 383 4359
C: Denver 00 1 303 592 5200
C: Kansas City 00 1 913 469 9786
C: Miami 00 1 305 374 1522
C: Nashville 00 1 615 743 3061
C: New Orleans 00 1 504 524 4180
C: Philadelphia 00 1 215 557 7665
C: Pittsburgh 00 1 412 624 4200
C: Portland 00 1 503 227 5669
C: Puerto Rico 00 1 787 758 9828
C: Salt Lake City 00 1 801 297 6922
C: San Diego 00 1 619 459 8231
C: Seattle 00 1 206 622 9255
C: Orlando 00 1 407 5254 3300

Uruguay
E: Montevideo 00 598 2 622 3630/50
www.britishembassy.org.uy

Uzbekistan
E: Tashkent 00 99871 120 6451/6288/7852-4
www.britain.uz

Vanuatu
HC: Suva 00 679 3229100
www.britishhighcommission.gov.uk/fiji

Venezuela
E: Caracas 00 58 212 263 8411   *www.britain.org.ve*
C: Maracaibo 00 58 2 61 797 7003
C: Margarita 00 0295 257 05 18
C: Mérida 00 0274 417 37 46
C: San Cristobal 00 58 276 356 67 32

Vietnam
E: Hanoi 00 84 4 936 0500   *www.uk-vietnam.org*
CG: Ho Chi Minh City 00 84 8 823 2862

Yemen
E: Sana'a 00 967 1 302450
www.britishembassy.gov.uk/yemen
C: Hodeidah 00 967 3 238130/1

Zambia
HC: Lusaka 00 260 1 251133
www.britishhighcommission.gov.uk/zambia

Zimbabwe
E: Harare 00 263 4 772990
www.britishembassy.gov.uk/zimbabwe

» WEBSITES
Where a website is not listed, visit
www.britishembassy.gov.uk for a country list

Agents

Alexander Personal Management
PO Box 834, Hemel Hempstead,
Hertfordshire HP3 9ZP
01442 252907
apm@apmassociates.net
www.apmassociates.net
Actors, voiceovers

Amanda Howard Associates
21 Berwick Street, London W1F 0PZ
020 7287 9277
mail@
    amandahowardassociates.co.uk
www.amandahowardassociates
    .co.uk
*Actors, directors, designers,
composers, voiceovers and writers*

Andrew Manson
288 Munster Road,
London SW6 6BQ
020 7386 9158
post@andrewmanson.com
www.talentroom.com
Actors, voiceovers (UK and US)

Another Tongue Voices
10–11 D'Arblay Street,
London W1F 8DS
020 7494 0300
info@anothertongue.com
www.anothertongue.com
Voiceovers

Arlington Enterprises
1–3 Charlotte Street,
London W1T 1RD
020 7580 0702
info@arlington-enterprises.co.uk
www.arlingtonenterprises.co.uk
TV presenters and actors

Billy Marsh Associates
76A Grove End Road,
St John's Wood, London NW8 9ND
020 7449 6930
talent@billymarsh.co.uk
www.billymarsh.co.uk
TV presenters and personalities

Blackburn Sachs Associates
2–4 Noel Street, London W1F 8GB
020 7292 7555
presenters@
    blackburnsachsassociates.com
www.blackburnsachsassociates
    .com
*TV and radio presenters and
personalities*

Bryan Drew
Mezzanine, Quadrant House,
80–82 Regent Street,
London W1B 5AU
020 7437 2293
bryan@bryandrewltd.com
Actors, writers, voiceovers

Calypso Voices
25–26 Poland Street,
London W1F 8QN
020 7734 6415
calypso@calypsovoices.com
www.calypsovoices.com
Actors for voiceover work

Castaway
Suite 3, 15 Broad Court,
London WC2B 5QN
020 7240 2345
sheila@castaway.org.uk
www.castaway.org.uk
Voiceovers and singers

Celebrity Management
12 Nottingham Place,
London W1M 3FA
0871 250 1234
info@celebrity.co.uk
www.celebrity.co.uk
Celebrity booking

Chase Personal Management
Model Plan 4th Floor,
4 Golden Square, London W1F 9HT
020 7287 8444
michelle@modelplanlondon.co.uk
www.modelplan.co.uk
*Presenters, actors, models and
celebrities*

Complete Talent Agency
200 London Road, Hadleigh,
Benfleet, Essex SS7 2PD
01702 427100
gary@entertainers.co.uk
www.entertainers.co.uk
*AV, celebrity guests, comedians, lights,
productions and speakers*
Also at:
    The Old Forge, Kingfield Road,
    Woking, Surrey GU22 9EG

Conway Van Gelder
3rd Floor, 18–21 Jermyn Street,
London SW1Y 6HP
020 7287 1070
kate@conwayvg.co.uk
www.conwayvangelder.com
*Actors, commercials, voiceovers,
directors*

Crawfords
PO Box 44394, London SW20 0YP
020 8947 9999
info@crawfordsagency.com
www.crawfords.tv
Actors and models for TV commercials

Curtis Brown Group
Haymarket House,
28–29 Haymarket,
London SW1Y 4SP
020 7393 4400
info@curtisbrown.co.uk
www.curtisbrown.co.uk
*Writers, directors, actors, playwrights
and celebrities*

Cut Glass Voices
7 Crouch Hall Road, Crouch End,
London, N8 8HT
020 8374 4701
info@cutglassproductions.com
www.cutglassproductions.com
Voiceovers

David Anthony Promotions
PO Box 286, Warrington,
Cheshire WA2 8GA
01925 632496
dave@davewarwick.co.uk
www.davewarwick.co.uk
TV presenters, actors

Downes Presenters Agency
96 Broadway, Bexleyheath,
Kent DA6 7DE
020 8304 0541
info@presentersagency.com
www.presentersagency.com
TV presenters

Dynamic FX
Regent House, 291 Kirkdale,
London SE26 4QD
0845 006 2442
mail@dynamicfx.co.uk
www.dynamicfx.co.uk
Magical entertainment

Eric Glass
25 Ladbroke Crescent,
Notting Hill, London W11 1PS
020 7229 9500
eglassltd@aol.com
Actors, writers

Evans O'Brien
115 Humber Road, London SE3 7LW
020 8293 7077
info@evansobrien.co.uk
www.evansobrien.co.uk
Voiceovers

Excellent Talent Company
19–21 Tavistock Street,
London WC2E 7PA
020 7520 5656
liz@excellentvoice.co.uk
www.excellentvoice.co.uk
Voiceovers and TV presenters

FBI Agency
PO Box 250, Leeds LS1 2AZ
07050 222747
casting@fbi-agency.ltd.uk
www.fbi-agency.ltd.uk
*Models, dancers, walk-ons, presenters,
actors, stand-ins*

Foreign Legion
1 Kendal Road London NW10 1JH
020 8450 4451
voices@foreignlegion.co.uk
www.foreignlegion.co.uk
*Foreign-language voiceovers and
translations*

Foreign Versions
60 Blandford Street,
London W1U 7JD
020 7935 0993
info@foreignversions.co.uk
www.foreignversions.com
*Translators and voiceovers in foreign
languages*

Gordon & French
12-13 Poland Street,
London W1F 8QB
020 7734 4818
mail@gordonandfrench.net
Actors and voiceovers

Harvey Voices
4th Floor, 54-55 Margaret Street,
London W1W 8SH
020 7952 4361
info@harveyvoices.co.uk
www.harveyvoices.co.uk
Voiceovers

Hobson's Voices
62 Chiswick High Road,
London W4 1SY
020 8995 3628
voices@
    hobson-international.com
www.hobsons-international.com
*Actors, voiceovers, children, singers,
studios*

ICM Artists (London)
4-6 Soho Square, London W1D 3PZ
020 7432 0800
infouk@icmtalent.com
www.icmtalent.com
Conductors and musicians

Icon Actors Management
Tanzaro House, Ardwick Green
North, Manchester M12 6FZ
0161 273 3344
info@iconactors.net
www.iconactors.net
Actors

International Artists
4th Floor, Holborn Hall,
193-197 High Holborn,
London WC1V 7BD
020 7025 0600
reception@
    internationalartistes.com
www.internationalartistes.com
Presenters, actors and comedians

J Gurnett Personal Management
12 Newburgh Street,
London W1F 7RP
020 7440 1850
info@jgpm.co.uk
www.jgpm.co.uk
TV and radio presenters

Jacque Evans Management
Suite 1, 14 Holmesley Road,
London SE23 1PJ
020 8699 1202
jacque@jacqueevans.com
www.jacqueevans.com
*Presenters, journalists, broadcasters
and experts*

James Grant Management
94 Strand on the Green,
London W4 3NN
020 8742 4950
enquiries@jamesgrant.com
www.jamesgrant.com
TV presenters

Jane Morgan Management
Thames Wharf Studios,
Rainville Road, London W6 9HA
020 7386 5345
enquiries@janemorganmgt.com
www.janemorganmgt.com

Jeremy Hicks Associates
114-115 Tottenham Court Road,
London W1T 5AH
020 7383 2000
info@jeremyhicks.com
www.jeremyhicks.com
Presenters, writers, comedians and chefs

JLA (Jeremy Lee Associates)
4 Stratford Place, London W1C 1AT
020 7907 2800
talk@jla.co.uk
www.jla.co.uk
Presenters, speakers, entertainers

John Miles Organisation
Cadbury Camp Lane,
Clapton-in-Gordano,
Bristol BS20 7SB
01275 854675
john@johnmiles.org.uk
www.johnmiles.org.uk
Presenters

John Noel Management
2nd Floor, 10A Belmont Street,
London NW1 8HH
020 7428 8400
john@johnnoel.com
www.johnnoelmanagement.com
TV presenters and radio Djs

Julie Ivelaw-Chapman
The Chase, Chaseside Close,
Cheddington, LU7 0SA
01296 662441
jivelawchapman@gmail.com
Broadcasters

KBJ Management
7 Soho Street, London W1D 3DQ
020 7434 6767
general@kbjmgt.co.uk
www.kbjmgt.co.uk
Presenters and comics

Knight Ayton Management
114 St Martin's Lane,
London WC2N 4BE
020 7836 5333
info@knightayton.co.uk
www.knightayton.co.uk
TV presenters and news broadcasters

Lip Service
60-66 Wardour Street,
London W1F 0TA
020 7734 3393
bookings@lipservice.co.uk
www.lipservice.co.uk
Voiceovers

Liz Hobbs Group
1st Floor, 65 London Road,
Newark, NG24 1RZ
0870 070 2702
info@lizhobbsgroup.com
www.lizhobbsgroup.com
Musical theatre, actors and presenters

Mark Summers
137 Freston Road, London W10 6TH
020 7229 8413
info@marksummers.com
www.marksummers.com
Casting, dance, extras, studios

**Markham & Froggatt Personal
Management**
4 Windmill Street, London W1T 2HZ
020 7636 4412
admin@markhamfroggatt.co.uk
www.markhamfroggatt.com
Actors, voiceovers and radio

McLean-Williams Management
Thames Wharf Studios, Rainville
Road, London, W6 9HA
020 7917 2806
alex@mclean-williams.com
Actors

MPC Entertainment
MPC House, 15-16 Maple Mews,
London NW6 5UZ
020 7624 1184
info@mpce.com
www.mpce.com
Radio, TV and sports personalities

NCI Management
51 Queen Anne Street,
London W1G 9HS
020 7224 3960
info@firstnci.com
www.nci-management.com
TV presenters

Noel Gay Artists
19 Denmark Street,
London WC2H 8NA
020 7836 3941
info@noelgay.com
www.noelgay.com
*TV presenters, voiceovers, writers,
directors*

Off The Kerb Productions
3rd Floor, Hammer House,
113-117 Wardour Street,
London W1F 0UN
020 7437 0607
info@offthekerb.co.uk
www.offthekerb.co.uk
Comedians
Also at:
22 Thornhill Crescent,
London N1 1BJ
020 7700 4477

PFD
Drury House, 34-43 Russell
Street, London WC2B 5HA
020 7344 1000
postmaster@pfd.co.uk
www.pfd.co.uk
*Writers, directors, producers, actors,
technicians, composers, sportsmen
and women, public speakers and
illustrators*

PHA Casting
Tanzaro House, Ardwick Green
North, Manchester M12 6FZ
0161 273 4444
info@pha-agency.co.uk
www.pha-agency.co.uk
Models, extras, actors

Princess Talent Management
Princess Studios, Whiteleys
Centre, 151 Queensway,
London W2 4SB
020 7985 1985
talent@princesstv.com
www.princesstv.com
TV and radio presenters

PVA Management
Hallow Park, Hallow,
Worcester WR2 6PG
01905 640663
pvamanltd@aol.com
www.pva.co.uk
*TV and radio presenters, voiceovers
and classical musicians*

Qvoice
4th Floor, Holborn Hall,
193–197 High Holborn,
London WC1V 7BD
020 7025 0660
info@qvoice.co.uk
www.qvoice.co.uk
Voiceovers

Rabbit Vocal Management
2nd Floor, 18 Broadwick Street,
London W1F 8HS
020 7287 6466
info@rabbit.uk.net
www.rabbit.uk.net
Voiceovers

Rhubarb
1st Floor, 1a Devonshire Road,
Chiswick, London W4 2EU
020 8742 8683
enquiries@rhubarb.co.uk
www.rhubarbvoices.co.uk
Voiceovers

Richard Stone Partnership
2 Henrietta Street,
London WC2E 8PS
020 7497 0849
all@thersp.com
www.thersp.com
*Actors, presenters, voiceovers,
comedians*

RK Commercials
205 Chudleigh Road,
London SE4 1EG
020 8690 6542
enquiries@rkcommercials.com
www.rkcommercials.com
*Actors for commercials and presenting
work*

Roseman Organisation
51 Queen Anne Street,
London W1G 9HS
020 7486 4500
info@
    therosemanorganisation.co.uk
www.therosemanorganisation
    .co.uk
News and TV presenters

Roxane Vacca Management
73 Beak Street, London W1F 9SR
020 7734 8085
roxane@
    roxanevaccamanagement.co.uk
www.roxanevaccamanagement.com
Actors and voiceovers

Sally Hope Associates
108 Leonard Street,
London EC2A 4XS
020 7613 5353
casting@sallyhope.biz
www.sallyhope.biz
*Actors, voiceovers, directors,
designers, lighting, hair and make-up*

Shining Management
12 D'Arblay Street,
London W1F 8DU
020 7734 1981
info@shiningvoices.com
www.shiningvoices.com
Voiceovers

Speak-Easy
PO Box 648, Harrington,
Northampton, NN6 9XT
0870 013 5126
enquiries@speak-easy.co.uk
www.speak-easy.co.uk
TV presenters and voiceovers

Storm
1st Floor, 5 Jubilee Place,
London SW3 3TD
020 7368 9967
info@stormmodels.com
www.stormmodels.com
Model and celebrity management

Susi Earnshaw Management
68 High Street, Barnet,
Herts EN5 5SJ
020 8441 5010
casting@susiearnshaw.co.uk
www.susiearnshaw.co.uk
Actors and musical theatre performers

Susy Wootton Voices
75 Shelley Street, Kingsley,
Northampton NN2 7HZ
0870 765 9660
suzy@suzywoottonvoices.com
www.suzywoottonvoices.com
Voiceovers

Take Three Management
110 Gloucester Avenue,
Primrose Hill, London NW1 8HX
020 7209 3777
info@take3management.com
www.take3management.co.uk
*TV presenters, commercials, radio,
after-dinner speakers*

Talking Heads
2/4 Noel Street, London W1F 8GB
020 7292 7575
voices@talkingheadsvoices.com
www.talkingheadsvoices.com
Voiceovers

Tongue & Groove
3 Stevenson Square,
Manchester M1 1DN
0161 228 2469
info@tongueandgroove.co.uk
www.tongueandgroove.co.uk
Voiceovers

Unique Management Group
Power Road Studios,114 Power
Road, Chiswick, London W4 5PY
020 8987 6406
jc@uniquemgt.co.uk
www.unique-management.co.uk
TV presenters, radio hosts

Upfront Celebrity Services
39–41 New Oxford Street,
London WC1A 1BN
020 7836 7702/3
info@upfronttv.com
www.celebritiesworldwide.com
Celebrity bookings

Vincent Shaw Associates
186 Shaftesbury Avenue,
London WC24 8JB
020 8509 2927
info@vincentshaw.com
www.vincentshaw.com
Actors

Vocal Point
25 Denmark Street,
London WC2H 8NJ
020 7419 0700
enquiries@vocalpoint.net
www.vocalpoint.net
Voiceovers

Voice & Script International
Aradco House, 132 Cleveland St,
London W1T 6AB
020 7692 7700
info@vsi.tv
www.vsi.tv
*Translators and voiceovers in foreign
languages*

Voice Shop
1st Floor, 1a Devonshire Road,
London W4 2EU
020 8742 7077
info@voice-shop.co.uk
www.voice-shop.co.uk
Voiceovers

Voice Squad
1 Kendal Road, London NW10 1JH
020 8450 4451
bookem@voicesquad.com
www.voicesquad.com
Voiceovers

**Voicebank, The Irish Voice-Over
Agency**
The Barracks, 76 Irishtown Road,
Dublin 4
00 353 1 668 7234
voicebank@voicebank.ie
www.voicebank.ie
Voiceovers

Voicecall
67A Gondar Gardens, Fortune
Green, London NW6 1EP
020 7209 1064
voicecall@blueyonder.co.uk
www.voicecall-online.co.uk
Voiceovers

The Voiceover Gallery
PO Box 213, Chorlton,
Manchester M21 9ED
0161 881 8844
info@thevoiceovergallery.co.uk
www.thevoiceovergallery.co.uk
Voiceovers

Whatever Artists Management
F24 Argo House, Kilburn Road,
London NW6 5LF
020 7372 4777
info@wamshow.biz
www.wamshow.biz
Artists in light entertainment

Yakety Yak
8 Bloomsbury Square,
London WC1A 2NE
020 7430 2600
info@yaketyyak.co.uk
www.yaketyyak.co.uk
Voiceove

Literary agents

» *see Books*   *page 349*

Associations

Agents Association
54 Keyes House, Dolphin Square,
London SW1V 3NA
020 7834 0515
association@agents-uk.com
www.agents-uk.com
*Trade association of entertainment
agents*

Association of Authors' Agents
Gillon Aitken Associates Ltd,
18–21 Cavaye Place,
London SW10 9PT
020 7373 8672
aaa@gillonaitken.co.uk
www.agentsassoc.co.uk

Personal Managers' Association
1 Summer Road, East Molesey,
Surrey KT8 9LX
020 8398 9796
aadler@thepma.com
www.thepma.com

Arts

Government departments

Culture, Media and Sport
020 7211 6200
www.culture.gov.uk
Press: 020 7211 6145

Arts councils

Arts Council England
0845 300 6200
www.artscouncil.org.uk
Press: 0845 300 6200

Arts Council for Northern Ireland
028 9038 5200
www.artscouncil-ni.org
Press: 028 9038 5263

Arts Council of Wales
029 2037 6500
www.artswales.org.uk
Press: 029 2037 6506

British Council
0161 957 7755
www.britishcouncil.org
Press: 020 7389 4939

Design Council
020 7420 5200
www.design-council.org.uk
Press: 020 7420 5248

Scottish Arts Council
0131 226 6051
www.scottisharts.org.uk
Press: 0131 240 2404

UK Film Council
020 7861 7861
www.ukfilmcouncil.org.uk
Press: 020 7861 7508

Galleries and museums

24 Hour Museum
01273 623266
www.24hourmuseum.org.uk

Ashmolean Museum, Oxford
01865 278000
www.ashmolean.org
Press: 01865 288298

Association of Independent Museums
023 9258 7751
www.aim-museums.co.uk

British Library
0870 444 1500
www.bl.uk
Press: 020 7412 7110

British Museum
020 7323 8000
www.thebritishmuseum.ac.uk
Press: 020 7323 8583

Gallery of Modern Art, Glasgow
0141 229 1996
www.glasgowmuseums.com
Press: 0141 287 0145

Geffrye Museum
020 7739 9893
www.geffrye-museum.org.uk

Imperial War Museum
020 7416 5320
www.iwm.org.uk
Press: 020 7416 5417

Institute of Contemporary Arts
020 7930 3647
www.ica.org.uk
Press: 020 7766 1406

Lowry, Salford
0870 787 5780
www.thelowry.com
Press: 0161 876 2044

Modern Art Oxford
01865 722733
www.modernartoxford.org.uk
Press: 01865 813813

Museum of London
0870 444 3852
www.museumoflondon.org.uk
Press: 020 7814 5503

Museums Association
020 7426 6970
www.museumsassociation.org

National Art Collections Fund
020 7225 4800
www.artfund.org
Press: 020 7225 4822

National Galleries of Scotland
0131 624 6200
www.nationalgalleries.org
www.natgalscot.ac.uk

National Gallery
020 7747 2885
www.nationalgallery.org.uk
Press: 020 7747 2865

National Maritime Museum
020 8858 4422
www.nmm.ac.uk
Press: 020 8312 6790

National Museum and Gallery of Wales
029 2039 7951
www.museumwales.ac.uk

National Museum of Science and Industry
0870 870 4771
www.nmsi.ac.uk
Press: 020 7942 4357

National Museums Liverpool
0151 207 0001
www.liverpoolmuseums.org.uk
Press: 0151 478 4612

National Museums of Scotland
0131 247 4422
www.nms.ac.uk

National Portrait Gallery
020 7306 0055
www.npg.org.uk
Press: 020 7312 2452

Natural History Museum
020 7942 5000
www.nhm.ac.uk
Press: 020 7942 5654

Royal Academy of Arts
020 7300 8000
www.royalacademy.org.uk
Press: 020 7300 5615

Royal College of Art
020 7590 4444
www.rca.ac.uk
Press: 020 7590 4114

Royal Marines Museum
023 9281 9385
www.royalmarinesmuseum.co.uk

Tate
020 7887 8000
www.tate.org.uk
Press: 020 7887 8730

Victoria and Albert Museum
020 7942 2000
www.vam.ac.uk
Press: 020 7942 2502

Performing arts

Almeida Theatre Company
020 7288 4900
www.almeida.co.uk
Press: 020 7292 8330

Barbican Centre
020 7638 4141
www.barbican.org.uk

BBC Proms
proms@bbc.co.uk
www.bbc.co.uk/proms
Press: 020 7765 5575

British Film Institute
020 7255 1444
www.bfi.org.uk
Press: 020 7957 8919

Celtic Connections
0141 353 8000
www.celticconnections.com
Press: 0141 353 8070

Earls Court
020 7385 1200
www.eco.co.uk

Edinburgh Festival Fringe
0131 226 0026
www.edfringe.com
Press: 0131 240 0024

English National Ballet
020 7581 1245
www.ballet.org.uk

English National Opera
020 7836 0111
www.eno.org
Press: 020 7845 9378

Glastonbury Festival
01458 834596
www.glastonburyfestivals.co.uk

Glyndebourne Festival
01273 812321
www.glyndebourne.com
Press: 01273 812321

London Astoria
020 7434 9592
www.meanfiddler.co.uk

Manchester Apollo
0161 273 6921
www.getlive.co.uk

Millennium Centre, Cardiff
029 2063 6400
www.wmc.org.uk

NEC, Birmingham
0121 780 4141
www.necgroup.co.uk
Press: 0121 780 2828

Ronnie Scott's
020 7439 0747
www.ronniescotts.co.uk

Royal Academy of Dance
020 7326 8000
www.rad.org.uk
Press: 020 7326 8003/8044

Royal Albert Hall
020 7589 3203
www.royalalberthall.com

Royal Ballet School
020 7836 8899
www.royal-ballet-school.org.uk
Press: 020 7845 7073

Royal College of Music
020 7589 3643
www.rcm.ac.uk
Press: 020 7591 4372

Royal Concert Hall, Glasgow
0141 353 8000
www.grch.com
Press: 0141 353 8070

Royal National Theatre
020 7452 3000
www.nt-online.org
Press: 020 7452 3235

Royal Opera House, Covent Garden
020 7240 1200
www.royaloperahouse.org

Royal Shakespeare Company
01789 296655
www.rsc.org.uk

Sage, Gateshead
0191 443 4666
www.thesagegateshead.org
Press: 0191 443 4613

South Bank Centre
020 7921 0600
www.southbankcentre.org.uk
Press: 020 7921 0888

Theatres Trust
020 7836 8591
www.theatrestrust.org.uk

Wembley Arena
020 8782 5500
www.wembley-arena.net
Press: 020 8782 5622/3

History and heritage

Alexandra Palace
020 8365 2121
www.alexandrapalace.com
Press: 020 8365 4328

Ancient Monuments Society
office@ancientmonuments
    society.org.uk
www.ancientmonumentssociety
    .org.uk

Architectural Heritage Fund
020 7925 0199
www.ahfund.org.uk

British Archaeological Association
www.britarch.ac.uk/baa

Civic Trust
020 7539 7900
www.civictrust.org.uk

Council for British Archaeology
01904 671417
www.britarch.ac.uk

English Heritage
0870 333 1181
www.english-heritage.org.uk
Press: 020 7973 3250

Garden History Society
020 7608 2409
www.gardenhistorysociety.org

Historic Royal Palaces
0870 751 5172
www.hrp.org.uk
Press: 020 3166 6166
Banqueting House
0870 751 5178
Hampton Court Palace
0870 752 7777
Kensington Palace State Apartments
0870 751 5170
Kew Palace and Queen Charlotte's Cottage
0870 751 5179
Tower of London
0870 756 6060

Historical Diving Society
enquiries@thehds.com
www.thehds.com

Historical Metallurgy Society
01792 233223
www.hist-met.org

Institute of Historic Building Conservation
01747 873133
www.ihbc.org.uk

International Council on Monuments & Sites in UK
020 7566 0031
www.icomos.org/uk

Jewish Historical Society of England
020 7723 5852
www.jhse.org

Keltek Trust
bells@keltek.org
www.keltek.org
Church bell preservation society

Landmark Trust
01628 825920
www.landmarktrust.org.uk

National Archives
020 8876 3444
www.nationalarchives.gov.uk
Press: 020 8392 5277

National Association of Decorative & Fine Arts Associations
020 7430 0730
www.nadfas.org.uk

National Trust
0870 458 4000
www.nationaltrust.org.uk
Press: 0870 600 2127

National Trust for Scotland
0844 493 2100
www.nts.org.uk
Press: 0131 243 9349

Royal Commission on the Ancient & Historic Monuments of Wales
01970 621200
www.rcahmw.org.uk

Save Britain's Heritage
020 7253 3500
www.savebritainsheritage.org

Scottish Railway Preservation Society
01506 825855
www.srps.org.uk

Society for the Protection of Ancient Buildings
020 7377 1644
www.spab.org.uk
Press: 020 7456 0905

Ulster Architectural Heritage Society
028 9055 0213
www.uahs.co.uk

United Kingdom Institute for Conservation of Historic & Artistic Works
020 7785 3807
www.icon.org.uk

Vivat Trust
0845 090 0194
www.vivat.org.uk

Books

Book publishers

A&C Black
(see Bloomsbury Publishing)

AA Publishing
The Automobile Association,
14th Floor, Fanum House,
Basingstoke, Hampshire RG21 4EA
01256 491519
ian.harvey@theaa.com
www.theaa.co.uk
Maps, atlases and guidebooks

Abacus
(see Time Warner Books)

ABC-Clio
7200 The Quorum, Oxford
Business Park North, Garsington
Road, Oxford OX4 2JZ
01865 481403
salesuk@abc-clio.com
www.abc-clio.com
Academic and general reference

Absolute Press
Scarborough House,
29 James Street West,
Bath BA1 2BT
01225 316013
office@absolutepress.co.uk
www.absolutepress.co.uk
Non-fiction

Abson Books London
5 Sidney Square, London E1 2EY
020 7790 4737
absonbooks@aol.com
www.absonbooks.co.uk
Language glossaries

Acair
7 James Street, Stornoway,
Isle of Lewis HS1 2QN
01851 703020
info@acairbooks.com
www.acairbooks.com
Scottish history and culture, Gaelic

Acumen Publishing
Stockfield Hall,
Stockfield NE43 7TN
01661 844865
steven.gerrard@
    acumenpublishing.co.uk
www.acumenpublishing.co.uk
*Philosophy, history, classics and
politics*

Addison-Wesley
(see Pearson Education)

African Books Collective
Unit 13, Kings Meadow,
Ferry Hinksey Road,
Oxford OX2 0DP
01869 349110
orders@africanbookscollective.com
www.africanbookscollective.com
*Publishing and distribution of African
books*

Age Concern England
1268 London Road,
London SW16 4ER
020 8765 7200
media@ace.org.uk
www.ageconcern.org.uk

Aidan Ellis Publishing
Whinfield, Herbert Road,
Salcombe, South Devon TQ8 8HN
01548 842755
mail@aidanellispublishing.co.uk
www.aepub.demon.co.uk
General publishing and non-fiction

Allen & Unwin
(see Orion Publishing Group)

Allen Lane
(see Penguin Books)

Allison & Busby
13 Charlotte Mews,
London W1T 4EJ
020 7580 1080
chiarapriorelli@
    allisonandbusby.com
www.allisonandbusby.com
Crime; literary fiction and non-fiction

Allyn & Bacon
(see Pearson Education)

Amber Lane Press
Cheorl House, Church Street,
Charlbury, Oxfordshire OX7 3PR
01608 810024
info@amberlanepress.co.uk
www.amberlanepress.co.uk
Plays and theatre

Andersen Press
20 Vauxhall Bridge Road,
London SW1V 2SA
020 7840 8701
andersoneditorial@
    randomhouse.co.uk
www.andersenpress.co.uk
Children's books and fiction

Anness Publishing
Hermes House,
88–89 Blackfriars Road,
London SE1 8HA
020 7401 2077
sbaldwin@anness.com
www.annesspublishing.com
General non-fiction

Anova Books
The Old Magistrates Court,
Soughcombe Street,
London W14 0RA
eproffit@anovabooks.com
www.anovabooks.com
- **Batsford** - *Specialist and technical
  illustrated non-fiction: embroidery,
  lace, chess, bridge, practical art, film
  and furniture*
- **Collins & Brown** - *Illustrated non-
  fiction: photography, crafts and
  practical arts; national magazine
  branded books; health, mind, body
  and spirit (formerly Vega)*

- **Conway Maritime** - *Maritime
  history, ship modelling and naval*
- **Pavilion** - *High-end coffee table
  books: celebrity, lifestyle, interiors,
  cookery, garden, art and
  photography*
- **Robson** - *Sports, humour and
  biography, especially celebrity; some
  fiction*

Anthem Press
(see Wimbledon Publishing Press)

Antique Collectors' Club
Sandy Lane, Old Martlesham,
Woodbridge, Suffolk IP12 4SD
01394 389950
sales@antique-acc.com
www.antiquecollectorsclub.com

Anvil Press Poetry
Neptune House, 70 Royal Hill,
London SE10 8RF
020 8469 3033
anvil@anvilpresspoetry.com
www.anvilpresspoetry.com
Poetry

APA Publications
58 Borough High Street,
London SE1 1XF
020 7403 0284
berlitz@apaguide.co.uk
www.berlitzpublishing.co.uk
*Owned by Langenscheidt Publishing
Group. Travel and languages. Imprint:
Berlitz Publishing*

Appletree Press
The Old Potato Station,
14 Howard Street South,
Belfast BT7 1AP
028 9024 3074
reception@appletree.ie
www.appletree.ie
*Cookery and Celtic interest, bespoke
publications*

Arc Publications
Nanholme Mill, Shaw Wood Road,
Todmorden, Lancashire OL14 6DA
01706 812338
info@arcpublications.co.uk
www.arcpublications.co.uk
Contemporary poetry

Arcadia Books
15–16 Nassau Street,
London W1W 7AB
020 7436 9898
info@arcadiabooks.co.uk
www.arcadiabooks.co.uk
*Literary fiction, crime, biography,
gender studies and travel*

**Architectural Association
Publications**
36 Bedford Square,
London WC1B 3ES
020 7887 4021
publications@aaschool.ac.uk
www.aaschool.info/publications
*Publishing arm of Architectural
Association School of Architecture*

Arcturus Publishing
26/27 Bickels Yard,
151–153 Bermondsey Street,
London SE1 3HA
020 7407 9400
info@arcturuspublishing.com
www.arcturuspublishing.com
Non-fiction

Arrow
(see Random House Group)

Ashgrove Publishing
27 John Street, London WC1N 2BX
020 7831 5013
gmo73@dial.pipex.com
www.ashgrovepublishing.com
Owned by Hollydata Publishers. Mind, body and spirit

Ashley Drake Publishing
PO Box 733, Cardiff CF14 7ZY
029 2056 0343
post@ashleydrake.com
www.ashleydrake.com
Imprints: Welsh Academic Press (academic titles in English); St David's Press (general trade); Y Ddraig Fach (children's books in Welsh); Gwasg Addysgol Cymru (educational in Welsh)

Ashmolean Museum Publications
(see Oxford University)

Atlantic Books
Ormond House,
26–27 Boswell Street,
London WC1N 3JZ
020 7269 1610
enquiries@groveatlantic.co.uk
www.groveatlantic.co.uk
Literary fiction, non-fiction and reference

Atom
(see Time Warner Books)

Aurum Press
7 Greenland Street,
London NW1 0ND
020 7284 7160
info@aurumpress.co.uk
www.aurumpress.co.uk
Non-fiction

Australian Consolidated Press UK
Moulton Park Business Centre,
10 Scirocco Close,
Moulton Park Office Village,
Northampton NN3 6AP
01604 642200
books@acpuk.com
www.acpuk.com
Home interest

Authentic Media
9 Holdom Avenue, Bletchley,
Milton Keynes MK1 1QR
01908 364200
info@authenticmedia.co.uk
www.authenticmedia.co.uk
Imprints: Authentic (Christian life); Paternoster (academic and theological titles and theses); Authentic Music

Autumn Publishing
Appledram Barns,
Birdham Road, near Chichester,
West Sussex PO20 7EQ
01243 531660
autumn@autumnpublishing.co.uk
www.autumnpublishing.co.uk
Early learning. Imprint: Byeway Books

Award Publications
The Old Riding School,
Welbeck Estate, Worksop,
Nottinghamshire S80 3LR
01909 478170
info@awardpublications.co.uk
www.awardpublications.co.uk
Children's fiction and reference.
Imprint: Horus Editions

Axis Publishing
8C Accommodation Road,
London NW11 8ED
020 8731 8080
admin@axispublishing.co.uk
www.axispublishing.co.uk
Illustrated full colour books

Bantam/Bantam Press
(see Random House Group)

Barefoot Books
124 Walcot Street, Bath BA1 5BG
01225 322400
info@barefootbooks.co.uk
www.barefootbooks.com
Highly illustrated children's picture books

Barny Books
The Cottage,
Hough on the Hill, near Grantham,
Lincolnshire NG32 2BB
01400 250246
Children's books, adult fiction and non-fiction

Barrington Stoke
18 Walker Street,
Edinburgh EH3 7LP
0131 225 4113
info@barringtonstoke.co.uk
www.barringtonstoke.co.uk
Remedial children's reading for dyslexic, struggling and reluctant readers.

Batsford
(see Anova Books)

BBC Bookshop
PO Box 308, Sittingbourne,
Kent ME9 8LW
0870 077 7001
bbcshop@bbc.co.uk
www.bbcshop.com

Benjamin Cummings
(see Pearson Education)

Berg Publishers
1st Floor Angel Court,
81 St Clements Street,
Oxford OX4 1AW
01865 245104
enquiry@bergpublishers.com
www.bergpublishers.com
Various academic

Berghahn Books
3 Newtec Place, Magdalen Road,
Oxford OX4 1RE
01865 250011
salesuk@berghahnbooks.com
www.berghahnbooks.com
Academic books and journals

BFI Publishing
British Film Institute,
21 Stephen Street, London W1T 1LN
020 7255 1444
publishing@bfi.org.uk
www.bfi.org.uk/books
Part of the British Film Institute

BFP Books
Focus House, 497 Green Lanes,
London N13 4BP
020 8882 3315
info@thebfp.com
www.thebfp.com
Publishing arm of the Bureau of Freelance Photographers

BIOS Scientific Publishers
(see T&F Informa)

Birlinn
West Newington House,
10 Newington Road,
Edinburgh EH9 1QS
0131 668 4371
info@birlinn.co.uk
www.birlinn.co.uk
History, folklore, Scottish interest and fiction

Black & White Publishing
99 Giles Street, Edinburgh EH6 6BZ
0131 625 4500
mail@blackandwhitepublishing
.com
www.blackandwhitepublishing
.com
General fiction and non-fiction

Black Spring Press
Curtain House,
134–146 Curtain Road,
London EC2A 3AR
020 7613 3066
general@blackspringpress.co.uk
www.blackspringpress.co.uk
Fiction and non-fiction

Black Swan
(see Random House Group)

Blackstaff Press
4c Heron Wharf,
Sydenham Business Park,
Belfast BT3 9LE
028 9045 5006
info@blackstaffpress.com
www.blackstaffpress.com
Fiction, non-fiction and poetry

Bloodaxe Books
Highgreen, Tarset,
Northumberland NE48 1RP
01434 240500
publicity@bloodaxebooks.com
www.bloodaxebooks.com
Poetry

Bloomsbury Publishing
36 Soho Square, London W1D 3QY
020 7494 2111
publicity@bloomsbury.com
www.bloomsbury.com
Adult and children's fiction and non-fiction (including Harry Potter)

A&C Black (Publishers)
Alderman House, 38 Soho Square,
London W1D 3HB
020 7758 0200
enquiries@acblack.com
www.acblack.com
Reference and non-fiction; Writers' and Artists' Yearbook

BMJ Books
(incorporated into Blackwell Publishing)

The Bodley Head
(see Random House Group)

Book Guild
Pavilion View, 19 New Road,
Brighton BN1 1UF
01273 720900
info@bookguild.co.uk
www.bookguild.co.uk
Fiction, non-fiction and children's.

**Boulevard Books &
The Babel Guides**
71 Lytton Road, Oxford OX4 3NY
01865 712931
info@babelguides.com
www.babelguides.com
*Contemporary world fiction and
guides*

Bowker (UK)
1st Floor, Medway House,
Canteloupe Road, East Grinstead,
West Sussex RH19 3BJ
01342 310450
sales@bowker.co.uk
www.bowker.co.uk
*Part of the Cambridge Information
Group (CIG). Reference and biography*

Boydell & Brewer
PO Box 9, Woodbridge,
Suffolk IP12 3DF
01394 610600
trading@boydell.co.uk
www.boydell.co.uk
Non-fiction, principally medieval studies

Boxtree
(see Macmillan Publishers)

Bradt Travel Guides
23 High Street, Chalfont St Peter,
Buckinghamshire SL9 9QE
01753 893444
info@bradtguides.com
www.bradtguides.com
Travel guides

Breedon Books Publishing Co
3 The Parker Centre, Mansfield
Road, Derby DE21 4SZ
01332 384235
sales@breedonpublishing.co.uk
www.breedonbooks.co.uk
Local history and heritage, sport

British Academy
10 Carlton House Terrace,
London SW1Y 5AH
020 7969 5200
secretary@britac.ac.uk
www.britac.ac.uk

British Library
96 Euston Road, London NW1 2DB
020 7412 7469
blpublications@bl.uk
www.bl.uk

British Museum Press
38 Russell Square,
London WC1B 3QQ
020 7323 1234
sales@britishmuseum.co.uk
www.britishmuseum.co.uk

Brooklands Books
PO Box 146, Cobham,
Surrey KT11 1LG
01932 865051
sales@brooklands-books.com
www.brooklands-books.com
Motoring titles and technical catalogues

Brown Watson
The Old Mill, 76 Fleckney Road,
Kibworth Beauchamp,
Leicestershire LE8 0HG
0116 279 6333
books@brownwatson.co.uk
www.brownwatson.co.uk
General children's interest

Brown, Son & Ferguson
4-10 Darnley Street,
Glasgow G41 2SD
0141 429 1234
info@skipper.co.uk
www.skipper.co.uk
Nautical textbooks and Scottish plays

Browntrout Publishers
Redland Office Centre,
157 Redland Road, Redland,
Bristol BS6 6YE
0117 973 9191
sales@browntroutuk.com
www.browntrout.com
Fine art and photography calendars

Brunner-Routledge
(see T&F Informa)

Bryntirion Press
Bryntirion, Bridgend,
Mid-Glamorgan CF31 4DX
01656 655886
office@emw.org.uk
www.emw.org.uk
*Owned by the Evangelical Movement of
Wales. Christian books in English and
Welsh*

Business Education Publishers
The Teleport, Doxford International,
Sunderland, Tyne & Wear SR3 3XD
0191 525 2410
info@bepl.com
www.bepl.com

Butterworth
(see Reed Elsevier)

Cadogan Guides
2nd Floor, 233 High Holborn,
London WC1V 7DN
020 7611 4660
info@cadoganguides.co.uk
www.cadoganguides.com
*Owned by US firm, Morris
Publications. Travel guides*

Calder Publications
51 The Cut, London SE1 8LF
020 7633 0599
info@calderpublications.com
www.calderpublications.com
*Formerly John Calder (Publishers).
Biography, drama, music, poetry and
translations*

Cambridge University Press
The Edinburgh Building,
Shaftesbury Road,
Cambridge CB2 2RU
01223 312393
information@cambridge.org
www.cambridge.org

Camden Press
43 Camden Passage,
London N1 8EA
020 7226 4673
Social issues. Imprint: Mindfield

Campbell Books
(see Macmillan Publishers)

Canongate Books
14 High Street, Edinburgh EH1 1TE
0131 557 5111
info@canongate.co.uk
www.canongate.net
Literary fiction and non-fiction, music

Capall Bann Publishing
Auton Farm, Milverton,
Somerset TA4 1NE
01823 401528
enquiries@capallbann.co.uk
www.capallbann.co.uk
British traditional works and folklore

Capstone Publishing
(see John Wiley & Sons)

Carcanet Press
4th Floor, Alliance House,
30 Cross Street,
Manchester M2 7AQ
0161 834 8730
info@carcanet.co.uk
www.carcanet.co.uk
*Poetry, academic works, literary
biography, fiction in translation*

Cardiff Academic Press
St Fagans Road, Fairwater,
Cardiff CF5 3AE
029 2056 0333
cap@drakeed.com
www.drakeed.com/cap

Carfax
(see T&F Informa)

Carlton Publishing Group
20 Mortimer Street,
London W1T 3JW
020 7612 0400
enquiries@carltonbooks.co.uk
www.carltonbooks.co.uk
*Illustrated entertainment and leisure
titles. Imprints: Carlton Books, Granada
Media, Manchester United Books,
Andre Deutsche and Prion Books*

Carroll & Brown Publishers
20 Lonsdale Road,
London NW6 6RD
020 7372 0900
mail@carrollandbrown.co.uk
www.carrollandbrown.co.uk
Lifestyle

**Cassell Reference/
Cassell Military**
(see Orion Publishing Group)

Catholic Truth Society (CTS)
40-46 Harleyford Road,
London SE11 5AY
020 7640 0042
editorial@cts-online.org.uk
www.cts-online.org.uk
*Roman Catholic books, including
Vatican documents*

Cavendish Publishing
2 Park Square, Milton Park,
Abingdon, Oxford, OX14 4RN
020 7017 6000
Webmaster.books@tandf.co.uk
www.tandf.co.uk
Academic and practitioner law books

CBA (Publishing Department)
St Marys House, 66 Bootham,
York YO30 7BZ
01904 671417
info@britarch.ac.uk
www.britarch.ac.uk
Publishing arm of the Council for
British Archaeology. Archaeology,
practical handbooks

CBD Research
Chancery House, 15 Wickham
Road, Beckenham, Kent BR3 5JS
020 8650 7745
cbd@cbdresearch.com
www.cbdresearch.com
Directories

Century
(see Random House Group)

Chambers Harrap Publishers
7 Hopetoun Crescent,
Edinburgh EH7 4AY
0131 556 5929
admin@chambersharrap.com
www.chambersharrap.com
Dictionaries and reference

Channel 4 Books
(see Random House Group)

Chapman Publishing
4 Broughton Place,
Edinburgh EH1 3RX
0131 557 2207
chapman-pub@blueyonder.co.uk
www.chapman-pub.co.uk
Scottish writers including poetry,
drama, short stories

Chartered Institute of Personnel
and Development
151 The Broadway,
London SW19 1JQ
020 8263 3387
publish@cipd.co.uk (books)
editorial@peoplemanagement
.co.uk
www.cipd.co.uk
Part of CIPD Enterprises (magazine)

Chatto & Windus
(see Random House Group)

Chicken House Publishing
2 Palmer Street, Frome,
Somerset BA11 1DS
01373 454488
chickenhouse@doublecluck.com
www.doublecluck.com
Children's fiction

Child's Play (International)
Ashworth Road, Bridgemead,
Swindon, Wiltshire SN5 7YD
01793 616286
office@childs-play.com
www.childs-play.com

Chris Andrews Publications
15 Curtis Yard, North Hinksey
Lane, Oxford OX2 0LX
01865 723404
chris.andrews1@btclick.com
www.oxfordpicturelibrary.co.uk
Owns the Oxford Picture Library. Coffee
table books, calendars and diaries

Christian Focus Publications
Geanies House, Fearn, Tain,
Rossshire IV20 1TW
01862 871011
info@christianfocus.com
www.christianfocus.com
Christian books for adults and children

Chrysalis Books
(incorporated into Anova Books)

Cicerone Press
2 Police Square, Milnthorpe,
Cumbria LA7 7PY
01539 562069
info@cicerone.co.uk
www.cicerone.co.uk
Guidebooks for outdoor enthusiasts

Cisco Press
(see Pearson Education)

Co & Bear Productions (UK)
63 Edith Grove, London SW10 0LB
020 7351 5545
bvincenzini@cobear.co.uk
www.scriptumeditions.co.uk
High quality illustrated books.
Imprint: Scriptum Editions

Colin Smythe
PO Box 6, Gerrards Cross,
Buckinghamshire SL9 8XA
01753 886000
sales@colinsmythe.co.uk
www.colinsmythe.co.uk
Anglo-Irish literature and criticism

Collins
(see HarperCollins Publishers)

Collins & Brown
(see Anova Books)

Colourpoint Books
Colourpoint House,
Jubilee Business Park,
21 Jubilee Road, Newtownards,
Co Down BT23 4YH
028 9182 0505
info@colourpoint.co.uk
www.colourpoint.co.uk
School textbooks, transport, Irish
interest

Compass Maps
The Coach House, Beech Court,
Winford BS40 8DW
01275 474737
info@popoutmaps.com
www.popout-travel.com
Pocket maps and guides

Compendium Publishing
1st Floor, 43 Frith Street,
London W1V 5TE
020 7287 4570
info@compendiumpublishing.com
Historical

Constable & Robinson
3, The Lanchesters,
162 Fulham Palace Road,
London W6 9ER
020 8741 3663
enquiries@constablerobinson.com
www.constablerobinson.com
Fiction and non-fiction: lifestyle,
reference, current affairs and politics

Continuum International
Publishing Group
(see Thompson Learning)

Conway Maritime
(see Anova Books)

Corgi
(see Random House Group)

Country Publications
The Watermill, Broughton Hall,
Skipton, North Yorkshire BD23 3AG
01756 701381
editorial@dalesman.co.uk
www.dalesman.co.uk
Magazines and regional books
(Countryman, Cumbria, Dalesman
and the Yorkshire nostalgia magazine
Down Your Way)

Countryside Books
Highfield House,
2 Highfield Avenue, Newbury,
Berkshire RG14 5DS
01635 43816
info@countrysidebooks.co.uk
www.countrysidebooks.co.uk
Local interest and walking books

CRC
(see T&F Informa)

Crecy Publishing
Unit 1a, Ringway Trading Estate,
Shadowmoss Road,
Manchester M22 5LH
0161 499 0024
enquiries@crecy.co.uk
www.crecy.co.uk
Aviation and naval military history

Cressrelles Publishing Co
10 Station Road Industrial Estate,
Colwall, Malvern,
Worcestershire WR13 6RN
01684 540154
simon@cressrelles.co.uk
Plays and theatre texts. Imprints:
Actinic Press

Crowood Press
The Stable Block, Crowood Lane,
Ramsbury, Marlborough,
Wiltshire SN8 2HR
01672 520320
enquiries@crowood.com
www.crowood.com
Aviation, military history, country,
sports, hobby and leisure pursuits

Curzon Press
(see T&F Informa)

CW Daniel Company
(see Random House Group)

Darton, Longman & Todd
1 Spencer Court,
140–142 Wandsworth High Street,
London SW18 4JJ
020 8875 0155
mail@
    darton-longman-todd.co.uk
www.darton-longman-todd.co.uk
Spirituality, theology and Christianity

David & Charles Publishers
Brunel House, Forde Close,
Newton Abbot, Devon TQ12 4PU
01626 323200
postmaster@davidandcharles.co.uk
www.davidandcharles.co.uk
Subsidiary of F&W, USA. Illustrated
non-fiction

David Fickling Books
(see Random House Group)

David Fulton (Publishers)
(see Granada Learning Group)

Debrett's
18–20 Hill Rise, Richmond,
Surrey TW10 6UA
020 8939 2250
people@debretts.co.uk
www.debretts.co.uk
Specialist reference works

Dedalus
Langford Lodge, St Judith's Lane,
Sawtry, Cambridgeshire PE28 5XE
01487 832382
info@dedalusbooks.com
www.dedalusbooks.com
*English contemporary fiction and
European fiction in translation,
concept books such as The Decadent
Handbook and The Dedalus Book of
Absinthe*

Dewi Lewis Publishing
8 Broomfield Road, Heaton Moor,
Stockport SK4 4ND
0161 442 9450
mail@dewilewispublishing.com
www.dewilewispublishing.com
Fiction, photography and visual arts

Dorling Kindersley
(see Penguin Books)

**Doubleday/
Doubleday Picture Books**
(see Random House Group)

Drake Educational Associates
St Fagans Road, Fairwater,
Cardiff CF5 3AE
029 2056 0333
info@drakeav.com
www.drakeav.com
Audio-visual, educational

Dref Wen
28 Church Road, Whitchurch,
Cardiff CF14 2EA
029 2061 7860
sales@drefwen.com
Welsh language

Duncan Baird Publishers
Castle House, 75–76 Wells Street,
London W1T 3QH
020 7323 2229
enquiries@dbp.co.uk
www.dbp.co.uk
General non-fiction

Duncan Petersen Publishing
C7, Old Imperial Laundry,
Warriner Gardens,
London SW11 4XW
020 7371 2356
charmingsmall.hotels@zen.co.uk
www.charmingsmallhotels.co.uk
Non-fiction

Ebury Press
(see Random House Group)

Eden
(see Random House Group)

Edinburgh University Press
22 George Square,
Edinburgh EH8 9LF
0131 650 4218
timothy.wright@eup.ed.ac.uk
www.eup.ed.ac.uk

Edward Elgar Publishing
Glensanda House,
Montpellier Parade, Cheltenham,
Gloucestershire GL50 1UA
01242 226934
info@e-elgar.co.uk
www.e-elgar.com
Economics, business and environment

Egmont Books
239 Kensington High Street,
London W8 6SA
020 7761 3500
info@euk.egmont.com
www.egmont.com
*Children's entertainment. Imprints:
Heinemann Young Books, Methuen
Children's Books, Hamlyn Children's
Books, Mammoth, Dean*

Eland Publishing
Third Floor, 61 Exmouth Market,
Clerkenwell, London EC1R 4QL
020 7833 0762
info@travelbooks.co.uk
www.travelbooks.co.uk
*Classic travel literature, Spirit of Place
novels, poetry and history of the
Islamic world*

Elliot Right Way Books
Kingswood Buildings,
Brighton Road, Lower Kingswood,
Tadworth, Surrey KT20 6TD
01737 832202
info@right-way.co.uk
www.right-way.co.uk
Practical non-fiction paperbacks

Elliott & Thompson
27 John Street, London WC1N 2BX
020 7831 5013
gmo73@dial.pipex.com
www.elliottthompson.com
History, biography, literary and fiction

Elm Consulting
Seaton House,
Kings Ripton, Huntingdon,
Cambridgeshire PE28 2NJ
01487 773254
sritchie@elm-training.co.uk
www.elm-training.co.uk
Educational aids

Elsevier
(see Reed Elsevier)

Emissary Publishing
PO Box 33, Bicester,
Oxfordshire OX26 4ZZ
01869 323447
www.manuscriptresearch.co.uk
www.peterpook.com
Humorous paperbacks

Emma Treehouse
2nd Floor, The Old Brewhouse,
Lower Charlton Trading Estate,
Shepton Mallet, Somerset BA4 5QE
01749 330529
treehouse-books@btconnect.com
www.emmatreehouse.com
Children's pre-school

Encyclopaedia Britannica (UK)
2nd Floor, Unity Wharf, Mill
Street, London SE1 2BH
020 7500 7800
enquiries@britannica.co.uk
www.britannica.co.uk

English Heritage (Publishing)
Kemble Drive, Swindon SN2 2GZ
01793 414619
customers@
english-heritage.org.uk
www.english-heritage.org.uk
General and specialist history

Enitharmon Press
26B Caversham Road,
London NW5 2DU
020 7482 5967
books@enitharmon.co.uk
www.enitharmon.co.uk
*Poetry, literary criticism, fiction, art
and photography, memoirs and
translations*

Euromonitor
60–61 Britton Street,
London EC1M 5UX
020 7251 8024
info@euromonitor.com
www.euromonitor.com
*Business reference, market analysis
and information directories*

Europa Publications
(see T&F Informa)

Evans Publishing Group
(see Thomson Learning)

Everyman
(see Orion Publishing Group)

Everyman's Library
Northburgh House,
10 Northburgh Street,
London EC1V 0AT
020 7566 6350
books@everyman.uk.com
*Imprint of Alfred A Knopf (subsidiary
of Random House, USA). Literature,
poetry, children's and travel*

Exley Publications
16 Chalk Hill, Watford,
Hertfordshire WD19 4BG
01923 248328
enquiries@exleypublications.co.uk
www.helenexleygiftbooks.com
*Giftbooks, quotation anthologies and
humour*

Expert Books
(see Random House Group)

FA Thorpe (Publishing)
(see Ulverscroft Group)

Faber & Faber
3 Queen Square, London WC1N 3AU
020 7465 0045
info@faber.co.uk
www.faber.co.uk
Fiction, non-fiction and poetry

Facet Publishing
7 Ridgmount Street,
London WC1E 7AE
020 7255 0590/0505 (text phone)
info@facetpublishing.co.uk
www.facetpublishing.co.uk
*Publishing arm of CILIP (Chartered
Institute of Library and Information
Professionals). Library and
information science*

Findhorn Press
305a The Park, Findhorn, Forres,
Morayshire IV36 3TE
01309 690582
info@findhornpress.com
www.findhornpress.com
*New Age, personal development and
alternative health*

First & Best in Education
Unit K, Earlstrees Court,
Earlstrees Road, Corby,
Northamptonshire NN17 4HH
01536 399005
info@firstandbest.co.uk
www.firstandbest.co.uk
*Educational books for schools.
Imprints: School Improvement Reports*

Fitzwarren Publishing
2 Orchard Drive,
Aston Clinton, Aylesbury,
Buckinghamshire HP22 5HR
01296 632627
pen2paper@btopenworld.com
Legal handbooks for the layman

Floris Books
15 Harrison Gardens,
Edinburgh EH11 1SH
0131 337 2372
floris@florisbooks.co.uk
www.florisbooks.co.uk
*Scientific, religion, holistic health,
children's, bio dynamics and organics*

Fodor's
(see Random House Group)

Folens Publishers
20 Apex Business Centre,
Boscombe Road,
Dunstable LU5 4RL
0870 609 1237
folens@folens.com
www.folens.com
Educational books. Imprint: Belair

Footprint Handbooks
6 Riverside Court,
Lower Bristol Road, Bath BA2 3DZ
01225 469141
ariddle@footprintbooks.com
www.footprintbooks.com
*Travel. Activity guides to hundreds of
cities and countries*

For Dummies
(see John Wiley & Sons)

Fountain Press
Newpro UK , Old Sawmills Road,
Faringdon, Oxfordshire SN7 7DS
01367 242411
sales@newprouk.co.uk
Photography and natural history

Fourth Estate
(see HarperCollins Publishers)

Frances Lincoln Publishers
4 Torriano Mews, Torriano
Avenue, London NW5 2RZ
020 7284 4009
reception@frances-lincoln.com
www.franceslincoln.com
Highly illustrated non-fiction

Frank Cass
(see T&F Informa)

Free Association Books
PO Box 37664, London NW7 2XU
020 8906 0396
info@fabooks.com
www.fabooks.com
*Psychoanalysis and psychotherapy,
social science, psychology*

Frommer's
(see John Wiley & Sons)

FT Prentice Hall
(see Pearson Education)

Gaia Books
2–4 Heron Quays, London E14 4JP
020 7531 8439
info@octopus-publishing.co.uk
www.octopus-publishing.co.uk
*Illustrated natural health, mind body
spirit, natural living and
environmental issues*

Garland Science
(see T&F Informa)

Garnet Publishing
8 Southern Court, South Street,
Reading, Berkshire RG1 4QS
0118 959 7847
enquiries@garnetpublishing.co.uk
www.garnetpublishing.co.uk
*Imprints: Garnet (Middle East); Ithaca
Press (business books)*

Geddes & Grosset
David Dale House,
New Lanark ML11 9DJ
01555 665000
info@geddesandgrosset.co.uk
www.geddesandgrosset.co.uk
*Children's and reference books.
Imprint: Beanobooks (children's)*

**Geological Society
Publishing House**
Unit 7, Brassmill Enterprise
Centre, Brassmill Lane,
Bath BA1 3JN
01225 445046
sales@geolsoc.org.uk
www.geolsoc.org.uk/bookshop
*Publishing arm of the Geological
Society. Undergraduate and
postgraduate texts in the earth sciences*

George Mann Books
PO Box 22, Maidstone,
Kent ME14 1AH
01622 759591
*Original non-fiction and selected
reprints*

Gibson Square Books
47, Lonsdale Square,
London N1 1EW
020 7096 1100
media@gibsonsquare.com
www.gibsonsquare.com/
*Biography and current issues.
Imprints: Gibson Square, New Editions*

Giles de la Mare Publishers
PO Box 25351, London NW5 1ZT
020 7485 2533
gilesdelamare@dial.pipex.com
www.gilesdelamare.co.uk
*Art and architecture, biography,
history, music*

Gollancz
(see Orion Publishing Group)

GMP (Gay Men's Press)
Unit M, Spectrum House,
32/34 Gordon House Road,
London NW5 1LP
020 7424 7400
www.millivres.co.uk
*Part of the Millivres Prowler Group.
Literary gay fiction. Imprint: Zipper
Books (gay male erotic fiction)*

Gomer Press
Llandysul, Ceredigion SA44 4JL
01559 362371
gwasg@gomer.co.uk
www.gomer.co.uk
*Adult fiction and non-fiction.
Imprint: Pont Books*

Good Web Guide
65 Bromfelde Road,
London SW4 6PP
020 7720 8919
marketing@
   thegoodwebguide.co.uk
www.thegoodwebguide.co.uk

Granada Learning Group
The Chiswick Centre, 414 Chiswick
High Road, London W4 5TF
020 8996 3333
info@granada-learning.co.uk
www.granada-learning.co.uk
nferNelson
The Chiswick Centre
020 8996 8444
information@nfernelson.co.uk
www.nfer-nelson.co.uk
*Tests, assessments and assessment
services*
SEMERC
Television Centre
0161 827 2927
www.semerc.com
ICT special needs

Granta Books
12 Addison Avenue,
London W11 4QR
020 7605 1360
lpaterson@granta.com
www.granta.com
Literary fiction and general non-fiction

Green Books
Foxhole, Dartington,
Totnes, Devon TQ9 6EB
01803 863260
edit@greenbooks.co.uk
www.greenbooks.co.uk
Green issues

Greenhill Books/Lionel Leventhal
Park House, 1 Russell Gardens,
London NW11 9NN
020 8458 6314
info@greenhillbooks.com
www.greenhillbooks.com
*Aviation, military, Napoleonic.
Imprint: Chatham Publishing (naval)*

Gresham Books
46 Victoria Road, Summertown,
Oxford OX2 7QD
01865 513582
info@gresham-books.co.uk
www.gresham-books.co.uk
Hymn and service books for children.

Griffith Institute
(see Oxford University)

Grub Street Publishing
4 Rainham Close, London SW11 6SS
020 7924 3966/7738 1008
post@grubstreet.co.uk
www.grubstreet.co.uk
Lifestyle and military

Guild of Master Craftsman Publications
166 High Street, Lewes,
East Sussex BN7 1XU
01273 477374
pubs@thegmcgroup.com
www.gmcbooks.com
Craft and woodworking

Guinness World Records
184-192 Drummond Street,
3rd Floor, London NW1 3HP
020 7891 4567
press@guinnessworldrecords.com
www.guinnessworldrecords.com

Gullane
(see Pinwheel)

Gwasg Carreg Gwalch
12 Iard yr Orsaf, Llanrwst,
Conwy LL26 0EH
01492 642031
llyrall@carreg-gwalch.co.uk
www.carreg-gwalch.co.uk
Welsh fiction and non-fiction; books on Wales

Hachette Group
338 Euston Road, London NW1 3BH
020 7873 6000
www.hodderheadline.co.uk

Halban Publishers
22 Golden Square,
London W1F 9JW
020 7437 9300
books@halbanpublishers.com
www.halbanpublishers.com
Fiction, memoirs, history, biography and books of Jewish interest

Halsgrove
Halsgrove House, Ryland Farm
Industrial Estate, Wellington,
Somerset TA21 9PZ
01823 653777
sales@halsgrove.com
www.halsgrove.com
South-west regional books, cookery, biography and art

Hambledon and London
102 Gloucester Avenue,
London NW1 8HX
020 7586 0817
office@hambledon.co.uk
www.hambledon.co.uk
History and biography

Hamish Hamilton
(see Penguin Books)

Harcourt Education
(see Reed Elsevier)

Harlequin Mills & Boon
Eton House, 18-24 Paradise Road,
Richmond, Surrey TW9 1SR
020 8288 2800
www.millsandboon.co.uk
Subsidiary of Harlequin, Canada. Popular fiction

Harley Books
Martins, Great Horkesley,
Colchester, Essex CO6 4AH
01206 271216
harley@harleybooks.co.uk
www.harleybooks.com
Natural history

HarperCollins Publishers
77-85 Fulham Palace Road,
London W6 8JB
020 8741 7070
webcontact@harpercollins.co.uk
www.harpercollins.co.uk
- Collins – www.collins.co.uk
  Reference books, cartography, education, dictionaries
- General books – www.harpercollinschildrensbooks.co.uk
  HarperCollins Childrens Books. Picture books, fiction and properties (Dr Seuss, Paddington Bear, Noddy etc.)
- HarperEntertainment – *Imprints: Entertainment (media-related); Collins Willow (sports); Tolkien and Estates (works by JRR Tolkien, Agatha Christie, CS Lewis); HarperCollins Audio*
- HarperFiction –
  www.voyager-books.co.uk
  www.readinggroups.co.uk
  Imprints: HarperCollins Fiction (crime and popular fiction); Voyager (sci-fi and fantasy)
- HarperPress – *Imprints: HarperCollins Non-Fiction (history, current affairs, travel and biography); Fourth Estate (innovative fiction and non fiction); HarperPerennial (literary paperbacks)*
- Thorsons – www.thorsons.co.uk
  Health, mind, body and spirit, personal development books. Imprint: Thorsons and Element (colour illustrated)

Harvard University Press/ MIT Press
Fitzroy House, 11 Chenies Street,
London WC1E 7EY
020 7306 0603
info@HUP-MITpress.co.uk
http://mitpress.mit.edu
European office of US company

Harvill Secker
(see Random House Group)

Haynes Publishing
Sparkford, Near Yeovil,
Somerset BA22 7JJ
01963 440635
www.haynes.co.uk
Car and motorcycle service and repair manuals

Heinemann
(see Random House)

Helicon Publishing
RM, New Mill House,
183 Milton Park, Abingdon,
Oxfordshire OX14 4SE
0870 920 0200
helicon@rm.com
www.helicon.co.uk
CD-Roms and online reference and cartography

Helm Information
Crowham Manor, Main Road,
Westfield, Hastings,
East Sussex TN35 4SR
01424 882422
amandahelm@
  helm-information.co.uk
www.helm-information.co.uk
Academic

Helter Skelter Publishing
South Bank House, Black Prince
Road, London SE1 7SJ
020 7463 2204
info@helterskelterpublishing.com
www.helterskelterbooks.com
Obscure music. Firefly Publishing (mainstream rock and pop)

Hesperus Press
4 Rickett Street, London SW6 1RU
020 7610 3331
info@hesperuspress.com
www.hesperuspress.com
Classic fiction in paperback

Hobsons Publishing
Challenger House, 42 Adler
Street, London E1 1EE
020 7958 5000
info@hobsons.co.uk
www.hobsons.com/uk
Part of the Daily Mail & General Trust. Course and career guides

Hodder Headline Group
338 Euston Road, London NW1 3BH
020 7873 6000
www.hodderheadline.co.uk and
www.madaboutbooks.com
Owned by Hachette Group

Hodder Headline Ireland
8 Castlecourt Centre,
Castleknock, Dublin 15
00 353 1 824 6288
Adult fiction and non-fiction. Imprint: HHI Lir (fiction)

Hodder Headline Scotland
2A Christie Street, Paisley PA1 1NB
0141 848 1609
bob.mcdevitt@hodder.co.uk
General
- Hodder & Stoughton – *Imprints: Sceptre (literary); NEL (crime); Coronet (commercial fiction); Mobius (mind, body & spirit); Flame (fiction)*
- Headline – *Imprints: Review (literary); Headline (commercial fiction and non-fiction)*
- John Murray – *Fiction, history, travel, literature and memoir*
Education
- Hodder Arnold – *Imprints: teach yourself (home reference); Hodder & Stoughton (reference including FA Guides and Michelle Thomas)*
- Hodder Murray – *Curriculum materials*
- Hodder Gibson – 0141 848 1609
  hoddergibson@hodder.co.uk
  Textbooks and revision support for the Scottish market

Religious
- **Hodder Religious** - *Imprints: Hodder & Stoughton (gift and inspirational); HY [help yourself] (home reference); HCB (Hodder Christian Books); NIV [New International Version] (bible translation)*

Children's
- **Hodder Children's Books** - *Fiction for children and young adults*
- **Hodder Wayland** - www.hodderwayland.co.uk *Non-fiction educational books*

Honeyglen Publishing
56 Durrels House, Warwick Gardens, London W14 8QB
020 7602 2876
History and fiction

Honno Welsh Women's Press
c/o Canolfan Merched Y Wawr, Vulcan Street, Aberystwyth, Ceredigion SY23 1JH
01970 623150
post@honno.co.uk
www.honno.co.uk
Reprints of classics, children's, fiction, poetry, short stories and Welsh women writers

House of Lochar
Isle of Colonsay, Argyll PA61 7YR
01951 200232
lochar@colonsay.org.uk
www.houseoflochar.com
Mostly Scottish titles. Imprint: Colonsay Books

How To Books
Spring Hill House, Spring Hill Road, Begbroke, Oxford OX5 1RX
01865 375794
info@howtobooks.co.uk
www.howtobooks.co.uk
Reference and self-help books

Hurst Publishers
41 Great Russell Street, London WC1B 3PL
020 7255 2201
hurst@atlas.co.uk
www.hurstpub.co.uk
Current affairs, politics, contemporary history

Hutchinson
(see Random House Group)

Ian Allan Publishing
Riverdene Business Park, Molesey Road, Hersham, Surrey KT12 4RG
01932 266600
info@ianallanpublishing.co.uk
www.ianallan.com
Maritime, road, rail, aviation, militaria and military history. Imprints: Midland Publishing, OPC Railway, Classic Publications, Lewis Masonic

Ian Henry Publications
20 Park Drive, Romford, Essex RM1 4LH
01708 749119
info@ian-henry.com
www.ian-henry.com
History and Sherlock Holmes

IB Tauris
(see Thomson Learning)

Icon Books
The Old Dairy, Brook Road, Thriplow, Cambridge SG8 7RG
01763 208008
info@iconbooks.co.uk
www.iconbooks.co.uk
History, game books, children's non-fiction, adult non-fiction

IMP Fiction
PO Box 69, Church Stretton, Shropshire SY6 6WZ
0169 472 0049
info@impbooks.com
www.impbooks.com
Music biographies

Independent Music Press
PO Box 69, Church Stretton, Shropshire SY6 6WZ
0169 472 0049
info@impbooks.com
www.impbooks.com
Music biography and youth culture

Interpet
Interpet House, Vincent Lane, Dorking, Surrey RH4 3YX
01306 873840
publishing@interpet.co.uk
Pet, aquatic and water gardening books

Inter-Varsity Press
Norton Street, Nottingham NG7 3HR
0115 978 1054
ivp@ivpbooks.com
www.ivpbooks.com
Christian belief and lifestyle. Imprints: IVP, Apollos, Crossway

Isis Publishing
(see Ulverscroft Group)

Ithaca Press
(see Garnet Publishing)

James Clarke & Co Lutterworth Press
PO Box 60, Cambridge CB1 2NT
01223 350865
publishing@jamesclarke.co.uk
www.lutterworth.com
Parent company of The Lutterworth Press. Theological, directory and reference

James Currey Publishers
73 Botley Road, Oxford OX2 0BS
01865 244111
editorial@jamescurrey.co.uk
www.jamescurrey.co.uk
Academic books on Africa and third world

Jane's Information Group
163 Brighton Road, Coulsdon, Surrey CR5 2YH
020 8700 3700
info@janes.com
www.janes.com
Defence, aerospace and transport

Janus Publishing Company
105–107 Gloucester Place, London W1U 6BY
020 7486 6633
publisher@januspublishing.co.uk
www.januspublishing.co.uk
Fiction and non-fiction. Imprint: Empiricus Books

Jarrold Publishing
Whitefriars, Norwich, Norfolk NR3 1JR
01603 763300
publishing@jarrold.com
www.jarrold-publishing.co.uk
Heritage and leisure, walking guides. Imprints: Pitkin, Unichrome

Jessica Kingsley Publishers
116 Pentonville Road, London N1 9JB
020 7833 2307
post@jkp.com
www.jkp.com
Social and behavioural sciences

John Blake Publishing
3 Bramber Court, 2 Bramber Road, London W14 9PB
020 7381 0666
words@blake.co.uk
www.blake.co.uk
General non-fiction, esp true crime, popular culture, general biography. Includes Richard Cohen, Smith Gryphon and Blake Publishing. Imprints: Metro Books (health, fitness, cookery and lifestyle)

John Hunt Publishing
The Bothy, Deershot Lodge, Park Lane, Ropley, Hampshire SO24 0BE
01962 773768
office1@o-books.net
www.johnhunt-publishing.com
www.o-books.net
World religions. Imprint: O Books (mind, body and spirit)

John Murray
(see Hodder Headline Group)

John Wiley & Sons
The Atrium, Southern Gate, Chichester PO19 8SQ
01243 779777
cs-books@wiley.co.uk
www.wileyeurope.com
Scientific, technical and medical; professional and trade; textbooks and educational materials.
- **Capstone Publishing** - *Business and personal development* www.capstoneideas.com
- **Fernhurst Books** - *Sailing and watersports*
- **For Dummies** - *Reference series*
- **Frommer's** - *Travel guides*
- **Jossey-Bass** - *Management, education and religion*
- **The Unofficial Guide** - *Travel, computing*
- **Visual/Redhat Press/Wrox** - *Computing*
- **Wiley** - *Scientific, technical and medical; professional and trade; textbooks and educational materials*
- **Wiley Interscience** - *Scientific, technical and medical; print and online reference materials*
- **Wiley-Academy** - *Architecture*
- **Wiley-Liss** - *Life and medical*
- **Wiley-VCH** - *Scientific, technical and medical*

Jonathan Cape
(see Random House Group)

Kahn & Averill
9 Harrington Road,
London SW7 3ES
020 8743 3278
kahn@averill23.freeserve.co.uk
Books on music

Kenilworth Press
Wykey House, Wykey,
Shrewsbury, Shropshire SY4 1JA
01939 261616
editorial@kenilworthpress.co.uk
www.kenilworthpress.co.uk
Equestrian

Kenneth Mason Publications
The Book Barn, Westbourne,
Emsworth, Hampshire PO10 8RS
01243 377977
info@researchdisclosure.com
www.researchdisclosure.com
*Lifestyle, nutrition and nautical.
Imprint: Research Disclosure*

Kevin Mayhew Publishers
Buxhall, Stowmarket,
Suffolk IP14 3BW
01449 737978
info@kevinmayhewltd.com
www.kevinmayhew.com
Christian music resources

Kingfisher Publications
New Penderel House,
283–288 High Holborn,
London WC1V 7HZ
020 7903 9999
sales@kingfisherpub.com
www.kingfisherpub.com
Children's fiction and non-fiction

Kogan Page
120 Pentonville Road,
London N1 9JN
020 7278 0433
kpinfo@kogan-page.co.uk
www.kogan-page.co.uk
Business and management

Kyle Cathie
122 Arlington Road,
London NW1 7HP
020 7692 7215
general.enquiries@kyle-cathie.com
www.KyleCathie.com
Lifestyle

Ladybird
(see Penguin Books)

Landmark Publishing
Ashbourne Hall, Cokayne Avenue,
Ashbourne, Derbyshire DE6 1EJ
01335 347349
landmark@clara.net
www.landmarkpublishing.co.uk
*Travel guides, and industrial and local
history*

Laurence King Publishing
361–373 City Road,
London EC1V 1LR
020 7841 6900
enquiries@laurenceking.co.uk
www.laurenceking.co.uk
Illustrated arts

Lawrence & Wishart
99A Wallis Road, London E9 5LN
020 8533 2506
lw@lwbooks.co.uk
www.lwbooks.co.uk
Current and world affairs

Leckie and Leckie
(see Granada Learning Group)

Lennard Associates
Windmill Cottage, Mackerye End,
Harpenden, Hertfordshire AL5 5DR
01582 715866
stephenson@lennardqap.co.uk
*Sporting yearbooks. Imprints and
divisions include: Lennard Publishing,
Queen Anne Press*

Letts Educational
(see Granada Learning Group)

LexisNexis
(see Reed Elsevier)

Lion Hudson
Mayfield House, 256 Banbury
Road, Oxford OX2 7DH
01865 302750
enquiries@lionhudson.com
www.lionhudson.com
*Formed through merger of Lion
Publishing and Angus Hudson.
Christian books. Imprints: Lion,
Lion Children's, Candle, Monarch*

Little, Brown
(see Hachette Group)

Little Tiger Press
Magi Publications, 1 The Coda
Centre, 189 Munster Road,
London SW6 6AW
020 7385 6333
info@littletiger.co.uk
www.littletigerpress.com
*Children's picture and novelty books.
Imprints: Little Tiger, Caterpillar Books*

Liverpool University Press
4 Cambridge Street,
Liverpool L69 7ZU
0151 794 2233
sbell@liv.ac.uk
www.liverpool-unipress.co.uk

Lonely Planet Publications
72–82 Rosebery Avenue,
Clerkenwell, London EC1R 4RW
020 7841 9000
go@lonelyplanet.co.uk
www.lonelyplanet.com
Travel guides

Longman
(see Pearson Education)

Lutterworth Press
(see James Clarke & Co
Lutterworth Press)

Macmillan Publishers
4 Crinan Street, London N1 9XW
020 7843 3600
www.macmillan.com

Nature Publishing Group
4 Crinan Street, London N1 9XW
020 7843 4000
www.nature.com
*Scientific journals and reference
publishing*

Macmillan Education
Macmillan Oxford,
4 Between Towns Road,
Oxford OX4 3PP
01865 405700
www.macmillaneducation.com
*ELT learning materials for
international markets*

Palgrave Macmillan
Brunel Road, Houndmills,
Basingstoke, Hampshire RG21 6XS
01256 329242
bookenquiries@palgrave.com
www.palgrave.com
*Academic, scholarly and reference
publishing in the social sciences and
humanities*

Pan Macmillan
20 New Wharf Road,
London N1 9RR
020 7014 6000
www.panmacmillan.com
*Fiction and non-fiction for adults and
children. Imprints: Macmillan, Pan,
Picador, Young Picador, Boxtree,
Sidgwick and Jackson, Papermac,
Macmillan Children's Books, Campbell
Books, Priddy Books. US imprints:
Picador USA; St Martin's Press; Farrar,
Straus and Giroux Inc.; Henry Holt;
Tor. Australian imprints: Pan
Macmillan Australia, Pancake. South
African imprints: Pan Macmillan
South Africa, Picador Africa. Irish
imprints: Gill and Macmillan*

Magna Large Print Books
(see Ulverscroft Group)

**Mainstream Publishing Co
(Edinburgh)**
7 Albany Street,
Edinburgh EH1 3UG
0131 557 2959
enquiries@
mainstreampublishing.com
www.mainstreampublishing.com
Non fiction

Management Books 2000
Forge House, Limes Road,
Kemble, Cirencester,
Gloucestershire GL7 6AD
01285 771441
info@mb2000.com
www.mb2000.com
Working books for working managers

Manchester University Press
Oxford Road, Manchester M13 9NR
0161 275 2310
mucp@manchester.ac.uk
www.manchesteruniversitypress
.co.uk

Manson Publishing
73 Corringham Road,
London NW11 7DL
020 8905 5150
www.mansonpublishing.com
*Scientific, technical, medical and
veterinary*

Marion Boyars Publishers
24 Lacy Road, London SW15 1NL
020 8788 9522
catheryn@marionboyars.com
www.marionboyars.co.uk
*Formerly Calder and Boyars. Literary
fiction, fiction in translation, social
affairs, film, music, drama*

Marshall Cavendish
119 Wardour Street,
London W1F 0UW
020 7565 6000
www.marshallcavendish.co.uk
Adults' and children's and educational

Marston House
Marston House, Marston Magna,
Yeovil, Somerset BA22 8DH
01935 851331
alphaimage@marstonhouse
.ndo.co.uk
www.marstonhouse.ndo.co.uk
*Fine art, architecture, ceramics and
horticulture*

Martin Dunitz
(see T&F Informa)

McGraw-Hill Education
Shoppenhangers Road,
Maidenhead, Berkshire SL6 2QL
01628 502500
www.mcgraw-hill.co.uk
*Business, economics, computing and
engineering*

Higher Education
*University textbooks on business,
economics, accounting, finance,
marketing, computing science,
decision sciences. Imprints: McGraw-
Hill Education, McGraw-Hill Irwin*

Open University Press
*Higher education, education, health
and social welfare, cultural and media
studies, psychology, criminology,
sociology, counselling, study guides*

Professional
*Professional, business and general
reference books covering computing,
science, technical and medical,
languages, architecture, careers,
politics, management, finance,
parenting, health, sports & fitness.
Imprints: McGraw-Hill Professional,
McGraw-Hill Trade, McGraw-Hill
Osborne, McGraw-Hill Medical
Publishing, McGraw-Hill Contemporary,
Harvard Business School Press,
Amacom, Berrett-Koehler, CMP*

Schools
*Early childhood, primary and
secondary school books. Imprints:
Kingscourt, Glencoe and SRA,
Macmillan, The Learning Group*

Mercat Press
10 Coates Crescent,
Edinburgh EH3 7AL
0131 225 5324
enquiries@mercatpress.com
www.mercatpress.com
*Fiction and non-fiction of Scottish
interest*

Merlin Press
96, Monnow Street,
Monmouth NP25 3EQ
01600 775663
info@merlinpress.co.uk
www.merlinpress.co.uk
*Economics, history, leftwing politics.
Imprints: Green Print, Merlin Press*

Merrell Publishers
81 Southwark Street,
London SE1 0HX
020 7928 8880
mail@merrellpublishers.com
www.merrellpublishers.com
*Art, architecture, design and
photography*

Methodist Publishing House
4 John Wesley Road,
Werrington, Peterborough,
Cambridgeshire PE4 6ZP
01733 325002
customer.services@mph.org.uk
www.mph.org.uk
*Owned by the Methodist Church
Christian books. Imprint: Epworth Press*

Methuen Publishing
11/12 Buckingham Gate,
London SW1E 6LB
020 7798 1600
sales@methuen.co.uk
www.methuen.co.uk
*General fiction and non-fiction.
Imprint: Politicos (politics)*

Michael Joseph
(see Penguin Books)

Michael O'Mara Books
9 Lion Yard, Tremadoc Road,
London SW4 7NQ
020 7720 8643
enquiries@mombooks.com
www.mombooks.com
*Biography, popular history, humour,
children's and pre-school*

Michelin Travel Publications
Hannay House,
39 Clarendon Road, Watford,
Hertfordshire WD17 1JA
01923 205240
www.michelin.co.uk
Travel books and maps

Microsoft Press
Thames Valley Park,
Reading, Berkshire RG6 1WG
0870 601 0100
mspinfo@microsoft.com
www.microsoft.com/mspress/uk
*Computing manuals to accompany
Microsoft products; also system
administration, business solutions
and security*

Miles Kelly Publishing
Unit 17 & 18, The Bardfield Centre,
Great Bardfield, Essex CM7 4SL
01371 811309
info@mileskelly.net
www.mileskelly.net
Children's titles

Milet Publishing
333 North Michigan Avenue,
Suite 330, Chicago IL6 6061
001 312 920 1828
info@milet.com
www.milet.com
Children's books

Millivres Prowler Group
Unit M, Spectrum House,
32/34 Gordon House Road,
London NW5 1LP
020 7424 7400
www.millivres.co.uk
*Zipper Books, Gay Men's Press, Gay
Times Books, Diva Books and Red Hot
Diva Books*

Mills & Boon
(see Harlequin Mills & Boon)

MIT Press
(see Harvard University Press/
MIT Press)

Motor Racing Publications
PO Box 1318, Croydon,
Surrey CR9 5YP
020 8654 2711
mrp.books@virgin.net
www.mrpbooks.co.uk
*Motor racing, road cars, performance
and classic cars*

MQ Publications
12 The Ivories,
6–8 Northampton Street,
London N1 2HY
020 7359 2244
kim@mqpublications.com
www.mqpublications.com
Illustrated cookbooks

Murdoch Books UK
Erico House, 6th Floor,
93–99 Upper Richmond Road,
Putney, London SW15 2TG
020 8785 5995
jpickett@murdochbooks.co.uk
*Food and drink, craft, gardening,
fiction and non-fiction*

National Trust Publications
Heelis, Kemble Drive, Swindon,
Wiltshire SN2 2NA
01793 817400
enquiries@thenationaltrust.org.uk
www.nationaltrust.org.uk/bookshop
Publishing arm of The National Trust

Nautical Data
The Book Barn, Westbourne,
Emsworth, Hampshire PO10 8RS
01243 389352
info@nauticaldata.com
www.nauticaldata.com

NCVO Publications
Regent's Wharf, 8 All Saints
Street, London N1 9RL
020 7713 6161
ncvo@ncvo-vol.org.uk
www.ncvo-vol.org.uk
*Publishing imprint of the National
Council for Voluntary Organisations.
Directories, public policy and
governance; trusteeship and HR in the
voluntary sector*

Neil Wilson Publishing
Suite EX8, 44 Washington Street,
Glasgow G3 8AZ
0141 221 1117
info@nwp.co.uk
www.nwp.co.uk
*Scottish and Irish interest: food and
drink, outdoor pursuits, history,
humour and biography*

Nelson Thornes
Delta Place, 27 Bath Road,
Cheltenham,
Gloucestershire GL53 7TH
01242 267100
info@nelsonthornes.com
www.nelsonthornes.com
*Part of the Wolters Kluwer Group.
Educational*

New Beacon Books
76 Stroud Green Road,
London N4 3EN
020 7272 4889
newbeaconbooks@btconnect.com
Black-oriented fiction, history, politics,
poetry and language

New Holland Publishers (UK)
Garfield House,
86–88 Edgware Road,
London W2 2EA
020 7724 7773
reception@nhpub.co.uk
www.newhollandpublishers.com
Non-fiction, lifestyle and
self-improvement

New Riders
(see Pearson Education)

nferNelson
(see Granada Learning Group)

Nicholas Brealey Publishing
3–5 Spafield Street,
London EC1R 4QB
020 7239 0360
publicity@nicholasbrealey.com
www.nicholasbrealey.com
Includes Intercultural Press.
Cultural business, self-help and travel.
US imprint: Intercultural Press

Nick Hern Books
The Glasshouse,
49a Goldhawk Road,
London W12 8QP
020 8749 4953
info@nickhernbooks.demon.co.uk
www.nickhernbooks.co.uk
Theatre and film

Nielsen BookData
3rd Floor, Midas House,
62 Goldsworth Road, Woking,
Surrey GU21 6LQ
0870 777 8710
sales@nielsenbookdata.co.uk
www.nielsenbookdata.co.uk
The Directory of UK and Irish Book
Publishers

NMS Enterprises
National Museums of Scotland,
Chambers Street,
Edinburgh EH1 1JF
0131 247 4026
publishing@nms.ac.uk
www.nms.ac.uk
History, art, archaeology, natural
history, popular Scottish history,
culture, biography and geology

Nottingham University Press
Manor Farm, Church Lane,
Thrumpton, Nottingham NG11 0AX
0115 983 1011
editor@nup.com
www.nup.com
Scientific textbooks

Oberon Books
521 Caledonian Road,
London N7 9RH
020 7607 3637
info@oberonbooks.com
www.oberonbooks.com
Play texts

Octagon Press
78 York Street, London W1H 1DP
020 7193 6456
admin@octagonpress.com
www.octagonpress.com
Philosophy, psychology, travel and
Eastern religion

Octopus Publishing Group
2–4 Heron Quays, London E14 4JP
020 7531 8400
info@octopus-publishing.co.uk
www.octopus-publishing.co.uk
www.conran-octopus.co.uk
www.hamlyn.co.uk
www.mitchell-beazley.co.uk
www.philips-maps.co.uk
Owned by Hachette. Illustrated adult
reference books

Oldcastle Books
PO Box 394, Harpenden,
Hertfordshire AL5 1XJ
01582 761264
info@noexit.co.uk;
info@pocketessentials.com
www.noexit.co.uk
www.pocketessentials.com
Imprints: No Exit Press and Crime
Time (crime/noir fiction);
Pocketessentials (compact reference
books on film, tv, literature, ideas and
history); High Stakes (gambling)

Omnibus Press
14–15 Berners Street,
London W1T 3LJ
020 7612 7400
music@musicsales.co.uk
www.omnibuspress.com
Imprints: Omnibus Press (music-
related biography); Vision On
(upmarket music-related photo books).
US imprint: Schirmer Books (self-help
books, music industry)

Oneworld
(see Thomson Learning)

Onlywomen Press
40 St Lawrence Terrace,
London W10 5ST
020 8354 0796
onlywomenpress@btconnect.com
www.onlywomenpress.com
Lesbian and feminist fiction,
non-fiction theory and poetry

Open University Press
(see McGraw-Hill Education)

Orbit Press
(see Time Warner Books)

Orion Publishing Group
Orion House, 5 Upper Saint
Martin's Lane, London WC2H 9EA
020 7240 3444
info@orionbooks.co.uk
www.orionbooks.co.uk
• Gollancz – *Sci-fi and fantasy*
• Orion Children's Books
• Weidenfeld & Nicolson – *History,*
  reference, non-fiction, illustrated
  and literary fiction, military
• Cassell Military – *Illustrated and*
  paperback
• Cassell Reference
• Everyman – *Classics in paperback*
• Phoenix – *Contemporary fiction*

Osprey Publishing
Midland House, West Way,
Oxford OX2 0PH
01865 727022
info@ospreypublishing.com
www.ospreypublishing.com
Military history, aviation

Oxford University
Ashmolean Museum Publications,
Ashmolean Museum,
Beaumont Street, Oxford OX1 2PH
01865 278000
publications@ashmus.ox.ac.uk
www.ashmolean.org
Art and archaeology
Griffith Institute
Sackler Library, 1 St John's Street,
Oxford OX1 2LG
01865 278099
griffith.institute@orinst.ox.ac.uk
www.ashmolean.museum
  /griffith.html
Egyptology
Oxford University Press
Great Clarendon Street,
Oxford OX2 6DP
01865 556767
enquiry@oup.com
www.oup.com
A department of Oxford University.
Academic. Imprint: Oxford Children's
Books

Palgrave Macmillan
(see Macmillan Publishers)

Pan/Pan Macmillan
(see Macmillan Publishers)

Papermac
(see Macmillan Publishers)

Paper Tiger
(see Anova Books)

Pavilion
(see Anova Books)

Peachpit Press
(see Pearson Education)

Pearson Education
Edinburgh Gate, Harlow,
Essex CM20 2JE
01279 623623
enquiries@pearson.com
www.pearsoned.co.uk
• Addison-Wesley – *Computer*
  programming
• Allyn & Bacon – *Education,*
  humanities and social sciences
• Benjamin Cummings – *Science*
• Cisco Press – *Cisco systems materials*
• FT Prentice Hall – *Global business*
• Longman – *Educational materials*
  for schools, English language
  teaching (ELT) materials, higher
  education textbooks (law,
  humanities, social sciences)
• New Riders – *Graphics and design*
• Peachpit Press – *Web development*
• Penguin Books – (*see separate entry*
  under Penguin Books)
• Penguin Longman – *ELT books*
• Penguin English (for teachers)
  – www.penguinenglish.com
• Penguin Readers (for students)
  – www.penguinreaders.com

- **Prentice Hall** - *Academic and reference textbooks: business, computer science, engineering and IT*
- **Prentice Hall Business** - *Practical and personal development*
- **QUE Publishing** - *Computing*
- **SAMS Publishing** - *Reference books for programmers and developers, web developers, designers, networking and system administrators*
- **York Notes** - *Literature guides for students*

Pegasus Elliot & Mackenzie Publishers
Sheraton House, Castle Park, Cambridge CB3 0AX
01223 370012
editors@pegasuspublishers.com
www.pegasuspublishers.com
Fiction and non-fiction, crime and erotica. Imprints: Vanguard Press, Nightingale Books, Chimera

Pen & Sword Books
47 Church Street, Barnsley, South Yorkshire S70 2AS
01226 734222
enquiries@pen-and-sword.co.uk
www.pen-and-sword.co.uk
Military, naval and aviation history. Imprints: Leo Cooper, Wharncliffe Publishing

Penguin Books
80 Strand, London WC2R 0RL
020 7010 3000
www.penguin.co.uk
Owned by Pearson
- **Dorling Kindersley** - *Information books and resources for children and adults*
- **ePenguin** - *ebooks*
- **Penguin Audiobooks**
- **Penguin General Books** - *Imprints: Penguin Paperbacks; Hamish Hamilton; Michael Joseph; Viking*
- **Penguin Press** - *Imprints: Allen Lane (reference inc. Roget's Thesaurus and Pears Cyclopaedia); Penguin Classics; Penguin Modern Classics*
- **Puffin** - *Children's*
- **Rough Guides** - roughguide@penguin.co.uk *Travel guides, phrase books, music guides and reference*
- **Warne** - *Children's, inc. Beatrix Potter, Spot, Ladybird*

Penguin Ireland
25 St Stephen's Green, Dublin 2
00 353 1 661 7695
info@penguin.ie
www.penguin.ie

Persephone Books
59 Lamb's Conduit Street, London WC1N 3NB
020 7242 9292
info@persephonebooks.co.uk
www.persephonebooks.co.uk
Reprint fiction and non-fiction, focus on women

Perseus Books Group
69-70 Temple Chambers, 3-7 Temple Avenue, London EC4Y 0HP
020 7353 7771
enquiries@perseusbooks.co.uk
www.perseusbooksgroup.com
UK office of US Perseus Books Group. Non-fiction. Imprints: PublicAffairs (current affairs); Da Capo Press (music, history, film and biography); Basic Books (current affairs, history, popular science); Counterpoint (literature and fiction); Basic Civitas Books (African American studies); Westview Press (social sciences, humanities, science)

Peter Haddock Publishing
Pinfold Lane, Bridlington, East Yorkshire YO16 6BT
01262 678121
sales@phpublishing.co.uk
www.phpublishing.co.uk
Children's books

Peter Owen Publishers
73 Kenway Road, London SW5 0RE
020 7373 5628
admin@peterowen.com
www.peterowen.com
Biography, non-fiction, literary fiction, literary criticism, history and the arts

Phaidon Press
18 Regent's Wharf, All Saints Street, London N1 9PA
020 7843 1000
enquiries@phaidon.com
www.phaidon.com
Arts

Pharmaceutical Press
1 Lambeth High Street, London SE1 7JN
020 7735 9141
enquiries@rpsgb.org
www.rpsgb.org
The publications division of the Royal Pharmaceutical Society of Great Britain. Medicine

Philip Berrill International
60 Leyland Road, Southport, Merseyside PR9 9JA
01704 534725
philipberrill@hotmail.com
Art and mind, body and spirit guides

Philip Wilson Publishers
109 Drysdale Street, The Timber Yard, London N1 6ND
020 7033 9900
pwilson@philip-wilson.co.uk
www.philip-wilson.co.uk
Art, museums and exhibition catalogues

Phillimore & Co
Madam Green Business Centre, Oving, Chichester, West Sussex PO20 2DD
01243 787636
bookshop@phillimore.co.uk
www.phillimore.co.uk
Local and family history

Phoenix
(see Orion Publishing Group)

Piatkus Books
5 Windmill Street, London W1T 2JA
020 7631 0710
info@piatkus.co.uk
www.piatkus.co.uk
Fiction, biography, history, health, business and personal development

Picador
(see Macmillan Publishers)

Piccadilly Press
5 Castle Road, London NW1 8PR
020 7267 4492
books@piccadillypress.co.uk
www.piccadillypress.co.uk
Children's, teenage and parental books

Pimlico
(see Random House Group)

Pinwheel (Division of Alligator books)
Winchester House, 259-269 Old Marylebone Road, London NW1 5XJ
020 7616 7200
www.pinwheel.co.uk
Imprints: Gullane (children's picture); Pinwheel (novelty); Andromeda (education)

Pluto Press
(see Thomson Learning)

Pocket Books
(see Simon & Schuster UK)

The Policy Press
University of Bristol, Fourth Floor, Beacon House, Queen's Road, Bristol BS8 1QU
0117 331 4054
tpp-info@bristol.ac.uk
www.policypress.org.uk
Social sciences

Politico's Publishing
(see Methuen Publishing)

Polity Press
65 Bridge Street, Cambridge CB2 1UR
01223 324315
info@polity.co.uk
www.polity.co.uk
General academic

Portland Press
3rd Floor, Eagle House, 16 Proctor Street, London WC1V 6NX
020 7280 4110
editorial@portlandpress.com
www.portlandpress.com
Biochemistry and medicine

Prentice Hall/Prentice Hall Business
(see Pearson Education)

Prestel Publishing
4 Bloomsbury Place, London WC1A 2QA
020 7323 5004
sales@prestel-uk.co.uk
www.prestel.com
Art, architecture, photography, design and fashion

Priddy Books
(see Macmillan Publishers)

Profile Books
3A Exmouth House, Pine Street,
Exmouth Market, London EC1R 0JH
020 7841 6300
info@profilebooks.com
www.profilebooks.com
Non-fiction. Imprint: Economist Books

Profile Sports Media
5th Floor, Mermaid House,
2 Puddledock, London EC4V 3DS
020 7332 2000
info@profilesportsmedia.com
www.profilesportsmedia.com
Sporting annuals and publications

**Proquest Information
and Learning**
The Quorum, Barnwell Road,
Cambridge CB5 8SW
01223 215512
marketing@proquest.co.uk
www.proquest.co.uk
Educational

Psychology Press
(see T&F Informa)

Publishing House
Trinity Place, Barnstaple,
Devon EX32 9HG
01271 328892
publishinghouse@
  vernoncoleman.com
www.vernoncoleman.com
*Fiction, health, humour, animals and
politics*

Puffin
(see Penguin Books)

Pushkin Press
12 Chester Terrace,
London NW1 4ND
020 7730 0750
info@pushkinpress.com
www.pushkinpress.com
*Translated classic and contemporary
European literature*

Quadrille Publishing
Alhambra House,
27-31 Charing Cross Road,
London WC2H 0LS
020 7839 7117
enquiries@quadrille.co.uk
www.quadrille.co.uk
Lifestyle

Quartet Books
27 Goodge Street, London W1T 2LD
020 7636 3992
quartetbooks@easynet.co.uk
*Part of the Namara Group.
Contemporary literary fiction*

Quarto Publishing
6 Blundell Street, London N7 9BH
020 7700 6700
info@quarto.com
www.quarto.com
Highly illustrated non-fiction

QUE Publishing
(see Pearson Education)

Radcliffe Publishing
18 Marcham Road, Abingdon,
Oxfordshire OX14 1AA
01235 528820
contact.us@radcliffemed.com
www.radcliffe-oxford.com

Random House Group
Random House, 20 Vauxhall
Bridge Road, London SW1V 2SA
020 7840 8400
enquiries@randomhouse.co.uk
www.randomhouse.co.uk
Random House Division
- **Arrow** - *Mass-market paperback
  fiction and non-fiction*
- **Century** - *General fiction and non-
  fiction including commercial fiction,
  autobiography, biography, history
  and self-help*
- **Chatto & Windus** - *Memoirs, current
  affairs, essays, literary fiction,
  history, poetry, politics, philosophy
  and translations*
- **Harvill Secker** - *Literary fiction,
  literature in translation, English
  literature, quality thrillers, some
  non-fiction*
- **Hutchinson** - *General fiction and
  non-fiction including belles-lettres,
  current affairs, politics, travel and
  history*
- **Jonathan Cape** - *Biography and
  memoirs, current affairs, fiction,
  history, photography, poetry, politics
  and travel*
- **Pimlico** - *Quality non-fiction
  paperbacks specialising in history,
  biography, popular culture and
  the arts*
- **Random House Business Books**
- **Vintage** - *Quality paperback fiction
  and non-fiction*
- **William Heinemann** - *General
  fiction and non-fiction especially
  history, literary fiction, crime,
  science, thrillers and women's fiction*
- **Yellow Jersey Press** - *Narrative
  sports books*

Ebury Press Division
- **Ebury Press** - *Autobiography,
  biography, popular history, cookery,
  popular science, humour, diet and
  health*
- **Fodor's** - *Travel guides*
- **Rider** - *Mind, body and spirit*
- **Vermilion** - *Popular reference,
  lifestyle, crafts, interior design*

Random House Children's Books
Transworld Publishers, 61-63
Uxbridge Road, London W5 5SA
020 8231 6800
*Imprints: Hutchinson, Jonathan Cape,
The Bodley Head, Doubleday Picture
Books, David Fickling Books, Corgi,
Red Fox*

Transworld Publishers
61-63 Uxbridge Road,
London W5 5SA
020 8579 2652
info@transworld-publishers.co.uk
www.booksattransworld.co.uk
*Imprints: Bantam, Bantam Press,
Corgi & Black Swan, Doubleday, Eden,
Expert Books, Channel 4 Books*

Ransom Publishing
Rose Cottage,
Howe Hill, Watlington,
Oxfordshire OX49 5HB
01962 862307
ransom@ransom.co.uk
www.ransom.co.uk
Education and children's fiction

Reader's Digest Association
11 Westferry Circus, Canary Wharf,
London E14 1HE
020 7715 8000
gbeditorial@readersdigest.co.uk
www.readersdigest.co.uk
*Cookery, history, reference, gardening
and DIY*

Reaktion Books
33 Great Sutton Street,
London EC1V 0DX
020 7253 1071
info@reaktionbooks.co.uk
www.reaktionbooks.co.uk
*Architecture, asian and cultural
studies, film, art and photography,
history and geography, biography*

Reardon Publishing
PO Box 919, Cheltenham,
Gloucestershire GL50 9AN
01242 231800
reardon@bigfoot.com
www.reardon.co.uk
*Member of the Outdoor Writers Guild.
Cotswold area local interest*

Red Bird Publishing
Kiln Farm, East End Green,
Brightlingsea, Colchester,
Essex CO7 0SX
01206 303525
info@red-bird.co.uk
www.red-bird.co.uk
Special-effects books for children

Red Fox
(see Random House Group)

Redhat Press
(see John Wiley & Sons)

Reed Elsevier
1-3 Strand, London WC2N 5JR
020 7930 7077
www.reedelsevier.com
Press: 020 7166 5657/5670
Business Division
Reed Business Information,
Quadrant House, The Quadrant,
Sutton, Surrey SM2 5AS
020 8652 3500
www.reedbusiness.co.uk
*Business directories, magazines,
e-newsletters, websites and cd-roms*
Press: 020 8652 3296
Education Division
Harcourt Education, Halley Court,
Jordan Hill, Oxford OX2 8EJ
01865 311366
uk.schools@
  harcourteducation.co.uk
www.harcourteducation.co.uk
*Textbooks and educational resources.
Imprints: Ginn; Heinemann (Primary,
Secondary, FE and Vocational);
Rigby UK*

Legal Division
LexisNexis Butterworths Tolley,
Halsbury House, 35 Chancery
Lane, London WC2A 1EL
020 7400 2500
competitive.intelligence@
lexis-nexis.com
www.lexisnexis.co.uk
*Legal and business materials in print
and online, including The Advertiser
Red Books. Butterworths Services
provide access to a library of UK law*
Press: 020 7400 2753

Medical Division
32 Jamestown Road, Camden
Town, London NW1 7BY
020 7424 4200
eurobkinfo@elsevier.com
www.elsevier-international.com
Press: pressoffice@elsevier.com
• **Elsevier Science and Technology -**
*Imprints: Academic Press (physical,
applied and life sciences); Morgan
Kaufmann (databases, computer
networking, human computer
interaction, computer graphics,
multimedia information and
systems, artificial intelligence, and
software engineering); Syngress
Media (computing reference works
for IT professionals)*
• **Elsevier Health Sciences -** *Imprints:
Saunders (medical); Mosby
(medicine, nursing, allied health and
veterinary medicine); Churchill
Livingstone (medical); Butterworth-
Heinemann (technology, medicine
and management); Hanley & Belfus
(medical); Bailliere Tindall (nursing
and midwifery); BC Decker
(medicine, health sciences, and
dentistry); GW Medical Publishing
(abuse, maltreatment, sexually
transmitted diseases, and domestic
violence)*

Regency House Publishing
Nial House, 24–26 Boulton Road,
Stevenage, Hertfordshire SG1 4QX
01438 314488
regency-house@btconnect.com
Art and transport

**Richmond House Publishing
Company**
70–76 Bell Street, Marylebone,
London NW1 6SP
020 7224 9666
sales@rhpco.co.uk
www.rhpco.co.uk
Theatre and entertainment directories

Rider
(see Random House Group)

Robert Hale
Clerkenwell House,
45–47 Clerkenwell Green,
London EC1R OHT
020 7251 2661
enquiries@halebooks.com
www.halebooks.com

Robson Books
(see Anova Books)

Rodale Books
7–10 Chandos Street,
London W1G 9AD
020 7291 6000
www.rodale.co.uk
Lifestyle

Roget's Thesaurus
(see Penguin Books)

RotoVision
Sheridan House, 112/116A Western
Road, Hove, East Sussex BN3 1DD
01273 727268
sales@rotovision.com
www.rotovision.com
Graphic arts and design

Rough Guides
(see Penguin Books)

Roundhouse Publishing
Millstone, Limers Lane, Northam,
North Devon EX39 2RG
01237 474474
roundhouse.group@ukgateway.net
www.roundhouse.net
Cinema and media

Routledge
(see T&F Informa)

Ryland, Peters & Small
20–21 Jockey's Fields,
London WC1R 4BW
020 7025 2200
info@rps.co.uk
www.rylandpeters.com
Illustrated lifestyle

SAF Publishing
149 Wakeman Road,
London NW10 5BH
020 8969 6099
info@safpublishing.co.uk
www.safpublishing.co.uk
*Experimental rock and jazz music.
Firefly Publishing (mainstream rock
and pop)*

Sage Publications
1 Olivers Yard, 55 City Road,
London EC1Y 1SP
020 7324 8500
market@sagepub.co.uk
www.sagepub.co.uk
*Social sciences and humanities.
Imprint: Paul Chapman (education
and training)*

Saint Andrew Press
Church of Scotland,
121 George Street,
Edinburgh EH2 4YN
0131 225 5722
standrewpress@cofscotland.org.uk
www.churchofscotland.org.uk
/standrewpress
*Owned by the Church of Scotland.
Christian, moral and ethical*

Samuel French
52 Fitzroy Street, London W1T 5JR
020 7387 9373
theatre@
samuelfrench-london.co.uk
www.samuelfrench-london.co.uk
Plays

SAMS Publishing
(see Pearson Education)

Sangam Books
57 London Fruit Exchange,
Brushfield Street, London E1 6EP
020 7377 6399
sangambks@aol.com
Educational textbooks

SB Publications
14 Bishopstone Road, Seaford,
East Sussex BN25 2UB
01323 893498
sbpublications@tiscali.co.uk
www.sbpublications.co.uk
Local history, travel, guides

Scholastic
Villiers House, Clarendon Avenue,
Leamington Spa,
Warwickshire CV32 5PR
01926 887799
enquiries@scholastic.co.uk
www.scholastic.co.uk
Education

Scholastic Children's Books
Euston House, 24 Eversholt
Street, London NW1 1DB
020 7756 7756
scbenquiries@scholastic.co.uk
www.scholastic.co.uk
Fiction. Imprints: Hippo, Point

SCM Canterbury Press
9–17 St Albans Place,
London N1 ONX
020 7359 8033
admin@scm-canterburypress.co.uk
www.scm-canterburypress.co.uk
Theology and hymn books

Scala Publishers
Northburgh House,
10 Northburgh Street,
London EC1V OAT
020 7490 9900
info@scalapublishers.com
www.scalapublishers.com
Art

**Scottish Cultural Press/
Scottish Children's Press**
Unit 6, Newbattle Abbey
Business Park, Newbattle Road,
Dalkeith EH22 3LJ
0131 660 6366
info@scottishbooks.com
www.scottishbooks.com
*Scottish-interest books for adult,
tourist and academic readers*

Search Press
Wellwood, North Farm Road,
Tunbridge Wells, Kent TN2 3DR
01892 510850
searchpress@searchpress.com
www.searchpress.com
Art and crafts

SEMERC
(see Granada Learning Group)

Seren
57 Nolton Street,
Bridgend CF31 3AE
01656 663018
general@seren-books.com
www.seren-books.com
Wales and Welsh authors

Serpent's Tail
3a Exmouth House, Pine Street,
London EC1R 0GH
020 7354 1949
info@serpentstail.com
www.serpentstail.com
*Contemporary and gay fiction and
non-fiction*

Severn House Publishers
9–15 High Street, Sutton,
Surrey SM1 1DF
020 8770 3930
info@severnhouse.com
www.severnhouse.com
*Hardback fiction for the library
market: romance, science fiction,
horror, fantasy and crime*

Shepheard-Walwyn (Publishers)
15 Alder Road, London SW14 8ER
020 8241 5927
books@shepheard-walwyn.co.uk
www.shepheard-walwyn.co.uk
*Ethical economics, perennial
philosophy, biography, gift books,
books of Scottish interest*

Shetland Times
Gremsta, Lerwick,
Shetland ZE1 0PX
01595 693622
adverts@shetland-times.co.uk
www.shetlandtoday.co.uk
Shetland interest

Shire Publications
Cromwell House, Church Street,
Princes Risborough,
Buckinghamshire HP27 9AA
01844 344301
shire@shirebooks.co.uk
www.shirebooks.co.uk
Original non-fiction paperbacks

Short Books
3a Exmouth House,
Pine Street, Exmouth Market,
London EC1R 0JH
020 7833 9429
emily@shortbooks.biz
www.shortbooks.co.uk
Non-fiction for adults and children

Sidgwick and Jackson
(see Macmillan Publishers)

Sigma Press
5 Alton Road, Wilmslow,
Cheshire SK9 5DY
01625 531035
info@sigmapress.co.uk
www.sigmapress.co.uk
Outdoor, heritage, myth, biography

Simon & Schuster UK
Africa House, 64–78 Kingsway,
London WC2B 6AH
020 7316 1900
enquiries@simonandschuster.co.uk
www.simonsays.co.uk
*General fiction and non-fiction.
Imprints: Simon & Schuster, Pocket,
Simon & Schuster Childrens Books,
Free Press, Scribner, Simon & Schuster
Audio, A CBS Company*

Soundings
(see Ulverscroft Group)

Souvenir Press
43 Great Russell Street,
London WC1B 3PD
020 7580 9307
souvenirpress@ukonline.co.uk
*Academic. Imprints include: Condor,
Human Horizons, Independent Voices,
Pictorial Presentations, Pop Universal,
The Story-Tellers*

Spon Press
(see T&F Informa)

Springer-Verlag London
Ashbourne House, The Guildway,
Old Portsmouth Road, Guildford,
Surrey GU3 1LP
01483 734433
jean.lovell-butt@springer.com
www.springer.com
*Computer science, medical,
engineering, astronomy, maths*

Stainer & Bell
PO Box 110, 23 Gruneisen Road,
London N3 1DZ
020 8343 3303
post@stainer.co.uk
www.stainer.co.uk
Music and hymns

Stanley Gibbons Publications
7 Parkside, Christchurch Road,
Ringwood, Hampshire BH24 3SH
01425 472363
rpurkis@stanleygibbons.co.uk
www.stanleygibbons.co.uk
*Philatelic reference catalogues and
handbooks*

TSO (The Stationery Office)
St Crispins, Duke Street, Norwich,
Norfolk NR3 1PD
01603 622211
customer.services@tso.co.uk
www.thestationeryoffice.com

Summersdale Publishers
46 West Street, Chichester,
West Sussex PO19 1RP
01243 771107
enquiries@summersdale.com
www.summersdale.com
*Travel, martial arts, self-help, cookery,
humour and gift books*

Summertown Publishing
Aristotle House, Aristotle Lane,
Oxford OX2 6TR
01865 454130
louis@summertown.co.uk
www.summertown.co.uk
English-language teaching

Sutton Publishing
The Mill, Brimscombe Port,
Phoenix, Stroud,
Gloucestershire GL5 2QG
01453 883300
sales@sutton-publishing.co.uk
www.suttonpublishing.co.uk
*Owned by Haynes Publishing.
Biography, countryside, history,
transport, military and aviation*

Sweet & Maxwell Group
100 Avenue Road,
London NW3 3PF
020 7393 7000
marketinginformation@
    sweetandmaxwell.co.uk
www.sweetandmaxwell.co.uk
*Part of the Thomson Corporation.
Legal and professional. Imprints:
W Green (Scotland); Round Hall*

T&F Informa
Mortimer House, 37–41 Mortimer
Street, London W1T 3JH
020 7017 5000
professional.enquiries@
    informa.com
www.informa.com
• **BIOS Scientific Publishers** – *Biology
  and medicine*
• **Brunner-Routledge** – *psychology
  and counselling*
• **Carfax** – *Social science and
  humanities*
• **CRC** – *Science and medical*
• **Curzon Press** – *Asian and Middle
  Eastern studies*
• **Europa Publications** – *International
  affairs, politics and economics*
• **Frank Cass** – *Military and strategic
  studies. Also Jewish interest
  imprints: Vallentine Mitchell, Jewish
  Chronicle Publications*
• **Garland Science** – *Biology*
• **Martin Dunitz** – *Medical*
• **Psychology Press** – *Psychology*
• **Routledge** – *Humanities & social
  sciences textbooks/ general non-fiction*
• **Routledge Curzon** – *Politics and
  Middle Eastern studies*
• **Routledge Falmer** – *Education*
• **Spon Press** – *Architecture and
  planning*
• **Taylor & Francis** – *Science and
  reference esp. ergonomics,
  geographical information systems,
  biotechnology and engineering*

Taschen UK
1 Heathcock Court, 5th Floor,
415 Strand, London WC2R 0NS
020 7845 8585
contact@taschen.com
www.taschen.com
*Architecture, art, atlases, collectors'
editions, film, lifestyle, photography
and pop culture*

Taylor & Francis
(see T&F Informa)

Telegram
26 Westbourne Grove,
London W2 5RH
020 7229 2911
editorial@telegrambooks.com
www.telegrambooks.com
*International literary fiction. Imprint:
Saqi fiction*

Templar Publishing
The Granary, North Street,
Dorking, Surrey RH4 1DN
01306 876361
alex.fieldus@templarco.co.uk
www.templarco.co.uk
Illustrated and novelty books for
children

Tempus Publishing
The Mill, Brimscombe Port,
Stroud, Gloucestershire GL5 2QG
01453 883300
info@tempus-publishing.com
www.spellmount.com
History and military history

Terence Dalton
Water Street, Lavenham,
Sudbury, Suffolk CO10 9RN
01787 249290
terence@lavenhamgroup.co.uk
www.terencedalton.com
Part of the Lavenham Group.
Non-fiction: aeronautical, aviation,
maritime and local interest

Thalamus Publishing
4 Attorney's Walk, Bull Ring,
Ludlow, Shropshire SY8 1AA
01584 874977
roger@thalamus-books.com
www.thalamus-books.com
Family reference

Thames & Hudson
181A High Holborn,
London WC1V 7QX
020 7845 5000
mail@thameshudson.co.uk
www.thamesandhudson.com
Cultural non-fiction

Third Millennium Publishing
2-5 Benjamin Street,
London EC1M 5QL
020 7336 0144
db@tmiltd.com
www.tmiltd.com

Thomas Cook Publishing
PO Box 227,
Unit 15/16 Coningsby Road,
Peterborough PE3 8SB
01733 416477
publishing-sales@
    thomascook.com
www.thomascookpublishing.com
Guide books and timetables

Thomson Learning
50-51 Bedford Row,
London WC1R 4LR
020 7067 2500
communications@
    thomsonlearning.com
www.thomsonlearning.co.uk
Part of the Thomson Corporation.
Educational. Imprints: Scientific
Press, Cherry Tree Books (children's),
Business Press, Arden Shakespeare,
Computer Press, Course Technology,
Premier Press, Texere, Wadsworth

Continuum International
Publishing Group
Tower Building, 11 York Road,
London SE1 7NX
020 7922 0880
info@continuumbooks.com
www.continuumbooks.com
Academic and religious. Imprints:
Athlone, Pinter, Sheffield Academic
Press, Geoffrey Chapman, Mowbray,
TandT Clark, Burns and Oates,
Morehouse, Claridge Press

Evans Publishing Group
2A Portman Mansions,
Chiltern Street, London W1U 6NR
020 7487 0920
sales@evansbrothers.co.uk
www.evansbooks.co.uk
Children's and educational. Imprints:
Cherrytree Books, Evans Brothers,
Zero to Ten

IB Tauris
6 Salem Road, London W2 4BU
020 7243 1225
enquiries@ibtauris.com
www.ibtauris.com
Culture, history and politics. Imprint:
New Press

Oneworld
185 Banbury Road, Oxford OX2 7AR
01865 310597
info@oneworld-publications.com
www.oneworld-publications.com
Religion, history, philosophy, popular
science and psychology

Pluto Press
345 Archway Road, Highgate,
London N6 5AA
020 8348 2724
pluto@plutobooks.com
www.plutobooks.com
Academic and political non-fiction

Thorsons
(see HarperCollins Publishers)

Time Out Group
Universal House,
251 Tottenham Court Road,
London W1T 7AB
020 7813 3000
www.timeout.com
Guide and travel books

Time Warner Books (UK)
Brettenham House, Lancaster
Place, London WC2E 7EN
020 7911 8000
email.uk@littlebrown.co.uk
www.littlebrownbookgroup.co.uk
Imprints: Little, Brown (non-fiction);
Abacus (fiction, travel); Time Warner
(paperback fiction); Virago Press
(women authors only: fiction, non-
fiction and poetry); Atom (teen sci-fi);
Orbit Press (sci-fi and fantasy)

Titan Publishing
144 Southwark Street,
London SE1 0UP
020 7620 0200
editorial@titanmail.com
www.forbiddenplanet.com
Comic books, graphic novels, spin-offs

Tolkien
(see HarperCollins Publishers)

Top That Publishing
Marine House, Tide Mill Way,
Woodbridge, Suffolk IP12 1AP
01394 386651
info@topthatpublishing.com
www.topthatpublishing.com
Children's imprints: Top that!, Kids and
Tide Mill Press: Adult imprint: Kudos

Transworld Publishers
(see Random House Group)

Travel Publishing
7A Apollo House, Calleva Park,
Aldermaston, Berkshire RG7 8TN
0118 981 7777
info@travelpublishing.co.uk
www.travelpublishing.co.uk
Imprints: Hidden Places, Hidden Inns,
Golfers Guides, Country Living Rural
Guides, Off the Motorway

Trentham Books
Westview House,
734 London Road, Stoke-on-Trent,
Staffordshire ST4 5NP
01782 745567
tb@trentham-books.co.uk
www.trentham-books.co.uk
Education, culture and law for
professional readers

Trident Press
Empire House, 175 Piccadilly,
London W1J 9TB
020 7491 8770
admin@tridentpress.com
www.tridentpress.com
TV tie-ins, history, travel, geography,
culture

Trotman & Co
2 The Green, Richmond,
Surrey TW9 1PL
020 8486 1200
mail@trotman.co.uk
www.trotman.co.uk
Careers and education

Tucann Books
19 High Street, Heighington,
Lincoln LN4 1RG
01522 790009
sales@tucann.co.uk
www.tucann.co.uk
Self-publishing

Ulverscroft Group
The Green, Bradgate Road,
Anstey, Leicester LE7 7FU
0116 236 4325
sales@ulverscroft.co.uk
www.ulverscroft.com

FA Thorpe Publishing
Fiction and non-fiction large print
books. Imprints and divisions include:
Linford Romance, Linford Mystery,
Linford Western, Charnwood and
Ulverscroft

Isis Publishing
7 Centremead, Osney Mead,
Oxford OX2 0ES
01865 250333
sales@isis-publishing.co.uk
www.isis-publishing.co.uk
Large-print books and audio books

Magna Large Print Books
Magna House,
Long Preston, Nr. Skipton,
North Yorkshire BD23 4ND
01729 840225
Large-print books; audio fiction and non-fiction

Soundings
Isis House, Kings Drive, Whitley Bay, Tyne and Wear NE26 2JT
0191 253 4155
mail@gillian2004.plus.com
Audio books

Ulverscroft Large Print Books
The Green, Bradgate Road,
Anstey, Leics LE7 7SU
0116 236 4325
Large-print books and audio books

University of Hertfordshire Press
Hatfield Campus, Learning
Resource Centre, College Lane,
Hatfield, Hertfordshire AL10 9AB
01707 284000
c.l.cox@herts.ac.uk
www.herts.ac.uk
Literary criticism and theatre studies, Romani studies, regional and local history, parapsychology. Imprints: Hertfordshire Publications

University of Wales Press
10 Columbus Walk, Brigantine
Place, Cardiff CF10 4UP
029 2049 6899
press@press.wales.ac.uk
www.uwp.co.uk
Imprints: GPC Books, Gwasg Prifysgol Cymru

University Presses of California, Columbia & Princeton
1 Oldlands Way, Bognor Regis,
West Sussex PO22 9SA
01243 843291
lois@upccp.demon.co.uk
www.ucpress.edu
www.columbia.edu/cu/cup
www.pup.princeton.edu

Unofficial Guides
(see John Wiley & Sons)

Usborne Publishing
83–85 Saffron Hill,
London EC1N 8RT
020 7430 2800
mail@usborne.co.uk
www.usborne.com
Non-fiction books for children, including computer guides, puzzle-books, pre-school and books on music

Vallentine Mitchell/ Jewish Chronicle Publications
(see Frank Cass, T&F Informa)

Vermilion
(see Random House Group)

Viking
(see Penguin Books)

Vintage
(see Random House Group)

Virago Press
(see Little Brown)

Virgin Books
Units 5 & 6, Thames Wharf Studios,
Rainville Road, London W6 9HA
020 7386 3300
info@virgin-books.co.uk
www.virginbooks.com
TV, film, music, sport and pop culture. Imprints: Black Lace and Nexus (erotic fiction)

Visual
(see John Wiley & Sons)

Voyager
(see HarperCollins Publishers)

W Foulsham & Co
The Publishing House,
Bennetts Close, Slough,
Berkshire SL1 5AP
01753 526769
info@foulsham.com
www.foulsham.com
Lifestyle

Walker Books
87 Vauxhall Walk, London SE11 5HJ
020 7793 0909
enquiry@walker.co.uk
www.walkerbooks.co.uk
Children's big books, book charts, game books. Series: Giggle Club

Wallflower Press
6 Market Place, London W1W 8AF
020 7436 9494
info@wallflowerpress.co.uk
www.wallflowerpress.co.uk
Film, media and cultural studies

Warne
(see Penguin Books)

Watts Publishing Group
338, Euston Road, London NW1 3BH
020 7873 6000
www.hodderheadline.co.uk
Children's non-fiction, reference, fiction, picture and novelty. Imprints: Franklin Watts, Orchard Books, Cats Whiskers, Aladdin/Watts

Weidenfeld & Nicolson
(see Orion Publishing Group)

Wharncliffe Publishing
(see Pen & Sword Books)

Which?
2 Marylebone Road,
London NW1 4DF
020 7770 7000
which@which.co.uk
www.which.co.uk
Publishing arm of the Consumers' Association

Whittet Books
Hill Farm, Stonham Road, Cotton,
Stowmarket, Suffolk IP14 4RQ
01449 781877
annabel@whittet.dircon.co.uk
www.whittetbooks.com
Natural history, pets and rural interest, livestock and horticulture

Wild Goose Publications
Iona Community,
4th Floor, The Savoy House,
140 Sauchiehall Street,
Glasgow G2 3DH
0141 332 6292
admin@ionabooks.com
www.iona.books.com
Publishing house of the Iona Community. Religion, spiritualism and human rights

Wiley
(see John Wiley & Sons)

Wiley Blackwell Publishing
9600 Garsington Road,
Oxford OX4 2DQ
01865 776868
www.blackwellpublishing.com
Journals and textbooks

William Heinemann
(see Random House Group)

Wimbledon Publishing Company
75–76 Blackfriars Road,
London SE1 8HA
020 7401 4200
info@wpcpress.com
www.anthempress.com
Textbooks for languages, maths, biology and accountancy. Imprint: Anthem Press

Windhorse Publications
11 Park Road, Moseley,
Birmingham B13 8AB
0121 449 9191
info@windhorsepublications.com
www.windhorsepublications.com
Meditation and Buddhism

WIT Press
Ashurst Lodge, Ashurst,
Southampton,
Hampshire SO40 7AA
023 8029 3223
marketing@witpress.com
www.witpress.com
Scientific and technical

Wolters Kluwer (UK)
145 London Road,
Kingston-on-Thames,
Surrey KT2 6SR
020 8247 1694
sales@kluwerlaw.com
www.kluwerlaw.com
Part of Aspen Publishers, a Wolters Kluwer company

Women's Press
27 Goodge Street, London W1T 2LD
020 7636 3992
sales@the-womens-press.com
www.the-womens-press.com
Part of the Namara Group

Woodhead Publishing
Abington Hall, Abington,
Cambridge CB1 6AH
01223 891358
wp@woodhead-publishing.com
www.woodheadpublishing.com
Formerly Abington Publishing. Engineering, textiles, finance and investment, food technology and environmental science

Wordsworth Editions
8b East Street, Ware,
Hertfordshire SG12 9HJ
01920 465167
enquiries@
wordsworth-editions.com
www.wordsworth-editions.com
*Literary classics, reference, poetry,
children's classics, mystery and the
supernatural*

Working White
Chancery Court,
Lincolns Inn, Lincoln Road,
High Wycombe HP12 3RE
01494 429318
info@workingwhite.co.uk
www.workingwhite.co.uk
*Children's big books, book charts,
game books. Series: Giggle Club*

Wrox
(see John Wiley & Sons)

WW Norton & Company
Castle House, 75–76 Wells Street,
London W1T 3QT
020 7323 1579
office@wwnorton.co.uk
Academic and professional non-fiction

X Press
PO Box 25694, London N17 6FP
020 8801 2100
vibes@xpress.co.uk
www.xpress.co.uk
Black interest. Imprints: Nia, 20/20

Y Lolfa Cyf
Talybont, Ceredigion SY24 5AP
01970 832304
ylolfa@ylolfa.com
www.ylolfa.com
*Welsh and Celtic interest. Imprints and
divisions include: Dinas*

Yale University Press (London)
47 Bedford Square,
London WC1B 3DP
020 7079 4900
sales@yaleup.co.uk
www.yalebooks.co.uk

Yellow Jersey Press
(see Random House Group)

York Notes
(see Pearson Education)

Young Picador
(see Macmillan Publishers)

Zambezi Publishing
PO Box 221, Plymouth,
Devon PL2 2YJ
01752 367300
info@zampub.com
www.zampub.com
New-age and self-help

Zed Books
7 Cynthia Street, London N1 9JF
020 7837 4014
www.zedbooks.co.uk
*International and third-world affairs
and development studies*

Literary agents

Abner Stein*
10 Roland Gardens,
London SW7 3PH
020 7373 0456
abner@abnerstein.co.uk
*US agents and authors, some full-
length fiction and general non-fiction*

The Agency (London)*
24 Pottery Lane, Holland Park,
London W11 4LZ
020 7727 1346
info@theagency.co.uk
www.theagency.co.uk
*Theatre, film, TV, radio and children's
writers and illustrators; also film and
TV rights in novels and non-fiction*

Aitken Alexander Associates*
18–21 Cavaye Place,
London SW10 9PT
020 7373 8672
reception@aitkenalexander.co.uk
Fiction and non-fiction

Alan Brodie Representation
6th Floor, Fairgate House,
78 New Oxford Street,
London WC1A 1HB
020 7079 7990
info@alanbrodie.com
www.alanbrodie.com
Theatre, film, TV and radio scripts

Alexandra Nye
Craigower, 6 Kinnoull Avenue,
Dunblane, Perthshire FK15 9JG
01786 825114
*Fiction and topical non-fiction, esp
literary fiction and history*

AM Heath & Co*
6 Warwick Court, London WC1R 5DJ
020 7242 2811
www.amheath.com
*Fiction, general non-fiction and
children's*

Andrew Lownie Literary Agency*
36 Great Smith Street,
London SW1P 3BU
020 7222 7574
mail@andrewlownie.co.uk
www.andrewlownie.co.uk
Non-fiction

Andrew Mann*
1 Old Compton Street,
London W1D 5JA
020 7734 4751
info@manscript.co.uk
*Fiction; general non-fiction; film, TV,
theatre and radio scripts*

Andrew Nurnberg Associates*
Clerkenwell House,
45–47 Clerkenwell Green,
London EC1R 0QX
020 7417 8800
all@nurnberg.co.uk
Foreign rights

Annette Green Authors' Agency*
1 East Cliff Road, Tunbridge Wells,
Kent TN4 9AD
01892 514275
annettekgreen@aol.com
www.annettegreenagency.co.uk
*Literary and general fiction, non-
fiction, fiction for teenagers, upmarket
popular culture*

Artellus
30 Dorset House, Gloucester
Place, London NW1 5AD
020 7935 6972
artellus@artellusltd.co.uk
General fiction and non-fiction

AP Watt*
20 John Street, London WC1N 2DR
020 7405 6774
apw@apwatt.co.uk
www.apwatt.co.uk
*Full-length typescripts, including
children's books, screenplays for film
and TV*

Barbara Levy Literary Agency*
64 Greenhill,
Hampstead High Street,
London NW3 5TZ
020 7435 9046
*General fiction, non-fiction, TV
presenters, film and TV rights*

**Bill McLean Personal
Management**
23B Deodar Road,
London SW15 2NP
020 8789 8191
Scripts for all media

Blake Friedmann*
122 Arlington Road,
London NW1 7HP
020 7284 0408
carole@blakefriedmann.co.uk
isobel@blakefriedmann.co.uk

BookBlast
PO Box 20184, London W10 5AU
020 8968 3089
gen@bookblast.com
www.bookblast.com
Selective fiction and non-fiction

Brie Burkeman*
14 Neville Court, Abbey Road,
London NW8 9DD
0709 223 9113
brie.burkeman@mail.com
*Commercial and literary fiction and
non-fiction, scripts. Independent film
and television consultant to literary
agents*

Bell Lomax Agency
James House, 1 Babmaes Street,
London SW1Y 6HF
020 7930 4447
agency@bell-lomax.co.uk
*Fiction and non-fiction, biography,
children's, business and sport*

Campbell Thomson & McLaughlin*
11-12 Dover Street, London W1S 4LJ
020 7399 2808
Fiction and general non-fiction

Capel & Land*
29 Wardour Street,
London W1D 6PS
020 7734 2414
abi@capelland.co.uk
www.capelland.com
*Fiction and non-fiction; film, TV, radio
presenters*

Caroline Davidson Literary Agency
5 Queen Anne's Gardens,
London W4 1TU
020 8995 5768
*High quality fiction of originality and
non-fiction*

Caroline Sheldon Literary Agency*
Thorley Manor Farm, Thorley,
Yarmouth PO41 0SJ
01983 760205
Fiction, commercial and literary novels, especially women's and children's fiction

Casarotto Ramsay and Associates
Waverley House, 7–12 Noel Street,
London W1F 8GQ
020 7287 4450
agents@casarotto.co.uk
www.casarotto.co.uk
Scripts for TV, theatre, film and radio

Cecily Ware Literary Agents
19C John Spencer Square,
London N1 2LZ
020 7359 3787
info@cecilyware.com
Scripts for TV and film in all areas

Chapman & Vincent*
The Mount, Sun Hill, Royston,
Herts SG8 9AT
01763 245005
info@chapmanvincent.co.uk
Non-fiction

Christine Green Authors' Agent*
6 Whitehorse Mews,
Westminster Bridge Road,
London SE1 7QD
020 7401 8844
info@christinegreen.co.uk
www.christinegreen.co.uk
Literary and general fiction and non-fiction

The Christopher Little Literary Agency*
10 Eel Brook Studios, 125 Moore Park Road, London SW6 4PS
020 7736 4455
info@christopherlittle.net
www.christopherlittle.net
Commercial and literary full-length fiction and non-fiction; film scripts for established clients

Conville & Walsh*
2 Ganton Street, Soho,
London W1F 7QL
020 7287 3030
sue@convilleandwalsh.com
Literary and commercial fiction; serious and narrative non-fiction; childrens books

Crawford and Pearlstine Associates
31 Ashley Gardens,
Ambrosden Avenue,
London SW1P 1QE
020 7828 4212
agents@capaltd.co.uk
General non-fiction and fiction, history, current affairs, biography, health and politics

Curtis Brown Group*
5th Floor, Haymarket House,
28/29 Haymarket,
London SW1Y 4SP
020 7393 4400
cb@curtisbrown.co.uk
www.curtisbrown.co.uk
Writers, directors, designers, presenters and actors

Darley Anderson Literary, TV & Film Agency*
Estelle House, 11 Eustace Road,
London SW6 1JB
020 7385 6652
enquiries@darleyanderson.com
www.darleyanderson.com
Fiction: young male, American, Irish, women's, crime/mystery and humour; non-fiction; children's fiction; selected scripts for film and TV

David Godwin Associates
55 Monmouth Street,
London WC2H 9DG
020 7240 9992
assistant@
   davidgodwinassociates.co.uk
Literary and general fiction, non-fiction, biography

David Grossman Literary Agency
118b Holland Park Avenue,
London W11 4UA
020 7221 2770
Full-length fiction and general non-fiction, esp controversial

David Higham Associates*
5–8 Lower John Street,
Golden Square, London W1F 9HA
020 7434 5900
dha@davidhigham.co.uk
www.davidhigham.co.uk
Fiction; general non-fiction: biography, history, current affairs; children's; scripts

David O'Leary Literary Agents
10 Lansdowne Court,
Lansdowne Rise, London W11 2NR
020 7229 1623
d.oleary@virgin.net
Fiction (popular and literary) and non-fiction, esp thrillers, history, popular science, Russia and Ireland (history and fiction)

Deborah Owen*
78 Narrow Street, Limehouse,
London E14 8BP
020 7987 51191
do@deborahowen.co.uk

Dench Arnold Agency
10 Newburgh Street,
London W1F 7RN
020 7437 4551
www.dencharnold.com
Scripts for TV and film

Dorian Literary Agency*
Upper Thornehill, 27 Church Road,
St Marychurch, Torquay,
Devon TQ1 4QY
01803 312095
General fiction especially popular

Dorie Simmonds Agency*
River Bank House, 1 Putney Bridge Approach, London SW6 3JD
020 7736 0002
dhsimmonds@aol.com
General fiction, including commercial women's fiction, historical fiction, thrillers; commercial non-fiction, including historical and contemporary biographies, self-help, cookery; children's books and associated rights throughout the world

Duncan McAra
28 Beresford Gardens,
Edinburgh EH5 3ES
0131 552 1558
duncanmcara@hotmail.com
Literary fiction and non-fiction

Ed Victor*
6 Bayley Street, Bedford Square,
London WC1B 3HE
020 7304 4100
Mostly commercial fiction and non-fiction; children's

Edwards Fuglewicz*
49 Great Ormond Street,
London WC1N 3HZ
020 7405 6725
ros@efla.co.uk
Fiction: literary, some commercial; non-fiction: biography, history, popular culture

Elaine Steel
110 Gloucester Avenue,
London NW1 8HX
020 8348 0918
ecmsteel@aol.com
Writers and directors in film, television and publishing

Elizabeth Puttick Literary Agency*
46 Brookfield Mansions,
Highgate West Hill, London N6 6AT
020 8340 6383
enquiries@puttick.com
www.puttick.com
General non-fiction, esp self-help, mind, body and spirit, health and fitness, lifestyle and business

Elspeth Cochrane Personal Management
16 Trinity Close, The Pavement,
London SW4 0JD
020 7622 3566
elspeth@elspethcochrane.co.uk
Fiction, non-fiction, biographies, screenplays, scripts for all media

Eric Glass
25 Ladbroke Crescent,
London W11 1PS
020 7229 9500
eglassltd@aol.com
Fiction, non-fiction and scripts

Eunice McMullen Children's Literary Agent
Low Ibbotsholme Cottage,
Off Bridge Lane, Troutbeck Bridge,
Windermere, Cumbria LA23 1HU
01539 448551
eunicemcmullen@totalise.co.uk
Children's material

Faith Evans Associates*
27 Park Avenue North,
London N8 7RU
020 8340 9920
Fiction and non-fiction

Felicity Bryan*
2A North Parade, Banbury Road,
Oxford OX2 6LX
01865 513816
agency@felicitybryan.com
Fiction and non-fiction

Felix de Wolfe
Kingsway House, 103 Kingsway,
London WC2B 6QX
020 7242 5066
info@felixdewolfe.com
Theatrical agency

Fox & Howard Literary Agency*
4 Bramerton Street,
London SW3 5JX
020 7352 8691
*Non-fiction: biography, history and
popular culture, reference, business
and lifestyle*

Frances Kelly Agency*
111 Clifton Road, Kingston Upon
Thames, Surrey KT2 6PL
020 8549 7830
Illustrated and academic non-fiction

Futerman, Rose & Associates*
17 Dean Hill Road,
London SW14 7DQ
020 8255 7755
guy@futermanrose.co.uk
www.futermanrose.co.uk
*Commercial fiction, non-fiction,
biography, film and television scripts
specialising in book-to-film projects*

Greene & Heaton*
37 Goldhawk Road,
London W12 8QQ
020 8749 0315
info@greeneheaton.co.uk
www.greeneheaton.co.uk
*Wide range of fiction and general
non-fiction (clients include Bill Bryson,
Hugh Fearnley-Whittingstall, Michael
Frayn, PD James and Sarah Waters)*

Gregory & Co*
3 Barb Mews, London W6 7PA
020 7610 4676
info@gregoryandcompany.co.uk
www.gregoryandcompany.co.uk
*Fiction: literary, commercial, crime,
suspense and thrillers; general non-
fiction*

ICM*
Oxford House, 76 Oxford Street,
London W1D 1BS
020 7636 6565
caronhurley@icmlondon.co.uk
Film, TV and theatre scripts

IMG Literary UK
McCormick House,
Burlington Lane, Chiswick,
London W4 2TH
020 8233 5000
www.imgworld.com
*Celebrity books, commercial fiction,
non-fiction, sports-related and
how-to business books*

Intercontinental Literary Agency*
Centric House, 390–391 Strand,
London WCTR OLT
020 7379 6611
ila@ila-agency.co.uk
Translation rights only

Jane Conway-Gordon*
1 Old Compton Street,
London W1D 5JA
020 7494 0148
Fiction and general non-fiction

Jane Judd Literary Agency*
18 Belitha Villas, London N1 1PD
020 7607 0273
*General fiction and non-fiction:
biography, investigative journalism,
health, women's interests and travel*

Janklow & Nesbit (UK)*
33 Drayson Mews, London W8 4LY
020 7376 2733
queries@janklow.co.uk
*Fiction and non-fiction, commercial
and literary; US and translation rights
handled by Janklow and Nesbit
Associates in New York*

Jeffrey Simmons
15 Penn House, Mallory Street,
London NW8 8SX
020 7224 8917
jasimmons@btconnect.com
*Biography, cinema and theatre, quality
and commercial fiction, history, law
and crime, politics and world affairs,
parapsychology and sport*

Jill Foster
9 Barb Mews, Brook Green,
London W6 7PA
020 7602 1263
Scripts for TV, film and radio

JM Thurley Management
Archery House, 33 Archery
Square, Walmer, Deal CT14 7JA
01304 371721
jmthurley@aol.com
*Full-length fiction, non-fiction, TV and
films*

Johnson & Alcock*
Clerkenwell House,
45/47 Clerkenwell Green,
London EC1R OHT
020 7251 0125
info@johnsonandalcock.co.uk
General fiction and non-fiction

**John Welch, Literary Consultant
& Agent**
Mill Cottage, Calf Lane,
Chipping Camden,
Gloucestershire GL55 6JQ
01386 840237
johnwelch@cyphus.co.uk
*Military, naval and aviation history,
general history, and a little biography*

Jonathan Clowes*
10 Iron Bridge House,
Bridge Approach, London NW1 8BD
020 7722 7674
jonathanclowes@aol.com
*Fiction and non-fiction; scripts,
especially situation comedy, film and
television rights (clients include Doris
Lessing, David Nobbs, Len Deighton)*

Josef Weinberger Plays
12-14 Mortimer Street,
London W1T 3JJ
020 7580 2827
general.info@jwmail.co.uk
www.josef-weinberger.com
*Scripts for the theatre; play publisher
and licensor of stage rights; publishes
plays and acts as UK agent for US agents
including the Dramatists Play Service*

Judith Chilcote Agency*
8 Wentworth Mansions,
Keats Grove, London NW3 2RL
020 7794 3717
judybks@aol.com
*Commercial fiction, TV tie-ins,
biography and lifestyle*

Judith Murdoch Literary Agency*
19 Chalcot Square, London NW1 8YA
020 7722 4197
Full-length fiction only

Judy Daish Associates
2 St Charles Place, London W10 6EG
020 8964 8811
judy@judydaish.com
Scripts for TV, theatre, film and radio

Juri Gabriel
35 Camberwell Grove,
London SE5 8JA
020 7703 6186
Quality fiction and non-fiction

Juvenilia
Avington, near Winchester,
Hampshire SO21 1DB
01962 779656
juvenilia@clara.co.uk
*Baby to teen fiction and picture books;
non-fiction and scripts for TV and radio*

Knight Features
20 Crescent Grove,
London SW4 7AH
020 7622 1467
peter@knightfeatures.co.uk
*Motorsports, cartoon books, puzzles,
business, history, factual and
biographical material*

Laurence Fitch
Mezzanine, Quadrant House,
80-82 Regent Street,
London W1B 5AU
020 7734 9911
information@laurencefitch.com
www.laurencefitch.com
*Children's and horror books, scripts
for theatre, film, TV and radio*

Lavinia Trevor Agency*
29 Addison Place, London W11 4RJ
020 7603 5254
*General literary and commercial
fiction; non-fiction including popular
science*

LAW (Lucas Alexander Whitley)*
14 Vernon Street, London W14 ORJ
020 7471 7900
*Commercial and literary fiction, non-
fiction and children's books; film and
TV scripts for established clients*

Limelight Management*
33 Newman Street,
London W1T 1PY
020 7637 2529
limelight.management@
   virgin.net
www.limelightmanagement.com
General non-fiction

Lisa Eveleigh Literary Agency
c/o Pollinger Limited, 9 Staple
Inn, Holborn, London WC1V 7QH
020 7399 2803
lisaeveleigh@dial.pipex.com
*Literary and commercial fiction,
non-fiction and children's fiction*

* Member of the Association of Authors' Agents

Louise Greenberg Books*
The End House, Church Crescent,
London N3 1BG
020 8349 1179
louisegreenberg@msn.com
Literary fiction and non-fiction

Lutyens and Rubinstein*
231 Westbourne Park Road,
London W11 1EB
020 7792 4855
susannah@lutyensrubinstein.co.uk
Adult fiction and non-fiction

Maggie Noach Literary Agency*
Unit 4, 246 Acklam Road,
London W10
01522 789438
m-noach@dircon.co.uk
Fiction and general non-fiction

Manuscript ReSearch
PO Box 33, Bicester,
Oxfordshire OX26 4ZZ
01869 323447
www.manuscriptresearch.co.uk
Scripts for film and TV

Margaret Hanbury Literary Agency*
27 Walcot Square, London SE11 4UB
020 7735 7680
maggie@hanburyagency.com
*Quality fiction and non-fiction
(clients include JG Ballard, Simon
Callow, George Alagiah, Judith
Lennox); children's books,
plays/scripts and poetry*

Marjacq Scripts
34 Devonshire Place,
London W1G 6JW
020 7935 9499
philip@marjacq.com
luke@marjacq.com
www.marjacq.com
*Fiction and non-fiction, screenplays,
radio plays and film and TV rights*

Mary Clemmey Literary Agency*
6 Dunollie Road, London NW5 2XP
020 7267 1290
*Fiction and non-fiction, high quality
for an international market*

MBA Literary Agents*
62 Grafton Way, London W1T 5DW
020 7387 2076
agent@mbalit.co.uk
*Fiction and non-fiction books, TV,
film, theatre and radio scripts*

Mic Cheetham Literary Agency
11-12 Dover Street, London W1S 4LJ
020 7495 2002
www.miccheetham.com
*General and literary fiction, fantasy
and science fiction, crime and some
specific non-fiction*

Micheline Steinberg Associates
Fourth Floor, 104 Great Portland
Street, London W1W 6PE
020 7631 1310
info@steinplays.com
Drama for stage, TV, radio and film

Michelle Kass Associates*
85 Charing Cross Road,
London WC2H 0AA
020 7439 1624
Literary fiction and film

Marsh Agency
11/12 Dover Street, London W1S 4LJ
020 7399 2800
enquiries@marsh-agency.co.uk
www.marsh-agency.co.uk
*International rights specialists selling
English and foreign-language writing*

Narrow Road Company
182 Brighton Road, Coulsdon,
Surrey CR5 2NF
020 8763 9895
richardireson@narrowroad.co.uk
Scripts for TV, theatre, film and radio

Paterson Marsh*
11/12 Dover Street, London W1S 4LJ
020 7399 2800
steph@patersonmarsh.co.uk
www.patersonmarsh.co.uk
*World rights, especially
psychoanalysis and psychotherapy*

Peake Associates*
14 Grafton Crescent,
London NW1 8SL
020 7482 0609
tony@tonypeake.com
www.tonypeake.com
Fiction and non-fiction

Peters Fraser & Dunlop Group (PFD)*
Drury House, 34-43 Russell
Street, London WC2B 5HA
020 7344 1000
postmaster@pfd.co.uk
www.pfd.co.uk
*Fiction and children's, plus scripts for
film, theatre, radio and TV*

Pollinger*
9 Staple Inn, Holborn,
London WC1V 7QH
020 7404 0342
info@pollingerltd.com
www.pollingerltd.com
*Formerly Laurence Pollinger and
Pearn, Pollinger & Higham. General
trade, non-fiction, children's fiction
and non-fiction*

PVA Management
Hallow Park, Worcester WR2 6PG
01905 640663
books@pva.co.uk
Non-fiction only

Real Creatives Worldwide
14 Dean Street, London W1D 3RS
020 7437 4188
business@realcreatives.com
www.realcreatives.com
*Represents writers and creative media
professionals*

Robert Smith Literary Agency*
12 Bridge Wharf, 156 Caledonian
Road, London N1 9UU
020 7278 2444
robertsmith.literaryagency@
    virgin.net
*Non-fiction; biography, health and
nutrition, lifestyle, showbusiness and
true crime*

Roger Hancock
4 Water Lane, London NW1 8NZ
020 7267 4418
info@rogerhancock.com
*Scripts for comedy, drama and light
entertainment*

Rogers, Coleridge & White*
20 Powis Mews, London W11 1JN
020 7221 3717
*Fiction, non-fiction and children's
books*

Rosemary Sandberg
6 Bayley Street, London WC1B 3HE
020 7304 4110
rosemary@sandberg.demon.co.uk
Children's picture books and novels

Rosica Colin
1 Clareville Grove Mews,
London SW7 5AH
020 7370 1080
*Full-length manuscripts plus theatre,
film, television and sound broadcasting*

Rupert Crew*
1A King's Mews, London WC1N 2JA
020 7242 8586
info@rupertcrew.co.uk
*Volume and subsidiary rights in fiction
and non-fiction properties*

Rupert Heath Literary Agency
177a Old Winton Road, Andover,
Hampshire SP10 2DR
020 7788 7807
rupert.heath@rupertheath.com
www.rupertheath.com
*Fiction, history, biography, science,
arts and popular culture*

Rod Hall Agency
6th Floor, Fairgate House,
78 New Oxford Street,
London WC1A 1HB
020 7079 7987
office@rodhallagency.com
www.rodhallagency.com
Drama for film, TV and theatre

Sayle Literary Agency*
1 Petersfield, Cambridge CB1 1BB
01223 303035
*Fiction, crime and general; general
non-fiction*

Sayle Screen
11 Jubilee Place, London SW3 3TD
020 7823 3883
info@saylescreen.com
www.saylescreen.com
*Writers and directors for film, TV,
theatre and radio*

Sharland Organisation
The Manor House,
Manor Street, Raunds,
Northamptonshire NN9 6JW
01933 626600
tsoshar@aol.com
*Scripts for film, TV, theatre and radio;
non-fiction; specialises in national and
international film, television and
theatre negotiations*

Sheil Land Associates*
52 Doughty Street,
London WC1N 2LS
020 7405 9351
info@sheilland.co.uk
*Full-length general, commercial
and literary fiction and non-fiction,
including theatre, film, radio and
TV scripts*

Sheila Ableman Literary Agency*
3rd Floor, Lyme House Studios,
38 Georgiana Street,
London NW1 0EB
020 7388 7222
sheila@sheilaableman.co.uk
*Non-fiction including history, science
and biography*

Shelley Power Literary Agency*
13 rue du Pre Saint Gervais,
75019 Paris, France
00 33 1 42 383649
shelley.power@wanadoo.fr
*Fiction, business, true crime, film and
entertainment, architecture, self-help
and popular psychology*

Sinclair-Stevenson
3 South Terrace, London SW7 2TB
020 7581 2550
*Biography, current affairs, travel,
history, fiction, the arts*

Susijn Agency
3rd Floor, 64 Great Titchfield
Street, London W1W 7QH
020 7580 6341
info@thesusijnagency.com
www.thesusijnagency.com
*Sells rights worldwide in English and
non-English language literature:
literary fiction and non-fiction*

Tanja Howarth Literary Agency*
19 New Row, London WC2N 4LA
020 7240 5553
tanja.howarth@btinternet.com
*Fiction and non-fiction from British
writers; represents German authors in
Britain on behalf of German publishers*

The Tennyson Agency
10 Cleveland Avenue,
Wimbledon Chase,
London SW20 9EW
020 8543 5939
agency@tenagy.co.uk
www.tenagy.co.uk
Theatre, film, radio and TV scripts

Teresa Chris Literary Agency*
43 Musard Road, London W6 8NR
020 7386 0633
TeresaChris@
  litagency.freeserve.co.uk
*Fiction: crime, general, women's,
commercial and literary and non-fiction*

Toby Eady Associates
3rd Floor, 9 Orme Court,
London W2 4RL
020 7792 0092
toby@tobyeady.demon.co.uk
www.tobyeadyassociates.co.uk
*Fiction, non-fiction, especially China,
Middle East, Africa and India*

Valerie Hoskins Associates
20 Charlotte Street,
London W1T 2NA
020 7637 4490
vha@vhassociates.co.uk
*Scripts for film, TV and radio, especially
feature films, animation and TV*

Vanessa Holt*
59 Crescent Road, Leigh-on-Sea,
Essex SS9 2PF
01702 473787
*General fiction especially crime,
commercial and literary; non-fiction;
non-illustrated children's*

Wade & Doherty Literary Agency
33 Cormorant Lodge, Thomas
More Street, London E1W 1AU
020 7488 4171
rw@rwla.com
www.rwla.com
*General fiction and non-fiction
including children's books*

Watson, Little Limited*
48-56 Bayham Place,
London NW1 0EU
020 7388 7529
office@watsonlittle.com
www.watsonlittle.co.uk
*Commercial and literary fiction and
non-fiction for adults and children*

The Wylie Agency (UK)
17 Bedford Square,
London WC1B 3JA
020 7908 5900
mail@wylieagency.co.uk
Fiction and non-fiction

William Morris Agency (UK)*
Centre Point, 103 New Oxford
Street, London WC1A 1DD
020 7534 6800
ldnmailroom@wma.com
www.wma.com
*Fiction; general non-fiction; TV and
film scripts*

William Neill-Hall
Old Oak Cottage, Ropewalk,
Mount Hawke, Truro,
Cornwall TR4 8DW
01209 891427
wneill-hall@msn.com
*General non-fiction (clients include
George Carey, Philip Yancey and
Eugene Peterson)*

Zebra Agency
Broadland House, 1 Broadland,
Shevington, Lancashire WN6 8DH
077193 75575
admin@zebraagency.co.uk
www.zebraagency.co.uk
*Non-fiction and general fiction; scripts
for TV, radio, film and theatre*

**Annual Bibliography of English
Language and Literature**
Modern Humanities Research
Association, Cambridge University
01223 333058
abell@bibl.org
www.mhra.org.uk/Publication
  /Journals/abell.html
*Annual. Editor: Gerard Lowe;
academic editor: Jennifer Fellows*

Books
Publishing News
0870 870 2345
mailbox@publishingnews.co.uk
www.publishingnews.co.uk
Weekly. Editor: Liz Thomson

Books in the Media
020 7420 6006
www.thebookseller.com
*Weekly. Editor: Neil Denny; news:
Joel Rickett*

The Bookseller
020 7420 6006
joel.rickett@bookseller.co.uk
www.thebookseller.com
*Weekly. Editor: Neil Denny; news:
Joel Rickett*

**Booksellers Association
Directory of Members**
The Booksellers Association
  of the UK and Ireland
020 7802 0802
mail@booksellers.org.uk
www.booksellers.org.uk
Annual. Editor: Meryl Halls

BookWorld Magazine
Christchurch Publishers
020 7351 4995
leonard.holdsworth@
  btopenworld.com
*Monthly. Editor: Leonard Holdsworth;
features: James Hughes*

**Digital Demand – The Journal
of Printing and Publishing
Technology**
PIRA International
01372 802080
publications@
  pira-international.com
www.piranet.com
12pa. Senior Editor: Sara Ver-Bruggen

London Review of Books
020 7209 1101
edit@lrb.co.uk
www.lrb.co.uk
Fortnightly. Editor: Mary-Kay Wilmers

Publishing News
Publishing News
0870 870 2345
mailbox@publishingnews.co.uk
www.publishingnews.co.uk
Weekly. Editor: Liz Thomson

Writers Forum
Writers International
01202 589828
editorial@writers-forum.com
www.writers-forum.com
*Monthly. Editor: John Jenkins;
assistant editor: Laura Fennimore*

* Member of the Association of Authors' Agents

Writers News/Writing Magazine
Warner Group Publications
0113 200 2929
hilary.gray@writersnews.co.uk
www.writersnews.co.uk
Monthly. Editor: Hilary Bowman

Associations

Academi (Yr Academi Gymreig)
Mount Stuart House, Mount
Stuart Square, Cardiff CF10 5FQ
029 2047 2266
post@academi.org
www.academi.org
*Welsh national literature promotion
agency*

Alliance of Literary Societies
22 Belmont Grove, Havant,
Hampshire PO9 3PU
023 9247 5855
rosemary.culley@ntlworld.com
www.alllitsoc.org.uk

Association for Scottish Literary Studies
c/o Department of Scottish
Literature, 7 University Gardens,
University of Glasgow,
Glasgow G12 8QH
0141 330 5309
office@asls.org.uk
www.asls.org.uk
*Charity promoting language and
literature of Scotland*

Association of Christian Writers
All Saints Vicarage,
43 All Saints Close, Edmonton,
London N9 9AT
020 8884 4348
admin@christianwriters.org.uk
www.christianwriters.org.uk
Support, training and encouragement

Association of Freelance Writers
The Writers Bureau,
Sevendale House, 7 Dale Street,
Manchester M1 1JB
0161 228 2362
studentservices@
    writersbureau.com
www.writersbureau.com
Correspondence college

Association of Illustrators
150 Curtain Road,
London EC2A 3AT
020 7613 4328
info@theaoi.com
www.theaoi.com
Trade association

Association of Learned and Professional Society Publishers
8 Rickford Road, Nailsea,
North Somerset BS48 4PY
01275 856444
ian.russell@alpsp.org
www.alpsp.org
*For not-for-profit academic and
professional publishers*

Audiobook Publishers' Association
c/o 18 Green Lanes, Hatfield,
Hertfordshire AL10 9JT
07971 280788
info@thepa.net
www.theapa.net
*The UK trade association of the
audiobook industry*

AuthorsOnline
19 The Cinques, Gamlingay, Sandy,
Bedfordshire SG19 3NU
0870 750 0544
theeditor@authorsonline.co.uk
www.authorsonline.co.uk
*Self-publishing and authors' services
worldwide*

Authors' Club
40 Dover Street, London W1S 4NP
020 7499 8581
mem@authorsclub.co.uk
www.authorsclub.co.uk
*Anyone involved with written words;
administers Best First Novel award
and Sir Banister Fletcher award*

Authors' Licensing & Collecting Society (ALCS)
The Writer's House, 13 Haydon
Street, London EC3N 1DB
020 7264 5700
alcs@alcs.co.uk
www.alcs.co.uk
*UK collecting society for writers and
successors*

Bibliographical Society
c/o The Institute of English
Studies, University of London,
Senate House, Malet Street,
London WC1E 7HU
020 7862 8679
admin@bibsoc.org.uk
www.bibsoc.org.uk
*Aims to encourage study of
bibliography and history of publishing*

Books 4 Publishing
Lasyard House, Underhill Street,
Bridgnorth, Shropshire WV16 4BB
0870 777 3339
editor@books4publishing.com
www.books4publishing.com
Online showcase for unpublished writers

Booksellers Association of the UK & Ireland
Minster House, 272 Vauxhall Bridge
Road, London SW1V 1BA
020 7802 0802
mail@booksellers.org.uk
www.booksellers.org.uk
*Trade association. Coordinates World
Book Day with Publishers' Association;
administers Costa Book Awards*

Booktrust
Book House, 45 East Hill,
London SW18 2QZ
020 8516 2977
info@booktrust.org.uk
www.booktrust.org.uk and
www.booktrusted.com
Educational charity

British Centre for Literary Translation
University of East Anglia,
Norwich, Norfolk NR4 7TJ
01603 592134/592785
bclt@uea.ac.uk
www.literarytranslation.com
Translation centre

British Copyright Council
Copyright House,
29-33 Berners Street,
London W1T 3AB
01986 788122
secretary@britishcopyright.org
www.britishcopyright.org
*Liaison committee for copyright
interest*

British Science Fiction Association
8a West Avenue Road,
London E17 9SE
bsfachair@gmail.com
www.bsfa.co.uk
*Also publishes Matrix, Vector and
Focus magazines*

British Society of Comedy Writers
61 Parry Road,
Ashmore Park, Wolverhampton,
West Midlands WW11 2PS
01902 722729
info@bscw.co.uk
www.bscw.co.uk
Society of comedy writers

Children's Books Ireland
First Floor, 17 North Great Georges
Street, Dublin 1, Ireland
00 353 1 872 7475
info@childrensbooksireland.com
www.childrensbooksireland.com
*Promotes children's literature and
publishes Inis magazine*

Clé, The Irish Book Publishers' Association
25 Denzille Lane, Dublin 2,
Republic of Ireland
00 353 1 639 4868
info@publishingireland.com
www.publishingireland.com
Provides expertise and resources

Combrogos
10 Heol Don, Whitchurch,
Cardiff CF14 2AU
029 2062 3359
*Arts and media research and editorial
services; books about Wales or by Welsh
authors; contact Dr Meic Stephens*

Crime Writers' Association (CWA)
info@thecwa.co.uk
www.thecwa.co.uk
Professional group of crime authors

Critics' Circle
c/o Catherine Cooper,
69 Marylebone Lane,
London W1U 2PH
020 7224 1410
www.criticscircle.org.uk
*Critics of drama, music, cinema &
dance, art and architecture*

Directory & Database Publishers Association
Queens House, 28 Kingsway,
London WC2B 6JR
020 7405 0836
christine@dpa.org.uk
www.dpa.org.uk
Trade association

Drama Association of Wales
The Old Library Building,
Singleton Road, Splott,
Cardiff CF24 2ET
029 2045 2200
aled.daw@virgin.net
www.amdram.co.uk/daw

English Association
University of Leicester,
University Road, Leicester LE1 7RH
0116 252 3982
engassoc@le.ac.uk
www.le.ac.uk/engassoc
Promotes knowledge, understanding and enjoyment of English language and literature

English PEN
6-8 Amwell Street,
London EC1R 1UQ
020 7713 0023
enquiries@englishpen.org
www.englishpen.org
Association of writers and literary professionals. Fights for right to freedom of expression

Federation of Worker Writers and Community Publishers (FWWCP)
Burslem School of Art, Queen
Street, Stoke on Trent ST6 3EJ
01782 822327
fwwcp@tiscali.co.uk
www.thefwwcp.org uk
For independent writing workshops and community publishers

Fellowship of Authors and Artists
PO Box 158, Hertford SG13 8FA
0870 747 2514
www.author-fellowship.co.uk
Promotes writing and art as therapy and self-healing

Garden Writers' Guild
c/o Institute of Horticulture,
14/15 Belgrave Square,
London SW1X 8PS
020 7245 6943
gwg@horticulture.org.uk
www.gardenwriters.co.uk
Promotes high-quality garden writing, photography and broadcasting

Gaelic Books Council (Comhairle nan Leabhraichean)
22 Mansfield Street,
Glasgow G11 5QP
0141 337 6211
brath@gaelicbooks.net
www.gaelicbooks.net

Horror Writers Association
244 5th Avenue, Suite 2767,
New York, NY 10001 USA
hwa@horror.org
www.horror.org
Worldwide organisation of writers and publishing professionals

Independent Publishers Guild
P O Box 93, Royston,
Hertfordshire SG8 5GH
01763 247014
info@ipg.uk.com
www.ipg.uk.com

Independent Theatre Council
12 The Leathermarket,
Weston Street, London SE1 3ER
020 7403 1727
admin@itc-arts.org
www.itc-arts.org
Offers legal advice and training opportunities

Institute of Linguists
Saxon House, 48 Southwark
Street, London SE1 1UN
020 7940 3100
info@iol.org.uk
www.iol.org.uk
Professional association; accredited exam board; commercial contracts for government

Institute of Translation and Interpreting (ITI)
Fortuna House,
South Fifth Street, Milton Keynes,
Buckinghamshire MK9 2EU
01908 325250
info@iti.org.uk
www.iti.org.uk

International Booksearch Service
07939 711039
sarah.fordham@btinternet.com
www.scfordham.com
Finds out-of-print books

Irish Writers Centre
19 Parnell Square, Dublin 1,
Republic of Ireland
00 353 1 872 1302
info@writerscentre.ie
www.writerscentre.ie
Promotes Irish writers, living in Ireland, organises readings and workshops
Also houses:
Irish Translators' and Interpreters' Association
translation@eircom.net
www.translatorsassociation.ie
Irish Writers' Union
iwu@ireland-writers.com
www.ireland-writers.com

ISBN Agency
3rd Floor, Midas House,
62 Goldsworth Road,
Woking GU21 6LQ
0870 777 8712
isbn@nielsenbookdata.co.uk
www.nielsenbookdata.co.uk
Book numbering agency

Manuscript ReSearch
PO Box 33, Bicester,
Oxfordshire OX26 4ZZ
01869 323447/322522
www.manuscriptresearch.co.uk
Services for self-publishing authors

Medical Writers' Group
The Society of Authors,
84 Drayton Gardens,
London SW10 9SB
020 7373 6642
info@societyofauthors.org
www.societyofauthors.org
Specialist group within Society of Authors

National Archives
Kew, Richmond, Surrey TW9 4DU
020 8876 3444
enquiry@nationalarchives.gov.uk
www.nationalarchives.gov.uk
National resource for documents relating to British history; brings together the Public Record Office and the Historical Manuscripts Commission

National Association for Literature Development
PO Box 49657, London N8 7YZ
020 7272 8386
director@nald.org
www.nald.org

National Association of Writers' Groups
The Arts Centre,
Biddick Lane, Washington,
Tyne & Wear NE38 2AB
01262 609228
nawg@tesco.net
www.nawg.co.uk
Connecting writers' groups around the country; yearly festivals and competitions

National Association of Writers in Education
PO Box 1, Sheriff Hutton,
York YO60 7YU
01653 618429
paul@nawe.co.uk
www.nawe.co.uk

New Writing North
Culture Lab,
Grand Assembly Rooms,
Newcastle University, King's Walk,
Newcastle upon Tyne NE1 7RU
0191 222 1332
mail@newwritingnorth.com
www.newwritingnorth.com
Literature development agency for north-east arts region

Nielsen BookData
3rd Floor, Midas House,
62 Goldsworth Road, Woking,
Surrey GU21 6LQ
0870 777 8710
info@nielsenbookdata.co.uk
www.nielsenbookdata.com
Bibliographic data

Nielsen BookScan
3rd Floor, Midas House,
62 Goldsworth Road, Woking,
Surrey GU21 6LQ
0870 777 8710
info@nielsenbookscan.co.uk
www.nielsenbookscan.co.uk
International sales data monitoring

Player-Playwrights
9 Hillfield Park, London N10 3QT
020 8883 0371
p-p@dial.pipex.com
www.playerplaywrights.co.uk
Gives opportunities to writers new to stage, radio and TV

Public Lending Right
Richard House, Sorbonne Close,
Stockton-on-Tees TS17 6DA
01642 604699
registrar@plr.uk.com
www.plr.uk.com
Distribute government funds to authors/libraries

Publishers Association
29B Montague Street,
London WC1B 5BH
020 7691 9191
mail@publishers.org.uk
www.publishers.org.uk
Trade association

Publishers Licensing Society
37–41 Gower Street,
London WC1E 6HH
020 7299 7730
pls@pls.org.uk
www.pls.org.uk
Licensing of photocopying materials in schools and universities

Publishers Publicity Circle
65 Airedale Avenue,
London W4 2NN
020 8994 1881
ppc-@lineone.net
www.publisherspublicitycircle.co.uk
Forum for book publicists and freelance PRs

Romantic Novelists' Association
jennyhaddon@dial.pipex.com
www.rna-uk.org

Royal Society of Literature
Somerset House, Strand,
London WC2R 1LA
020 7845 4676
info@rslit.org
www.rslit.org
Holds monthly lectures promoting literature and spoken word. Annual prizes

Science Fiction Foundation
28 St Johns Road,
Guildford GU2 7UH
sff.chair@gmail.com
www.sf-foundation.org
Writers, academics and critics with an active interest in science fiction

Scottish Book Trust
Sandeman House, Trunk's Close,
55 High Street, Edinburgh EH1 1SR
0131 524 0160
info@scottishbooktrust.com
www.scottishbooktrust.com
Arts organiser, promotes reading and writing in Scotland; holds a resource library

Scottish Print Employers Federation
48 Palmerston Place,
Edinburgh EH12 5DE
0131 220 4353
info@spef.org.uk
www.spef.org.uk
Advice, expertise, education and training

Publishing Scotland
Scottish Book Centre, 137 Dundee Street, Edinburgh EH11 1BG
0131 228 6866
enquiries@publishingscotland.org
www.publishingscotland.org
Networking and information services. Lobbying organisation for book publishing issues

Scottish Youth Theatre
Old Sheriff Court, 105 Brunswick Street, Glasgow G1 1TF
0141 552 3988
info@scottishyouththeatre.org
www.scottishyouththeatre.org
Giving young people in Scotland opportunity to explore and reach their creative potential through art

Society for Children's Book Writers & Illustrators
8271 Beverley Boulevard,
Los Angeles, CA 90048, USA
001 323 782 1010
scbwi@scbwi.org
www.scbwi.org

Society for Editors and Proofreaders (SfEP)
Riverbank House, 1 Putney Bridge Approach, London SW6 3JD
020 7736 3278
administration@sfep.org.uk
www.sfep.org.uk
Non-profit body promoting high editorial standards and recognition of the professional status of its members

Society of Authors
84 Drayton Gardens,
London SW10 9SB
020 7373 6642
info@societyofauthors.org
www.societyofauthors.org
Trade union for professional authors

Society of Civil and Public Service Writers
Adrian Danson, Editor,
78 Palace View, Bromley BR1 3EL
adriand@onetel.com
www.scpsw.co.uk

Society of Indexers
Woodbourn Business Centre,
10 Jessell Street, Sheffield S9 3HY
0114 244 9561
info@indexers.org.uk
www.indexers.org.uk

Society of Young Publishers
Endeavour House, 189 Shaftesbury Avenue, London WC2H 8TJ
info@thesyp.org.uk
www.thesyp.org.uk
Provides a forum, organises readings and meetings

Sports Writers' Association of Great Britain
244 Perry Street, Billericay,
Essex CM12 0QP
01277 657708
trevjanbond1@aol.com

Translators Association
84 Drayton Gardens,
London SW10 9SB
020 7373 6642
info@societyofauthors.org
www.societyofauthors.org

Welsh Books Council (Cyngor Llyfrau Cymru)
Castell Brychan, Aberystwyth,
Ceredigion SY23 2JB
01970 624151
castellbrychan@cllc.org.uk
www.cllc.org.uk and
www.gwales.com
For Welsh writers

West Country Writers' Association
1 Moreton Avenue, Crown Hill,
Plymouth PL6 5AZ
01752 785540
www.westcountrywriters.co.uk
Annual congress in May

Women in Publishing
info@wipub.org.uk
www.wipub.org.uk

Writernet
Cabin V, Clarendon Buildings,
25 Horsell Road, Highbury,
London N5 1XL
020 7609 7474
info@writernet.org.uk
www.writernet.org.uk
Information and guidance for playwrights and performance writers

Writers, Artists and their Copyright Holders (Watch)
David Sutton, Director of Research Projects, University of Reading Library, PO Box 223, Whiteknights, Reading RG6 6AE
0118 931 8783
D.C.Sutton@reading.ac.uk
www.watch-file.com
Database of copyright holders

Writers' Guild of Great Britain
15 Britannia Street,
London WC1X 9JN
020 7833 0777
admin@writersguild.org.uk
www.writersguild.org.uk
Trade union for professional writers

Business

Government departments

Treasury
020 7270 4558
www.hm-treasury.gov.uk
Press: 020 7270 5238

Trade and Industry
020 7215 5000
www.dti.gov.uk
Press: 020 7215 5961/5967/6405

Work and Pensions
020 7238 0800
www.dwp.gov.uk
Press: 020 3267 5144

Central banks

Bank of England
020 7601 4444
www.bankofengland.co.uk
Press: 020 7601 4411

European Central Bank
00 49 69 13440
www.ecb.int

Businesses

● Business associations

Trade Association Forum
020 7395 8283
www.taforum.org

Confederation of British Industry
020 7379 7400
www.cbi.org.uk
Press: 020 7395 8239

Ethnic Business Support Programme
029 2045 5334
www.ebsp.org

Federation of Small Businesses
01253 336000
www.fsb.org.uk
Press: 020 7592 8100

● FTSE 100 companies

3i Group
020 7928 3131
www.3i.com
Press: 020 7975 3573

Alliance & Leicester
0116 201 1000
www.alliance-leicester
-group.co.uk
Press: 0116 200 3355

Alliance Boots
0115 950 6111
www.allianceboots.com
Press: 020 7138 1164

Anglo American
020 7968 8888
www.angloamerican.co.uk
Press: 020 7698 8555

Antofagasta
020 7808 0988
www.antofagasta.co.uk

Associated British Foods
020 7399 6500
www.abf.co.uk

AstraZeneca
01582 836000
www.astrazeneca.co.uk

Aviva
020 7283 2000
www.aviva.com
Press: 020 7662 8221

BAE Systems
01252 373232
www.baesystems.com
Press: 01252 384605

Barclays
0800 282390
www.barclays.co.uk
Press: 020 7116 64755

Barratt Developments
0191 227 2000
www.barratthomes.co.uk

BG Group
0118 935 3222
www.bggroup.com
Press: 0118 929 3717

BHP Billiton
020 7802 4000
www.bhpbilliton.com
Press: 020 7802 4195

BP
020 7496 4000
www.bp.com
Press: 020 7496 4076

British Airways
0870 850 9850
www.britishairways.com
Press: 020 8738 5100

British American Tobacco
020 7845 1000
www.bat.com
Press: 020 7845 2888

British Land
020 7486 4466
www.britishland.com
Press: 020 7467 2961

BSkyB
0870 240 3000
www.sky.com
Press: 020 7705 3000

BT Group
020 7356 5000
www.btplc.com
Press - national: 020 7356 5369

Cable & Wireless
01908 845 000
www.cw.com
Press: 01344 818888

Cadbury Schweppes
020 7409 1313
www.cadburyschweppes.com
Press:020 7830 5011

Capita Group
020 7799 1525
www.capita.co.uk
Press: 0870 240 0488

Carnival
001 305 599 2600
www.carnivalcorp.com

Centrica
01753 494000
www.centrica.co.uk
Press: 01753 494085

Compass Group
01932 573000
www.compass-group.com
Press: 01932 573116

Daily Mail & General Trust
020 7938 6349
www.dmgt.co.uk

Diageo
020 7927 5200
www.diageo.com

Drax Group Plc
01757 618381
www.draxgroup.plc.uk

DSGI PLC
0870 850 3333
www.dsgiplc.com

Enterprise Inns
0121 733 7700
www.enterpriseinns.com

Experian Group Limited
www.experian.co.uk
00 353 1 846 9100
Press: 0115 934 4486

Friends Provident
0870 607 1352
www.friendsprovident.co.uk
City and corporate press:
0845 641 7833

Glaxo SmithKline
020 8047 5000
www.gsk.com
Press: 020 8047 5502

Hammerson
020 7887 1000
www.hammerson.com
Press: 020 7887 1881

Hanson
020 7245 1245
www.hansonplc.com
Press: 01454 316000

HBOS
0870 600 5000
www.hbosplc.com
Press - general:
pressoffice@HBOSplc.com
01422 333829
Bank of Scotland:
0131 243 7195,
Bank of Scotland corporate:
0845 606 6696
Bank of Scotland Press:
0845 606 6696
Halifax: 01422 333256

Home Retail
0845 603 6677
www.homeretailgroup.com
Press: 020 7251 3801
Argos:
0845 124 0044
Homebase:
0845 601 6911

HSBC
020 7991 8888
www.hsbc.com
Press: 020 7992 1573

ICAP
020 7000 5000
www.icap.com

ICI
020 7009 5000
www.ici.com
Press: 020 7009 5000

Imperial Tobacco
0117 963 6636
www.imperial-tobacco.com
Press: 0117 933 7241

Intercontinental Hotel Group
01753 410100
www.intercontinental.com

International Power
020 7320 8600
www.ipplc.com

Invesco
020 7065 4000
www.invesco.com

ITV
0844 881 8000
www.itv.com

Johnson Matthey
020 7269 8400
www.matthey.com
Press: 020 7269 8469

Kazakhmys
0845 080 2369
www.kazakhmys.com

Kelda Group
01274 600111
www.keldagroup.com

Kingfisher
020 7372 8008
www.kingfisher.co.uk
Press: 020 7644 1030

Land Securities Group
020 7413 9000
www.landsecurities.co.uk
Press: 020 7024 5421

Legal & General Group
020 7528 6200
www.legalandgeneral.com
Press: 01737 376024

Liberty International
020 7960 1200
www.liberty-international.co.uk
Press: 020 7887 7029

Lloyds TSB
020 7626 1500
www.lloydstsb.com
Press: 020 7356 2493

Lonmin
020 7201 6000
www.lonmin.com

Man Group
020 7144 1000
www.mangroupplc.com

Marks & Spencer
020 7935 4422
www.marksandspencer.com
Press: 020 8718 1919

Morrison Supermarkets
0845 611 5000
www.morrisons.co.uk
Press: 0845 611 6111

National Grid Transco
01926 653000
www.nationalgrid.com/uk

Next
0845 456 7777
www.next.co.uk
Press: 0845 456 7808

Northern Rock
0191 285 7191
www.northernrock.co.uk
Press: 0191 279 4676

Old Mutual
020 7002 7000
www.oldmutual.com
Press: 020 7002 7133

Pearson
020 7010 2000
www.pearson.com
Press - general: 020 7825 8076
corporate: 020 7010 2314/07
FT Group: 020 7873 3000
Pearson Education:
01279 623623
Penguin UK: 020 7010 3000

Persimmon
01904 642199
www.persimmon.plc.uk

Prudential
020 7334 9000
www.prudential.co.uk
Press - general: 020 7548 3719
M&G: 020 7624 4588
UK insurance: 020 7334 9000

Punch Taverns
01283 501600
www.punchtaverns.com

Reckitt Benckiser
01753 217800
www.reckitt.com

Reed Elsevier
020 7930 7077
www.reed-elsevier.com
Press - general: 020 7166 5646
Reed business information:
020 8652 3296
legal: 001 937 865 8838
science and medical:
020 7400 2500

Resolution
020 7489 4880
www.resolutionplc.com
020 7002 1080

Reuters Group
020 7250 1122
www.reuters.com

Rexam
020 7227 4100
www.rexam.com
Press: 020 7227 4141

Rio Tinto
020 7930 2399
www.riotinto.com
Press: 020 7753 2305

Rolls Royce
020 7222 9020
www.rolls-royce.com

Royal & Sun Alliance
01403 232323
www.royalsunalliance.com
Press - UK: 020 7337 5146
world: 020 7111 7047

Royal Bank of Scotland
020 7250 1122
www.rbs.co.uk
Press - general: 0131 523 4414
Corporate banking and
financial markets:
0131 523 4414
Churchill: 020 8313 3030
Coutts: 020 7957 2427
Direct Line: 0141 308 4100
Lombard: 020 7672 1921
NatWest: 020 7672 1932/31/27
One Account: 01603 707154
RBS: 020 7672 1928
RBS cards: 020 7672 1922/1817
RBS insurance: 0845 878 2367
Ulster Bank: 00 353 1 608 4280/
4344

Royal Dutch Shell
020 7934 1234
www.shell.com
Press: 020 7934 3505

SABMiller
020 7659 0100
www.sabmiller.com
Press: 01483 264115

Sage Group
0191 294 3000
www.sage.co.uk
Press: 0191 294 3036

Sainsbury (J)
020 7695 6000
www.j-sainsbury.co.uk
Press: 020 7695 7295

Schroders
020 7658 6000
www.schroders.com

Scottish & Newcastle
0131 528 1000
www.scottish-newcastle.com
Press: 0131 203 2137

Scottish & Southern Energy
0845 143 4005
www.scottish-southern.co.uk

Severn Trent
0121 722 4000
www.stwater.co.uk
Press - general: 0121 722 4273

**Slough Estates Shire
Pharmaceuticals**
01256 894 000
www.shiregroup.com
Press: 01256 894610

Smith & Nephew
020 7401 7646
www.smith-nephew.com
Press: 020 7831 3113

Smiths Group
020 8458 3232
www.smiths-group.com
Press: 020 8457 8403

Standard Chartered
020 7280 7500
www.standardchartered.com
Press: 020 7280 7708

Standard Life
0131 225 2552
www.ukgroup.standardlife.com
Press: 0131 245 5916

Tate & Lyle
020 7626 6525
www.tateandlyle.com

Tesco
01992 632222
www.tesco.com
Press: 01992 644645

Unilever
020 7822 5252
www.unilever.co.uk

United Utilities
01925 237000
www.unitedutilities.com
Press: 01925 537366

Vedanta Resources
020 7499 5900
www.vedantaresources.com

Vodafone
01635 33251
www.vodafone.co.uk
Press - group: 01635 674268

Whitbread
020 7806 5480
www.whitbread.co.uk
Premier Travel Inn:
  www.premiertravelinn.com
Costa Coffee
  www.costa.co.uk
David Lloyd Leisure
  www.davidlloydleisure.co.uk
Brewer's Fayre
  www.brewersfayre.co.uk
Beefeater
  www.beefeater.co.uk
T.G.I. Friday's
  www.tgifridays.co.uk
Press: 01582 424200

Wolseley
0118 929 8700
www.wolseley.com

WPP Group
020 7408 2204
www.wpp.com
Press: 020 7408 2204

Xstrata
020 7968 2800
www.xstrata.com
Press: 020 7968 2812

Yell Group
0118 959 2111
www.yellgroup.com
Press: 0118 950 6999

Watchdog

● Regulators and government agencies

Advertising Standards Authority
020 7492 2222
www.asa.org.uk
Press: 020 7492 2123

British and Irish Ombudsman Association
020 8894 9272
www.bioa.org.uk

British Board of Film Classification
020 7440 1570
www.bbfc.co.uk
Press: 020 7440 3285

British Standards Institution
020 8996 9000
www.bsi-global.com
Press: 020 8996 6330

Competition Commission
020 7271 0100
www.competition-commission
  .org.uk
Press: 020 7271 0242

Council of Mortgage Lenders
020 7437 0075
www.cml.org.uk

Financial Ombudsman Service
020 7964 1000
www.financial-ombudsman
  .org.uk

Financial Services Authority
020 7066 1000
www.fsa.gov.uk

Food Standards Agency
020 7276 8000
www.food.gov.uk

Health and Safety Executive
0845 345 0055
www.hse.gov.uk

Health and Safety Executive for Northern Ireland
0800 032 0121
028 9024 3249
www.hseni.gov.uk

Independent Committee for the Supervision of Telephone Information Services
020 7940 7474
www.icstis.org.uk
Press: 020 7940 7408

Information Commissioner
01625 545 700
www.ico.gov.uk
Press: 020 7025 7580

National Lottery Commission
020 7016 3400
www.natlotcomm.gov.uk
Press: 020 7016 3430

Ofcom
020 7981 3000
www.ofcom.org.uk
Press: 020 7981 3033

Office of Fair Trading
0845 722 4499
www.oft.gov.uk

Office of the Rail Regulator
020 7282 2000
www.rail-reg.gov.uk
Press: 020 7282 2007

Ofgem
020 7901 7000
www.ofgem.gov.uk
Press: 020 7901 7225

Ofwat
0121 625 1300/1373
www.ofwat.gov.uk
Press: 0121 625 1442

Ombudsman for Estate Agents
01722 333306
www.oea.co.uk

Pensions Ombudsman
020 7834 9144
www.pensions-ombudsman
  .org.uk

Serious Fraud Office
020 7239 7272
www.sfo.gov.uk

Trading Standards Institute
0870 872 9000
www.tsi.org.uk
Press: 0870 872 9030

● Consumer bodies

Which?
020 7770 7000
0845 307 4000
www.which.co.uk
Press: 020 7770 7062/7373

General Consumer Council for Northern Ireland
028 9067 2488
www.consumercouncil.org.uk

National Association of Citizens Advice Bureaux
020 7833 7000
www.adviceguide.org.uk

National Consumer Council
020 7730 3469
www.ncc.org.uk

Scottish Consumer Council
0141 226 5261
www.scotconsumer.org.uk

Welsh Consumer Council
029 2025 5454
www.wales-consumer.org.uk

● Employment bodies

Employment Tribunals
Enquiry line: 0845 795 9775
www.employmenttribunals.gov.uk

Equal Opportunities Commission (EOC)
020 7222 1110
www.eoc.org.uk

Equality Commission for Northern Ireland
028 90 500 0600
www.equalityni.org

Investors in People UK
020 7467 1900
www.investorsinpeople.co.uk

Labour Relations Agency
028 9032 1442
www.lra.org.uk

Low Pay Commission
020 7215 8495
www.lowpay.gov.uk
Press: 020 7215 8199

Pay & Employment Rights Service
01924 439587
www.pers.org.uk

● Unions

Trades Union Congress
020 7636 4030
www.tuc.org.uk
Press: 020 7467 1248

Abbey National Group Union
01442 891122
www.angu.org.uk

Accord
0118 934 1808
www.accord-myunion.org
HBOS Group employees

Alliance and Leicester Group Union of Staff
0116 285 6585
www.algus.org.uk

Amicus
020 8462 7755
www.amicustheunion.org
Manufacturing, technical and skilled workers

Aslef
020 7317 8600
www.aslef.org.uk
Associated Society of Locomotive Engineers and Firemen
Press: 020 7317 8607

Aspect
01226 383420
www.aspect.org.uk

Association for College Management
01858 461110
www.acm.uk.com

Association of Educational Psychologists
0191 384 9512
www.aep.org.uk

Association of Flight Attendants
001 202 434 1300
www.afanet.org

Association of Magisterial Officers
020 7403 2244
www.amo-online.org.uk

Association of Teachers and Lecturers
020 7930 6441
www.askatl.org.uk
Press: 020 7782 1589

Bakers, Food and Allied Workers Union
01707 260150
www.bfawu.org

Britannia Staff Union
01538 399627
www.britanniasu.org.uk

British Air Line Pilots Association
020 8476 4000
www.balpa.org.uk

British and Irish Orthoptic Society
020 7387 7992
www.orthoptics.org.uk

British Association of Colliery Management — Technical, Energy and Administrative Management
01302 815551
www.bacmteam.org.uk

British Dietetic Association
0121 200 8080
www.bda.uk.com
Press: 0870 850 2517

Broadcasting, Entertainment, Cinematograph and Theatre Union
020 7346 0900
www.bectu.org.uk

Card Setting Machine Tenters Society
01924 400206

Ceramic and Allied Trades Union
01782 272755
www.catu.org.uk

Chartered Society of Physiotherapy
020 7306 6666
www.csp.org.uk

Communication Workers Union
020 8971 7200
www.cwu.org

Community and District Nursing Association
020 8231 0180
www.cdna.tvu.ac.uk

Community and Youth Workers' Union
0121 643 6221
www.cywu.org.uk

Connect
020 8971 6000
www.connectuk.org
Communications professionals
Press: 020 8971 6027

Diageo Staff Association
020 8978 6069
Staff grades at Diageo, including Guinness, in the UK

Educational Institute of Scotland
0131 225 6244
www.eis.org.uk

Equity
020 7379 6000
www.equity.org.uk
Performers and artists

FDA
0845 470 1111
www.fda.org.uk
Senior managers and professionals in public service
Press: 020 7343 5588

Fire Brigades Union
020 8541 1765
www.fbu.org.uk

General Union of Loom Overlookers
01254 51760

GMB
020 8947 3131
www.gmb.org.uk
General union
Press: 020 8971 4224

Hospital Consultants and Specialists Association
01256 771777
www.hcsa.com

ISTC
020 7239 1200
www.istc-tu.org
Steel and metal industry and communities

Musicians' Union
020 7582 5566
www.musiciansunion.org.uk

NASUWT
0121 453 6150
www.nasuwt.org.uk
National Association of Schoolmasters Union of Women Teachers

National Association of Colliery Overmen, Deputies and Shotfirers
01226 203743
www.nacods.co.uk

National Association of Cooperative Officials
0161 351 7900
www.businesslink.gov.uk

National Association of Probation Officers
020 7223 4887
www.napo.org.uk

National Union of Domestic Appliances and General Operatives
020 7387 2578
www.gftu.org.uk

National Union of Journalists
020 7278 7916
www.nuj.org.uk

National Union of Knitwear, Footwear and Apparel Trades
020 7239 1200
www.kfat.org.uk
Manufacturing, retail and logistics

National Union of Lock and Metal Workers
01902 366651

National Union of Marine, Aviation and Shipping Transport Officers
020 8989 6677
www.nautilist.uk

National Union of Mineworkers
01226 215555
www.num.org.uk

National Union of Teachers
020 7388 6191
www.teachers.org.uk

Nationwide Group Staff Union
01295 710767
www.ngsu.org.uk

Prison Officers Association
020 8803 0255
www.poauk.org.uk

Professional Footballers' Association
0161 236 0575
www.givemefootball.com

Prospect
020 7902 6600
www.prospect.org.uk
Engineers, scientists, managers and specialists

Public and Commercial Services Union
020 7924 2727
www.pcs.org.uk
Press: 020 7801 2820

RMT
020 7387 4771
www.rmt.org.uk
Rail, maritime and transport workers
Press: 020 7529 8803

Society of Chiropodists and Podiatrists
0845 450 3720
www.feetforlife.org

Society of Radiographers
020 7740 7200
www.sor.org

Transport and General Workers' Union
020 7611 2500
www.tgwu.org.uk
Press: 020 7611 2555

Transport Salaried Staffs' Association
020 7387 2101
www.tssa.org.uk

UBAC
01653 697634
Staff at Bradford and Bingley Group and Alltel Mortgage Solutions

UCAC National Union of Welsh Teachers
01970 639950
www.athrawon.com

UCU
020 7690 9700
info@ucu.org.uk
www.ucu.org.uk
Press: 020 7670 9705

Union of Construction, Allied Trades and Technicians
020 7622 2442
www.ucatt.org.uk
Press: 020 7622 2422

Union of Shop, Distributive and Allied Workers
0161 224 2804/249 2400
www.usdaw.org.uk

Unison
0845 355 0845
www.unison.org.uk
Public service union

Writers' Guild of Great Britain
020 7833 0777
www.writersguild.org.uk

Yorkshire Independent Staff Association
01274 472453
www.businesslink.gov.uk

Media diversity associations

Age Concern
Astral House, 1268 London Road, London SW16 4ER
020 8765 7200
ace@ace.org.uk
www.ageconcern.co.uk

Age Positive
Department for Work and Pensions, Room W8d, Moorfoot, Sheffield S1 4PQ
Press: 020 7299 8757
agepositive@dwp.gsi.gov.uk
www.agepositive.gov.uk/
Age diversity in employment

Bird's Eye View
Unit 310A, Aberdeen Centre, 22-24 Highbury Grove, London N5 2EA
020 7288 7444
rosiestrang@birds-eye-view.co.uk
www.birds-eye-view.co.uk
Platform for emerging female film-makers

Employers' Forum on Disability
Broadcaster and Creative Industries Disability Network, Nutmeg House, 60 Gainsford Street, London SE1 2NY
020 7403 3020
jenny.stevens@
    employers-forum.co.uk
www.employers-forum.co.uk
Employers' organisation

Commission for Racial Equality (CRE)
St Dunstan's House, 201-211 Borough High Street, London SE1 1GZ
020 7939 0000
info@cre.gov.uk
www.cre.gov.uk

The Creative Collective
The Business Design Centre, Suite Forum P, 52 Upper Street, Islington, London N1 0QH
020 7359 3535
info@thecreativecollective.com
www.thecreativecollective.com
Aims to develop social policy on diversity and to empower community groups to harness media

Cultural Diversity Network (CDN)
c/o ITV, London Television Centre, Upper Ground, London SE1 9LT
020 7261 3006
cdnetwork@itv.com
www.itv.com
Online directory of black, Asian and other ethnic minority TV freelancers and staff

Digital Media Access Group
Applied Computing, University of Dundee, Dundee DD1 4HN
01382 345050
dmag@computing.dundee.ac.uk
www.dmag.org.uk
Promotes new media accessibility

Disability Rights Commission
Freepost MID02164, Stratford upon Avon CV37 9BR
0845 762 2633
enquiry@drc-gb.org
www.drc-gb.org

Emma Awards
67-69 Whitfield Street, London W1T 4HF
020 7636 1233
mail@emma.tv
www.emma.tv
Multicultural media awards and online humanitarian information portal

Equal Opportunities Commission
Arndale House, Arndale Centre, Manchester M4 3EQ
0845 601 5901
info@eoc.org.uk
www.eoc.org.uk

International Association of Women in Radio and Television
nik@netactive.co.za
www.iawrt.org

International Women's Media Foundation
1625K Street NW, Suite 1275, Washington, DC 20006, USA
001 202 496 1992
info@iwmf.org
www.iwmf.org

Ligali
PO Box 1257, London E5 0UD
020 8986 1984
mail@ligali.org
www.ligali.org
African British equality organisation

MediaWise Trust
38 Easton Business Centre, Felix Road, Bristol BS5 0HE
0117 941 5889
pw@mediawise.org.uk
www.mediawise.org.uk
Independent media ethics charity

Society of Women Writers & Journalists
Calvers Farm, Thelveton, Diss IP21 4NG
01379 740550
zoe@zoeking.com
www.swwj.co.uk

Women and Equality Unit
1 Victoria Street, London SW1H OET
020 7215 5000
info-womenandequalityunit@
  dti.gsi.gov.uk
www.womenandequalityunit.gov.uk

Women in Film and Television
6 Langley Street,
London WC2H 9JA
020 7240 4875
angela@wftv.org.uk
www.wftv.org.uk

Women in Publishing
c/o Multilingual Matters,
Channel View Publications,
Frankfurt Lodge, Clevedon Hall,
Victoria Road, Clevedon BS21 7HH
info@wipub.org.uk
www.wipub.org.uk

Women's Radio Group
27 Bath Road, London W4 1LJ
020 8995 5442
wrg@zelo.demon.co.uk
www.womeninradio.org.uk
Training, info and production facilities

Careers and training

Government department

Education and Skills
0870 000 2288
www.dfes.gov.uk
Press: 020 7925 6789

Government agencies

Arts and Humanities Research Council
0117 987 6500
www.ahrc.ac.uk

Becta
020 7641 6994
www.becta.org.uk

Council for Science and Technology
020 7215 6518
www.cst.gov.uk

Education and Learning Wales
0845 608 8066
www.elwa.ac.uk

Higher Education Funding Council for England (HEFCE)
0117 931 7317
www.hefce.ac.uk
Press: 0117 931 7363/7431

Learning and Skills Council
0870 900 6800
www.lsc.gov.uk

Learning and Skills Network
020 7297 9000
www.lsneducation.org.uk

Learning and Teaching Scotland
0870 010 0297
www.ltscotland.org.uk

Ofsted
0845 640 4045
www.ofsted.gov.uk
Press: 020 7421 6617

Qualifications and Curriculum Authority
020 7509 5555
www.qca.org.uk
Press: 020 7509 6789

Quality Assurance Agency for Higher Education
01452 557000
www.qaa.ac.uk
Press: 01452 557074

Scottish Qualifications Authority
0845 279 1000
www.sqa.org.uk

Sector Skills Development Agency
01709 765444
www.ssda.org.uk

Student Loans Company
0800 405010
www.slc.co.uk
Press: 0141 306 2120

Teacher Development Agency (TDA)
020 023 2001
www.tda.gov.uk

Ucas
01242 222444
www.ucas.com

Professional bodies

Association of Teachers and Lecturers
020 7930 6441
www.atl.org.uk
Press: 020 7782 1541

Association of University Administrators
0161 275 2063
www.aua.ac.uk

British Educational Research Association
01625 504062
www.bera.ac.uk

National Association of School-masters Union of Women Teachers
0121 453 6150
www.nasuwt.org.uk

National Union of Students
England: 020 7561 6577
Wales: 029 2068 0070
Scotland: 0131 556 6598
Ireland: 028 9024 4641
www.nus.org.uk

National Union of Teachers
020 7388 6191
www.teachers.org.uk

UCU
020 7690 9700
info@ucu.org.uk
www.ucu.org.uk
Press: 020 7670 9705
Association of schools and universities

1994 Group
020 7164 2094
www.1994group.ac.uk
19 small and medium-sized universities

Boarding Schools' Association
020 7798 1580
www.boarding.org.uk

Girls' Schools Association
0116 254 1619
www.gsa.uk.com

Independent Schools Association
01799 523619
www.isaschools.org.uk

National Association of Independent Schools and Non-Maintained Special Schools
01904 621243
www.nasschools.org.uk

National Grammar Schools Association
01543 251517
www.ngsa.org.uk

Russell Group
020 7872 5802
www.russellgroup.ac.uk
20 major research-intensive universities, including Oxford and Cambridge

State Boarding Schools' Association
020 7798 1580
www.sbsa.org.uk

Universities UK
020 7419 4111
www.universitiesuk.ac.uk

Voluntary bodies

Afasic
020 7490 9410
www.afasic.org.uk
Speech, language and communication charity

Campaign for Learning
020 7930 1111
www.campaign-for-learning.org.uk

ContinYou
024 7658 8440
www.continyou.org.uk

Learning Through Action
0870 770 7985
www.learning-through-action.org.uk

Life Education Centres
020 7831 9311
www.lifeeducation.org.uk

National Literacy Trust
020 7587 1842
www.literacytrust.org.uk

UFI/Learn Direct
0114 291 5000
www.ufi.com

General media See also PR, marketing and advertising
Press, journalism and writing See also publishing and broadcasting
TV, radio and film See also press and multimedia
PR, marketing and advertising
Publishing See also press and multimedia
Multimedia Includes new media, photography, animation, special effects, art and design
Music See also broadcasting

	general media	press, journalism & writing	TV, radio & film	PR, marketing & advertising	publishing	multimedia	music
Aberdeen, University of			•				•
Abertay, Dundee, University of	•			•		•	
Adam Smith College, Fife		•		•		•	
Anglia Ruskin University	•		•	•		•	•
Arts Institute at Bournemouth			•			•	
Aston University				•		•	
Barnsley, University Centre		•			•	•	•
Basingstoke College of Technology	•					•	
Bath Spa University College	•	•				•	•
Bath, University of		•		•		•	
Bedfordshire, University of	•	•	•	•		•	•
Birkbeck, University of London	•	•	•	•		•	•
Birmingham College of Food, Tourism and Creative Studies				•			
Birmingham Conservatoire							•
Birmingham, University of	•	•	•	•		•	
Blackburn College		•	•		•	•	•
Bolton, University of	•	•	•	•		•	
Bournemouth University	•	•	•	•		•	•
Bradford College		•	•			•	•
Bradford, University of	•	•	•	•		•	•
Brighton, University of	•	•	•	•		•	•
Bristol, University of		•				•	•
Brunel University	•	•	•	•		•	•
Buckingham, University of	•	•		•		•	
Bucks Chilterns University College	•	•	•	•		•	•
Camberwell College of Arts					•	•	
Cambridge, University of							•
Canterbury Christ Church University College	•	•	•			•	•
Canterbury College	•		•	•		•	•
Cardiff University	•	•	•	•		•	•
Cardonald College	•	•	•				
Central England in Birmingham, University of	•	•	•	•		•	•
Central Lancashire, University of	•	•	•	•		•	•
Central Saint Martins College of Art and Design	•	•	•			•	
Central School of Speech and Drama		•	•				•
Central Sussex College	•		•				
Chelsea College of Art and Design				•		•	
University College Chester	•	•	•	•		•	•
Chichester College	•		•				
Chichester, University College		•				•	•
City College Brighton and Hove		•	•			•	•
City Lit		•	•	•	•	•	•
City Of Wolverhampton College	•	•					•
City University, London	•	•	•		•	•	•
Cleveland College of Art & Design		•				•	

381

	general media	press, journalism & writing	TV, radio & film	PR, marketing & advertising	publishing	multimedia	music
Coleg Gwent		●	●			●	●
Coleg Menai						●	
Coleg Sir Gar (Carmarthenshire College)			●			●	●
Conservatoire for Dance and Drama			●				
Cornwall College		●	●			●	
Coventry University	●	●	●	●		●	●
Cumbria University		●	●			●	
Darlington College of Technology	●	●	●	●		●	●
De Montfort University	●	●	●	●		●	●
Derby, University of	●	●	●	●		●	●
Doncaster College		●		●		●	●
Dublin Institute of Technology	●	●				●	●
Dundee, University of						●	
Durham University							●
Ealing, Hammersmith and West London College	●					●	●
East Anglia, University of	●	●	●	●		●	●
East London, University of	●	●	●	●		●	●
East Surrey College	●		●			●	●
Edge Hill College of Higher Education	●	●	●	●		●	
Edinburgh College of Art			●			●	
Edinburgh, University of		●	●			●	●
Editorial Centre		●	●			●	
Editorial Training Consultants	●	●	●	●	●	●	
Essex, University of		●	●			●	●
Exeter, University of	●	●	●				
Falmouth, University College	●	●	●	●		●	
Glamorgan, University of	●	●	●	●		●	●
Glasgow Caledonian University		●		●		●	●
Glasgow Metropolitan College		●	●	●	●	●	
Glasgow School of Art						●	
Glasgow, University of	●		●			●	●
Gloucestershire, University of		●	●	●	●	●	
Goldsmiths College	●	●	●			●	●
Greenwich, University of	●	●	●	●		●	●
Grimsby Institute of Further & Higher Education	●	●	●	●		●	●
Guildford College	●		●	●		●	
Harlow College		●				●	●
Harrow College	●	●	●			●	●
Henley College Coventry	●		●			●	
Hertfordshire, University of			●	●		●	●
Highbury College, Portsmouth	●	●	●		●	●	●
Huddersfield, University of	●	●	●	●		●	●
Hull, University of	●	●	●	●		●	●
Journalism Training Centre		●					
Keele, University of	●			●			●
Kensington and Chelsea College						●	●
Kent Institute of Art and Design			●	●		●	
Kent, University of		●	●			●	●
King's College London	●		●			●	●
Kingston University	●	●	●	●		●	●
Lambeth College	●	●	●			●	
Lampeter, University of Wales	●	●	●				
Lancaster University	●	●	●	●		●	●

	general media	press, journalism & writing	TV, radio & film	PR, marketing & advertising	publishing	multimedia	music
Leeds College of Art and Design				●		●	
Leeds College of Music			●				●
Leeds Metropolitan University	●		●	●		●	●
Leeds Trinity & All Saints	●	●	●	●			
Leeds, University of		●	●	●		●	●
Leicester, University of			●	●			
Lincoln, University of	●	●	●	●		●	●
Liverpool Community College	●	●	●			●	●
Liverpool Hope University College	●		●	●			●
Liverpool John Moores University	●	●	●	●		●	●
Liverpool, University of	●		●	●		●	●
London Business School				●			
London College of Communication	●	●	●	●	●	●	●
London College of Fashion		●		●		●	
London Film School			●				
London Metropolitan University	●	●	●	●		●	●
London School of Economics and Political Science	●			●		●	
London School of Journalism		●					
London South Bank University	●	●	●	●		●	
London, University College			●		●		
Manchester Metropolitan University	●	●	●	●		●	
Manchester, University of	●	●	●				●
Marjon, College of St Mark & St John	●	●		●			
Mid-Cheshire College						●	●
Middlesex University	●	●	●	●	●	●	●
Mid-Kent College	●		●		●		●
Napier University	●	●	●	●	●	●	●
National Broadcasting School			●				
National Film and Television School			●			●	●
Neath Port Talbot College			●			●	●
New College Nottingham	●		●			●	●
Newcastle College			●			●	
Newcastle Upon Tyne, University of	●	●	●	●		●	
Newport, University of Wales	●	●	●	●		●	●
North East Surrey College of Technology (NESCOT)	●		●			●	●
North East Wales Institute of Higher Education	●	●		●		●	●
North East Worcestershire College	●		●			●	●
North West Kent College	●	●				●	●
Northbrook College Sussex			●	●		●	●
Northampton, University of	●	●	●	●			
Northumbria University	●	●	●	●		●	●
Norwich School of Art and Design		●			●	●	
noSweat Journalism Training		●					
Nottingham Trent University	●	●	●	●		●	
Nottingham, University of			●				●
Open University	●						
Oxford Brookes University			●	●	●	●	●
Oxford, University of		●					●
Peterborough Regional College	●	●	●				●
Plymouth College of Art and Design			●		●	●	●
Plymouth, University of	●	●	●	●	●	●	●

	general media	press, journalism & writing	TV, radio & film	PR, marketing & advertising	publishing	multimedia	music
PMA Training	●	●	●	●		●	
Portsmouth, University of	●	●	●	●		●	●
Queen Margaret University College, Edinburgh	●		●	●			
Queen Mary, University of London			●			●	●
Queen's University Belfast			●				●
Radio and TV School			●				
Ravensbourne College of Design and Communication		●			●	●	
Robert Gordon University		●		●	●	●	
Roehampton University	●	●	●	●	●	●	●
Royal Academy of Music							●
Royal College of Music							●
Royal Holloway, University of London		●	●			●	●
Royal Northern College of Music							●
Royal Scottish Academy of Music and Drama							●
Royal Welsh College of Music and Drama			●				●
St Helens College, Merseyside			●			●	●
St Martin's College, Lancaster		●					
St Mary's College, Twickenham		●	●			●	
Salford, University of	●	●	●	●		●	●
Salisbury College			●			●	●
School of Oriental and African Studies	●	●					●
Sheffield College, The	●	●				●	●
Sheffield Hallam University	●	●	●	●		●	
Sheffield, University of	●	●	●				●
Solihull College	●			●			
South Birmingham College			●	●		●	
South Devon College	●		●				
South East Essex College	●	●	●		●	●	●
South Kent College	●		●	●			●
South Nottingham College			●			●	
South Thames College	●		●			●	●
Southampton Solent University	●	●	●	●		●	●
Southampton, University of			●			●	●
Staffordshire University	●	●	●			●	●
Stevenson College Edinburgh			●	●			●
Stirling, University of	●	●	●	●	●		
Stockport College of Further and Higher Education	●		●			●	
Strathclyde, University of		●		●		●	●
Sunderland, University of	●	●	●	●		●	
Surrey, University of			●				●
Sussex, University of	●	●	●			●	●
Sutton Coldfield College	●	●				●	
Swansea Institute of Higher Education		●	●	●		●	●
Swansea University	●	●	●	●			
Tameside College			●			●	
Teesside, University of	●	●	●	●		●	
Thames Valley University	●	●	●	●		●	●
Trinity College, Carmarthen	●	●	●	●			
Trinity College of Music							●
Tyne Metropolitan College			●			●	
UHI Millennium Institute	●		●	●		●	●

	general media	press, journalism & writing	TV, radio & film	PR, marketing & advertising	publishing	multimedia	music
University College for the creative arts at Canterbury, Epsom, Farnham, Maidstone and Rochester	●	●	●	●		●	
Ulster, University of	●	●	●	●		●	●
Wakefield College	●					●	●
University of Wales, Aberystwyth	●		●	●			
University of Wales, Bangor	●	●	●	●		●	●
University of Wales Institute, Cardiff		●	●			●	●
Warwick, University of	●	●	●	●			
Warwickshire College		●		●	●		
West Herts College			●	●			
West Kent College	●	●					
West of England, University of the	●	●	●	●	●	●	●
West of Scotland, University of the	●	●	●	●	●	●	●
Westminster, University of	●	●	●	●	●	●	●
Winchester, University of	●	●	●			●	
Wirral Metropolitan College	●		●				●
Wolverhampton, University of	●	●	●	●		●	●
Worcester, University of	●		●			●	
York St John College	●	●				●	●
York, University of			●			●	●
Yorkshire Coast College of Further Education						●	

Careers & training contacts

Aberdeen, University of
King's College, Aberdeen AB24 3FX
01224 272000
communications@abdn.ac.uk
www.abdn.ac.uk
• MA (ug) film • BMus music

Abertay, Dundee, University of
40 Bell Street, Dundee DD1 1HG
01382 308000
enquiries@abertay.ac.uk
www.abertay.ac.uk
• BA (Hons) media, culture and society • BA (Hons) marketing and business • BSc (Hons) web design and development. BA (Hons) computer arts. BSc multimedia development (no year 4)

Adam Smith College, Fife
St Brycedale Avenue, Kirkcaldy, Fife, Scotland KY1 1EX
0800 413280
enquiries@fife.ac.uk
www.fife.ac.uk
Formerly Fife College of Further and Higher Education and Glenrothes College
• HNC/HND practical journalism • HNC/HND communication with media; events management • HNC/HND interactive multimedia. BA Visual communication and digital publishing. BSc multimedia development

Anglia Ruskin University
East Road, Cambridge CB1 1PT
Bishop Hall Lane, Chelmsford, Essex CM1 1SQ
0845 271 3333
answers@apu.ac.uk
www.apu.ac.uk
• BA (Hons) film, film and art history, media studies
• BA (Hons) marketing. BA (Hons) Media studies
• BA (Hons) illustration and animation; graphic design; graphic and typographic design; web design
• BA (Hons) music and drama, English. MA music

Arts Institute at Bournemouth
Wallisdown, Poole, Dorset BH12 5HH
01202 533011
general@aib.ac.uk
www.aib.ac.uk
• BA (Hons) acting for theatre, film and TV; film production
• Fdg commercial photography; visual communication; commercial photography; interactive media; interactive media. BA (Hons) graphic design; film production; photography; animation production

Aston University
Aston Triangle, Birmingham B4 7ET
0121 204 3000
www.aston.ac.uk
• BSc marketing • BSc multimedia tech; multimedia digital systems

Barnsley, University Centre

PO Box 266, Church Street, Barnsley S70 2YW
01226 216267
admissions@barnsley.ac.uk
www.barnsley.ac.uk

• *Fdg journalism and media production* • *FdSc multimedia.
BSc creative multimedia tech (top-up)* • *BA (Hons) creative
music tech and sound recording; pop; NatDip drama; e-media;
games design; media publishing; moving image production*

Basingstoke College of Technology

Worting Road, Basingstoke RG21 8TN
01256 354141
info@bcot.ac.uk
www.bcot.ac.uk

• *BTec FirstDip/NatDip media* • *BTec NatDip/NatCert graphic
design; multimedia. OCN level 3 photography. Short courses:
intro to using a digital camera; web page design with
Dreamweaver*

Bath Spa University College

Newton Park, Newton St Low, Bath BA2 9BN
01225 875875
enquiries@bathspa.ac.uk
www.bathspa.ac.uk

• *BA/BSc (Hons) media communication (joint)* • *MA creative
writing; writing for young people* • *Fdg design for digital tech.
PgCert/PgDip/MA interactive multimedia* • *Fdg commercial
music; Broadcast media: process and production. PgCert/
PgDip/BA(Hons)/MA creative music tech. BA (Hons) music*

Bath, University of

Claverton Down, Bath BA2 7AY
01225 388388
admissions@bath.ac.uk
www.bath.ac.uk

• *Fdg digital media arts (moving image production) (Wiltshire
College, Chippenham 01249 464644)* • *Fdg digital media arts
(multimedia) (Wiltshire College, Trowbridge 01225 766241)
journalism (reporting and interviewing); news and
scriptwriting; production using Cool Edit Pro)* • *DipHE/CertHE
communication. Short course in marketing*

Birkbeck, University of London

Malet Street, Bloomsbury, London WC1E 7HX
020 7631 6000
info@bbk.ac.uk
www.bbk.ac.uk

• *Fdg media and business application. BA media and
humanities* • *Cert/MA creative writing. BA film and media.
PhD/MPhil film; TV; media. MA/MRes history of film and
visual media.* • *Dip science communication. Dip multimedia
and new media authoring; new media management; web design and
development* • *Cert/Dip, short courses: musical techniques
and composition; opera studies, journalism, film and media
studies, humanities, media practice, screenwriting. Fcourse/
Dip/AdvDip performance studies: concert singing, opera,
dance. Short courses in music; PR; film; history of cinema;
radio, docs and video*

Birmingham College of Food, Tourism and Creative Studies

Summer Row, Birmingham B3 1JB
0121 604 1000
marketing@bcftcs.ac.uk
www.bcftcs.ac.uk

• *Fdg/BA(Hons) marketing management; marketing with
events/ hospitality management. FdA business and marketing*

Birmingham Conservatoire

Paradise Place, Birmingham B3 3HG
0121 331 5901/2
conservatoire@uce.ac.uk
www.conservatoire.uce.ac.uk

• *HND music performance, popular music studies.
BMus (Hons) jazz; music. BSc (Hons) music tech.
Post graduate courses in music.*

Birmingham, University of

Edgbaston, Birmingham B15 2TT
0121 414 3344
postmaster@bham.ac.uk
www.bham.ac.uk

• *BA culture, society and communication (Europe); media,
culture and society (single and joint)* • *BA (Hons) creative
writing* • *MPhil American film and literature; film; history,
film and TV* • *MSc marketing* • *BEng/MEng computer
interactive systems (business management option). BSc/MSc
multimedia computer systems. MEng computer interactive
systems with international study. MSc/PgDip/PgCert comms
engineering; multimedia computer systems, computer
science* • *BMus/ BA (joint)/BMus with modern languages.
MPhil/MLitt/MMus/PhD music*

Blackburn College

Feilden Street, Blackburn BB2 1LH
01254 55144
studentservices@blackburn.ac.uk
www.blackburn.ac.uk

• *BA (Hons) Creative writing; graphic design; BTec NatDip
media (moving image); photography. Pre-entry media
production. Cert/Dip/PgDip marketing professional* • *BTec
NatDip multimedia; photography. HND photography. Fdg
multimedia (Lancaster University)* • *NOCN IntDip/ AdvDip
contemporary and pop*

Bolton, University of

Deane Road, Bolton BL3 5AB
01204 900600
enquiries@bolton.ac.uk
www.bolton.ac.uk

• *BA (Hons) fashion media** • *BA (Hons) media; film and
media; writing and production; creative writing; animation
and illustration marketing; creative advertising.* • *MA creative
writing, photography. MSc e-business.* • *HND/BSc (Hons)
multimedia and website development; creative technologies.
Short courses in internet site design, web site promotion*

Bournemouth University

Bournemouth Media School, Weymouth House,
Fern Barrow, Poole, Dorset BH12 5BB
01202 524111
bms@bournemouth.ac.uk
www.bournemouth.ac.uk

• *BA (Hons) communication and media (University Centre
Yeovil)* • *MA magazine journalism;* • *Fdg video production
(Weymouth College). BA (Hons) scriptwriting for film and TV;
TV production; media production (top-up Bournemouth and
Poole College/ Weymouth College/University Centre Yeovil);
radio production (Bournemouth and Poole College). MA TV
production; radio production; screenwriting; broadcast and
film management* • *Fdg marketing (Bournemouth and Poole
College). BA (Hons) PR; ad and marketing comms; marketing;
international marketing; international leisure marketing
(top-up); international retail marketing (top-up); marketing
comms. MA corporate/political comms; PR practice.*
• *Fdg multimedia (Bournemouth and Poole College);
CAD - 3D computer modelling and animation (Bournemouth
and Poole College/Salisbury College); CAD - engineering
modelling and animation (Bournemouth and Poole
College/Cornwall College); CAD - design engineering
(Cornwall College)/ CAD - graphics and packaging (University
Centre Yeovil). BA (Hons) multimedia journalism; interactive
media production; computer visualisation and animation;
photomedia (top-up at Salisbury College). BSc (Hons) CAD
- 3D computer/engineering modelling and animation (both
top-up at Bournemouth and Poole College). MA multimedia
journalism: (post-production - sound design/editing;
interactive media; 3D computer animation; digital effects).
MSc computer animation* • *Fdg music (at Weymouth College);
music tech (at Weymouth College) BA (Hons) music design
(top-up). MA post-production: composing*

Bradford College
Great Horton Road, Bradford BD7 1AY
01274 433333
admissions@bradfordcollege.ac.uk
www.bradfordcollege.ac.uk
• *BTec HNC advertising and marketing comms. HND marketing comms and advertising. BA (Hons) advertising and marketing comms; marketing comms.. NatDip business and marketing. PgDip/MA marketing practice. HE courses in law and marketing • BTec HND computing (software development). BTec NatDip multimedia design. Dip digital applications. HND media and special effects (beauty therapy). BA (Hons) graphic media communication; interactive multimedia. Short courses in multimedia design (photography, web page design, animation, CD-Rom design, digital moving image) • NatDip music performance; music tech*

Bradford, University of
Richmond Road, Bradford BD7 1DP
01274 232323
course-enquiries@bradford.ac.uk
www.brad.ac.uk
• *BA/BSc media (with many post-production options). BSc media tech and production. EurMA media, communication and cultural studies • BA creative writing and identity; creative media technologies • BA music tech (joint) • BA cinematics (joint); TV (joint). PgDip/MSc entertainment tech; radio frequency comms engineering • BSc marketing (options) • BA/BSc computer animation and special effects; e-commerce tech; internet, law and society; multimedia computing. BA digital media; digital tech (joint). BEng electronic, telecomms and internet engineering. PgDip/MSc personal, mobile and satellite comms; creative media and tech (options). EurMA computer animation and special effects*

Brighton, University of
Mithras House, Lewes Road, Brighton BN2 4AT
01273 600900
admissions@brighton.ac.uk
www.brighton.ac.uk
• *BA (Hons) English • BA (Hons) modern languages and media; sport journalism (NCTJ) • FCert eSystems design and tech. BSc (Hons) digital media development; MSc digital television management and production • BA (Hons) communication and media; communication and digital media • FCert graphics communication. FCert/BA (Hons) multimedia. BA (Hons) graphic design • FCert music production. BA (Hons) digital music; music and visual art; music composition for professional media music performance; music production; documentary practice; performance research*

Bristol, University of
Senate House, Tyndall Avenue, Bristol BS8 1TH
0117 928 9000
Press: public-relations@bristol.ac.uk
www.bris.ac.uk
• *BA drama: theatre, film and TV. MA cinema; film and TV production; TV • BSc/MEng, computer science; MSc advanced computing (character animation; global computing and multimedia; internet tech; machine learning and data mining) • BA music. MA music: advanced musical studies; composition of music for film and television; music and modern languages*

Brunel University
Uxbridge, Middlesex UB8 3PH
01895 274000
admissions@brunel.ac.uk
www.brunel.ac.uk
• *MSc health, risk and the media; risk, insecurity and the media • BA English with creative writing. MA creative and transactional writing • BA film and TV; English, drama, music options. • MA documentary practice • BSc social anthropology and communication; sociology and communication; communication and media. MSc marketing, business and management; public affairs and lobbying. MA public policy; media and comms • BSc multimedia tech and design. MSc multimedia computing; digital broadcast systems; globalisation and new media; multimedia computing • BA music (also with drama, English, film, TV); creative music tech. MA creative music*

Buckingham, University of
Hunter Street, Buckingham MK18 1EG
01280 814080
admissions@buckingham.ac.uk
www.buckingham.ac.uk
• *BA (Hons) English with multimedia journalism, media comms and other options • BSc economics with business journalism • BSc (Hons) marketing with media comms (and other options). MSc international marketing management • BA (Hons) English literature with multimedia journalism*

Bucks Chilterns University College
Queen Alexander Road, High Wycombe, Bucks HP11 2JZ
01494 522141
marketing@bcuc.ac.uk
www.bcuc.ac.uk
• *BA (Hons) media (joint and with options) • BA (Hons) creative writing (joint and with options); journalism (joint) • HNC/HND live TV production. BA applied performing arts (top-up); applied TV production (top-up). BA (Hons) video production; drama production; film or film studies (all joint and with options) • BA (Hons) ad and promotions management; business and ad management; business and marketing management; business management with marketing; business management with marketing comms; marketing (joint and with options); PR management. PgDip marketing (CIM) • BA applied graphic studies (top-up); applied photography and digital imaging (top-up). BA (Hons) design for digital media; graphic design and advertising. BSc (Hons) multimedia tech (options). • BSc (Hons) audio and music tech. BA (Hons) international music management; music entertainment and arts management; music industry management*

Cambridge, University of
The Old Schools, Trinity Lane, Cambridge CB2 1TN
01223 333308
admissions@cam.ac.uk
www.cam.ac.uk
• *BA (Hons) music*

Canterbury Christ Church University College
Department of Media, North Holmes Road, Canterbury, Kent CT1 1QU
01227 767700
admissions@cant.ac.uk
www.cant.ac.uk
• *BA (Hons) media and cultural studies (also joint and with options). MA popular culture and the media • BA/BSc journalism; MA creative writing • BA (Hons) film, radio and TV (joint and with options). PgDip/MA broadcast journalism. MA media production • DipHE/ BA (Hons) digital media. BA (Hons) digital culture, arts and media (joint and with options) • Cert/Dip music. BA (Hons) music (also joint and with options); commercial music. MMus music*

Canterbury College

New Dover Road, Canterbury, Kent CT1 3AJ
01227 811111
courseenquiries@cant-col.ac.uk
www.cant-col.ac.uk
• BTec NatDip media (including moving image pathway)
• HND media production. OCN intro to scriptwriting • HND
graphic design and advertising. BA (Hons) visual art and
communication, theatre production* • HNC/HND CAD and 3D
animation (various) • BTec FirstDip/NatDip music tech. BTec
NatDip music. HND music production. BA (Hons) creative
music production.

Cardiff University

Student Recruitment Office, Cardiff University,
46 Park Place, Cardiff CF10 3XQ
029 2087 4000
prospectus@cardiff.ac.uk
www.cardiff.ac.uk
• BA language and communication. MA teaching and practice
of creative writing • BA journalism film and media. PgDip/MA
journalism studies. MA international journalism; political
communication . Short courses: writing, exploring media
• PgDip public and media relations. MA international PR;
political communication. MSc strategic marketing; science,
media and communication • Short courses in photography,
creative website design, creative digital video production
• BMus/BA (Hons - single and joint) music. MA musicology;
music, culture and politics; performance studies;
composition. Short courses in music

Cardiff, University of Wales Institute

PO Box 377, Western Avenue, Cardiff CF5 2SG
029 2041 6070
uwicinfo@uwic.ac.uk
www.uwic.ac.uk
• BA (Hons) art and creative writing; writing for the creative
arts; media studies and visual cultures; broadcast media with
popular culture • HND business information tech. BA (Hons)
graphic communication; design for interactive media. BSc
(Hons) business information systems • HND/BSc (Hons)
music and audio electronic systems

Cardonald College

690 Mosspark Drive, Glasgow G52 3AY
0141 272 3333
enquiries@cardonald.ac.uk
www.cardonald.ac.uk
• HNC/HND media and comms • Prelim Cert journalism (NCTJ).
HNC/ HND practical journalism • HNC/HND TV operations and
production; communication. NatCert/Dip media studies

Central England in Birmingham, University of

Perry Barr, Birmingham B42 2SU
0121 331 5000
info@ucechoices.com
www.uce.ac.uk
• BA/MA/PgCert/PgDip (Hons) media and communication
• BA (Hons) media and communication (journalism)
• BA (Hons) media and communication (routes: radio
production; TV and video; music industries; web and new
media); TV tech and production • BA (Hons) advertising (joint
only); marketing (options); marketing, advertising and PR;
media and communication (PR); PR. CIM Dip marketing
• HND digital media tech; multimedia; multimedia and
networks tech. BA (Hons) multimedia tech; sound and
multimedia • BSc (Hons) music tech; sound and multimedia;
sound engineering and audio production

Central Lancashire, University of

Preston, Lancashire PR1 2HE
01772 201201
cenquiries@uclan.ac.uk
www.uclan.ac.uk
• BA (Hons) creative writing (joint course) • BA (Hons) digital
journalism production; international journalism; journalism;
journalism and English lang or lit; sports journalism.
MA/PgDip broadcast/newspaper/ online journalism. MA
international journalism; magazine journalism • BA (Hons)
film, media and American studies; film, media and visual
culture; film and media; TV (minor). BSc (Hons) media
production and tech (AV media, journalism options); TV
production; screenwriting. MA experimental film • BA (Hons)
advertising (options); communication studies; digital comms;
management and PR; marketing (options); press comms; PR
(also with management/marketing). BSc (Hons) marketing.
MA/PgDip/PgCert strategic communication. MA marketing.
MSc international applied communication; fundraising and
sponsorship; marketing management • BSc (Hons) interactive
digital media; web and multimedia (also with business
information systems) • BA(Hons) multimedia and sonic arts;
music practice; music theatre

Central School of Speech and Drama

Embassy Theatre, Eton Avenue, London NW3 3HY
020 7722 8183
enquiries@cssd.ac.uk
www.cssd.ac.uk
• MA writing for stage and broadcast media • MA theatre
(inc theatre journalism). MA acting for screen. Short course:
intro to acting for screen • MA advanced theatre practice
(visual media for performance) • BA theatre practice (theatre
sound); acting (music theatre). MA acting musical theatre;
advanced theatre practice (sound design and music for
performance). Short course in singing; PGCE in drama;
media studies (14-19)

Central Sussex College

College Road, Crawley, West Sussex RH10 1NR
01293 442200
information@crawley-college.ac.uk
www.crawley-college.ac.uk
• BTec Dip media • BTec NatDip media production; NCFE video
production

University of Chester

Parkgate Road, Chester CH1 4BJ
01244 511000
enquiries@chester.ac.uk
www.chester.ac.uk
• BA (Hons) media studies (with film, PR, graphic design,
journalism, multimedia, radio or TV production, sport
development, film studies) ; cultural studies. MA media and
cultural studies • BA (Hons) journalism • BA (Hons) film;
media (TV/radio production). MA TV production • BA (Hons)
communication studies; advertising; marketing • BA (Hons)
graphic design; multimedia tech; photography. BSc/BA (Hons)
multimedia tech; fine art: new media • BA (Hons) media
(commercial music production); pop

Chichester College

Westgate Fields, Chichester, West Sussex PO19 1SB
01243 786321
info@chichester.ac.uk
www.chichester.ac.uk
• NatDip media production • HND media (radio production)

Chichester, University College

Bishop Otter Campus, College Lane, Chichester,
West Sussex PO19 6PE
01243 816000
admissions@ucc.ac.uk
www.chi.ac.uk
• BA (Hons) English and creative writing; MA creative writing
• Fdg instrumental and vocal teaching; music tech. BA (Hons)
music. MA music performance; MA fine art*

City College Brighton and Hove
Pelham Street, Brighton, East Sussex BN1 4FA
01273 667788
info@ccb.ac.uk
www.ccb.ac.uk
• Cert periodical, magazine or newspaper journalism (NCTJ); OCN level 3 print journalism • OCN level 3 video production; animation • Short courses: 3D Studio Max, animation, digital imaging for managers, digital photography, Quark, Flash animation, intro to digital imaging, multimedia, web design, PhotoShop for photographers, • Short courses: intro to music tech; Cubase SX for PC; Logic Audio for Apple Mac

City Lit
Keeley Street, London WC2B 4BA
020 7492 2600
infoline@citylit.ac.uk
www.citylit.ac.uk
• Short courses in creative writing, freelance journalism, travel journalism, computer skills for journalists, etc • Short courses in broadcast journalism, writing comedy, scriptwriting, screenwriting • Short course in how to write a press release • Short course in how to get published • Short courses: HTML, web design and hosting, Dreamweaver and Fireworks, Javascript, using Apple computers, sound and video editing, desktop video and digital editing, Premiere, Final Cut, After Effects, producing animated titles, PhotoShop, digital techniques for printmakers, animation, Maya and 3D animation, digital imaging, digital photography, colour management • Short courses: Cubase sequencing, Pro-tools, Logic Pro, digital music production techniques, Loop-based music using Ableton Live, Reason, Sibelius, Mixing and mastering techniques, drum-and-bass masterclass with Davide Carbone

City of Wolverhampton College
Wulfrun Campus, Paget Road,
Wolverhampton WV6 0DU
01902 836000
mail@wolverhamptoncollege.ac.uk
www.wolverhamptoncollege.ac.uk;
www.mediacove.com
• Dip/NatDip media; moving image media; performing arts • Pre-entry journalism (NCTJ). OCN level 3 art of writing • NatCert music tech; BA (Hons) journalism and editorial design

City University, London
Department of Journalism, Northampton Square,
London EC1V 0HB
020 7040 5060; journalism: 020 7040 8221
ugadmissions@city.ac.uk; journalism@city.ac.uk
www.city.ac.uk
• MSc media research and analysis. MA transnational media and society • BA journalism with social science or contemporary history. PGDip newspaper journalism; magazine journalism (PTC). PgDip/MA international journalism. MA creative writing (novels/plays and scripts) • PGDip broadcast journalism (BJTC)/ TV current affairs journalism • PgDip/MA publishing studies; electronic publishing. • BSc computer science with games tech; music informatics. BEng multimedia communication systems. BSc/BEng multimedia and internet systems • BMus/BSc music. MA musicology; music performance studies. PgDip/ MSc music IT. Various short and part-time courses open to the public, covering film, filmmaking, cinema history and computing.

Cleveland College of Art & Design
Green Lane, Linthorpe, Middlesbrough TS5 7RJ
01642 288000
StudentRecruitment@ccad.ac.uk
www.ccad.ac.uk
• BTec Dip media (moving image). Fdg TV and film production; commercial photography • NatDip multimedia; BA (Hons) photography

Coleg Gwent
The Rhadyr, Usk NP15 2FD
01495 333333
info@coleggwent.ac.uk
www.coleggwent.ac.uk
• OCN writing for the media • BTec NatDip media (moving image). OCN live production; video and editing production • BTec Dip multimedia and animation. BTec NatDip/HNC/HND graphic design. BTec NatDip photography and digital imaging; multimedia. HND photography and digital imaging. Fdg multimedia. C&G 9231/6922/6923/OCN photography. OCN web design; animation; cartooning and comic strip; CEL animation (traditional); computer graphics and animation; electronic imaging • BTec Dip performing arts (music/rock and pop). BTec NatDip music practice (performing, performance); music tech. OCN music tech; percussion and guitar; level 1 guitar

Coleg Menai
Ffriddoedd Road, Bangor, Gwynedd,
North Wales LL57 2TP
01248 370125
student.services@menai.ac.uk
www.menai.ac.uk
• Dip/NatDip e-media and e-media2; NatCert/Dip media (moving image); performing arts. HND media; VTCTDip photography

Coleg Sir Gar (Carmarthenshire College)
Graig Campus, Sandy Road, Llanelli,
Carmarthenshire SA15 4DN
01554 748000
admissions@colegsirgar.ac.uk
www.colegsirgar.ac.uk
• NatDip media (moving image). EdexcelCert film & TV acting • OCN web page design • Dip performing arts – music. NatDip music tech. Short course in music composition portfolio development; BA (Hons) graphic design; media production; photography. HND/HND multimedia computing. NVQ Level3 in TV, theatre and media make-up. Short courses: shooting single camera drama; digital photography

Conservatoire for Dance and Drama
1–7 Woburn Walk, London WC1H 0JJ
020 7387 5101
info@cdd.ac.uk
www.cdd.ac.uk
• MA dance for the screen (London Contemporary Dance School). DipHE costume for theatre, film and TV (Bristol Old Vic Theatre School)

Cornwall College
Trevenson Road, Pool, Redruth, Cornwall TR15 3RD
01209 611611
enquiries@cornwall.ac.uk
www.cornwall.ac.uk
• HNC media (writing). Fdg newspaper and magazine journalism. PGDip journalism (NCTJ). Short course in creative writing • NatDip media (moving image). • BTec NatDip media (e-media). HNC creative photography in commercial practice. HND multimedia. Fdg animation; multimedia design; graphic and communication design

Coventry University
Priory Street, Coventry CV1 5FB
024 7688 7688
rao.cor@coventry.ac.uk
www.coventry.ac.uk
• BA (Hons) communication, culture and media; media.
MA communication, culture and media; media arts
• BA (Hons) journalism and English; journalism and media.
MA automotive journalism; international media journalism
• BA (Hons) media production • BA (Hons) advertising and
business/media; creative industries management; marketing
(joint and options); marketing management. MA marketing.
MSc communication management • BA (Hons) creative
computing; digital entertainment tech; English; graphic
design; media; multimedia computing. BSc/BEng (Hons)
multimedia computing. MA design and digital media; media
arts • BA (Hons) music composition and professional practice.
BEng (Hons) music tech. BA (Hons) music and professional
practice

Cumbria University
Brampton Road, Carlisle, Cumbria CA3 9AY
01228 400300; enquiries: 0845 607 6563
info@cumbria.ac.uk
www.cumbria.ac.uk
• BA (Hons) journalism (NCTJ, BJTC); creative writing and
contemporary culture; creative writing and film • BA (Hons)
media production; film and creative writing; film and
contemporary culture. Fdg multimedia • MA graphic design;
digital media; media futures. • BA (Hons) photography;
graphic design; multimedia design and digital animation;
multimedia learning technologies

Darlington College Of Technology
Cleveland Avenue, Darlington, County Durham DL3 7BB
01325 503050
enquire@darlington.ac.uk
www.darlington.ac.uk
• NatDip media • Pre-entry journalism (NCTJ) • NatDip media
production (moving image) • ProfDip marketing (CIM)
• NatDip multimedia. Level4 Cert digital photo journalism
(NCTJ*) • NatCert audio production

De Montfort University
The Gateway, Leicester LE1 9BH
0116 255 1551
enquiry@dmu.ac.uk
www.dmu.ac.uk
• BA (Hons) media • BA (Hons) journalism. PgDip journalism
(NCTJ) • BSc (Hons) media production; media tech;
broadcast tech. BA (Hons) film. MA TV scriptwriting
• BA (Hons) arts management; marketing; advertising and
marketing comms; design management and innovation
• BA (Hons) Design, pathways: graphic/interactive/animation/
game art design; internet computing; photography and video.
BSc (Hons) multimedia computing; tech. MA/PgDip
photography. MSc/PgDip/PgCert multimedia comms
engineering • HND music tech. BA/BSc (Hons) music, tech
and innovation (BA for creative musicians working with
technology). BSc (Hons) audiology; radio production

Derby, University of
School of Arts, Design & Technology, Kedleston Road,
Derby DE22 1GB
01332 590500
admissions@derby.ac.uk
www.derby.ac.uk
• BA media; popular culture and media (with options)
• BA media writing (with options) • Fdg/BA (top-up) video
and photography; video production. BA broadcast media
(options); film and TV (single and with options); film and
video; film • BA/PgCert/ PgDip/MA marketing and broadcast
management. Cert/Dip/ PgDip marketing (CIM) • BSc
computer games programming; design tech; multimedia
tech • BA web design and digital media (top-up); illustration
for animation • BSc multimedia tech and music production;
music tech and audio system design; sound, light and live
event tech. BA pop with music tech. PgDip acoustics and noise
control. MSc applied acoustics

Doncaster College
Waterdale, Doncaster DN1 3EX
01302 553553
infocentre@don.ac.uk
www.don.ac.uk
• BA (Hons) scriptwriting • Cert/Dip/PgDip marketing (CIM).
• HNC computing general. Fdg animation and games art. BA
(Hons) theatre or dance practice with digital performance. MA
digital performance • NCFE InterCert music tech (mix DJ
skills); BA (Hons) music tech (top-up); music (top-up);
applied new music; creative music tech

Dublin Institute of Technology
Fitzwilliam House, 30 Upper Pembroke Street, Dublin 2
00 353 1 402 3000
school of media: 00 353 1 402 3098
www.dit.ie
• BA media arts • BA (Hons) journalism with a language; media
arts; performing arts. MA journalism • MA PR • BA (Hons)
photography. MA digital media tech • FCert music. BMus
(Hons). MMus performance

Dundee, University of
Nethergate, Dundee DD1 4HN
01382 344000
srs@dundee.ac.uk
www.dundee.ac.uk and www.imaging.dundee.ac.uk
• BA (Hons) animation and electronic media; time-based art;
illustration. MSc animation and visualisation; electronic
imaging

Durham University
University Office, Old Elvet, Durham DH1 3HP
0191 334 2000
admissions@durham.ac.uk
www.dur.ac.uk
• BA (Hons) music; education studies with music

Ealing, Hammersmith and West London College
Gliddon Road, Barons Court, London W14 9BL
0800 980 2175
Marketing@wlc.ac.uk
www.wlc.ac.uk
• BTec FirstDip/NatDip media • BTec NatDip/HND multimedia.
BTec Dip design. BTec NatDip graphic design; multimedia;
graphics. Fdg digital animation. Short course in web page
creation and other IT courses • BTec NatAward/NatDip music
tech. BTec Dip performing arts (music). BTec NatDip music
practice

East Anglia, University of
Norwich, Norfolk NR4 7TJ
01603 456161
admissions@uea.ac.uk
www.uea.ac.uk
• BA politics with media; society, culture and media. MA economics of the mass media • BA English literature with creative writing. MA creative writing • BA film with American studies, English studies, TV. MA film; film with archiving; studies in fiction • MA culture and communication
• BA music; music with computing; music with mathematics. MMus music performance studies

East London, University of
Docklands Campus, University Way, London E16 2RD
020 8223 3000
admiss@uel.ac.uk
www.uel.ac.uk
• BA (Hons) media and creative industries; media. MA media; global media • BA (Hons) creative writing; journalism
• BA (Hons) film and video: theory and practice/ film history.
• BA (Hons) media and advertising; communication studies
• BA (Hons) photographic and print media. • HND multimedia tech. BA (Hons) digital arts; interactive media. BSc (Hons) multimedia; multimedia tech. MA interactive media practice; cybernetic culture • BA (Hons) music culture: theory and production. MA sonic culture

East Surrey College
Reigate School of Art Design and Media, Gatton Point, Claremont Road, Redhill, Surrey RH1 2JX
01737 772611
studentservices@esc.ac.uk
www.esc.ac.uk
• FDip art, design and media • HNC/HND 3D media crafts and sculpture; moving image production. InterDip media: audio, video and photography. NatDip media (moving image)
• InterDip multimedia. NatDip photography. HNC/Dip digital photography • NatDip media (audio)

Edge Hill College of Higher Education
St Helen's Road, Ormskirk, Lancashire L39 4QP
01695 575171
enquiries@edgehill.ac.uk
www.edgehill.ac.uk
• BA (Hons) media • BA (Hons) journalism (NCTJ). BSc (Hons) creative writing. PgDip print journalism • BA (Hons) media (film and TV); film; film with film and TV production. PgDip broadcast journalism • BA (Hons) media (advertising); PR
• BA (Hons) media (digital media design); animation; Graduate diplomas in print and broadcast journalism

Edinburgh College of Art
Lauriston Place, Edinburgh EH3 9DF
0131 221 6000
registry@eca.ac.uk
www.eca.ac.uk
• BA (Hons)/MDes/Dip visual communication - animation; film and TV, graphic design; illustration; photography. MA/MFA film directing.

Edinburgh, University of
57 George Square, Edinburgh EH8 9JU
0131 650 1000
sra.enquiries@ed.ac.uk
www.ed.ac.uk
• MA/MSc English literature: creative writing; culture; writing and cultural politics • PhD/MSc film • MSc sound design; design and digital media • MA (Hons) (undergrad) music; music tech. MSc research music. Dip music therapy (Nordoff-Robbins). MMus composition; keyboard performance studies; musicology; organology

Editorial Centre
Hanover House, Marine Court, St Leonards-on-Sea, East Sussex TN38 0DX
01424 435991
enquiries@editorial-centre.co.uk
www.editorial-centre.co.uk
• NatDip journalism (15-week pre-entry newspaper journalism, Newspaper Qualifications Council). Dip journalism (overseas); subediting; press photography. Short courses inc reporting, writing, features, subediting, desk editing, editing, design, law, government, FoI, photography, pictures, publishing business, marketing, Quark, InDesign, PhotoShop, etc • Short courses in video camera and editing, presenting for TV and multimedia, reporting for TV and multimedia, editing for TV and multimedia, radio • Short course in multimedia basics, designing for the web, subediting, editorial staff and the web

Editorial Training Consultants
13 Petworth Road, Haslemere, Surrey GU27 2JB
01428 644123
info@etc-online.co.uk
www.etc-online.co.uk
• Short tailored courses for businesses. Media law: IP inc copyright, defamation update, IP update. Journalism skills: interviewing, style, styles of writing, subbing, research, shorthand, etc.. PR: marketing, presentation, creative thinking, writing, media training etc. Publishing: editorial management and craft skills. • New media: online writing and research; improving site traffic. Design training. Academic journalism. Graduate programme. Team days for magazines or websites.

Essex, University of
Wivenhoe Park, Colchester CO4 3SQ
01206 873333
admit@essex.ac.uk
www.essex.ac.uk
• BA journalism (South East Essex College) • BA film and literature/ history of art; history with film; American studies with film. MACert film; film and literature • BSc multimedia production and internet tech (taught in conjunction with South East Essex College) • BA music production (South East Essex College)

Exeter, University of
The Queen's Drive, Exeter, Devon EX4 4QJ
01392 661000
www.ex.ac.uk
• BA English, also with film. • MA/PhD creative writing
• BA film (cinema and practice)/ film with a modern language; MA film; PhD film by practice

Falmouth, University College
Woodlane Campus, Falmouth, Cornwall TR11 4RH
01326 211077
admissions@falmouth.ac.uk
www.falmouth.ac.uk
• BA (Hons) English with creative writing; journalism; media studies. BA (Hons) graphic design. BA (Hons)/MA photography. BA (Hons) film; broadcasting. BA (Hons) PR.
• MA interactive art and design MA international journalism
• PgDip/MA broadcast journalism (BJTC) (MA options in arts, media, travel/investigative/science/sports journalism; TV production • PgDip/MA professional writing. PgDip creative advertising

Glamorgan, University of

Pontypridd, Wales CF37 1DL
0800 716925
enquiries@glam.ac.uk
www.glam.ac.uk
• BA (Hons) English, also with media; drama (theatre and media); media and communication studies; media, with options • BA (Hons) creative and professional writing; journalism. BSc (Hons) creative technologies: broadcast; multimedia; lighting tech; live event tech. BA (Hons) film and TV set design; film (joint); film, radio and TV; media production (with options); media production (radio). BSc (Hons) media production with marketing; drama (minor/joint film studies), multimedia; multimedia tech. • HND/Fdg/BSc/ BSc (Hons) music tech; sound tech. BA (Hons) pop. MSc advanced music production; music engineering and production. MPhil/PhD film practice. MSc film producing and business management •. MPhil writing; MA scriptwriting. • HND/Fdg/BSc/BSc (Hons) music tech; sound tech. BA (Hons) pop. MSc advanced music production; music engineering and production FCert media and information tech. BSc (Hons) interactive new media tech; media tech (also as BSc); multimedia; multimedia tech. BA (Hons) media production (photography)

Glasgow Caledonian University

70 Cowcaddens Road, Glasgow G4 0BA
0141 331 3000
enquiries@gcal.ac.uk
www.gcal.ac.uk
• BA/BA (Hons) journalism (NCTJ). PGDip journalism studies (NCTJ) • BA (Hons) marketing • Dip multimedia visualisation with product design. BSc multimedia tech. MA digital media design • BSc/BSc (Hons) audio tech with electronics; multimedia

Glasgow Metropolitan College

60 North Hanover Street, Glasgow G1 2BP
0141 566 6226
enquiries@glasgowmet.ac.uk
www.gcbp.ac.uk
• HNC/HND journalism: broadcast and print • HNC/HND TV operations and production • HNC/HND event management • HNC/HND digital media for publishing and print; publishing. • HNC/HND interactive multimedia creation; radio; graphic design; TV production; visual information: design and illustration. HND professional photography and digital imaging. AdvDip illustrative photography

Glasgow School of Art

167 Renfrew Street, Glasgow G3 6RQ
0141 353 4500
registry@gsa.ac.uk
www.gsa.ac.uk
• MPhil 2D/3D motion graphics; BA (Hons)/ PhD visual communication;

Glasgow, University of

Glasgow G12 8QQ
0141 330 2000
admissions@gla.ac.uk
www.gla.ac.uk
• MA (Hons) creative and cultural studies (undergraduate) • MA (Hons) theatre; film and TV (undergrad). MLitt theatre; film and TV • MA (Hons) arts and media informatics (undergrad) • BMus/MA (Hons) music

Gloucestershire, University of

The Park, Cheltenham GL50 2RH
0870 721 0210
admissions@glos.ac.uk
www.glos.ac.uk
• BA (Hons) print journalism; creative writing • BA (Hons) broadcast journalism; film; media comms BA (Hons) advertising; PR; marketing, advertising and communications; media and music management • BA (Hons) multimedia; digital film production; publishing. PhD Media, art and communication.

Goldsmiths College

Dept of Media and Communications,
University of London, New Cross, London SE14 6NW
020 7919 7171
media-comms@gold.ac.uk
www.goldsmiths.ac.uk
• BA media and anthropology/sociology/modern literature/comms; international media; transnational comms and global media. MPhil/PhD/MRes/FCert/BA media and comms. Practice courses in journalism, radio, TV, film, photography, surrealism in the cinema • MA journalism; practical journalism (accredited by PTC and recognised by NUJ) • MA political communications; feature films; filmmaking; TV journalism; radio (BJTC); screen documentary; scriptwriting • MA digital media: tech and cultural form; image and communication (photography or electronic graphics); interactive media: critical theory and practice • BMus music; music (extension degree); pop studies. PgCert music. MMus composition; contemporary music studies; ethnomusicology; historical musicology; music theory and analysis; performance and related studies. MPhil/PhD music. Dip jazz and pop. PgDip music teaching to adults. Cert music studies; music workshop skills. FCert integrated degree in music

Greenwich, University of

Old Royal Naval College, Park Row, Greenwich,
London SE10 9LS
020 8331 8000
courseinfo@greenwich.ac.uk
www.gre.ac.uk
• BA (Hons) creative industries; media and comms • HND professional writing. BA creative writing (options). BA (Hons) media writing (options) • HND TV production tech. BA film (with options) • BA(Hons) marketing comms. • HNC/HND/BA (Hons) graphic and digital design. HND photography. Fdg creative industries (multimedia; image-based media)*. BA (Hons) photography*; 3D digital design and animation. BSc (Hons) multimedia and internet tech; multimedia tech (options); entertainment tech; interactive multimedia games development. BEng (Hons) games and entertainment systems. MA critical studies, media, arts, philosophy and practice; website design and content planning. Fdg creative industries (music production)

Grimsby Institute of Further & Higher Education

Nuns Corner, Grimsby DN34 5BQ
01472 311222
infocent@grimsby.ac.uk
www.grimsby.ac.uk
• Dip media; bespoke media law training • NatDip media (journalism and publishing). OCN novel/short story writing. BA (Hons) professional writing; digital media production - journalism (both with Lancaster University) • HND media production; media (TV, film and video). NatDip media (moving image). Fdg (applied) digital media (broadcast). BA (Hons) digital media production - TV, film, video (with Lancaster University). OCN intro to script writing. ProfCert video journalism; digital video editing • BTec NatDip e-media; games media development. HNC photography and digital imaging. HNC/HND interactive media. HND multimedia. BA (Hons) digital media production - photography; multimedia (with Lancaster University) • ProfCert digital audio editing. HND music production. Dip performing arts (music). NatDip music tech.

Guildford College

Stoke Park, Guildford, Surrey GU1 1EZ
01483 448500
info@guildford.ac.uk
www.guildford.ac.uk
• NatCert media • NatDip media (moving image). HND/ BA (Hons) media production. • IntroCert/ ProfCert/Dip/PgDip marketing (CIM) • SROCN level 2 and 3/NatDip photography. Short courses in PhotoShop and Quark Xpress on the Mac

Harlow College

Velizy Avenue, Town Centre, Harlow, Essex CM20 3LH
01279 868000
full-time@harlow-college.ac.uk
www.harlow-college.ac.uk
• *One-year journalism: newspapers (NCTJ). BA (Hons) journalism (Middlesex University). Pg journalism: newspapers (NCTJ); magazines (NCTJ, PTC)* • *NatDip graphic design. Short courses: Apple Mac workshop, webpage design, digital photography, advanced digital photography* • *NatDip pop. Short course in music tech*

Harrow College

Brookshill, Harrow Weald, Middlesex HA3 6RR
020 8909 6000
enquiries@harrow.ac.uk
www.harrow.ac.uk
• *BTec NatCert/NatDip media* • *Short courses: creative writing* • *Short courses speaking with confidence* • *Short courses in using digital photography (PhotoShop), web design using Dreamweaver/ Front Page* • *Short courses in music theory beginner to grade 5, piano keyboard, singing and vocal workout*

Henley College Coventry

Henley Road, Bell Green, Coventry CV2 1ED
024 7662 6300
info@henley-cov.ac.uk
www.henley-cov.ac.uk
• *BTec Dip/HND media* • *BTec NatDip media - moving image* • *BTec NatDip e-media; photography; media production*

Hertfordshire, University of

College Lane, Hatfield AL10 9AB
01707 284000
admissions@herts.ac.uk
www.herts.ac.uk
• *BSc (Hons) media tech and digital broadcast* • *BA (Hons) programmes: digital animation, 2D and 3D; graphic design; digital and lens media; model design; special effects; character creation and soft effects. BA/BSc (Hons) software systems for the arts and media. BSc (Hons) digital media tech with modern languages; internet tech and e-commerce* • *BSc (Hons) music composition and tech; music; commercial composition and tech; music tech; sound design tech BA (Hons) programmes: screen cultures (with options); philosophy with media cultures; philosophy/journalism with media; English language with film or media communications; film and television entertainment. BSc journalism with mathematics, or most social sciences (excluding modern languages)*

Highbury College, Portsmouth

Dept of Media and Journalism, Dovercourt Road, Portsmouth, Hampshire PO6 2SA
023 9238 3131
info@highbury.ac.uk
www.highbury.ac.uk
• *BTec Dip art, design and media; media* • *Pre-entry newspaper journalism (NCTJ); magazine journalism (PTC). HND media (journalism). Short course introduction to newspaper and magazine journalism* • *Pre-entry broadcast journalism (BJTC). BTec NatDip media production (moving image). HND media (moving image).* • *BTec NatDip media production (publishing)* • *BTec NatDip multimedia;* • *BTec NatDip music tech*

Huddersfield, University of

Queensgate, Huddersfield HD1 3DH
01484 422288
admissions@hud.ac.uk
www.hud.ac.uk
• *BA (Hons) English (with media, creative writing, journalism); media and sports journalism; drama and media* • *BA (Hons) media and print journalism* • *BA (Hons) media and TV production.* • *BA (Hons) advertising with media and design management; creative imaging (advertising); marketing with innovation; PR with media; PR with media and design management* • *HNC/HND multimedia. BA (Hons) creative imaging (graphic design/illustration/media and animation); interactive multimedia and design; multimedia with installation art; multimedia (options); video, 3D and popular music; video and 3D for popular music; virtual reality design with animation. BSc (Hons)/BSc multimedia computing. BSc (Hons) new media innovation. MA creative imaging. MSc electronic and computer based systems design. MA/MSc innovation for the digital future; interactive multimedia production. PgCert/PgDip/MSc multimedia and e-learning* • *BMus (Hons) music; creative music tech. BA (Hons) drama with music; music tech; music tech and pop; music with a modern language; music with English; pop production; media and radio journalism. BSc (Hons) music tech software development; music tech and audio systems; pop production. PgDip/ MA music (single and joint); music (composition; electro-acoustic composition; performance; performance; contemporary music studies; historical musicology). MA music (musicology)*

Hull, University of

Cottingham Road, Hull HU6 7RX
01482 346311
admissions@hull.ac.uk
www.hull.ac.uk
• *BA media, culture and society* • *BA creative writing (options). Cert creative writing* • *BA film studies (with options). MA contemporary literature and film* • *BA marketing (options)* • *BA creative music tech with digital arts; design for digital media; digital arts. BSc creative media computing. BSc internal computing with creative media; creative music tech; design for digital media. BSc computer science with games development.* • *BA music; creative music tech (single or with digital arts); drama and music; English and music; music and modern languages; modern languages and film studies. BSc music tech and computing. BMus music; jazz and popular music. MMus music (musicology, composition, performance). MRes creative music tech. MPhil/PhD music; creative music tech. BA theatre and performance; drama with various options (languages, social sciences and media)*

Journalism Training Centre

29 Harley Street, London W1G 9QR
020 7798 5618
info@jtc.co.uk
www.jtc.co.uk
• *Dip periodicals journalism (NUJ). Short courses: subediting, feature writing, media law, computer skills, page design and layout, news writing, shorthand, editorial managing.*

Keele, University of

Keele, Staffordshire ST5 5BG
01782 621111
www.keele.ac.uk
• *BA/BSc media, comms and culture (with options); marketing* • *BA/BSc music (options); music tech (options)*

Kensington and Chelsea College

Hortensia Road, London SW10 0QS
020 7573 5333
enquiries@kcc.ac.uk
www.kcc.ac.uk

• BTec NatCert/HNC multimedia; graphic design; LOCN web page design Flash, Dreamweaver, Fireworks; e-commerce and business websites with Dreamweaver, PHP and Apache • BTec FirstDip performing musician (in partnership with Access to Music). LOCN music tech. Music tech with Deep Recording Studios. LOCN studio programming level 1, 2 and 3.

Kent Institute of Art and Design

Oakwood Park, Maidstone, Kent ME16 8AG
01622 620000
info@kiad.ac.uk
www.kiad.ac.uk

• BA (Hons) video media arts; video and photography. MA artists' film, video and photography • BA (Hons) design, branding and marketing; fashion promotion. • BA (Hons) illustration • BTec NatDip multimedia. Fdg graphic communication. BA (Hons) animation; digital 3D design; graphic design; photography; photography and media arts. PgCert contemporary photographic practice; graphic design. MA graphic design; photography

Kent, University of

The Registry, Canterbury, Kent CT2 7NZ
01227 764000
recruitment@kent.ac.uk
www.kent.ac.uk

• MA English and American literature and creative writing • BA (Hons) American studies (art and film); European studies (film); film; film and contemporary arts; visual and performed arts. MA/MPhil/PhD film • BA (Hons) multimedia tech and design. MRes/MPhil/PhD cartoons and caricature. MSc computer animation • BA (Hons) music tech

King's College London

School of Humanities, Strand, London WC2R 2LS
020 7836 5454
ceu@kcl.ac.uk
www.kcl.ac.uk

• MA cultural and creative industries • BA English with film; film and American studies; other BA honours programmes with film. MA contemporary cinema cultures • MA digital culture and tech. MSc information tech and internet law • BMus music; BA German or French and music; languages with digital humanities; music with digital humanities. MMus music.

Kingston University

River House, 53–57 High Street,
Kingston-upon-Thames, Surrey KT1 1LQ
020 8547 2000
admissions-info@kingston.ac.uk
www.kingston.ac.uk

• BA (Hons) visual and material culture; BSc (Hons) media tech. • BA (Hons) creative writing (joint); journalism. MA creative writing • BA (Hons) history of art, design and film/TV; TV design and production; film. MA production design/screen design for film and TV • Fdg graphic comms. MA communication design; marketing; strategic marketing management • BA (Hons) graphic design. BA (Hons) media and cultural studies (with options) • BA (Hons) live arts. BMus (Hons) music. MA composing for film and TV; music; music composition; music education; musicology; music performance; pop; screen design for film and TV; film studies: contemporary developments

Lambeth College

45 Clapham Common South Side, London SW4 9BL
020 7501 5100
courses@lambethcollege.ac.uk
www.lambethcollege.ac.uk

• BTec FirstDip media • Fdg journalism. Pre-entry newspaper journalism (NCTJ) • BTec NatDip media production (moving image). Level2 NatAward radio. C&G Cert media video production techniques. • OCNLR video, photography and digital publishing; web design and animation. C&G Dip/ AdvDip web design. BTec FirstDip multimedia and photography (beginners and intermediate). OCNLR web design and animation (e-media)

Lampeter, University of Wales

Ceredigion SA48 7ED
01570 422351
dept of film and media: 01570 424790
admissions@lamp.ac.uk
www.lamp.ac.uk

• BA media production. MA/PgDip Welsh media • BA English with creative writing. MA/PgDip creative writing • BA film/ MPhil and PhD; film and media studies. BA/MA/PgDip media production, e-commerce. MA/PgDip screenwriting (bilingual); screen studies; interactive media

Lancaster University

Bailrigg, Lancaster LA1 4YW
01524 65201
ugadmissions@lancaster.ac.uk
www.lancs.ac.uk

• BA (Hons) contemporary arts; English language and the media; media and cultural studies. MA globalisation and the information age; visual culture • BA (Hons) English language or literature with creative writing. MA creative writing; women's writing • BA (Hons) film and cultural studies; film and philosophy; sociology. PgDip/MSc media production and distribution • BA (Hons) advertising and marketing. BSc (Hons) marketing; marketing management. MSc advanced marketing management • BSc (Hons) computer science with multimedia systems. BSc (Hons)/MSc communication and computer systems. PgDip/MA/MRes IT, management and organisational change. MSc mobile and ubiquitous computing; multimedia networking. PgDip/MSc mobile game design and m-commerce systems*; multimedia courseware engineering • BA (Hons)/BSc (Hons) computer science and music. BA (Hons) music tech; musicology. BA (Hons)/BMus (Hons) music. MMus music; music theory

Leeds College of Art and Design

Blenheim Walk, Leeds, West Yorkshire LS2 9AQ
0113 202 8000
info@leeds-art.ac.uk
www.leeds-art.ac.uk

• Fdg advertising. BA (Hons) visual comms
• Fdg photography; digital media

Leeds College of Music

3 Quarry Hill, Leeds LS2 7PD
0113 222 3400
enquiries@lcm.ac.uk
www.lcm.ac.uk

• Fdg music production for film and television • BA (Hons) jazz studies; music studies; pop studies; music production. MMus jazz studies; music studies. PgCert advanced piano performance; NatDip in music technology; popular music

Leeds Metropolitan University

Civic Quarter, Leeds LS1 3HE
0113 812 3113
course-enquiries@leedsmet.ac.uk
www.leedsmet.ac.uk

• BA (Hons) media and popular culture • CertHE/Fdg film and TV production. BA (Hons) film and moving image production • HND business and PR; consumer marketing; BA (Hons) PR; PR with a European language; consumer marketing; marketing. • BA/BA (Hons) managing cultural and major events; BA (Hons) entertainment management. MA PR management; PR. MSc marketing • Fdg creative music and sound tech. HND/BSc (Hons) games design; multimedia tech. BSc (Hons) animation tech and special effects. BA (Hons) web media management. BA/BSc (Hons) education and new media; interactive media tech. MSc digital imaging tech; web engineering • BSc (Hons) design tech for music; music tech; music and new media tech. MSc music tech. MA screen media cultures.

Leeds Trinity & All Saints

Brownberrie Lane, Horsforth, Leeds LS18 5HD
0113 283 7100
admissions@tasc.ac.uk
www.leedstrinity.ac.uk

• BA English, also with film, media and other options. BA media; media and marketing. Cert media education • BA sports journalism; business journalism*. PgDip/MA bi-media (radio and TV); radio or print journalism (NCTJ) • BA film • PgDip/MA public communication. BA marketing (options)

Leeds, University of

Leeds LS2 9JT
0113 243 1751
enquiry@leeds.ac.uk
www.leeds.ac.uk

• BA creative writing. MA international journalism: production; media management • PgDip/MA creative writing • BA broadcast journalism; cinema, photography and TV. MA scriptwriting for TV • BA comms. MA comms studies; international comms; media management; political communication • BA new media, communication studies • BA/BMus music. BA/BSc music, multimedia and electronics. BA popular and world music; music - philosophy; music - theology and religious studies. MMus music (composition; musicology; performance; tech and computer music). PgCert/ PgDip/MA music and liturgy

Leicester, University of

University Road, Leicester LE1 7RH
0116 252 2522
admissions@le.ac.uk
www.le.ac.uk

• BA film and the visual arts. MA humanities and film • BSc comms, media and society. MA/PGDip mass comms; globalisation and comms; media and communication research

Lincoln, University of

Brayford Pool, Lincoln LN6 7TS
01522 882000
enquiries@lincoln.ac.uk
www.lincoln.ac.uk

Some courses held at Hull School of Art & Design • BA (Hons) media, culture and comms (with American studies; PR; journalism; marketing). MA/MRes/MPhil/PhD media and cultural studies • BA (Hons) journalism • BA (Hons) contemporary lens media; digital and interactive TV (at Hull) BA (Hons)/MA media production. MA documentary and factual programme production • BA (Hons) advertising and art direction; marketing. MSc international marketing strategy. MBA strategic marketing • BA (Hons) animation; games design; interactive and screen-based graphics; interactive multimedia; web design. BSc (Hons) media tech; multimedia tech. BSc (Hons)/MSc games computing • BSc audio tech

Liverpool Community College

Broad Green Road, Old Swan, Liverpool L13 5SQ
0151 252 1515
www.liv-coll.ac.uk

• BTec FirstDip/HND/Fdg media • Pre-entry journalism (NCTJ). Dip print/periodical journalism (fast-track, NCTJ) • BTec NatDip media (moving image) • BTec NatDip multimedia; photography. Fdg digital media design; media production. • BTec FirstDip/NatAward/ NatDip music tech. ProfDip creative music tech. CollegeFirst in media skills; evening classes in multimedia.

Liverpool Hope University College

Hope Park, Liverpool L16 9JD
0151 291 3000
admission@hope.ac.uk
www.hope.ac.uk

• BA creative and performing arts; media (single and joint, with social and physical sciences) • BA film (joint) • BA marketing (joint) • BA music (joint); music, pop, music tech. MA music

Liverpool John Moores University

Roscoe Court, 4 Rodney Street, Liverpool L1 2TZ
0151 231 5090
recruitment@ljmu.ac.uk
www.ljmu.ac.uk

• BA (Hons) media and cultural studies; media, cultural studies and marketing; mass communications • BA (Hons) journalism (NCTJ); international journalism (NCTJ); imaginative writing. MA journalism; international journalism; writing • BA (Hons) media professional studies; screen studies. MA screen writing • BA (Hons) business and PR; marketing; business and information. BSc (Hons) e-business tech and management • PgDip/MA information management • BA (Hons) English literature and electronic creative tech; BSc (Hons) multimedia systems • BA (Hons) pop studies

Liverpool, University of

Liverpool L69 3BX
0151 794 2000
uksro@liv.ac.uk
www.liv.ac.uk

• BA (Hons) English and communication studies (joint) • BA (Hons) film (European) and a modern language • BA (Hons) communication and business studies (joint); politics and communication studies; marketing. MA politics and the mass media •BEng (Hons)/ MEng (Hons) wireless comms and 3G tech. MSc internet computing • BA (Hons) communication, media and pop (joint). BA (Hons) music/ pop. MA pop studies. MMus music

London Business School

Regent's Park, London NW1 4SA
020 7000 7000
www.london.edu

• MBA marketing strategy (full-time executive MBA)

London — University of the Arts

www.arts.ac.uk

Camberwell College of Arts

Peckham Road, London SE5 8UF
020 7514 6302
www.camberwell.arts.ac.uk

• BA/MA conservation; illustration. MA book arts • BA photography. BA/MA graphic design. MA digital arts; digital arts online; short courses: next generation desktop publishing; guerrilla film-making; animation; portrait photography

Central St Martin's College of Art & Design
020 7514 7000
www.csm.arts.ac.uk
• MA creative practice for narrative environments
• BA criticism, communication and curation for arts and design; fashion communication with promotion. MA fashion journalism • BA acting; directing. MA European classical acting; performance (pathways in screen acting, directing, scriptwriting, movement direction); scenography • BA graphic design. PgCert professional studies: photography. PgDip character animation. MA communication design

Chelsea College of Art & Design
16 John Islip Street, London SW1P 4JP
020 7514 7751
enquiries@chelsea.arts.ac.uk
www.chelsea.arts.ac.uk
 BA design communication • BA fine art: new media

London College of Communication
Elephant & Castle, London SE1 6SB
020 7514 6500
www.lcc.arts.ac.uk
• Fdg media practice. BA media and cultural studies • Fdg/BA/ PgDip/MA journalism. GradCert periodical journalism
• BA film and video. MA screenwriting; documentary research. PgDip broadcast journalism and documentary photography
• Fdg/BA marketing and advertising. BA/MA PR. MA marketing and comms • Dip print production. BA print media, marketing and advertising. GradCert bookbinding and restoration/publishing. Postgraduate programme in publishing/publishing production • Dip animation; pro photography practice; 3D modelling and animation; new media publishing. NatDip/BA graphic and media design. Fdg digital media production; interactive games production; photojournalism; design for graphic; display design. GradCert photography practice; design for visual communication. BA digital media production; photography. MA/PgDip interactive media. MSc digital colour imaging. MA digital media and print; photography; graphic design. Short courses: digital orientation/ media • Dip sound design and music tech. BA sound arts and design. GradCert sonic arts; music publishing

London College of Fashion
20 John Prince's Street, London W1G 0BJ
020 7514 7500
www.fashion.arts.ac.uk
• PgCert fashion and lifestyle journalism. MA fashion journalism • Fdg fashion marketing and promotion (also online); fashion design and marketing. GradCert fashion marketing. BA fashion promotion. MA fashion photography; digital fashion

Wimbledon College of Art
Main Building, Merton Hall Road, London SW19 3QA
020 7514 9641
www.wimbledon.arts.ac.uk
MA or BA: Fine art; theatre. Short courses: art theory; creative software; design; film and photography; fine art; theatre, costume and screen.

London College of Music & Media
see Thames Valley University

London Film School
24 Shelton Street, London WC2H 9UB
020 7836 9642
info@lfs.org.uk
www.lfs.org.uk
• MA filmmaking; screenwriting

London Metropolitan University
31 Jewry Street, London EC3N 2EY
020 7423 0000
admissions@londonmet.ac.uk
www.londonmet.ac.uk
• BA (Hons) media • BA (Hons) creative writing. Fdg/BA (Hons) journalism. MA professional writing • Fdg audio production for broadcast media. BA (Hons) film; film and broadcast production. PgCert/PgDip/MA screenwriting. MA AV production; filmmaking • BA (Hons) advertising, marketing communication and media*; arts management (joint); comms and visual culture; events management and music and media management; marketing; PR. HND/BA (Hons) events management. BSc mass comms with media. MA international marketing comms; marketing; mass comms; sport management • Fdg/ BSc (Hons) multimedia. BSc (Hons) digital media; computer animation; computer visualisation and games; digital media and mass comms. MA digital information management/media/media management/ moving image. MSc multimedia systems • Fdg musical instruments. /BA (Hons) music and media management. BSc (Hons) music tech (audio systems). BA (Hons) sound and media. Cert sound recording tech

London School of Economics and Political Science
Houghton Street, London WC2A 2AE
020 7405 7686
stu.rec@lse.ac.uk
www.lse.ac.uk
• MSc gender and the media • MSc global media and comms; media and comms; media and comms regulation and policy; politics and communication; social and public communication
• MSc new media, information and society

London School of Journalism
126 Shirland Road, Maida Vale, London W9 2BT
020 7289 7777
info@lsjournalism.com
www.lsj.org
• PgDip journalism (also online) (NUJ). Short and distance courses inc news/feature/internet/freelance journalism, sub-editing, novel/short story writing, writing for children, law etc

London South Bank University
90 London Road, London SE1 6EN
020 7815 7815
enquiries@lsbu.ac.uk
www.lsbu.ac.uk
• BA (Hons) English/ media; BSc (Hons) media and society; MA creative/digital media arts (cultural and media; digital film production; media education; media writing; new media)
• BA (Hons) creative writing and English • BA (Hons) film (joint) • BA (Hons) arts management; marketing. MSc/PgDip international marketing. E-marketing award (CIM)
• BA (Hons) digital photography/media arts; game cultures. MSc/PgDip/PgCert internet and multimedia computing/engineering • BA (Hons) sonic media; writing for media arts; digital photography

London, University College
Gower Street, London WC1E 6BT
020 7679 2000
www.ucl.ac.uk
• MA film studies • MA library and information studies. PgCert/PgDip/MA publishing (with various pathways)

Bedfordshire, University of
Park Square, Luton, Beds LU1 3JU
01582 489286
enquiries@beds.ac.uk
www.beds.ac.uk
• MA media, culture and tech. MRes media arts • BA (Hons) creative writing; journalism; journalism and public relations. MRes creative writing • Fdg media production (Barnfield/ Bedford/ Dunstable/Milton Keynes). BA (Hons) media performance; TV production. MA international cinema; media production (documentary) • Fdg ad and marketing comms. BA (Hons) marketing; marketing and media practices; PR; media advertising; media practices (mass comms). MSc marketing and business management; marketing comms. MA media arts (mass comms) • Fdg creative and editorial photography (Dunstable College); graphic design for digital media (Milton Keynes College); media art and design. BA (Hons) digital photography and video art; animation. BSc (Hons) computer games development. MA art design and internet tech; children's literature and culture; new media and internet tech. MSc computer animation • Fdg music tech; music production (Bedford). BA (Hons) music tech

Manchester, University of
Oxford Road, Manchester M13 9PL
0161 306 6000
www.manchester.ac.uk
• BA (Hons) media, culture and society • MA/PhD creative writing • BA (Hons) film with options • BMus (Hons) music. BA (Hons) music and drama. MMus musicology; composition; electroacoustic music composition. MPhil/PhD musicology; composition

Manchester Metropolitan University
All Saints Building, All Saints, Manchester M15 6BH
0161 247 2000
enquiries@mmu.ac.uk
www.mmu.ac.uk
• MA media arts; representation in cinema and media; design and art direction • BA (Hons) English and creative writing • BA (Hons) English and film; contemporary film and video; film and media BA (Hons) digital media (with options, urban studies, languages, social sciences, multimedia, psychology, mathematics) • BA (Hons) ad and brand management; communication; corporate communication; communication in culture and media; human communication; interactive arts • Fdg new media design. BSc (Hons) multimedia tech; media tech; multimedia computing. BA (Hons) photography

Marjon, College of St Mark & St John
Derriford Road, Plymouth, Devon PL6 8BH
01752 636700
admissions@marjon.ac.uk
www.marjon.ac.uk
• BA (Hons) media (combined Hons available); contemporary culture, media and society • BA (Hons) writing for the media; creative writing • BA (Hons) creative media practice • BA (Hons) PR

Mid-Cheshire College
Hartford Campus, Chester Road, Northwich,
Cheshire CW8 1LJ
01606 74444
info@midchesh.ac.uk
www.midchesh.ac.uk
• BTec NatDip multimedia; media (moving image); graphic design; photography. Fdg new and interactive media; contemporary photography practice. • BTec NatDip music practice; music tech. BTec FirstDip in media (moving image)

Middlesex University
Admissions Enquiries, North London Business Park,
London N11 1QS
020 8411 5555
admissions@mdx.ac.uk
www.mdx.ac.uk
• BA (Hons) media and cultural studies • BA (Hons) writing and publishing; creative and media writing; journalism and communication studies; journalism. MA writing (prose fiction, poetry or scriptwriting) • BA film arts/ filmmaking. BA (Hons) film studies; film video interactive arts; TV production • MA media and comms management. BA marketing • BA (Hons) magazine publishing; publishing, journalism and media • HND/HNC graphic design. DipHE visual communication design - graphic design. BA (Hons) Journalism (with options) Fdg graphic design. BA (Hons) graphic/games design; illustration; photography. MA/MSc design for interactive media. MA electronic arts; graphic design • BA (Hons) music; music and arts management; theatre arts (various genres). BA/BSc (Hons)/MA sonic arts. MA music

Mid-Kent College
Horsted Centre, Maidstone Road, Chatham,
Kent ME5 9UQ
01634 402020
www.midkent.ac.uk
• BTec IntroDip art, design and media • BTec FirstDip media • BTec NatDip media (publishing); media (moving image) • BTec NatDip music tech. BTec NatAward music tech

Napier University
Craiglockhart Campus, Edinburgh EH14 1DJ
0845 260 6040
info@napier.ac.uk
www.napier.ac.uk
• BA/BA (Hons) culture, media and society • BA/BA (Hons) journalism. MSc/PgDip journalism • MA screen project development; screenwriting • BA (Hons) communication; marketing management. MSc/PgDip creative advertising; international communication; marketing • BA/BA (Hons) publishing media. MSc/ PgDip publishing • BA/BA (Hons) design futures; photography, film and imaging. BEng / BEng (Hons) internet computing; multimedia systems; multimedia technology; software engineering. MDes interdisciplinary design • BMus/ BMus (Hons) music. • BA/BA (Hons) popular music

National Broadcasting School
The Innovation Centre, University of Sussex,
Brighton BN1 9SB
01273 704510
www.nationalbroadcastingschool.com
• PgDip NBS radio presentation and production; radio journalism

National Film and Television School
Beaconsfield Studios, Station Road, Beaconsfield,
Bucks HP9 1LG
01494 731425/13
info@nftsfilm-tv.ac.uk
www.nftsfilm-tv.ac.uk
• Dip script development; sound recording for film and TV. MA producing; production design; screenwriting; sound post-production; cinematography; documentary direction; editing; producing for TV entertainment. Doc summer school. Short courses in art and design; camera and lighting; directing; editing; production; sound; writing SFX/VFX • Dip digital post production; visual and special effects producing. MA animation direction • MA composing for film and TV

Neath Port Talbot College
Dwr-y-Felin Road, Neath SA10 7RF
01639 648000
enquiries@nptc.ac.uk
www.nptc.ac.uk
• HNC/HND media production (creative industries) • HNC/HND computing (multimedia) • HND music performance (pop). BA (Hons) music performance and production

New College Nottingham

City Campus, Adams Building, Stoney Street,
Lace Market, Nottingham NG1 1NG
0115 910 0100
enquiries@ncn.ac.uk
www.ncn.ac.uk
• BTec FirstDip/NatDip/HND media • C&G TV and video
production. BTec ProfCert digital video editing • BTec NatDip
e-media production. Fdg digital design (and media top-up).
HND music performance; music production. FirstDip/NatDip
music practice (pop); music tech. Short course music
production. FdA multimedia

Newcastle College

Rye Hill Campus, Scotswood Road, Newcastle NE4 5BR
0191 200 4000
enquiries@ncl-coll.ac.uk
www.ncl-coll.co.ac.uk
• Fdg TV and media practice (and top-up); editorial and news
media design (2 campuses); animation and illustration; web
design and development; creative advertising; commercial
photography • HNC interactive media/graphic design. Fdg
multimedia design; illustration and animation; graphic design;
graphics design for news media. BTec NatDip interactive
media; HEFC art and design; film studies; photography.

Newcastle Upon Tyne, University of

Newcastle NE1 7RU
0191 222 6000
enquiries@ncl.ac.uk
www.ncl.ac.uk
• BA (Hons) media, communication and cultural studies;
BA (Hons) modern languages and film studies • PgCert/MA
creative writing. MA literary studies: writing, memory, culture
• MA film: history theory and practice; MA modern and
contemporary studies; MA media and journalism; MLitt and
PhD: American and English film • BA (Hons) marketing and
management. BSc (Hons) marketing; Short course:
understanding film • MSc e-business and information
systems; system design for internet apps; cross-cultural
communication and international management

Newport, University of Wales

Caerleon Campus, PO Box 179, Newport,
South Wales NP18 3YG
01633 432432
uic@newport.ac.uk
www.newport.ac.uk
• MA sports media; marketing; telecoms; film • BA (Hons)
creative writing • BA (Hons) documentary film and TV; film
and video. BA (Hons) advertising. BSc marketing • BA (Hons)
interactive media; animation; computer games design.
BSc (Hons) games development and artificial intelligence;
internet and multimedia tech. BA (Hons)/MA animation
• BA (Hons) creative sound and music. Short courses: basic
computing and webpage design.

North East Surrey College of Technology (NESCOT)

Reigate Road, Ewell, Epsom, Surrey KT17 3DS
020 8394 1731
info@nescot.ac.uk
www.nescot.ac.uk
• FirstDip media; media (moving image) • NatDip media
production; performing arts; music tech • NatDip multimedia.
Fdg interactive media; media and multimedia (OUVS);
photography and digital imaging (OUVS). BA (Hons)
photography and imaging. HND media production

North East Wales Institute of Higher Education

Plas Coch, Mold Road, Wrexham LL11 2AW
01978 290666
enquiries@newi.ac.uk
www.newi.ac.uk
• BA (Hons) media (with options) • BA (Hons) writing • BA
(Hons) media comms; marketing. ProfCert/ProfDip/ PgDip
marketing (CIM) • HND internet and multimedia computing;
graphic design. Fdg (Hons) internet and multimedia
computing. Fdg digital media. BA (Hons) animation;
graphic/multimedia; design (various pathways). BSc (Hons)
internet and multimedia computing. MA animation; digital
sound and video process • Fdg sound/studio tech. BSc (Hons)
studio recording and performance tech. FdA digital media.
HNC internet and multimedia computing (with options)

North East Worcestershire College

Peakman Street, Redditch, Worcestershire B98 8DW
01527 570020
info@ne-worcs.ac.uk
www.ne-worcs.ac.uk
• BTec FirstDip/NatDip media; media and music • HNC/HND
media (moving image); multimedia development • BTec
FirstDip performing arts, media and music tech. NatDip music
tech; make-up artistry. BA (Hons) media (2 campuses).
Fdg: theatre and the community

North West Kent College

Oakfield Lane, Dartford, Kent DA1 2JT
0800 074 1447
course.enquiries@nwkcollege.ac.uk
www.nwkcollege.ac.uk
• BTec IntroDip art, design and media; graphics;
3D design; photography; BTec NatDip media; video media
• Fdg professional writing • BTec NatDip graphic design;
multimedia. • InterDip music tech; performance.
Dip advanced music tech; advanced acting and music

Northbrook College Sussex

Little Hampton Road, Worthing, West Sussex BN12 6NU
01903 606060; 0800 183 6060
enquiries@nbcol.ac.uk
www.northbrook.ac.uk
• HND media, the moving image; journalism • BA (Hons)
communication design • ABC Dip/BTec NatDip media arts
• BTec NatDip music tech. HND music performance (pop).
Fdg music production. BA (Hons) music composition;
performance; production (top-up). BA (Hons) communication
design; music composition for professional media;
contemporary media arts practice/photography practice

Northampton, University Of

Park Campus, Boughton Green Road,
Northampton NN2 7AL
0800 358 2232
study@northampton.ac.uk
www.northampton.ac.uk
• BA (Hons) media (with social sciences options)
• HND/BA (Hons) journalism; media production.
• BA (Hons) creative writing • HND digital film-making;
multimedia. BA (Hons) contemporary media practice; film
and TV • BA (Hons) marketing

Northumbria University

Ellison Place, Newcastle Upon Tyne NE1 8ST
0191 232 6002
er.admissions@northumbria.ac.uk
www.northumbria.ac.uk
• BA (Hons) media, culture and society; media practice; media
cultures. • MA creative writing • BA (Hons) media and
journalism; journalism and English; English and film; film and
TV studies; media production; history of modern art, design
for industry • BSc (Hons) communication. BA (Hons) politics
and media • BA (Hons) contemporary photographic
practice/multimedia design. BSc (Hons) multimedia and
digital entertainment computing; multimedia computing;
multimedia and web applications. MA art practices (media)
• BA (Hons) performance; theatre and performance practice
(at the Live Theatre, Newcastle) . MA music management and
promotion

Norwich School of Art and Design

Francis House, 3-7 Redwell Street, Norwich,
Norfolk NR2 4SN
01603 610561
info@nsad.ac.uk
www.nsad.ac.uk
• BA (Hons) creative writing. MA writing the visual
• BA (Hons) graphic design (design for publishing)
• Fdg games art and design; film and video; surface design;
graphic design. BA (Hons) graphic communication; graphic
design; photography; games art and design. MA animation
and sound design; digital practices

noSweat Journalism Training

16/17 Clarkenwell Close, London EC1R OAN
020 7490 2006
info@nosweatjt.co.uk
www.nosweatjt.co.uk
• Prelim Cert newspaper journalism (NCTJ). Dip magazine
journalism

Nottingham Trent University

Burton Street, Nottingham NG1 4BU
0115 941 8418
advice.shop@ntu.ac.uk
www.ntu.ac.uk
• BA (Hons) media (with pathways in communications,
creative industries, film and TV, journalism studies, media
practices and popular culture) (options with social and
physical sciences and languages); media and communication
& society. PgDip/MA media and globalisation • BA (Hons)
English with creative writing. PGDip/MA newspaper
journalism; television journalism; radio journalism; online
journalism (all also international). MA photography. PgCert/
PgDip/MA creative writing • BA (Hons) broadcast journalism.
BA (Hons) print journalism. • BA(Hons)/MA fashion
marketing and communication. ProfDip/ PgDip marketing
(CIM) • BA (Hons) photography; photography in Europe.
BA/BSc (Hons) multimedia. BSc (Hons) computer science
(games tech; imaging and display tech); PgDip/MSc computer
games systems; multimedia engineering/games engineering

Nottingham, University of

University Park, Nottingham NG7 2RD
0115 951 5151
undergraduate-enquiries@nottingham.ac.uk
postgraduate-enquiries@nottingham.ac.uk
www.nottingham.ac.uk
• BA film and American studies/sociology/theology.
• BA (Hons) film and TV (with options). MA/PgDip film.
Research opportunities: institute welcomes applications from
students interested in analysis of film and TV production and
consumption • BA music; music and philosophy

Open University

Walton Hall, Milton Keynes MK7 6AA
01908 274066
general-enquiries@open.ac.uk
www.open.ac.uk
• MA cultural and media

Oxford Brookes University

Headington Campus, Oxford OX3 0BP
01865 484848
query@brookes.ac.uk
www.brookes.ac.uk
• BA/BSc (Hons) film (joint); communications, media and
culture (with options) • BA/BSc (Hons) arts management and
administration (joint); communication, media and culture
(single or joint) • BA/BSc (Hons) publishing (single or joint).
MA education/educational studies with publishing;
international publishing; publishing; publishing and language.
MBA (specialism in publishing) • Fdg art and design. BA/ BSc
(Hons) fine art (single or joint); multimedia systems (joint).
BSc (Hons) media tech (joint); multimedia production (joint).
MA interactive media publishing. MSc digital media
production; e-commerce computing; web tech • BA/BSc
(Hons) music (single or joint). BSc (Hons) sound tech and
digital music. MA composition and sonic art; contemporary
arts and music

Oxford, University of

St Aldate's, Oxford OX1 1DB
01865 276125
www.music.ox.ac.uk
• Dip/MStud creative writing • BA (Hons) music

Peterborough Regional College

Park Crescent, Peterborough PE1 4DZ
01733 767366
info@peterborough.ac.uk
www.peterborough.ac.uk
• BTec FirstDip/HNC/HND media • BA (Hons) media. C&G
7790 journalism (media techniques). HNC/HND journalism
• BTec NatDip media (moving image, video) • BTec NatDip
media (audio/radio); music practice

Plymouth College of Art and Design

Tavistock Place, Plymouth PL4 8AT
01752 203434
enquiries@pcad.ac.uk
www.pcad.ac.uk
• NatDip moving image. Fdg media environmental arts;
BA (Hons) environmental media practice • NatDip media
publishing • NatDip interactive media; graphic design;
photography. BA (Hons) photomedia and design
communication (and top-up). Fdg film and animation;
photography and electronic imaging; graphic design and
production • NatAward music tech (music for media).
Fdg music and sound for film and TV

Plymouth, University of

Drake Circus, Plymouth, Devon PL4 8AA
01752 600600
prospectus@plymouth.ac.uk
www.plymouth.ac.uk
• BA (Hons) media arts (with options); media practice and
society; science and the media. BSc (Hons) science and the
media • PgDip/MA creative writing • MA contemporary film
practice • BA (Hons) marketing • PgDip/MA publishing
• BA (Hons) design: illustration; photography. BA/BSc (Hons)
digital art and tech. BSc (Hons) media lab arts; multimedia
production and tech; media advertising. MA/MSc/MRes
digital art and tech. MA/MSc digital futures • BA (Hons)
music; sonic arts. MA music education. FdA media writing;
journalism and practical media; media arts and design; media
advertising; media production and the environment;
multimedia design; internet and multimedia tech. HNC digital
media production; graphic design; multimedia tech; media
production; media moving image.

PMA Training

PMA Group, PMA House, Free Church Passage,
St Ives, Cambs PE27 5AY
020 7278 0606
training@pma-group.com
www.pma-group.com
• One- to three-day short courses, covering the following
areas of media practice. Journalism: news, features, style,
subediting and proofing, writing for different mediums,
production, investigation, launching a publication etc; also
two-day journalism school for school and college leavers;
nine-week postgrad course in magazine journalism (PTC).
Broadcasting: writing, interviewing and public speaking PR:
law, writing, strategy, event management, pitching, internal
comms etc. Software: Quark XPress, Adobe Illustrator/
Photoshop/ Acrobat, PowerPoint, HTML, Macromedia Flash/
Dreamweaver, DVD Studio Pro, Adobe Premiere, Final Cut Pro.
Also media law; marketing; blogging; public speaking,
interviewing and presentation skills

Portsmouth, University of

University House, Winston Churchill Avenue,
Portsmouth PO1 2UP
023 9284 8484
info.centre@port.ac.uk
www.port.ac.uk

• *BA (Hons) English with media, creative writing and film
as options* • *BA (Hons) creative writing and drama; English
lang/lit and journalism; languages and creative writing.
MA creative writing; film and TV studies* • *BA (Hons) film
with options including entertainment tech, creative writing,
drama, languages. BA (Hons) media (single or with creative
writing, drama, entertainment tech)* • *BA (Hons) ; marketing.
MA communication and language skills; technical
communication; BA (Hons) communication and English
studies. MPA masters in public administration (with English)*
• *BA (Hons) animation; communication design; design for
interactive media; 3D design; video production. BSc (Hons)
computer animation; computer games tech; creative
computing tech; digital media; digital video tech; enterprise
in computer games tech/entertainment tech; entertainment
tech; multimedia programming. MA art, design and media;
design for digital media; real-time media comms. MSc
computer animation; digital media; scientific and technical
comms* • *MSc creative and computational sound*

Queen Margaret University, Edinburgh

Corstophine Campus, Clerwood Terrace,
Edinburgh EH12 8TS
0131 317 3000
marketing@qmu.ac.uk
www.qmu.ac.uk

• *BA (Hons) media; media and culture; psychology and media*
• *BA (Hons) film and media; sociology and culture; drama
and theatre arts. MFA/MA/PgDip advanced screen practice*
• *BA (Hons) marketing (options); PR and media/marketing/
psychology; event management. CIPR diploma. MSc PR*

Queen Mary, University of London

Mile End Road, London E1 4NS
020 7882 5555
admissions@qmul.ac.uk
www.qmul.ac.uk

• *MA/BA film (with options)* • *BEng/MEng multimedia
systems tech* • *MSc digital music processing. BSc interactive
media design.*

Queen's University Belfast

University Road, Belfast BT7 1NN
028 9024 5133
admissions@qub.ac.uk
www.qub.ac.uk

• *BA (Hons)/MA/MPhil film* • *BSc (Hons) music tech.
BA (Hons)/BMus music*

Radio and TV School

High Street, Staplehurst, Kent TN12 0AX
01580 895256
mail@radioschool.co.uk
www.radioschool.co.uk

• *One-to-one radio courses, covering presentation styles,
techniques and production values. Core 1 for beginners with
no technical or radio experience, one-day courses; Core 2 for
hospital/University/RSL presenters and nightclub DJs; Core 3
for pro and semi-pro broadcasters working on-air now. One-
to-one TV presenter mini-courses for demos and showreels*

Ravensbourne College of Design and Communication

Walden Road, Chislehurst, Kent BR7 5SN
020 8289 4900
info@rave.ac.uk
www.ravensbourne.ac.uk

• *Fdg broadcast post-production; broadcast operations and
production; broadcast media tech. BA (Hons) broadcasting;
content creation for broadcasting and new media (fast track).
BSc (Hons) broadcast tech (top-up)* • *Fdg computer
visualisation and animation. BA (Hons) animation (top-up).
MA interactive digital media; networked media environments*
• *Fdg creative sound design; BA (Hons) design for moving
image/interaction/ digital live arts: performance video*

Robert Gordon University

School Hill, Aberdeen AB10 1FR
01224 262000
admissions@rgu.ac.uk
www.rgu.ac.uk

• *BA/BA (Hons) corporate communication* • *BA/BA (Hons)
publishing; publishing with journalism* • *BA (Hons)
photographic and electronic media. BSc (Hons) graphics
design; graphic/production design (for printing). BSc/BSc
(Hons) internet and multimedia. BDes (Hons) (graphic) design
for digital media*

Roehampton University

Erasmus House, Roehampton Lane, London SW15 5PU
020 8392 3000
enquiries@roehampton.ac.uk
www.roehampton.ac.uk

• *BA media and culture. PgDip/MA media and cultural studies*
• *BA/BSc creative writing; journalism and news media.
PgDip/MA translation (AV); creative and professional writing;
women, gender and writing* • *BA film and screen practice.
BA/BSc film* • *BSc marketing; business information
management* • *PgCert/PgDip/MA children's literature*
• *BA/BSc internet and multimedia computing; computing*
• *BMus/BA/BSc music. PgDip/MA choral education and music
education; music and culture*

Royal Academy of Music

Marylebone Road, London NW1 5HT
020 7873 7373
go@ram.ac.uk
www.ram.ac.uk

• *BMus (4yr) composition; performance. PgDip performance
(options in musical theatre and opera). MMus/MPhil/PhD
composition; performance*

Royal College of Music

Prince Consort Road, London SW7 2BS
020 7589 3643
info@rcm.ac.uk
www.rcm.ac.uk

• *BMus (Hons) music. PGDip/MMus integrated masters
programme in performance*

Royal Holloway, University of London

Egham, Surrey TW20 0EX
01784 434455
admissions@rhul.ac.uk
www.rhul.ac.uk

• *MA creative writing* • *MA doc by practice; feature film
screenwriting (MAFFS); producing film and TV; screen
studies; screenwriting for TV and film (retreat programme)*
• *BA media arts* • *BMus music. MMus composition;
performance studies (joint with Royal College of Music);
advanced musical studies (composition; ethnomusicology;
historical musicology; opera studies; performance;
performance studies; theory and analysis)*

Royal Northern College of Music
124 Oxford Road, Manchester M13 9RD
0161 907 5200
info@rncm.ac.uk
www.rncm.ac.uk
• BMus(Hons). PGDip performance; composition; repetiteur studies. MMus/MPhil/PhD performance; composition

Royal Scottish Academy of Music and Drama
100 Renfrew Street, Glasgow G2 3DB
0141 332 4101
registry@rsamd.ac.uk
www.rsamd.ac.uk
• BA (Hons) music; Scottish music; Scottish music - piping. MMus performance; opera. Master of opera. MMus composition; conducting. PgDip music. Master of performance in musical theatre

Royal Welsh College of Music and Drama
Castle Grounds, Cathays Park, Cardiff CF10 3ER
029 2034 2854
info@rwcmd.ac.uk
www.rwcmd.ac.uk
• BA (Hons)/PgDip acting; stage management; theatre design • PgDip/MA arts management • BMus (Hons) music. PgDip/MA music therapy

St Helens College
Brook Street, St Helens, Merseyside WA10 1PZ
01744 733766
enquire@sthelens.ac.uk
www.sthelens.ac.uk
• BA (Hons) digital arts; TV and video production (Liverpool John Moores University). • HNC media (writing); multimedia (design route). BTec NatCert multimedia. Fdg interactive multimedia arts and animation (Liverpool John Moores University). BA (Hons) digital arts (LJM Uni) • NatCert music tech. Fdg music tech and audio technology; video games production; radio production

St Martin's College
Bowerham Road, Lancaster LA1 3JD
01524 384384
www.ucsm.ac.uk
• PgCert/PgDip/MA/BA (Hons) creative writing

St Mary's College
Waldegrave Road, Twickenham TW1 4SX
020 8240 4000
recruit@smuc.ac.uk
www.smuc.ac.uk
• BA (Hons) professional and creative writing (single or with options) • BA Hons film and TV (joint) • BA (Hons) media arts (joint)

Salford, University of
Salford, Greater Manchester M5 4WT
0161 295 5000
course-enquiries@salford.ac.uk
www.salford.ac.uk
• BA (Hons) media • BA (Hons) journalism (options); English and creative writing • HND media production; media performance; audio and video systems. BSc (Hons) media tech. BA (Hons) media and performance; TV and radio; journalism and broadcasting • BA (Hons) advertising design • BA (Hons) digital 3D design; visual arts; animation. BSc (Hons) computer and video games; multimedia and internet tech • BA (Hons) pop and recording; music. BSc (Hons) audio, video and broadcast engineering

Salisbury College
Southampton Road, Salisbury, Wiltshire SP1 2LW
01722 344344
enquiries@salisbury.ac.uk
www.salisbury.ac.uk
• BTec NatAward/Dip/NatDip performing arts. BTec NatDip media (moving image) • BTec Dip design; art. BTec FDip/NatDip art and design. HNC/ HND fine art • BTec Dip/NatDip pop. BTec NatDip music tech. HND/BA (Hons) (top-up) film and television; photography

School of Oriental and African Studies
Thornaugh Street, Russell Square, London WC1H 0XG
020 7637 2388
study@soas.ac.uk
www.soas.ac.uk
• MA critical media and cultural studies; anthropology of media; global media and postnational communication • MA cinemas of Asia and Africa • BA music. MMus ethnomusicology; performance

Sheffield College, The
The Norton Centre, Dyche Lane, Sheffield S8 8BR
0114 260 3603
course-enquiries@sheffcol.ac.uk
www.sheffcol.ac.uk
• BTec media • Short courses: reporter journalism (NCTJ), journalism/photography (NCTJ), press photography • BTec NatDip media; multimedia; media production • BTec Dip/NatDip music practice

Sheffield Hallam University
City Campus, Howard Street, Sheffield S1 1WB
0114 225 5555
admissions@shu.ac.uk
www.shu.ac.uk
• BA (Hons)/MA/PgDip/PgCert media • MA/PgDip/PgCert broadcast journalism; international broadcast journalism; writing • BA (Hons) film and literature; film and media production; film and visual effects; film and history; film. MA/PgDip/PgCert film and media production • BA (Hons) communication studies; animation. MA/PgDip/ PgCert communication studies; corporate/professional/tech communication • BA (Hons) photographic practice; multimedia and communication design; interactive media design; digital media production. BSc (Hon) software development (games). MSc/PgDip/PgCert multimedia and internet; entertainment software development

Sheffield, University of
Western Bank, Sheffield S10 2TN
0114 222 2000
www.shef.ac.uk
• BA (Hons)/MA journalism studies (options). PGDip/MA print journalism. • MA web journalism; print journalism; human communication studies • PGDip/MA broadcast journalism (BJTC) • MA musicology; music theatre studies; BMus music.

Solihull College
Blossomfield Road, Solihull B91 1SB
0121 678 7000
enquiries@solihull.ac.uk
www.solihull.ac.uk
• BTec Dip/NatDip media • Cert sales and marketing (Level 2 and3) (ISMM). FCert marketing (CIM). Cert marketing (Stage 1) (CIM). ProfDip marketing (Stage 2) (CIM). ProfPgDip marketing (Stage 3) (CIM)

South Birmingham College
High Street, Deritend, Digbeth, Birmingham B5 5SU
0121 694 5000
info@sbc.ac.uk
www.sbc.ac.uk
• BTec NatDip media: audio and visual/ moving image production/ games development/ e-media production. BTec HND media, communication and production. NatCert photography; video production; web broadcasting

South Devon College
Vantage Point, Long Road, Paignton TQ4 7EJ
01803 540540
enquiries@southdevon.ac.uk
www.southdevon.ac.uk
• *FirstDip media* • *BTec NatDip media (moving image)*
• *FirstDip music production. NatDip music tech (audio engineering; studio production) NatDip/Fdg art and design (lens-based media, digital arts and moving-image)*

South East Essex College
Luker Road, Southend-on-Sea, Essex SS1 1ND
01702 220400
learning@southend.ac.uk
www.southend.ac.uk
• *BTec FirstDip media* • *BA (Hons) journalism. Short courses: writing your first novel, creative writing* • *BTec NatDip moving image. BA (Hons) TV production and screen media; short course TV presenting skills* • *BTec NatDip publishing* • *BTec NatDip digital animation; multimedia. Short course: basic 3D animation* • *HND performing arts (music production). BTec FirstDip/NatDip contemporary music; music tech. BTec NatDip radio. BA (Hons) music production*

South Kent College
Folkestone Campus, Shorncliffe Road, Folkestone, Kent CT20 2TZ
01303 858200
www.southkent.ac.uk
• *Dip media* • *FirstDip/NatCert/NatDip performing arts. NatDip/HND media (moving image) production* • *IntroCert/ ProfCert/ProfDip/ PgDip marketing (CIM)* • *InterCert/NatCert/ NatDip music tech. NatAward music tech - DJ skills*

South Nottingham College
Greythorn Drive, West Bridgford, Nottingham NG2 7GA
0115 914 6400
enquiries@snc.ac.uk
www.snc.ac.uk
• *HNC/HND media production* • *HNC/HND multimedia; photography and digital imaging; print, media and digital design*

South Thames College
Wandsworth High Street, London SW18 2PP
020 8918 7777
studentservices@south-thames.ac.uk
www.south-thames.ac.uk
• *BTec Dip/NatDip media; HNC media (creative sound and vision); film and TV. BTec NatDip media (moving image). HNC 16mm film making; TV production; media production* • *Dip design. NatCert multimedia (graphics and photography). ProfDev Cert graphic design. HNC graphic design; photography; art and design (graphic design)* • *Entry-level course music, TV and video production. C&G/BTec Dip/NatCert/NatDip music tech. BTec NatAward music production. BTec NatAward/NatDip music performance; music production and performance. NCFE Intermediate music tech -audio pathway*

Southampton Solent University
East Park Terrace, Southampton, Hampshire SO14 0YN
023 8031 9000
enquiries@solent.ac.uk
www.solent.ac.uk
• *BA (Hons) media with cultural studies. MA media. MProf media practice.* • *BA (Hons) journalism (NCTJ, PTC, BJTC); media writing; writing fashion and culture; writing popular fiction* • *BSc (Hons) film and video tech (BKSTS); media tech. BA (Hons) film and TV; film; screenwriting; TV production (directing performance/ editing/ online/ screenwriting). MA film and filmmaking; media writing; media; interactive production* • *HND advertising and media comms. Dip marketing (CIM). BA (Hons) marketing with media and design; PR and communication; music promotion; popular music and record production.* • *BA (Hons) animation; digital media; multimedia design; photography* • *BSc (Hons) audio tech (BKSTS); music studio tech (BKSTS). BA (Hons) pop and record production.*

Southampton, University of
University Road, Highfield, Southampton SO17 1BJ
023 8059 5000
www.soton.ac.uk
• *BA film (with options)* • *BSc/MEng computer science with image and multimedia systems* • *BA music (options). BEng/MEng acoustical engineering*

Staffordshire University
Stoke-on-Trent, Staffordshire ST4 2DE
01782 294000
study@staffs.ac.uk
www.staffs.ac.uk
• *BA media* • *BA (Hons) English and journalism (NCTJ)* • *BA (Hons)/MA broadcast journalism (BJTC). BA film; film, TV and radio studies; music technology; TV and radio studies; media production* • *BA multimedia graphics; graphics; animation; design innovation. MA media futures; interactive multimedia* • *BA music broadcasting*

Stevenson College Edinburgh
Bankhead Avenue, Edinburgh EH11 4DE
0131 535 4600; course enquiries: 0131 535 4700
info@stevenson.ac.uk
www.stevenson.ac.uk
• *HNC/HND AV tech. HND TV operations. Fdg film and TV* • *HNC advertising and PR* • *Fdg classical music. HND/Fdg pop*

Stirling, University of
Stirling FK9 4LA
01786 473171
admissions@stir.ac.uk
www.stir.ac.uk
• *MSc/PGDip media management (available online); media research* • *BA (Hons) journalism studies* • *BA (Hons) film and media; European film and media* • *BA (Hons)/PgDip/MSc marketing. PGDip/MSc PR (online learning available)* • *MLitt publishing studies*

Stockport College of Further and Higher Education
Wellington Road South, Stockport, Cheshire SK1 3UQ
0161 958 3100
enquiries@stockport.ac.uk
www.stockport.ac.uk
• *Dip media. IntroDip art, design and media* • *FirstDip/HND media; Fdg TV production (moving image - broadcasting). NatDip media broadcasting. NatCert/NatDip performing arts: media make-up. BA (Hons) design and visual arts (graphic design/illustration/multimedia pathways)*

Strathclyde, University of
16 Richmond Street, Glasgow G1 1XQ
0141 552 4400
www.strath.ac.uk
• *BA (Hons) journalism and creative writing (joint).* • *BA applied music; BSc internet computing; software engineering. MLitt/PgDip in journalism studies (Scottish Centre for Journalism with Glasgow Caledonian - 0141 950 3281)* • *BA/MRes/MSc/PgDip marketing. MSc/PgDip marketing, international. MSc marketing, international (online)* • *MSc/PgDip/PgCert digital creativity; computer and internet tech.*

Sunderland, University of

Edinburgh Building, Chester Road, Sunderland SR1 3SD
0191 515 3000
student-helpline@sunderland.ac.uk
www.sunderland.ac.uk

• *BA (Hons) media, culture and communication. • BA (Hons)/ MA journalism studies* (NCTJ); BA (Hons) English and film; broadcast journalism; news journalism*; magazine journalism*; film and media; media writing (film and TV); media production (TV and radio/video and new media) • BA (Hons) music*
• *BA (Hons) photography, video and digital imaging; media production (video and new media); animation and design; design: multimedia and graphics; illustration and design; 3D design innovation; graphic communication; graphic design (top-up). BSc (Hons) product design• BA (Hons) marketing; PR (CIPR); ads and design • MA/PgDip/PgCert film and cultural studies; media production (TV and video); MA/PgDip/ PgCert media and cultural studies •Fdg creative multimedia). MA/PgDip/PgCert design: multimedia and graphics; illustration and design. 3D design innovation; design studies; photography (top-up). MA/PgDip/PgCert radio (production and management)*

Surrey, University of

Guildford, Surrey GU2 7XH
01483 300800
information@surrey.ac.uk
www.surrey.ac.uk

• *BA (Hons) media studies; media engineering; sound recording. MA/PgDip audiovisual translation. MPhil/PhD culture, media and communication • BMus (Hons) music (also with professional placement year, or with computer sound design) MMus/PgDip/MRes/MPhil/PhD music; MRes musicology*

Sussex, University of

Falmer, Brighton BN1 9RH
01273 606755
information@sussex.ac.uk
www.sussex.ac.uk

• *BA media; media practice and theory; media and anthropology; media and modern languages; sociology and media. PgDip/MA/MPhil/DPhil/BA media and cultural studies. MA gender and media. MSc social research methods (media and cultural studies) • MPhil/DPhil creative and critical writing. MA English literature: creative and critical writing; dramatic writing • BA film (with options); BSc multimedia and digital systems. MA film • MA digital media ; digital documentary • BA music; music and cultural studies; music and film; music with languages. BA/BSc music informatics. MA music*

Sutton Coldfield College

Lichfield Road, Sutton Coldfield,
West Midlands B74 2NW
0121 355 5671
infoc@sutcol.ac.uk
www.sutcol.ac.uk

• *HND media and communication. • Pre-entry Cert newspaper journalism (NCTJ). C&G desktop publishing; 7500 Cert in media techniques: journalism and radio competences. Various part-time Certs in photography; media production; writing skills; photojournalism and digital techniques.*

Swansea Institute of Higher Education

Mount Pleasant, Swansea SA1 6ED
01792 481000
enquiry@sihe.ac.uk
www.sihe.ac.uk

• *BA (Hons) photojournalism • BA (Hons) English studies, video; documentary video; HNC/HND theatre; technical theatre • BA (Hons) design for advertising; marketing. PgDip marketing (CIM) • HND/BA/BSc (Hons) 3D computer animation; multimedia. BSc (Hons) computer games development. BA (Hons) creative computer games design; photojournalism (contemporary practice); photography in the arts; performance and theatre studies. MA photography; visual arts enterprise; visual communication. MA 3D computer animation. MSc multimedia • BSc (Hons) music tech*

Swansea University

Singleton Park, Swansea SA2 8PP
01792 205678
admissions@swansea.ac.uk
www.swansea.ac.uk

• *BA (Hons) media (with options). MA media talk*
• *MA comparative journalism; creative and media writing*
• *BA (Hons) screen studies (options) • BA (Hons) public and media relations*

Tameside College

Beaufort Road, Ashton-under-Lyne,
Greater Manchester OL6 6NX
0161 908 6600
info@tameside.ac.uk
www.tameside.ac.uk

• *NatDip media (moving image) • NatDip multimedia. HNC/NatDip photography. FirstDip media production.*

Teesside, University of

Middlesbrough, Tees Valley TS1 3BA
01642 218121
registry@tees.ac.uk
www.tees.ac.uk

• *BA (Hons) creative media; English with media; media; media with history • Fdg journalism • Fdg TV and film production; performance and event production; digital media; radio production. BA (Hons) media production professional practice; TV production professional practice; performance and event production* • BA (Hons) marketing; marketing and retail management/ad management; PR; marketing and PR. PgCert professional development: marketing. PgDip marketing (CIM). MSc marketing management • HND web design/development. Fdg digital media. BA (Hons) computer animation; creative digital media/ visualisation; computer games art/design; digital character animation; web design. BSc (Hons) computer games programming/ science; computer graphics science; web development. MA computer animation; computer games art; web design; creative digital media. MSc visual and web apps; web enterprise; web services development • HND music tech. BSc (Hons) media and music tech; digital music.*

Thames Valley University

St Mary's Road, Ealing, London W5 5RF
020 8579 5000
learning.advice@tvu.ac.uk
www.tvu.ac.uk

• *BA (Hons) media studies (options); media arts; broadcasting. MA/PgDip/MPhil/PhD media • BA (Hons) new media journalism (options); new media journalism and radio broadcasting; drama: acting for stage and media. MPhil/PhD journalism • BA (Hons) digital broadcast media. BA (Hons)/DipHE/MA film: video production with film. MA film and the moving image • BA (Hons) advertising (options); creative advertising (options). PR (options) • BA (Hons)/DipHE photography and digital imaging. BA (Hons)/MPhil/PhD digital arts (options). MA photography; computer arts • Fdg music and multimedia tech; music performance; musical theatre; pop studies. HND music production (music tech); music practice; performing arts (theatre). BA (Hons)/DipHE music tech. BMus (Hons)/DipHE pop performance. BA (Hons) music and event management; music and media; combinations of the above; music: performance/ composition (options); music tech (options). BSc (Hons) performance tech. BMus (Hons) music (performance, composition). MA audio tech. MMus composing concert music; composing for film and television; composing for musical theatre. MPhil/PhD music; music tech*

Trinity College Carmarthen

Wales SA31 3EP
01267 676767
registry@trinity-cm.ac.uk
www.trinity-cm.ac.uk

• *BA media • BA/MA creative writing • BA film • BA advertising • MBA arts management*

Trinity College of Music
King Charles Court, Old Royal Naval College,
Greenwich, London SE10 9JF
020 8305 4444
admissions@tcm.ac.uk
www.tcm.ac.uk
• *Provides intensive performance-centred training and individualised programmes of study in music, at both undergraduate and postgraduate levels. BMus (Hons) Indian music; performance. FdA MT musical theatre. PGCE musicians in education. Master of Music: 1,2,3-4 years.*

Tyne Metropolitan College
Embleton Avenue, Wallsend, Tyne and Wear NE28 9NJ
0191 229 5000
enquiries@tynemet.ac.uk
www.tynemet.ac.uk
• *HND TV and video* • *HNC graphic design*

UHI Millennium Institute
Executive Office, Ness Walk, Inverness IV3 5SQ
01463 279000
eo@uhi.ac.uk
www.uhi.ac.uk
• *BA (Hons) Gaelic and media* • *HND TV and multimedia; visual communications* • *HNC/HND advertising and PR; creative industries: TV; creative industries: radio; HNC/HND interactive multimedia creation; music. BA (Hons) pop performance*

Ulster, University of
Cromore Road, Co Londonderry,
Northern Ireland BT52 1SA
0870 040 0700
online@ulster.ac.uk
www.ulster.ac.uk
• *BA media (options in languages and social sciences); journalism (with options); media arts. BSc (Hons) business with media. BA (Hons) English with media. PgDip/MA international media* • *MA journalism* • *BA Hons film (options)* • *BSc (Hons) PR; government/politics with PR; communication (options); communication, advertising and marketing; marketing; government with communication; leisure events and cultural management. BDes design and communication. MSc film and television management policy. PgDip/MDes design communication* • *BSc (Hons) interactive multimedia design; multimedia computer games. BDes design for visual communication. BA (Hons) tech and design* • *BMus (Hons). BA Hons music (options). MMus music*

University College for the Creative Arts at Canterbury, Epsom, Farnham, Maidstone and Rochester
01622 620000
www.ucreative.ac.uk
01622 620164
• *BA (Hons) arts and media* • *BA (Hons) journalism (PTC, BJTC, recognised by NUJ); fashion journalism* • *BA (Hons) film and video (BKSTS). MA film and video* • *BA (Hons) ad and brand management* • *BA (Hons) animation; digital screen arts; photography. MA animation; photography; digital games design; graphic design and communication (branding, printed and interactive media); graphic design and new media*

Wakefield College
Margaret Street, Wakefield, West Yorks WF1 2DH
01924 789789
info@wakcoll.ac.uk
www.wakcoll.ac.uk
• *HND media (games design); interactive media; photography; graphic design* • *FirstDip pop music*

University of Wales, Aberystwyth
Old College, King Street, Aberystwyth,
Ceredigion SY23 2AX
01970 623111
ug-admissions@aber.ac.uk
www.aber.ac.uk
• *BA/MA/MPhil/PhD media and communication studies*
• *BA/MA/MPhil/ PhD television; film; scriptwriting. BSc marketing; drama: Welsh or English; performance studies; film and TV studies; scenographic studies.*

University of Wales, Bangor
Gwynedd LL57 2DG
01248 351151
admissions@bangor.ac.uk
www.bangor.ac.uk
• *BA (Hons) creative studies; theatre and media. MA creative studies* • *BA (Hons) history with journalism; creative writing; journalism and media; journalism and languages.* • *BA Hons English with film; English language with film; history with film* • *BA (Hons) entertainment industries with law; theatre and media studies; communication and media (Welsh)*
• *BA (Hons) (part time) internet, learning and organisations*
• *BA (Hons)/BMus (Hons) music. MA music*

Warwick, University of
Coventry CV4 7AL
024 7652 3523
www.warwick.ac.uk
• *BA English literature and creative writing. MA ancient visual and material culture; creative and media enterprises* • *MA writing* • *BA theatre, film and literature; film and literature; film with TV. MA film and TV* • *MSc marketing and strategy*

Warwickshire College
Leamington Centre, Warwick New Road, Leamington Spa, Warwickshire CV32 5JE
0800 783 6767
enquiries@warkscol.ac.uk
www.warkscol.ac.uk
• *Pre-entry journalism (NCTJ)* • *BTec Multimedia (Visual Communications)* • *BTec art & design*

West Herts College
Watford Campus, Hempstead Road, Watford,
Herts WD17 3EZ
01923 812345
admissions@westherts.ac.uk
www.westherts.ac.uk
• *BTec NatDip multimedia; photography; media; media (moving image). Fdg/BA (Hons) media, design and production* • *Fdg business (with advertising, PR, marketing). BA (Hons) advertising and marketing comms. Part time courses: creative writing; digital photography; photoshop.*

West Kent College
Brook Street, Tonbridge, Kent TN9 2PW
01732 358101
enquiries@wkc.ac.uk
www.wkc.ac.uk
• *BA (Hons) media and communication* • *Pre-entry newspaper journalism (NCTJ)* • *HND TV production tech*

West of England, University of the
Frenchay Campus, Coldharbour Lane, Bristol BS16 1QY
0117 965 6261
enquiries@uwe.ac.uk
www.uwe.ac.uk
• BA (Hons)/MA cultural and media (with options). PhD media
practice: theory • BA (Hons) film. • BA/BSc marketing
(options). MA marketing; media (animation/graphic
arts/interactive arts/screenwriting/video arts) • BA (Hons)
animation; graphic design; media practice. BSc (Hons)
internet computing; internet tech and multimedia computing;
multimedia computing; games technology. MA media
(animation/interactive media/ research); multimedia
(research) • BSc (Hons) creative music tech; music systems
engineering; web design. BA (Hons) journalism (options);
media and cultural studies; (options from social sciences and
languages); new media photography.

West of Scotland, University of the
Almada Street, Hamilton, Lanarkshire ML3 0JB
01698 283100
enquiries@bell.ac.uk
www.bell.ac.uk

High Street, Paisley, Scotland PA1 2BE
0141 848 3000
info@paisley.ac.uk
www.paisley.ac.uk
• BA journalism*; Prelim journalism (NCTJ). NatCert
journalism (NCTJ). Block-release newspaper journalism. Short
courses in subediting, shorthand, law, freelancing, features
• PgDip broadcast journalism. Short courses: freelance
broadcasting, moviemaking without budget, radio • BA (Hons)
media • BA (Hons) cinema; screen practice • BA (Hons)
marketing; international marketing. MSc international
marketing • BSc (Hons) multimedia tech; media tech;
multimedia with interactive entertainment tech*; computer
games tech; computer animation; digital art • BA (Hons)
commercial music; music tech

Westminster, University of
309 Regent Street, London W1B 2UW
020 7911 5000
www.wmin.ac.uk
• BA (Hons) media; journalism; photography. PgDip
journalism (NCTJ). MA journalism studies (part-time);
journalism for international students. All with print and online
journalism options • BA (Hons) media (TV/radio production
pathways); film and TV production; internet multimedia
communications; contemporary media practice; graphic
information design. PgDip journalism (broadcast pathway).
MA journalism (part-time; broadcast pathway); journalism
for international students (broadcast pathway); screenwriting
and producing for film and TV; film: culture and industry
• BA (Hons) media (PR; radio production; TV production
pathways). MA communication; communications policy;
design for communication; global media; international
journalism. MSc interactive multimedia; MRes media, art and
design. BSc media tech; multimedia computing. • BA (Hons)
commercial music. MA audio production; music business
management

Winchester, University Of
Hampshire SO22 4NR
01962 841515
admissions@winchester.ac.uk
www.winchester.ac.uk
• Fdg creative industries. BA media; drama • BA journalism;
creative writing (joint). MA creative and critical writing;
writing for children • BA film and cinema technologies; film;
media production; media studies

Wirral Metropolitan College
Conway Park Campus, Europa Boulevard,
Conway Park, Birkenhead, Wirral CH41 4NT
0151 551 7777
enquiries@wmc.ac.uk
www.wmc.ac.uk
• BA media • Short courses: writing film scripts, writing
scripts for film and TV • BTec FirstDip performing arts
(music). BTec NatCert music tech. BTec NatDip music practice;
media (video and sound)

Wolverhampton, University of
Wulfruna Street, Wolverhampton WV1 1SB
01902 321000
enquiries@wlv.ac.uk
www.wlv.ac.uk
• BA (Hons) media and cultural studies • BA (Hons) creative
and professional writing; journalism and editorial design
• Fdg (arts) broadcast journalism (top up: BA (Hons)).
BA (Hons) film studies; literary, film and theatre studies
• BA (Hons) media and comms studies; marketing; PR; public
services • HNC/HND/ BA (Hons) photography. BA (Hons)
animation; computer games design; design; design for
multimedia; digital + arts media; interactive multimedia.
BSc (Hons) computer science (games development, software
engineering); computing (multimedia); design tech;
multimedia apps development; mobile computing; web
computing • BA (Hons) music; music tech and music; music
tech and pop; pop; pop (top-up from HND)

Worcester, University Of
Henwick Grove, Worcester WR2 6AJ
01905 855000
study@worc.ac.uk
www.worc.ac.uk
• HND media; media (moving image). BA (Hons) media and
cultural studies • BA (Hons) drama and performance;
performance costume and make-up (top-up) • BA (Hons)
visual arts; creative digital media; interactive digital media;
time-based digital media/digital film production. MA/MSc
creative digital media.

York St John University
Lord Mayor's Walk, York YO31 7EX
01904 624624
admissions@yorksj.ac.uk
www.yorksj.ac.uk
• BA (Hons) media; communication; film studies • PgDip/MA
literature studies and creative writing • Fdg creative industries
and tech • BA (Hons) performance: music; dance; theatre.

York, University of
Heslington, York YO10 5DD
01904 430000
admissions@york.ac.uk
www.york.ac.uk
• BA/MA writing and performance (drama, film, TV).
• BEng/MEng media tech • BA music. BEng/MEng music tech
systems. MA music; community music. Dip/MPhil/PhD/MA/
MSc music tech

Yorkshire Coast College
Lady Edith's Drive, Scarborough,
North Yorks YO12 5RN
01723 372105
admissions@ycoastco.ac.uk
www.yorkshirecoastcollege.ac.uk
• Fdg applied digital media (design). BA (Hons) costume.

In-house training courses

Archant
Prospect House, Rouen Road,
Norwich, Norfolk NR1 1RE
paul.durrant@archant.co.uk
www.archant.co.uk
*EDP assistant editor: Paul Durrant.
Takes applicants within, or with strong
link to, circulation area. Ask in July for
info on following year's recruitment.
One month induction, followed by fast-
track training course*

**BBC Training and development:
Broadcast Training**
35 Marylebone High Street,
London W1U 4PX
0870 122 0216
training@bbc.co.uk
www.bbctraining.com
*External development executive:
Andrew Carmichael. All strands of
broadcast training*

Johnston Training Centre
Upper Mounts,
Northampton NN1 3HR
01604 477755
www.johnstonpress.co.uk
PO Box 168, Wellington Street,
Leeds, LS1 1RS
0113 243 2701
*Most training for Johnston Group at
theses two offices. No external trainees.*

Midland News Association
51-53 Queen Street,
Wolverhampton,
West Midlands, WV61 1ES
01902 313131
c.clark@expressandstar.co.uk
www.expressandstar.com
*Training coordinator: Crispin Clark.
Recruits non-company editorial
trainees, usually eight per year*

Newsquest Media Group
58 Church Street,
Weybridge KT13 8DP
01932 821212
www.newsquest.co.uk
*Each region operates its own training
system*

The Press Association
Bridgegate, Howden,
East Yorks, DN14 7AE
tony.johnston@
    pressassociation.co.uk
www.pa.press.net
*Head of PA editorial training: Tony
Johnston. In-house trainee journalist
programmes in multimedia, sport and
production*
Thomson House, Groat Market,
Newcastle-upon-Tyne NE1 1ED
0191 201 6043
paul.jones@pa-training.co.uk
www.editorial.com
*Formerly Trinity Mirror Group
Training Centre. Foundation course
leader: Paul Jones 0191 201 6039. 16-
week preliminary course, primarily in-
house but external places available.*

Media Recruitment companies

Career Moves
London: 020 7908 7900
www.cmoves.co.uk
Leed Recruitment
Ipswich: 01473 289000
www.leedrecruitment.co.uk
Marketing Stars
Isleworth: 020 8892 1848
www.marketingstars.co.uk
Media Contacts
London: 020 7359 8244
www.media-contacts.co.uk
The Media Exchange
London: 020 7636 6777
www.themediaexchange.com
The Media Network
London: 020 7637 9227
www.tmn.co.uk
MediaCentrix
London: 020 7812 7180
www.mediacentrix.com
Michael Page Marketing
Birmingham: 0121 634 6920
Bristol: 0117 927 6509
Edinburgh: 0131 243 2900
Glasgow: 0141 331 7900
Leeds: 0113 242 3530
London: 020 7831 2000
Manchester: 0161 819 5500
St Albans: 01727 730111
Weybridge: 01932 264 000
www.michaelpage.co.uk
Moriati Media
London: 020 7307 1280
www.moriati.co.uk
Network Recruitment
London: 020 7580 5151
www.networkdesign.cc
Online Content UK
Harpenden: 0845 123 5717
www.onlinecontentuk.org
Pathfinders
London: 020 7434 3511
www.pathfindersrecruitment.com
Phee Farrer Jones
London, Manchester
0870 048 9100
www.pfj.co.uk
Price Jamieson
London: 020 7580 7702
www.pricejam.com
Profiles Creative
London, Leeds, Reading
0870 414 6288
www.profilescreative.com
Real Recruitment
London: 020 7499 5955
www.real-recruitment.com/
Recruit Media
London: 020 7758 4550
www.recruitmedia.co.uk
Reilly People
London: 020 7240 8080
www.reillypeople.co.uk
Swindale Parks Recruitment
Halesowen: 0121 585 6079
www.swindaleparks.co.uk

Workstation
London: 020 7371 7161
www.workstation.co.uk
Xchangeteam
London: 020 7025 4400
www.xchangeteam.com

Media training associations

**BKSTS — The Moving Image
Society**
Pinewood Studios, Iver Heath,
Bucks SL0 0NH
01753 656656
info@bksts.com
www.bksts.com
*Film foundation, TV and digital tech,
foundation sound for film and video,
broadcasting engineering*

**British Universities Film & Video
Council**
77 Wells Street, London W1T 3QJ
020 7393 1500
ask@bufvc.ac.uk
www.bufvc.ac.uk
*To promote the use of media within
higher education*

**Broadcast Journalism Training
Council**
The Secretary, 18 Miller's Close,
Rippingale, Lincolnshire PE10 0TH
01778 440025
sec@bjtc.org.uk
www.bjtc.org.uk
Accredits courses

City & Guilds
1 Giltspur Street, London EC1A 9DD
020 7294 2800
enquiry@city-and-guilds.co.uk
www.city-and-guilds.co.uk
Vocational qualifications

**FT2 — Film and Television
Freelance Training**
Fourth Floor, Warwick House,
9 Warwick Street, London W1B 5LY
020 7407 0344
info@ft2.org.uk
www.ft2.org.uk
Training for new broadcast freelancers

Film Education
21-22 Poland Street,
London W1F 8QQ
020 7851 9450
postbox@filmeducation.org
www.filmeducation.org

First Film Foundation
info@firstfilm.co.uk
www.firstfilm.co.uk
*Training for new film writers,
producers and directors*

**National Council for the Training
of Journalists**
The New Granary, Station Road,
Newport, Saffron Walden,
Essex CB11 3PL
01799 544014
info@nctj.com
www.nctj.com
*Runs schemes for print journalists.
Accredits courses*

Periodicals Training Council
Queens House, 28 Kingsway,
London WC2B 6JR
020 7400 7533
www.ppa.co.uk
Training arm of PPA

**Skillset: The Sector Skills Council
for the Audio Visual Industries**
Prospect House,
80–110 New Oxford Street,
London WC1A 1HB
020 7520 5757
info@skillset.org
www.skillset.org
*Owned by broadcast industry;
accredits courses, publishes handbooks
and runs Skillsformedia
(www.skillsformedia.com)*

yourcreativefuture.org
education@designcouncil.org.uk
www.yourcreativefuture.org
*Guide to a creative career; sponsored
by government, Design Council and
Arts Council*

Diversity

Age Concern
Astral House, 1268 London Road
London SW16 4ER
020 8765 7200
ace@ace.org.uk
www.ageconcern.co.uk

Bird's Eye View
Unit 306A Aberdeen Centre,
22-24 Highbury Grove
London N5 2EA
020 7704 6500
rosiestrang@birds-eye-view.co.uk
www.birds-eye-view.co.uk
Platform for emerging female film-makers

Employers' Forum on Disability
Nutmeg House, 60 Gainsford
Street, London SE1 2NY
020 7403 3020
jenny.stevens@
    employers-forum.co.uk
www.employers-forum.co.uk
Employers' organization

Commission for Racial Equality (CRE)
St Dunstan's House,
201-211 Borough High Street,
London SE1 1GZ
020 7939 0000
info@cre.gov.uk
www.cre.gov.uk

The Creative Collective
The Business Design Centre,
Suite Forum P, 52 Upper Street,
London N1 0QH
020 7359 3535
info@thecreativecollective.com
www.thecreativecollective.com
*Aims to develop social policy on
diversity and to empower community
groups to harness media*

Cultural Diversity Network (CDN)
c/o Sky, 123 Buckingham Palace
Road, London SW1W
www.cdnetwork.org.uk
*Network of black, Asian and other
ethnic minority TV freelancers and staff*

Digital Media Access Group
Applied Computing, University
of Dundee, Dundee DD1 4HN
01382 345050
dmag@computing.dundee.ac.uk
www.dmag.org.uk
Promotes new media accessibility

Disability Rights Commission
Freepost MID02164,
Stratford upon Avon CV37 9BR
0845 762 2633
enquiry@drc-gb.org
www.drc-gb.org

Emma Awards
67-69 Whitfield Street,
London W1T 4HF
020 7636 1233
mail@emma.tv
www.emmaglobalvillage.com
*Multicultural media awards and online
humanitarian information portal*

Equal Opportunities Commission
Arndale House, Arndale Centre,
Manchester M4 3EQ
0845 601 5901
info@eoc.org.uk
www.eoc.org.uk

International Association of Women in Radio and Television
nik@netactive.co.za
www.iawrt.org

International Women's Media Foundation
1625K Street NW, Suite 1275,
Washington DC 20006   USA
001 202 496 1992
info@iwmf.org
www.iwmf.org

Ligali
PO Box 1257, London E5 0UD
020 8986 1984
mail@ligali.org
www.ligali.org
African British equality organization

MediaWise Trust
University of the West of England,
Oldbury Court Road,
Bristol BS16 2JP
0117 939 9333
pw@mediawise.org.uk
www.mediawise.org.uk
Independent media ethics charity

Women in Film and Television
Unit 2 Wedgwood Mews, 12-13
Greek Street, London W1D 4BB
020 7287 1400
karen.venn@wftv.org.uk
www.wftv.org.uk

Women in Publishing
c/o Multilingual Matters , Channel
View Publications, Frankfurt
Lodge, Clevedon Hall, Victoria
Road, Clevedon BS21 7HH
info@wipub.org.uk
www.wipub.org.uk

Women's Radio Group
27 Bath Road, London W4 1LJ
020 8995 5442
wrg@zelo.demon.co.uk
www.womeninradio.org.uk
Training, info and production facilities

Environment

Government and agencies

Department for the Environment, Food and Rural Affairs
020 7238 6000
www.defra.gov.uk
Press -
 animal welfare: 020 7238 6044
 environment: 020 7238 6054
 rural affairs: 020 7238 5608
 sustainable farming and food:
  020 7238 6146

British Waterways Board
01923 201120
www.britishwaterways.co.uk
Press: 01923 201329

Environment Agency
0870 850 6506
www.environment-agency.gov.uk
Press: 020 7863 8710

Food Standards Agency
020 7276 8000
www.foodstandards.gov.uk
Press: 020 7276 8888

Forestry Commission
0131 334 0303
www.forestry.gov.uk
Press: 0131 334 0303

Meat and Livestock Commission
01908 677577
www.mlc.org.uk
Press: 01908 844106

The Pesticides Safety Directorate
01904 640500
www.pesticides.gov.uk
Press: 020 7238 6698

United Kingdom Atomic Energy Authority
01235 820220
www.ukaea.org.uk
Press: 01235 435234

Rural and environmental bodies

Country Land and Business Association
020 7235 0511
www.cla.org.uk
Press: 020 7460 7936

English Heritage
0870 333 1181
www.english-heritage.org.uk
Press: 020 7973 3250

Natural England
01733 455000
www.naturalengland.org.uk
Press: 01733 455190

Friends of the Earth
020 7490 1555
www.foe.co.uk
England, Wales and Northern Ireland
Press: 020 7566 1649

Friends of the Earth Scotland
0131 554 9977
www.foe-scotland.org.uk

Game Conservancy Trust
01425 652381
www.gct.org.uk
Press: 01425 651000

Greenpeace
020 7865 8100
www.greenpeace.org.uk
Press: 020 7865 8255

National Farmers Union
024 7685 8500
www.nfuonline.com
Press: 024 7685 8686

National Trust
0870 242 6620
www.nationaltrust.org.uk

National Trust for Scotland
0131 243 9300
www.nts.org.uk
Press: 0131 243 9349

Ramblers Association
020 7339 8500
www.ramblers.org.uk
Press: 020 7339 8531/2

Worldwide Fund for Nature UK
01483 426444
www.wwf-uk.org

National Parks

Brecon
01874 624437
www.breconbeacons.org

Dartmoor
01626 832093
www.dartmoor-npa.gov.uk

Exmoor
01398 323665
www.exmoor-nationalpark.gov.uk

Lake District
01539 724555
www.lake-district.gov.uk

Norfolk & Suffolk Broads
01603 610734
www.broads-authority.gov.uk

Northumberland
01434 605555
www.northumberland-national
 -park.org.uk

North Yorkshire Moors
01439 770657
www.moors.uk.net

Peak District
01629 816200
www.peakdistrict.org

Pembrokeshire Coast
0845 345 7275
www.pcnpa.org.uk

Snowdonia
0845 130 6229
www.ccw.gov.uk

Yorkshire Dales
0870 166 6333
www.yorkshiredales.org.uk

Voluntary sector

● Animal welfare

Animal Aid
01732 364546
www.animalaid.org.uk

Animal Defenders
020 8846 9777
www.animaldefenders.org.uk

Animal Health Trust
0870 050 2424
www.aht.org.uk

Bat Conservation Trust
020 7627 2629
www.bats.org.uk

Battersea Dogs Home
020 7622 3626
www.dogshome.org
Press: 020 7627 9294

Blue Cross
01993 822651
www.bluecross.org.uk
Pet welfare charity

British Deer Society
01425 655434
www.bds.org.uk

British Hedgehog Protection Trust
01584 890801
www.britishhedgehogs.org.uk

British Union for Abolition of Vivisection
020 7700 4888
www.buav.org

Brooke Hospital for Animals
020 7930 0210
www.thebrooke.org
Working animals in developing world

Butterfly Conservation Trust
0870 774 4309
www.butterfly-conservation.org

Cat Action Trust
01555 660784
www.catactiontrust.co.uk

Cats Protection
0870 209 9099
www.cats.org.uk

Celia Hammond Animal Trust
01892 783367
www.celiahammond.org

Dog Trust
020 7837 0006
www.dogstrust.org.uk

Donkey Sanctuary
01395 578222
www.thedonkeysanctuary.org.uk

Farm Animal Welfare Council
020 7904 6534
www.fawc.org.uk

Fauna & Flora International
01223 571000
www.fauna-flora.org

Federation of Zoos
www.zoofederation.org.uk
Feline Advisory Board
0870 742 2278
www.fabcats.org
Humane Slaughter Society
01582 831919
www.hsa.org.uk
Hunt Saboteurs Organisation
0845 450 0727
www.huntsabs.org.uk
International Dolphin Watch
01482 632650
www.idw.org
International Fund for Animal Welfare
020 7587 6700
www.ifaw.org
International League for the Protection of Horses
0870 870 1927
www.ilph.org
League Against Cruel Sports
0845 330 8486
www.league.uk.com
London Wildlife Trust
020 7261 0447
www.wildlondon.org.uk
Mammal Society
020 7350 2200
www.abdn.ac.uk/mammal
Mare & Foal Sanctuary
01626 355969
www.mareandfoal.org.uk
Marine Conservation Society
www.mcsuk.org
National Federation of Badger Groups
020 7228 6444
www.nfbg.org.uk
Otter Trust
01986 893470
www.ottertrust.org.uk
People and Dogs Society
01924 897732
01977 678593
www.padsonline.org
People for the Ethical Treatment of Animals (PETA)
020 7357 9229
www.peta.org
People's Dispensary for Sick Animals (PDSA)
01952 290999
www.pdsa.org.uk
Rare Breeds Survival Trust
www.rarebreeds.com
Redwings Horse Sanctuary
01508 481000
www.redwings.co.uk
Royal Society for the Prevention of Cruelty to Animals
0870 555 5999
www.rspca.org.uk
Press: 0870 754 0288/44
Royal Society for the Protection of Birds
01767 680551
www.rspb.org.uk
Press: 01767 681577

Save the Rhino
020 7357 7474
www.savetherhino.org
Scottish Society for the Prevention of Cruelty to Animals
0131 339 0222
www.scottishspca.org
Scottish Wildlife Trust
0131 312 7765
www.swt.org.uk
Society for the Protection of Animals Abroad
020 7831 3999
www.spana.org
TRAFFIC
01223 277427
www.traffic.org
Combats damaging trade in plants & animals
Ulster Wildlife Trust
028 4483 0282
www.ulsterwildlifetrust.org
Uncaged
0114 272 2220
www.uncaged.co.uk
Anti-vivisection campaigner
Veteran Horse Society
01239 881300
www.veteran-horse-society.co.uk
Whale & Dolphin Conservation Society
0870 870 0027
www.wdcs.org.uk
Wildfowl & Wetlands Trust
01453 891900
www.wwt.org.uk
The Wildlife Trusts
0870 036 7711
www.wildlifetrusts.org
Wood Green Animal Shelters
0870 190 4090
www.woodgreen.org.uk
World Society for the Protection of Animals
020 7587 5000
www.wspa-international.org
www.wspa.org.uk
WWF UK
01483 426444
www.wwf.org.uk

● Conservation

Black Environment Network
01286 870715
www.ben-network.co.uk
British Association for Shooting and Conservation
01244 573000
www.basc.org.uk
Press: 01244 573031
British Trust for Conservation Volunteers
01302 388888
www.btcv.org
Campaign for Real Events
www.c-realevents.demon.co.uk
Provides renewable energy and 'alt tech' support for events

Campaign to Protect Rural England
020 7981 2800
www.cpre.org.uk
Carbon Neutral Company
020 7833 6000
www.carbonneutral.com
Centre for Alternative Technology
01654 705950
www.cat.org.uk
Community Composting Network
0114 258 0483
0114 255 3720
www.communitycompost.org
Community Service Volunteers — Environment
020 7278 6601
www.csv.org.uk
Conservation Foundation
020 7591 3111
www.conservationfoundation.co.uk
Council for Environmental Education
0118 950 2550
www.cee.org.uk
Council for National Parks
020 7924 4077
www.cnp.org.uk
Earth First! In Britain
www.earthfirst.org.uk
Earth Rights
01279 870391
www.earthrights.org.uk
Environmental public interest law firm
Earthwatch Institute
01865 318838
www.uk.earthwatch.org
Conservation of natural environments and cultural heritage
Eco-Village Network
0117 373 0346
www.evnuk.org.uk
Energywatch
0845 906 0708
www.energywatch.org.uk
Environmental Campaigns
01942 612621
www.encams.org
European Rivers Network
00 33 05 71 03 11 47
www.rivernet.org
Based in southern France
Forest Action Network
www.fanweb.org
Forum for the Future
020 7324 3630
www.forumforthefuture.org.uk
Game Conservancy Trust
01425 652381
www.gct.org.uk
People and Planet
01865 245678
www.peopleandplanet.org
UK student action on human rights, poverty and the environment
Rising Tide
07708 794665
www.risingtide.org.uk
Action against climate change

Royal Society for Nature Conservation
0870 036 1000
www.wildlifetrusts.org
Solar Energy Society
07760 163559
www.thesolarline.com
Surfers Against Sewage
0845 458 3001
www.sas.org.uk
UNEP World Conservation Monitoring Centre
01223 277314
www.unep-wcmc.org
Woodland Trust
01476 581111
www.woodland-trust.org.uk

● Farming and food

Farm Animal Welfare Council
020 7904 6534
www.fawc.org.uk
Farming & Wildlife Advisory Group
024 7669 6699
www.fwag.org.uk
Biodynamic Agricultural Association
01453 759501
www.biodynamic.org.uk
Campaign for Real Ale
01727 798443
www.camra.org.uk
Compassion in World Farming
01730 264208
www.ciwf.org.uk
Dig It Up!
www.dig-it-up.uk.net
Action against planting of GM rape crops
Eat the View
01242 533222
www.countryside.gov.uk/lar
/landscape/etv/index.asp
FARMA
0845 458 8420
www.farma.org.uk
Food from Britain
020 7233 5111
www.foodfrombritain.com
Promoting sustainable local products
Five Year Freeze Campaign
020 7837 0642
www.fiveyearfreeze.org
Anti-GM activists group
Food & Drink Federation
020 7836 2460
www.fdf.org.uk
Food Dudes
01248 388201
www.fooddudes.co.uk
Teaching children about healthy eating
Foundation for Local Food Initiatives
0845 458 9525
www.localfood.org.uk
Free Range Activism Website
www.fraw.org.uk

Future Harvest
001 703 548 4540
www.futureharvest.org
Promoting environmentally sound agricultural methods
Garden Organic
024 7630 3517
www.gardenorganic.org.uk
Researches and promotes organic methods and produce
Herb Society
01295 768899
www.herbsociety.co.uk
Herbs for health
National Federation of City Farms
0117 923 1800
www.farmgarden.org.uk
Permaculture Society
0845 458 1805
www.permaculture.org.uk
Pesticide Action Network
020 7065 0905
www.pan-uk.org
Soil Association
0117 314 5000
www.soilassociation.org
Sustain
020 7837 1228
www.sustainweb.org
Alliance for better food and farming
UK Food Group
020 7523 2369
www.ukfg.org.uk
Network for NGOs working on global food and agriculture issues
Veggies Catering Campaign
0845 458 9595
www.veggies.org.uk
Willing Workers on Organic Farms
01273 476286
www.wwoof.org/wwoof_uk

● Gardening

Royal Horticultural Society
020 7834 4333
www.rhs.org.uk

Health

Government departments

Department of Health
020 7210 4850
www.dh.gov.uk
Press: 020 7210 5221

Scottish Executive DoH
0131 556 8400
www.scotland.gov.uk
Press: 0131 244 2797

Northern Ireland DoH
028 9052 0500
www.dhsspsni.gov.uk
Press: 028 9052 0636

Government agencies

Health and Safety Executive
0845 345 0055
www.hse.gov.uk
Press: 020 7717 6700
out of hours: 020 7928 8382

Health Care Commission
020 7448 9200
www.healthcarecommission.org.uk
Press: 020 7448 9210

Health Professions Council
020 7582 0866
www.hpc-uk.org

Health Protection Agency
020 7759 2700/1
www.hpa.org.uk

Health Service Ombudsman
0845 015 4033
www.ombudsman.org.uk

Human Fertilisation and Embryology Authority
020 7291 8200
www.hfea.gov.uk

Human Genetics Commission
020 7972 4351
www.hgc.gov.uk
Press: 020 8675 1066

Medical Research Council
020 7636 5422
www.mrc.ac.uk

Medicines and Healthcare products Regulatory Agency
020 7084 2000
www.mhra.gov.uk
Press: 020 7084 2657

National Blood Service
0845 771 1711
www.blood.co.uk

National Institute for Health and Clinical Excellence (NICE)
020 7067 5800
www.nice.org.uk

National Patient Safety Agency
020 7927 9500
www.npsa.nhs.uk

NHS Executive
0113 254 5000
www.nhs.uk
Press: 020 7210 5221

NHS Health Scotland
0131 536 5500
www.healthscotland.com

NHS Quality Improvement, Scotland
0131 623 4300
www.nhshealthquality.org

NHS State Hospitals Board for Scotland
01555 840293
www.show.scot.nhs.uk
/tshProfessional bodies

Professional bodies

Royal College of Anaesthetists
020 7092 1500
www.rcoa.ac.uk

Royal College of General Practitioners
020 7581 3232
www.rcgp.org.uk
Press: 020 7344 3135/29/37

Royal College of Nursing
020 7409 3333
www.rcn.org.uk
Press: 020 7647 3633

Royal College of Obstetricians & Gynaecologists
020 7772 6200
www.rcog.org.uk
Press: 020 7772 6357

Royal College of Ophthalmologists
020 7935 0702
www.rcophth.ac.uk

Royal College of Paediatrics and Child Health
020 7307 5600
www.rcpch.ac.uk

Royal College of Pathologists
020 7451 6700
www.rcpath.org
Press: 020 7451 6752

Royal College of Physicians of Edinburgh
0131 225 7324
www.rcpe.ac.uk
Press: 0131 247 3693

Royal College of Physicians of Ireland
00 353 1 863 9700
www.rcpi.ie

Royal College of Physicians of London
020 7935 1174
www.rcplondon.ac.uk
Press: x254, x468

Faculty of Public Health Medicine
020 7935 0243
www.fphm.org.uk
Press: 020 7487 1185

Royal College of Physicians & Surgeons of Glasgow
0141 221 6072
www.rcpsglasg.ac.uk

Royal College of Psychiatrists
020 7235 2351
www.rcpsych.ac.uk
Press: x154, x127

Royal College of Radiologists
020 7636 4432
www.rcr.ac.uk
Press: x1138

Royal College of Surgeons of Edinburgh
0131 527 1600
www.rcsed.ac.uk

Royal College of Surgeons of England
020 7405 3474
www.rcseng.ac.uk
Press: 020 7869 6045

Royal College of Surgeons in Ireland
00 353 1 402 2100
www.rcsi.ie
Press: 00 353 1 402 8610

Patient Groups

Patients Association
020 8423 9111
www.patients-association.com

Voluntary sector

● General health

Action Medical Research
01403 210406
www.action.org.uk
Press: 01403 327404

Alzheimer's Society
020 7306 0606
www.alzheimers.org.uk
Press: 020 7306 0813/39

Arthritis Care
020 7380 6500
www.arthritiscare.org.uk
Press: 020 7380 6551

Arthritis Research Campaign
0870 850 5000
www.arc.org.uk
Press: 01246 541107

Association for International Cancer Research
01334 477910
www.aicr.org.uk

Bliss
020 7378 1122
www.bliss.org.uk
National charity for premature or sick babies

Breakthrough Breast Cancer
020 7025 2400
www.breakthrough.org.uk
Press: 020 7025 2432/2460

Breast Cancer Campaign
020 7749 3700
www.bcc-uk.org

Breast Cancer Care
020 7384 2984
www.breastcancercare.org.uk
Press: 020 7384 4696

British Dietetic Association
0121 200 8080
www.bda.uk.com

British Heart Foundation
020 7935 0185
www.bhf.org.uk
Press: 020 7487 7172 (24 hour)

British Pregnancy Advisory Service
0870 365 5050
www.bpas.org
Press: 020 7612 0206;
07788 725185

CLIC Sargent
0845 301 0031
www.clicsargent.org.uk
Children's cancer charity
Press: 0117 314 8621

Cancer Research UK
020 7121 6699
www.cancerresearchuk.org
Press: 020 7061 8300

Consensus Action on Salt and Health
020 8725 2409
www.actiononsalt.org.uk
020 8853 1349

Cystic Fibrosis Trust
020 8464 7211
www.cftrust.org.uk
Press: 020 7940 3800

Diabetes UK
020 7424 1000
www.diabetes.org.uk
Press: 020 7424 1165

Eating Disorders Association
0870 770 3256
www.edauk.com
Press: 0870 770 3221

Epilepsy Action
0113 210 8800
www.epilepsy.org.uk

Great Ormond St Children's Charity
020 7916 5678
www.gosh.org

Guy's & St Thomas' Charity
020 7188 7700
www.gsttcharity.org.uk
Press: 020 7188 1218

HIT
0870 990 9702
www.hit.org.uk
Campaigning and providing helplines

Institute of Cancer Research
020 7352 8133
www.icr.ac.uk
Press: x5312, x5359

International HIV/AIDS Alliance
01273 718900
www.aidsalliance.org

International Obesity Taskforce
020 7691 1900
www.iotf.org

Leukaemia Research Fund
020 7405 0101
www.lrf.org.uk
Press: 020 7269 9019

Macmillan Cancer Support
020 7840 7840
www.macmillan.org.uk
Press: 020 7840 7821

Marie Curie Cancer Care
020 7599 7777
www.mariecurie.org.uk
Press: 020 7599 7700

Marie Stopes International
020 7574 7400
www.mariestopes.org.uk
Reproductive healthcare worldwide
Press: 020 7574 7353

Meningitis Trust
01453 768000
www.meningitis-trust.org

Mind
020 8519 2122
www.mind.org.uk
National Association for Mental Health
Press: 020 8522 1743

Motor Neurone Disease Association
01604 250505
www.mndassociation.org
Press: 01604 611840

Multiple Sclerosis Society
020 8438 0700
www.mssociety.org.uk
Press: 020 8438 0763

Muscular Dystrophy Campaign
020 7720 8055
www.muscular-dystrophy.org

National Asthma Campaign
020 7786 4900
www.asthma.org.uk
Press: 020 7786 4949

National Heart Forum
020 7383 7638
www.heartforum.org.uk

National Kidney Research Fund
0845 070 7601
www.kidneyresearchuk.org

Parkinson's Disease Society of the UK
020 7931 8080
www.parkinsons.org.uk

St John Ambulance
0870 010 4950
www.sja.org.uk
Press: 020 7324 4210

Stroke Association
020 7566 0300
www.stroke.org.uk
Press: 020 7566 1500

Terrence Higgins Trust
0845 1221 200
www.tht.org.uk
HIV/Aids
Press: 020 7812 1600

The Wellcome Trust
020 7611 8888
www.wellcome.ac.uk
Health research charity
Press: 020 7611 8866

World Cancer Research Fund UK
020 7343 4200
www.wcrf-uk.org

Yorkshire Cancer Research
01423 501269
www.ycr.org.uk

● Drugs, alcohol and addiction

Addaction
020 7251 5860
www.addaction.org.uk

Adfam
020 7553 7640
www.adfam.org.uk
Families, drugs and alcohol

Alchemy Project
0845 165 1197
www.alchemyproject.co.uk

Alcohol Concern
020 7264 0510
www.alcoholconcern.org.uk

Alcohol Focus Scotland
0141 572 6700
www.alcohol-focus
-scotland.org.uk

Alcoholics Anonymous
01904 644026
www.alcoholics-anonymous
.org.uk

The National Criminal Justice Drug Workers Forum
01484 437905
www.drugreferral.org
Support for workers on drugs referral projects

ASH: Action on Smoking and Health
020 7739 5902
www.ash.org.uk

Association of Nurses in Substance Abuse
0870 241 3503
www.ansa.uk.net

Clouds
01747 830733
www.clouds.org.uk
Treatment for addiction

Crew 2000
0131 220 3404
www.crew2000.co.uk
Drug advice service

Drugscope
020 7928 1211
www.drugscope.org.uk
Information resource

European Association for the Treatment of Addiction
020 7553 9580
www.eata.org.uk

Legalise Cannabis Alliance
07984 255015
www.lca-uk.org

Life or Meth
www.lifeormeth.com
Methamphetamine awareness campaign

Narcotics Anonymous
020 7251 4007
www.ukna.org

National Treatment Agency
020 7261 8801
www.nta.nhs.uk

No Smoking Day — March 8
0870 770 7909
www.nosmokingday.org.uk

Promis Recovery Centre
01304 841700
www.promis.co.uk
Multi-addiction awareness and treatment

Release
020 7729 5255
www.release.org.uk
Provides for health, welfare and legal needs of drug users

Re-Solv
01785 817885
www.re-solv.org
Society for prevention of solvent abuse

Ride Foundation
01372 467708
www.ridefoundation.org.uk
Drug awareness programmes for schools

Scottish Drugs Forum
0141 221 1175
www.sdf.org.uk

Substance Misuse Management in General Practice
www.smmgp.org.uk

Transform
0117 941 5810
www.tdpf.org.uk
Anti-prohibition campaign

UK Harm Reduction Alliance
www.ukhra.org
Campaigning for health and ethical treatment of drug users

Health helplines

NHS Direct
0845 4647

Alcoholics Anonymous
0845 769 7555

Alzheimers Helpline
0845 300 0336

Arthritis Care Helpline
0808 800 4050

Asthma UK Advice Line
0845 701 0203

British Allergy Foundation Helpline
01322 619898

Carers Line
0808 808 7777

Diabetes UK Careline
0845 120 2960

Doctors' Supportline
0870 765 0001

Drinkline
0800 917 8282

Eating Disorders Association Helpline
0845 634 1414

Eating Disorders Association Youth Helpline
0845 634 7650

Epilepsy Action Helpline
0808 800 5050

Frank (National Drugs Helpline)
0800 776600

Miscarriage Association Helpline
01924 200799

NHS Asian Tobacco Helpline
0800 169 0881 (Urdu)
0800 169 0882 (Punjabi)
0800 169 0883 (Hindi)
0800 169 0884 (Gujerati)
0800 169 0885 (Bengali)

NHS Pregnancy Smoking Helpline
0800 169 9169

NHS Smoking Helpline
0800 169 0169

Organ Donor Line
0845 606 0400

Parents Against Drug Abuse
0845 702 3867

Re-Solv
0808 800 2345

RNID Tinnitus Helpline
0808 808 6666

Sexual Health Direct
0845 310 1334

Sexual Health Information Line
0800 567123

Smokers Quitline
0800 002200

Still Births and Neonatal Deaths Helpline
020 7436 5881

Women's Health Concern Helpline
0845 123 2319

The NHS

● Strategic health authorities, England

East Midlands Strategic Health Authority
0115 968 4444
www.eastmidlands.nhs.uk

East of England Strategic Health Authority
01223 597500
www.eoe.nhs.uk

London Strategic Health Authority
020 7016 8872
www.london.nhs.uk

North East Strategic Health Authority
0191 210 6400
www.northeast.nhs.uk

North West Strategic Health Authority
0161 237 2397
www.northwest.nhs.uk

South Central Strategic Health Authority
01865 337000
www.southcentral.nhs.uk

South East Coast Strategic Health Authority
01293 778899
www.southeastcoast.nhs.uk

South West Strategic Health Authority
01935 384000
www.southwest.nhs.uk

West Midlands Strategic Health Authority
0121 695 2222
www.westmidlands.nhs.uk

Yorkshire and The Humber Strategic Health Authority
0113 295 2000
www.yorksandhumber.nhs.uk

● Local health boards, Wales

Anglesey
01248 751229
www.wales.nhs.uk

Blaenau Gwent
01495 325400
www.wales.nhs.uk

Bridgend
01656 754400
www.wales.nhs.uk

Caerphilly
01495 241200
www.wales.nhs.uk

Cardiff
029 2055 2212
www.wales.nhs.uk

Carmarthenshire
01554 744400
www.wales.nhs.uk

Ceredigion
01570 424100
www.wales.nhs.uk

Conwy
01492 536586
www.wales.nhs.uk
Denbighshire
01745 589601
www.wales.nhs.uk
Flintshire
01352 803434
www.wales.nhs.uk
Gwynedd
01286 672451
www.gwyneddhealth.org
Merthyr Tydfil
01685 358500
www.wales.nhs.uk
Monmouthshire
01600 710000
www.wales.nhs.uk
Neath/Port Talbot
01639 890916
www.wales.nhs.uk
Newport
01633 261430
www.wales.nhs.uk
Pembrokeshire
01437 771220
www.wales.nhs.uk
Powys
01874 711661
www.wales.nhs.uk
Rhondda Cynon Taff
01443 744800
www.wales.nhs.uk
Swansea
01792 784800
www.wales.nhs.uk
Torfaen
01495 332200
www.wales.nhs.uk
Vale of Glamorgan
029 2035 0600
www.wales.nhs.uk
Wrexham
01978 346500
www.wales.nhs.uk

● **NHS boards, Scotland**

Argyll and Clyde
0141 842 7200
www.nhsac.scot.nhs.uk
Ayrshire and Arran
01563 52113
www.nhsayrshireandarran.com
Borders
01896 825500
www.nhsborders.org.uk
Dumfries and Galloway
01387 246246
www.nhsdg.scot.nhs.uk
Fife
01592 643355
www.nhsfife.scot.nhs.uk
Forth Valley
01786 463031
www.nhsforthvalley.com
Grampian
0845 456 6000
www.nhsgrampian.org

Greater Glasgow and Clyde
0141 201 4444
www.nhsggc.org.uk
Press: 0141 201 4429
Highland
01463 717123
www.nhshighland.scot.nhs.uk
Lanarkshire
01698 281313
www.nhslanarkshire.co.uk
Lothian
0131 536 9000
www.nhslothian.scot.nhs.uk
Orkney
01856 888000
www.show.scot.nhs.uk/ohb
Shetland
01595 743060
www.show.scot.nhs.uk/shb
Tayside
01382 818479
www.nhstayside.scot.nhs.uk
Western Isles
01851 702997
www.wihb.scot.nhs.uk
Scottish Ambulance Service
0131 446 7000
www.scottishambulance.com

● Health & social
   services boards,
   Northern Ireland

Eastern
028 9032 1313
www.ehssb.n-i.nhs.uk
Northern
028 2531 1000
www.nhssb.n-i.nhs.uk
Southern
028 3741 0041
www.shssb.n-I.nhs.uk
Western
028 7186 0086
www.whssb.n-I.nhs.uk

● NHS foundation trusts

Monitor
020 7340 2400
www.monitor-nhsft.gov.uk
Monitor and independent regulator of
NHS foundation trusts
Press: 020 7340 2440
Aintree University Hospitals
NHSFT
0151 525 5980
Barnsley Hospital NHS
Foundation Trust
01226 730000
Basildon and Thurrock Hospitals
NHSFT
01268 533911
Basingstoke and North
Hampshire NHSFT
01256 473202
Berkshire Healthcare NHSFT
01344 415600
Birmingham Children's Hospital
NHSFT
0121 333 9999

Bradford Teaching Hospitals
NHSFT
01274 542200
Calderdale and Huddersfield
NHSFT
01484 342000
Cambridge University Hospitals
NHSFT
01223 245151
Central and North West London
NHSFT
020 8237 2000
Chelsea and Westminster
Hospital NHSFT
020 7746 8000
Cheshire and Wirral Partnership
NHSFT
0124 436 5000
Chesterfield Royal Hospital
NHSFT
01246 277271
City Hospitals Sunderland NHSFT
0191 565 6256
Clatterbridge Centre for
Oncology NHSFT
0151 334 1155
Countess of Chester Hospital
NHSFT
01244 365000
County Durham and Darlington
NHSFT
0191 333 2333
Derby Hospitals NHSFT
01332 347141
Doncaster and Bassetlaw
Hospitals NHSFT
01302 366666
Dorset County Hospital NHSFT
01305 251150
Dorset HealthCare NHSFT
01202 303400
Frimley Park Hospital NHSFT
01276 604604
Gateshead Health NHSFT
0191 482 0000
Gloucestershire Hospitals NHSFT
0845 422 2222
Gloucestershire Partnership
NHSFT
01452 891000
Guy's and St Thomas's NHSFT
020 7188 7188
Harrogate and District NHSFT
01423 885959
Heart of England NHSFT
0121 424 2000
Heatherwood and Wexham Park
Hospitals NHSFT
01753 633000
Homerton University Hospital
NHSFT
020 8510 5555
James Paget University Hospitals
NHSFT
01493 452452
King's College Hospital NHSFT
020 3299 9000
Lancashire Teaching Hospitals
NHSFT
01772 716565
Liverpool Women's NHSFT
0151 708 9988

Luton and Dunstable Hospital NHSFT
0845 127 0127

Moorfields Eye Hospital NHSFT
020 7253 3411

The Newcastle Upon Tyne Hospitals NHSFT
0191 233 6161

Northern Lincolnshire and Goole Hospitals NHSFT
01472 874111

Northhumbria Healthcare NHSFT
0191 259 6660

The Royal Orthopaedic Hospital NHSFT
0121 685 4000

Papworth Hospital NHSFT
01480 830541

Peterborough and Stamford Hospitals NHSFT
01733 874000

Queen Victoria Hospital NHSFT
01342 414000

The Rotherham NHSFT
01709 820000

The Royal Berkshire NHSFT
0118 322 5111

The Royal Bournemouth & Christchurch Hospitals NHSFT
01202 303626

Royal Devon & Exeter NHSFT
01392 411611

The Royal Marsden NHSFT
020 7352 8171

The Royal National Hospital for Rheumatic Diseases NHSFT
01225 465941

Salford Royal NHSFT
0161 789 7373

Salisbury NHSFT
01722 336262

Sheffield Children's NHSFT
0114 271 7000

Sheffield Teaching Hospital NHSFT
0114 271 1900

Sherwood Forest Hospitals NHSFT
01623 622515

South Devon Healthcare NHSFT
01803 614567

South Essex Partnership NHSFT
01375 364650

South London and Maudsley NHSFT
020 3228 6000

South Staffordshire and Shropshire Healthcare NHSFT
01785 257888

South Tyneside NHSFT
0844 811 3030

Southend University Hospital NHSFT
01702 221100

Stockport NHSFT
0161 483 1010

Tavistock and Portman NHSFT
020 7435 7111

University College London Hospitals NHSFT
0845 155 5000

University Hospital Birmingham NHSFT
0121 432 3232

University Hospital of South Manchester NHSFT
0161 998 7070

Wirral University Teaching Hospital
0151 678 5111

Yeovil District Hospital NHSFT
01935 384825

York Hospitals NHSFT
01904 631313

A

Abingdon Community Hospital, Abingdon
01235 205700

Accrington Victoria Community Hospital, Accrington
01254 295636

Addenbrooke's Hospital, Cambridge
01223 245151

Airedale General Hospital, Keighley
01535 652511

Alcester Hospital, Alcester
01789 762470

Alder Hey Children's Hospital, Liverpool
0151 228 4811

Alderney Hospital, Poole
01202 735537

Alexandra Hospital, Chatham
01634 687166

Alexandra Hospital, Redditch
01527 503030

Alfred Bean Hospital, Driffield
01377 241124

Alnwick Infirmary
01665 626700

Altrincham General Hospital, Altrincham
0161 928 6111

Amberstone Hospital, Hailsham
01323 440022

Amersham Hospital, Amersham
01494 526161

Arrowe Park Hospital, Wirral
0151 678 5111

Ashburton & Buckfastleigh Hospital
01364 652203

Ashfield Community Hospital, Kirkby in Ashfield
01636 681681

Ashford Hospital
01784 884488

Ashton House Hospital, Merseyside
0151 653 9660

Ashworth Hospital, Liverpool
0151 473 0303

Axminster Hospital, Axminster
01297 630400

B

Babington Hospital, Belper
01773 824171

Barking Hospital, Essex
020 8983 8000

Barnet Hospital, London
0845 111 4000

Barnsley District General Hospital
01226 730000

Basildon Hospital, Essex
01268 533911

Bassetlaw Hospital, Worksop
01909 500990

Beccles & District Hospital
01502 719800

Beckenham Hospital
01689 863000

Bedford Hospital, Bedford
01234 355122

Beighton Community Hospital, Sheffield
0114 271 6500

Bensham Hospital, Gateshead
0191 482 0000

Berkeley Hospital, Berkley
01453 562000

Berwick Infirmary, Berwick-on-Tweed
01289 356600

Beverley Westwood Hospital
01482 886600

Bexhill Hospital, Bexhill-on-Sea
01424 755255

Bicester Hospital
01869 604000

Bickley Day Hospital, Norfolk
01953 457342

Bingley Hospital
01274 563438

Birch Hill Hospital, Rochdale
01706 377777

Birmingham Children's Hospital
0121 333 9999

Birmingham Dental Hospital
0121 236 8611

Birmingham Heartlands Hospital
0121 424 2000

Birmingham Women's Hospital
0121 472 1377

Bishop Auckland General Hospital
01388 455000

Bishops Castle Community Hospital
01588 638220

Blackberry Hill Hospital, Bristol
0117 965 6061

Blackburn Royal Infirmary, Blackburn
01254 263555

Blackpool Victoria Hospital
01253 300000

Blandford Community Hospital
01258 456541

Blyth Community Hospital
01670 396400

Bodmin Hospital
01208 251301

Bolingbroke Hospital, London
020 7223 7411

Booth Hall Children's Hospital, Manchester
0161 795 7000

Bovey Tracey Hospital, Bovey Tracey
01626 832279

Bradford Royal Infirmary
01274 542200

Bradford-on-Avon Community Hospital
01225 862975

Bradwell Hospital, Newcastle
01782 425400

Brampton War Memorial Community Hospital, Brampton
01697 72534

Bridgnorth Hospital
01746 762641

Bridgwater Community Hospital
01278 451501

Bridlington & District Hospital
01262 606666

Bridport Community Hospital
01308 422371

Brighton General Hospital
01273 696011

Bristol Eye Hospital
0117 928 4771

Bristol General Hospital
0117 928 6223

Bristol Homoeopathic Hospital
0117 973 1231

Bristol Royal Hospital for Children
0117 927 6998

Bristol Royal Infirmary
0117 923 0000

Brixham Hospital
01803 882153

Broadgreen Hospital, Liverpool
0151 282 6000

Broadmoor Hospital
01344 773111

Bromyard Community Hospital
01885 485700

Broomfield Hospital, Chelmsford
0844 822 0002

Buckland Hospital, Dover
01304 201624

Bucknall Hospital, Stoke-on-Trent
01782 273510

Budleigh Salterton Hospital
01395 442020

Burnham-on-Sea War Memorial Hospital
01278 773118

Burnley General Hospital
01282 425071

Bushey Fields Hospital, Dudley
01384 457373

Buxton Hospital
01298 214 000

C

Calderdale Royal Hospital, Halifax
01422 357171

Calderstones Hospital, Clitheroe
01254 822121

Camborne/Redruth Community Hospital, Redruth
01209 881688

Cannock Chase Hospital, Cannock
01543 572757

Carlton Court, Lowestoft
01502 527900

Carshalton War Memorial Hospital
020 8770 8000

Cassell Hospital, Richmond
020 8483 2900

Castle Hill Hospital, Cottingham
01482 875875

Castleberg Hospital, Settle
01729 823515

Castleford & Normanton District Hospital
01924 327000

Caterham Dene Hospital
01883 837500

Central Middlesex Hospital, London
020 8965 5733

Chantry House Day Hospital, Frome
01373 455817

Chapel Allerton Hospital, Leeds
0113 262 3404

Chard & District Hospital
01460 238220

Charing Cross Hospital, London
020 8846 1234

Charles Clifford Dental Hospital, Sheffield
0114 271 7800

Chase Farm Hospital, Enfield
0845 111 4000

Chase Hospital, Bordon
01420 488801

Cheadle Hospital, Stoke-on-Trent
01538 487500

Chelsea and Westminster Hospital, London
020 8746 8000

Cheltenham General Hospital
0845 422 2222

Cherry Knowle Hospital, Sunderland
0191 565 6256

Cherry Tree Hospital, Stockport
0161 483 1010

Chester le Street Hospital
0191 333 6262

Chesterfield Royal Hospital
01246 277271

Chingford Hospital
020 8529 7141

Chippenham Community Hospital
01249 447100

Chipping Norton Community Hospital
01608 648450

Chorley & South Ribble District General Hospital, Chorley
01257 261222

Christchurch Hospital
01202 486361

Christie Hospital, Manchester
0161 446 3000

Churchill Hospital, Headington
01865 741841

Cirencester Hospital
01285 655711

City General Hospital, Stoke-on-Trent
01782 715444

City Hospital, Birmingham
0121 554 3801

Clacton Hospital
01255 201717

Clatterbridge Hospital, Wirral
0151 334 4000

Clayton Hospital, Wakefield
01924 201688

Clifton Hospital, Lytham St Annes
01253 306204

Clitheroe Hospital
01200 427311

Cobham Cottage Hospital
01932 588400

Cockermouth Cottage Hospital, Cockermouth
01900 822226

Colchester General Hospital
01206 747474

Colman Hospital, Norwich
01603 286286

Congleton & District War
Memorial Hospital, Congleton
01260 294800
Conquest Hospital,
St Leonards on Sea
01424 755255
Cookridge Hospital, Leeds
0113 267 3411
Coppetts Wood Hospital, London
020 7794 0500
Coquetdale Cottage Hospital,
Morpeth
01669 620555
Corbett House, Stourbridge
01384 456111
Corby Community Hospital
01536 400070
Coronation Hospital, Ilkley
01943 609666
Cossham Hospital, Bristol
0117 967 1661
Countess of Chester Hospital
01244 365000
County Hospital, Durham
0191 333 6262
Coventry and Warwickshire
Hospital, Coventry
024 7696 4000
Crawley Hospital
01293 600300
Crediton Hospital
01363 775588
Crewkerne Hospital
01460 72491
Cromer Hospital
01263 513571
Crowborough War Memorial
Hospital
01892 652284
Cumberland Infirmary, Carlisle
01228 523444

D

Danesbury Hospital, Welwyn
01438 714447
Danetre Hospital, Daventry
01327 708100
Darent Valley Hospital, Dartford
01322 428100
Darlington Memorial Hospital
01325 380100
Dartmouth & Kingswear Hospital,
Dartmouth
01803 832255
Dawlish Hospital, Dawlish
01626 868500
Delancey Hospital, Cheltenham
01242 222222
Derby City General Hospital
01332 340131
Derby Royal Infirmary
01332 347141
Derbyshire Children's Hospital,
Derby
01332 340131
Dereham Hospital
01362 692391
Derriford Hospital, Plymouth
0845 155 8155
Devizes Community Hospital
01380 723511
Devonshire Road Hospital,
Blackpool
01253 303364

Dewsbury and District Hospital
0844 811 8110
Diana, Princess of Wales
Hospital, Grimsby
01472 874111
Didcot Hospital
01235 205860
Dilke Memorial Hospital,
Gloucester
01594 598100
Doncaster Gate Hospital,
Rotherham
01709 304802
Doncaster Royal Infirmary
01302 366666
Dorking Hospital
01306 887150
Dorset County Hospital,
Dorchester
01305 251150
Dunston Hill Hospital, Gateshead
0191 482 0000

E

Ealing Hospital, Southall
020 8967 5000
Earls House Hospital, Durham
0191 333 6262
East Surrey Hospital, Redhill
01737 768511
Eastbourne District General
Hospital, Eastbourne
01323 417400
Eastman Dental Hospital, London
020 7915 1000
Edenbridge & District War
Memorial Hospital, Edenbridge
01732 862137
Edgware Community Hospital
020 8952 2381
Edward Hain Hospital, St Ives
01736 576100
Ellen Badger Hospital,
Shipston-on-Stour
01608 661410
Ellesmere Port Hospital
01244 365000
Elmwood Day Hospital, Chester
01244 364122
Epsom General Hospital
01372 735735
Erith & District Hospital
020 8308 3131
Essex County Hospital,
Colchester
01206 747474
Evesham Community Hospital
01386 502345
Exmouth Hospital
01395 282000

F

Fairfield General Hospital, Bury
0161 764 6081
Fairford Hospital
01285 712212
Faversham Cottage Hospital
01795 562066
Feilding Palmer Hospital,
Lutterworth
01455 552150
Felixstowe General Hospital
01394 458848

Fenwick Hospital, Lyndhurst
023 8028 2782
Fieldhead Hospital, Wakefield
01924 327000
Finchley Memorial Hospital,
London
020 8349 6300
Fleetwood Hospital
01253 306000
Fordingbridge Hospital
01425 652255
Fowey Hospital
01726 832241
Freeman Hospital,
Newcastle-upon-Tyne
0191 233 6161
Frenchay Hospital, Bristol
0117 970 1212
Friarage Hospital, Northallerton
01609 779911
Frimley Park Hospital, Frimley
01276 604604
Frome Victoria Hospital
01373 463591
Furness General Hospital,
Barrow-in-Furness
01229 870870

G

George Eliot Hospital, Nuneaton
024 7635 1351
Glenfield Hospital, Leicester
0116 287 1471
Gloucestershire Royal Hospital,
Gloucester
01452 528555
Goldie Leigh Hospital, London
020 8319 7100
Good Hope Hospital, Sutton
Coldfield
0121 378 2211
Goole & District Hospital
01405 720720
Gordon Hospital, London
020 8746 5505
Gorse Hill Hospital, Leicester
0116 225 5400
Goscote Hospital, Walsall
01922 721172
Gosport War Memorial Hospital
023 9252 4611
Grantham & District Hospital
01476 565232
Gravesend & North Kent Hospital
01474 360500
Great Ormond Street Hospital for
Children, London
020 7405 9200
Great Western Hospital, Swindon
01793 604020
Green Lane Hospital, Devizes
01380 731200
Greenfields Hospital,
Birmingham
0121 465 8750
Guest Hospital, Dudley
01384 456111
Guisborough General Hospital
01287 284000
Guy's Hospital, London
020 7188 7188

H

Halstead Hospital
01787 291022

Halton Hospital, Runcorn
01928 714567

Haltwhistle War Memorial
Hospital
01434 320225

Hammersmith Hospital, London
020 8383 1000

Hammerwich Hospital,
Burntwood
01543 412900

Harefield Hospital
01895 823737

Harpenden Memorial Hospital
01582 760196

Harplands Hospital, Stoke-on-
Trent
01782 441600

Harrogate District Hospital
01423 885959

Harry Watton House, Birmingham
0121 685 6001

Harwich Hospital
01255 201200

Havant War Memorial Hospital
023 9248 4256

Hawkhurst Cottage Hospital,
Hawkhurst
01580 753345

Haywood Hospital, Stoke-on-
Trent
01782 715444

Heanor Memorial Hospital
01773 710711

Heartlands Hospital, Birmingham
0121 424 2000

Heath Lane Hospital, West
Bromwich
0845 146 1800

Heatherwood Hospital, Ascot
01344 623333

Heavitree Hospital, Exeter
01392 411611

Hellesdon Hospital, Norwich
01603 421421

Helston Hospital
01326 435800

Hemel Hempstead General
Hospital
01442 213141

Herbert Hospital, Bournemouth
01202 584300

Hereford County Hospital
01432 355444

Hertford County Hospital
01438 314333

Herts & Essex Hospital,
Bishop's Stortford
01279 655191

Hexham General Hospital
01434 655655

Highbury Hospital, Nottingham
0115 977 0000

Highfield Day Hospital,
Chester le Street
0191 333 6262

Highfield Hospital, Widnes
0151 495 5079

Hill Crest Mental Health Unit,
Redditch
01527 500575

Hillingdon Hospital, Uxbridge
01895 238282

Hinchingbrooke Hospital,
Huntingdon
01480 416416

Holbeach Hospital, Spalding
01406 422283

Holme Valley Memorial Hospital,
Holmfirth
01484 681711

Homeopathic Hospital,
Tunbridge Wells
01892 522598

Homerton University Hospital,
London
020 8510 5555

Honiton Hospital
01404 540540

Hope Hospital, Salford
0161 789 7373

Hornsea Cottage Hospital
01964 533146

Horsham Hospital
01403 227000

Horton Hospital, Banbury
01295 275500

Hospital for Tropical Diseases,
London
0845 155 5000

Hospital of St Cross, Rugby
01788 572831

Huddersfield Royal Infirmary
01484 342000

Hull Royal Infirmary
01482 328541

Hundens Lane Day Hospital,
Darlington
01325 380100

Hunters Moor Hospital,
Newcastle-upon-Tyne
0844 811 5522

Hurstwood Park Neurosciences
Centre, Haywards Heath
01444 441881

Hyde Hospital, Cheshire
0161 604 3445

Hythe Hospital, Southampton
023 8084 5955

I

Ilkeston Community Hospital
0115 930 5522

Ipswich Hospital
01473 712233

J

James Cook University Hospital,
Middlesbrough
01642 850850

James Paget Hospital, Great
Yarmouth
01493 452452

John Coupland Hospital,
Gainsborough
01427 816500

John Radcliffe Hospital, Oxford
01865 741166

Johnson Hospital, Spalding
01775 722386

Julian Hospital, Norwich
01603 421800

K

Kendray Hospital, Barnsley
01226 777811

Kent & Canterbury Hospital,
Canterbury
01227 766877

Kent and Sussex Hospital,
Tunbridge Wells
01892 526111

Kettering General Hospital
01536 492000

Kidderminster Hospital
01562 823424

King Edward VII Hospital,
Windsor
01753 860441

King George Hospital, Ilford
020 8983 8000

King's College Hospital, London
020 3299 9000

King's Mill Hospital, Sutton in
Ashfield
01623 622515

Kings Park Hospital,
Bournemouth
01202 303757

Kingston Hospital,
Kingston-upon-Thames
020 8546 7711

Knutsford and District
Community Hospital
01565 757220

L

Lady Eden Hospital, Bishop
Auckland
01388 455060

Launceston General Hospital
01566 765650

Leatherhead Hospital
01372 384384

Leeds Dental Hospital
0113 244 0111

Leeds General Infirmary
0113 243 2799

Leek Moorlands Hospital
01538 487100

Leicester General Hospital,
Leicester
0116 249 0490

Leicester Royal Infirmary,
Leicester
0116 254 1414

Leigh Infirmary, Leigh
01942 672333

Leighton Hospital, Crewe
01270 255141

Leominster Community Hospital,
Leominster
01568 614211

Lewes Victoria Hospital
01273 474153

Lincoln County Hospital
01522 512512

Lings Bar Hospital, Nottingham
0115 945 5577

Liskeard Community Hospital
01579 335600

Lister Hospital, Stevenage
01438 314333

Little Brook Hospital, Dartford
01322 622222

Little Court Day Hospital,
Burnham-on-Sea
01278 786876

Liverpool Women's Hospital,
Liverpool
0151 708 9988

Livingstone Hospital, Dartford
01322 622222

London Chest Hospital
020 7377 7000

Longton Cottage Hospital,
Stoke-on-Trent
01782 425600

Louth County Hospital
01507 600100

Lowestoft Hospital
01502 587311

Lucy Baldwyn Hospital,
Stourport-on-Severn
01299 827327

Ludlow Hospital
01584 872201

Luton & Dunstable Hospital
0845 127 0127

Lydney and District Hospital
01594 598220

Lymington Hospital
01590 677011

Lynfield Mount Hospital,
Bradford
01274 494194

Lytham Hospital, Lytham St
Annes
01253 303953

M

Macclesfield District General
Hospital, Macclesfield
01625 421000

Maidstone Hospital, Maidstone
01622 729000

Malmesbury Community Hospital
01666 823358

Malton and Norton Hospital
01653 693041

Malvern Community Hospital,
Malvern
01684 612600

Manchester Royal Eye Hospital
0161 276 5526

Manchester Royal Infirmary
0161 276 1234

Manor Hospital, Walsall
01922 721172

Mansfield Community Hospital
01623 785050

Market Harborough & District
Hospital, Market Harborough
01858 410500

Mary Hewetson Community
Hospital, Keswick
01768 767000

Maudsley Hospital, London
020 7703 6333

Mayday University Hospital,
Croydon
020 8401 3000

Medway Maritime Hospital,
Gillingham
01634 830000

Melksham Community Hospital
01225 701000

Melton War Memorial Hospital,
Melton Mowbray
01664 854800

Memorial Hospital, London
020 8836 8500

Mile End Hospital, London
020 7377 7000

Milford-on-Sea Hospital
01590 648110

Mill View Hospital, Hove
01273 696011

Millom Hospital, Cumbria
01229 772631

Milton Keynes General Hospital
01908 660033

Minehead Hospital
01643 707251

Montagu Hospital, Mexborough
01709 585171

Moore Hospital, Cheltenham
01451 820228

Moorgreen Hospital,
Southampton
023 8047 2258

Moreton-in-Marsh Hospital
01608 650456

Moretonhampstead Hospital,
Newton Abbot
01647 440217

Morpeth Cottage Hospital
01670 395600

Moseley Hall Hospital,
Birmingham
0121 442 4321

Mount Gould Hospital, Plymouth
01752 268011

Mount Vernon Hospital, Barnsley
01226 777835

Mount Vernon Hospital,
Northwood
01923 826111

Musgrove Park Hospital, Taunton
01823 333444

N

National Hospital for Neurology
& Neurosurgery, London
020 7837 3611

Nelson Hospital, London
020 8296 2000

Nevill Hospital, Hove
01273 821680

New Cross Hospital,
Wolverhampton
01902 307999

New Epsom and Ewell Cottage
Hospital
01372 734834

Newark Hospital
01636 681681

Newcastle Dental Hospital,
Newcastle upon Tyne
0191 233 6161

Newcastle General Hospital,
Newcastle upon Tyne
0191 233 6161

Newham General Hospital,
London
020 7476 4000

Newport Hospital, Shropshire
01952 820893

Newquay and District Hospital
01637 893600

Newton Abbot Hospital
01626 354321

Newton Community Hospital,
Newton-le-Willows
01925 222731

Newtown Hospital, Worcester
01905 763333

Norfolk & Norwich University
Hospital
01603 286286

North Devon District Hospital,
Barnstaple
01271 322577

North Hampshire Hospital,
Basingstoke
01256 473202

North Manchester General
Hospital
0161 795 4567

North Middlesex University
Hospital, London
020 8887 2000

North Tyneside General Hospital,
North Shields
0191 259 6660

Northampton General Hospital
01604 634700

Northern General Hospital,
Sheffield
0114 243 4343

Northgate Hospital, Great
Yarmouth
01493 337652

Northgate Hospital, Morpeth
01670 394000

Northwick Park Hospital, Harrow
020 8864 3232

Norwich Community Hospital
01603 776776

Nottingham City Hospital
0115 969 1169

O

Okehampton Community
Hospital
01837 658000

Ongar War Memorial Hospital
01277 362629

Orchard Hill Hospital
020 8770 8000

Ormskirk and District General
Hospital, Ormskirk
01695 577111

Orpington Hospital
01689 863000

Orsett Hospital
01268 533911

Ottery St Mary Hospital
01404 816000

Oxford Community Hospital
01865 225501

P

Paignton Hospital
01803 557425

Palmer Community Hospital,
Jarrow
0191 451 6000

Papworth Hospital, Cambridge
01480 830541

Patrick Stead Hospital,
Halesworth
01986 872124

Paulton Memorial Hospital, Bristol
01761 412315

Peasley Cross Hospital, St Helens
01744 458380

Pembury Hospital, Tunbridge Wells
01892 823535

Pendle Community Hospital, Nelson
01282 425071

Penrith Hospital
01768 245300

Pershore Cottage Hospital, Worcestershire
01386 502070

Peterborough District Hospital
01733 874000

Peterlee Community Hospital
0191 586 3474

Petersfield Hospital
01730 263221

Pilgrim Hospital, Boston
01205 364801

Pinderfields General Hospital, Wakefield
0844 811 8110

Plympton Hospital, Plymouth
01752 314500

Poltair Hospital, Penzance
01736 575570

Pontefract General Infirmary
0844 811 8119

Poole Hospital
01202 665511

Portland Hospital, Dorset
01305 820341

Potters Bar Community Hospital
01707 653286

Preston Hall Hospital, Aylesford
01622 710161

Primrose Hill Hospital, Jarrow
0191 451 6375

Princess Alexandra Hospital, Harlow
01279 444455

Princess Anne Hospital, Southampton
023 8077 7222

Princess Louise Hospital, London
020 8962 6112

Princess Marina Hospital, Northampton
01604 752323

Princess of Wales Community Hospital, Bromsgrove
01527 488000

Princess of Wales Hospital, Ely
01353 652000

Princess Royal Hospital, Haywards Heath
01444 441881

Princess Royal Hospital, Hull
01482 701151

Princess Royal Hospital, Telford
01952 641222

Princess Royal University Hospital, Orpington
01689 863000

Prospect Park Hospital, Reading
0118 960 5000

Prudhoe Hospital
01670 394000

Purley War Memorial Hospital
020 8401 3000

Q

Queen Alexandra Hospital, Portsmouth
023 9228 6000

Queen Charlotte's Hospital
020 8383 1111

Queen Elizabeth Hospital, Gateshead
0191 482 0000

Queen Elizabeth Hospital, King's Lynn
01553 613613

Queen Elizabeth Hospital, London
020 8836 6000

Queen Elizabeth II Hospital, Welwyn Garden City
01707 328111

Queen Elizabeth Medical Centre, Birmingham
0121 472 1311

Queen Elizabeth The Queen Mother Hospital, Margate
01843 225544

Queen Mary's Hospital, Roehampton, London
020 8487 6000

Queen Mary's Hospital, Sidcup
020 8302 2678

Queen Victoria Hospital, East Grinstead
01342 414000

Queen Victoria Hospital, Morecambe
01524 405700

Queen Victoria Memorial Hospital, Herne Bay
01227 594700

Queen's Hospital, Burton-upon-Trent
01283 566333

Queens Medical Centre, Nottingham
0115 924 9924

Queens Park Hospital, Blackburn
01254 263555

R

Radcliffe Infirmary, Oxford
01865 741166

Ramsbottom Cottage Hospital, Bury
01706 823123

Redcliffe Day Hospital, Wellingborough
01933 440181

Retford Hospital
01777 274400

Ribbleton Hospital, Preston
01772 401600

Richardson Hospital, Barnard Castle
01833 696500

Ridge Lea Hospital, Lancaster
01524 586200

Ridley Day Hospital, Wincanton
01963 34708

Ripley Hospital, Derbyshire
01773 743456

Ripon Community Hospital, Ripon
01765 602546

Robert Jones and Agnes Hunt Orthopaedic Hospital, Oswestry
01691 404000

Roborough Day Hospital, Eastbourne
01323 638972

Rochdale Infirmary
01706 377777

Romsey Hospital, Romsey
01794 834700

Ross Community Hospital, Ross-on-Wye
01989 562100

Rossall Hospital, Fleetwood
01253 655101

Rossendale Hospital
01706 215151

Rotherham District General Hospital
01709 820000

Rowan House EMI Facility and Day Hospital, Malvern
01684 612763

Rowley Regis Hospital
0121 553 1831

Roxbourne Hospital, Harrow
020 8237 2000

Royal Albert Edward Infirmary, Wigan
01942 244000

Royal Alexandra Hospital for Sick Children, Brighton
01273 696955

Royal Berkshire Hospital, Reading
0118 322 5111

Royal Bolton Hospital
01204 390390

Royal Bournemouth General Hospital
01202 303626

Royal Brompton Hospital, London
020 7352 8121

Royal Cornwall Hospital, Truro
01872 250000

Royal Devon and Exeter Hospital
01392 411611

Royal Eye Infirmary, Plymouth
01752 315123

Royal Free Hospital, London
020 7794 0500

Royal Hallamshire Hospital, Sheffield
0114 271 1900

Royal Hampshire County Hospital, Winchester
01962 863535

Royal Lancaster Infirmary, Lancaster
01524 65944

Royal Leamington Spa Rehabilitation Hospital, Warwick
01926 317700

Royal Liverpool Children's Hospital, Alder Hey
0151 228 4811

Royal Liverpool University Dental Hospital
0151 706 2000

Royal Liverpool University Hospital
0151 706 2051

Royal London Homeopathic
Hospital
020 7391 8833
Royal London Hospital
020 7377 7000
Royal Manchester Children's
Hospital
0161 794 4696
Royal Marsden Hospital, London
020 7352 8171
Royal Marsden Hospital, Sutton
020 8642 6011
Royal National Hospital for
Rheumatic Diseases, Bath
01225 465941
Royal National Orthopaedic
Hospital, London
020 8954 2300
Royal National Throat, Nose and
Ear Hospital, London
020 7915 1300
Royal Oldham Hospital
0161 624 0420
Royal Orthopaedic Hospital,
Birmingham
0121 685 4000
Royal Preston Hospital
01772 716565
Royal Shrewsbury Hospital
01743 261000
Royal South Hants Hospital,
Southampton
023 8063 4288
Royal Surrey County Hospital,
Guildford
01483 571122
Royal Sussex County Hospital,
Brighton
01273 696955
Royal United Hospital, Bath
01225 428331
Royal Victoria Hospital,
Folkestone
01303 850202
Royal Victoria Infirmary,
Newcastle-upon-Tyne
0191 233 6161
Royston Hospital
01763 242134
Rushden Hospital
01933 440666
Russells Hall Hospital, Dudley,
01384 456111
Ruth Lancaster James Hospital,
Alston
01434 381218
Rutland Memorial Hospital,
Oakham
01572 722552
Ryhope General Hospital,
Sunderland
0191 521 0541

S

Saffron Walden Community
Hospital
01799 562900
St Albans City Hospital
01727 866122
St Andrew's Hospital, London
020 7476 4000
St Ann's Hospital, Poole
01202 708881

St Anne's Hospital, Altrincham
0161 928 5851
St Anne's Orchard Psychiatric Day
Hospital, Malvern
01684 561659
St Austell Community Hospital
01726 291199
St Barnabas Hospital, Saltash
01752 857400
St Bartholomew's Day Hospital,
Liverpool
0151 489 6241
St Bartholomew's Hospital,
London
020 7377 7000
St Barholomew's Hospital,
Rochester
01634 810900
St Catherine's Hospital,
Birkenhead
0151 678 7272
St Charles Hospital, London
020 8969 2488
St Christopher's Hospital,
Fareham
01329 286321
St Clement's Hospital, Ipswich
01473 329000
St Clement's Hospital, London
020 8880 6296
St George's Hospital, Lincoln
01522 512512
St George's Hospital, London
020 8672 1255
St George's Hospital, Stafford
01785 257888
St Helens Hospital
01744 26633
St Helier Hospital, Carshalton
020 8296 2000
St James' Hospital, Portsmouth
023 9282 2444
St James's University Hospital,
Leeds
0113 243 3144
St John's Hospital, Chelmsford
0844 822 0002
St Leonard's Community
Hospital, Ringwood
01202 584200
St Luke's Hospital, Bradford
01274 734744
St Luke's Hospital, Market
Harborough
01858 410300
St Luke's Hospital,
Middlesbrough
01642 516147
St Margaret's Hospital, Epping
01992 902010
St Mark's Hospital, Maidenhead
01628 632012
St Mark's Hospital, Harrow
020 8235 4000
St Martin's Hospital, Bath
01225 831500
St Martin's Hospital, Canterbury
01227 459584
St Mary's Hospital, Isle of Wight
01983 524081
St Mary's Hospital, Isles of Scilly
01720 422392
St Marys Hospital, Kettering
01536 410141

St Mary's Hospital, London
020 7886 6666
St Mary's Hospital, Manchester
0161 276 1234
St Mary's Hospital, Melton
Mowbray
01664 854800
St Mary's Hospital, Portsmouth
023 9228 6000
St Michael's Hospital, Braintree
01245 440761
St Michael's Hospital, Bristol
0117 921 5411
St Michael's Hospital, Hayle
01736 753234
St Michael's Hospital, Warwick
01926 406789
St Monica's Hospital, York
01347 821214
St Nicholas Hospital,
Newcastle-upon-Tyne
0191 213 0151
St Pancras Hospital, London
020 7530 3500
St Peter's Hospital, Chertsey
01932 872000
St Peter's Hospital, Maldon
01621 725323
St Richard's Hospital, Chichester
01243 788122
St Thomas' Hospital, London
020 7188 7188
Salisbury District Hospital,
Salisbury
01722 336262
Sandwell General Hospital,
West Bromwich
0121 553 1831
Savernake Hospital, Marlborough
01672 517200
Scarborough General Hospital
01723 368111
Scott Hospital, Plymouth
01752 314343
Scunthorpe General Hospital
01724 282282
Seacroft Hospital, Leeds
0113 264 8164
Seasons Day Hospital, Clevedon
01275 335300
Seaton Hospital
01297 23901
Sedgefield Community Hospital,
Stockton-on-Tees
01740 626600
Selby War Memorial Hospital
01757 702664
Selly Oak Hospital, Birmingham
0121 627 1627
Sevenoaks Hospital
01732 470200
Sheffield Children's Hospital
0114 271 7000
Shelton Hospital, Shrewsbury
01743 261000
Sheppey Community Hospital,
Isle of Sheppey
01795 879100
Shepton Mallet Community
Hospital
01749 342931
Shipley Hospital
01274 773390
Shotley Bridge Hospital, Consett
0191 333 2333

Sir Alfred Jones Memorial
Hospital, Liverpool
0151 494 3198
Sir GB Hunter Memorial Hospital,
Wallsend
0191 220 5953
Sir Robert Peel Hospital,
Tamworth
01827 263800
Sittingbourne Memorial Hospital
01795 418300
Skegness & District General
Hospital
01754 762401
Skipton General Hospital
01756 792233
Solihull Hospital
0121 424 2000
South Hams Hospital,
Kingsbridge
01548 852349
South Moor Hospital, Stanley
0191 333 6262
South Petherton Hospital
01460 240333
South Shore Hospital, Blackpool
01253 306106
South Tyneside District General
Hospital, South Shields
0844 811 3030
Southampton General Hospital
023 8077 7222
Southend Hospital,
Westcliff-on-Sea
01702 435555
Southlands Hospital,
Shoreham-by-Sea
01273 455622
Southmead Hospital, Bristol
0117 950 5050
Southport & Formby District
General Hospital, Southport
01704 547471
Southport General Infirmary
01704 547471
Southwold Hospital, Suffolk
01502 723333
Springfield University Hospital,
London
020 8672 9911
Staffordshire General Hospital,
Stafford
01785 257731
Stamford and Rutland Hospital
01780 764151
Stead Memorial Hospital, Redcar
01642 282282
Stepping Hill Hospital, Stockport
0161 483 1010
Stewart Day Hospital, St Helens
01744 458393
Stoke Mandeville Hospital,
Aylesbury
01296 315000
Stone House Hospital, Dartford
01322 622222
Stratford Hospital,
Stratford-upon-Avon
01789 205831
Stratton Hospital, Bude
01288 287700
Stretford Memorial Hospital,
Manchester
0161 881 5353

Stroud General Hospital
01453 562200
Stroud Maternity Hospital
01453 562140
Sunderland Eye Infirmary
0191 565 6256
Sunderland Royal Hospital
0191 565 6256
Surbiton Hospital
020 8399 7111
Sussex Eye Hospital, Brighton
01273 606126
Swanage Hospital, Swanage
01929 422282

T

Tameside General Hospital,
Ashton-under-Lyne
0161 331 6000
Tavistock Hospital
01822 612233
Teddington Memorial Hospital
020 8714 4000
Teignmouth Hospital
01626 772161
Tenbury and District General
Hospital, Tenbury Wells
01584 810643
Tewkesbury Hospital
01684 293303
Thornbury Hospital, Bristol
01454 412636
Tickhill Road Hospital, Doncaster
01302 796000
Tiddington Fields,
Stratford-upon-Avon
01789 261455
Tiverton & District Hospital
01884 235400
Tolworth Hospital, Surrey
020 8390 0102
Tonbridge Cottage Hospital
01732 353653
Torbay District General Hospital,
Torquay
01803 614567
Totnes Hospital
01803 862622
Trafford General Hospital,
Manchester
0161 748 4022
Trengweath Hospital, Redruth
01209 881900
Trowbridge Community Hospital
01225 752558

U

Uckfield Hospital
01825 769999
Ulverston Hospital
01229 484045
University College Hospital,
London
0845 155 5000
University Dental Hospital,
Manchester
0161 275 6666
University Hospital Aintree,
Liverpool
0151 525 5980
University Hospital Lewisham,
London
020 8333 3000

University Hospital of Hartlepool
01429 266654
University Hospital of North
Durham
0191 333 2333
University Hospital of North
Tees, Stockton-on-Tees
01429 266654
University of Bristol Dental
Hospital
0117 928 4383
Upton Hospital, Slough
01753 821441

V

Verrington Hospital, Wincanton
01963 32006
Victoria Central Hospital,
Merseyside
0151 678 7272
Victoria Cottage Hospital, Havant
01243 376041
Victoria Cottage Hospital,
Maryport
01900 812634
Victoria Hospital, Deal
01304 865400
Victoria Hospital, Lichfield
01543 442000
Victoria Hospital, Sidmouth
01395 512482
Victoria Infirmary, Northwich
01606 564000

W

Walkergate Hospital, Newcastle
upon Tyne
0191 233 6161
Wallingford Community Hospital
01491 208500
Walsgrave Hospital, Coventry
024 7660 2020
Walton Hospital, Chesterfield
01246 515151
Walton Hospital, Liverpool
0151 525 3611
Wansbeck General Hospital,
Ashington
01670 521 212
Wantage Hospital
01235 205801
Wareham Community Hospital
01929 552433
Warminster Community Hospital
01985 212076
Warrington Hospital
01925 635911
Warwick Hospital
01926 495321
Waterside Mental Health Day
Hospital
01386 502510
Watford General Hospital
01923 244366
Wathwood Hospital, Rotherham
01709 870800
Weardale Hospital, Stanhope
01388 528233
Welland Hospital, Spalding
01476 565232
Wellington & District Cottage
Hospital
01823 662663

West Cornwall Edward Bolitho
House Hospital
01736 575555
Wembley Community Hospital,
London
020 8903 1323
Wesham Hospital Rehabilitation
Unit, Preston
01253 655411
West Berkshire Community
Hospital, Thatcham
01635 273300
West Cornwall Hospital,
Penzance
01736 874000
West Cumberland Hospital,
Whitehaven
01946 693181
West Heath Hospital,
Birmingham
0121 627 1627
West Mendip Community
Hospital
01458 836450
West Middlesex University
Hospital, Isleworth
020 8560 2121
West Park Hospital,
Wolverhampton
01902 444000
West Suffolk Hospital,
Bury St Edmunds
01284 713000
West View Hospital, Tenterden
01580 261500
Westbourne Green Hospital,
Bradford
01274 227599
Westbury Community Hospital
01373 823616
Western Community Hospital,
Southampton
023 8047 5401
Western Eye Hospital, London
020 7886 6666
Westhaven Hospital, Weymouth
01305 786116
Westminster Memorial Hospital,
Shaftesbury
01747 851535
Westmorland General Hospital,
Kendal
01539 732288
Weston General Hospital,
Weston-super-Mare
01934 636363
Weston Park Hospital, Sheffield
0114 226 5000
Westwood Hospital, Beverley
01482 886600
Wexham Park Hospital, Slough
01753 633000
Weymouth Community Hospital
01305 760022
Wharfedale Hospital, Otley
01943 465522
Whelley Hospital, Wigan
01942 244000
Whipps Cross University Hospital,
London
020 8539 5522
Whiston Hospital, Prescot
0151 426 0611
Whitby Community Hospital
01947 604851

Whitchurch Hospital
01948 666292
Whitstable & Tankerton Hospital
01227 594400
Whittington Hospital, London
020 7272 3070
Whitworth Hospital, Matlock
01629 580211
Wigton Hospital, Cumbria
01697 366600
Willesden Hospital, London
020 8438 7000
William Harvey Hospital, Ashford
01233 633331
William Julien Courtauld
Hospital, Braintree
0844 822 0002
Williton Hospital
01984 635600
Wimborne Hospital
01202 858200
Winchcombe Hospital,
Cheltenham
01242 602341
Withernsea Community Hospital
01964 614666
Withington Hospital, Manchester
0161 434 5555
Witney Community Hospital
01993 209400
Woking Community Hospital
01483 715911
Wokingham Hospital
0118 949 5000
Wolverhampton and Midland Eye
Infirmary
01902 307999
Woodlands Hospital, St Leonards
on Sea
01424 755470
Woods Hospital, Glossop
01457 860783
Worcestershire Royal Hospital,
Worcester
01905 763333
Workington Infirmary
01946 693181
Worthing Hospital
01903 205111
Wotton Lawn, Gloucester
01452 891500
Wrightington Hospital, Wigan
01257 252211
Wycombe Hospital, High
Wycombe
01494 526161
Wythenshawe Hospital,
Manchester
0161 998 7070

Y

Yeatman Hospital, Sherborne
01935 813991
Yeovil District Hospital
01935 475122
York Hospital
01904 631313

*NHS England hospitals © NHS
Connecting for Health*

NHS hospitals: Wales

Aberbargoed Hospital
01443 828728
Aberdare General Hospital
01685 883811
Abergele Hospital
01745 832295
Abertillery & District Hospital
01495 214123
Amman Valley Hospital,
Ammanford
01269 822226
Barry Hospital
01446 704000
Blaenavon Hospital
01495 790236
Blaina & District Hospital,
Nantyglo
01495 293250
Bodnant EMI Unit, Llandudno
01492 862347
Brecon War Memorial Hospital,
Brecon
01874 622443
Bro Cerwyn Day Hospital,
Haverfordwest
01437 773157
Bro Ddyfi Community Hospital,
Powys
01654 702266
Bron y Garth Hospital, Gwynedd
01766 770310
Bronglais General Hospital,
Aberystwyth
01970 623131
Bronllys Hospital, Brecon
01874 711255
Bryn Beryl Hospital, Pwllheli
01758 701122
Bryn y Neuadd Hospital, Conwy
01248 682682
Brynmair Day Hospital, Llanelli
01554 772768
Bryntirion Hospital, Llanelli
01554 756567
Builth Wells Hospital
01982 552221
Caerphilly and District Miners'
Hospital
029 2085 1811
Cardiff Royal Infirmary
029 2049 2233
Cardigan and District Memorial
Hospital
01239 612214
Cefn Coed Hospital, Swansea
01792 561155
Cefni Hospital, Anglesey
01248 750117
Chepstow Community Hospital,
Chepstow
01291 636636
Chirk Community Hospital
01691 772430
Cimla Hospital, Neath
01639 862000
Colwyn Bay Community Hospital
01492 515218
Conwy Hospital
01492 564300
County Hospital, Torfeen
01495 768768

Dan-y-Bryn Unit, Ebbw Vale
01495 353700
Deeside Community Hospital,
Deeside
01244 830461
Denbigh Infirmary
01745 812624
Dewi Sant Hospital, Pontypridd
01443 486222
Dolgellau Hospital
01341 422479
Eryri Hospital, Caernarfon
01286 672481
Fairwood Hospital, Swansea
01792 203192
Ffestiniog Memorial Hospital
01766 831281
Flint Community Hospital
01352 732215
Garngoch Hospital, Swansea
01792 892921
Gellinudd Hospital, Swansea
01792 862221
Glan Clwyd District General
Hospital, Rhyl
01745 583910
Glanrhyd Hospital, Bridgend
01656 752752
Glantraeth Day Hospital, Rhyl
01745 443270
Gorseinon Hospital, Swansea
01792 702222
Gorwelion Day Hospital,
Aberystwyth
01970 615448
Groeswen Hospital, Port Talbot
01639 862000
Hill House Hospital, Swansea
01792 203551
HM Stanley Hospital, St Asaph
01745 583275
Holywell Community Hospital
01352 713003
Knighton Hospital
01547 528633
Llandough Hospital, Penarth
029 2071 1711
Llandovery Hospital
01550 722200
Llandrindod Wells Hospital
01597 822951
Llandudno General Hospital
01492 860066
Llanfrechfa Grange Hospital,
Cwmbran
01633 623623
Llangollen Community Hospital
01978 860226
Llanidloes War Memorial Hospital
01686 412121
Lluesty Hospital, Holywell
01352 710581
Llwynypia Hospital, Rhondda
01443 440440
Maesteg Community Hospital
01656 752752
Maindiff Court Hospital,
Abergavenny
01873 735500
Minfordd Hospital, Bangor
01248 352308
Mold Community Hospital
01352 758744

Montgomery County Infirmary,
Newtown
01686 617200
Morriston Hospital, Swansea
01792 702222
Mountain Ash General Hospital
01685 872411
Mynydd Mawr Hospital, Llanelli
01269 841343
Neath Port Talbot Hospital, Port
Talbot
01639 862000
Oakdale Hospital, Blackwood
01495 225207
Pontypridd & District Cottage
Hospital
01443 486144
Prestatyn Community Hospital
01745 853487
Prince Charles Hospital, Merthyr
Tydfil
01685 721721
Prince Phillip Hospital, Llanelli
01554 756567
Princess of Wales Hospital,
Bridgend
01656 752752
Redwood Memorial Hospital,
Rhymney
01685 840314
Rookwood Hospital, Cardiff
029 2041 5415
Royal Alexandra Hospital, Rhyl
01745 443000
Royal Glamorgan Hospital,
Llantrisant
01443 443443
Royal Gwent Hospital, Newport
01633 234234
Ruthin Hospital
01824 702692
St Brynach's Day Hospital,
Haverfordwest
01437 773157
St Cadoc's Hospital, Newport
01633 436700
St David's Hospital, Cardiff
029 2053 6666
St David's Hospital, Carmarthen
01267 237481
St Tydfil's Hospital, Merthyr
Tydfil
01685 723244
St Woolos Hospital, Newport
01633 234234
Singleton Hospital, Swansea
01792 205666
South Pembrokeshire Hospital,
Pembroke Dock
01646 682114
Swn-y-Gwynt Day Hospital,
Ammanford
01269 595473
Tenby Cottage Hospital
01834 842040
Tonna Hospital, Neath
01639 862000
Tredegar General Hospital
01495 722271
Tregaron Hospital
01974 298203
Trevalyn Hospital
01244 570446

Ty Sirhowy Health Centre,
Blackwood
01495 229010
Tywyn & District War Memorial
Hospital, Tywyn
01654 710411
University Dental Hospital,
Cardiff
029 2074 7747
University Hospital of Wales,
Cardiff
029 2074 7747
Victoria Memorial Hospital,
Welshpool
01938 553133
Whitchurch Hospital, Cardiff
029 2069 3191
Withybush General Hospital,
Haverfordwest
01437 764545
Wrexham Maelor Hospital,
Wrexham
01978 291100
Ysbyty George Thomas, Treorchy
01443 440440
Ysbyty Gwynedd, Bangor
01248 384384
Ysbyty Penrhos Stanley, Anglesey
01407 766000
Ysbyty'r Tri Chwm, Blaenau
Gwent
01495 353200
Ystrad Mynach Hospital,
Hangoed
01443 811411
Ystradgynlais Community
Hospital, Swansea
01639 844777

NHS hospitals: Scotland

Abbotsford Park Hospital,
Edinburgh
0131 447 2674, 653 4100
Aberdeen Maternity Hospital,
Aberdeen
0845 456 6000
Aberdeen Royal Infirmary
0845 456 6000
Aberfeldy Community Hospital
01887 820314
Aboyne Community Hospital
01339 886433
Adamson Hospital, Fife
01334 652901
Ailsa Hospital, Ayr
01292 610556
Annan Hospital
01461 203425
Arbroath Infirmary
01241 872584
Argyll & Bute Hospital, Argyll
01546 602323
Arran War Memorial Hospital,
Lamlash
01770 600777
Ashludie Hospital, Angus
01382 423000
Astley Ainslie Hospital,
Edinburgh
0131 537 9000
Ayr Hospital
01292 610555

Ayrshire Central Hospital
01294 274191
Balfour Hospital, Kirkwall
01856 888000
Bannockburn Hospital
01786 813016
Belford Hospital, Fort William
01397 702481
Belhaven Hospital, Dunbar
01368 862246
Benbecula Hospital
01870 603603
Biggart Hospital
01292 470611
Birch Avenue Day Hospital, Perth
01738 553920
Blairgowrie Community Hospital
01250 874466
Blawarthill Hospital
0141 211 9030
Bo'ness Hospital
01506 829580
Bonnybridge Hospital
01324 814685
Borders General Hospital,
Melrose
01896 826000
Brechin Infirmary
01356 622291
Brooksby Day Hospital
01475 676318
Caithness General Hospital, Wick
01955 605050
Cameron Hospital, Fife
01592 712472
Campbell Hospital, Banff
01261 842202
Campbell House, Gartnavel Royal
Hospital, Glasgow
0141 211 3600
Campbeltown Hospital, Argyll
01586 552224
Castle Douglas Hospital
01556 502333
Chalmers Hospital, Banff
01261 812567
Chalmers Hospital, Edinburgh
0131 536 1000
City Hospital, Edinburgh
0131 536 6000
Clackmannan County Hospital,
Alloa
01259 727374
Coathill Hospital, Coatbridge
01236 707769
Corstorphine Hospital, Edinburgh
0131 537 5000
County Community Hospital,
Invergordon
01349 852496
Crieff Community Hospital
01764 653173
Crosshouse Hospital, Kilmarnock
01563 521133
Dalrymple Hospital, Stranraer
01776 707707
Davidson Cottage Hospital,
Girvan
01465 712571
Dr Gray's Hospital, Elgin
01343 543131

Dr Mackinnon Memorial Hospital,
Isle of Skye
01471 822491
Drumchapel Hospital, Glasgow
0141 211 6000
Dumbarton Joint Hospital
01389 812036
Dumfries and Galloway Royal
Infirmary, Dumfries
01387 246246
Dunaros Hospital, Isle of Mull
01680 300392
Dunbar Hospital, Thurso
01847 893263
Dundee Dental Hospital
01382 660111
Dunoon General Hospital
01369 704341
Dunrowan Day Hospital, Falkirk
01324 639009
Dykebar Hospital, Paisley
0141 884 5122
East Ayrshire Community Hospital
01290 429429
Edenhall Hospital, Musselburgh
0131 536 8000
Edinburgh Dental Hospital,
Edinburgh
0131 536 4900
Edinburgh Orthopaedic Trauma
Unit
0131 536 1000
Edington Cottage Hospital, North
Berwick
01620 897040
Eyemouth Day Hospital
01890 752600
Falkirk & District Royal Infirmary,
Falkirk
01324 624000
Fleming Hospital, Aberlour
01340 871464
Forth Park Hospital, Kirkcaldy
01592 643355
Fraserburgh Hospital
01346 513151
Garrick Hospital, Stranraer
01776 707707
Gartnavel General Hospital,
Glasgow
0141 211 3000
Gilbert Bain Hospital, Lerwick
01595 743000
Glasgow Dental Hospital
0141 211 9600
Glasgow Homoeopathic Hospital
0141 211 1600
Glasgow Royal Infirmary
0141 211 4000
Glaxo Day Hospital, Monifieth
01382 527831
Glen O'Dee Hospital, Banchory
01330 822233
Glencoe Hospital, Glencoe
01855 811254
Glenrothes Hospital
01592 743505
Hairmyres Hospital, East Kilbride
01355 585000
Hartwood Hill Hospital, Shotts
01501 824575
Hawick Cottage Hospital
01450 372162

Hawick Day Hospital
01450 364300
Hawkhill Day Hospital, Dundee
01382 668300
Hay Lodge Hospital, Peebles
01721 722080
Herdmanflat Hospital,
Haddington
0131 536 8300
Holmhead Hospital, Cumnock
01290 422220
Ian Charles Hospital,
Grantown-on-Spey
01479 872528
Insch Hospital
01464 820213
Inverclyde Royal Hospital,
Greenock
01475 633777
Inverurie Hospital
01467 620454
Irvine Memorial Hospital,
Pitlochry
01796 472052
Islay Hospital, Isle of Islay
01496 301000
Johnstone Hospital, Johnstone
01505 331471
Kello Hospital, Biggar
01899 220077
Kelso Community Hospital
01573 223441
Kildean Hospital, Stirling
01786 446615
Kilsyth Victoria Memorial
Hospital
01236 822172
Kirkcudbright Hospital
01557 330549
Kirklands Hospital, Bothwell
01698 245000
Knoll Hospital, Duns
01361 883373
Lady Home Hospital, Lanark
01555 851210
Lady Margaret Hospital, Isle of
Cumbrae
01475 530307
Lawson Memorial Hospital,
Golspie
01408 633157
Leanchoil Hospital, Forres
01309 672284
Lightburn Hospital, Glasgow
0141 211 1500
Little Cairnie Hospital, Arbroath
01241 872584
Loanhead Hospital, Edinburgh
0131 440 0174
Lochmaben Hospital
01387 810255
Lorn and Islands District General
Hospital, Oban
01631 567500
Lynebank Hospital, Fife
01383 623623
Mackinnon Memorial Hospital,
Isle of Skye
01471 822491
Macmillan House, Perth
01738 639303
Maud Hospital
01771 613236

Merchiston Hospital, Johnstone
01505 328261
Mid Argyll Hospital, Argyll
01546 602449
Migdale Hospital, Bonar Bridge
01863 766211
Moffat Hospital
01683 220031
Monklands Hospital, Airdrie
01236 748748
Montrose Royal Infirmary
01674 830361
Murray Royal Hospital, Perth
01738 621151
Netherlea Hospital,
Newport-on-Tay
01382 543223
Newton Stewart Hospital
01671 402015
Ninewells Hospital, Dundee
01382 660111
Orchard House Day Hospital,
Stirling
01786 849717
Orleans Day Hospital, Dundee
01382 667322
Parkhead Hospital, Glasgow
0141 211 8300
Perth Royal Infirmary, Perth
01738 623311
Peterhead Community Hospital
01779 478234
Portree Hospital, Skye
01478 613200
Princess Alexandra Eye Pavilion,
Edinburgh
0131 536 1000
Princess Royal Maternity
Hospital, Glasgow
0141 211 5400
Queen Margaret Hospital,
Dunfermline
01383 623623
Queen Mother's Hospital,
Glasgow
0141 201 0550
Raigmore Hospital, Inverness
01463 704000
Randolph Wemyss Memorial
Hospital, Buckhaven
01592 712427
Ravenscraig Hospital, Greenock
01475 633777
Roodlands Hospital, Haddington
0131 536 8300
Ross Memorial Hospital, Dingwall
01349 863313
Rosslynlee Hospital, Midlothian
0131 536 7600
Roxburghe House, Aberdeen
0845 456 6000
Royal Aberdeen Children's
Hospital
0845 456 6000
Royal Alexandra Hospital, Paisley
0141 887 9111
Royal Cornhill Hospital,
Aberdeen
0845 456 6000
Royal Dundee Liff Hospital
01382 423000
Royal Edinburgh Hospital
0131 537 6000

Royal Hospital for Sick Children,
Edinburgh
0131 536 0000
Royal Hospital for Sick Children,
Glasgow
0141 201 0000
Royal Infirmary of Edinburgh
0131 536 1000
Royal Northern, Inverness
01463 704000
Royal Scottish National Hospital,
Larbert
01324 570700
Royal Victoria Hospital, Dundee
01382 423000
Royal Victoria Hospital,
Edinburgh
0131 537 5000
St Andrews Memorial Hospital,
Fife
01334 472327
St Brendan's Hospital, Isle of
Barra
01871 810465
St John's Hospital at Howden,
Livingston
01506 419666
St Margaret's Hospital,
Auchterarder
01764 662246
St Michael's Hospital, Linlithgow
01506 842053
St Vincent's Hospital, Kingussie
01540 661219
Seafield Hospital, Buckie
01542 832081
Southern General Hospital,
Glasgow
0141 201 1100
Spynie Hospital, Elgin
01343 567101
Stephen Hospital, Dufftown
01340 820215
Stirling Royal Infirmary, Stirling
01786 434000
Stobhill Hospital, Glasgow
0141 201 3000
Stracathro Hospital, Brechin
01356 647291
Strathclyde Hospital, Motherwell
01698 245000
Stratheden Hospital, Fife
01334 652611
Strathmartine Hospital, Dundee
01382 423000
Sunnyside Royal Hospital,
Montrose
01674 830361
Thomas Hope Hospital,
Langholm
01387 380417
Thornhill Hospital
01848 330205
Threshold Day Hospital, Dundee
01382 322026
Tippethill House, West Lothian
01501 745917
Town & County Hospital,
Caithness
01955 880389
Town & County Hospital, Nairn
01667 452101

Turner Memorial Hospital, Keith
01542 882526
Turriff Hospital
01888 563293
Udston Hospital, Hamilton
01698 723200
Ugie Hospital, Peterhead
01779 472011
Uist and Barra Hospital
01870 603603
Vale of Leven District General
Hospital, Alexandria
01389 754121
Victoria Hospital, Isle of Bute
01700 503938
Victoria Infirmary, Glasgow
0141 201 6000
Victoria Infirmary, Helensburgh
01436 672158
Westbank Day Hospital, Falkirk
01324 624111
Wester Moffat Hospital, Airdrie
01236 763377
Western General Hospital,
Edinburgh
0131 537 1000
Western Infirmary, Glasgow
0141 211 2000
Western Isles Hospital,
Stornoway
01851 704704
Weston Day Hospital, Fife
01334 652163
Whitehills Hospital, Angus
01307 475222
Whytemans Brae Hospital, Fife
01592 643355
Wishaw General Hospital
01698 361100
Woodend Hospital, Aberdeen
0845 456 6000

NHS hospitals: Northern Ireland

Alexandra Gardens Day Hospital,
Belfast
028 9080 2150
Altnagelvin Area Hospital,
Londonderry
028 7134 5171
Antrim Hospital
028 9442 4000
Ards Hospital, Newtownards
028 9181 2661
Armagh Community Hospital
028 3752 2281
Bangor Community Hospital
028 9147 5100
Belvoir Park Hospital, Belfast
028 9032 9241
Belfast City Hospital
028 9032 9241
Braid Valley Hospital, Ballymena
028 2563 5200
Causeway Hospital, Coleraine
028 7032 7032
Craigavon Area Hospital
028 3833 4444
Daisy Hill Hospital, Newry
028 3083 5000

Dalriada Hospital, Ballycastle
028 2766 6600
Downe Hospital, Downpatrick
028 4461 3311
Erne Hospital, Enniskillen
028 6638 2000
Forster Green Hospital, Belfast
028 9094 4444
Gransha Hospital, Londonderry
028 7186 0261
Holywell Hospital, Antrim
028 9441 3620
Knockbracken Mental Health
Services, Belfast
028 9056 5656
Lagan Valley Hospital, Lisburn
028 9266 5141
Longstone Hospital, Armagh
028 3752 2381
Lurgan Hospital
028 3832 3262
Mater Hospital, Belfast
028 9074 1211
Mid-Ulster Hospital, Magherafelt
028 7963 1031
Mourne Hospital, Co Down
028 4176 2235
Moyle Hospital, Larne
028 2827 5431
Muckamore Abbey Hospital,
Muckamore
028 9446 3333
Mullinure Hospital, Armagh
028 3752 2381
Musgrave Park Hospital, Belfast
028 9090 2000
Royal Belfast Hospital for Sick
Children, Belfast
028 9024 0503
Royal Maternity Hospital, Belfast
028 9024 0503
Royal Victoria Hospital, Belfast
028 9024 0503
St Luke's Hospital, Armagh
028 3752 2381
Shaftesbury Square Hospital,
Belfast
028 9032 9808
South Tyrone Hospital,
Dungannon
028 8772 2821
Tyrone and Fermanagh Hospital,
Omagh
028 8283 3100
Tyrone County Hospital, Omagh
028 8283 3100
Ulster Hospital, Dundonald
028 9048 4511
Whiteabbey Hospital,
Newtownabbey
028 9086 5181

Private healthcare

● Main private healthcare providers

Abbey Hospitals
020 7384 0978
www.abbeyhospitals.co.uk
Alliance Healthcare
01926 482000
www.alliancemedical.co.uk
BMI Healthcare
020 7009 4500
www.bmihealthcare.co.uk
British Pregnancy Advisory Service
0870 365 5050
www.bpas.org
Press: 020 7612 0206
BUPA Hospitals
020 7656 2000
www.bupahospitals.co.uk
Capio Healthcare
01234 273473
www.capio.co.uk
Clinicenta
01865 893293
www.clinicenta.co.uk
Four Seasons Health Care
01625 417800
www.fshc.co.uk
HCA International
020 7616 4848
www.hcainternational.com
Mercury Health
0118 952 1900
www.mercuryhealth.co.uk
Nations Healthcare
020 7034 5250
www.nationshealthcare.com
Netcare
020 8232 5100
www.netcareuk.com
Nuffield Hospitals
020 8390 1200
www.nuffieldhospitals.org.uk
Partnerships in Care
01763 255600
www.partnershipsincare.co.uk
Priory Healthcare
01372 860400
www.prioryhealthcare.co.uk
UK Specialist
020 7601 1060
www.ukspecialisthospitals.co.uk

Law

Government

Home Office
020 7035 4848
www.homeoffice.gov.uk
Press: 020 7035 4381

Attorney General's Office
020 7271 2440
Press: 020 7271 2465

Ministry of Justice
020 7210 8500
www.justice.gov.uk
Press: 020 7210 8913

Scottish Executive
0131 556 8400
www.scotland.gov.uk
Press office, justice desk:
0131 244 1111

● Government agencies

Law Commission
020 7453 1220
www.lawcom.gov.uk

Legal Services Commission
020 7759 0000
www.legalservices.gov.uk

The legal system

● Ombudsmen

Legal Services Ombudsman
0845 601 0794
www.olso.org

Scottish Legal Services Ombudsman
0131 556 9123
www.slso.org.uk

● Law associations

Administrative Law Bar Association
www.adminlaw.org.uk

Association of Personal Injury Lawyers
0115 958 0585
www.apil.com

Bar Council
020 7242 0082
www.barcouncil.org.uk
Press: 020 7222 2525

Chancery Bar Association
020 8883 1700
www.chba.org.uk

Commercial Bar Association
020 7404 2022
www.combar.com

Family Law Bar Association
020 7242 1289
www.flba.co.uk

Institute of Barristers' Clerks
020 7831 7144
www.barristersclerks.com

Institute of Legal Executives
01234 841000
www.ilex.org.uk
Press: 01234 845713

Justices' Clerks' Society
0151 255 0790
www.jc-society.co.uk

Law Society
020 7242 1222
www.lawsoc.org.uk
Press: 020 7320 5764

Legal Aid Practitioners' Group
020 7960 6068
www.lapg.co.uk

Magistrates' Association
020 7387 2353
www.magistrates-association
.org.uk

Solicitors' Criminal Law Association
01273 676725
www.clsa.co.uk

Solicitors' Family Law Association
01689 850227
www.sfla.org.uk
Press: 020 7357 9215

The judiciary

● Justice agencies

Tribunals Service
020 7712 2600
www.tribunals.gov.uk

Children and Family Court Advisory and Support Service (Cafcass)
020 7510 7000
www.cafcass.gov.uk
See website for details of regional offices

Civil Justice Council
020 7947 6670
www.civiljusticecouncil.gov.uk

Court Service, Northern Ireland
028 9032 8594
www.courtsni.gov.uk
Press: 028 9041 2345

Courts Service
020 7189 2000
www.hmcourts-service.gov.uk

Criminal Cases Review Commission
0121 633 1800
www.ccrc.gov.uk

Criminal Records Bureau
0870 909 0811
www.crb.gov.uk

Crown Office and Procurator Fiscal Service, Scotland
0131 226 2626
www.crownoffice.gov.uk

Crown Prosecution Service
020 7796 8000
www.cps.gov.uk
Press: 020 7796 8127

HM Revenue & Customs
0845 010 9000
www.hmrc.gov.uk
Press –
business: 020 7147 2328/0798
personal: 020 7147 2318/319/333
law enforcement:
020 7147 0052/2314/2331
social: 020 7147 0452/2337/0051

Inspectorate of Court Administration
020 7217 4355
www.hmica.gov.uk

Scottish Courts Administration
0131 229 9200
www.scotcourts.gov.uk

Youth Justice Boards for England and Wales
020 7271 3033
www.yjb.gov.uk
Press: 020 7271 3014/2988

● Appeal courts

Court of Appeal
020 7947 6000

High Court
020 7947 6000

Judicial Committee of the Privy Council
020 7276 0483/5/7

Supreme Courts, Scotland
0131 225 2595
High Court (criminal) and Court of Session (civil)

High Court of Justiciary, Scotland
0131 240 6900
Press: 0131 225 2595

Supreme Court of Northern Ireland
028 9072 4661
Press: 028 9041 2385

● Crown courts

Central Criminal Court – Old Bailey
020 7248 3277

Aylesbury
01296 434401

Barnstaple
01271 373286

Basildon Combined Court
01268 458000

Birmingham
0121 681 3300

Blackfriars
020 7922 5800

Bolton Combined Court Centre
01204 392881

Bournemouth
01202 502800

Bradford Combined Court Centre
01274 840274

Bristol
0117 976 3030

Burnley Combined Court Centre
01282 416899

Bury St Edmunds
01473 228585

Caernarfon
01286 675753

Cambridge
01223 488321

Canterbury Combined Court Centre
01227 819200

Cardiff
029 2041 4400

Carlisle Combined Court Centre
01228 520619

Chelmsford
01245 603000

Chester
01244 317606

Chichester Combined Court Centre
01243 520700

Coventry Combined Court Centre
024 7653 6166

Croydon
020 8410 4700

Derby Combined Court Centre
01332 622600

Dolgellau
01341 423081

Doncaster
01302 322211

Dorchester
01305 752510

Durham
0191 386 6714

Exeter Combined Court Centre
01392 415300

Gloucester
01452 420100

Great Grimsby Combined Court Centre
01472 265250

Guildford
01483 468500

Harrow
020 8424 2294

Hereford
01432 276118

Hove Trial Centre
01273 229200

Inner London
020 7234 3100

Ipswich
01473 228 585

Isleworth
020 8380 4500

King's Lynn
01553 760847

Kingston-upon-Hull Combined Court Centre
01482 586161

Kingston-upon-Thames
020 8240 2500

Knutsford
01565 624020

Lancaster Crown Court
01772 844700

Leeds Combined Court Centre
0113 306 2800

Leicester Crown Court
0116 222 5800

Lewes Combined Court Centre
01273 480400

Lincoln
01522 525222

Liverpool
0151 473 7373

Luton
01582 522000

Maidstone
01622 202000

Manchester (Crown Square)
0161 954 1800

Manchester at Minshull St
0161 954 7500

Merthyr Tydfil Combined Court Centre
01685 358222

Middlesex Guildhall
020 7202 0370

Mold
01352 707340

Newcastle upon Tyne Combined Court Centre
0191 201 2000

Newport (South Wales)
01633 266211

Newport, I.O.W.
01983 535100

Northampton Combined Court
01604 470400

Norwich Combined Court Centre
01603 728200

Nottingham
0115 910 3551

Oxford Combined Court Centre
01865 264200

Peterborough Combined Court Centre
01733 349161

Plymouth Combined Court
01752 677400

Portsmouth Combined Court Centre
023 9289 3000

Preston Combined Court Centre
01772 844700

Reading
0118 967 4400

Salisbury Combined Court Centre
01722 325444

Sheffield Combined Court Centre
0114 281 2400

Shrewsbury
01743 260820

Snaresbrook
020 8530 0000

Southampton Combined Court Centre
023 8021 3200

Southwark
020 7522 7200

St. Albans
01727 753220

Stafford Combined Court Centre
01785 610730

Stoke-on-Trent Combined Court
01782 854000

Swansea
01792 637000

Swindon Combined Court
01793 690500

Taunton
01823 281100

Teesside Combined Court Centre
01642 340000

Truro
01872 222328

Warrington Combined Court Centre
01925 256700

Warwick Combined Court Centre
01926 495428

Welshpool
01938 553144

Weymouth and Dorchester Combined Court Centre
01305 752510

Winchester Combined Court Centre
01962 814100

Wolverhampton Combined Court Centre
01902 481000

Wood Green
020 8826 4100

Woolwich
020 8312 7000

Worcester Combined Court Centre
01905 730800

York
01904 645121

● County courts

Aberdare
01685 888575

Aberystwyth
01970 636370

Accrington
01254 237490

Aldershot & Farnham
01252 796800

Altrincham
0161 975 4760

Ashford
01233 632464

Aylesbury
01296 393498

Banbury
01295 452090

Barnet
020 8343 4272

Barnsley
01226 777550

Barnstaple
01271 372252

Barrow-In-Furness
01229 840370

Basildon Combined Court
01268 458000

Basingstoke
01256 318200

Bath
01225 310282

Bedford
01234 760400

Birkenhead
0151 666 5800

Birmingham Civil Justice Centre
0121 681 4441

Bishop Auckland
01388 660251

Blackburn
01254 680640

Blackpool
01253 754020

Blackwood
01495 223197

Bodmin
01208 74224/73735

Bolton Combined Court
01204 392881

Boston
01205 366080

Bournemouth
01202 502800

Bow
020 8536 5200

Bradford Combined Court Centre
01274 840274

Brecknock
01874 622993

Brentford
020 8231 8940

Bridgend
01656 673 833

Brighton
01273 674421

Brighton County Court Family Centre
01273 811333

Bristol
0117 910 6700

Bromley
020 8290 9620

Burton Upon Trent County Court
01283 568241

Burnley Combined Court
01282 416899

Bury
0161 447 8699

Bury St Edmunds
01284 753254

Buxton
01298 23734

Caernarfon
01286 684600

Cambridge
01223 224500

Canterbury Combined Court
01227 819200

Cardiff Civil Justice Centre
029 2037 6400

Carlisle Combined Court Centre
01228 520619

Carmarthen
01267 228010

Central London
020 7917 5000

Cheltenham
01452 834900

Chelmsford
01245 264670

Chester Civil Justice Centre
01244 404200

Chesterfield
01246 501200

Chichester
01243 520700

Chorley
01257 262778

Clerkenwell
020 7250 7200

Colchester
01206 717200

Consett
01207 502854

Conwy & Colwyn
01492 530807

Coventry Combined Court Centre
024 7653 6166

Crewe
01270 539300

Croydon Combined Court
020 8410 4797

Darlington
01325 463224

Dartford
01322 629820

Derby Combined Court
01332 622600

Dewsbury
01924 466135

Doncaster
01302 381730

Dudley
01384 480799

Durham
0191 3865941

Eastbourne
01323 727518

Edmonton
020 8884 6500

Epsom
01372 721801

Evesham
01386 442287

Exeter Combined Court
01392 415300

Gateshead
0191 477 2445

Gloucester
01452 834900

Grantham
01476 539030

Gravesend
01322 629820

Great Grimsby Combined Court
01472 265200

Guildford
01483 405300

Halifax
01422 344700

Harlow
01279 443291

Harrogate
01423 503921

Hartlepool
01429 268198

Hastings
01424 435128

Haverfordwest
01437 772060

Haywards Heath
01444 447970

Hertford
01992 503954

Hereford
01432 357233

High Wycombe
01494 651011

Hitchin
01462 443750

Horsham
01403 252474

Huddersfield
01484 421043

Huntingdon
01480 450932

Ilford
020 8477 1920

Ipswich
01473 214256

Keighley
01535 602803

Kendal
01539 721218

Kettering
01536 512471

Kidderminster
01562 822480

King's Lynn
01553 772067

Kingston upon Hull
01482 586161

Kingston-upon-Thames
020 8972 8700

Lambeth
020 7091 4410/20

Lancaster
01524 68112

Leeds
0113 306 2800

Leicester
0116 222 5700

Leigh
01942 673639

Lewes Combined Court
01273 480400

Lincoln Combined Court
01522 883000

Liverpool Combined Court
0151 296 2200

Llanelli
01554 757171

Llangefni
01248 750225

Lowestoft
01502 501060

Ludlow
01584 872091

Luton
01582 506700

Macclesfield
01625 412800

Maidstone Combined Court
01622 202000

Manchester
0161 954 1800

Mansfield
01623 656406

Mayor's & City Of London Court
020 7796 5400

Medway
01634 810720

Melton Mowbray
01664 485100

Merthyr Tydfil Combined Court
01685 358200

Middlesborough County Court at
Teesside Combined Court
01642 340000

Milton Keynes
01908 302800

Mold
01352 707330

Morpeth & Berwick
01670 512221

Neath and Port Talbot
01639 642267

Nelson
01282 601177

Newark
01636 703607

Newbury County Court
01635 642210

Newcastle Combined Court
0191 201 2000

Newport (Gwent) County Court
01633 227150

Newport (Isle Of Wight)
01983 535100

North Shields
0191 2982339

Northampton Combined Court
01604 470400

Northwich
01606 338508

Norwich Combined Court
01603 728200

Nottingham
0115 910 3500

Nuneaton
024 7648 2970

Oldham
0161 290 4200

Oswestry
01691 652127

Oxford Combined Court Centre
01865 264200

Penrith
01768 862535

Penzance
01736 362987

Peterborough Combined Court
01733 349161

Plymouth Combined Court
01752 677400

Pontefract
01977 702357

Pontypool
01495 762248

Pontypridd
01443 490800

Poole
01202 741150

Portsmouth Combined Court
023 9289 3000

Preston Combined Court
01772 844700

Rawtenstall
01706 214614

Reading
0118 987 0500

Redditch
01527 67822

Reigate
01737 763637

Rhyl
01745 352940

Romford
01708 775353

Rotherham
01709 364786

Rugby
01788 542543

St Albans
01727 856925

St Helens
01744 27544

Salford
0161 745 7511

Salisbury
01722 325444

Scarborough
01723 366361

Scunthorpe
01724 289111

Sheffield Combined Court
0114 281 2400

Shrewsbury
01743 289069

Skegness
01205 366080

Skipton
01756 692650

Slough
01753 690300

South Shields
0191 456 3343

Southampton Combined Court
023 8021 3200

Southend
01702 601991

Southport
01704 531541

Stafford
01785 610730

Staines
01784 459175

Stockport
01614 747707

Stoke On Trent Combined Court
01782 854000

Stourbridge
01384 394232

Stratford upon Avon
01789 293056

Sunderland
0191 568 0750

Swansea Civil Justice Centre
01792 510350

Swindon Combined Court
01793 690500

Tameside
0161 331 5614

Tamworth
01827 62664

Taunton
01823 281110

Teesside Combined Court
01642 340000

Telford
01952 238280

Thanet
01843 221722

Torquay & Newton Abbot
01803 616791

Trowbridge
01225 752101

Truro Combined Court
01872 222340

Tunbridge Wells
01892 515515

Uxbridge
020 8756 3520

Wakefield
01924 370268

Walsall
01922 728855

Wandsworth
020 8333 4351

Warrington Combined Court
01925 256700

Warwick Combined Court Centre
01926 492276

Watford
01923 699400/1

Wellingborough
01933 226168/222393

Welshpool And Newtown
01938 552004

West London
020 8600 6868

Weston Super Mare
01934 626967

Weymouth & Dorchester
01305 752510

Whitehaven
01946 67788

Wigan
01942 246481

Winchester Combined Court
01962 814100

Willesden
020 8963 8200

Wolverhampton Combined Court
01902 481000

Woolwich
020 8301 8700

Worcester Combined Court
01905 730800

Worksop
01909 472358

Worthing
01903 221920

Wrexham
01978 296140

Yeovil
01935 382150

York
01904 688550

● Sheriff courts, Scotland

Aberdeen
01224 657200
Airdrie
01236 751121
Alloa
01259 722734
Arbroath
01241 876600
Ayr
01292 268474
Banff
01261 812140
Campbeltown
01586 552503
Cupar
01334 652121
Dingwall
01349 863153
Dornoch
01862 810224
Dumbarton
01389 763266
Dumfries
01387 262334
Dundee
01382 229961
Dunfermline
01383 724666
Dunoon
01369 704166
Duns
01835 863231
Edinburgh
0131 225 2525
Elgin
01343 542505
Falkirk
01324 620822
Forfar
01307 462186
Fort William
01397 702087
Glasgow
0141 429 8888
Greenock
01475 787073
Haddington
01620 822936
Hamilton
01698 282957
Inverness
01463 230782
Jedburgh
01835 863231
Kilmarnock
01563 550024
Kirkcaldy
01592 260171
Kirkcudbright
01557 330574
Kirkwall
01856 872110
Lanark
01555 661531

Lerwick
01595 693914
Linlithgow
01506 842922
Livingston
01506 462118
Lochmaddy
01876 500340
Oban
01631 562414
Paisley
0141 887 5291
Peebles
01721 720204
Perth
01738 620546
Peterhead
01779 476676
Portree
01478 612191
Rothesay
01700 502982
Selkirk
01750 21269
Stirling
01786 462191
Stonehaven
01569 762758
Stornoway
01851 702231
Stranraer
01776 702138
Tain
01862 892518
Wick
01955 602846

● Northern Ireland courts

Antrim
028 9446 2661
Armagh
028 3572 2816
Ballymena
028 2564 9416
Banbridge
028 4062 3622
Bangor
028 9147 2626
Belfast
028 9032 8594
Coleraine
028 7034 3437
Craigavon
028 3834 1324
Derry
028 7136 3448
Downpatrick
028 4461 4621
Dungannon
028 8772 2992
Enniskillen
028 6632 2356
Larne
028 2827 2927
Limavady
028 7772 2688
Lisburn
028 9267 5336

Londonderry
028 7136 3448
Magherafelt
028 7963 2121
Newry
028 3025 2040
Newtownards
028 9181 4343
Omagh
028 8224 2056
Strabane
028 7138 2544

Law centres

Law Centres Federation
020 7428 4400
www.lawcentres.org.uk

Avon & Bristol
0117 924 8662
Barnet
020 8203 4141
Battersea
020 7585 0716
Bradford
01274 306617
Brent Community
020 8451 1126
Bury
0161 272 0666
Cambridge House Law Centre
020 7703 3051
Camden Community
020 7284 6510
Cardiff
029 2049 8117
Carlisle
01228 515129
Central London
020 7839 2998
Chesterfield
01246 550674
Coventry
024 7622 3053
Croydon & Sutton Law Centre (SWLLC)
020 8667 9226
Derby
01332 344557
Devon
01752 519794
Enfield Law Centre
020 8807 8888
Gateshead
0191 440 8585
Gloucester
01452 423492
Greenwich Community
020 8305 3350
Hackney Community
020 8985 8364
Hammersmith & Fulham
020 8741 4021
Harehills & Chapeltown
0113 249 1100
Haringey
020 8808 5354

Hillingdon
020 8561 9400
Hounslow
020 8570 9505
Isle of Wight Law Centre
01983 524715
Islington
020 7607 2461
Kingston & Richmond Law Centre (SWLLC)
020 8547 2882
Lambeth
020 7737 9780
Leicester
0116 242 1160
Lewisham
020 8692 5355
Liverpool
0151 709 7222
Luton
01582 481000
Newcastle
0191 230 4777
North Kensington
020 8969 7473
North Manchester
0161 205 5040
Nottingham
0115 978 7813
Oldham
0161 627 0925
Paddington
020 8960 3155
Plumstead Community
020 8855 9817
Rochdale
01706 657766
Rotherham
01709 838988
Saltley & Nechells
0121 328 2307
Sheffield
0114 273 1501
South Manchester
0161 225 5111
Southwark
020 7732 2008
Springfield
020 8767 6884
Stockport
0161 476 6336
Streetwise Community
020 8778 5854
Surrey
01483 215 000
Thamesmead
020 8311 0555
Tottenham
020 8808 5354
Tower Hamlets
020 7247 8998
Trafford Law Centre
0161 872 3669
Vauxhall Law and Information Centre
0151 482 2001
Wandsworth & Merton
020 8767 2777

Warrington Community
01925 651104
Wiltshire
01793 486926
Wythenshawe
0161 498 0905/6

NORTHERN IRELAND

Northern Ireland: Belfast
028 9024 4401
Northern Ireland: western area
028 7126 2433

Prisons

● Prison services

National Offender Management Service
0870 000 1585
www.noms.homeoffice.gov.uk
Victim helpline: 0845 758 5112
Press: 020 7035 4381
Her Majesty's Inspectorate of Prisons for England and Wales (HMIP)
020 7035 2136
www.homeoffice.gov.uk
Northern Ireland Prison Service
028 9052 5065
www.niprisonservice.gov.uk
Parole Board for England and Wales
0870 420 3505
www.paroleboard.gov.uk
Prisons Ombudsman for England and Wales
020 7035 2876
www.ppo.gov.uk
Scottish Parole Board
0131 244 8373
www.scottishparoleboard.gov.uk
Scottish Prison Service
0131 244 8745
www.sps.gov.uk
Scottish Prisons Inspectorate
0131 244 8481

● Professional bodies

Prison Governors Association
020 7217 8591
www.prisongovernors.org.uk
Prison Officers Association
020 8803 0255
www.poauk.org.uk
National Association of Probation Officers (Napo)
020 7223 4887
www.napo.org.uk
Trade union and professional association for family court and probation staff

● Campaign groups

Action for Prisoners' Families
020 8812 3600
www.prisonersfamilies.org.uk
Apex Trust
020 7638 5931
www.apextrust.com
Campaign for Freedom of Information
020 7831 7477
www.cfoi.org.uk
Committee on the Administration of Justice (Northern Ireland)
028 9096 1122
www.caj.org.uk
Howard League for Penal Reform
020 7249 7373
www.howardleague.org
Inquest
020 7263 1111
www.inquest.org.uk
Justice
020 7329 5100
www.justice.org.uk
Liberty
020 7403 3888
www.liberty-human-rights.org.uk
Press: 020 7378 3656
Minority Rights Group
020 7422 4200
www.minorityrights.org
National Association for the Care and Resettlement of Offenders
020 7582 6500
www.nacro.org.uk
Prison Reform Trust
020 7251 5070
www.prisonreformtrust.org.uk
Prisoners Advice Service
020 7253 3323
www.prisonersadviceservice.org.uk
Prisoners Family and Friends
020 7403 4091/9359
www.prisonersfamiliesandfriends
.org.uk
Unit for the Arts and Offenders
01227 470629
www.apcentre.org.uk
Unlock
01634 247350
www.unlock.org.uk
National association of ex-offenders
Women in Prison
020 7226 5879
www.womeninprison.org.uk

● Prisons for men

Acklington
01670 762300
Albany
01983 556300
Altcourse*
0151 522 2000
Ashfield*
0117 303 8000
Ashwell
01572 884100
Aylesbury
01296 444000
Bedford
01234 373000
Belmarsh
020 8331 4400
Birmingham
0121 345 2500
Blakenhurst
01527 400500
Blantyre House
01580 213200
Blundeston
01502 734500
Brinsford
01902 532450
Bristol
0117 372 3100
Brixton
020 8588 6000
Brockhill
01527 552650
Bullingdon
01869 353100
Bullwood Hall
01702 562800
Camp Hill
01983 554600
Canterbury
01227 862800
Cardiff
02920 923100
Castington
01670 382100
Channings Wood
01803 814600
Chelmsford
01245 272000
Coldingley
01483 804300
Dartmoor
01822 892000
Deerbolt
01833 633200
Doncaster*
01302 760870
Dorchester
01305 214500
Dovegate*
01283 829400
Downview
020 8929 3300
Durham
0191 332 3400
Edmunds Hill
01440 743500

Elmley
01795 882000
Erlestoke
01380 814250
Everthorpe
01430 426500
Featherstone
01902 703000
Feltham
020 8844 5000
Ford
01903 663000
Forest Bank*
0161 925 7000
Frankland
0191 332 3000
Full Sutton
01759 475100
Garth
01772 443300
Gartree
01858 436600
Glen Parva
0116 228 4100
Gloucester
01452 453000
Grendon
01296 443000
Guys Marsh
01747 856400
Haverigg
01229 713000
Hewell Grange
01527 552000
High Down
020 8722 6300
Highpoint
01440 743100
Hindley
01942 855000
Hollesley Bay
01394 412400
Holme House
01642 744000
Hull
01482 282200
Huntercombe
01491 643100
Kennet
0151 527 3500
Kingston
023 9295 3100
Kirkham
01772 675400
Kirklevington Grange
01642 792600
Lancaster Castle
01524 565 100
Lancaster Farms
01524 563450
Latchmere House
020 8588 6650
Leeds
0113 203 2600
Leicester
0116 228 3000
Lewes
01273 785100

Leyhill
01454 264000
Lincoln
01522 663000
Lindholme
01302 524700
Littlehey
01480 333000
Liverpool
0151 530 4000
Long Lartin
01386 835100
Lowdham Grange*
0115 966 9200
Maidstone
01622 775300
Manchester
0161 817 5600
Moorland
01302 523000
The Mount
01442 836300
Northallerton
01609 785100
North Sea Camp
01205 769300
Norwich
01603 708600
Nottingham
0115 872 3000
Onley
01788 523400
Parc*
01656 300200
Parkhurst
01983 554000
Pentonville
020 7023 7000
Peterborough*
01733 217500
Portland
01305 825600
Prescoed
01291 675000
Preston
01772 444550
Ranby
01777 862000
Reading
0118 908 5000
Risley
01925 733000
Rochester
01634 803100
Rye Hill*
01788 523300
Send
01483 471000
Shepton Mallett
01749 823300
Shrewsbury
01743 273000
Spring Hill
01296 443000
Stafford
01785 773000
Standford Hill
01795 884500

Stocken
01780 795100
Stoke Heath
01630 636000
Sudbury
01283 584000
Swaleside
01795 804100
Swansea
01792 485300
Swinfen Hall
01543 484000
Thorn Cross
01925 805100
Usk
01291 671600
The Verne
01305 825000
Wakefield
01924 246000
Wandsworth
020 8588 4000
Warren Hill
01394 412400
Wayland
01953 804100
Wealstun
01937 4444000
Wellingborough
01933 232700
Werrington
01782 463300
Wetherby
01937 544200
Whatton
01949 803200
Whitemoor
01354 602350
Winchester
01962 723000
Wolds*
01430 428000
Woodhill
01908 722000
Wormwood Scrubs
020 8588 3200
Wymott
01772 442000

● Prisons for women

Askham Grange
01904 772000
Bronzefield*
01784 425690
Buckley Hall
01706 514300
Cookham Wood
01634 202500
Drake Hall
01785 774100
East Sutton Park
01622 845000
Eastwood Park
01454 382100
Exeter
01392 415650

private prisons

435

Foston Hall
01283 584300
Holloway
020 7979 4400
Low Newton
0191 376 4000
Morton Hall
01522 666700
New Hall
01924 803000
Peterborough*
01733 217500
Styal
01625 553000

● Prisons in Scotland

Aberdeen
01224 238300
Barlinnie
0141 7702000
Castle Huntly
01382 319333
Cornton Vale
01786 832591
Dumfries
01387 261218
Edinburgh
0131 444 3000
Glenochil
01259 760471
Greenock
01475 787801
Inverness
01463 229000
Kilmarnock*
01563 548800
Low Moss
0141 7624848
Noranside
01382 319333
Perth
01738 622293
Peterhead
01779 479101
Polmont
01324 711558
Shotts
01501 824000

● Prisons in
  Northern Ireland

Hydebank Wood
028 9025 3666
Maghaberry
028 9261 1888
Magilligan
028 7776 3311

● Immigration
  removal centres

Dover
01304 246400
Haslar
023 9260 4000

Legal advice

Activists Legal Project
www.activistslegalproject.org.uk
Legal information for activists
Asylum Aid
020 7354 9631
www.asylumaid.org.uk
Advice line: 020 7354 9264
CHAS Central London
020 7723 5928
www.chascl.org.uk
Housing and debt advice
Children's Legal Centre
01206 872466
www.childrenslegalcentre.com
Community Legal Service
0845 345 4345
www.clsdirect.org.uk
Counsel & Care
020 7241 8555
www.counselandcare.org.uk
Advice line: 0845 300 7585
Disability Law Service
020 7791 9800
Environmental Law Foundation
020 7404 1030
www.elflaw.org
Housing Justice
020 7723 7273
www.housingjustice.org.uk
**Joint Council for the Welfare of
Immigrants**
020 7251 8708
www.jcwi.org.uk
Legal Action Group
020 7833 2931
www.lag.org.uk
Legal Services Research Centre
www.lsrc.org.uk
**Liberty (the National Council for
Civil Liberties)**
www.yourrights.org.uk
Advice line: 0845 123 2307
National Youth Advocacy Service
0151 649 8700
www.nyas.net
Young people helpline:
  0800 616101
Prisoners' Families Helpline
0808 808 2003
www.prisonersfamilieshelpline
.org.uk
Public Law Project
020 7697 2190
www.publiclawproject.org.uk
Refugee Legal Centre
020 7780 3200
www.refugee-legal-centre.org.uk
Advice line: 020 7780 3220
UK Legal
0845 280 1976
www.uklegal.com

Libraries and research

Specialists libraries and archives

Bank of England Information Centre
Threadneedle Street,
London EC2R 8AH
020 7601 4715
enquiries@bankofengland.co.uk
www.bankofengland.co.uk
Central banking and finance

Barbican Library
Silk Street, London EC2Y 8DS
020 7638 0569
barbicanlib@cityoflondon.gov.uk
www.cityoflondon.gov.uk
Lending library with strong arts and music sections

BBC Written Archives Centre
Peppard Road, Caversham Park,
Reading, Berkshire RG4 8TZ
0118 948 6281
heritage@bbc.co.uk
www.bbc.co.uk/heritage

BFI
21 Stephen Street, London W1T 1LN
020 7255 1444
library@bfi.org.uk
www.bfi.org.uk/nationallibrary
World's largest collection of documentation on film and television

British Architectural Library
Royal Institute of British
Architects, 66 Portland Place,
London W1B 1AD
020 7580 5533
bal@inst.riba.org
www.architecture.com

British Library
96 Euston Road, London NW1 2DB
0870 444 1500
reader-admissions@bl.uk
www.bl.uk

British Newspaper Library
Colindale Avenue,
London NW9 5HE
020 7412 7353
newspaper@bl.uk
www.bl.uk/collections
/newspapers.html

CAA Library and Information Centre
Aviation House, Gatwick Airport,
West Sussex RH6 0YR
01293 573725
infoservices@caa.co.uk
www.caa.co.uk

Catholic National Library
St Michael's Abbey, Farnborough
Road, Farnborough GU14 7NQ
01252 543818
library@catholic-library.org.uk
www.catholic-library.org.uk

City Business Library
1 Brewers' Hall Garden,
London EC2V 5BX
020 7332 1812
cbl@cityoflondon.gov.uk
www.cityoflondon.gov.uk
/citybusinesslibrary

City of Westminster Archives Centre
10 St Ann's Street,
London SW1P 2DE
020 7641 5180
archives@westminster.gov.uk
www.westminster.gov.uk/archives

DigiReels Media Monitoring
45 Foubert's Place,
London W1F 7QH
020 7575 1880
info@xtremeinformation.com
www.ads.xtremeinformation.com
Online ad database

Foreign and Commonwealth Office
Maughan Library, Kings College,
Chancery Lane, London WC2A 1LR
020 7270 3925
library.enquiries@fco.gov.uk
www.fco.gov.uk

Forestry Commission Library
Forest Research Station, Alice
Holt Lodge, Wrecclesham,
Farnham, Surrey GU10 4LH
01420 222555
research.info@forestry.gsi.gov.uk
www.forestry.gov.uk/forestry
/library

French Institute Library
Institut Francais, 17 Queensberry
Place, London SW7 2DT
020 7073 1354
library@ambafrance.org.uk
www.institut.ambafrance.org.uk

Goethe-Institut Library
50 Princes Gate, Exhibition Road,
London SW7 2PH
020 7596 4000
library@london.goethe.org
www.goethe.de/london
German literature and reference

Harry Price Library of Magical Literature
University of London Library,
Senate House, Malet Street,
London WC1E 7HU
020 7862 8470
historic@ull.ac.uk
www.ull.ac.uk/historic/hpl.shtml
Magic literature

Institute of Education Library (London)
20 Bedford Way, London WC1H 0AL
020 7612 6080
lib.enquiries@ioe.ac.uk
www.ioe.ac.uk
Over 300,000 volumes including special sections on educational studies. 2,000 periodicals

Instituto Cervantes
102 Eaton Square,
London SW1W 9AN
020 7201 0757
biblon@cervantes.es
www.cervantes.es
Spain

International Booksearch Service
020 7639 8900
admin@scfordham.com
www.scfordham.com
Finds out-of-print books

Italian Cultural Institute
39 Belgrave Square,
London SW1X 8NX
020 7235 1461
icilondon@esteri.it
www.icilondon.esteri.it

Linen Hall Library
17 Donegall Square North,
Belfast BT1 5GB
028 9032 1707
info@linenhall.com
www.linenhall.com
Ireland and politics

Llyfrgell Genedlaethol Cymru/ National Library of Wales
Aberystwyth, Ceredigion SY23 3BU
01970 632800
holi@llgc.org.uk
www.llgc.org.uk

London Metropolitan Archives (LMA)
40 Northampton Road,
Clerkenwell, London EC1R 0HB
020 7332 3820
ask.lma@cityoflondon.gov.uk
www.cityoflondon.gov.uk/lma
Largest local authority archive in the UK

Murder Files
Dommett Hill Farm,
Hare Lane, Buckland St Mary,
Somerset TA20 3JS
01460 234065
enquiry@murderfiles.com
www.murderfiles.com
UK murders since 1400

National Archives
Kew, Richmond, Surrey TW9 4DU
020 8876 3444
www.nationalarchives.gov.uk
11th-20th-century national records

National Film and TV Archive
Kingshill Way, Berkhamsted,
Herts HP4 3TP
01442 876301
darren.long@bfi.org.uk
www.bfi.org.uk/nftva
Contains more than 275,000 films and
200,000 TV programmes, dating from
1895 to the present

National Library for the Blind
Far Cromwell Road, Bredbury,
Stockport SK6 2SG
0161 355 2000
enquiries@nlbuk.org
www.nlb-online.org

National Library of Scotland
George IV Bridge,
Edinburgh EH1 1EW
0131 623 3700
enquiries@nls.uk
www.nls.uk

National Meteorological Archive
FitzRoy Road, Exter, Devon EX1 3PB
01392 360987
metarc@metoffice.gov.uk
www.metoffice.gov.uk/corporate
/library

National Museum of Scotland
NMS Enterprises, Chambers
Street, Edinburgh EH1 1JF
0131 247 4422
info@nms.ac.uk
www.nms.ac.uk

Natural History Museum Library
Cromwell Road, London SW7 5BD
020 7942 5460
library@nhm.ac.uk
www.nhm.ac.uk/research
-curation/library/index.html

Office for National Statistics
1 Drummond Gate,
London SW1V 2QQ
0845 601 3034
info@statistics.gov.uk
www.statistics.gov.uk

Polish Library
238-246 King Street,
London W6 0RF
020 8741 0474
polish.library@posk.org
www.posk.org

**Royal Geographical Society
Library (with the Institute of
British Geographers)**
1 Kensington Gore,
London SW7 2AR
020 7591 3000
press@rgs.org
www.rgs.org

Royal Society Library
6-9 Carlton House Terrace,
London SW1Y 5AG
020 7451 2500
library@royalsoc.ac.uk
www.royalsoc.ac.uk
Science

Royal Society of Medicine Library
1 Wimpole Street, London W1G 0AE
020 7290 2940
library@rsm.ac.uk
www.rsm.ac.uk

**Science Fiction Foundation
Research Library**
Liverpool University Library,
PO Box 123, Liverpool L69 3DA
0151 794 2696
asawyer@liverpool.ac.uk
www.liv.ac.uk/~asawyer
/sffchome.html

Science Museum Library
Imperial College Road,
London SW7 5NH
020 7942 4242
smlinfo@nmsi.ac.uk
www.sciencemuseum.org.uk

**Theatre Museum Library and
Archive**
1E Tavistock Street,
London WC2E 7PR
020 7943 4700
tmenquiries@vam.ac.uk
www.theatremuseum.org

Westminster Music Library
Victoria Library, 160 Buckingham
Palace Road, London SW1W 9UD
020 7641 1300
musiclibrary@westminster.gov.uk
www.westminster.gov.uk
/libraries/special/music

Wiener Library
4 Devonshire Street,
London W1W 5BH
020 7636 7247
info@wienerlibrary.co.uk
www.wienerlibrary.co.uk
Modern Jewish history, the Holocaust
and German 20th-century history

Women's Library
25 Old Castle Street, London E1 7NT
020 7320 2222
moreinfo@thewomenslibrary.ac.uk
www.londonmet.ac.uk
/thewomenslibrary

Zoological Society Library
Regent's Park, London NW1 4RY
020 7449 6293
library@zsl.org
www.zsl.org

Research data

AC Nielsen
ACNielsen House, London Road,
Headington, Oxford OX3 9RX
01865 742742
www.acneilson.com
Marketing research worldwide

Audit Bureau of Circulations (ABC)
Saxon House, 211 High Street,
Berkhamsted,
Hertfordshire HP4 1AD
01442 870800
abcpost@abc.org.uk
www.abc.org.uk
Circulation figures for newspapers and
magazines

**Broadcasters' Audience
Research Board (Barb)**
2nd Floor, 18 Dering Street,
London W15 1AQ
020 7529 5531
enquiries@barb.co.uk
www.barb.co.uk
TV audience data

Communications Research Group
Anvic House, 84 Vyse Street,
Jewellery Quarter,
Birmingham B18 6HA
0121 523 9595
research@crghq.com
www.crghq.com
Market and audience research

National Readership Survey (NRS)
40 Parker Street, London WC2B 5PQ
020 7242 8111
stevemillington@nrs.co.uk
www.nrs.co.uk
Newspaper and magazine readership
estimates

Nielsen BookScan
3rd Floor Midas House,
62 Goldsworth Road, Woking,
Surrey GU21 6LQ
01483 712222
jim.king@nielsen.com
www.bookscan.co.uk
International sales data monitoring
and analysis service for the English-
language book industry worldwide

Rajar
Paramount House, 162-170 Wardour
Street, London W1F 8XZ
020 7292 9040
info@rajar.co.uk
www.rajar.co.uk
Measures and profiles the audiences of
UK radio stations

Media Monitoring

Precise Media Group
The Registry, Royal Mint Court,
London EC3N 4QN
020 7264 4700
sales.admin@precise-media.co.uk
www.precise-media.co.uk
*Media monitoring across print, web
and broadcast*

Library associations

**Association of Independent
Libraries**
Leeds Library,
18 Commercial Street, Leeds,
West Yorkshire LS1 6AL
0113 245 3071
admin@hlsi.demon.co.uk
www.independentlibraries.co.uk

Association of UK Media Libraries
Editorial Information Services,
Financial Times, One Southwark
Bridge, London SE1 9HL
020 7873 3920
www.aukml.org.uk
Represents librarians in media industry

**Chartered Institute of Library
and Information Professionals**
7 Ridgmount Street,
London WC1E 7AE
020 7255 0500
info@cilip.org.uk
www.cilip.org.uk

**Chartered Institute of Library
and Information Professionals
in Scotland**
1st Floor, Building C, Brandon Gate,
Leechlee Road, Hamilton ML3 6AU
01698 458888
scotearl@slainte.org.uk
www.slainte.org.uk

Focal International
Pentax House, South Hill Avenue,
South Harrow HA2 0DU
020 8423 5853
info@focalint.org
www.focalint.org
*Represents commercial
film/audiovisual, stills and sound
libraries, plus facility houses, film
researchers and producers*

**Museum Libraries & Archives
Council**
Victoria House, Southampton
Row, London, WC1B 4EA
020 7273 1444
www.mla.gov.uk
*Development agency for museums,
libraries and archives*

Media awards

Press

Amnesty International Media Awards
020 7033 1500
www.amnesty.org.uk
Human rights journalism

BAPLA Picture Editor's Award
020 7713 1780
www.pbf.org.uk
For nationals and regionals that show best practice in crediting images

British Garden Writers' Guild
020 7245 6943
www.gardenwriters.co.uk/awards/2007/awards2k.html

British Press Awards
020 8565 4392
www.britishpressawards.com
Organised by Press Gazette

British Society of Magazine Editors
020 8906 4664
www.bsme.com

Emmas (Ethnic Multicultural Media Academy awards)
020 7636 1233
www.emma.tv
Multicultural media awards

Foreign Press Association Annual Media Awards
020 7930 0445
www.foreign-press.org.uk
International journalism by British media

Glenfiddich Food & Drink awards
020 7355 0655
http://events.glenfiddich-whisky.co.uk/food-and-drink-awards

Guardian Student Media Awards
01727 898141
http://media.guardian.co.uk/studentmediaawards
Student journalists, designers and photographers
Press: 020 7713 4087

The Herald Scottish Student Press Awards 2003
0141 302 7000
www.theherald.co.uk
Open to full-time students in Scotland

ICIJ Award for Outstanding International Investigative Reporting
001 202 466 1300
www.icij.org

Local Reporting Awards
020 7632 7400
www.newspapersoc.org.uk
Under-30s

Medical Journalism Awards
023 8037 2414
www.norwichunion.co.uk/medical_journalism_awards

Newspaper Awards
01869 340788
www.newspaperawards.co.uk
Technical innovation in newspaper and new media production

Observer Hodge Award
01727 799987
www.observer.guardian.co.uk/hodgeaward
Young photographers

Picture Editors' Awards
administrator@pictureawards.net
www.pictureawards.net
Photographic journalism

Plain English Media Awards
01663 744409
www.plainenglish.co.uk/mediaawards
Campaign against gobbledygook

PPA Awards
020 7404 4166
www.ppa.co.uk
www.magazines2007.com
Periodicals

Press Gazette Regional Press Awards
020 7549 8719
www.regionalpressawards.co.uk
Organised by Press Gazette

Press Gazette Student Journalism Awards
020 7549 8719
www.studentjournalismawards.co.uk
Open to students enrolled on a journalism course

PTC New Journalist of the Year Awards
020 7404 4168
www.ptcnewjournalist.com
Open to journalists, designers or section editors with fewer than three years' working experience in the role

Race in the Media Awards
020 7939 0000
www.cre.gov.uk
Organised by Commission for Racial Equality

Smedias
00 353 1 406 2421
www.oxygen.ie/page/726
Open to full-time students of the Republic of Ireland and Northern Ireland. Print, media and multimedia

What the Papers Say Awards
020 7620 1620
www.granadamedia.com
National newspaper journalists

TV and film

Academy Awards (US)
001 310 247 3000
www.oscars.org
Film

Bafta Awards
020 7734 0022
www.bafta.org
Film, TV and interactive industries

British Comedy Awards
020 8987 6400
www.britishcomedyawards.com

British Independent Film Awards
020 7287 3833
www.bifa.org.uk

Broadcast Awards
020 7505 8017
www.broadcastnow.co.uk
Programme ideas and execution

BTJC Awards
01778 440025
www.bjtc.org.uk
Students on BTJC accredited courses

Emmy Awards (US)
001 818 754 2800
www.emmys.tv
TV
Press: 001 323 965 1990

Evening Standard British Film Awards
020 7938 6247
www.thisislondon.co.uk

First Light Film Awards
0121 753 4866
www.firstlightmovies.com/awards
Short films made by 5- to 18-year-olds

Golden Globes (US)
001 310 657 1731
www.hfpa.org
TV and film, worldwide

Indie Awards (Pact)
020 7067 4367
www.pact.co.uk
Film, TV, animation and new media producers

National TV Awards
020 7486 4443
Winners picked by viewers

Royal Television Society Awards
020 7822 2810
www.rts.org.uk
Best audiovisual work created by full- or part-time students as part of their course

Radio

Arquiva Commercial Radio Awards
020 7306 2603
www.crca.co.uk

Sony Radio Academy Awards
020 7723 0106
www.radioawards.org

Student Radio Awards
events@studentradio.org.uk
www.studentradio.org.uk
/awards/2007

Music

Brits
020 7803 1301
www.brits.co.uk
Press: 020 7439 7222

BT Digital Music Awards
info@btdma.com
www.btdma.com

Classical Brit Awards
020 7803 1301
www.classicalbrits.co.uk

Grammys (US)
00 1 310 392 3777
www.grammy.com

Gramophone Awards
020 8267 5136
www.gramophone.co.uk
Classical music

Ivor Novello Awards
www.theivors.org
British songwriters, composers and music publishers
Press: 020 7436 3632
TV and radio: 020 7299 7979

Kerrang Awards
020 7436 1515
www.kerrangawards.com
Rock

Mobo Awards
www.mobo.com
020 7419 8055
Music of black origin
Press: press@mobo.com

MTV Europe Awards
www.mtve.com

Music Week Awards
020 7921 8308
www.musicweekawards.com

NME Awards
020 7261 5564
www.nme.com/awards
Voted for by NME readers

Nationwide Mercury Prize
020 8964 9964
www.nationwidemercurys.com
Best album in UK and Ireland

Q Awards
020 7312 8182
www.qawards.co.uk

Radio 3 Awards for World Music
020 7765 5887
www.bbc.co.uk/radio3/worldmusic

Books

British Book Design and Production Awards
020 7915 8334
www.britishbookawards.com

Costa Book Awards
01582 844346
dionne.parker@whitbread.com
www.costabookawards.com
Contemporary British writing
Press: 07748 321557

Guardian First Book Award
020 7278 2332
www.guardian.co.uk/firstbook
First-time writers of fiction, poetry, biography, memoirs, history, politics, science and current affairs
Press: 020 7713 4087

Orange Prize for Fiction
www.orangeprize.co.uk
Women's fiction
Press: 020 7544 3894

The Man Booker Prize
www.themanbookerprize.com
Best novel in English by citizen of Commonwealth, Ireland, Pakistan or South Africa
Press: 020 7631 2666

Advertising and PR

Advertising, Marketing & Digital Media Awards
020 7693 0428
www.newspapersoc.org.uk

British Television Advertising Awards
01376 562122
www.btaa.co.uk

Campaign Direct/Media/Poster Advertising Awards
020 8267 4042
www.brandrepublic.com
/campaign/events/awards/1082

Cannes Lions International Advertising Festival Awards
020 7239 3400
www.canneslions.com

Communicators in Business Awards
01908 313755
www.cib.uk.com

Creative Juice Awards
020 7632 7400
www.newspapersoc.org.uk
Young creative teams with maximum of three years' experience

Institute of Public Relations Excellence Awards
020 7766 3333
www.ipr.org.uk

London International Advertising Awards
020 8426 1670
www.liaawards.com

Marketing Week Effectiveness Awards
020 7970 4772
www.marketingweekawards.co.uk

Media Week Awards
020 8267 4344
www.mediaweekawards.co.uk

PR Week Awards
020 8267 4017
www.prweek.com

The Pride Awards
01158 419699
www.cipr.org.uk/prideawards

TUC/Bank of Scotland Press and PR Awards
020 7467 1242
www.tuc.org.uk
Journalism about Scottish issues and in Scottish publications

New Media

AOP Online Publishing Awards
020 7400 7532
www.ukaop.org.uk/events
/annual-awards

Bafta Games Awards
020 7734 0022
www.bafta.org
Video games

Bloggies
2007.bloggies.com

New Media Age Awards
020 7970 4848
www.nma.co.uk

New Statesman New Media Awards
020 7730 3444
www.newstatesman.co.uk/nma

Revolution Awards
020 8267 4947
www.revolutionmagazine.com
/awards
Digital marketing and business

Webby Awards
001 212 675 3555
www.webbyawards.com
Press: 001 212 627 8098

Picture libraries

British Association of Picture Libraries and Agencies
18 Vine Hill, London EC1R 5DZ
020 7713 1780
enquiries@bapla.org.uk
www.bapla.org

Picture Research Association
c/o 1 Willow Court, Off Willow Street, London EC2A 4QB
020 7739 8544
chair@picture-research.org.uk
www.picture-research.org.uk
Fine arts collection for museums throughout the world

4Corners Images
The Lightbox, 111 Power Road,
London W4 5PY
020 8811 1010
info@4cornersimages.com
www.4cornersimages.com

A1PIX
40 Bowling Green Lane, Finsbury
Business Centre, London EC1R ONE
020 7415 7045
london@a1pix.com
a1pix.com
*Travel, business, lifestyle, children,
nature, animals and illustrations.
Hi-res download facility, personal
search service*

AA World Travel Library
13th Floor, Fanum House,
Basing View, Basingstoke RG21 4EA
01256 491588
travel.images@theaa.com

ACESTOCK.COM
Satellite House, 2 Salisbury Road,
Wimbledon, London SW19 4EZ
020 8944 9944
library@acestock.com
www.acestock.com

Action Images
Image House, Station Road,
London N17 9LR
020 8885 3000
info@actionimages.com
www.actionimages.com

Action Library
Bretton Court, Bretton,
Peterborough PE3 8DZ
0870 062 4849
info@actionlibrary.com
www.actionlibrary.com

Action Plus Sports Images
54/58 Tanner Street,
London SE1 3PH
020 7403 1558
osha@actionplus.co.uk
www.actionplus.co.uk

Adam (Amnesty Digital Asset Management)
Audio Visual Resources, Amnesty
International, International
Secretariat, 1 Easton Street,
London WC1X ODW
020 7413 5893
audiovis@amnesty.org

Adams Picture Library
Unit 1 Canalot Production Studios,
222 Kensal Road, London W10 5BN
020 8964 8007
mail@adamspicturelibrary.com
www.adamspicturelibrary.com

Advertising Archives
45 Lyndale Avenue,
London NW2 2QB
020 7435 6540
library@advertisingarchives.co.uk
www.advertisingarchives.co.uk
*British and American press ads,
magazine illustration*

africanpictures.net
Leighton Street No. 17,
Pietermaritzburg, KwaZulu-Natal,
South Africa 3201
00 27 33 345 9445
pictures@africanpictures.net
www.africanpictures.net

Agripicture Images
1 Bowdens Lane, Shillingford,
Tiverton, Devon EX16 9DG
01398 331598
info@agripicture.com
www.agripicture.com

akg-images
5 Melbray Mews, 158 Hurlingham
Road, London SW6 3NS
020 7610 6103
enquiries@akg-images.co.uk
www.akg-images.co.uk

Alamy Images
Central 127 Milton Park,
Abingdon, Oxfordshire OX14 4SA
01235 844600
sales@alamy.com
www.alamy.com

Alinari Archives
Largo Fratelli Alinari 15,
50123 Firenze, Italy 50123
00 39 055 239 5239
fototeca@alinari.it
www.alinariarchives.it

All Action Digital
Pavilion House, 16 Castle
Boulevard, Nottingham NG7 1FL
0115 844 7447
info@empics.com
www.empics.com

AllStar & Sportsphoto
20 Clifton Street,
Scarborough YO12 7SR
01723 367264
library@allstarpl.com
www.allstarpl.com
Worldwide sports, politics, travel

Alpine Club Photo Library
55 Charlotte Road,
London EC2A 3QF
photos@alpine-club.org.uk
www.alpine-club.org.uk

Alvey & Towers
The Springboard Centre,
Mantle Lane, Coalville,
Leicestershire LE67 3DW
01530 450011
office@alveyandtowers.com
www.alveyandtowers.com
Transport

Ancient Art & Architecture Collection Library
Suite 1, 410–420 Rayners Lane,
Pinner, Middlesex HA5 5DY
020 8429 3131
library@aaacollection.co.uk
www.aaacollection.com

Andes Press Agency
26 Padbury Court, London E2 7EH
020 7613 5417
apa@andespressagency.com
www.andespressagency.com
*Travel and social documentary
worldwide, Latin America, UK,
Middle East*

Andreas von Einsiedel Archive
72–80 Leather Lane,
London EC1N 7TR
020 7242 7674
federica@einsiedel.com
www.einsiedel.com

Andrew N Gagg's Photo Flora
Town House Two, Fordbank Court,
Henwick Road, Worcester WR2 5PF
01905 748515
andrew.n.gagg@ntlworld.com
homepage.ntlworld.com
 /a.n.gagg/photo/photoflora.html

Angelo Hornak Library
17 Alwyne Villas, London N1 2HG
020 7354 1790
angelohornak@mac.com
www.angelohornak.co.uk

Animal Photography
EC1 Studio 140–142 Saint John's
Street, London EC1V 4UA
020 7193 4778
stephen@
 animal-photography.co.uk
www.animal-photography.co.uk

Ann & Bury Peerless Picture Library
22 Kings Avenue, Minnis Bay,
Birchington On Sea, Kent CT7 9QL
01843 841428
ann@peerlessmail.com;
picturelibrary@peerlessmail.com
www.peerlessimages.com

Anthony Blake Photo Library
20 Blades Court, Deodar Road,
Putney, London SW15 2NU
020 8877 1123
info@abpl.co.uk
www.abpl.co.uk

Antiquarian Images
PO Box 20, Chislehurst,
Kent BR7 5SZ
020 8467 6297
enquiries@antiquarianimages.co.uk
www.antiquarianimages.com

Aquarius Library
PO Box 5, Hastings,
East Sussex TN34 1HR
01424 721196
aquarius.lib@clara.net
www.aquariuscollection.com

Arcaid Picture Library
Parc House, 25-37 Cowleaze Road,
Kingston upon Thames,
Surrey KT2 6DZ
020 8546 4352
arcaid@arcaid.co.uk
www.arcaid.co.uk

arcblue.com
93 Gainsborough Road,
Richmond TW9 2ET
020 8940 2227
info@arcblue.com
www.arcblue.com

**Architectural Association
Photo Library**
36 Bedford Square,
London WC1B 3ES
020 7887 4066
valerie@aaschool.ac.uk
www.aaschool.ac.uk/photolib

Ardea
35 Brodrick Road,
London SW17 7DX
020 8672 2067
ardea@ardea.com
www.ardea.com
Wildlife, pets, environment

ArenaPAL
Lambert House, 55 Southwark
Street, London SE1 1RU
020 7403 8542
searches@arenapal.com
www.arenapal.com

Arkreligion.com
57 Burdon Lane, Cheam,
Surrey SM2 7BY
020 8642 3593
images@artdirectors.co.uk
www.arkreligion.com
www.artdirectors.co.uk

Aroomwithviews
Bluff House, Stoulgrove Lane,
Woodcroft, Chepstow NP16 7QE
01594 529111
aroomwithviews@
    molyneuxassociates.com
www.aroomwithviews.com

Art Archive, The
2 The Quadrant, 135 Salusbury
Road, London NW6 6RJ
020 7624 3500
info@picture-desk.com
www.picture-desk.com

**Art Directors and Trip Photo
Library**
57 Burdon Lane, Cheam,
Surrey SM2 7BY
020 8642 3593
images@artdirectors.co.uk
www.artdirectors.co.uk
Worldwide countries and religion

artimagedirect.com
29 High Street, Stalham,
Norwich NR12 9AH
01692 580205
enquiries@artimagedirect.com
www.artimagedirect.com

ARWP
Studio 444, 80 High Street,
Winchester SO23 9AT
01264 731238
sales@andyrouse.co.uk
www.andyrouse.co.uk

Aspect Picture Library
40 Rostrevor Road,
London SW6 5AD
020 7736 1998
aspect.Ldn@btinternet.com
www.aspect-picture-library.co.uk

Associated Press Images
Associated Press House, 12 Norwich
Street, London EC4A 1BP
020 7427 4333
london_photolibrary@ap.org
www.apimages.com

Atmosphere Picture Library
Willis Vean, Mullion, Helston,
Cornwall TR12 7DF
01326 240180
pix@atmosphere.co.uk
www.atmosphere.co.uk

Auto Express Picture Library
Dennis Publishing, 30 Cleveland
Street, London W1T 4JD
020 7907 6132
pictures@dennis.co.uk
www.autoexpressimages.co.uk

Aviation Picture Library
30 Wyndham Road, West Ealing,
London W13 9TE
07860 670073
avpix@aol.com
www.aviationpictures.com
Aviation, aerial, architecture and travel

Aviation-Images.com
42 Queens Road, Wimbledon,
London SW19 8LR
020 8944 5225
pictures@aviation-images.com
www.aviation-images.com
Aviation and aerial photography

Axel Poignant Archive
115 Bedford Court Mansions,
Bedford Avenue, London WC1B 3AG
020 7636 2555
rpoignant@aol.com
Anthropology, ethnography

Axiom Photographic Agency
020 8964 9970
jen@axiomphoto.co.uk
jennifer.dove@axiomphoto.co.uk
www.axiomphoto.co.uk

BAA Aviation Photo Library
Green Dragon Vaults, Parliament
Square, Hertford SG14 1PT
01992 501134
sales@in-press.co.uk
www.baa.com/photolibrary

BananaStock
Jupiterimages UK Ltd., Unit 5,
Finch Drive, Springwood,
Braintree, Essex, CM7 2SF
01376 333780
team@bananastock.com
www.bananastock.com

Barnardos'
Tanners Lane, Barkingside, Ilford,
Essex IG6 1QG
020 8498 7345
stephen.pover@barnardos.org.uk
www.barnardos.org.uk

BBC Photo Library
B116 BBC Television Centre,
Wood Lane, London W12 7RJ
020 8225 7193
Research-Central@bbc.co.uk
www.bbcresearchcentral.com

BDI Images
56 Five Ash Down, Uckfield,
East Sussex TN22 3AL
01825 732006
info@bdi-images.com
www.bdi-images.com

Beachfeature.com
41 Trebarwith Crescent, Newquay,
Cornwall TR7 1DX
01637 870430
info@beachfeature.com
www.beachfeature.com

Beken of Cowes
16 Birmingham Road, Cowes,
Isle of Wight PO31 7BH
01983 297311
beken@beken.co.uk
www.beken.co.uk

The Best of Morocco
38 Market Place, Chippenham,
Wiltshire SN15 3HT
01380 828533
steve@realmorocco.com
www.realmorocco.com

BFI Stills, Posters and Designs
21 Stephen Street, London W1T 1LN
020 7957 4797
stills.films@bfi.org.uk
www.bfi.org.uk

Big Pictures
50-54 Clerkenwell Road,
London EC1M 5PS
020 7250 3555
alan.williams@bigpictures.co.uk
www.bigpicturesphoto.com

Birmingham Central Library
Chamberlain Square,
Birmingham B3 3HQ
0121 303 4439
pete.james@birmingham.gov.uk
www.birmingham.gov.uk

**Birmingham Museums & Art
Gallery Picture Library**
Chamberlain Square,
Birmingham B3 3DH
0121 303 3155
picture_library@birmingham.gov.uk
www.bmag.org.uk

Birmingham Picture Library
14 St. Bernard's Road, Olton,
Solihull B92 7BB
0121 765 4114
office@bplphoto.co.uk
www.bplphoto.co.uk

Bluegreen Pictures
11 Bath Road, Cowes,
Isle of Wight PO31 7QN
01983 282233
info@bluegreenpictures.com
www.bluegreenpictures.com

BM Totterdell Photography
Constable Cottage, Burlings Lane,
Knockholt, Sevenoaks TN14 7PE
01959 532001
btrial@btopenworld.com

Bridgeman Art Library
17–19 Garway Road, London W2 4PH
020 7727 4065
admin@bridgeman.co.uk
www.bridgeman.co.uk

Britain on View
Thames Tower, Black's Road,
Hammersmith, London W6 9EL
020 8563 3120
bovsales@visitbritain.org
www.britainonview.com

British Antarctic Survey
High Cross, Madingley Road,
Cambridge CB3 0ET
01223 221400
pictures@bas.ac.uk
www.antarctica.ac.uk
www.photo.antarctic.ac.uk

**British Geological Survey –
National Archive of Geological
Photographs (NAGP)**
Murchison House, West Mains
Road, Edinburgh EH9 3LA
0131 650 0335
nagp@bgs.ac.uk
www.bgs.ac.uk

British Library Imaging Services
96 Euston Road, London NW1 2DB
020 7412 7614
imagesonline@bl.uk
www.bl.uk/imagesonline
Images, maps, historical and engravings

**British Motor Industry Heritage
Trust**
Heritage Motor Centre, Banbury
Road, Gaydon, Warwick CV35 0BJ
01926 645073
photo@bmiht.com
www.heritage-motor-centre.co.uk

**British Museum Photography
and Imaging**
The British Museum Company,
38 Russell Square,
London WC1B 3QQ
020 7079 0944
customerservices@bmimages.com
www.bmimages.com

**Bryan and Cherry Alexander
Photography**
Higher Cottage, Manston,
Sturminster Newton,
Dorset DT10 1EZ
01258 473006
alexander@arcticphoto.co.uk
www.arcticphoto.com
Arctic and Antarctic specialists

Bubbles Photolibrary
3 Rose Lane, Ipswich IP1 1XE
01473 288605
info@bubblesphotolibrary.co.uk
www.bubblesphotolibrary.co.uk

Built Vision
49 Lucknow Drive,
Nottingham NG3 5EU
0115 962 1112
office@builtvision.co.uk
www.builtvision.co.uk

**Buzz Pictures
Fifth Dimension**
36 Byron Hill Road, Harrow on the
Hill, Middlesex, HA2 0HY
020 8864 0155
Info@fifthdimension.co.uk
www.buzzpictures.co.uk

Cadenza Archive
81 Clifton Road, Wokingham,
Berkshire RG41 1NJ
0118 979 1404
peter@cadenza-archive.co.uk
www.cadenza-archive.co.uk

Camera Press
21 Queen Elizabeth Street,
London SE1 2PD
020 7378 1300
sales@camerapress.com
www.camerapress.com
Worldwide photographic library

Capital Pictures
85 Randolph Avenue,
London W9 1DL
020 7286 2212
sales@capitalpictures.com
www.capitalpictures.com

CartoonStock
Unit 2, Lansdown Mews,
Bath BA1 5DY
01225 789600
admin@cartoonstock.com
www.cartoonstock.com

Celebrity Pictures
98 De Beauvoir Road,
London N1 4EN
020 7275 2700
steve@celebritypictures.co.uk
www.celebritypictures.co.uk

Cephas Picture Library
A1 Kingsway Business Park,
Oldfield Road, Hampton,
Middlesex TW12 2HD
020 8979 8647
pictures@cephas.com
www.cephas.com
*Wine and vineyards, whisky and
brandy, food and drink*

Chatsworth Photo Library
Chatsworth, Bakewell,
Derbyshire DE45 1PP
01246 565300
photolibrary@chatsworth.org
www.chatsworth.org

Chris Bonington Picture Library
Badger Hill, Hesket Newmarket,
Wigton, Cumbria CA7 8LA
01697 478286
frances@bonington.com
www.bonington.com

**Chris Howes/Wild Places
Photography**
PO Box 100, Abergavenny NP7 9WY
01873 737707
photos@wildplaces.co.uk
*Travel, topography and natural
history, plus action sports and caving*

Christian Aid Photo Section
PO Box 100, London SE1 7RT
020 7523 2235
jcabon@christian-aid.org

Christian Him's Jazz Index
26 Fosse Way, London W13 0BZ
020 8998 1232
christianhim@jazzindex.co.uk
www.jazzindex.co.uk

Christie's Images
1 Langley Lane, Vauxhall,
London SW8 1TJ
020 7582 1282
imageslondon@christies.com
www.christiesimages.com
Fine and decorative art

**Christopher Hill Photographic
Library**
17 Clarence Street, Belfast BT2 8DY
028 9024 5038
sales@scenicireland.com
www.scenicireland.com

CIRCA Photo Library
Icorec 3, Wynnstay Grove,
Fallowfield, Manchester M14 6XG
0161 248 5731
joanner@arcworld.org

Collections
13 Woodberry Crescent,
London N10 1PJ
020 8883 0083
collections@btinternet.com
www.collectionspicturelibrary.co.uk
*Britain and Ireland: people and
traditional culture*

Construction Photography
2 Whitacre Mews, 26–34 Stannary
Street, London, SE11 4AB
020 7820 6200
Lucy@
   constructionphotography.com
www.constructionphotography.com

Corbis
111 Salusbury Road,
London NW6 6RG
0800 731 9995
info@corbis.com
www.corbis.com

Cornish Picture Library
Trelawney Lodge, Keveral Lane,
Seaton, Cornwall PL11 3JJ
01503 250673
info@imageclick.co.uk
www.imageclick.co.uk

Cornwall, Norways in
Parc Webban, Gulval Churchtown,
Penzance, Cornwall TR18 3BB
01736 365056
graeme@norways.co.uk
www.norways.co.uk

Country Life Picture Library
King's Reach Tower, Stamford
Street, London SE1 9LS
020 3148 4474
clpicturelibrary@ipcmedia.com
www.clpicturelibrary.co.uk
*Architecture, country pursuits,
gardens, crafts, black and white
pictures*

**Natural England and the
Commission for Rural
Communities' Photographic
Library**
John Dower House, Crescent
Place, Cheltenham,
Gloucestershire GL50 3RA
01242 521381

**Courtauld Institute of Art Image
Libraries**
Somerset House, Strand,
London WC2R 0RN
020 7848 2879
galleryimages@courtauld.ac.uk
www.courtauld.ac.uk and
www.artandarchitecture.org.uk

Crafts Council Picture Library
44a Pentonville Road, Islington,
London N1 9BY
020 7806 2503
photostore@craftscouncil.org.uk
www.craftscouncil.org.uk
/photostore

Crash Picture Agency
No1 Innovation Centre,
Silverstone Circuit, Silverstone,
Northamptonshire NN12 8GX
0870 350 5044
photos@crash.net
www.crashpa.net

Create Online
The Mansion, Bletchley Park,
Milton Keynes MK3 6EB
0845 658 2470
enquiries@createonline.net
www.createonline.net

Creative Image Library
Brook Cottage, Hale Oak Road,
Weald, Sevenoaks TN14 6NQ
01892 723388
sales@creativeimagelibrary.com
www.creativeimagelibrary.com

The Culture Archive
193 Ditchling Road,
Brighton BN1 6JB
01273 552929
culture@pavilion.co.uk
www.fulltable.com/index.htm

Cumbria Photo
Ashleigh, Holly Road,
Windermere, Cumbria LA23 2AQ
bbarden@gocumbria.org
www.cumbriaphoto.co.uk

**Dance Picture Library and Circus
Images**
4 Ongar Place, Addlestone,
Surrey KT15 1JF
07956 319362
linda-rich@
dancepicturelibrary.com
www.dancepicturelibrary.com

David Hoffman Photo Library
c/o Bapla office, 18 Vine Hill,
London EC1R 5DZ
020 8981 5041
lib@hoffmanphotos.com
www.hoffmanphotos.com
*Social issues, built from journalistic
work since the 1970s*

David King Collection
90 St Pauls Road, London N1 2QP
020 7226 0149
postmaster@
davidkingcollection.com
www.davidkingcollection.com
*Soviet Union and other images of the
Communist movements*

David Noble Photography
Longleigh, 28 Coolinge Lane,
Folkestone, Kent CT20 3QT
01303 254263
djn@noblepics.co.uk
www.noblepics.co.uk

David Tipling Photo Library
9 Eccles Road, Holt,
Norfolk NR25 6HJ
01263 711496
dt@windrushphotos.demon.co.uk
www.davidtipling.com

David Williams Picture Library
50 Burlington Avenue,
Glasgow G12 0LH
0141 339 7823
david@scotland-guide.co.uk

**Dee Conway Ballet & Dance
Picture Library**
110 Sussex Way, London N7 6RR
020 7272 7845
www.ddance.co.uk

The Defence Picture Library
1 Creykes Court, Plymouth,
Devon PL1 3JY
01752 312061
pix@defencepictures.com
www.defencepictures.com

Diomedia
4, 34–35 Grand Parade,
London N4 1AQ
020 7193 1389
info@diomedia.com
www.diomedia.com

DIY Photolibrary
The Covert, Pickhurst Rise,
West Wickham, Kent BR4 0AA
020 8777 5025
info@diyphotolibrary.com
www.diyphotolibrary.com

DK Images
80 Strand, London WC2 0RL
020 7010 4500
enquiries@dkimages.com
www.dkimages.com

DN – Images
Cambridge Lodge, Gate Lane,
Freshwater Bay,
Isle of Wight PO40 9QD
01983 759918
info@dn-images.com
www.dn-images.com

Dominic Photography
4b Moore Park Road,
London SW6 2JT
020 7381 0007
office@catherineashmore.co.uk

dopeshots.com
27 Orchard Park, Holmer Green,
Buckinghamshire HP15 6QX
01494 717118
info@dopeshots.com
www.dopeshots.com

Double Red Photographic
Unit 4, Gateway Court,
Dankerwood Road, Gateway Park,
Lincoln, LN6 9UL
01522 693278
s.ward@doublered.co.uk
pix@doublered.co.uk
www.doublered.co.uk
Motorsport photography

Heritage Image Partnership
4th Floor, 18-20 Saint John
Street, London, EC1M 4NX
020 7251 5091
Angela.davies@
heritage-images.com
www.heritage-images.com
*World religion, heritage and
architecture*

Ecoscene
Empire Farm, Throop Road,
Templecombe, Somerset BA8 0HR
01963 371700
pictures@ecoscene.com
www.ecoscene.com

Edifice
Cutterne Mill, Southwood,
Evercreech, Somerset BA4 6LY
01749 831400
info@edificephoto.com
www.edificephoto.com
*Buildings, architecture and exteriors of
all kinds*

Education Photos
8 Whitemore Road, Guildford,
Surrey, GU1 1QT
01483 511666
johnwalmsley@
educationphotos.co.uk
www.educationphotos.co.uk
Education, work, homes, signs

Elizabeth Whiting & Associates
70 Mornington Street,
London NW1 7QE
020 7388 2828
ewa@elizabethwhiting.com
www.elizabethwhiting.com

EMRIC Images
64 Union Street, Barnet,
London EN5 4HZ
020 8364 9506
emric-images@virgin.net
www.emric-images.com

English Heritage Photo Library
NMRC, Kemble Drive,
Swindon SN2 2GZ
01793 414903
photo.library@
english-heritage.org.uk
www.english-heritage.org.uk

**English Heritage, National
Monuments Record**
English Heritage, Kemble Drive,
Swindon SN2 2GZ
01793 414600
nmrinfo@english-heritage.org.uk
www.english-heritage.org.uk

Environmental Investigation Agency
62–63 Upper Street,
London N1 0NY
020 7354 7968
tomthistlethwaite@
    eia-international.org
www.eia-international.org

ePicscotland.com
Unit 5 Hathaway Business Centre,
21/29 Hathaway Street,
Glasgow G20 8TD
0141 945 0000
info@epicscotland.com
www.epicscotland.com

Eric Hepworth Golf Course Picture Library
72 Apley Road, Hyde Park,
Doncaster DN1 2AY
01302 322674
eric@
    hepworthgolfphotography.com
www.hepworthgolfphotography
    .com

Esler Crawford Photography
37a Lisburn Road, Belfast BT9 7AA
028 9032 6999
esler.crawford@btclick.com
www.eslercrawford.com

Everynight Images
Top Floor Studio, 127 Strathleven
Road, Brixton, London SW2 5JS
020 7738 7297
info@everynight.co.uk
www.everynight.co.uk

EWA Stock
70 Mornington Street,
London NW1 7QE
020 7388 2828
info@ewastock.com
www.ewastock.com

Exile Images
4 Clarence Road, Stratford on
Avon, Warwickshire, CV37 9DL
01789 262151
pics@exileimages.co.uk
www.exileimages.co.uk
Refugees, protest, asylum seekers,
conflict. Middle East, Balkans,
south-east Asia

Eye Ubiquitous/Hutchison
65 Brighton Road, Shoreham-by-
sea, West Sussex BN43 6RE
01273 440113
library@eyeubiquitous.com
www.eyeubiquitous.com

eyevine
3 Mills Film Studios, Three Mill
Lane, London E3 3DU
020 8709 8709
info@eyevine.com
www.eyevine.com

Fairfaxphotos.com
201 Sussex Street,
Sydney 2000, Australia
00 61 2 9282 2429
fairfaxphotos@fairfax.com.au
www.fairfaxphotos.com

Famous
13 Harwood Road,
London SW6 4QP
020 7731 9333
info@famous.uk.com
www.famous.uk.com

ffotograff
10 Kyveilog Street, Cardiff CF11 9JA
029 2023 6879
ffotograff@easynet.co.uk
www.ffotograff.com
Travel, exploration, arts, architecture,
culture, Wales, Middle East, Far East

FilmMagic
101 Bayham Street,
London NW1 0AG
020 7868 8940
billy.robertson@filmmagic.com
www.filmmagic.com

Financial Times Pictures
1 Southwark Bridge,
London SE1 9HL
020 7873 3000
photosynd@ft.com
www.ft.com

Fine Art Photographic Library
2a Milner Street, London SW3 2PU
020 7589 3127
info@fineartphotolibrary.com
www.fineartphotolibrary.com

Firepix International
68 Arkles Lane, Anfield,
Liverpool L4 2SP
0151 260 0111
info@firepix.com
www.firepix.com

The Flight Collection
Quadrant House, The Quadrant,
Sutton SM2 5AS
020 8652 8888
qpl@rbi.co.uk
www.theflightcollection.com

Floramedia
The Octagon, Middlebrough
Colchester Essex CO1 1TG
0870 728 7222

Flowerphotos
71 Leonard Street,
London EC2A 4QU
020 7684 5668
sales@flowerphotos.com
www.flowerphotos.com

FLPA – Images of Nature
Pages Green House, Wetheringsett,
Stowmarket IP14 5QA
01728 860789
pictures@flpa-images.co.uk
www.flpa-images.co.uk

Fogden Wildlife Photographs
16 Locheport, North Uist,
Western Isles HS6 5EU
01876 580245
susan.fogden@virgin.net
www.fogdenphotos.com

Food Features
Stream House, West Flexford Lane,
Wanborough, Guildford GU3 2JW
01483 810840
frontdesk@foodpix.co.uk
www.foodfeatures.net

foodanddrinkphotos
Studio 4, Sun Studios,
30 Warple Way, London W3 0RX
020 8740 6610
info@foodanddrinkphotos.com
www.foodanddrinkphotos.com

Forest Commission Life Picture Library
231 Corstorphine Road,
Edinburgh EH12 7AT
0131 314 6411
neil.campbell@forestry.gsi.gov.uk
www.forestry.gov.uk

Fortean Picture Library
Henblas, Mwrog Street,
Ruthin LL15 1LG
01824 707278
janet.bord@forteanpix.demon.co.uk
www.forteanpix.demon.co.uk

fotoLibra
22 Mount View Road,
London N4 4HX
020 8348 1234
professionals@fotolibra.com
www.fotolibra.com

Fotomas Index UK
12 Pickhurst Rise,
West Wickham BR4 0AL
020 8776 2772

Francis Frith Collection, The
Frith's Barn, Teffont,
Salisbury SP3 5QP
01722 716376
sales@francisfrith.co.uk
www.francisfrith.co.uk

Frank Lane Picture Agency
Pages Green House, Pages Green,
Wetheringsett, Suffolk IP14 5QA
01728 860789
pictures@flpa-images.co.uk
www.flpa-images.co.uk
Natural history, environment, pets,
weather

FremantleMedia Stills Library, The
Unit 5, Teddington Business Park,
Station Road, Teddington,
Middlesex TW11 9BQ
020 8977 2134
stills.library@fremantlemedia.com
www.fremantlemediastills.com

Galaxy Picture Library
34 Fennels Way, Flackwell Heath,
High Wycombe HP10 9BY
01628 521338
robin@galaxypix.com
www.galaxypix.com
Astronomy and the sky

GAP Photos Ltd
Knowles Farm, Wycke Hill,
Maldon, Essex, CM9 6SH
01621 858379
info@gapphotos.com
www.gapphotos.com

Garden and Wildlife Matters Photo Library
Marlham, Watermill Lane,
Henley's Down, Battle,
East Sussex TN33 9BN
01424 830566
gardens@gmpix.com
www.gardenmatters.uk.com

The Garden Collection
6 Dorset Road, Harrow,
Middlesex HA1 4JG
020 8863 8298
info@garden-collection.com
www.garden-collection.com

Garden Exposures Photo Library
316 Kew Road, Kew Gardens,
Richmond, Surrey TW9 3DU
020 8287 0600
pictures@gardenexposures.co.uk
www.gardenexposures.co.uk

Garden Photo Library
239a Hook Road, Chessington,
Surrey KT9 1EQ
020 8397 3761
derek@gardenphotolibrary.com
www.gardenphotolibrary.com

Garden Picture Library
Unit 12, Ransome's Dock,
35 Parkgate Road,
London SW11 4NP
020 7228 4332
sales@gardenpicture.com
www.gardenpicture.com
Gardening

Garden World Images
Grange Studio, Woodham Road,
Battlesbridge, Wickford,
Essex SS11 7QU
01245 325725
info@gardenworldimages.com
www.gardenworldimages.com

Geo Aerial Photography
4 Christian Fields,
London SW16 3JZ
0115 981 9418
geo.aerial@geo-group.co.uk
www.geo-group.co.uk

Geoff Wilkinson Image Library
4 Rectory Crescent, Wanstead,
London E11 2LE
020 8530 4612
mjw@gwimlib.com
www.gwimlib.com

GeoScience Features Picture Library
6 Orchard Drive, Wye,
Kent TN25 5AU
01233 812707
gsf@geoscience.demon.co.uk
www.geoscience.demon.co.uk

Geoslides Photography
4 Christian Fields,
London SW16 3JZ
0115 981 9418
geoslides@geo-group.co.uk
www.geo-group.co.uk
Landscape and human interest

Getty Images
101 Bayham Street,
London NW1 0AG
0800 376 7977
sales@gettyimages.co.uk
www.gettyimages.co.uk
Live feed photo agency

Glasgow Museums Photo Library
The Burrell Collection, Pollok
Country Park, 2060 Pollokshaws
Road, Glasgow G43 1AT
0141 287 2595
photolibrary@cls.glasgow.gov.uk
www.glasgowmuseums.com

Golf Picture Library
7 Bourne Road, Berkhamstead,
Hartfordshire HP4 3JU
01442 863434
requests@golfpicturelibrary.com
www.golfpicturelibrary.com

Great Stock Photo Library
PO Box 87622, Houghton,
Johannesburg, South Africa 2041
00 27 11 880 7826
enquiries@greatstock.co.za
www.greatstock.co.za

Greenpeace Images
Canonbury Villas, London N1 2PN
020 7865 8294
pix@uk.greenpeace.org
www.greenpeace.org.uk

Greenpeace International Images
Photo Library, Otto Heldringstraat
5, Amsterdam 1066 AZ
00 31 20 718 2116
julieanne.wilce@int.greenpeace.org
www.greenpeace.org

Guzelian
5 Victoria Road, Saltaire, Bradford,
Yorkshire BD18 3LA
01274 532300
pictures@guzelian.co.uk
www.guzelian.co.uk

Hali Archive
Hali Publications Ltd,
St Giles House, 50 Poland Street,
London W1F 7AX
020 7970 4600
hali@centaur.co.uk
www.hali.com

Harpur Garden Library
44 Roxwell Road,
Chelmsford, Essex CM1 2NB
01245 257527
info@harpurgardenlibrary.com
www.harpurgardenlibrary.co.uk

Heather Angel/Natural Visions
6 Vicarage Hill, Farnham,
Surrey GU9 8HG
01252 716700
hangel@naturalvisions.co.uk
www.naturalvisions.co.uk
Online images of worldwide wildlife and plants

Heritage Image Partnership
18–20 St John Street, Islington,
London EC1M 4NX
020 7251 5091
info@heritage-images.com
www.heritage-images.com

Heseltine Archive
Mill Studios, Frogmarsh Mills,
South Woodchester,
Gloucestershire GL5 5ET
01453 873792
john@heseltine.co.uk
www.heseltine.co.uk

Historic Royal Palaces
Apartment 25, Hampton Court
Palace, East Molesey,
Surrey KT8 9AU
020 3166 6633
annie.heron@hrp.org.uk
www.hrp.org.uk

Historic Scotland Photographic Library
Historic Scotland, Longmore
House, Salisbury Place,
Edinburgh EH9 1SH
0131 668 8647
hs.images@scotland.gsi.gov.uk
www.historic-scotland.gov.uk

History of Advertising Trust Archive (HAT)
HAT House, 12 Raveningham
Centre, Raveningham, NR14 6NU
01508 548623
enquiries@hatads.org.uk
www.hatads.org.uk

Historystore
29 Churton Street,
London SW1V 2LY
020 7976 6040
claire@historystore.ltd.uk
www.historystore.ltd.uk

Hobbs Golf Collection
5 Winston Way,
New Ridley, Stocksfield,
Northumberland NE43 7RF
01661 842933
info@hobbsgolfcollection.com
www.hobbsgolfcollection.com

Holt Studios
Pages Green House, Wetheringsett,
Stowmarket IP14 5QA
01728 860789
jean@flpa-images.co.uk
www.holt-studios.co.uk
World agriculture and horticulture, wildlife, pests and diseases

Houghton's Horses
Radlet Cottage, Spaxton,
Bridgwater, Somerset TA5 1DE
01278 671362
kit@enterprise.net
www.houghtonshorses.com

Hungry Eye Images
Ground Floor, 25 Phipp Street,
London EC2A 4NP
020 7033 0022
info@hungryeye.co.uk
www.hungryeyeimages.com

Hutchison Picture Library
65 Brighton Road, Shoreham on
sea, West Sussex BN43 6RE
01273 440113
library@hutchisonpictures.co.uk
www.hutchisonpictures.co.uk
Worldwide contemporary images

ICCE Photolibrary
Burcott House, Wing,
Leighton Buzzard LU7 0JU
01296 688245
jacolyn@iccephotolibrary.co.uk
www.iccephotolibrary.co.uk

Idols Licensing and Publicity
593–599 Fulham Road,
London SW6 5UA
020 7385 5121
info@idols.co.uk
www.idols.co.uk

Illustrated London News Picture Library
20 Upper Ground, London SE1 9PF
020 7805 5585
research@ilnpictures.co.uk
www.ilnpictures.co.uk

Image Quest Marine
1 Eynsham Park Workshops.
Cuckoo Lane, North Leigh,
Oxfordshire OX29 6PS
01993 882333
info@imagequestmarine.com
www.imagequestmarine.com

Image Solutions
P.O Box 62429, UAE
00 971 4 340 4092
info@gulfimages.com
www.gulfimages.com

Image Source
41 Great Pulteney Street,
London W1F 9NZ
020 7851 5700
info@imagesource.com
www.imagesource.com

Images of Africa Photobank
11 The Windings, Lichfield,
Staffordshire WS13 7EX
01543 262898
info@imagesofafrica.co.uk
www.imagesofafrica.co.uk
130,000 images of 20 African countries

Images of Empire
British Empire & Commonwealth
Museum, Temple Meads,
Bristol BS1 6QH
0117 929 3851
jo.hopkins@empiremuseum.co.uk

Imagestate
18-20 St John Street,
London EC1M 4NX
020 7734 7344
sales@imagestate.co.uk
www.imagestate.com

Imperial Images.com
Porta Leacach House, Kildonan,
Isle of Arran KA27 8SD
01770 820644
inquiries@imperialimages.com
www.imperialimages.com

Imperial War Museum
Photograph Archive,
All Saints Annexe, Austral Street,
London SE11 4SL
020 7416 5333
photos@iwm.org.uk
www.iwm.org.uk

Infoterra
Atlas House, 41 Wembley Road,
Leicester LE3 1UT
0116 273 2314
info@infoterra-global.com
www.infoterra-global.com

Inmagine Limited
7th Floor, 52-54 Gracechurch
street, London EC3V OEH
0808 222 8888
info.uk@inmagine.com
www.inmagine.com

Inpho Sports Photography
15A Lower Baggot Street, Dublin 2
00 353 1 7088 084
norman@inpho.ie
www.inpho.ie

**Institution of Mechanical
Engineers**
1 Birdcage Walk, London SW1H 9JJ
020 7222 7899
m_claxton@imeche.org.uk
www.imeche.org.uk

Interior Archive
1 Ruston Mews, London W11 1RB
020 7221 9922
karen@
   interior-archive.netkonect.co.uk
www.interiorarchive.com

International Photobank
PO Box 6554, Dorchester DT1 9BF
01305 854145
peter@
   internationalphotobank.co.uk
www.internationalphotobank.co.uk
400,000 travel images

Irish Image Collection
Unit 507 Clerkenwell Workshops,
London
020 7014 3404
info@irishimagecollection.com

Irish Picture Library
69b Heather Road, Sandyford
Industrial Estate, Dublin 18
00 353 1 2950 799
info@fatherbrowne.com
www.fatherbrowne.com/ipl

Jacqui Hurst
66 Richford Street, London W6 7HP
020 8743 2315
jacquih@dircon.co.uk
www.jacquihurstphotography.co.uk
*Designers and applied artists, regional
food producers and markets*

**Jaguar Daimler
Photographic Library**
B/1/002, Browns Lane, Allesley,
Coventry CV5 9DR
024 7620 2743
kram4@jaguar.com
www.jdht.com

James Davis Worldwide
65 Brighton Road, Shoreham on
sea, West Sussex BN43 6RE
01273 452252
library@eyeubiquitous.com
www.eyeubiquitous.com
Travel collection

Janine Wiedel Photo Library
8 South Croxted Road,
London SE21 8BB
020 8761 1502
wiedelphoto@compuserve.com
www.wiedel-photo-library.com

Jellypics Limited
25 Kellerton Road,
London SE13 5RB
020 8852 0352
info@jellypics.com
www.jellypics.com

Jessica Strang
504 Brody House, Strype Street,
London E1 7LQ
020 7247 8982
jessica@jessicastrang.plus.com
Architecture, interiors and gardens

Jim Henderson Photography
Crooktree, Kincardine O'Neil,
Aboyne, Aberdeenshire AB34 4JD
01339 882149
JHende7868@aol.com
www.jimhendersonphotography
   .com
*Aberdeenshire, aurora borealis,
ancient Egypt*

**John Birdsall Social Issues
Photo Library**
89 Zulu Road, New Basford,
Nottingham NG7 7DR
0115 978 2645
photos@johnbirdsall.co.uk
www.johnbirdsall.co.uk

**John Cleare/Mountain Camera
Picture Library**
Hill Cottage, Fonthill Gifford,
Salisbury SP3 6QW
01747 820320
cleare@btinternet.com
www.mountaincamera.com
*Landscapes of the UK and worldwide -
mountains and trekking*

John Heseltine Archive
Mill Studio, Frogmarsh Mills,
South Woodchester,
Gloucester GL5 5ET
01453 873792
john@heseltine.co.uk
www.heseltine.co.uk
*Landscapes, architecture, food and
travel: Italy and UK*

**John Warburton-Lee
Photography**
Broad Oak, Whitchurch, Salop,
SY13 3AQ
01948 780725
info@johnwarburtonlee.com
www.johnwarburtonlee.com

Jon Arnold Images
7 Rydes Avenue, Guildford GU2 9SR
01483 451245
info@jonarnoldimages.com
www.jonarnold.com

Jupiterimages
5 Finch Drive, Springwood
Industrial Estate, Braintree,
Essex CM7 2SF
0800 056 7533
sales@jupiterimages.co.uk
www.jupiterimages.co.uk

Just-London.com
Unit K, Suite 3, Kemp Road,
Chadwell Heath, Essex RM8 1SL
020 8598 9317
info@just-london.com
www.just-london.com

Katz
109 Clifton Street,
London EC2A 4LD
020 7749 6000
info@katzpictures.com
www.katzpictures.com

The Kennel Club
1-5 Clarges Street,
London WIJ 8AB
0870 606 6750
picturelibrary@
   the-kennel-club.org.uk
www.the-kennel-club.org.uk

Kevin Allen Photography
The Malthouse, Low Road,
Tasburgh, Norfolk NR15 1AR
01508 470030
kevin_allen@mac.com
www.kevinallenphotography.co.uk

Kobal Collection
2 The Quadrant, 135 Salusbury
Road, London NW6 6RJ
020 7518 1035
info@picture-desk.com
www.picture-desk.com

Kos Picture Source
7 Spice Court, Ivory Square,
Plantation Wharf, London SW11 3UU
020 7801 0044
images@kospictures.com
www.kospictures.com
Water-based images

Kumara Images
020 8150 9120

LAT Photographic
Somerset House, Somerset Road,
Teddington, Middlesex TW11 9BE
020 8251 3000
zoe.mayho@haynet.com
www.latphoto.co.uk

Latent Light
P.O Box 1426, Mangotsfield,
Bristol BS16 9ZJ
0870 043 5536
enquiries@latentlight.com
www.latentlight.com

**Lebrecht Music and Arts
Photo Library**
3 Bolton Road, London NW8 0RJ
020 7625 5341
pictures@lebrecht.co.uk
www.lebrecht.co.uk

Lee Miller Archives
Farley Farmhouse, Muddles Green,
Chiddingly, East Sussex BN8 6HW
01825 872691
archives@leemiller.co.uk
www.leemiller.co.uk

Leonard Smith Collection
Greenacre, Brantham Hill,
Brantham, Manningtree,
Essex CO11 1TB
01206 393321
library@leonardsmith.co.uk
www.leonardsmith.co.uk

Lesley & Roy Adkins
10 Acre Wood, Whitestone,
Exeter EX4 2HW
01392 811357
mail@adkinsarchaeology.com
www.adkinsarchaeology.com
Archaeology and heritage

Lickerish
36 Eastcastle Street,
London W1W 8DP
020 7323 1999
robert@lickerish.biz
www.lickerish.biz

**Lindley Library, Royal
Horticultural Society**
80 Vincent Square,
London SW1P 2PE
020 7821 3051
picturelibrary@rhs.org.uk
www.rhs.org.uk

Link Picture Library
41A The Downs, London SW20 8HG
020 8944 6933
library@linkpicturelibrary.com
www.linkphotographers.com

London Aerial Photo Library
Studio D1, Fairoaks Airport,
Chobham, Surrey GU24 8HU
01276 855997
info@londonaerial.co.uk
www.londonaerial.co.uk
*Aerial imagery (oblique and vertical)
covering most of the UK*

Londonstills.com
5 Keswick Road, Putney,
London SW15 2HL
020 8874 4905
info@londonstills.com
www.londonstills.com

Lonely Planet Images
72–82 Rosebery Avenue,
Clerkenwell, London EC1R 4RW
020 7841 9062
lpi@lonelyplanet.co.uk
www.lonelyplanetimages.com

Loop Images
The Studio, 61 Park Road,
Woking, Surrey GU22 7BZ
01483 830120
paul@loopimages.com
www.loopimages.com

Loupe Images
20–21 Jockey's Fields,
London WC1R 4BW
020 7025 2249
info@loupeimages.com
www.loupeimages.com

**MacQuitty International
Photographic Collection**
7 Elm Lodge, River Gardens,
Stevenage Road, London SW6 6NZ
020 7385 5606
miranda.macquitty@
  btinternet.com

Magnum Photos
Ground Floor, 63 Gee Street,
London EC1V 3RS
020 7490 1771
magnum@magnumphotos.co.uk
www.magnumphotos.com

**Manchester Art Gallery
Picture Library**
Mosley Street, Manchester M2 3JL
0161 235 8863
t.walker@manchester.gov.uk
www.manchestergalleries.org

**Mander and Mitchenson Theatre
Collection**
Jerwood Library of the Performing
Arts, Trinity College of Music,
King Charles Court, Old Royal
Naval College, London SE10 9JF
020 8305 4426
rmangan@tcm.ac.uk
www.mander-and-mitchenson
.co.uk

Marianne Majerus Photography
1 Mason's Place, off Moreland
Street, London EC1V 8DU
020 7253 5551
mm@mariannemajerus.com
www.mariannemajerus.com

Marsden Archive, The
The Presbytery, Hainton, Market
Rasen, Lincolnshire LN8 6LR
01507 313646
info@marsdenarchive.com
www.marsdenarchive.com

Marx Memorial Library Pictures
37a Clerkenwell Green,
London EC1R 0DU
020 7253 1485
marx.library@britishlibrary.net
www.marxlibrary.net

Mary Evans Picture Library
59 Tranquil Vale, Blackheath,
London SE3 0BS
020 8318 0034
pictures@maryevans.com
www.maryevans.com
Historical images

Masterfile UK Limited
1 Quality Court, Chancery Lane,
London WC2A 1HR
0870 351 7928
sales.london@masterfile.com
www.masterfile.com

Massive Pixels
07956 505186
info@massivepixels.com
www.massivepixels.com

mattonimages.co.uk
2 Western Avenue Business Park,
Mansfield Road, London W3 0BZ
020 8753 7000
info@mattonimages.co.uk
www.mattonimages.co.uk

M–Dash
11 Sandringham Drive, Bramcote,
Nottingham NG9 3EA
0115 925 8802
info@m-dash.com
www.m-dash.com

Mediablitz Images (UK) Ltd
11 Beaumont Road, Canford Cliffs,
Poole, Dorset BH13 7JJ
01202 701584
enquiries@mediablitzimages.com
www.mediablitzimages.com

Mediscan
2nd Floor, Patman House,
23–27 Electric Parade, George
Lane, London E18 2LS
020 8530 7589
info@mediscan.co.uk
www.mediscan.co.uk

Merseyside Photo Library
Suite 6 , Egerton House, Tower
Road, Birkenhead, Wirral CH41 1FN
0151 666 2289
ron@rja-mpl.com
www.merseysidephotolibrary.com

Michael Cole Camerawork
The Coach House, 27 The Avenue,
Beckenham, Kent BR3 5DP
020 8658 6120
mikecole@dircon.co.uk
www.tennisphotos.com

Moodboard Images
52 Lime Street, London EC3M 7NL
020 7469 6946
hello@moodboard.com
www.moodboard.com

Millennium Images
48 Belsize Square,
London NW3 4HN
020 7794 9194
mail@milim.com
www.milim.com

Mirrorpix
21 Bruton Street, Mayfair,
London W1J 6QD
020 7293 3700
desk@mirrorpix.com
www.mirrorpix.com

Monitor Picture Library
The Forge, Roydon, Harlow,
Essex CM19 5HH
01279 792700
sales@monitorpicturelibrary.com
www.monitorpicturelibrary.com
UK and international personalities

Mooney Photo
25 Armitage Bridge Mills, Armitage
Bridge, Huddersfield HD4 7NR
01484 663698
keely@mooney-photo.co.uk
www.mooney-photo.co.uk

Mother & Baby Picture Library
Emap Esprit, Greater London
House, Hampstead Road,
London NW1 7EJ
020 7347 1867
mother.baby.pl@emap.com
www.motherandbaby
picturelibrary.com

Motoring Picture Library
National Motor Museum,
Beaulieu, Brockenhurst,
Hampshire SO42 7ZN
01590 614656
motoring.pictures@beaulieu.co.uk
www.motoringpicturelibrary.com

Moviestore Collection
2nd Floor, Chartwell House, 61–65
Paulet Road, London SE5 9HW
020 7733 9990
sales@moviestorecollection.com
www.moviestorecollection.com

Museum of Antiquities
The University, Newcastle NE1 7RU
0191 222 7846
l.allason-jones@ncl.ac.uk
www.museums.ncl.ac.uk

Museum of English Rural Life
The University of Reading,
Redlands Road, Reading RG1 5EX
0118 378 8660
merl@reading.ac.uk
www.merl.org.uk

**Museum of London
Picture Library**
London Wall, London EC2Y 5HN
020 7814 5604/12
picturelib@
museumoflondon.org.uk
www.museumoflondon.org.uk

nagelestock.com
Parkgate, West Approach Drive,
Cheltenham GL52 3AD
01242 242952
look@nagelestock.com
www.nagelestock.com

Narratives (Interiors Food Travel)
11 Gibraltar Walk, London E2 7LH
020 7366 6658
pictures@narratives.co.uk
www.narratives.co.uk

**National Archives Image Library
(Public Record Office)**
Ruskin Avenue, Kew,
Richmond TW9 4DU
020 8392 5225
image-library@
nationalarchives.gov.uk
www.nationalarchives.gov.uk
British and colonial history

National Army Museum
Royal Hospital Road, Chelsea,
London SW3 4HT
020 7730 0717
photo@
national-army-museum.ac.uk
www.national-army-museum.ac.uk

National Galleries of Scotland
Picture Library, The Dean Gallery,
73 Belford Road,
Edinburgh EH4 3DS
0131 624 6258
picture.library@
nationalgalleries.org
www.nationalgalleries.org

**National Gallery of Ireland
Picture Library**
Merrion Square West, Dublin 2
00 353 1 6633 526/7
mmcfeely@ngi.ie
www.nationalgallery.ie

National Gallery Picture Library
St Vincent House, 30 Orange
Street, London WC2H 7HH
020 7747 5994
picture.library@
nationalgallery.co.uk
www.nationalgalleryimages.co.uk

National Maritime Museum
Picture Library, National Maritime
Museum, Greenwich,
London SE10 9NF
020 8312 6645
picturelibrary@nmm.ac.uk
www.nmm.ac.uk/picturelibrary

National Museums Liverpool
127 Dale Street, Liverpool L2 2JH
0151 478 4657
photography@
liverpoolmuseums.org.uk
www.liverpoolmuseums.org.uk

**National Museums of Scotland
Picture Library**
Chambers Street,
Edinburgh EH1 1JF
0131 247 4236
h.osmani@nms.ac.uk
www.nms.ac.uk

**National Portrait Gallery
Picture Library**
St Martin's Place,
London WC2H OHE
020 7312 2475
picturelibrary@npg.org.uk
www.npg.org.uk/picturelibrary
Portraits

The National Trust for Scotland
28 Charlotte Square,
Edinburgh EH2 4ET
0131 243 9315
irobertson@nts.org.uk
www.nts.org.uk

National Trust Photo Library
Heelis, Kemble Drive,
Swindon SN2 2NA
01793 817400
photo.library@nationaltrust.org.uk
www.nationaltrust.org.uk
/photolibrary

**Natural History Museum
Picture Library**
Cromwell Road, South Kensington,
London SW7 5BD
020 7942 5401
nhmpl@nhm.ac.uk
www.nhm.ac.uk/piclib

Natural Science Photos
PO Box 397, Welwyn Garden City,
Hertfordshire AL8 6LG
01707 690561
natasha@naturalsciencephotos.com
www.naturalsciencephotos.com

Nature Photographers
West Wit, New Road Little London,
Tadley, Hampshire RG26 5EU
01256 850661
paul@naturephotographers.co.uk
www.naturephotographers.co.uk
Worldwide natural history

Nature Picture Library
BBC Broadcasting House,
Whiteladies Road, Bristol BS8 2LR
0117 974 6720
info@naturepl.com
www.naturepl.com
Wildlife

Neil Williams Classical Collection
22 Avon Hockley, Tamworth,
Staffordshire B77 5QA
01827 286086
neil@classicalcollection.co.uk
Classical music

**Neill Bruce's Automobile
Photo Library**
Grange Cottage, Harts Lane,
Burghclere, Newbury RG20 9JN
01635 278342
neillb@brucephoto.co.uk
www.brucephoto.co.uk

Network Photographers
32 Paul Street, London EC2A 4LF
020 739 9000
sales@alamy.com
www.alamy.com

News Team International
41-43 Commercial Street,
Birmingham, B1 1RS
0121 246 5510
syndication@newsteam.co.uk
www.newsteam.co.uk

NewsCast
The Coach House, 4 Cannon Hill,
London N14 7HG
020 8886 5895
contact@newscast.co.uk;
photo@newscast.co.uk
www.newscast.co.uk

NewsCom
700 12th Street NW, Suite 1000,
Washington DC 20005, USA
001 202 664 3864
support@newscom.com
www.newscom.com

Newspix
2 Holt Street, Level 2, Sydney
NSW 2010, Australia
00 61 2 9288 2829
newspix@newsltd.com.au
www.newspix.com.au

Newsquest (Herald & Times)
200 Renfield Street,
Glasgow G2 3QB
0141 302 6188
rights@glasgow.newsquest.co.uk
www.thepicturedesk.co.uk

NHPA Ltd/Photoshot Holdings
29-31 Saffron Hill,
London EC1N 8SW
020 7421 6003
nhpa@nhpa.co.uk
www.nhpa.co.uk
Natural history

NI Syndication
1 Virginia Street, London E98 1SY
020 7711 7888
enquiries@nisyndication.com
www.nisyndication.com

Novosti Photo Library
3 Rosary Gardens,
London SW7 4NW
020 7370 1873
photos@novosti.co.uk
http://en.rian.ru

Nunn Syndication
PO Box 56303, London SE1 2TD
020 7357 9000
production@
   nunn-syndication.com
www.nunn-syndication.com

Oceans-Image Pictures
2nd Floor, 83-84 George Street,
Richmond TW9 1HE
020 8332 8422
matthew@oceans-image.com
www.oceans-image.com

Offside Sports Photography
271-273 City Road,
London EC1V 1LA
020 7253 3344
mail@welloffside.com
www.welloffside.com

OnAsia
30 Cecil Street, Prudential Tower,
Level 15, Singapore 049712
00 66 2655 4680
info@onasia.com
www.onasia.com

Organics Image Library
The Studios, 27 Hogarth Road,
Brighton & Hove BN3 5RH
01273 701557
info@organicsimagelibrary.com
www.organicsimagelibrary.com

The Original Double Red Photographic
Unit 4, Gatewat Court,
Dankerwood Road, Gateway Park,
Lincoln, LN6 9UL
01469 531416
doublered@atlas.co.uk
www.doublered.co.uk

Oxford Picture Library
15 Curtis Yard, North Hinksey
Lane, Oxford OX2 0LX
01865 723404
opl@cap-ox.com
www.cap-ox.com

Oxford Scientific (OSF)
Ground Floor, Network House,
Station Yard, Thame,
Oxfordshire OX9 3UH
01844 262370
enquiries@osf.co.uk
www.osf.co.uk

PA Photos
292 Vauxhall Bridge Road,
London, SW1V 1AE
020 7963 7022
www.paphotos.com

Panos Pictures
1 Honduras Street,
London EC1Y 0TH
020 7253 1424
pics@panos.co.uk
www.panos.co.uk
Documentary library specialising in developing world

Papilio
155 Station Road, Herne Bay,
Kent CT6 5QA
01227 360996
library@papiliophotos.com
www.papiliophotos.com
Natural history subjects worldwide

Patrick Eagar Photography
1 Queensberry Place, Richmond,
Surrey TW9 1NW
020 8940 9269
patrick@patrickeagar.com
www.patrickeagar.com

PBPA – Paul Beard Photo Agency
PBPA House, 33 Sanctuary Close,
St John's, Worcester WR2 5PY
0845 644 7975
Paul@pbpa.co.uk
www.pbpa.co.uk

Peter Dazeley Photography
The Studios, 5 Heathman's Road,
Parsons Green, London SW6 4TJ
020 7736 3171
studio@peterdazeley.com

Peter Sanders Photography
24 Meades Lane, Chesham,
Buckinghamshire HP5 1ND
01494 773674
photos@petersanders.com
www.petersanders.com

PGI-Images
64 Union Street, Barnet,
London EN5 4HZ
020 8364 9506
emric-images@virgin.net

Phil Sheldon Golf Picture Library
Southcroft, 40 Manor Road,
Barnet EN5 2JQ
020 8440 1986
info@philsheldongolfpics.co.uk;
Gill@philsheldongolfpics.co.uk
www.golfsnap.com
More than 500,000 images of golf

Photofusion Picture Library
17a Electric Lane, Brixton,
London SW9 8LA
020 7733 3500
library@photofusion.org
www.photofusionpictures.org
Contemporary social and environmental issues

Photolibrary Wales
2 Bro-Nant, Church Road,
Pentyrch, Cardiff CF15 9QG
029 2089 0311
info@photolibrarywales.com
www.photolibrarywales.com

photolibrary.com
4th Floor, 83-84 Long Acre,
Covent Garden, London WC2E 9NG
020 7836 5591
uksales@photolibrary.com
www.photolibrary.com

Photomax Specialist Aquarium Picture Library
118-122 Magdalen Road,
Oxford OX4 1RQ
01865 372981
info@photomax.org.uk
www.photomax.org.uk

Photos 12
57 Boulevard Arago, 72030 Paris
00 33 1 5680 1440
meurin@photo12.com
www.photo12.com

Photos Horticultural
PO Box 105, Ipswich IP1 4PR
01473 257329
library@photos-horticultural.com
www.photos-horticultural.com

Photoshot
29-31 Saffron Hill,
London EC1N 8SW
020 7421 6000
charles@uppa.co.uk
www.photoshot.com

Photostage
8 Drakes Mews, Crownhill
Industry, Milton Keynes MK8 0ER
01908 262324
info@photostage.co.uk
www.photostage.co.uk

Pictoreal
26 Spring Meadow, Tipton,
West Midlands DY4 7BA
0121 520 7881
peter.smith@pictoreal.com
www.pictoreal.com

Picture Business
PO Box 6275, Wareham BH20 9AG
020 7731 6076
picturebusiness@easynet.co.uk
www.picturebusiness.co.uk

The Picture Library
16 Crescent Road, London N22 7RS
020 8365 8389
joanne@thepicturelibraryltd.net
www.alandavidson.net

PictureBank Photo Library
Parman House, 30-36 Fife Road,
Kingston Upon Thames KT1 1SY
020 8547 2344
info@picturebank.co.uk
www.picturebank.co.uk

Pictures Colour Library
10 James Whatman Court,
Turkey Mill, Ashford Road,
Maidstone ME14 5SS
01622 609809
enquiries@
   picturescolourlibrary.co.uk
www.picturescolourlibrary.co.uk

Pictures of Britain
Alma House, 73 Rodney Road,
Cheltenham GL50 1HT
01242 537923
info@picturesofbritain.co.uk
www.picturesofbritain.co.uk

picturesofmanchester.com
13 Alan Road, Withington,
Manchester M20 4NQ
0161 445 3681
info@picturesofmanchester.com
www.picturesofmanchester.com

Poker Images
1 Barb Mews, London W6 7PA
020 7605 8018
sales@pokerimages.com
www.pokerimages.com

Popstar Ltd
Central Warehouse, North London
Freight Terminal, York Way,
London N1 0UZ
020 7833 1066
www.popstarpictures.co.uk
Glamour and celebrity pictures

PPL Photo Agency
Booker's Yard, The Street,
Walberton, near Arundel,
Sussex BN18 0PF
01243 555561
ppl@mistral.co.uk
www.pplmedia.com
Watersports, sub-aqua, business, travel,
Sussex scenes and historical images

Practical Pictures
Hermes House, 88-89 Blackfriars
Road, London SE18HA
020 7775 4407
piclibrary@anness.com
www.practicalpictures.com

Premaphotos Wildlife
Amberstone, 1 Kirland Road,
Bodmin, Cornwall PL30 5JQ
01208 78258
enquiries@premaphotos.com
www.premaphotos.com
Natural history worldwide

Print Fair Ltd
Glaisdale Drive East,
Nottingham NG8 4JJ
0115 929 3419
davidhyams@print-fair.com
www.print-fair.com

Professional Sport UK
18-19 Shaftesbury Quay,
Hertford SG14 1SF
01992 505000
pictures@prosport.co.uk
www.professionalsport.com

Proper Gander Imaging
94 Leonard Street,
London EC2A 4RH
020 7617 7564
info@proper-gander.co.uk
www.proper-gander.co.uk

Pulse Picture Library
CMP Information Ltd, Ludgate
House, 245 Blackfriars Road,
London SE1 9UY
020 7921 8099
mcollard@cmpinformation.com
www.cmpimages.com

Punch Cartoon Library
87-135 Brompton Road,
Knightsbridge, London SW1X 7XL
020 7225 6710
punch.library@harrods.com
www.punch.co.uk

PunchStock
101 Bayham Street,
London NW1 0AG
020 7424 8100
service@punchstock.co.uk
www.punchstock.co.uk

PYMCA
St John's Building, 2nd Floor,
43 Clerkenwell Road,
London EC1M 5RS
020 7251 8338
info@pymca.com
www.pymca.com

QA Photos
Ladwood Farm, Acrise,
Folkestone CT18 8LL
01303 894141
pix@qaphotos.com
www.qaphotos.com

Rail Images
5 Sandhurst Crescent,
Leigh-on-Sea, Essex SS9 4AL
01702 525059
info@railimages.co.uk
www.railimages.co.uk

Railways - Milepost 92 $^1/_2$
Milepost 92 $^1/_2$, Newton Harcourt,
Leicestershire LE8 9FH
0116 259 2068
contacts@milepost92-half.co.uk
www.railphotolibrary.com

Raleigh International
Raleigh House, Third Floor,
207 Waterloo Road,
London SE1 8XD
020 7371 8585
www.raleighinternational.org

Raymond Mander & Joe
Mitchenson Theatre Collection
Jerwood Library of Performing
Arts, Trinity College of Music,
King Charles Court, Old Royal
Naval College, London SE10 9JF
020 8305 4426
rmangan@tcm.ac.uk
www.mander-and-mitchenson
.co.uk

Red Cover
Unit 7, Aura House, 53 Oldridge
Road, London SW12 8PP
020 8772 1110
info@redcover.com
www.redcover.com

Redferns Music Picture Library
7 Bramley Road, London W10 6SZ
020 7792 9914
info@redferns.com
www.redferns.com

Repfoto London
74 Creffield Road, Acton,
London W3 9PS
020 8992 2936
repfoto@btinternet.com

Report Digital
4 Clarence Road,
Stratford upon Avon CU37 9DL
01789 262151
info@reportdigital.co.uk
www.reportdigital.co.uk
Work issues and occupations, leisure,
economy, health, education, politics,
social issues, protest, trades union,
environmental issues and culture

reportphotos.com
15 Pembroke Road
London N10 2HR
07973 219201
library@reportphotos.com
www.reportphotos.com

Retna Pictures
Units 1a &1b, Farm Lane
Trading Estate, 101 Farm Lane,
London SW6 1QJ
0845 034 0645
info@retna.co.uk
www.retna.co.uk
Celebrity music and lifestyle

Retrograph Archive Collection
10 Hanover Street, Brighton,
East Sussex BN2 9SB
01273 687554
retropix1@aol.com
www.retrograph.com
Vintage consumer advertising, art,
decorative art

Reuters
The Reuters Building,
South Colonnade, Canary Wharf,
London E14 5EP
020 7542 4899
kim.lee@reuters.com
www.reuters.com/pictures

Rex Features
18 Vine Hill, London EC1R 5DZ
020 7278 7294
info@rexfeatures.com
www.rexfeatures.com

Rex Interstock
18 Vine Hill, London EC1R 5DZ
020 7278 6989
interstock@rexfeatures.com
www.rexinterstock.com

Robbie Jack Photography
45 Church Road, Hanwell,
London W7 3BD
020 8567 9616
robbie@robbiejack.com
www.robbiejack.com
Performing arts

Robert Estall Photo Agency
12-14 Swan Street, Boxford,
Sudbury, Suffolk CO10 5NZ
01787 210111
robertestall@mac.com
www.africanceremonies.com

Robert Forsythe Picture Library
16 Lime Grove, Prudhoe,
Northumberland NE42 6PR
01661 834511
robert@forsythe.demon.co.uk
www.forsythe.demon.co.uk
Original ephemera and transparencies
of industrial and transport heritage

Robert Harding World Imagery
58–59 Great Marlborough Street,
London W1F 7JY
020 7478 4000
info@robertharding.com
www.robertharding.com

Ronald Grant Archive
The Masters House,
The Old Lambeth Workhouse,
2 Dugard Way, off Renfrew Road,
London SE11 4TH
020 7840 2200
pixdesk@rgapix.com
www.ronaldgrantarchive.com

Round the World Images
Wrotham Business Park, Barnet,
Hertfordshire EN5 4SZ
020 8275 1040
martin.smith@worldonfilm.com
www.worldonfilm.com

Royal Air Force Museum
Grahame Park Way, Hendon,
London NW9 5LL
020 8205 2266
photographic@rafmuseum.org
www.rafmuseum.org

Royal Armouries Image Library
Royal Armouries, Armouries Drive,
Leeds LS10 1LT
0113 220 1832
image.library@armouries.org.uk
www.armouries.org.uk

Royal Collection Enterprises
Picture Library, St James's Palace,
London SW1A 1JR
020 7839 1377
picturelibrary@
    royalcollection.org.uk
www.royalcollection.org.uk
Royal family

**Royal Geographical Society
Picture Library**
1 Kensington Gore,
London SW7 2AR
020 7591 3060
pictures@rgs.org
www.rgs.org/picturelibrarys

RSPB Images
The Old Dairy, Broadfield Road,
Sheffield S8 0XQ
0114 258 001
rspb@thatsgood.biz
www.rspb-images.com

RSPCA Photolibrary
Wilberforce Way, Southwater,
Horsham, West Sussex RH13 9RS
0870 754 0150
pictures@rspcaphotolibrary.com
www.rspcaphotolibrary.com

Russia and Eastern Images
Sonning, Cheapside Lane, Denham,
Uxbridge, Middlesex UB9 5AE
01895 833508
easteuropix@btinternet.com
www.easteuropix.com

S&O Mathews Photography
Little Pit Place, Brighstone,
Isle of Wight PO30 4DZ
01983 741098
oliver@mathews-photography.com
www.mathews-photography.com
Gardens, plants and landscapes

Sally and Richard Greenhill
357 Liverpool Road, London N1 1NL
020 7607 8549
sr.greenhill@virgin.net
www.srgreenhill.co.uk

Scala, London
1 Willow Court, off Willow Street,
London EC2A 4QB
020 7782 0044
info@scala-art.demon.co.uk
www.scalarchives.it
Art and culture

Science & Society Picture Library
Science Museum, Exhibition Road,
London SW7 2DD
020 7942 4400
piclib@nmsi.ac.uk
www.scienceandsociety.co.uk
*Science Museum, National Railway
Museum; photography, film and
television*

Science Photo Library
327–329 Harrow Road,
London W9 3RB
020 7432 1100
info@sciencephoto.com
www.sciencephoto.com

Scope Features & Scope Beauty
26–29 St Cross Street, Hatton
Garden, London EC1N 8UH
020 7405 2997
images@scopefeatures.com
www.scopefeatures.com

**Scott Polar Research Institute
Picture Library**
University of Cambridge, Lensfield
Road, Cambridge CB2 1ER
01223 336547
picture.library@spri.cam.ac.uk
www.spri.cam.ac.uk/lib/pictures

Scottish Viewpoint
64 Polwarth Gardens,
Edinburgh EH11 1LL
0131 622 7174
info@scottishviewpoint.com
www.scottishviewpoint.com

**Shell Photographic Services
and Library**
Shell International Limited,
Shell Centre, London SE1 7NA
020 7934 4820
photographicservices@shell.com

SIN
89a North View Road, Crouch
End, London N8 7LR
020 8348 8061
sales@sin-photo.co.uk
www.sin-photo.co.uk

Skishoot-Offshoot
Hall Place, Upper Woodcott,
Whitchurch, Hampshire RG28 7PY
01635 255527
info@skishoot.co.uk
www.skishoot.co.uk
Winter sports

Skyscan Photolibrary
Oak House, Toddington,
Cheltenham GL54 5BY
01242 621357
info@skyscan.co.uk
www.skyscan.co.uk
Aviation and aerial sports

**Snookerimages (Eric Whitehead
Photography)**
Larch House, 10 Brow Close,
Bowness on Windermere,
Cumbria LA23 2HA
01539 448894
snooker@snookerimages.co.uk
www.snookerimages.co.uk

SNS Group
15 Fitzroy Place, Glasgow G3 7RW
0141 221 3602
info@snspix.com
www.snspix.com

SOA Photo Agency
The Stables, 9 Rose Lane,
Crewkerne TA18 7ER
020 7870 6437
info@pictureocean.net
www.pictureocean.net
*Humour, sports, travel, modern
European*

**Société Jersiaise Photographic
Archive**
7 Pier Road, St Helier,
Jersey JE2 4XW
01534 758314
photoarchive@
    societe-jersiaise.org
www.societe-jersiaise.org

Sonia Halliday Photographs
22 Bates Lane, Weston Turville,
Buckinghamshire HP22 5SL
01296 612266
info@soniahalliday.com
www.soniahalliday.com

Sotheby's Picture Library
Level 2 Olympia, Hammersmith
Road, London W14 8UX
020 7293 5383
piclib@sothebys.com
www.sothebys.com

South American Pictures
48 Station Road, Woodbridge,
Suffolk IP12 4AT
01394 383963
morrison@
    southamericanpictures.com
www.southamericanpictures.com

Splash News UK Limited
105-107 Farringdon Road,
London EC1R 3BU
020 7107 2666
dellis@splashnews.com
www.splashnews.com

SplashdownDirect.com
1 Glen Cottages, Sandy Lane,
Abbots Leigh, Bristol BS8 3SE
01275 375520
tom@splashdowndirect.com
www.splashdowndirect.com

Stay Still
29–31 Saffron Hill,
London EC1N 8SW
020 7421 6008
staystill@staystill.com
www.staystill.com

Steve Bloom Images
Middlefield House, Olantigh Road,
Wye, Ashford, Kent TN25 5EP
01233 813777
kathy@stevebloom.com
www.stevebloom.com

Still Moving Picture Company
1c Castlehill, Doune,
Edinburgh FK16 6BU
01786 842790
info@stillmovingpictures.com
www.stilldigital.co.uk
Scotland and sport

Still Pictures – The Whole Earth Photo Library
199 Shooters Hill Road,
Blackheath, London SE3 8UL
020 8858 8307
info@stillpictures.com
www.stillpictures.com
Environment, nature, social and developing world issues

Stock Scotland
The Croft Studio, Croft Roy,
Crammond Brae, Tain,
Ross-shire IV19 1JG
01862 892298
info@stockscotland.com
www.stockscotland.com

Stockfile
5 High Street,
Sunningdale SL5 0LX
01344 872249
info@stockfile.co.uk
www.stockfile.co.uk
Mountain biking and cycling

StockShot
2b St Vincent Street,
Edinburgh EH3 6SH
0845 370 0663
info@stockshot.co.uk
www.stockshot.co.uk

Sue Anderson Island Focus Scotland
Pony Park, Letterwalton,
Benderloch, Oban,
Argyll PA37 1SA
01387 375051
info@islandfocus.co.uk
www.islandfocus.co.uk

Sue Cunningham Photographic
56 Chatham Road,
Kingston Upon Thames KT1 3AA
020 8541 3024
info@scphotographic.com
www.scphotographic.com

Superstock
1st Floor Grayton House, 498–502
Fulham Road, London SW6 5NH
020 7386 4380
info@superstock.co.uk
www.superstock.co.uk

Surfpix
1 High Street, St Davids,
Pembrokeshire SA62 6SA
01437 721188
info@surfpix.co.uk
www.surfpix.co.uk

Sutton Motorsport Images
The Chapel, 61 Watling Street,
Towcester, Northants NN12 6AG
01327 352188
customerservices@
    sutton-images.com
www.sutton-images.com

Swift Imagery
The Old Farm House, Hexworthy,
Yelverton, Devon PL20 6SD
01364 631405
info@theswiftgroup.co.uk
www.theswiftgroup.co.uk

Sylvia Cordaiy Photo Library
45 Rotherstone, Devizes,
Wiltshire SN10 2DD
01380 728327
info@sylvia-cordaiy.com
www.sylvia-cordaiy.com
170 countries, from obscure to stock images

Tate Images
The Lodge, Millbank,
London SW1P 4RG
020 7887 8890
picture.library@tate.org.uk
www.tate.org.uk

Tessa Traeger
7 Rossetti Studios, 72 Flood
Street, London SW3 5TF
020 7352 3641
info@tessatraeger.com
www.tessatraeger.com

Theimagefile.com
3000 Hillswood Drive, PO Box
241, Chertsey, Surrey KT16 0YZ
0870 224 2454
sales@theimagefile.com
www.theimagefile.com

Thoroughbred Photography
The Hornbeams, 2 The Street,
Worlington, Suffolk IP28 8RU
01638 713944
mail@thoroughbredphoto.com
www.thoroughbredphoto.com

Tibet Images
3rd Floor, 5 Torrens Street,
London EC1V 1NQ
020 7278 2377
info@tibetimages.co.uk
www.tibetimages.co.uk

Tim Graham
020 7435 7693
mail@timgraham.co.uk
www.royalphotographs.com

TimeArts Picture Library
29–31 Distons Lane, Chipping
Norton, Oxfordshire OX7 5NY
01608 643334
info@3sco.co.uk
www.3sco.co.uk

TIPS Images
3000 Hillswood Drive, PO Box
241, Chertsey, Surrey KT16 0YZ
ossie@tipsimages.com
www.tipsimages.com

Tom Hanley
41 Harefield, Hinchley Wood,
Esher, Surrey KT10 9TG
020 8972 9165
tomhanley31@hotmail.com

TopFoto
PO Box 33, Edenbridge,
Kent TN8 5PF
01732 863939
requests@topfoto.co.uk
www.TopFoto.co.uk

Travel Ink Photo Library
The Old Coach House,
14 High Street, Goring on Thames,
Reading RG8 9AR
01491 873011
info@travel-ink.co.uk
www.travel-ink.co.uk

The Travel Library
Unit 7, The Kiln Workshops,
Pilcot Road, Crookham Village,
Fleet GU51 5RY
01252 627233
info@travel-library.co.uk
www.travel-library.co.uk

travel-shots.com
3b Uplands Close,
London SW14 7AS
020 8878 2226
sales@travel-shots.com
www.travel-shots.com

Trevillion Images
1 Bellman's Court, 2 Reform
Street, Beith KA15 2AE
0845 223 5451
info@trevillion.com
www.codyimages.com

TRH Pictures
1 Bellman's Court, 2 Reform
Street, Beith KA15 2AE
020 7520 7647
www.codyimages.com

TROPIX Photo Library
44 Woodbines Avenue, Kingston
upon Thames, Surrey KT1 2AY
020 8546 0823
veronica@tropix.co.uk
www.tropix.co.uk

True North Photo Library
Louper Weir, Ghyll Head,
Windermere, Cumbria LA23 3LN
07941 630420
hurlmere@btinternet.com
Picture collection of landscapes and life of the North

UKstockimages
St Cross, Havant,
Hampshire PO9 2QR
023 9247 8643
grant@ukstockimages.com
www.ukstockimages.com

Ulster Museum Picture Library
Botanic Gardens, Belfast BT9 5AB
028 9038 3113
patricia.maclean@magni.org.uk
www.ulstermuseum.org.uk
Art, archaeology, ethnography, natural history, Irish history

Universal Pictorial Press and Agency/Photoshot
29–31 Saffron Hill,
London EC1N 8SW
020 7421 6000
ctaylor@uppa.co.uk
www.uppa.co.uk

Untitled
Radar Studio, Coldblow Lane,
Thurnham, Maidstone ME14 3LR
01622 737722
info@untitled.co.uk
www.untitled.co.uk

urbanlip.com
Ivy Cottage, Lampard Lane,
Churt, Surrey GU10 2HJ
01428 717548
team@urbanlip.com
www.urbanlip.com

V&A Images
Victoria and Albert Museum,
Cromwell Road, South
Kensington, London SW7 2RL
020 7942 2489
vanda.images@vam.ac.uk
www.vandaimages.com

**Vaughan Williams
Memorial Library**
Cecil Sharpe House, Regents Park
Road, London NW1 7AY
020 7485 2206
info@efdss.org
www.efdss.org
Traditional music and culture

View Pictures
14 The Dove Centre,
109 Bartholomew Road,
London NW5 2BJKU
020 7284 2928
info@viewpictures.co.uk
www.viewpictures.co.uk

VinMag
84–90 Digby Road, London E9 6HX
020 8533 7588
piclib@vinmag.com
www.vinmagarchive.com
*Twentieth-century history: books,
newspapers, posters, adverts, photos,
film, ephemera*

VK Guy
Browhead Cottage, Troutbeck,
Windermere, Cumbria LA23 1PG
01539 433519
mike@vkguy.co.uk
www.vkguy.co.uk

**Volunteering England Image
Bank**
Regent's Wharf, 8 All Saints
Street, London N1 9RL
0845 305 6979
marketing@
    volunteeringengland.org
www.volunteering.org.uk
    /imagebank

Waterways Photo Library
39 Manor Court Road, Hanwell,
London W7 3EJ
020 8840 1659
watphot39@aol.com
www.waterwaysphotolibrary.com
Inland waterways

**Wellcome Trust Medical
Photographic Library**
183 Euston Road, London NW1 2BE
020 7611 8348
images@wellcome.ac.uk
http://images.wellcome.ac.uk

Werner Forman Archive
36 Camden Square,
London NW1 9XA
020 7267 1034
wfa@btinternet.com
www.werner-forman-archive.com

Wilderness Photographic Library
4 Kings Court, Kirkby Lonsdale,
Cumbria LA6 2BP
01524 272149
wildernessphoto@btinternet.com
www.wildernessphoto.co.uk

**Window on the World
Picture Library**
124 Cornwall Road,
London SE1 8TQ
020 7928 3448
usill@winworld.co.uk
www.winworld.co.uk

WireImage
101 Bayham Street,
London NW1 0AG
020 7868 8940
captions@wireimage.com
www.wireimage.com

Woodfall Wild Images
17 Bull Lane, Denbigh LL16 3SN
01745 815903
wwimages@woodfall.com
www.woodfall.com

Woodland Trust
Autumn Park, Dysart Road,
Grantham, Lincolnshire NG31 6LL
01476 581111
woodlandpictures@
    woodland-trust.org.uk
www.woodlandpictures.com

**World Entertainment News
Network Ltd**
35 Kings Exchange, Tileyard Road,
London N7 9AH
020 7607 2757
lloyd@wenn.com
www.wenn.com

World Pictures
Photoshot Holdings Ltd. 29-31
Saffron Hill, London EC1N 8SW
020 7421 6000
worldpictures@btinternet.com
www.worldpictures.co.uk
Travel

World Religions Photo Library
57 First Avenue, Katoomba, Blue
Mountains, New South Wales
2780 Australia
co@worldreligions.co.uk
www.worldreligions.co.uk

Writer Pictures
33/5 Mertoun Place,
Edinburgh EH11 1JX
020 8241 0039
info@writerpictures.com
www.writerpictures.com

WWF-UK Photo-Library
Panda House, Weyside Park,
Godalming, Surrey GU7 1XR
01483 412336
phototemp@wwf-uk.org
www.wwf-uk.org

www.cumbriaphoto.co.uk
Ashleigh, Holly Road,
Windermere, Cumbria LA23 2AQ
01539 822222
bbarden@gocumbria.org
www.cumbriaphoto.co.uk

Xposure Photo Agency Limited
32-38 Scrutton Street,
London EC2A 4SS
020 7377 2770
david@xposurephotos.com
www.xposurephotos.com

**York Archaeological Trust
Picture Library**
47 Aldwark, York, YO1 7BX
01904 663000
enquiries@yorkarchaeology.co.uk
www.yorkarchaeology.co.uk
Archaeology in York area

Zoological Society of London
Regents Park, London NW1 4RY
020 7449 6274
leonie.lambert@zsl.org
www.zsl.org

Press agencies

National Association of Press Agencies
41 Lansdowne Crescent,
Leamington Spa,
Warwickshire CV32 4PR
01926 424181
secretariat@napa.org.uk
www.napa.org.uk

24/7 Media (Photography)
200 St Andrews Road, Bordesley
Village, Birmingham,
West Midlands B9 4JG
0121 753 1329
Jamie Jones: 07976 400043
Photographer covering news, sports, features, PR and commercial

Advance Media Information
Princess Court, 1 Horace Road,
Kingston-upon-Thames,
Surrey KT1 2SL
020 8547 0077
Accounts: 020 8547 9173
sales@amiplan.com
www.amiplan.com
Future news, entertainment, lifestyle and business events

Agence France-Presse, UK
3rd Floor, 78 Fleet Street,
London EC4Y 1NB
020 7353 7461
london.bureau@afp.com
www.afp.com
Major agency, claiming to be the world's oldest established agency

Agencia EFE
299 Oxford Street, 6th Floor,
London W1C 2DZ
020 7493 7313
efelondon@btclick.com
www.efe.com
Spanish news agency

Airtime Television News
PO Box 258, Maidenhead SL6 9YR
01753 785799
info@airtimetv.co.uk
www.airtimetv.co.uk
Heathrow airport

Allscot News Agency
PO Box 6, Haddington EH41 3NQ
01620 822578
101324.2142@compuserve.com
Scottish news

Anglia Press Agency
17A Whiting Street, Bury St
Edmunds, Suffolk IP33 1NR
01284 702421
news@angliapressagency.co.uk
East Anglia, words and pictures

ANSA News Agency
Essex House, 12–13 Essex Street,
London WC2R 3AA
020 7240 5514
ansalondra@yahoo.com
www.ansa.it
News worldwide

Apex News and Picture Agency
Priests Court, Main Road,
Exminster, Exeter EX6 8AP
01392 824024
info@apexnewspix.com
www.apexnewspix.com
Based in south-west. All news and features

AP Television News
The Interchange, Oval Road,
Camden Lock, London NW1 7DZ
020 7482 7400
aptninfo@ap.org
www.aptn.com
International newsgathering

Associated Press News Agency
12 Norwich Street,
London EC4A 1BP
020 7353 1515
www.ap.org
Worldwide all news

Associated Sports Photography
21 Green Walk, Leicester LE3 6SE
0116 232 0310
asp@sports-photos.co.uk
www.sporting-heroes.net
Worldwide sports, travel

Australian Associated Press
Associated Press Building,
12 Norwich Street,
London EC4A 1QJ
020 7353 0153
news.london@aap.com.au
www.aap.com.au
European news to Australia

Big Pictures
50–54 Clerkenwell Road,
London EC1M 5PS
020 7250 3555
picturedesk@bigpictures.co.uk
www.bigpictures.co.uk
Celebrities

Bloomberg LP
City Gate House, 39–45 Finsbury
Square, London EC2A 1PQ
020 7330 7500
newsdesk@bloomberg.net
www.bloomberg.com
Worldwide financial

Bournemouth News & Picture Service
Unit 1, 1st Floor, 40–44
Holdenhurst Road,
Bournemouth BH8 8AD
01202 558833
news@bnps.co.uk
www.bnps.co.uk
News and features

Calyx Multimedia
41 Churchward Avenue,
Swindon SN2 1NJ
01793 520131
richard@calyxpix.com
www.calyxpix.com
Stills, news and freelance camerawork

Capital Press Agency
14 Canongate Venture, New
Street, Edinburgh EH8 8BH
0131 652 3999
capitalnews@hemedia.co.uk,
capitalpix@hemedia.co.uk
www.hemedia.co.uk
Edinburgh, Lothians and borders

Capital Pictures
85 Randolph Avenue,
London W9 1DL
020 7286 2212
sales@capitalpictures.com
www.capitalpictures.com
International celebrities

Cassidy & Leigh Southern News Service
Exchange House, Hindhead Road,
Hindhead GU26 6AA
01428 607330
denis@cassidyandleigh.com
news@cassidyandleigh.com
News and pictures

Caters News Agency
Queens Gate, Suite 40,
121 Suffolk Street Queensway,
Birmingham B1 1LX
0121 616 1100
news@catersnews.com,
features@catersnews.com
West Midlands news, features & pictures

Cavendish Press and CPMedia
3rd Floor, Albert House, 17 Bloom
Street, Manchester M1 3HZ
0161 237 1066
newsdesk@cavendish-press.co.uk
www.cavendish-press.co.uk
www.cpmedia.co.uk
News and pictures

Celtic News
Box 101, Powys NP8 1WZ
01874 731185
features@celticnews.co.uk
www.sellmystory.co.uk
UK-wide features for nationals and magazines

Central News Network
Suite 7, 350 Main Street, Canelon,
Falkirk FK1 4EG
01324 630505
jimdavisofcnn@aol.com
Central Scotland news features

Centre Press Agency
M8 Business Park, 259 Summerlee
Street, Glasgow, G33 4DB
0141 332 8888
centrenews@hemedia.co.uk,
centrepix@hemedia.co.uk
www.hemedia.co.uk
Central and southern Scotland

Chapman & Page
Dengate House, Amber Hill,
Boston PE20 3RL
01205 290477
chapmanpage@
    internett.demon.co.uk
Syndicated features agency

Chester Press Bureaux
Riverside House, Brymau 3 Trading Estate, River Lane Saltney, Chester CH4 8RQ
01244 678575
ron@chesterpb.freeserve.co.uk
North-west area press agency and contract publishing

Computer Wire
Charles House, 108–110 Finchley Road, London NW3 5JJ
020 7675 7000
euroinfo@datamonitor.com
www.computerwire.com
Worldwide IT index links

Copyline Scotland
70 Tomnahurich Street, Inverness IV3 5DT
01463 231415
copylinescotland@aol.com
Scottish Highlands

Cotswold & Swindon News Service
256 Marlborough Road, Swindon SN3 1NR
01793 485461
cotswin@stares.co.uk
www.stares.co.uk
Swindon area

Coventry News Service
4 Edison Building, Electric Wharf, Sandy Lane, Coventry CV1 4JA
024 7663 3636
adent@
advent-communications.co.uk
www.advent-communications
.co.uk
Coventry area

DBSP
112 Cornwall Street South, Glasgow G41 1AA
0141 427 5344
stewart.mcdougall@btclick.com
Worldwide sport

Dobson Agency
20 Seafield Avenue, Osgodby, Scarborough YO11 3QG
01723 585141/356555
pix@dobsonagency.co.uk
www.dobsonagency.co.uk
Covering Yorkshire, Cleveland, Humberside and rest of UK

Double Red Photographic
Unit 4, Gateway Court, Dankerwood Road, Gateway Park, Lincoln LN6 9UL
01522 693278
s.ward@doublered.co.uk
info@doublered.co.uk
www.doublered.co.uk
Motorsport photography

Dow Jones Newswires
10 Fleet Place, Limeburner Lane, London EC4M 7QN
020 7842 9900
adam.howes@dowjones.com
www.djnewswires.com
International financial news

DPA (German Press Agency)
30 Old Queen Street, St James's Park, London SW1H 9HP
020 7233 2888
london@dpa.com
www.dpa.com
Global media services, in English and German

Dragon News & Picture Agency
21 Walter Road, Swansea SA1 5NQ
01792 464800
mail@dragon-pictures.com
www.dragon-pictures.com
All news and PR

Emirates News Agency
The Studio, 143 Lavender Hill, London SW11 5QJ
020 7228 1060
mia@mia.gb.com
www.mia.gb.com
News from Arab peninsula

Entertainment News
Dragon Court, 27–29 Mackin Street, London WC2B 5LX
020 7190 7788
info@entnews.co.uk
www.entnews.co.uk
Diary for entertainment news

Essex News Service
2 The Street, Great Tay, Colchester CO6 1AE
01206 211413
perfect@teynews.fsnet.co.uk
Essex area news and features

Evertons News Agency
1st Floor Offices, Hayley Green Court, 130 Hagley Road, Halesowen, West Midlands B63 1DY
0121 585 9188
clive.everton@talk21.com
Snooker and golf. Magazine journalist

Feature Story News
The Interchange, Oval Road, London NW1 7DZ
020 7485 0303
drewc@featurestory.com
www.featurestory.com and
www.featurestorynews.com
Domestic and international radio and TV news

Ferrari Press Agency
7 Summerhill Road, Dartford, Kent DA1 2LP
01322 628444
news@ferraripress.com
www.ferraripress.com
Kent, south London, south Essex, East Sussex, Calais and Boulogne etc

Foresightnews
Dragon Court, 27–29 Mackin Street, London WC2B 5LX
020 7190 7788
info@foresightnews.co.uk
www.foresightnews.co.uk
Forward planning media news diary

Frank Ryan News Service
Cargenriggs, Islesteps, Dumfries DG2 8ES
01387 253700
smeddum@btinternet.com
South-west Scotland, general news, features and photography

Freemans Press Agency
3 Youlston Close, Shirwell, Barnstable EX31 4JW
01271 850255
freemans.pa@virgin.net
www.bipp.com
All news, north Devon

Future Events News Service
FENS House, 8–10 Wiseton Road, London SW17 7EE
020 8672 3191
editorial@fensintl.com
www.fens.com
Diary news service, UK and international. Entertainment and business

Getty Images
101 Bayham Street, London NW1 1OG
0800 376 7977
sales@gettyimages.co.uk
www.gettyimages.com
Images of news

Gloucestershire News Service
Maverdine Chambers, 26 Westgate Street, Gloucester GL1 2NG
01452 522270
john.hawkins@glosnews.com
www.glosnews.com
Gloucester general news

Gosnay's Sports Agency
Park House, 356 Broadway, Horsforth, Leeds LS18 4RE
0113 258 5864
gosnays@aol.com
Sports journalism

Government News Network
London
Hercules House, Hercules Road, London SE1 7DU
020 7261 8325
london@gnn.gsi.gov.uk
www.gnn.gov.uk
Government press office
West Midlands
5 St Phillips Place, Birmingham B3 2PW
0121 352 5500
birmingham@gnn.gsi.gov.uk
www.gnn.gov.uk
East Midlands
Belgrave Centre, Stanley Place, Talbot Street, Nottingham NG1 5GG
0115 971 2780
nottingham@gnn.gsi.gov.uk
www.gnn.gov.uk
North-west
25th Floor, Sunley Tower, Piccadilly Plaza, Manchester M1 4BT
0161 952 4513
manchester@gnn.gsi.gov.uk
www.gnn.gov.uk
All north-west, Carlisle to Stoke
North-east
Citygate, Gallowgate, Newcastle upon Tyne NE1 4WH
0191 202 3600
newcastle@gnn.gov.uk
www.gnn.gov.uk

Yorkshire & Humber
1st Floor, City House,
New Station Street, Leeds LS1 4JG
0113 341 3170
leeds@gnn.gsi.gov.uk
www.gnn.gov.uk

Harrison Photography
37/39 Great Northern Street,
Belfast BT9 7FJ
028 9066 3100
mail@harrisonphotography.co.uk
www.harrisonphotography.co.uk
All Northern Ireland. Business, PR, photography

Hayters Teamwork
Image House, Station Road,
London N17 9LR
020 8808 3300
info@haytersteamwork.com
www.haytersteamwork.com
Home and international sports

IPS Photo Agency
21 Delisle Road, London SE28 0JD
020 8331 0207
info@ipsphotoagency.co.uk
www.ips-net.co.uk
Agents in Japan, Italy, Germany, Spain, France, Scandinavia

Independent Radio News (IRN)
ITN Radio, 200 Gray's Inn Road,
London WC1X 8XZ
020 7430 4814
irn@itn.co.uk
www.irn.co.uk
National and international news

Independent Sports Network
London Television Centre,
Upper Ground, London SE1 9LT
020 7827 7700
jane.tatnall@isntv.co.uk
www.isntv.co.uk
UK sport transmissions

Islamic Republic News Agency (IRNA)
3rd Floor, Imperial Life House,
390–400 High Road, Wembley,
Middlesex HA9 6AS
020 8903 5531
irna@irna.ir
www.irna.ir
Islamic Republic news agency

Information Telegraph Agency of Russia (ITAR-TASS)
Suite 12–20, 2nd Floor, Morley
House, 314–320 Regent Street,
London W1B 3BD
020 7580 5543
iborisenko@yahoo.co.uk
www.itar-tass.com
Russian business news agency

Jarrold's Press Agency
68 High Street, Ipswich IP1 3QJ
01473 219193
jarroldspress@cix.compulink.co.uk
Suffolk, north Essex, south Norfolk, East Anglia and football coverage

Jenkins Group
Berkeley House, 186 High Street,
Rochester ME1 1EY
01634 830888
nickandmarion@hotmail.com
PR worldwide

Jewish Chronicle News Agency
25 Furnival Street,
London EC4A 1JT
020 7415 1500
marketing@thejc.com
www.thejc.com
Worldwide news

JIJI Press
4th Floor, International Press
Centre, 76 Shoe Lane,
London EC4A 3JB
020 7936 2847
edit@jiji.co.uk
www.jiji.co.jp
Japanese news agency

John Connor Press Associates
57a High Street, Lewes BN7 1XE
01273 486851
pictures@jcpa.co.uk
www.jcpa.co.uk
News and features in Sussex

John Fairfax (UK)
1 Bath Street, London EC1V 9LB
020 7688 2777
linda@fairfaxbn.com
Worldwide news

John Wardle Agency
Trafalgar House, 5 High Lane,
Manchester M21 9DJ
0161 861 8015
iwhittell@aol.com
Sports agency nationwide

Kuwait News Agency (KUNA)
6th Floor, New Premier House,
150 Southampton Row,
London WC1B 5AL
020 7278 5445
kuwait@btclick.com
www.kuwait-info.com
News around the world

Lakeland Press Agency
16 Stonecroft, Ambleside,
Lancashire LA22 0AU
01539 431749
craigwilson23@yahoo.co.uk
Cumbria/Lake District. All news and features

M&Y News Agency
65 Osborne Road, Southsea,
Portsmouth PO5 3LS
023 9282 0311
mynews@dircon.co.uk
www.mynewsagency.co.uk
News, sports and pictures. Hampshire, Sussex, Dorset, Isle of Wight

M2 Communications
PO Box 505, Coventry CV1 1ZQ
020 7047 0200
info@m2.com
www.m2.com
Global news

Maghreb Arabe Press
35 Westminster Bridge Road,
London SE1 7JB
020 7401 8147/07832 147146
aouifia@aol.com
mapldn@aol.com
www.map.ma/eng
News in North Africa, Middle East and Mediterranean

Market News International
Ocean House, 50 Cannon Street,
London EC4N 6JJ
020 7634 1666
ukeditorial@marketnews.com
www.marketnews.com
International economics, politics and financial markets

Marshall's Sports Service
2 Newfield Drive,
Kingswinford DY6 8HY
01384 274877
marshall@
   bham-sport.demon.co.uk
West Midlands sports

Masons News Service
Unit 2, Clare Hall, Parsons Green,
St Ives, Cambridgeshire PE27 4WY
01480 302302
newsdesk@masons-news.co.uk
www.campix.co.uk
News and pictures from East Anglia

Media Features
36 Holcroft Court, Carburton
Street, London W1W 5DJ
020 7436 3678
leozanelli@aol.com
Worldwide press syndication

Mercury Press Agency
Suite 218, Century Buildings,
Tower Street, Liverpool L3 4UE
0151 709 6707
reporters@mercurypress.co.uk
www.mercurypress.co.uk
Merseyside, Lancashire, Cheshire, parts of North Wales

National News Agency
4–5 Academy Buildings,
Fanshaw Street, London N1 6LQ
020 7684 3000
pix@nationalnews.co.uk
www.nationalpictures.co.uk
General news. London and south-east

News Limited of Australia
1 Virginia Street, London E98 1NL
020 7702 1355
pj.wilson@newsint.co.uk
www.news.com.au
Australian news

News Team International
41–43 Commercial Street,
Birmingham B1 1RS
0121 246 5511
picture.desk@newsteam.co.uk
www.newsteam.co.uk
Midlands, London news

Newsflash Scotland
21a Port Street, Stirling,
Scotland, FK8 2EJ
01786 477310
news@nflashed.co.uk
www.newsflashscotland.com
Scotland

North News and Pictures
The Newgate Centre,
69 Grainger Street,
Newcastle upon Tyne NE1 5JE
0191 233 0223
news@northnews.co.uk
www.northnews.co.uk
North-east England, Cumbria and borders

North West News Service
10 Broseley Avenue,
Manchester M20 6JX
07980 006606
northwestnews@ntlworld.com
www.nw-news.co.uk

Northscot Press Agency
18 Adelphi, Aberdeen AB11 5BL
01224 212141
northscotnews@hemedia.co.uk,
northscotpix@hemedia.co.uk
www.hemedia.co.uk
Grampian and Highlands

Nunn Syndication
PO Box 56303, London SE1 2TD
020 7357 9000
production@
    nunn-syndication.com
www.nunn-syndication.com
London press agency

PA Photos
Pavilion House, 16 Castle
Boulevard, Nottingham NG7 1FL
0115 844 7447
www.paphotos.com
Sports worldwide, celebrities

Press Association (PA)
292 Vauxhall Bridge Road,
London SW1V 1AE
020 7963 7000
information@pa.press.net
www.pa.press.net
*National news agency of UK and
Ireland; provider of real-time news
and sports information and images*

PA News Birmingham
312–313 The Custard Factory,
Gibb Street, Digbeth,
Birmingham B9 4AA
0121 224 7686
pa_birmingham@hotmail.com
www.pa.press.net

PA News Liverpool
PO Box 48, Old Hall Street,
Liverpool L69 3EB
0151 472 2548
paliverpool@pa.press.net
www.pa.press.net

PA News Howden
Bridgegate, Howden,
East Yorkshire DN14 7AE
0870 830 6725
pahowden@pa.press.net
www.thepagroup.com

PA News Scotland
1 Central Quay, Glasgow G3 8DA
0870 830 6725
news@
    scottishpressassociation.co.uk
www.thepagroup.com

PA News Bristol
5th Floor, BEP Building,
Temple Way, Bristol BS99 7HD
0117 934 3605
www.pa-entertainment.co.uk

Press Gang News
137 Endlesham Road, Balham,
London SW12 8JN
020 8673 4229
mail@pressgangnews.co.uk
www.pressgangnews.co.uk

Pacemaker Press International
787 Lisburn Road, Belfast BT9 7GX
028 9066 3191
david@pacemakerpressintl.com
www.pacemakerpressintl.com
Northern Ireland, Republic of Ireland

Page One Photography
11 West Avenue, West Bridgeford,
Nottingham, NG2 7NL
0115 981 8880
pictures@
    pageonephotography.com
www.pageonephotography.com
*Central and East Midlands. Corporate
and editorial photography*

**Parliamentary Monitoring
Services**
19 Douglas Street, Westminster,
London SW1P 4PA
020 7233 8283
info@
    parliamentary-monitoring.co.uk
www.parliamentary-monitoring
.co.uk
Parliamentary news service

The Picture Library
16 Crescent Road, London N22 7RS
020 8365 8389
joanne@thepicturelibraryltd.net
www.alandavidson.net

Press Agency (Gatwick)
1a Sunview Avenue,
Peacehaven BN10 8PJ
01273 583103
petershirley2@hotmail.com
*Gatwick and south coast, mostly
national press*

Press Team Scotland
22 St John's Street, Coatbridge,
Lanarkshire ML5 3EJ
01236 440077
news@pressteam.co.uk
www.pressteam.co.uk
Lanarkshire, Glasgow and west Scotland

Press Trust of India
PTI Building, 4 Parliament Street,
New Delhi 110 001
00 91 11 031 61872
trans@pti.com
www.ptinews.com
Worldwide news and photos

Profile Group (UK)
Dragon Court, 27–29 Macklin
Street, London WC2B 5LX
020 7190 7777
info@profilegroup.co.uk
www.profilegroup.co.uk
Future events info and business leads

Racenews
85 Blackstock Road,
London N4 2JW
020 7704 0326
racenews@compuserve.com
www.racenews.co.uk
Worldwide horse racing

Raymonds Press Agency
3rd Floor Abbots Hill Chambers,
Gower Street, Derby DE1 1SD
01332 381347
news@raymondspress.com
Sports, news and photography

Reuters
The Reuters Building, South
Colonnade, Canary Wharf E14 5EP
020 7250 1122
robert.woodward@reuters.com
www.reuters.com
Worldwide news and features

Rex Features
18 Vine Hill, London EC1R 5DZ
020 7278 7294
rex@rexfeatures.com
www.rexfeatures.com
International and US picture agency

Richard Harris News
Woody Glen, How Mill,
Branton CA8 9JY
01228 670381
richardwjharris@aol.com
News in north Cumbria

Richard Lappas Images
7 Waylands Road, Tiverton,
Devon EX16 6UT
01884 254555
lappas@freeuk.com
www.richardlappasimages.com
Devon, Cornwall, Somerset, Dorset

Ross Parry Agency
40 Back Town Street, Farsley,
Leeds LS28 5LD
0113 236 1842
newsdesk@rossparry.co.uk
www.rossparry.co.uk
Yorkshire, news features and photos

**Russian Information Agency —
Novosti (RIA-Novosti)**
3 Rosary Gardens,
London SW7 4NW
020 7370 3002
ria@novosti.co.uk
en.rian.ru
Russia

Scottish News Agency
Avian House, 4 Lindsay Court,
Dundee Technology Park,
Dundee DD2 1SW
01382 427035
newsdesk@scottishnews.com
*East and central Scotland, Perthshire,
Fife, Edinburgh, Lothians and Borders*

Scottish News & Sport
15 Fitzroy Place, Glasgow G3 7RW
0141 221 3602
info@snspix.com
www.snspix.com
Scotland sport

Shetland News Agency
The Knowes, Lunning, Vidlin,
Shetland
01806 577332
hans@shetland-news.co.uk
www.shetland-news.co.uk

Smith Davis Press
Queens Chambers,
8 Westport Road, Burslem,
Stoke on Trent ST6 4AW
01782 829850
smith-davis@smith-davis.co.uk
www.smith-davis.co.uk
*Photography, graphic design, freelance
journalists and contract publishing*

Snowmedia Consultancy
Unit G4, Broadway Studio,
28 Tooting High Street,
London SW17 0RG
020 8672 9800
info@snowmedia.net
www.snowmedia.net
*Nationwide lifestyle profiles on health
and sport*

Solent News and Photo Agency
23 Mitchell Point, Ensign Way,
Hamble, Southampton SO31 4RF
023 8045 8800
news@solentnews.biz
www.solentnews.biz
*Hampshire, Wiltshire, Isle of Wight
news features for all national media*

Somerset News Service
3 Lewis Road, Taunton,
Somerset TA2 6DU
01823 331856
somersetnews@boltblue.com
Contact: Richard Briers

Somerset Photo News
12 Jellalabad Court, The Mount,
Taunton, Somerset TA1 3RZ
01823 282053, 07860 207333
somersetphotonews@
  boltblue.com
Somerset

South Beds News Agency
Bramingham Park Business
Centre, Enterprise Way,
Bramingham Park, Luton,
Bedfordshire LU3 4BU
01582 572222
southbedsnews@btconnect.com
*Hertfordshire, Bedfordshire,
Buckinghamshire, Northamptonshire*

South West News & Picture Service
Media Centre, Abbeywood Park,
Bristol BS34 7JU
0117 906 6500
news@swns.com
www.swns.com
*South-west general news, features and
photos*

Space Press News and Pictures
Bridge House, Blackden Lane,
Goostrey, Cheshire CW4 8PZ
01477 533403
scoop2001@aol.com
*Knutsford, Macclesfield, Crewe,
Nantwich, Wilmslow, Alderley Edge,
Northwich, Cheshire, Shropshire and
North-west*

Specialist News Services
27 Newton Street,
London WC2B 5EL
020 7831 3267
desk@snsnews.co.uk
www.specialistnews.co.uk
*National. Consumer, media, city,
travel and motor industry, advertising
and marketing, new products, science
and nature*

Speed Media One
3 Kings Court, Horsham RH13 5UR
01403 259661
info@speedmediaone.co.uk,
greg@speedmediaone.co.uk
www.croxby.com/speedmedia
*General news and features. Sport,
sport development, education, local
government, environment, overseas
property, investments*

Sport & General Press Agency
63 Gee Street, London EC1V 3RS
020 7253 7705
info@alphapress.com
www.alphapress.com

Sportsphoto
20 Clifton Street,
Scarborough YO12 7SR
01723 367264
stewart@sportsphoto.co.uk
www.allstarpl.com
*All sport and entertainment, national
and international*

Thompson Financial News
Finsbury Tower, 103–105 Bunhill
Row, London EC1Y 8TN
020 7422 4870
john.manley@afxnews.com
info@afxnews.com
www.afxnews.com
International financial news

Tim Wood Agency
Press Room, Central Criminal
Courts, London EC4M 7EH
020 7248 3277
www.old-bailey.com
obinsight@hotmail.com
*Court cover at Old Bailey, Southwark
and Blackfriars crown courts*

Tony Scase News Service
Little Congham House,
Congham, Kings Lynn PE32 1DR
01485 600650
news@scase.co.uk
www.scase.co.uk
East Anglia news

TV News
Feature Story News,
The Interchange, Oval Road,
London NW1 7DZ
020 7485 0303
newsdesk3@featurestory.com
www.featurestorynews.com
*TV news for north America, south-east
Asia, southern Africa*

UK Press
Jubilee House, 3 The Drive,
Great Warley, Brentwood,
Essex CM13 3FR
0870 114 2855
info@ukpress.com
www.ukpress.com
UK and European photography

Unique Entertainment News
50 Lisson Street, London NW1 5DF
020 7453 1650
philip.chryssikos@
  entertainmentnews.co.uk
www.entertainmentnews.co.uk
Purely entertainment news

Universal Pictorial Press & Agency
29–31 Saffron Hill,
London EC1N 8SW
020 7421 6000
contacts@uppa.co.uk
maurice@uppa.co.uk
www.photoshot.com
*Press and worldwide commercial
photography, celebrities, sport,
politicians*

Wales News & Picture Service
Market Chambers, 5–7 St Mary's
Street, Cardiff CF10 1AT
029 2066 6366
news@walesnews.com
www.walesnews.com
Wales. General news and features

Warwickshire News & Picture Agency
41 Lansdowne Crescent,
Leamington Spa CV32 4PR
01926 424181
barrie@tracynews.co.uk
*Midlands. General news, features and
pictures*

Wessex Features and Photos Agency
Neates Yard, 108 High Street,
Hungerford RG17 0NB
01488 686810
news@britishnews.co.uk
www.britishnews.co.uk
Women's and news, nationwide

West Coast News
Renaissance House, Parracombe,
Barnstaple, Devon EX31 4QH
01598 763296
westcoast.news@dial.pipex.com
Devon, Cornwall, west Somerset

White's Press Agency
446 London Road, Heeley,
Sheffield S2 4HP
0114 255 3975
news@whites-press-sheffield.co.uk
Men's sport

Wireimage UK
101 Bayham Street,
London NW1 0AG
020 7868 8940
jc@wireimage.com
www.wireimage.com
*Worldwide coverage of entertainment
news and sport*

World Entertainment News Network
35 Kings Exchange, Tileyard Road,
London N7 9AH
020 7607 2757
enquiries@wenn.com
yasmin@wenn.com
www.wenn.com
Worldwide entertainment and photos

Xinhua News Agency of China
8 Swiss Terrace, Belsize Road,
Swiss Cottage, London NW6 4RR
020 7586 8437
xinhua@easynet.co.uk
www.xinhuanet.com
News of China

Religion

Inter Faith Network for the UK
020 7931 7766
ifnet@interfaith.org.uk
www.interfaith.org.uk

Anglicanism

Anglican Communion
020 7313 3900
www.anglicancommunion.org
Archbishop of Canterbury
020 7898 1200
www.archbishopofcanterbury.org
Archbishop of York
01904 707021
www.bishopthorpepalace.co.uk
/archbishop.html
Church in Wales
029 2034 8200
suebrookman@churchinwales
.org.uk
www.churchinwales.org.uk
Church of England
020 7898 1000
www.cofe.anglican.org
Press: 020 7898 1326
Church of Ireland
00 353 1 497 8422
enquiries@ireland.anglican.org
www.ireland.anglican.org
Press: 028 9023 2909
Record Centre
020 7898 1400
www.lambethpalacelibrary.org
Scottish Episcopal Church
0131 225 6357
office@scotland.anglican.org
www.scotland.anglican.org
Press:
press@scotland.anglican.org

Catholicism

Catholic Church
020 7630 8220
www.catholicchurch.org.uk
Media Office: 00 353 1 505 3000
Provinces/ Archbishops
Armagh 028 3752 2045
Birmingham 0121 236 5535
Edinburgh 0131 452 8244
Glasgow 0141 226 5898
Cardiff 029 2022 0411
Liverpool 0151 522 1000
Southwark 020 7928 5592
Westminster 020 7798 9055
Catholic Enquiry Office
020 8458 3316
www.life4seekers.co.uk

Other Christian

Baptist Union
01235 517700
www.baptist.org.uk
Church of Christ, Scientist
001 617 450 2000
www.themotherchurch.org
Church of Jesus Christ of Latter Day Saints (Mormons)
0121 712 1207
www.lds.org
Church of Scotland
0131 225 5722
www.churchofscotland.org.uk
Churches Together in Britain & Ireland
020 7654 7254
www.ctbi.org.uk
Churches Together in England
020 7529 8141
www.churches-together.org.uk
Congregational Federation
0115 911 1460
www.congregational.org.uk
Association of Interchurch Families
www.interchurchfamilies.org
Eastern Orthodox Churches
Greek: 020 7723 4787
Russian: 020 7584 0096
Free Church of England
admin@fce-ec.org.uk
www.fce-ec.org.uk
Free Presbyterian Church of Scotland
daross@donaldalexander
.freeserve.co.uk
www.fpchurch.org.uk
Independent Methodist Churches
emoore@fimc.org.uk
www.fimc.org.uk
International Churches of Christ
info@icoc.org.uk
www.icoc.org.uk
Jehovah's Witnesses
020 8906 2211
www.watchtower.org
Jesus Army
0845 123 5550
www.jesus.org.uk
Press: 01327 344566
Lutheran Council of GB
020 7554 2900
www.lutheran.org.uk
Methodist Church
020 7467 5221
www.methodist.org.uk
Moravian Church
020 8883 3409
www.moravian.org.uk
New Testament Church of God
01604 643311
www.ntcg.org.uk
Assemblies of God
0115 921 7272
www.aog.org.uk

Presbyterian Church in Ireland
028 9032 2284
www.presbyterianireland.org
Presbyterian Church of Wales
029 2062 7465
www.ebcpcw.org.uk
Quakers
020 7663 1000
www.quaker.org.uk
Salvation Army
020 7332 0101
www.salvationarmy.org
Seventh Day Adventist Church
01923 672251
www.adventist.org.uk
Unitarian Churches
020 7240 2384
www.unitarian.org.uk
United Free Church of Scotland
0141 332 3435
www.ufcos.org.uk
United Reform Church
020 7916 2020
www.urc.org.uk
World Council of Churches
00 41 22 791 6111
www.wcc-coe.org

Buddhism

BuddhaNet
bdea@buddhanet.net
www.buddhanet.net
London Buddhist Centre (LBC)
0845 458 4716
www.lbc.org.uk
London Buddhist Vihara
020 8995 9493
www.londonbuddhistvihara.org
The Buddhist Society
020 7834 5858
www.thebuddhistsociety.org
Cardiff Buddhist Centre
029 2046 2492
www.cardiffbuddhistcentre.com
Edinburgh Buddhist Centre
0131 662 6699
www.edinburghbuddhistcentre
.org.uk
Friends of the Western Buddhist Order
0845 458 4716
www.fwbo.org
Network of Buddhist Organisations
0845 345 8978
www.nbo.org.uk
Potala Buddhist Centre, Belfast
028 9023 8090
www.potalacentre.org.uk
Society Krishna Consciousness
01923 857244
www.iskcon.org.uk

Islam

Islamic Centre of England
020 7604 5500
www.ic-el.org
Islamic Cultural Centre
020 7724 3363
www.iccuk.org
Islamic Digest
00 255 744 078830
www.islamicdigest.net
Muslim Council of Britain
0845 262 6786
www.mcb.org.uk
Muslim Directory
020 8799 4455
www.muslimdirectory.co.uk

Hinduism

Hindu Centre, London
020 7485 8200
Hindunet
hsc@hindunet.org
www.hindunet.org
Hindu Links
www.hindulinks.org

Judaism

Board of Deputies of British Jews
020 7543 5400
www.bod.org.uk
The Jewish Leadership Council
020 7242 9734
www.jlc.gb.com
Jewish Network
07976 220273
www.jewish.co.uk
United Synagogue
020 8343 8989
www.unitedsynagogue.org.uk

Sikhism

Sikh Missionary Society
020 8574 1902
www.sikhs.org
Sikhnet
00 505 753 3117
www.sikhnet.com
Sikh Women's Network
info@sikhwomen.com
www.Sikhwomen.com

Spiritualism and paganism

Aetherius Society
020 7736 4187
www.aetherius.org
British Druid Order
sparrowhawk@
    britishdruidorder.co.uk
www.britishdruidorder.co.uk
Order of Bards, Ovates & Druids
01273 470888
www.druidry.org
Pagan Federation
07986 034378
www.paganfed.org
Press: 01458 835518
Satanism
HPNadramia@churchofsatan.com
www.churchofsatan.com
Spiritualist Association of Great Britain
020 7235 3351
info@spiritualuk.com
www.spiritualuk.com
Spiritualists' National Union
0845 458 0768
snu@snu.org.uk
www.snu.org.uk
Theosophical Society
020 7563 9815
info@thesociety.org
www.theosophical-society.org.uk
Transcendental Meditation
0870 514 3733
www.transcendental-meditation
    .org.uk.

Other religions

Baha'i Community of UK
020 7584 2566
www.bahai.org.uk
Church of Scientology
01342 318229
www.scientology.org
Jainism
vinod@jainworld.com
www.jainworld.com
World Zoroastrian Organisation
President@w-z-o.org
www.w-z-o.org

Humanism and atheism

Association of Irish Humanists
00 353 1841 3116
www.humanism.ie
British Humanist Assoc
020 7079 3580
www.humanism.org.uk
Gay and Lesbian Humanist Association
01926 858450
www.galha.freeserve.co.uk
    /galha.htm
International Humanist and Ethical Union
0870 288 7631
www.iheu.org
National Secular Society
020 7404 3126
www.secularism.org.uk
Rationalist Press Association
020 7436 1151
www.rationalist.org.uk
South Place Ethical Society
020 7242 8037
library@ethicalsoc.org.uk
www.ethicalsoc.org.uk

Society

Government

Department for Communities and Local Government
020 7944 4400
www.communities.gov.uk

Health
020 7210 4850
www.dh.gov.uk
Press: 020 7210 5221

Home Office
020 7035 4848
www.homeoffice.gov.uk
Press: 020 7035 4381

Work and Pensions
020 7238 0800
www.dwp.gov.uk
Press: 020 3267 5113

Government agencies

Charity Commission
0845 300 0218
www.charity-commission.gov.uk
Press: 020 7674 2323/32/33

Children and Family Court Advisory Service
020 7510 7000
www.cafcass.gov.uk
Press: 020 7510 7036

Child Support Agency
0845 713 3133
www.csa.gov.uk
Press: 020 7238 0725

Commission for Racial Equality (CRE)
020 7939 0000
www.cre.gov.uk
Press: 020 7939 0106

Connexions
0808 001 3219
www.connexions.gov.uk
Advice and support for 13-19-year-olds

Housing Corporation
0845 230 7000
www.housingcorp.gov.uk
Funding and regulation of housing associations

Immigration Directorate
0870 606 7766
www.bia.homeoffice.gov.uk

Office of the Immigration Services Commissioner
020 7211 1500
www.oisc.gov.uk

Charity association

Institute of Fundraising
020 7840 1000
www.institute-of-fundraising.org.uk

Media Trust
020 7874 7600
www.mediatrust.org
Helping charities communicate

Major charities

Action for Blind People
020 7635 4800
www.afbp.org
Press: 020 7635 4921

ActionAid
020 7561 7561
www.actionaid.org
Press: 020 7561 7614

Age Concern England
020 8765 7200
www.ageconcern.org.uk

Alzheimer's Society
020 7306 0606
www.alzheimers.org.uk
Press: 020 7306 0813/39

ARC Addington Fund
024 7669 0587
www.arc-addingtonfund.org.uk

Arthritis Research Campaign
0870 850 5000
www.arc.org.uk
Press: 01246 541107

Association for International Cancer Research
01334 477910
www.aicr.org.uk

Asthma UK
020 7786 4900
www.asthma.org.uk
Press: 020 7786 4949

Barnardo's
020 8550 8822
www.barnardos.org.uk
Press: 020 8498 7555

Battersea Dogs' & Cats' Home
020 7622 3626
www.dogshome.org
Press: 020 7627 9294

BBC Children in Need Appeal
020 8576 7788
www.bbc.co.uk/pudsey

Benenden Hospital Trust
01580 240333
www.benendenhospital.org.uk
Press: 01580 242472

Birmingham Diocesan Trust
0121 236 5535
www.birminghamdiocese.org.uk
Press: 0121 427 2780

Blue Cross
01993 822651
www.bluecross.org.uk
Press: 020 7932 4060

British and Foreign Bible Society
01793 418100
www.biblesociety.org.uk
Press: 01793 418241

British Heart Foundation
020 7935 0185
www.bhf.org.uk
Press: 020 7487 7172
out of hours: 07764 290381

British Red Cross
0870 170 7000
www.redcross.org.uk
Press: 020 7877 7046

British Tennis Foundation
020 8487 7000
www.lta.org.uk
Press: 020 8487 7000

Cambridge Foundation
01223 332288
www.foundation.cam.ac.uk
Press: 01223 332300

Cancer Research UK
020 7121 6699
www.cancerresearchuk.org
Press: 020 7061 8300

Catholic Agency for Overseas Development
020 7733 7900
www.cafod.org.uk
Press: 020 7326 5557

Cats Protection
0870 209 9099
www.cats.org.uk
Press: 0870 770 8612

ChildLine
020 7650 3200
www.childline.org.uk
Press: 020 7825 2516

Children with Leukaemia Foundation
020 7404 0808
www.leukaemia.org

Children's Society
0845 300 1128
www.childrenssociety.org.uk

Choice Support
020 7261 4100
www.choicesupport.org.uk

Christian Aid
020 7620 4444
www.christian-aid.org.uk
Press: 020 7523 2421

Christian Vision
0121 522 6087
www.christianvision.com

Christie Hospital Charitable Fund
0161 446 3988
www.christies.org
Press: 0161 446 3613

Church of Jesus Christ of Latter Day Saints Great Britain
0121 712 1207
www.lds.org.uk

Church of Scotland Unincorporated Boards and Committees
0131 225 5722
www.churchofscotland.org.uk
Press: 0131 240 2243

Comic Relief
020 7820 5555
www.comicrelief.com

Community Integrated Care
0151 420 3637
www.c-i-c.co.uk
Press: 0151 422 5352

Concern Worldwide
0800 032 4000
www.concern.net
Press: 020 7906 4629

Diabetes UK
020 7424 1000
www.diabetes.org.uk
Press: 020 7424 1165

Disasters Emergency Committee
020 7387 0200
www.dec.org.uk

Dogs Trust
020 7837 0006
www.dogstrust.org.uk
Press: 020 7837 0006

Donkey Sanctuary
01395 578222
www.thedonkeysanctuary.org.uk
Press: 01395 573097

Fremantle Trust
01296 393055
www.fremantletrust.org

Great Ormond St Children's Charity
020 7916 5678
www.gosh.org

Guide Dogs for the Blind Association
0118 983 5555
www.guidedogs.org.uk
Press: 0118 983 8380

Help the Aged
020 7278 1114
www.helptheaged.org.uk
Press: 020 7239 1942

International Planned Parenthood Federation
020 7939 8200
www.ippf.org
Press: 020 7939 8233

Islamic Relief
0121 605 5555
www.islamic-relief.com/uk
Press: 0121 605 0663

Jewish Care
020 8922 2000
www.jewishcare.org
Press: 020 8922 2812

Leonard Cheshire
020 7802 8200
www.leonard-cheshire.org
Provider of support to disabled people

Leukaemia Research Fund
020 7405 0101
www.lrf.org.uk
Press: 020 7269 9019

Liverpool Roman Catholic Archdiocesan Trust
0151 522 1000
www.archdiocese
   -of-liverpool.co.uk
Press: 0151 522 1007

Macmillan Cancer Relief
020 7840 7840
www.macmillan.org.uk
Press: 020 7840 7821

Marie Curie Cancer Care
020 7599 7777
www.mariecurie.org.uk
Press: 020 7599 7700

Mencap
020 7454 0454
www.mencap.org.uk
Press: 020 7696 5524

Mind
020 8519 2122
www.mind.org.uk
National Association for Mental Health
Press: 020 8522 1743

Motability
01279 635999
www.motability.co.uk
Press: 01279 632024

Multiple Sclerosis Society
020 8438 0700
www.mssociety.org.uk
Press: 020 7082 0820

National Council of YMCAs
020 8520 5599
www.ymca.org.uk
Press: 020 7061 3324

National Galleries of Scotland
0131 624 6200
www.nationalgalleries.org
www.natgalscot.ac.uk

National Missing Persons Helpline
020 8392 4545
www.missingpersons.org
Press: 020 8392 4510-3

National Museum of Science and Industry
0870 870 4771
www.nmsi.ac.uk
Press: 020 7942 4357

National Society for the Prevention of Cruelty to Children (NSPCC)
020 7825 2500
www.nspcc.org.uk
Press: 020 7825 2514/1373

National Trust
0870 458 4000
www.nationaltrust.org.uk
Press: 0870 600 2127

National Trust for Scotland
0131 243 9300
www.nts.org.uk
Press: 0131 243 9349

NCH
020 7704 7000
www.nch.org.uk
Press: 020 7704 7111

Oxfam
0870 333 2700
www.oxfam.org.uk
Press: 01865 472498

Parkinson's Disease Society of the UK
020 7931 8080
www.parkinsons.org.uk

PDSA
0800 917 2509
www.pdsa.org.uk
Press: 01952 290999

Plan UK
020 7482 9777
www.plan-uk.org

Portsmouth Roman Catholic Diocesan Trustees Registered (PRCDTR)
01329 835583
www.portsmouthdiocese.org.uk
Press: 07770 538693

Prince's Trust
020 7543 1234
www.princes-trust.org.uk
Press: 020 7543 1318

Royal National Institute of the Blind (RNIB)
020 7388 1266
www.rnib.org.uk
Press: 020 7391 2223

Royal National Institute for Deaf People (RNID)
020 7296 8000
www.rnid.org.uk
Press: 020 7296 8137

Roman Catholic Diocese of Hexham & Newcastle
0191 243 3300
www.rcdhn.org.uk
Press: 0191 228 0003

Roman Catholic Diocese of Southwark
020 7928 2495
www.rcsouthwark.co.uk

Royal British Legion
020 7973 7200
www.britishlegion.org.uk
www.poppy.org.uk
Press: 020 7973 7296

Royal Horticultural Society
020 7834 4333
www.rhs.org.uk
Press: 020 7821 3043

Royal Marsden Hospital Charity
020 7352 8171
www.royalmarsden.org
Press: 020 7808 2605

Royal National Lifeboat Institution (RNLI)
0845 122 6999
www.rnli.org.uk
Press: 01202 662218
   /663184/663127

Royal Society for the Prevention of Cruelty to Animals (RSPCA)
Helpline: 0870 555 5999
enquiries: 0870 333 5999
www.rspca.org.uk
Press: 0870 754 0244

Royal Society for the Protection of Birds (RSPB)
01767 680551
www.rspb.org.uk

Salford Diocesan Trust
0161 736 1421
www.salforddiocese.org.uk
Press: 0161 330 2777

Salvation Army
020 7367 4500
www.salvationarmy.org.uk
Press: 020 7367 4700

Samaritan's Purse International
020 8559 2044
www.samaritanspurse.org.uk
Press: 0131 624 1155

Save the Children (UK)
020 7012 6400
www.savethechildren.org.uk
Press: 020 7012 6841

Scope
020 7619 7100
www.scope.org.uk
Press: 020 7619 7200

Sense
020 7272 7774
www.sense.org.uk
Press: 020 7561 3405

Sheffield City Trust
0114 243 5355
www.sivltd.com
Press: 0114 221 0380

Shelter
0845 458 4590
www.shelter.org.uk
Press: 020 7505 2162

Sightsavers
01444 446600
www.sightsavers.org.uk
Press: 01444 446655

St John Ambulance
0870 010 4950
www.sja.org.uk
Press: 020 7324 4210

Stewardship
0845 226 2627
www.stewardship.org.uk

Stroke Association
020 7566 0300
www.stroke.org.uk
Press: 020 7566 1500

Tate
020 7887 8000
www.tate.org.uk
Press: 020 7887 8730

Tear Fund
0845 355 8355
www.tearfund.org
Press: 020 8943 7779

Unicef
020 7405 5592
www.unicef.org.uk
Press: 020 7430 0162

United Jewish Israel Appeal
020 8369 5000
www.ujia.org
Press: 020 8369 5028

Victoria and Albert Museum
020 7942 2000
www.vam.ac.uk
Press: 020 7942 2502

Watch Tower Bible and Tract Society of Britain
020 8906 2211
www.watchtower.org

WaterAid
020 7793 4500
www.wateraid.org.uk
Press: 020 7793 4793

Westminster Roman Catholic Diocesan Trust
020 7798 9036
www.rcdow.org.uk
Press: 020 7798 9031

World Emergency Relief
0870 429 2129
www.wer-uk.org

World Vision UK
01908 841000
www.worldvision.org.uk
Press: 01908 841020

WWF UK
01483 426444
www.wwf.org.uk
Press: 01483 412383

Other charities and campaign groups

● Children

4Children
020 7512 2112
www.4children.org.uk

Acorns Children's Hospice Trust
0845 128 4444
www.acorns.org.uk

Adoption and Fostering Information Line
0800 783 4086
www.adoption.org.uk

Anna Freud Centre
020 7794 2313
www.annafreudcentre.org
Psychoanalysis for children

Barnardo's
020 8550 8822
www.barnardos.org.uk

BBC Children in Need
020 8576 7788
www.bbc.co.uk/pudsey

Bliss
020 7378 1122
www.bliss.org.uk
National charity for premature or sick babies

Care and Relief For The Young
01489 788300
www.cry.org.uk

Child Concern
0161 832 8113
www.childconcern.org.uk

ChildHope
020 7065 0950
www.childhopeuk.org
Defending street children worldwide

ChildLine
020 7650 3200
www.childline.org.uk

Children and Armed Conflict Unit
01206 873483
www.essex.ac.uk/armedcon

Children with Leukaemia Foundation
020 7404 0808
www.leukaemia.org

Children's Society
0845 300 1128
www.childrenssociety.org.uk

CLIC Sargent
0845 301 0031
www.clicsargent.org.uk
Children's cancer charity

Coram Family
020 7520 0300
www.coram.org.uk
Working with vulnerable children

End Child Poverty
020 7278 6541
www.ecpc.org.uk

EveryChild
020 7749 2468
www.everychild.org.uk

Foyle Foundation
020 7430 9119
www.foylefoundation.org.uk
Distributes grants to arts, health and learning charities

Girlguiding UK
020 7834 6242
www.girlguiding.org.uk

Great Ormond St Children's Charity
020 7916 5678
www.gosh.org

Hope
01442 234561
www.hope-for-children.org
International charity for handicapped, orphaned, poor and exploited children

Hope and Homes for Children
01722 790111
www.hopeandhomes.org

Hyperactive Children's Support Group
01243 539966
www.hacsg.org.uk

International Planned Parenthood Federation
020 7939 8200
www.ippf.org

National Children's Bureau
020 7843 6000
www.ncb.org.uk

National Youth Agency
0116 242 7350
www.nya.org.uk

NCH
020 7704 7000
www.nch.org.uk
Support for vulnerable children

NSPCC
020 7825 2500
www.nspcc.org.uk
Press: 020 7825 2514

Plan UK
020 7482 9777
www.plan-uk.org
Children in developing countries

Prince's Trust
020 7543 1234
www.princes-trust.org.uk

Relate
0845 1 304016
www.relate.org.uk
Relationship guidance
Press: 0845 456 1210

Ride Foundation
01372 467708
www.ridefoundation.org.uk
Drug awareness, life skills and citizenship programmes for schools

Save the Children (UK)
020 7012 6400
www.savethechildren.org.uk

Second Chance
023 9287 2790
www.second-chance.org.uk
*Camping and fishing for
disadvantaged children*

The Site
020 7250 5700
www.thesite.org.uk
Advice and help for young people
Press: 020 7226 8008

Task Brasil Trust
020 7735 5545
www.taskbrasil.org.uk
UK charity for street children in Brazil

Trident Trust
020 7014 1400
www.thetridenttrust.org.uk

Unicef
020 7405 5592
www.unicef.org.uk

United Kingdom Missing Children
www.missingkids.co.uk

Variety Club Children's Charity
020 7428 8100
www.varietyclub.org.uk

War Child UK
020 7916 9276
www.warchild.org.uk

Whizz Kidz
020 7233 6600
www.whizz-kidz.org.uk
Children with disabilities

World Villages for Children
020 7629 3050
www.worldvillages.org

Young Enterprise
01865 776845
www.young-enterprise.org.uk

● Citizenship

Association for Citizenship Teaching
020 7566 4133
www.teachingcitizenship.org.uk
*Information and direct action across a
number of areas*

Citizenship Foundation
020 7566 4141
www.citizenshipfoundation.org.uk

● Community

Anchor Trust
020 7759 9100
www.anchor.org.uk
Press: 020 7759 9104

Army Benevolent Fund
0845 241 4820
www.armybenfund.org

Business in the Community
0870 600 2482
www.bitc.org.uk

Changemakers
020 7702 1511
www.changemakers.org.uk

Citizens Advice Bureaux
020 7833 2181
www.citizensadvice.org.uk

Civil Service Benevolent Fund
020 8240 2400
www.csbf.org.uk

Coalfields Regeneration Trust
0800 064 8560
www.coalfields-regen.org.uk

Common Purpose
020 7608 8100
www.commonpurpose.org.uk

Communities that Care
020 7922 7788
www.communitiesthatcare.org.uk

Community Development Foundation
020 7833 1772
www.cdf.org.uk

Community Foundation
0191 222 0945
www.communityfoundation.org.uk
*Serving Tyne & Wear and
Northumberland*

Community Integrated Care
0151 420 3637
www.c-i-c.co.uk

Community Service Volunteers
020 7278 6601
www.csv.org.uk

Directory of Social Change
0845 077 7707
www.dsc.org.uk

Duke of Edinburgh's Award
01753 727400
www.theaward.org

Erskine Home
0141 812 1100
www.erskine.org.uk
For ex-servicemen

Groundwork
0121 236 8565
www.groundwork.org.uk
*Community improvement schemes in
rundown areas*

Gurkha Welfare Trust
020 7251 5234
www.gwt.org.uk

Nacro
020 7582 6500
www.nacro.org.uk
Crime reduction charity

**National Federation of
Community Organisations**
020 7837 7887
www.communitymatters.org.uk

Neighbourhood Initiatives Foundation
0870 770 0339
www.nif.co.uk

Neighbourhood Renewal Unit
0845 082 8383
www.neighbourhood.gov.uk

Norwood Ravenswood Foundation
020 8954 4555
www.norwood.org.uk

Outward Bound Trust
01931 740000
www.outwardbound.org.uk

Police Rehabilitation Centre
01491 874499
www.flinthouse.co.uk

Prince's Trust
020 7543 1234
www.princes-trust.org.uk

Princess Royal Trust for Carers
020 7480 7788
www.carers.org

Raleigh International Trust
020 7371 8585
www.raleighinternational.org

Rathbone
0161 236 5358
www.rathbonetraining.co.uk
*Learning and training support for the
disadvantaged*

Royal Air Force Benevolent Fund
020 7580 8343
www.rafbf.org.uk

Royal Air Forces Association
020 8286 6667
www.rafa.org.uk

Royal British Legion
0845 772 5725
www.britishlegion.org.uk
www.poppy.org.uk

**Royal Commonwealth
Ex-Services League**
020 7973 7263
www.bcel.org.uk

Samaritans
020 8394 8300
www.samaritans.org

Scottish Community Foundation
0131 524 0300
www.scottishcommunity
foundation.com

**Soldiers, Sailors, Airmen and
Families Association — Forces Help**
020 7403 8783
www.ssafa.org.uk

Sue Ryder Care
020 7400 0440
www.suerydercare.org
*National volunteering campaign for
community welfare*

Time Bank
0845 456 1668
www.timebank.org.uk

Victim Support
020 7735 9166
www.victimsupport.org
Helps victims of crime

Voluntary Service Overseas
020 8780 7200
www.vso.org.uk

● Disability

Disability Rights Commission
0845 762 2633
www.drc-gb.org
Independent body established by statute

Action for Blind People
020 7635 4800
www.afbp.org
Press: 020 7635 4898

Afasic
020 7490 9410
www.afasic.org.uk
*For children and young adults with
communication impairments*

Christian Blind Mission
01223 484700
www.cbmuk.org.uk

Council for Disabled Children
020 7843 6000
www.ncb.org.uk

Dogs For the Disabled
0870 077 6600
www.dogsforthedisabled.org

Elizabeth Foundation for Pre-School Deaf Children
023 9237 2735
www.elizabeth-foundation.org

Employment Opportunities for People with Disabilities
020 7448 5420
www.opportunities.org.uk

Guide Dogs for the Blind
0118 983 5555
www.guidedogs.org.uk

Leonard Cheshire
020 7802 8200
www.leonard-cheshire.org
Creating opportunities with disabled people

Mencap
020 7454 0454
www.mencap.org.uk

Motability
01279 635999
www.motability.co.uk

National Autistic Society
020 7833 2299
www.nas.org.uk

National Deaf Children's Society
020 7490 8656
www.ndcs.org.uk

National Library for the Blind
0161 355 2000
www.nlb-online.org

Northern Counties School for the Deaf
0191 281 5821
www.northern-counties -school.co.uk

Physically Handicapped and Able Bodied Children
020 8667 9443
www.phabengland.org.uk

Riding for the Disabled
0845 658 1082
www.riding-for-disabled.org.uk

Royal National Institute of the Blind (RNIB)
020 7388 1266
www.rnib.org.uk

Royal National Institute for Deaf People (RNID)
020 7296 8000
www.rnid.org.uk

Royal Hospital for Neuro-disability
020 8780 4500
www.rhn.org.uk

Royal London Society for the Blind
01732 592500
www.rlsb.org.uk

Royal Star and Garter Home
020 8439 8000
www.starandgarter.org

St Dunstan's
020 7723 5021
www.st-dunstans.org.uk

Scope
020 7619 7100
www.scope.org.uk

Sense – National Deafblind and Rubella Association
020 7272 7774
www.sense.org.uk

Sightsavers
01444 446600
www.sightsavers.org.uk

The Shaw Trust
01225 716300
www.shaw-trust.org.uk
Provides training and work opportunities

United Response
020 8246 5200
www.unitedresponse.org.uk
Support for those with learning difficulties and mental health problems

West Midlands Special Needs Transport
0121 333 3107
www.ringandride.org.uk

Westminster Society for Mentally Handicapped Children and Adults
020 8968 7376
www.wspld.org.uk

WheelPower
01296 395995
www.wheelpower.org.uk

World Vision UK
01908 841000
www.worldvision.org.uk

● Diversity

Equal Opportunities Commission
0845 601 5901
www.eoc.org.uk

AGE

Age Concern England
020 8765 7200
www.ageconcern.org.uk

Age Positive
0113 232 4444
www.agepositive.gov.uk
Age diversity in employment
Press: 020 3267 5144

Help the Aged
020 7278 1114
www.helptheaged.org.uk

RACE

1990 Trust
020 7582 1990
www.blink.org.uk
Black community organisation

Black Enterprise
Helper@colourfulnetwork.net
www.blackenterprise.co.uk

Ethnic Minority Foundation
020 8432 0307
www.emf-cemvo.co.uk

SEXUALITY

Armed Forces Lesbian and Gay Association
0870 740 7755
www.aflaga.org.uk

Gay and Lesbian Association of Doctors and Dentists
0870 765 5606
www.gladd.org.uk

Lesbian and Gay Christian Movement
020 7739 1249
www.lgcm.org.uk
Press: 01633 215841

Lesbian and Gay Foundation
0161 235 8035
www.lgf.org.uk
Press: 0161 2358001

Metro Centre
020 8265 3311
www.metrocentreonline.org
Services for people questioning their sexuality

Outrage
020 8240 0222
outrage@blueyonder.co.uk
Direct action for gay rights

Queerspace
info@queerspace.org.uk
www.queerspace.org.uk
Northern Ireland

Stonewall
020 7593 1850
www.stonewall.org.uk

UK Lesbian and Gay Immigration Group
www.uklgig.org.uk

» *Diversity in the media*
see page 378

● Housing

Broadway
020 7089 9500
www.broadwaylondon.org
Working to house the homeless

Centrepoint
0845 466 3400
www.centrepoint.org.uk
Agency for young homeless

Chartered Institute of Housing
024 7685 1700
www.cih.org
Promoting high standards in housing provision

Connection at St Martin's
020 7766 5544
www.connection-at -stmartins.org.uk
Facilities for London's homeless

Crash
020 8742 0717
www.crash.org.uk
Construction and property industry homeless charity

Crisis
0870 011 3335
www.crisis.org.uk
Homeless charity

Defend Council Housing
020 7987 9989
www.defendcouncilhousing.org.uk

Empty Homes Agency
020 7828 6288
www.emptyhomes.com

FEANTSA
00 32 2 538 6669
www.feantsa.org
European federation of homeless organisations

Foyer Federation
020 7430 2212
www.foyer.net
Accommodation and opportunities for the young

Groundswell
020 7737 5500
www.groundswell.org.uk
Support projects for the homeless

Homeless Link
020 7960 3010
www.homeless.org.uk
UK membership network for homeless agencies

Homes for Homeless People
01582 481426/481484
www.homeline.dircon.co.uk

Housing Quality Network
01723 350099
www.hqnetwork.org.uk
Aims to improve quality of housing services

Joseph Rowntree Foundation
01904 629241
www.jrf.org.uk
Policy research and action on housing and social care

National Housing Federation
020 7067 1010
www.housing.org.uk
Representing the independent social housing sector

Paddington Churches Housing Association
020 8150 4200
www.pcha.org.uk
London housing association founded 1965

Peabody Trust
020 7021 4000
www.peabody.org.uk
London housing association

ROOMatRTPI
01789 763006
www.room.org.uk
Forum for debate on housing and regeneration issues

Rural Housing Trust
020 7793 8114
www.ruralhousing.org.uk
Affordable housing in English villages

Shelter
0845 458 4590
www.shelter.org.uk

Thames Reach Bondway
020 7702 4260
www.thamesreachbondway.com
London homeless charity
Press: 020 7702 5646

UK Co-Housing Network
johnston@garradhassan.com
www.cohousing.org.uk
Network of resident-developed neighbourhoods

● Immigration and refugees

Asylum Aid
020 7354 9631
www.asylumaid.org.uk

COSLA Refugee &Asylum Seekers Consortium
0141 248 2396
www.asylumscotland.org.uk

Immigration Advisory Service
020 7967 1200
www.iasuk.org

Immigration Law Practitioners' Association
020 7251 8383
www.ilpa.org.uk

Information Centre about Asylum & Refugees
020 7040 4596
www.icar.org.uk

Joint Council for the Welfare of Immigrants
020 7251 8708
www.jcwi.org.uk
Human rights for immigrants and asylum seekers in UK

Migration Research Unit
020 7679 7569
www.geog.ucl.ac.uk/mru

Refugee Action
020 7654 7700
www.refugee-action.org.uk

Refugee Council
020 7346 6700
www.refugeecouncil.org.uk

Scottish Refugee Council
0141 248 9799
www.scottishrefugeecouncil.org.uk

● Women

Abortion Rights
020 7923 9792
www.abortionrights.org.uk

Breast Cancer Campaign
020 7749 3700
www.bcc-uk.org

Breast Cancer Care
020 7384 2984
www.breastcancercare.org.uk

British Association of Women Entrepreneurs
01786 446044
www.bawe-uk.org

Campaign Against Domestic Violence
020 8520 5881
www.cadv.org.uk

Child and Woman Abuse Studies Unit
020 7133 5014
www.cwasu.org

Emily's List
contact@emilyslist.org.uk
www.emilyslist.org.uk
Campaign for Labour women MPs

European Women's Lobby
00 32 2 217 9020
www.womenlobby.org

Everywoman
0870 746 1800
www.everywoman.co.uk

The Fawcett Society
020 7253 2598
www.fawcettsociety.org.uk
Equality campaign

Justice for Women
0113 262 5101
www.jfw.org.uk

League of Jewish Women
020 7242 8300
www.theljw.org

Marie Stopes International
020 7574 7400
www.mariestopes.org.uk
Reproductive healthcare worldwide

Meet A Mum Association
0845 120 3746
www.mama.co.uk

National Association for Premenstrual Syndrome
0870 777 2178
www.pms.org.uk

National Council of Women
01325 367375
www.ncwgb.org

National Federation of Women's Institutes
020 7371 9300
www.womens-institute.co.uk

Older Feminist Network
020 8346 1900
www.ofn.org.uk

Rights of Women
020 7251 6575
www.row.org.uk

Scottish Women's Aid
0131 226 6606
www.scottishwomensaid.co.uk

Single Parent Action Network
0117 951 4231
www.spanuk.org.uk

Suzy Lamplugh Trust
020 7091 0014
www.suzylamplugh.org
Personal safety

Womankind Worldwide
020 7549 0360
www.womankind.org.uk

Women and Manual Trades
020 7251 9192
www.wamt.org

Women's Aid
0117 944 4411
www.womensaid.org.uk

Women's Aid, Ireland
028 2563 2136
www.womens-aid.org.uk

The Women's Library
020 7320 2222
www.thewomenslibrary.ac.uk

Women's Link
0800 652 3167
www.womenslink.org.uk
Women's National Commission
020 7944 0585
www.thewnc.org.uk
YWCA (London)
01865 304200
www.ywca-gb.org.uk

Useful Helplines

Afasic
0845 355 5577
Benefit Enquiry Line
0800 882200
Childline
0800 1111
Churches Child Protection Advisory Service
0845 120 4550
Deafblind UK
0800 132 320
Disability Living Allowance
0845 712 3456
Elder Abuse Response line
0808 808 8141
Gamblers Anonymous
0870 050 8880
Gingerbread Advice Line
0800 018 4318
Healthy Start
0845 607 6823
Kidscape
0845 120 5204
Learning Disability Helpline
0808 808 1111
National Missing Persons Helpline
0500 700700
NSPCC National Child Protection Helpline
0808 800 5000
Parent Line
0808 800 2222
Refugee Helpline
0800 413 848
Relate
0845 130 4016
Runaway Helpline
0808 800 7070
Samaritans
0845 790 9090
Saneline
0845 767 8000
Shelter London Line
0808 800 4444
Supportline for Survivors of Professional Abuse
0845 450 0300
Victim Supportline
0845 303 0900
Winter Warmth Advice Line
0800 085 7000
Women's Aid National Domestic Violence Helpline
0808 200 0247

Sport

Government department

Department for Culture, Media and Sport
020 7211 6200
www.culture.gov.uk
Press:
Sport, Lottery and Gambling
020 7211 6970
Culture 020 7211 6272
Tourism 020 7211 6271

Official bodies

UK Sport
020 7211 5100
www.uksport.gov.uk
Press: 020 7211 5106
Sport England
0845 850 8508
London: 020 7273 1963
East: 020 7273 1817
East Midlands: 020 7273 1751
North-east 020 7273 1691
North-west: 020 7273 1717
South-east: 020 7273 1921
South-west: 020 7273 1840
Yorkshire: 020 7273 1639
www.sportengland.org
Sport Scotland
0131 317 7200
Glenmore Lodge: 01479 861256
Cumbrae: 01475 530757
Inverclyde: 01475 674666
www.sportscotland.org.uk
Press: 0131 472 3309
Sports Council for Northern Ireland
028 9038 1222
www.sportni.net
Sports Council for Wales
0845 045 0904
www.sports-council-wales.co.uk

Olympics and Paralympics

London 2012
020 3201 2000
www.london2012.com
Press: 020 8211 6145
British Olympic Association
020 8871 2677
www.olympics.org.uk
Press: 020 8871 2677 x233
British Paralympic Association
020 7211 5222
www.paralympics.org.uk
Press: 020 72115240
International Olympic Committee
00 41 21 621 6111
www.olympic.org
International Paralympic Committee
00 49 228 209 7200
www.paralympic.org

Football

● Governing bodies

Fifa
00 41 222 7777
www.fifa.com
Deutsche Fussball-Bund (German FA)
00 49 69 67880
www.dfb.de
UEFA
00 41 0848 00 2727
www.uefa.com
Press: 00 41 0848 04 2727
Euro 2008, Austria and Switzerland
00 41 848 002008
Press: 00 41 22 707 2002
FA
020 7745 4545
www.thefa.com
Press: 020 7745 4720
Women's Football
www.thefa.com/womens
FA Premier League
020 7864 9000
www.premierleague.com
Press: 020 7864 9190
Football League
020 7864 9000
www.football-league.co.uk
Press: 020 7864 9190
Nationwide Conference
conference@fastwebmedia.co.uk
www.footballconference.co.uk
Press: pressoffice@
footballconference.co.uk
Irish Football Association
028 9066 9458
www.irishfa.com
Scottish Football Association
0141 616 6000
www.scottishfa.co.uk
Football Association of Wales
029 2043 5830
www.faw.org.uk

● National stadiums

Millennium Stadium, Cardiff
0870 558 2582
www.millenniumstadium.com
Wembley Stadium
0844 980 8001
www.wembleystadium.com

● Premiership 2007–08

Arsenal FC
020 7704 4000
www.arsenal.com
Press: 020 7704 4010
Aston Villa FC
0121 327 2299
www.avfc.co.uk
Press: 0121 326 1561
Birmingham City FC
0871 226 1875
www.blues.premiumtv.co.uk
Press: 0121 244 1501
Blackburn Rovers FC
0870 111 3232
www.rovers.co.uk
Press: 01254 296171
Bolton Wanderers FC
01204 673673
www.bwfc.co.uk
Press: 01204 673675
Chelsea FC
0870 300 1212
www.chelseafc.co.uk
Press: 020 7957 8285
Derby County FC
01332 202202
www.dcfc.co.uk
Press: 01332 667553
Everton FC
0151 330 2200
www.evertonfc.com
Press: 0151 330 2278
Fulham FC
0870 442 1222
www.fulham-fc.co.uk
Press: 020 8336 7510
Liverpool FC
0151 263 2361
www.liverpoolfc.net
Press: 0151 230 5721
Manchester City FC
0161 231 3200
www.mcfc.co.uk
Press: 0161 438 7631
Manchester United FC
0161 868 8000
www.manutd.com
Press: 0161 868 8720
Middlesbrough FC
0870 421 1986
www.mfc.co.uk
Press: 01325 729916
Newcastle United FC
0191 201 8400
www.nufc.co.uk
Press: 0191 201 8420
Portsmouth FC
023 9273 1204
www.pompeyfc.co.uk
Reading FC
0118 968 1100
www.readingfc.co.uk

Sunderland FC
0191 551 5000
www.safc.com
Press: 0191 551 5060

Tottenham Hotspur FC
0870 420 5000
www.spurs.co.uk
Press: 020 8506 9043

West Ham United FC
020 8548 2748
www.whufc.co.uk

Wigan Athletic FC
01942 774000
www.wiganathletic.tv
Press: 01942 770411

● Coca-Cola Football League Championship

Barnsley FC
01226 211211
www.barnsleyfc.co.uk

Burnley FC
0870 443 1882
www.burnleyfootballclub.com

Cardiff City FC
029 2022 1001
www.cardiffcityfc.co.uk

Charlton AFC
020 8333 4000
www.cafc.co.uk

Colchester United FC
01206 508800
www.cu-fc.com

Coventry City FC
0870 421 1987
www.ccfc.co.uk

Crystal Palace FC
020 8768 6000
www.cpfc.co.uk

Hull City FC
0870 837 0003
www.hullcityafc.net

Ipswich Town FC
01473 400500
www.itfc.co.uk

Leicester City FC
0870 040 6000
www.lcfc.co.uk

Norwich City FC
01603 760760
www.canaries.co.uk

Plymouth Argyle FC
01752 562561
www.pafc.co.uk

Preston North End FC
0870 442 1964
www.pnefc.net

Queens Park Rangers FC
020 8743 0262
www.qpr.co.uk

Scunthorpe United FC
0871 221 1899
www.scunthorpe-united.co.uk

Southampton FC
0845 688 9448
www.saintsfc.co.uk

Stoke City FC
0871 663 2008
www.stokecityfc.premiumtv.co.uk

Watford FC
0870 111 1181
www.watfordfc.co.uk

Wolverhampton Wanderers FC
0870 442 0123
www.wolves.co.uk

● Coca-Cola League One

AFC Bournemouth
01202 726300
www.afcb.co.uk

Blackpool FC
0870 443 1953
www.blackpoolfc.co.uk

Brentford FC
0845 345 6442
www.brentfordfc.co.uk

Brighton and Hove Albion FC
01273 695400
www.seagulls.co.uk

Carlisle United FC
01228 526237
www.carlisleunited.premiumtv.co.uk

Cheltenham Town FC
01242 573558
www.ctfc.com

Crewe Alexandra FC
01270 213014
www.crewealex.net

Doncaster Rovers FC
01302 764664
www.doncasterroversfc.co.uk

Gillingham FC
01634 300000
www.gillinghamfootballclub.com

Hartlepool United
01429 272584
www.hartlepoolunited.co.uk

Huddersfield Town FC
01484 484100
www.htafc.com

Leeds United
0113 367 6000
www.leedsunited.com

Leyton Orient FC
020 8926 1111
www.leytonorient.net

Millwall FC
020 723 21222
www.millwallfc.co.uk

Northampton Town FC
01604 757773
www.ntfc.co.uk

Nottingham Forest FC
0115 982 4444
www.nottinghamforest.co.uk

Oldham Athletic FC
08712 262235
www.oldhamathletic.co.uk

Port Vale FC
01782 655800
www.port-vale.co.uk

Southend United
01702 304050
www.southendunited.co.uk

Swansea City FC
01792 616600
www.swanseacity.net

Tranmere Rovers FC
0151 609 3333
www.tranmererovers.co.uk

Wallsall FC
0871 221 0442
www.saddlers.co.uk

Yeovil Town FC
01935 423662
www.ytfc.net

● Coca-Cola League Two

Accrington Stanley FC
01254 356950
www.accringtonstanley.co.uk

Barnet FC
020 8441 6932
www.barnetfc.premiumtv.co.uk

Bradford City FC
01274 773355
www.bradfordcityfc.co.uk

Bury FC
0161 764 4881
www.buryfc.co.uk

Chester City FC
01244 371376
www.chestercityfc.net

Chesterfield FC
01246 209765
www.chesterfield-fc.co.uk

Dagenham and Redbridge FC
020 8592 1549
www.daggers.co.uk

Darlington FC
01325 387000
www.darlington-fc.net

Grimsby Town FC
01472 605050
www.gtfc.co.uk

Hereford United FC
01432 276666
www.herefordunited.co.uk

Lincoln City FC
0870 899 2005
www.redimps.com

Macclesfield Town FC
01625 264686
www.mtfc.co.uk

Mansfield Town FC
0870 756 3160
www.mansfieldtown.net

Milton Keynes Dons FC
01908 607090
www.mkdons.com

Morecambe FC
01524 411797
www.morecambefc.com

Notts County FC
0115 952 9000
www.nottscountyfc.co.uk

Peterborough United FC
01733 563947
www.theposh.com

Rochdale FC
01706 644648
www.rochdaleafc.co.uk

Rotherham FC
01709 512434
www.themillers.co.uk

Shrewsbury Town FC
01743 360111
www.shrewsburytown.co.uk

Stockport County FC
0161 286 8888
www.stockportcounty.com

Wrexham AFC
01978 262129
www.wrexhamafc.co.uk

Wycombe Wanderers FC
01494 472100
www.wycombewanderers.co.uk

● Scottish premier league

Aberdeen FC
01224 650400
www.afc.co.uk
Press: 01224 650406

Celtic FC
0845 226 1888
www.celticfc.co.uk
Press: 0141 551 4276

Dundee United FC
01382 833166
www.dundeeunitedfc.co.uk

Falkirk FC
01324 624121
www.falkirkfc.co.uk

Gretna
01461 337602
www.gretnafootballclub.co.uk

Hearts of Midlothian FC
0131 200 7200
www.heartsfc.co.uk

Hibernian FC
0131 661 2159
www.hibernianfc.co.uk

Inverness Caledonian Thistle FC
01463 222880
www.caleythistleonline.com

Kilmarnock FC
01563 545300
www.kilmarnockfc.co.uk

Motherwell FC
01698 333333
www.motherwellfc.co.uk

Rangers FC
0870 600 1972
www.rangers.co.uk

St Mirren FC
0141 889 2558
www.saintmirren.net

● Football: other bodies

Professional Footballers' Association
0161 236 0575
www.givemefootball.com

Referees Association
024 7660 1701
www.footballreferee.org

Football Supporters' Federation
0191 567 9100
www.fsf.org.uk

Kick It Out
020 7684 4884
www.kickitout.org
Football's anti-racism campaign

Show Racism the Red Card
0191 291 0160
www.srtrc.org

Supporters Direct
0870 160 0123
www.supporters-direct.org

Other sports

AMERICAN FOOTBALL

British American Football Association
01661 843179
www.bafa.org.uk

ANGLING

National Federation of Anglers
0115 981 3535
www.nfadirect.com

National Federation of Sea Anglers
01364 644643
www.nfsa.org.uk

Salmon and Trout Association
020 7283 5838
www.salmon-trout.org

ARCHERY

The Grand National Archery Society
01952 677888
www.gnas.org

ATHLETICS

British Athletics
0161 406 6320
www.britishathletics.info

International Association of Athletics Federations
00 377 9310 8888
www.iaaf.org

BADMINTON

Badminton Association of England
01908 268400
www.baofe.co.uk

Welsh Badminton Union
029 2049 7225
www.welshbadminton.net

Scottish Badminton Union
0141 445 1218
www.scotbadminton.demon.co.uk

Badminton Union of Ireland
00 353 1 839 3028
www.badmintonireland.com

BALLOONING

British Balloon & Airship Club
0117 953 1231
www.bbac.org

BASEBALL

British Baseball Federation
020 7453 7055
www.baseballsoftballuk.com

BASKETBALL

English Basketball Association
0870 774 4229
www.englandbasketball.co.uk

Basketball Association of Wales
01443 771576
www.basketballwales.com

Basketball Scotland
0131 317 7260
www.basketball-scotland.com

BIATHLON

British Biathlon Union
01874 730562
www.britishbiathlon.com

BOBSLEIGH

British Bobsleigh Association
01225 386802
www.british-bobsleigh.com

BOWLING

English Bowling Association
01903 820222
www.bowlsengland.com

Welsh Bowling Association
www.welshbowlingassociation
.co.uk

Scottish Bowling Association
01292 294623
www.scottish-bowling.co.uk

Irish Bowling Association
028 2827 0008
www.bowlsireland.com

BOXING

Amateur Boxing Association of England
0114 223 5654
www.abae.co.uk

Amateur Boxing Scotland
07900 003206
www.garnockboxing.com

British Boxing Board of Control
029 2036 7000
www.bbbofc.com

International Boxing Federation
001 973 414 0300
www.ibf-usba-boxing.com

Irish Amateur Boxing Association
00 353 1 453 3371
www.iaba.ie

World Boxing Association (Venezuela)
00 58 244 663 1584
www.wbaonline.com

World Boxing Organisation
001 787 765 4444
www.wbo-int.com

CANOEING

British Canoe Union
0845 370 9500
www.bcu.org.uk

CAVING

British Caving Association
www.british-caving.org.uk

CRICKET

England and Wales Cricket Board
020 7432 1200
www.ecb.co.uk

Cricket Scotland
0131 313 7420
www.cricketscotland

Marylebone Cricket Club (Lord's)
020 7616 8500
www.lords.org.uk

CROQUET

Croquet Association
01242 242318
www.croquet.org.uk

CURLING

British Curling Association
01234 315174
www.britishcurlingassociation
.org.uk

Royal Caledonian Curling Club
0131 333 3003
www.royalcaledoniancurlingclub
.org

CYCLING

British Cycling Federation
0870 871 2000
www.bcf.uk.com

EQUESTRIANISM

British Equestrian Federation
024 7669 8871
www.bef.co.uk

British Show Jumping Association
024 7669 8800
www.bsja.co.uk

FENCING

British Fencing Association
020 8742 3032
www.britishfencing.com

GOLF

English Golf Union
01526 354500
www.englishgolfunion.org

Welsh Golfing Union
01633 436040
www.welshgolf.org

Scottish Golf Union
01382 549500
www.scottishgolfunion.org

Golfing Union of Ireland, Ulster branch
00 353 1 505 4000
www.gui.ie

Ladies Golf Union
01334 475811
www.lgu.org

R&A, St Andrews
01334 460000
www.randa.org
Open Championship
www.opengolf.com
St Andrews Links
01334 466666
www.standrews.org.uk

GYMNASTICS

British Gymnastics
01952 820330
www.baga.co.uk

HANDBALL

England Handball
01706 229354
www.englandhandball.com

HOCKEY

English Hockey Association
01908 544644
www.englandhockey.co.uk

Welsh Hockey Union
029 2057 3940
www.welsh-hockey.co.uk

Scottish Hockey Union
0131 453 9070
www.scottish-hockey.org.uk

Irish Hockey Assoc
00 353 1 260 0028
www.hockey.ie

HORSE RACING

The Horse Racing Association
020 7189 3800
www.thehra.org

Ascot
0870 727 4321
www.ascot.co.uk

Aintree (Grand National)
0151 523 2600
www.aintree.co.uk

Epsom (Derby)
01372 726311
www.epsomderby.co.uk

ICE HOCKEY

Ice Hockey UK
07713 590506
www.icehockeyuk.co.uk

ICE SKATING

National Ice Skating Association of UK
0115 988 8060
www.iceskating.org.uk

MARTIAL ARTS

British Aikido Board
020 8304 8430
www.aikido-baa.org.uk

British Ju-Jitsu Association
01254 396806
www.bjjagb.com

British Judo Association
01509 631670
www.britishjudo.org.uk

British Kendo Association
president@kendo.org.uk
www.kendo.org.uk

English Karate Governing Body
01628 487555
www.ekgb.org.uk

Tae Kwon-Do Association of Great Britain
0800 052 5960
www.tagb.biz

KORFBALL

British Korfball Association
chairman@korfball.co.uk
www.korfball.co.uk

LACROSSE

English Lacrosse Association
0161 227 3626
www.englishlacrosse.co.uk

LUGE

Great Britain Luge Association
01684 576604
www.gbla.org.uk

MODERN PENTATHLON

Modern Pentathlon Association of Great Britain
01225 386808
www.mpagb.org.uk

MOTOR SPORTS

Auto-Cycle Union
01788 566400
www.acu.org.uk

Federation Internationale de L'Automobile (FIA)
00 33 1 4312 4455
www.fia.com

Royal Automobile Club Motor Sports Association
01753 765000
www.msauk.org

MOUNTAINEERING

British Mountaineering Council
0870 010 4878
www.thebmc.co.uk

NETBALL

All England Netball Association
01462 442344
www.england-netball.co.uk

Welsh Netball Association
029 2023 7048
www.welshnetball.co.uk

Netball Scotland
0141 572 0114
www.netballscotland.com

ORIENTEERING

British Orienteering Federation
01629 734042
www.britishorienteering.org.uk

PARACHUTING

British Parachute Association
0116 278 5271
www.bpa.org.uk

PETANQUE

British Petanque Association
www.britishpetanque.org.uk

POLO

Hurlingham Polo Association
01367 242828
www.hpa-polo.co.uk

POOL

English Pool Association
07726 846 839
www.epa.org.uk

ROUNDERS

National Rounders Association
0114 248 0357
www.nra-rounders.co.uk

ROWING

Amateur Rowing Association
0870 060 7100
www.ara-rowing.org

RUGBY

The Rugby Football League
0844 477 7113
www.rfl.uk.com

British Amateur Rugby League Association
01484 544131
www.barla.org.uk

Rugby Football Union
020 8892 2000
www.rfu.com

Welsh Rugby Union
0870 013 8600
www.wru.co.uk

Scottish Rugby Union
0131 346 5000
www.sru.org.uk

Irish Rugby Union
00 353 1 647 3800
www.irishrugby.ie

Rugby Football Union for Women
020 8831 7996
www.rfu-women.co.uk

SAILING

Royal Yachting Association
0845 345 0400
www.rya.org.uk

SCUBA DIVING

British Sub-Aqua Club
0151 350 6200
www.bsac.com

SHOOTING

Great Britain Target Shooting Federation
01483 486948
www.gbtsf-worldclass.co.uk

SKIING AND SNOWBOARDING

British Ski & Snowboard Federation
0131 445 7676
www.snowsportgb.com

Snowsport Scotland
0131 445 4151
www.snowsportscotland.org

SOFTBALL

British Softball Federation
020 7453 7055
www.baseballsoftballuk.com

SQUASH

England Squash
0161 231 4499
www.englandsquash.com

Scottish Squash
0131 317 7343
www.scottishsquash.org

Squash Wales
01633 682108
www.squashwales.co.uk

Ulster Squash
028 9038 1222
www.ulstersquash.com

SURFING

British Surfing Association
01637 876474
www.britsurf.co.uk

SWIMMING

Amateur Swimming Federation of Great Britain
01509 618700
www.britishswimming.org

TABLE TENNIS

English Table Tennis Association
01424 722525
www.englishtabletennis.org.uk

TENNIS

Lawn Tennis Association
020 8487 7000
www.lta.org.uk

Tennis and Rackets Association
020 8333 4267
www.irtpa.com

TENPIN BOWLING

British Tenpin Bowling Association
020 8478 1745
www.btba.org.uk

TRIATHLON

British Triathlon Association
01509 226161
www.britishtriathlon.org

VOLLEYBALL

English Volleyball Association
01509 631699
www.volleyballengland.org

WATER SKIING

British Water Ski Federation
01932 570885
www.britishwaterski.co.uk

WEIGHTLIFTING

British Weight Lifting Association
01952 604201
www.bawla.com

WRESTLING

British Amateur Wrestling Association
01246 236443
www.britishwrestling.org

YOGA

British Wheel of Yoga
01529 306851
www.bwy.org.uk

Institutes of sport

English Institute of Sport
0870 759 0400
www.eis2win.co.uk
Press: 07866 495872

Scottish Institute of Sport
01786 460100
www.sisport.com
Press: 01786 460119

National sports centres

Bisham Abbey, Bucks
01628 476911
www.bishamabbeynsc.co.uk

Crystal Palace, South London
020 8778 0131

Cumbrae, Ayrshire
01475 530757

Glenmore Lodge, Aviemore
01479 861256
www.glenmorelodge.org.uk

Inverclyde, Largs
01475 674666
www.nationalcentreinverclyde
.org.uk

Lilleshall, Shropshire
01952 603003
www.lilleshallnsc.co.uk

National Water Sports Centre — Holme Pierrepont, Nottinghamshire
0115 982 1212
www.nationalsportscentres.co.uk

Plas Menai, Gwynedd
01248 673943
www.plasmenai.co.uk

Plas y Brenin, Conwy
01690 720214
www.pyb.co.uk

Tollymore, County Down
028 4372 2158
www.tollymore.com

Welsh Institute, Cardiff
0845 045 0902
www.welsh-institute-sport.co.uk

Sport and disability

British Amputee and Les Autres Sports Association
01773 7159847

British Blind Sport
0870 078 9000
www.britishblindsport.org.uk

British Deaf Sports Council
Fax: 01268 510621
www.britishdeafsportscouncil
.org.uk

Wheelpower British Wheelchair Sports
01296 395995
www.wheelpower.org.uk

Sports and education

British Universities Sports Association
020 7633 5080
www.busa.org.uk

Central Council of Physical Recreation
020 7854 8500
www.ccpr.org.uk

National Council for School Sport
0115 923 1229
www.yst.org.uk/ncss

Physical Education Association of UK
0118 931 6240
www.pea.uk.com

Youth Sport Trust
01509 226600
www.youthsporttrust.org

Other bodies

The Big Lottery Fund
0845 410 2030
www.biglotteryfund.org.uk

Sports Aid Foundation
020 7273 1975
www.sportsaid.org.uk

Sports Coach UK
0113 274 4802
www.sportscoachuk.org

Women's Sports Foundation
020 7273 1740
www.wsf.org.uk

Travel

Department for Transport
020 7944 8300
www.dft.gov.uk
Press:
roads: 020 7944 3066
marine, aviation: 020 7944 3232
railways: 020 7944 3248
Commission for Integrated Transport
cfit@dft.gsi.gov.uk
www.cfit.gov.uk

Urban Transport

● London

Transport for London
020 7222 5600
www.tfl.gov.uk/tfl
Press: 0845 600 4141
Congestion charging
0845 900 1234
www.cclondon.com
London Buses
0845 300 7000
www.tfl.gov.uk/buses
London River Services
020 7941 2400
www.tfl.gov.uk/river
London Underground
020 7222 5600
www.tube.tfl.gov.uk
Docklands Light Rail
020 7363 9700
www.tfl.gov.uk/dlr
London Cycling Campaign
020 7234 9310
www.lcc.org.uk
London Travel Watch
020 7505 9000
www.londontravelwatch.org.uk
Press: 020 7726 9953

● The regions

Centro
0121 200 2787
www.centro.org.uk
West Midlands
Press: 0121 214 7073
GMPTE
0161 242 6000
www.gmpte.gov.uk
Greater Manchester
Press: 0161 244 1055
Merseytravel
0151 227 5181
www.merseytravel.gov.uk
Merseyside
Press: 0151 330 1151
Metro
0113 251 7272
www.wymetro.com
West Yorkshire
Press: 0113 251 7213

Nexus
0191 203 3333
www.nexus.org.uk
Tyne & Wear
Press: 0191 203 3112
South Yorkshire
0114 276 7575
www.sypte.co.uk
Press: 0114 221 1335
Strathclyde
0141 332 6811
www.spt.co.uk
Press: 0141 333 3282
Passenger Transport Executive Group
0113 251 7204
www.pteg.net
Association of all seven passenger transport executives
Press: 0113 251 7445

Rail

● Rail companies

Network Rail
020 7557 8000
www.networkrail.co.uk
Infrastructure operator
National press: 020 7557 8292/3
London and south-east:
020 7094 43411/4380
Midlands: 0121 345 3100
North-east: 01904 383180
North-west: 0161 261 6093
Scotland: 0141 555 4109
Wales and West Country:
01793 515267
Arriva Trains Wales
0845 6061 660
www.arrivatrainswales.co.uk
Press: 029 2072 0522
C2C
0845 601 4873
www.c2c-online.co.uk
Press: 020 7713 2168
Central Trains
0121 634 2040
www.centraltrains.co.uk
Press: 0121 654 1278
Chiltern Railways
0845 600 5165
www.chilternrailways.co.uk
Press: 020 7282 2930
English Welsh & Scottish Railways
0870 140 5000
www.ews-railway.co.uk
First Capital Connect
0845 026 4700
www.firstcapitalconnect.co.uk
Press: 0845 470 0789
First Great Western Link
0845 700 0125
www.firstgreatwesternlink.co.uk
Press: 01793 499499

First Scotrail
0845 601 5929
www.firstgroup.com
Press: 0141 335 4788
Freightliner
020 7200 3974
www.freightliner.co.uk
Press: 020 7200 3900/2
Gatwick Express
0845 850 1530
www.gatwickexpress.co.uk
Press: 020 8750 6622
GNER
0845 722 5225
www.gner.co.uk
Press: 01904 523072
Heathrow Express
0845 600 1515
www.heathrowexpress.co.uk
Press: 020 8750 6680
Hull Trains
0845 071 0222
www.hulltrains.co.uk
Press: 01482 867867
Island Line
01983 812591
www.island-line.co.uk
One
0845 600 7245
www.onerailway.com
Press: 01206 363947/8/9
Midland Mainline
0845 722 1125
www.midlandmainline.com
Press: 01332 262010
Northern Rail
0845 000 0125
www.northernrail.org
Press: 01904 568670
Silverlink
0845 601 4867/8
www.silverlink-trains.com
Press: 020 7713 2168
Southern
0845 127 2920
www.southcentraltrains.co.uk
Press: 020 8929 8673
South West Trains
0845 600 0650
www.swtrains.co.uk
Press: 020 7620 5229
Translink
028 9066 6630
www.translink.co.uk
Press: 028 9089 9455
Virgin Trains
0870 789 1234
www.virgintrains.co.uk
Press: 0870 789 1111

Overseas rail travel

EuRail
www.eurail.com
Press: 00 31 30 750 83 92

Eurostar
01777 777879
www.eurostar.com
Press: 020 7922 6030/4494

Rail Europe
0870 584 8848
www.raileurope.co.uk
Main distributor of continental rail travel in the UK; including Eurostar, Inter-Rail, Snow Trains, French Motorail and TGV
Press: 01732 526729/14

Rail associations

Association of Train Operating Companies
020 7841 8000
www.atoc.org
Trade association
Press: 020 7841 8020

National Rail Enquiries
0845 748 4950
www.nationalrail.co.uk

Passenger Focus
0845 302 2022
www.railpassengers.org.uk

General Consumer Council Northern Ireland
028 9067 2488
www.gccni.org.uk

Government and agencies

Health and Safety Executive: railways
020 7717 6533
www.hse.gov.uk/railways

Office of the Rail Regulator
020 7282 2000
www.rail-reg.gov.uk
library: 020 7282 2001

Rail Safety and Standards Board
020 7904 7777
www.railwaysafety.org.uk

Air Travel

Airports

BAA
020 8745 9800
www.baa.co.uk
Operates UK's biggest airports
Press: 0870 000 0123

London City
020 7646 0088
www.londoncityairport.com
Press: 020 7646 0054

London Gatwick
0870 000 2468
www.baa.co.uk/main/airports /gatwick
Press: 01293 505000

London Heathrow
0870 000 0123
www.baa.com/main/airports /heathrow
Press: 020 8745 7224

London Heliport (Battersea)
020 7228 0181/2
www.weston-aviation.com

London Luton
01582 405100
www.london-luton.co.uk
Press: 01582 395119

London Stansted
0870 000 0303
www.baa.com/main/airports /stansted
Press: 01279 680534

Aberdeen
0870 040 0006
www.aberdeenairport.com
Press: 0131 272 2111

Alderney
01481 822624
www.alderney.gov.gg/index .php/pid/40

Barrra
01871 890212
www.hial.co.uk/barra-airport.html

Belfast International Airport (Aldergrove)
028 9448 4848
www.belfastairport.com
Press: 07766 475453

Benbecula
01870 602051
www.hial.co.uk/benbecula-airport .html

Biggin Hill
01959 578500
www.bigginhillairport.com

Birmingham
0870 733 5511
www.bhx.co.uk
Press: 0121 767 7074

Blackpool
0870 027 3777
www.blackpoolairport.com

Bournemouth
01202 364000
www.bournemouthairport.com
Press: 0845 108 8542

Bristol
0870 121 2747
www.bristolairport.co.uk

RAF Brize Norton
01993 842551
www.raf.mod.uk/rafbrizenorton

Cambridge City Airport
01223 373765
www.cambridgecityairport.com

Campbeltown
01586 553797
www.hial.co.uk/campbeltown -airport.html

Cardiff International Airport
01446 711111
www.cial.co.uk

Carlisle
01228 573641
www.carlisleairport.co.uk

Coventry
024 7630 8600
www.coventryairport.co.uk

RNAS Culdrose
01326 574121
www.royal-navy.mod.uk

Doncaster Sheffield Robin Hood Airport
0870 833 2210
www.robinhoodairport.com

Dundee
01382 662200
www.dundeecity.gov.uk/airport

East Midlands
0871 919 9000
www.eastmidlandsairport.com
Press: 0845 108 8542

Edinburgh
0870 040 0007
www.edinburghairport.com
Press: 0131 272 2111

Exeter
01392 367433
www.exeter-airport.co.uk
Press: 01392 354945

George Best Belfast (City)
028 9093 9093
www.belfastcityairport.com
Press: 028 9448 4035

Glasgow
0870 040 0008
www.glasgowairport.com
Press: 0131 272 2111

Gloucester
01452 857700
www.gloucestershireairport.co.uk

Guernsey
01481 237766
www.guernsey-airport.gov.gg

Inverness
01667 464000
www.hial.co.uk/inverness -airport.html

Islay
01496 302361
www.hial.co.uk/islay-airport.html

Isle of Man (Ronaldsway)
01624 821600
www.iom-airport.com

Jersey
01534 492000
www.jersey-airport.com

Kent International, Manston
01843 823600
www.kia-m.com

Lands End
01736 788771

Leeds Bradford International Airport
0113 250 9696
www.lbia.co.uk
Press: 0113 391 3333

Liverpool John Lennon Airport
0870 750 8484
www.liverpooljohnlennonairport
.com
Press: 0151 907 1622

London Ashford Airport
01797 322411
www.lydd-airport.co.uk

Manchester
0161 489 3000
www.manairport.co.uk
Press: 0871 882 1121

Newcastle
0870 122 1488
www.newcastleairport.com
Press: 0191 214 3568

Newquay Cornwall Airport
01637 860600
www.newquayairport.com

Norwich
01603 411923
www.norwichairport.co.uk

Orkney (Kirkwall)
01856 886210
www.hial.co.uk/kirkwall-
airport.html

Penzance Heliport
01736 363871
www.islesofscillyhelicopter.com

Plymouth City Airport
01752 204090
www.plymouthairport.com
Press: 01872 276276

Prestwick
0871 223 0700
www.gpia.co.uk

St Mary's, Isles of Scilly
01720 422677

Sheffield City Airport
0114 201 1998
www.sheffieldcityairport.com

Shetland
01950 461000

Shoreham (Brighton City)
01273 467373
www.shorehamairport.co.uk

Southampton
0870 040 0009
www.southamptonairport.com
Press: 023 8062 7141

Southend
01702 608100
www.southendairport.net

Stornoway
01851 707400
www.hial.co.uk/stornoway
-airport.html

Sumburgh
01950 461000
www.hial.co.uk/sumburgh
-airport.html

Teesside
01325 332811
www.teessideairport.com

Tiree
01879 220456
www.hial.co.uk/tiree-airport.html

Tresco Heliport
01720 422970
www.tresco.co.uk

Wick
01955 602215
www.hial.co.uk/wick-airport.html

● Airlines

Aer Lingus
00 353 818 365 044
www.aerlingus.ie
Press: 00 353 1 886 3420

Aeroflot
001 212 944 2300
www.aeroflot.com

Air Berlin
0870 738 8880
www.airberlin.com
Press: 00 49 30 3434 1510

Air Canada
0871 220 1111
www.aircanada.ca

Air France
0870 142 4343
www.airfrance.com
Press: mail.mediarelations.gbi@
airfrance.fr

Air India
020 7495 7950
www.airindia.com

Air Malta
00 356 22 999 208
www.airmalta.com

Air New Zealand
0800 028 4149
www.airnewzealand.com

Air Seychelles
01293 596656
www.airseychelles.net

Ajet
00 357 24 815 735
www.ajet.com

Alitalia
020 8814 7700
www.alitalia.com

Alaska Airlines
01992 441517
www.alaskaair.com

America West Airlines
001 480 693 0800
www.americawest.com
Press: 001 480 693 5729

American Airlines
0845 778 9789
www.aa.com
Press: 020 8577 4804

ANA Europe
0870 837 8866
www.anaskyweb.com

ATA
001 800 435 9282
www.ata.com

Austrian Airlines
020 7766 0300
www.aua.com

Avianca (Colombia)
0870 576 7747
www.avianca.com

British Airways
0870 850 9850
www.british-airways.com
Press: 020 8738 5100

BMI (British Midland)
01332 854000
www.britishmidland.com
Press: 01332 854687

Cathay Pacific
020 8834 8888
www.cathaypacific.com
Press: 020 8834 8800

China Airlines
020 7436 9001
www.china-airlines.com

Continental Airlines
www.continental.com

Cyprus Airways
020 8359 1333
www.cyprusair.com
Press: 020 8359 1366

Delta Express
001 404 715 2600
www.delta.com

EasyJet
0871 244 2366
www.easyjet.com
Press: 01582 525252

El Al Israel Airlines
020 7121 1450
www.elal.com
Press: 020 7121 1455

Emirates
0870 243 2222
www.emirates.com
Press: 020 7861 2424

Finnair
0870 241 4411
www.finnair.com

Flybe
01392 366669
www.flybe.com
Press: 0845 675 0681

Flyglobespan
0871 271 0515
www.flyglobespan.com

GB Airways
01293 664239
www.gbairways.com
Press: 01293 664000

Germanwings
0870 252 1250
www.germanwings.com
Press: presse@germanwings.com

Gulf Air
0870 777 1717
www.gulfairco.com

HLX (Hapag-Lloyd Express)
0870 606 0519
www.hlx.com

Iberia
0870 609 0500
www.iberia.com

Icelandair
0870 787 4020
www.icelandair.net
Press: 020 7874 1007

Japan Airlines
0845 774 7700
www.jal.com

JAT – Yugoslav Airlines
020 7629 2007
www.jat.com

Jet 2
0871 226 1737
www.jet2.com

Kenya Airways
01784 888222
www.kenya-airways.com

KLM Royal Dutch
0870 243 0541
www.klm.com

Kuwait Airways
020 7412 0006
www.kuwait-airways.com

LanChile
0800 917 0572
www.lan.com

LOT — Polish Airlines
0870 414 0088
www.lot.com

Lufthansa
0870 837 7747
www.lufthansa.com
Press: 020 8750 3415

Malaysia Airlines
020 7341 2000
www.malaysia-airlines.com

Monarch
01582 400000
www.monarch-airlines.com
Press: 01582 398146

Olympic Airways
0870 606 0460
www.olympic-airways.gr
Press: 00 30 210 926 7251

Portugalia Airlines
0161 250 0385
www.pga.pt

Qantas Airways
0845 774 7767
www.qantas.com.au
Press: 020 8846 0501

Royal Air Maroc
020 7307 5800
www.royalairmaroc.com

Royal Jordanian Airlines
020 7878 6300
www.rja.com.jo
Press: 020 7878 6337

RyanAir
0871 246 0000
www.ryanair.co.uk
Press: 00 353 181 21212

SAS Scandinavian Airlines
00 46 8 797 0000
www.scandinavian.net
Press: 00 46 70 997 4893

Saudi Arabian Airlines
020 7798 9898
www.saudiairlines.com

Singapore Airlines
0844 800 2380
www.singaporeair.com
Press: 020 8563 6788/41

Sky Europe
0905 722 2747
www.skyeurope.com

South African Airways
020 8897 3645
www.flysaa.com

Sri Lankan Airlines
020 8538 2001
www.srilankan.aero

Swiss
0845 758 1333
www.swiss.com

TAP Air Portugal
0870 607 2024
www.tap.pt
Press: 00 351 21 841 5000

Thai Airways
020 7491 7953
www.thaiairways.com
Press: 020 7907 9524

Transavia
020 7365 4997
www.transavia.com

United Airlines
0845 844 4777
www.ual.com
Press: 020 8276 6800

Varig – Brazilian Airlines
www.varig.co.uk

Virgin Atlantic
01293 562345
www.virgin-atlantic.com
Press: 01293 747373

Volare
00 380 44 537 52 96
www.volare.kiev.ua

Wizz Air
00 48 22 351 9499
www.wizzair.com

Yemen Airways
020 8759 0385
www.yemenairways.co.uk

● Air associations
  and authorities

Air Accidents Investigation Branch
01252 510300
24-hour accident reporting line:
01252 512299
www.aaib.dft.gov.uk

Air Transport Users Council
020 7240 6061
www.auc.org.uk

Airport Operators Association
020 7222 2249
www.aoa.org.uk

British Airline Pilots Association
020 8476 4000
www.balpa.org
Press: 020 7924 7555

Civil Aviation Authority
020 7379 7311
www.caa.co.uk
Regulator

International Air Transport Association
www.iata.org

National Air Traffic Services
020 7309 8666
www.nats.co.uk
Press: 01489 615945

Water Travel

● Ports

Aberdeen
01224 597000
www.aberdeen-harbour.co.uk

Ayr
01292 281687
www.abports.co.uk

Barrow
01229 822911
www.abports.co.uk

Barry
0870 609 6699
www.abports.co.uk

Belfast
028 9055 4422
www.belfast-harbour.co.uk

Boston
01205 365571
www.portofboston.co.uk

Brightlingsea
01206 302200
www.brightlingseaharbour.org

Bristol
0117 982 0000
www.bristolport.co.uk

Brixham
01803 853321

Cardiff
0870 609 6699
www.abports.co.uk

Cowes
01983 293952
www.cowes.co.uk

Dartmouth
01803 832337
www.dartharbour.org.uk

Dover
01304 240400
www.doverport.co.uk
Press: x4806

Dundee
01382 224121
www.forthports.co.uk

**Ellesmore Port
(Manchester Ship Canal)**
01928 508550
www.shipcanal.co.uk

Eyemouth
01890 750223

Falmouth
01326 312285
www.falmouthport.co.uk

Felixstowe
01394 604500
www.portoffelixstowe.co.uk

Fife
0131 554 2703
www.forthports.co.uk

479

Fleetwood
01253 872323
www.abports.co.uk
Folkestone
01303 254597
www.folkestoneharbour.com
Garston
0151 427 5971
www.abports.co.uk
Goole
01482 327171
www.abports.co.uk
Grangemouth
01324 482591
www.forthports.co.uk
Great Yarmouth
01493 335500
www.gypa.co.uk
Grimsby
01472 359181
www.abports.co.uk
Harwich
01255 243030
www.hha.co.uk
Heysham
01524 852373
Hull
01482 327171
www.abports.co.uk
Immingham
01472 359181
www.abports.co.uk
Inverness Harbour Trust
01463 715715
www.invernessharbour.co.uk
Ipswich
01473 231010
www.abports.co.uk
Isle of Man
01624 686628
King's Lynn
01553 691555
www.abports.co.uk
Larne
028 2887 2100
www.portoflarne.co.uk
Leith
0131 555 8750
www.forthports.co.uk
Lerwick
01595 692991
www.lerwick-harbour.co.uk
Liverpool
0151 949 6000
www.merseydocks.co.uk
Port of London
01474 562200
www.portoflondon.co.uk
Londonderry
028 7186 0555
www.londonderryport.com
Lowestoft
01553 691555
www.abports.co.uk
Medway Ports
01795 596596
www.medwayports.com
Milford Haven
01646 696100
www.mhpa.co.uk

Montrose Port Authority
01674 672302
www.montroseport.co.uk
Mostyn Docks, Holywell
01745 560335
Newport
0870 609 6699
www.abports.co.uk
Peterhead
01779 483600
www.peterheadport.co.uk
Plymouth
01752 662191
www.abports.co.uk
Poole
01202 440200
www.phc.co.uk
Portsmouth
023 9229 7395
www.portsmouthand.co.uk
Port Talbot
0870 609 6699
www.abports.co.uk
Ramsgate
01843 587661
www.ramsgatenewport.co.uk
Rosyth
01383 413366
www.forthports.co.uk
Saundersfoot
01834 812094
Scarborough
01947 602354
Seaham
0191 516 1700
www.victoriagroup.co.uk
Shoreham
01273 598100
www.portshoreham.co.uk
Silloth
01697 331358
www.abports.co.uk
Southampton
023 8048 8800
www.abports.co.uk
Stonehaven
01569 762741
Stornoway
01851 702688
www.stornoway-portauthority.com
Sunderland
0191 553 2100
www.portofsunderland.org.uk
Swansea
0870 609 6699
www.abports.co.uk
Tees & Hartlepool
01642 877000
www.thpal.co.uk
Teignmouth
01626 774044
www.abports.co.uk
Tilbury
01375 852200
www.forthports.co.uk
Troon
01292 281687
www.abports.co.uk

Tyne, Port of
0191 455 2671
www.portoftyne.com
Weymouth
01305 838000
www.weymouth.gov.uk
Whitby, Port of
01947 602354
www.portofwhitby.co.uk

● Ferries and cruises

Brittany Ferries
0870 366 5333
www.brittany-ferries.com
Caledonian MacBrayne
01475 650100
www.calmac.co.uk
Condor Ferries
01202 207207
www.condorferries.co.uk
Cunard Cruise Line
0845 071 0300
www.cunard.com
DFDS Seaways
0870 252 0524
www.dfdsseaways.co.uk
EasyCruise
0871 210 0001
www.easycruise.com
Fjord Line
www.fjordline.com
Hoverspeed
0870 240 8070
www.hoverspeed.com
Press: 020 7805 5845
Hovertravel
01983 811000
www.hovertravel.co.uk
Irish Ferries
0870 517 1717
www.irishferries.com
**Isle of Man Steam Packet
Company**
01624 645645
www.steam-packet.com
Norfolk Line
00 31 7035 27400
www.norfolkline.com
Orkney Ferries
01856 872044
www.orkneyferries.co.uk
P&O Cruises
0845 678 0014
www.pocruises.com
P&O Ferries
0870 520 2020
www.poferries.com
Press: 01304 863833
Red Funnel Ferries
0870 444 8898
www.redfunnel.co.uk
**Sea Containers Irish Sea
Operations**
020 7805 5000
www.seacontainers.com
SeaFrance
01304 828300
www.seafrance.com
Press: 020 7902 2990

Stena Line
0870 570 7070
www.stenaline.com

Superfast Ferries Scotland
0870 234 0870
www.superfast.com

Swansea Cork Ferries
01792 474354
www.swansea-cork.ie

Thomson Cruises
0870 607 1642
www.thomson-cruises.co.uk

Wightlink
0870 582 7744
www.wightlink.co.uk

Woolwich Ferry
020 8921 5978

● Water travel associations and authorities

Associated British Ports
020 7430 1177
www.abports.co.uk
Press: 020 7430 6820/60

Association of Inland Navigation Authorities
0113 243 3125
www.aina.org.uk

British Marine Federation
01784 223634
www.britishmarine.co.uk

British Ports Association
020 7242 1200
www.britishports.org.uk

British Waterways
01923 201120
www.britishwaterways.co.uk
Press: 01923 201350

Hydrographic Office
01823 723366
www.hydro.gov.uk

Inland Waterways Association
01923 711114
www.waterways.org.uk

International Maritime Organisation
020 7735 7611
www.imo.org

Lloyd's Register – Fairplay
01737 379000
www.fairplay.co.uk

Lloyd's Register
020 7709 9166
www.lr.org

Lloyd's List
0220 7017 5531
www.lloydslist.com

Maritime & Coastguard Agency
023 8032 9100
www.mcga.gov.uk

Royal Institute of Navigation
020 7591 3130
www.rin.org.uk

Royal Yachting Association
0845 345 0400
www.rya.org.uk

Road travel

● Motoring bodies

AA
0870 600 0371
www.theaa.co.uk
Press: 01256 492927

British Motorcyclists Federation
0116 284 5380
www.bmf.co.uk

British Parking Association
01444 447300
www.britishparking.co.uk

Coach Operators Federation
01934 832074
http://users.tinyworld.co.uk /somerbus/index.htm

Confederation of Passenger Transport
020 7240 3131
www.carlton-group.co.uk /passtransport.html

DVLA (Drivers & Vehicles Licensing Authority)
01792 782341
www.dvla.gov.uk
Press: 01792 782318

Greenflag
0845 246 1557
www.greenflag.com
Press: 0113 399 1427

Institute of Logistics & Transport
01536 740104
www.iolt.org.uk

Institute of the Motor Industry
01992 511521
www.motor.org.uk

International Road Transport Union
www.iru.org

Licensed Taxi Drivers Association
020 7286 1046
www.ltda.co.uk

Motor Industry Research Association
01268 290100
www.mira.co.uk

National Federation of Bus Users
023 9281 4493
www.nfbu.org

RAC
01922 727313
www.rac.co.uk
Press: 01603 688263

Road Haulage Association
01932 841515
www.rha.net

Road Operators Safety Council
01865 775552
www.rosco.org.uk

Society of Motor Manufacturers
020 7235 7000
www.smmt.co.uk

Transport & General Workers Union
020 7611 2500
www.tgwu.org.uk

World Road Association (PIARC)
00 33 1 47 96 81 21
www.piarc.org

● Pedestrians, cyclists and campaign groups

Brake
01484 559909
www.brake.org.uk
Road safety charity

British Cycling Federation
0870 871 2000
www.bcf.uk.com
pressoffice@britishcycling.org.uk

Campaign Against Drinking & Driving
0845 123 5541
www.cadd.org.uk

Cycle Campaign Network
ccn@cyclenetwork.org.uk
www.cyclenetwork.org.uk

Cyclists Touring Club
0870 873 0060
www.ctc.org.uk
Press: 0870 873 0063

Environmental Transport Association
0800 212810
www.eta.co.uk
Environmental campaigner and provider of roadside recovery service

European Federation of Road Victims
fevr@worldcom.ch
www.fevr.org

Lift Share
0870 078 0225
www.liftshare.com
Online car-sharing scheme

Living Streets
020 7820 1010
www.livingstreets.org.uk
Fighting for cleaner, safer streets

London Cycling Campaign
020 7234 9310
www.lcc.org.uk

Motorcycle Action Group
0870 444 8448
www.mag-uk.org

National Cycle Network
0845 113 0065
www.sustrans.org.uk
Press: 0117 927 7555

Nationwide Cycle Registration
0117 964 2187
www.cycleregistration.com

Ramblers Association
020 7339 8500
www.ramblers.org.uk
Press: 020 7339 8531/8532

Reclaim the Streets
rts@gn.apc.org
http://rts.gn.apc.org

RoadPeace
020 8838 5102
www.roadpeace.org

Slower Speeds Initiative
0845 345 8459
www.slower-speeds.org.uk

Sustrans
0845 113 0065
www.sustrans.org.uk
Sustainable transport charity
Press: 0117 927 7555

● Buses

Arriva
0191 520 4000
www.arriva.co.uk
Press: 0191 520 4106

Firstgroup
020 7291 0505
www.firstgroup.com
Press: 0161 627 7218

The Go-ahead Group
0191 232 3123
www.go-ahead.com

London United Busways
020 8400 6665
www.lonutd.co.uk

Lothian Buses
0131 554 4494
www.lothianbuses.co.uk
Press: 0131 555 6363

Metroline
020 8218 8888
www.metroline.co.uk

National Express
0870 580 8080
www.nationalexpress.com
Press: 0121 625 1122

Scottish Citylink
0141 332 9644
www.citylink.co.uk
Press: 0141 333 9585

Stagecoach
01738 442111
www.stagecoachplc.com

Translink
028 9066 6630
www.translink.co.uk

Tourism

● Major tour operators

First Choice
0870 750 0001
www.firstchoice.co.uk
Press: 01293 588762

MyTravel
01706 742000
www.mytravel.com
Press: 0161 232 6464

Thomas Cook
01733 417100
www.thomascook.com
Press: 01733 417272

Thomson
0870 165 0079
www.thomson.co.uk

● Tourism associations

Air Travel Organisers' Licensing (ATOL)
020 7453 6424
www.caa.co.uk/cpg/atol
Press: 020 7453 6030

Association of British Travel Agents
020 7637 2444
www.abtanet.com
Press: 020 7307 1900

British Tourist Authority
020 8846 9000
www.visitbritain.com
Press: 020 8563 3220

Tourism Concern
020 7133 3330
www.tourismconcern.org.uk

Visit London
020 8234 5000
www.visitlondon.com

Youth Hostels Association
01629 592600
www.yha.org.uk
Press: 01629 592575

Utilities

Energy

● Energy companies

BNFL
01925 832000
www.bnfl.com
British Nuclear Fuels
Press: 01925 834075

British Gas
0845 600 0560
www.house.co.uk
Gas and electricity supplier.
Owned by Centrica
Press: 01784 874433

British Energy
01452 652222
www.british-energy.com
Electricity producer
Press: 01506 408801

Ecotricity
01453 756111
www.ecotricity.co.uk
Electricity supplier
Press: 01453 769317

EDF Energy
020 7242 9050
www.edfenergy.com
Gas and electricity supplier. Owns
SWEB, Seeboard and London Energy
Press: 020 7752 2266

Green Energy UK
0845 456 9550
www.greenenergy.uk.com

Good Energy
0845 456 1640
www.good-energy.co.uk
Renewable electricity supplier.
Owned by Monkton Group

National Grid
020 7004 3000
www.nationalgrid.com
Energy distribution
Press: 020 7004 3147

Powergen
024 7642 4000
www.powergen.co.uk
Gas and electricity supplier.
Owned by E.ON UK
Press: 024 7642 5741

RWE npower
01793 877777
www.rwenpower.com
Gas and electricity supplier
Press: 0845 070 2807

Scottish and Southern
01738 456000
www.scottish-southern.co.uk
Gas and electricity supplier
Press: 0870 900 0410

Scottish Power
0141 248 8200
www.scottishpower.com
Gas and electricity supplier
Press: 0141 636 4515

● Energy bodies and associations

British Hydropower Association
01202 886622
www.british-hydro.org
Trade association

British Nuclear Energy Society
020 7222 7722
www.bnes.com

British Wind Energy Association
020 7689 1960
www.bwea.com
Trade association

Centre for Sustainable Energy
0117 929 9950
www.cse.org.uk
Charity

Energy Retail Association
020 7930 9175
www.energy-retail.org.uk
Press: 07730 898 641

Energywatch
0845 906 0708
www.energywatch.org.uk
Independent watchdog
Press: 020 799 8340

National Energy Foundation
01908 665555
www.natenergy.org.uk
Charity

Nuclear Industry Association
020 7766 6640
www.niauk.org
Trade association
Press: 020 7766 6640

Solar Trade Association
01908 442290
www.greenenergy.org.uk/sta
Trade association

● Government and regulation

Defra
0845 933 5577
www.defra.gov.uk

DTI Energy Group
020 7215 5000
www.dti.gov.uk/energy
Press: 020 7215 6407

Nuclear Decommissioning Authority
01925 802001
www.nda.gov.uk
Press: 01925 802075

Ofgem
020 7901 7000
www.ofgem.gov.uk
Official regulator
Press: 020 7901 7006

Water

● Water companies

Anglian Water
0845 714 5145
www.anglianwater.co.uk
Press: 0870 600 5600

Dwr Cymru Welsh Water
01443 452300
www.dwrcymru.com
Press: 029 2055 6140

Northumbrian Water
0870 608 4820
www.nwl.co.uk

Scottish Water
0845 601 8855
www.scottishwater.co.uk
Press: 01383 848445

Severn Trent Water
0800 783 4444
www.stwater.co.uk
Press: 0121 722 4555

South West Water
01392 446688
www.southwestwater.co.uk
Press: 01392 443020

Southern Water
0845 272 0845
www.southernwater.co.uk

Thames Water
0845 920 0800
www.thames-water.com

United Utilities
01925 234000
www.unitedutilities.com
Press: 01925 537366

Wessex Water
01225 526000
www.wessexwater.co.uk
Press: 01225 526323/9

Yorkshire Water
01274 691111
www.yorkshirewater.com

● Water associations

British Water
020 7957 4554
www.britishwater.co.uk
Trade association

Water UK
020 7344 1844
www.water.org.uk
Trade association

● Government and regulation

Defra
0845 933 5577
www.defra.gov.uk
Drinking Water Inspectorate
020 7082 8024
www.dwi.gov.uk
Watchdog
Ofwat
0121 625 1300/73
www.ofwat.gov.uk
Regulator
Press: 0121 625 1416/96/42
Water Industry Commissioner for Scotland
01786 430200
www.watercommissioner.co.uk

Post

Royal Mail
0845 774 0740
www.royalmail.com

● Regulator

Postcomm (Postal Services Commission)
020 7593 2100
www.postcomm.gov.uk
Press: 020 7593 2114
info@psc.gov.uk

Telecoms

British Telecom
020 7356 5000
www.bt.com
Press: 020 7356 5369
Cable and Wireless
01908 845000
www.cw.com
Press: 01344 818888
Colt
0207 390 3900
www.colt.net
Press: 07017 100100
Hutchinson 3G
0870 733 0333
www.three.co.uk
Kingston Communications
01482 602100
www.kcom.com
Press: 01482 602711
O2
0113 272 2000
www.o2.com
Orange
0870 376 8888
www.orange.co.uk
Press: 0870 373 1501
Thus
0800 027 5848
www.thus.co.uk
Press: 0141 567 1234
T-Mobile
01707 315000
www.t-mobile.co.uk
Press: 07017 150150
Verizon
0118 905 5000
www.verizon.com
Virgin Media
01256 752000
www.virginmedia.co.uk
Vodafone
01635 33251
www.vodafone.co.uk
Press: 07000 500100

● Regulator

Ofcom
020 7981 3040
www.ofcom.org.uk
Press: 020 7981 3033

Emergency and services

Police

Government and agencies

Home Office
020 7035 4848
www.homeoffice.gov.uk
Press: 020 7035 4381

Forensic Science Service
0121 329 5200
www.forensic.gov.uk
Press: 0121 329 5225

HM Inspectors of Constabulary
01527 882000
www.inspectorates.homeoffice
.gov.uk/hmic

Independent Police Complaints Commission (IPCC)
0845 300 2002
www.ipcc.gov.uk
Press: 020 7166 3214

» *Police forces*
see pages 487–489

Police services

Police Service
www.police.uk

National Policing Improvement Agency
01256 602100
National police training
Press: 01256 602949

Civil Nuclear Constabulary (CNC)
01245 466666
www.cnc.police.uk

Interpol
00 33 4 7244 7000
www.interpol.int

Northern Ireland Police Service
028 9065 0222
www.psni.police.uk
Press: 028 9070 0084

Northern Ireland Policing Board
028 9040 8500
www.nipolicingboard.org.uk
Press: 028 9040 8562

Police Forces in Scotland
www.scottish.police.uk

Police IT Organisation
020 8358 5555
www.pito.org.uk
National computer

Scottish Drug Enforcement Agency
0141 302 1000
www.sdea.police.uk

Scottish Police Information Strategy
0141 582 1000
www.spis.police.uk

Serious Organised Crime Agency (SOCA)
0870 268 8100
www.soca.gov.uk

Professional bodies

Association of Chief Police Officers
020 7084 8950
www.acpo.police.uk
Press: 020 7084 8945

Association of Chief Police Officers in Scotland
0141 532 2052
www.scottish.police.uk
Press: 0141 532 2658

Association of Police Authorities
020 7664 3185
www.apa.police.uk

British Association for Women in Policing
0870 766 4056
www.bawp.org

Institute of Traffic Accident Investigators
01332 292447
www.itai.org

Police Federation
020 8335 1000
www.polfed.org

Police Federation for Northern Ireland
028 9076 4200
www.policefed-ni.org.uk

Police Superintendents' Association
0118 984 4005
www.policesupers.com

Fire

Office of the Deputy Prime Minister
020 7944 4400
www.communities.gov.uk
Press: 020 7944 4297

FRS Development Division
020 7944 8194
www.frsonline.fire.gov.uk

Chief Fire and Rescue Advisors
020 7944 5569

» *Fire and rescue authorities*
see pages 487–489

Professional bodies

Fire Brigades Union
020 8541 1765
www.fbu.org.uk
Press: 07736 818 100

Chief Fire Officers' Association (CFOA)
01827 302300
www.cfoa.org.uk

Fire Protection Association
01608 812500
www.thefpa.co.uk

Ambulance

Department of Health
020 7210 4850
www.dh.gov.uk
Press: 020 7210 5221

» *Ambulance services*
see pages 487–489

Ambulance associations

Ambulance Service Association
020 7928 9620
www.asa.uk.net

Association of Professional Ambulance Personnel
0870 167 0999
www.apap.org.uk

Search and rescue

Maritime and Coastguard Agency
0870 600 6505
www.mcga.gov.uk

Mountain Rescue Council of England and Wales
0870 240 4024
www.mountain.rescue.org.uk
Network of voluntary rescue teams

RAF Mountain Rescue Association
www.rafmountainrescue.com

Search and Rescue Dog Association
chairman@nsarda.org.uk
www.nsarda.org.uk

Military

Ministry of Defence
020 7218 9000
www.mod.uk
Press: 020 7218 7907

British Army
www.army.mod.uk
Press: 020 7218 7907

Royal Air Force
www.raf.mod.uk
Press: 020 7218 7907

Royal Navy
www.royal-navy.mod.uk
Press: 020 7218 7907

Army Training and Recruitment Agency
01980 615041

Information Coherence Authority
01793 555391

Computer Emergency Response Team
020 7218 2640

Defence Analytical Services Agency
www.dasa.mod.uk
UK defence statistics

Defence Procurement Agency
0117 913 0000
www.mod.uk/defenceinternet
/microsite/dpa
Press: 0117 913 0257

Defence Scientific Advisory Council
020 7218 9000
www.dsac.mod.uk
*Provides independent advice to the
defence secretary*

**GCHQ (Government Communications
Headquarters)**
01242 221491
www.gchq.gov.uk
Press: 01242 221491 x33847

International Visits Control Office
ivco@dpa.mod.uk
www.mod.uk/ivco
*Provides security clearance and advice
for visitors to and from the UK defence
industry*

Ministry of Defence Police
01371 854444
www.mdp.mod.uk
Press: 01371 854416

Sabre
0800 389 5459
www.sabre.mod.uk
*Supports Britain's reservists and
employers*

Territorial Army
0845 603 8000
www.ta.mod.uk
Reserve force

Veterans Agency
0800 169 2277, 01253 866043
www.veteransagency.mod.uk
*MoD contact for veterans and
dependants*

MI5
www.mi5.gov.uk
*UK's defensive security intelligence
agency*
Press: 020 7035 3535 (Home
Office)

MI6
www.fco.gov.uk
Secret intelligence service
Press: 020 7008 3100 (Foreign
Office)

● Military associations

Army Base Repair Organisation
01264 383295
www.abro.mod.uk

**Commonwealth War Graves
Commission**
01628 634221
www.cwgc.org
Press: 01628 507163

Military Heraldry Society
01952 270221

Military Historical Society
020 7730 0717

**Orders and Medals Research
Society**
01494 441207
www.omrs.org.uk

**Reserve Forces' and Cadets'
Associations' in Scotland**
Lowland: 0141 945 4951
Highland: 01382 668283
www.rfca.org.uk

Royal British Legion
020 7973 7200
www.britishlegion.org.uk
www.poppy.org.uk
Press: 020 7973 7296

SSAFA Forces Help
020 7403 8783
www.ssafa.org.uk
*National charity helping serving and
ex-service men, women and their
families*

Emergency planning

● Government

**Air Accidents Investigation
Branch**
01252 510300
24-hour accident reporting line:
01252 512299
www.aaib.dft.gov.uk
Press: 020 7944 3387

Civil Contingencies Secretariat
020 7276 3267
www.cabinetoffice.gov.uk
*Formerly the Emergency Planning
Division*
Press: 020 7276 1191

**Emergency Planning College,
Easingwold**
01347 821406
www.ukresilience.info/college
Government training college

**London Fire and Emergency
Planning Authority**
020 7587 2000
www.london-fire.gov.uk

London Prepared
enquiries-lrt@gol.gsi.gov.uk
www.londonprepared.gov.uk

**National Infrastructure Security
Co-ordination Centre (NISCC)**
020 7821 1330
www.niscc.gov.uk

**Health Protection Agency,
Centre for Radiation, Chemical
and Environmental Hazards,
Radiation Protection Division**
01235 831600
www.hpa.org.uk/radiation

**Scottish Executive Justice
Department**
0131 556 8400
www.scotland.gov.uk

Anti-Terrorist Hotline
0800 789321

● Professional body

Emergency Planning Society
0845 600 9587
www.the-eps.org

Voluntary services

Basics
0870 165 4999
www.basics.org.uk
Medical help at disasters

British Red Cross
0870 170 7000
www.redcross.org.uk

Casualties Union
0870 078 0590
www.casualtiesunion.org.uk
*Simulated injuries for emergency
exercises*

Crimestoppers
020 8254 3200
Hotline: 0800 555111
www.crimestoppers-uk.org

Royal Life Saving Society
01789 773994
www.lifesavers.org.uk

**Royal National Lifeboat
Institution**
0845 122 6999
www.rnli.org.uk

**St Andrews Ambulance
Association**
Aberdeen: 01224 877271
Dundee: 01382 322389
Fife: 01592 631758
Edinburgh: 0131 229 5419
Glasgow: 0141 332 4031
www.firstaid.org.uk

St John Ambulance
0870 010 4950
www.sja.org.uk

Victim Support
020 7735 9166
Victim support line:
0845 303 0900
www.victimsupport.org
Supports victims of crime
Press: 020 7896 3809

Fire, police and ambulance

England

Avon
FIRE: 0117 926 2061
PRESS: x216
POLICE: 0845 456 7000
PRESS: 01275 816350
AMBULANCE: 0117 927 7046
PRESS: 0117 928 0271

Bedfordshire
FIRE: 01234 351081
PRESS: 01234 326198
POLICE: 01234 841212
PRESS: 01234 842390
AMBULANCE: 01234 408999
PRESS: 01707 362505

Berkshire
FIRE: 0118 945 2888
PRESS: 0118 932 2214/83
POLICE: 0845 850 5505
PRESS: 01865 846699
AMBULANCE: 0118 936 5500

Buckinghamshire
FIRE: 01296 424666
POLICE: 0845 850 5505
PRESS: 01865 846699
AMBULANCE: 01908 262422

Cambridgeshire
FIRE: 01480 444500
PRESS: 01480 444558
POLICE: 0845 456 4564
PRESS: 01480 422393
AMBULANCE: 01603 424255
PRESS: 01865 740100

Cheshire
FIRE: 01606 868700
PRESS: 01606 868657/
   868422/868786
POLICE: 01244 350000
PRESS: 01244 612030
AMBULANCE: 0151 260 5220
PRESS: 0151 261 2585

Cleveland
FIRE: 01429 872311
POLICE: 01642 326326
PRESS: 01642 301245/54
AMBULANCE: 01904 666000
PRESS: 01904 666041

Cornwall
FIRE: 01872 273117
PRESS: 01872 322785
POLICE: 0845 277 7444
PRESS: 01392 452151/200
AMBULANCE: 01392 261500
PRESS: 01392 261506

Cumbria
FIRE: 01900 822503
POLICE: 01768 891999
PRESS: 0845 330 0247
AMBULANCE: 01228 596909
PRESS: 01228 403006

Derbyshire
FIRE: 01332 771221
POLICE: 0845 123 3333
PRESS: 01773 572033/034/979
AMBULANCE: 0115 929 6151

Devon
FIRE: 01392 872200
PRESS: 01392 872318
POLICE: 0845 277 7444
PRESS: 01392 452151/200
AMBULANCE: 01392 261500
PRESS: 01392 261506

Dorset
FIRE: 01305 251133
PRESS: 01305 252084
POLICE: 01202 222222
PRESS: 01202 223893
AMBULANCE: 01202 851640

Durham
FIRE: 0191 384 3381
POLICE: 0845 606 0365
PRESS: 0191 375 2157
AMBULANCE: 0191 273 1212

East Sussex
FIRE: 0845 130 8855
PRESS: 01323 462388
POLICE: 0845 607 0999
PRESS: 01273 404173
AMBULANCE: 01273 489444
PRESS: 01273 897859

Essex
FIRE: 01277 222531
POLICE: 01245 491491
PRESS: 01245 452450
AMBULANCE: 01245 443344
PRESS: 01245 444444

Gloucestershire
FIRE: 01452 753333
POLICE: 0845 090 1234
PRESS: 01242 276070
AMBULANCE: 01452 753030

Greater Manchester
FIRE: 0161 736 5866
PRESS: 0161 608 4090
POLICE: 0161 872 5050
PRESS: 0161 856 2220
AMBULANCE: 0161 796 7222
PRESS: 0161 828 5400

Hampshire
FIRE: 023 8064 4000
PRESS: 023 8062 6812
POLICE: 0845 045 4545
PRESS: 01962 871619
AMBULANCE: 01962 863511
PRESS: 01962 843165

Hereford & Worcester
FIRE: 01905 24454
PRESS: 01905 725060
POLICE: 0845 744 4888
PRESS: 01432 347340
AMBULANCE: 01886 834200

Hertfordshire
FIRE: 01992 507507
PRESS: 01992 507546
POLICE: 0845 330 0222
PRESS: 01707 354588
AMBULANCE: 01234 408999

Humberside
FIRE: 01482 565333
PRESS: 07860 280044
POLICE: 0845 606 0222
PRESS: 01482 578372
AMBULANCE: 01904 666000
PRESS: 01904 666041

Isle of Wight
FIRE: 01983 823194
POLICE: 0845 045 4545
PRESS: 01962 871619
AMBULANCE: 01983 534111
PRESS: 01983 534184

Kent
FIRE: 01622 692121
PRESS: 01622 692121
POLICE: 01622 690690
PRESS: 01622 652231-3
PORT OF DOVER POLICE:
   01304 240400
AMBULANCE: 01622 747010
PRESS: 01622 740331

Lancashire
FIRE: 01772 862545
PRESS: 01772 866939,
   07769 907887
POLICE: 01772 614444
PRESS: 01772 412658/444
AMBULANCE: 01772 862666
PRESS: 01207 498400

Leicestershire
FIRE: 0116 287 2241
POLICE: 0116 222 2222
PRESS: x2798
AMBULANCE: 0115 929 6151

Lincolnshire
FIRE: 01522 582222
PRESS: 01522 552302
POLICE: 01522 532222
PRESS: 01522 558026
AMBULANCE: 0845 045 0422
PRESS: 01522 580322

London
FIRE: 020 7587 2000
PRESS: 020 7587 4064
METROPOLITAN POLICE:
   020 7230 1212
PRESS: 020 7230 2171
CITY OF LONDON POLICE:
   020 7601 2222
PRESS: 020 7601 2220
AMBULANCE: 020 7921 5100
PRESS: 020 7921 5113

Merseyside
FIRE: 0151 296 4000
PRESS: 0151 296 4417/06
POLICE: 0151 709 6010
PRESS: 0151 777 8566
AMBULANCE: 0151 260 5220
PRESS: 0151 261 2585

Norfolk
FIRE: 01603 810351
PRESS: 01603 819759
POLICE: 0845 456 4567
PRESS: 01953 423666/
07626 952342
AMBULANCE: 01603 424255
PRESS: 01603 422729

North Yorkshire
FIRE: 01609 780150
PRESS: 0870 774 9992
POLICE: 0845 606 0247
PRESS: 01609 789959
AMBULANCE: 01904 666000
PRESS: 01904 666041

Northamptonshire
FIRE: 01604 797000
PRESS: 01536 516400
POLICE: 01604 700700
PRESS: 01604 703197
AMBULANCE: 01908 262422
PRESS: 01865 740100

Northumberland
FIRE: 01670 533000
PRESS: 01670 583252
POLICE: 01661 872555
AMBULANCE: 0191 273 1212

Nottinghamshire
FIRE: 0115 967 0880
PRESS: 0115 977 4918
POLICE: 0115 967 0999
PRESS: 0115 967 2080
AMBULANCE: 0115 929 6151
PRESS: 0115 929 6151

Oxfordshire
FIRE: 01865 842999
PRESS: 01865 842999
POLICE: 0845 850 5505
PRESS: 01865 846699
AMBULANCE: 01865 740100
PRESS: 01865 740117

Rutland
FIRE: 0116 287 2241
PRESS: 0116 287 2241
POLICE: 0116 222 2222
PRESS: x2798
AMBULANCE: 0115 929 6151
PRESS: 0115 929 6151

Shropshire
FIRE: 01743 260200
PRESS: 01743 260286
POLICE: 0845 744 4888
PRESS: 01743 237491
AMBULANCE: 01384 215555
PRESS: 01384 246496

Somerset
FIRE: 01823 364500
PRESS: 01823 364582
POLICE: 0845 456 7000
PRESS: 01275 816350
AMBULANCE: 01392 261500
PRESS: 01392 261506

South Yorkshire
FIRE: 0114 272 7202
PRESS: 0114 253 2353
POLICE: 0114 220 2020
PRESS: 0114 252 3848
AMBULANCE: 01709 820520
PRESS: 01709 302026

Staffordshire
FIRE: 0845 122 1155
PRESS: 01785 898941
POLICE: 0845 330 2010
PRESS: 01785 234864
AMBULANCE: 01785 253521
PRESS: 01785 273309

Suffolk
FIRE: 01473 588888
PRESS: 01473 264392
POLICE: 01473 613500
PRESS: 01473 613996/7
AMBULANCE: 01603 424255
PRESS: 01603 422729

Surrey
FIRE: 01737 242444
PRESS: 01737 224027
POLICE: 0845 125 2222
PRESS: 01483 482322
AMBULANCE: 01737 353333
PRESS: 01737 363815

Tyne and Wear
FIRE: 0191 444 1500
PRESS: 0191 444 1542
POLICE: 01661 872555
AMBULANCE: 0191 273 1212
PRESS: 0191 273 1212

Warwickshire
FIRE: 01926 412513
PRESS: 01926 423231
POLICE: 01926 415000
PRESS: NORTH: x3366;
SOUTH: x4266
AMBULANCE: 01926 881331
PRESS: 01384 215555

West Midlands
FIRE: 0121 359 5161
PRESS: 0121 380 6101
POLICE: 0845 113 5000
PRESS: 0121 626 5858
AMBULANCE: 01384 215555
PRESS: 01384 246496

West Sussex
FIRE: 01243 786211
PRESS: 01243 752448
POLICE: 0845 607 0999
PRESS: 01273 404173
AMBULANCE: 01273 489444
PRESS: 01273 897859

West Yorkshire
FIRE: 01274 682311
PRESS: 01274 655717
POLICE: 0845 606 0606
PRESS: 01924 292045
AMBULANCE: 01924 582000
PRESS: 01924 582204

Wiltshire
FIRE: 01380 723601
POLICE: 0845 408 7000
PRESS: 01380 734126
AMBULANCE: 01249 443939
PRESS: 01249 858740

Worcestershire

» *see Hereford & Worcester*

Wales

Mid Wales
FIRE: 0870 606 0699
PRESS: 01267 226866
POLICE: 01267 222020
PRESS: 01267 222274
AMBULANCE: 01745 532900
PRESS: 029 2034 4888

West Wales
FIRE: 0870 606 0699
PRESS: 01267 226866
POLICE: 0845 330 2000
PRESS: 01267 222274
AMBULANCE: 01745 532900
PRESS: 029 2034 4888

North Wales
FIRE: 01745 343431
PRESS: 01745 535283
POLICE: 01492 517171
PRESS: 01492 511157-9
AMBULANCE: 01745 532900
PRESS: 029 2034 4888

South Wales
FIRE: 01443 232000
PRESS: 01443 232164
POLICE: 01656 655555
PRESS: 01656 869291
AMBULANCE: 01745 532900
PRESS: 029 2034 4888

Scotland

Central Scotland
FIRE: 01324 716996
PRESS: 01324 710221
POLICE: 01786 456000
PRESS: 01786 456370
AMBULANCE: 0131 446 7000
PRESS: 07974 017937

Dumfries and Galloway
FIRE: 01387 252222
PRESS: 01387 242253
POLICE: 0845 600 5701
PRESS: 01387 260576
AMBULANCE: 0131 446 7000
PRESS: 07974 017937

Fife
FIRE: 01592 774451
PRESS: x2711
POLICE: 01592 418888
PRESS: 01592 418813
AMBULANCE: 0131 446 7000
PRESS: 07974 017937

Grampian
FIRE: 01224 696666
POLICE: 0845 600 5700
PRESS: 01224 386431
AMBULANCE: 0131 446 7000
PRESS: 07974 017937

Highland and Islands
FIRE: 01463 227000
POLICE: 01463 715555
PRESS: 01463 720396
AMBULANCE: 0131 446 7000
PRESS: 07974 017937

Lothian and Borders
FIRE: 0131 228 2401
POLICE: 0131 311 3131
PRESS: 0131 311 3423
AMBULANCE: 0131 446 7000
PRESS: 07974 017937

Strathclyde
FIRE: 01698 300999
POLICE: 0141 532 2000
PRESS: 0141 532 2658
AMBULANCE: 0131 446 7000
PRESS: 07974 017937

Tayside
FIRE: 01382 322222
PRESS: 01382 322222
POLICE: 01382 223200
PRESS: 01382 596730
AMBULANCE: 0131 446 7000
PRESS: 07974 017937

Northern Ireland

HQ, Lisburn
FIRE: 028 9266 4221
PRESS: 028 9266 4221
POLICE: 028 9065 0222
PRESS: 028 9070 0084
AMBULANCE: 028 9040 0999
PRESS: 028 9040 0999

British Transport Police

020 7830 8800

PRESS

London and south-east
Breaking news:
    020 7957 1527
Follow-ups:
London Underground:
    020 7918 3547
South London and south-east:
    020 7023 6973
North London through East
Anglia:
    020 7830 8854

Midlands, Wales and west
Breaking news: 0121 228 2244
Follow-ups: 0121 654 2076

North-east
Breaking news: 0113 245 9149
Follow-ups: 0113 247 9550

North-west
Breaking news: 0161 228 5685
Follow-ups: 0161 228 4074

Scotland
Breaking news: 0141 335 3198
Follow-ups: 0141 335 2814

National and policy enquiries
020 7830 8854

PA Photos

News, sport and showbiz pictures, past and present

paphotos.com

Bournemouth University

UK FILM|COUNCIL
LOTTERY FUNDED

skillset
Screen
Academy ✓

The Media School

Make sure you're in
the media spotlight.

Bournemouth University is the largest centre of professional education for the media industries in the UK and has a range of industry accreditations in its specialist subject areas:

- Computer Animation
- Corporate & Marketing Communications
- Journalism & Communication
- Media Production.

The Media School offers high-quality, industry-recognised undergraduate and postgraduate programmes and funded PhD studentships.

Students benefit from:

- Academic expertise and increasing research profile
- Close links with industry and professional bodies
- High-profile guest lecturers
- Industry-standard equipment
- Excellent employment record
- Superb placement opportunities
- Studying at the only government-designated Centre for Excellence in Media Practice, the Bournemouth Screen Academy and The National Centre for Computer Animation.

**If you would like to know more about
The Media School, contact us:
t: 01202 965360 e: media@bournemouth.ac.uk
www.bournemouth.ac.uk/media**

Broadcasters turn to GlobeCast for content management and delivery with

GLOBAL REACH

Be *content* in a world powered by

Study the 'why' and the 'how'

Choose the following degrees within our lively, multi-cultural, internationally-known five star RAE rated department. Benefit from: teaching by internationally leading researchers and media professionals; sessions from visiting professionals from London's media and cultural industries; excellent employment record – former students work across the sector.

Undergraduate level

Media and Communications; Media Studies with Digital Content Creation; or Media combined with Anthropology; Modern Literature; or Sociology.

Postgraduate level

MAs in Digital Media; Feature Film; Film Making (January start); Image and Communication; Journalism (PTC accredited covering newspapers, magazines and web); Media and Communications; Political Communications; Radio (BJTC accredited); Screen Documentary; Script Writing; Screen Studies; Television Journalism (BJTC accredited); Transnational Communications and Global Media; MRes, MPhil and PhD.

Other programmes in related areas include

Journalism and media practice; photography and urban cultures; interactive media; gender and culture.

Open Days

November, February and June.

For more information:

www.goldsmiths.ac.uk
admissions@gold.ac.uk
call 020 7919 7766

Committed to equal opportunities

Goldsmiths
UNIVERSITY OF LONDON

The UK's fastest growing search engine marketing agency.

www.ispysearch.com

Contact **Nick Jones: nick@ispysearch.com**

Media at Southampton Solent University

Here at Southampton Solent University we believe in equipping our students with the skills, confidence and knowledge they need to succeed in their media careers. That's why 80% of our graduates go straight into employment after leaving us.

All of our courses are based on industry practices, taught by lecturers and technicians with extensive experience. Our industry-standard equipment includes digital multi-camera television studios, specialist 3D multimedia areas, digital and 16mm film editing, plus the latest in recording and music studio technology.

You can't beat hands-on experience so we offer a unique range of work experience opportunities. We have links with large multi-national organisations and small specialist companies and our students have worked on projects at large outdoor venues like Southampton Football Club and Glastonbury Festival. Students also have the chance to work on their own projects with our student-run radio station, film society and record label.

Film and Television

- BA (Hons) Film
- BA (Hons) Film and Television Studies
- BA (Hons) Television and Video Production
- BA (Hons) Television Production (Design)
- BA (Hons) Television Production (Directing Performance)
- BA (Hons) Television Production (Editing)
- BA (Hons) Television Production (Events Management)
- BA (Hons) Television Production (Location)
- BA (Hons) Television Production (Online)
- BA (Hons) Television Production (Screenwriting)
- BA (Hons) Television Production (Special Effects)
- BA (Hons) Television Production (Sound)
- MA Directing for Film and Television
- MA Editing and Digital Post Production
- MA Film
- MA Producing for Film and Television
- MA Television

www.solent.ac.uk

Media and Production

- BA (Hons) Interactive Media (Advertising)
- BA (Hons) Interactive Media (Entertainment)
- BA (Hons) Interactive Media (Events)
- BA (Hons) Interactive Media (Marketing)
- BA (Hons) Interactive Media (Production)
- BA (Hons) Media Culture and Production
- BA (Hons) Radio
- MA Media
- MA Interactive Production
- MProf Media Practice

Music

- BA (Hons) Music Promotion
- BA (Hons) Popular Music and Record Production
- BA (Hons) Popular Music Journalism
- BA (Hons) Popular Music Performance
- BA (Hons) Popular Music Radio
- BA (Hons) Popular Music Studies

- BA (Hons) Urban and Electronic Music
- MA Popular Music Studies
- MA Popular Music (Performance)
- MA Popular Music (Production)
- MA Popular Music (Promotion and Management)

Performing Arts

- BA (Hons) Comedy: Writing and Performance
- BA (Hons) Dance
- BA (Hons) Performance

To find out more about studying at Southampton Solent University, click your way to www.solent.ac.uk give us a call, or drop us an e-mail.
T: 023 8031 9039   E: enquiries@solent.ac.uk

Southampton
SOLENT
University

Index

C

H

J

S

X

Y

Z